The Human Self and Allah

The Human Self and Allah
(The Quranic Concept of God)

G. A. Parwez

That introduction of Allah which He Himself has expounded in His Own Book and from which this reality also becomes evidently clear as to what is the mutual relationship between Allah and Man.

Tolu-e-Islam Trust (Regd.)
25 B, Gulberg-II, LAHORE
Islamicdawn.com

ALL RIGHTS RESERVED

Title of the book: The Human Self and Allah
                     (Translation of *Mann o Yazdan*)

Author: Ghulam Ahmad Parwez

Translated and Edited: Dr. Ejaz Rasool (UK)

Technical Assistance: Mr. Sheraz Akhter (Norway)

ISBN: 9781 725783805

Contact: Tolu-e-Islam Trust
                     25 B Gulberg-II
                     Lahore-54660 Pakistan
                     www.islamicdawn.com

Tolu-e-Islam Trust®

Copyright © 2019

List of Other Works by the Author

1. Exposition of the Quran
2. Islam: A Challenge to Religion
3. What is Islam? (Available from Amazon)
4. The Book of Destiny
5. The Quranic Laws
6. Reasons for the Decline of Muslims
7. Letters to Tahira
8. *Iblees* and Adam
9. *Lughat-ul-Quran* (Dictionary of Quranic words and terms) – Volume I and II (Available from Amazon)
10. The Quranic System of Sustenance (Available from Amazon)
11. The Life in the Hereafter: What Does the Quran Say? (Available from Amazon)
12. The Status of Hadeeth in Islam. (Available from Amazon)

These books are available free for download at:

http://www.Islamicdawn.com/

These books are also available from:

Tolu-e-Islam Trust
25 – B Gulberg 2
LAHORE – 54660, PAKISTAN
E mail: tolueislam@gmail.com
Telephone: 00 92 (0)42 35753666

About the Author

Ghulam Ahmad Parwez was born in Batala, Punjab, in British India on 9th July 1903 into a profoundly religious family. His grandfather, who was deeply religious and belonged to the Hanafi school of thought, was a renowned religious scholar who intended to make the author inherit his knowledge and religious understanding. As a consequence, his education and training were carried out under the direction of his grandfather. While he studied the traditional religious teachings, he also had the desire and inkling to question its content using his intellect and reasoning. This led to his inner conflict with the external religious environment and he continued to question the prevalent religious concepts and practices. He noticed that whatever was being taught as part of the religion was being referred to some Imam or religious scholar for authority. It was also noted in the religious literature, that whatever the forefathers had followed should be obeyed without any question, and this was considered to be a requirement of Islam.

For Parwez this did not satisfy his desire to seek reason and logic in every claim and statement made within the religious literature. However, he could not express these doubts and reservations initially due to his respect for his grandfather, and the constraints of the religious environment which prevailed at the time in his town. Later, due to his employment, he moved to Lahore (now part of Pakistan), and found a degree of freedom to question some of these religious concepts and beliefs. After the death of his grandfather, he found complete freedom to pursue his line of enquiry and research into the prevalent Islamic beliefs, doctrines, ideologies, and religious practices.

This led to his discovering that most of these have been acquired from others. He tried to study the Quran using the traditional religious approach but was unable to find the answers to all his doubts, which required satisfaction from a logical point of view. He also studied the life of the last messenger and the establishment of the Islamic State in the seventh century in his quest to determine the cause which contributed to this greatest revolution based on the Quran. He especially paid attention to the statement from the last messenger, 'The Quran is not a product of my thinking or that of any other human being' and that this is the message from Allah. He soon learnt the procedure to understand the Quran.

Through his contact with the famous philosopher and poet, Allama Iqbal, who had a deep interest in the Quran, Parwez concluded that to understand the Quran one has to understand three fundamentally important points:

1

(1) The Quran calls itself Light (*Nur*) and a light does not need any external source or aid to make itself visible. It makes itself evident and also exposes the reality of those things which are within its domain.

(2) The Quran is revealed in the Arabic language and, to understand it correctly, one needs to understand the Arabic context which was prevalent at the time of its revelation.

(3) The Quran has guided us by saying that through *Tasreef-ul-Ayat* (through cross reference within the verses of the Quran) it makes its guidance clear e.g. see (6:106).

In order to meet the second requirement regarding the precise meaning of the Arabic words in the Quran, he researched and compiled a *Lughat-ul-Quran* (now translated into English), which is a dictionary of all the words and terms used in the Quran and which includes the meanings which were prevalent among the Arabs at the time of the Quranic Revelation. For the third requirement of *Tasreef-ul-Ayat*, the Quran is different from books written by human beings, where the latter are usually divided based on various subjects - the Quran is based on mentioning a reality in one verse or verses and then its further explanation is noted in another place or places. For example, in *Surah Inaam* the Quran states:

And thus do We explain the signs by various verses, so that they acknowledge 'You have explained them', and We make the Quran clear for a people who know. (6:105)

In order to meet this requirement, Parwez felt the need to compile all the verses under one subject as referred in various verses of the Quran and he compiled a book in Urdu titled *Tabweeb-ul-Quran* i.e. Classification of the Quran. This made it easy to refer to various subjects and look at all the verses mentioned in the Quran relating to a subject.

Along with writing and producing literature on the Quran, Parwez also held a regular weekly meeting in Lahore to deliver a *Dars* (lecture explaining the Quran) in Urdu, and these are also available in audio and video recordings. He dedicated most of his life to researching the Quran and its significance in relation to presenting an alternative solution to human problems, and answering questions relating to human creation, its purpose and the question of death and the next life.

He also participated in the struggle for Independence during the period 1938-1947 and the creation of Pakistan, which was based on the ideology of the Quran, with a view to establishing an Islamic State for the Muslims of the sub-continent. He worked very closely with the founder of Pakistan, Muhammad Ali Jinnah (*Quaid-e-Azam* or Great Leader) and had regular discussions with him on various aspects of the message of the Quran. In order to support the movement for a separate

State for the Muslims of India and to counter the arguments put forward by some of the religious lobby who opposed the creation of Pakistan, he published a monthly journal called Tolu-e-Islam (Dawn of Islam), commencing in 1938.

Parwez joined the Indian Civil Service in the Home Department in 1927, and after the creation of Pakistan he migrated to Karachi and continued to serve in the same department till 1955, when he took early retirement and devoted the rest of his life fully to his work on the Quran. He moved to Lahore from Karachi and settled there.

He left this life on 24th February 1985 in Lahore and his body was laid to rest in Lahore.

FOREWORD

In connection with the understanding of the Quran (*Mafhoom ul Quran*), the series of '*Maarif ul Quran*' by Parwez commenced in 1941, when the first volume of this was published in Delhi (India). The second edition was also published there in 1947, the title of this volume was 'Allah'. After this, other links in this series, Volume I, Volume II, Volume III etc. were published. When the time arrived for the publication of their latest editions, advice was given that since each volume is about a permanent subject, hence, instead of calling them first, second and third volume, every volume should have a separate title according to its subject. This was sensible advice therefore it was accepted. According to this decision, the title of the first volume was suggested as '*Mann O Yazdan*', and the succeeding volumes were published with titles of *Iblees O Adam, Jooy e Nur, Barq e Tur, Shola e Mastoor, Mairaaj e Insaniyat* etc.

This book was published in Pakistan under the title '*Mann O Yazdan*', which remained unavailable for a while. Now the fresh edition (i.e. fourth edition of the original book) has been published after revision of the author. In the previous editions a permanent and long chapter on '*Mashe'at*'[1] was also included. But during this period, the book titled 'The Book of Destiny' by Parwez was published, in the presence of which the need for the chapter on '*Mashe'at*' to be included is considered to be unnecessary. Hence this chapter has been removed.

In this time when the prices of essential commodities are sky high, the publication of new editions of these books is a daunting task. Keeping in mind their importance and due to the demands of members, fresh editions of all of these books have been published. Only one book, *Shola e Mastoor*, remains, which is going into press. During this time, some new writings of Parwez have also been published. The latest book is '*Shah Kar e Risalat*' – Umer Farooq[2], which has earned fame far and wide. Tolu-e-Islam is a missionary institution whose aim is to disseminate and communicate the Quranic thinking of Parwez. May Allah grant us strength for this work!

In the writings of Parwez the reference to the verses of the Quran is like this – the number of Surah comes first followed by the number of the verse.
Salaam!

Tolu-e-Islam Trust
25 – B, Gulberg II, Lahore, Pakistan
March 1974

---

[1] *Mashe'at* – the word here means Allah's Will.
[2] The second Caliph in the early Islamic era.

EDITOR'S NOTE

This book is a translation of the Urdu book '*Mann-o-Yazdan*' by G. A. Parwez, which is a title taken from the Persian language by the author. The literal translation is '*Man and God*'. However, since the purpose of the human creation is to provide an opportunity for man to develop his self, therefore the book has been titled '*The Human Self and Allah*', as the author has discussed in the book, Allah and God are not interchangeable. This is the reason that wherever God of the Quran is referred to by the author, the term Allah is used to differentiate between the two. Similarly, the author has used the term Deen[3] as noted in the Quran, as it refers to a system in its own right. Hence, the word religion has not been used in the book when referring to the Islam of the Quran. The English translation of the Quranic verses is mostly based on the work of Abdullah Yousuf Ali. The term Rasul-ullah refers to the last messenger of Allah, Muhammad (peace be upon him).

Arguments about the existence of God and His nature are ongoing, and these will continue till the end of time. In our time this debate has become more intense, and religions have come under more intense scrutiny. This book throws light on the concept put forward by the Quran, and aids in comprehending the concept of Allah, and its application, need and role in the development of the human self. The Quran repeatedly draws our attention to all the vast array of physical and non-physical signs which are dispersed throughout the universe, including planet earth - an abode selected for man to live his earthly life as a first stage in his life. It repeatedly invites us to question both our existence and the existence of the universe. The Quran's addressee is the human mind i.e. the faculties of intellect and reasoning, the meta-cognitive ability which is exclusively made available to man in order to carry out the purpose of human creation. Then the Quran makes it easy to reflect by pointing first of all to the signs in the outer physical world, and then brings attention back to the inner self of man. It answers all of the requisite questions which can possibly arise in the human mind in all times to provide the most logical answer and evidence which can appeal to human reason. The question of death, and the next life in the hereafter, is discussed in detail and can be understood at an intellectual level by anyone who is looking for a logical explanation of such an important concluding event for every human being in this life. The Quran presents man as being the most important creation at the heart of this universe for whom the universe owes its existence, and it states:

Allah created the heavens and the earth for just ends, and in order that each self may find the recompense of what it has earned, and none of them be wronged. (45:22)

---

[3] Deen is commonly translated as religion which is incorrect. Deen denotes the system by which to manage human affairs within the confines of the Permanent Values of the Quran. This aspect is discussed in detail in the book by the author titled '*What is Islam?*'. (Ed)

In order to explore this verse further, please refer to the book titled *The Life in the Hereafter: What does the Quran say?* by the author. This is a very comprehensive book in which the author has discussed Allah and His attributes in detail as noted in the Quran. The history of the concept of god, and its evolution in relation to the various religions, provides the background to this age-old concept. The concept of Allah as revealed in the Quran is unique, as it is based on Divine attributes which serve as a model for the development of the human self. i.e. since man has a self, hence there is a need for a higher self to serve as a model for man. This is an important point to understand as it changes human outlook and brings a new understanding of human life and its purpose. It also solves the issue of the purpose of death, and casts light on life after death and the immense possibilities which await man for his further development. At the level of the human self, the Quran points to the fact that life continues as one entity and declares physical death to be just the conclusion of the first phase of human existence on this planet called Earth.[4]

In the world today, which is full of conflict amongst people and nations, this and other books by the author provide food for thought regarding an alternative system of life, which can not only accommodate the physical needs of this world, but can also effectively cater for the development of the human self which no man-made system has the ability to do, since human beings cannot reach this comprehension without the aid of the guidance of the Quran. Recognition of the existence of a self within us is the first step towards realising its need for development, and the Quran draws our attention to this fact, and then presents guidance as a perquisite for the development of this self. This takes away all competitiveness, greed and desire for power over other human beings, and once man engages in considering the possibility of no death occurring at the level of the self, then the whole of human outlook becomes focused on the correct priorities in life in this world. This then provides a logical basis for resolving the issue of death which has confused man for centuries. The needs of the human self are different from those of the physical body, and both this book and the book 'Life in the Hereafter' discuss this aspect in detail.

Having convinced our intellect of the presence of a self, we then proceed to convince our intellect of the need to develop it with a view to living a better life in this world and of being assured of the opportunity of further development in the life in the hereafter. However, human intellect only pursues what it considers to be beneficial to its own interest. The question which arises here is, 'how to convince oneself of the need for Quranic guidance?' The Quran draws our attention to its guidance firstly by stating that the purpose of human creation is

---

[4] The Quran points to the universality of human physical death from the viewpoint of the *Nafs* (self), stating: '*Every self will taste death...*' (3:185). The human self does not die as it is non-physical.

accountability[5]; secondly, by pointing towards the outer universe and its laws; thirdly, asking us to examine our inner world and to reflect and reason using our intellectual faculties; and fourthly, points to our death as a fact, and to the possibility of life beyond our physical existence. Allah then invites us to assume the role of a junior companionship, by establishing an order based on the Permanent Values of the Quran, in order to first develop our own self and then help others on His behalf on a global basis. This will not only remove differences and conflicts, which will otherwise always exist without this Divine guidance, but will create an environment in which every individual will benefit from no man-made subjugation, no slavery, complete true freedom to enjoy the benefits of possessing free will and will then live a life free from fear and grief. The Quran declares that this is not a Utopian idea, but it will come to pass eventually at some stage in this world (9:33) – otherwise, this whole creation of Allah's would be aimless and without any long-term purpose, and both the Quran and the evidence presented by the universe point to this fact that Allah does not do this.

In order to understand the solution presented by the Quran to resolve human issues in this life, the reader can refer to three other books by the author.[6] This book is divided into twenty-six chapters of various lengths. All the major Divine attributes have been discussed with their meanings and significance in relation to development of the human self, and their application in the context of establishment of Deen as an Islamic system in the world for the good of the whole of mankind.

I am profoundly grateful to my wife for her help in editing and revising the book. I also acknowledge the help of Mr. Asif Jalil from Karachi, Pakistan in elucidation of some of the terms used in the Urdu version. I am also grateful to Mr. Hussain Kaisrani of Tolu-e-Islam Trust for providing support for this project.

Finally, this work is a translation and as such any ambiguity in the text in the English version which is not present in the Urdu version is my responsibility as a translator and editor and not of the original author. If readers have any question or comment after reading this book, they are welcome to contact the Tolu-e-Islam Trust.

Ejaz Rasool
Glasgow, UK
May 2019

---

[5] Taking responsibility for one's actions is the starting point in the creation of our new self based on *Eimaan,* and as we begin to live our life with an awareness of this responsibility, life becomes more meaningful. In the words of the Quran, this gives birth to a new life e.g. see verse (8:24).
[6] These books are: *What is Islam?, The Life in the Hereafter, What Does the Quran Say?,* and *The Quranic System of Sustenance.*

Table of Contents

10

1   The Human Self and Allah

No-one can deny this fact that the basis of religion is on belief in God. The name of God will change within different religions but acceptance of His existence and belief in Him will be the first condition[7] everywhere. From this the questions which necessarily arise are: what is God? What is He like? Why it is necessary to believe in Him? What happens by not believing in Him? What is the mutual relationship between man and God?

1.1 The Importance of this Question

These questions are, as is obvious, very important, very difficult and very sensitive, and since the time that the human consciousness has awakened, it has been busy making efforts in investigating to find a satisfactory answer.

The Quran has also raised the edifice of Deen on the foundations of *Eimaan* in Allah (*Eimaan Billah*). Therefore, these questions which are mentioned above also confront a student of the Quran. Because the importance of these questions was also in front of the Quran, it has therefore provided answers to them with great detail and emphasis. But it is obvious that each and every individual can only comprehend these kinds of lofty, abstract truths according to his own personal vision and understanding. In the following passages I have attempted to present in brief words that which I have been able to comprehend in this connection according to my own vision. Since (as noted above) this subject is very difficult and these issues are very delicate, I am sure that readers will peruse whatever is said with full concentration and interest and will attempt to comprehend it with extreme attention and reflection. It may happen that as a result of this hard work and endeavour, even greater avenues of Quranic understanding are opened up to us.

If you traverse any period of human history and cast an eye on any part of the earth, you will find that there is one thing every place, every nation and every era has in common, and that is that people will have devised some sort of Being (either a tangible or abstract thing, or an intangible perceptive power) in front of which they bow down, which they worship, and of whose anger or displeasure they are fearful and whose pleasure they consider to be a reason for blessings and approval for themselves. Leaving aside the civilized and developed nations, if you go to such an island where no outsider has previously stepped (according to history), then no matter how different the population residing there may be in other matters, in this

---

[7] There is no doubt in this that some religions e.g. Buddhism are such which deny the existence of God but the state of Buddhists themselves is such that they worship Buddha like a God. Therefore the difference is in name only, the concept being the same everywhere.

common issue their practice too will be equivalent. The famous Greek historian Plutarch (42-107 AD) writes in this regard:

In wandering over the earth, you can find cities without walls, without science, without rulers, without palaces, without treasures, without money, without gymnasium or theatre, but a city without temples to gods, without prayer, oaths and prophecy - such a city no mortal has yet seen and will never see.[8]

1.2 Differences in Concept

Along with this it is also a fact that while such an awareness exists everywhere about such a power, its concept and details are different in every place. Within even one country the 'god' of one tribe does not match the 'god' of another tribe. The 'God' of one country is different from the 'God' of another country. The 'deity' of one nation is distinct from the 'deity' of another nation. The '*Eishwar*' (idol) of one sect is disparate from the '*Eishwar*' of another sect. Until a short time previously, the thinking of one group of Western thinkers was that (and it is possible that there may still be supporters of this idea present there) when early man of the initial era observed that some such disasters occurred (e.g. sudden changes in weather, storms and hurricanes, or epidemics of disease etc.) whose causes and remedies were concealed from his eyes and his mind could not grasp them, then there arose in his heart this idea that it could be that there were very great forces present behind these events which were not visible to him. In this way the concept of 'God' was born in the human mind. This concept varied in different countries according to their circumstances and conditions, and in different tribes according to their situation and environment. After this, as time passed and man made continuous progress, this concept also evolved and in this way, gradually, that concept of 'God' came into existence which is presented by the higher religions of the world. This doctrine is called the 'evolution of the concept of God', details of which will be found in Grant Allen's book *The Evolution of the Idea of God*, or in I.G. Frazer's books titled *Golden Bough* etc.

1.3 Repudiation of This

But later thinkers countered this doctrine and asserted that the correct concept of God has always remained the same right from the very beginning. The question of progression and evolution in this simply does not arise. So much so that the modern famous historian, Dr. Arnold Toynbee, has written the following in his book titled *An Historian's Approach to Religion*:

---

[8] W. M. Urban, *Humanity and Deity*, p. 15

Professor Schmidt's research shows that the concept of the worship of god presented by developed religions is not a new concept which they have invented. The oldest religion of mankind was also this, which has been renewed by developed religions.[9]

Prof. Schmidt's book, *The Origin and Growth of Religion*, from which Dr. Toynbee has quoted the above conclusion, is considered to be the best book on this subject in modern times. In this, he has noted in clear words that '*the concept of that higher deity which exists in the early social life of man, was that very same concept which has been presented by the flag bearers of the monotheistic religions. Therefore, it can be stated with certainty regarding most of the oldest tribes of the human race that this was their concept about God too. Hence, the doctrine of evolutionary religion has been proven to be absolutely bankrupt in the whole field of sociology*'. Since the subject of our book is not to trace the history of the concept of or belief in God, we do not consider it necessary to elaborate further on this point.

1.4 Concept of the Quran

For the purpose in front of us, it will suffice to say only this, that the Quran has informed us that ever since social consciousness awakened in man, guidance of *Wahi* (Divine revelation) commenced descending through the *Anbiya*[10] from Allah. The focal point of this teaching was the correct concept of God, and it is obvious that when the source of this knowledge (*Wahi*) was only one (God), then this concept will also remain one from the beginning to the end (and was only one). But what used to happen was that a messenger would come and would present this high and supreme concept about Allah with great clarity; after some time, this reality would disappear from the eyes of the people, and man, engrossed in his physical senses, would begin mixing the colours of his own thoughts into this clear and transparent concept of Divinity. Sometimes he would make these things his god from which he was afraid and fearful; sometime into those things from which he had some expectations; sometimes he would erect statues of those mental and imagined gods because of their greatness and holiness and carve idols. Hence, these different gods and goddesses – *Inder*, *Agnee*, sun, moon, Ganges, Jumna, snake, cow, bull – all are varying forms of the manifestation of this sentiment of fear and hope (i.e. of dispelling pain and accruing benefit). When, in this way, the darknesses of superstition enveloped the human mind, then another messenger would come and deliver the pure concept of Allah to the people via *Wahi*, and would inform them in clear words that it is the things of the universe which bow to man, not man to the universe: such potentials have been placed in him as a result of which he can harness the things of nature and make use of these according to his choice. The roar of the oceans, the weighty loads of the

---

[9] A. Toynbee, *An Historian's Approach to Religion*, p. 18

[10] *Anbiya* – plural of *Nabi*, which denotes the status of a messenger of Allah as a recipient of *Wahi*. (Ed)

mountains, the eruptions of the volcanoes deep in the earth, the twinkling lights and movements of the milky way, the fearsome torrents and steady, calm drift of rivers, the fast and furious gusts of stormy winds, the desolation and awesomeness of petrifying deserts – so much so, that this whole universe and its different and contrasting images are, every one of them, standing with their hands tied before man in his service. Therefore, to bow down before these things and to conceive of them as masters and rulers - means what?

Thus, this process of *Wahi* continued in this pattern and form until the human mind reached nearer to full adulthood; then this virtuous and pristine, pure and transparent, lofty and supreme concept of Allah was given within the Quran in a complete form, and this heavenly Book was preserved and protected for all times. Therefore, the correct concept of Allah[11] (which Allah Himself has detailed) is within the folds of the Quran in its original and true form (in which there is not an iota of adulteration by the human mind) and is nowhere outside of it. This is because no world religion of today can claim that the book which they call a Divine book is word for word the same one that their messenger received from Allah Himself.[12] Hence, whichever individual wishes that he could obtain that concept about Allah which Allah Himself has detailed, he has no other option except to turn to the Quran for that. The purpose and intent of this book is to explain what is the concept of Allah which is put forward by the Quran.

1.5 The Divine Self

This is obvious that as far as the Self of Allah is concerned comprehending its form and reality, state and composition, is not a matter within the grasp of the human mind. A finite mind can never even begin to conceive of an infinite one. Leaving aside an immense concept such as Allah, modern philosophers and scientists tell us that time has no beginning and space has no limit. In other words, it is wrong to say that time began at such and such a moment and that some corner of the universe is the final frontier. Neither time started from some point, nor is there any final boundary of the universe – we are informed of this by philosophy and science. But if you exert your mind and try to imagine some space which is 'without a beginning' or 'without an end', you will see that such a concept simply cannot be grasped by your mind. The more pressure you put on your mind the sooner you will become uneasy. So if this is the state of affairs regarding the concept of time and space[13], then how can the concept of Allah's Self (Who is the

---

[11] This concept of Allah will also lead to the confirmation of His existence. It will become clear as we go through the book that this concept cannot be invented by the human mind. (Ed)

[12] Details of this can be found in my book titled *Divine Books of the World Religions* (Urdu).

[13] Time and space are in any case abstract entities; the state of the human mind is such that we teach a child in the first lesson of geometry that a point has neither length nor width, nor does it gather space, yet it is visible despite this. You cannot even conceive of such a thing which has no

Creator of time and space) come within the domain of human cognition? This is the reason why the Quran has not stated anything about the reality and form of the Divine Self. It has only informed us as to what His attributes are.

1.6 Divine Attributes

The fundamental aspect of the great and unparalleled Quranic teaching is this, that the concept of Allah which arises before us according to these attributes, no higher, purer and more complete concept can be found anywhere else. The truth is that (as will be explained later) ascertaining the purpose and destination of human life itself is dependent on the concept of Allah. Whatever kind of concept an individual has of God, the life of that individual and the social map of that group (or nation) will be of the same kind. It was probably the Western thinker Kant who said that tell me what type of god a nation has adopted for worship and I will tell you everything about the culture and social structure of that nation. Indeed, it is obvious that when the concept of God which is presented by the Quran is unparalleled and without any visible example anywhere, then the purpose and destination which will be that of human life according to this concept, and the paths which will have been put forward by the Quran in order to achieve these, will also be unparalleled and without any visible example (which is called the guidance of *Wahi*). This is the reason why the guidance which the caravan of humanity receives from the Quran cannot be obtained from anywhere else.

1.7 Human Life

We have noted above that whatever type of concept of God (i.e. Divine attributes) is in front of us, our life (individual and collective) will be of the same kind. It is apparent from this that our life has a very profound and fundamental relationship with the concept of God. This is a very important point which it is essential to understand extremely well. One level of human life is that which is called the animal level. This life is one of purely physical existence (water and mud), whose purpose (like other animals) is preservation of self and procreation. This life is the physical life of this world and it ends with death. It is called the materialistic concept of life. But the Quran tells us that human life is not defined by physical existence (animalistic) alone; there is another thing contained within it which is called personality or human self or 'I' or ego. The Quran denotes it using the term 'Divine energy' and calls it '*Nafs*'. The Quran states:

> *...And breathed into him something of His Ruh (energy) ...(32:9)*

---

length, width and volume, and which is visible despite this and can be perceived. Despite this, we accept the existence of a point, because it is on this very definition that the structure of an important subject like geometry is raised.

The human body keeps changing from moment to moment whereas the human self is not affected by external influences, and if suitable development of the human self takes place, then man can live beyond his physical death and achieve immortality[14].

1.8 Human Self

By denoting the human self using the term 'Divine Energy', the Quran has pointed towards a great truth. It has stated:

(1) Allah has a personality and man also has a personality. It should be clear that the self of man is bestowed on him by Allah and is not a part of the Self of Allah. Personality is an indivisible unity which cannot be divided into parts, and when the human self is not a portion (i.e. part) of the Divine Self, then this belief (of *Vedant*[15] or Mysticism) that the human self will ultimately merge with the Divine Self and in this way the part will join with the whole (as a droplet merges into a river), is contrary to the Quran.

(2) Wherever there is a personality (self), its basic characteristics will be the same.[16]

(3) Since the personality of Allah is the most complete and highest Self, therefore its attributes and traits are also the most complete and highest. The Quran denotes these as *Asma-al-Husna*[17] – these are the different aspects of this Self.

(4) The human self in its miniature form (in comparison with the Divine Self) is finite. Therefore, its attributes are also finite (in comparison with the Divine attributes). But at the same time, all those attributes (in finite form) are present in it which are termed *Asma-al-Husna* in relation to Allah, excepting those attributes which are related to Allah's infiniteness (further details about this will be provided later).

---

[14] I have dealt with this subject in detail in several other works, such as *Iblees O Adam* (Devil and Man), *Insaan Ney Kiya Socha* (What Man Thought*), Islam Kiya Hai* (What is Islam), *Jahaan e Farda* (The Life in the Hereafter) etc. In *Insaan Ney Kiya Socha* in particular, I have shown with evidence that modern thinkers and scientists are gradually coming closer to the Quran's concept of human personality and accepting that death is not necessarily the end of human existence.

[15] *Vedant* – Hindu belief in reincarnation. (Ed)

[16] Every personality (self) of man will be indivisible, possess free will and the freedom to choose, and the potential to develop etc. (Ed)

[17] *Asma-al-Husna* – the literal translation is balanced names. These are Allah's attributes as noted in the Quran. (Ed)

(5) In the Self of Allah His attributes manifest their glory in their completest form. In the human self these attributes are present as realisable possibilities or in a latent, potent or dormant form. The manifesting or actualising of these is the purpose of human life. This is, in essence, what is termed as development of the human self.

(6) It is obviously necessary for a self which is at a lower level that it should keep some higher self as a standard in front of it for its accomplishment. If man does not have such a standard in front of him then he can never say with certainty and assurance that his self is developing, and if it is, then to what extent. In fact, this is also possible that development of his self (*Tazkia-Nafs*[18]) is not occurring at all, while he is absorbed in this self-deception that development of his self is taking place. Hence, it is essential for man that he should keep the Divine attributes in front of him as a standard for the development of his self.

It is for this very reason that the Quran has explained these Divine attributes with such detail and clarity, beauty and proportion, so that there remains no doubt or misgiving, ambiguity or vagueness for these to become a standard for a human being. As these attributes continue to manifest in the human self, he (in the words of the Quran) is 'coloured in the colours of Allah', or he continues achieving 'nearness' to Him.

(7) The display of these attributes in the human self is not such a matter about which no-one else can have any knowledge of – the manifestation of these attributes occurs through the character and conduct of man which presents itself in a tangible and concrete form in front of everyone. This is essentially what is known as the character of man. Bear in mind that according to the Quran the highest character is the eminence of humanity; there is no concept of 'spirituality' (*Ruhaniyat*) other than this. In the Quran there is no mention even of the word 'spirituality'. It has been stated even about Rasul-ullah[19] himself that he was the possessor of *Khulq e Azeem* i.e. holder of the highest character (68:4).

(8) Keeping the Divine attributes as a standard in front of oneself, and declaring the manifestation of these in one's self as being the purpose of life, is called *Eimaan* in Allah.

(9) As previously stated, the human self is received by every individual from Allah but it is received in an undeveloped form. The human self will be

---

[18] *Tazkia-Nafs* – the Arabic term used for the development of the self e.g. (53:32). (Ed)
[19] Rasul-ullah - this term means the messenger of Allah. Here it refers to Muhammad, the last messenger of Allah. (Ed)

strengthened by whichever deed of man is according to the Quranic programme; whichever is contrary to this, will result in weakening and degradation in it (this is called the Law of Requital). The effects of these deeds become apparent in this world as well as in the life after death. Therefore, the meaning of *Eimaan* in the human self means having *Eimaan* in Allah, *Eimaan* in His Law of Requital and *Eimaan* in the life of the hereafter.

From this it is apparent what the fundamental relationship between Allah and man is, and therefore how important it is to have the Divine attributes before us in their true and unadulterated form. The essential consequence of having *Eimaan* in Allah is of man having *Eimaan* in the existence of his own self which takes him far higher than life at an animal level. This is the fundamental difference between the Western materialistic (mechanical) concept of life and the Quranic concept of life, and it is due to this very difference that the paths of both diverge completely from each other – different paths as well as different destinations. Hear this once again - that for the person who does not have *Eimaan* in his own self, his *Eimaan* in Allah means nothing.

1.9 Basic Attributes of the Self

Now let us proceed a step further. Though every personality trait is significant in its own place, two among these are such that they can be declared as being fundamental i.e. freedom and independence. Independence means not to be dependent on another with regards to one's self i.e. to remain established by oneself without any external support (in Quranic terminology this is called *Samdeat*). And freedom (*Hurriyat*) means to be the possessor of the freedom to choose and of the ability to make decisions. Allah, Who is an Absolute Self and complete, in infinite form is:

...and know Allah is free from all wants and worthy of all praise (admiration).
(2:267)

...for your Sustainer is the (sure) Accomplisher of what He plans. (11:107)

This means that in Him the attributes of independence and freedom are infinite (we will discuss *Samdeat* elsewhere). As far as freedom is concerned Allah is the Master of absolute power and limitless authority. But despite this He has Himself imposed some constraints on His powers and controls i.e. self-imposed limitations. For example, the Quran states:

...He has inscribed for Himself (the rule of) mercy ...(6:12)

Allah has made the *Rabubiyat* of the things of the universe His duty (i.e. to provide sustenance and nourishment to them). See! this is a constraint. But by these kinds of constraints no aspersion is cast on the freedom (*Hurriyat*) of this Self. It does not become subservient to another by this. Obedience to external imposed constraints is known as subservience. Obedience to self-imposed constraints is not called bondage. If you reach some place at a specified time by command of another, then this is servitude; however, if you are punctual of your own accord, then this will not be servitude but will be called being principled.

This imposition of limitations by Allah Himself on His absolute powers is the demonstration of a great truth. This means that Allah does not use His powers and forces like an absolute dictator, rather uses these according to laws and procedures. And laws and procedures mean that whatever the demand is of circumstances in the universe, the same kind of Divine attribute manifests. In other words, you can understand it as whatever kind of circumstance there is in the outside world, there is a reaction[20] according to it from Allah.

1.10   Meaning of *Sunnat-Ullah*[21]

This reality that in a specific situation a specific attribute of Allah manifests is called the Divine law. And since the attributes of Allah are immutable, therefore the Divine laws are also immutable. The Quran states:

> *...no change can there be in the Words of Allah...(10:64)*

> *...no change will you find in Allah's way (of dealing): no turning off will you find in Allah's way (of dealing). (35:43)*

The pronouncement of this great truth is that you will never find any alteration or modification in the Divine laws. This means that the system of the universe is not functioning according to 'blind forces of nature' but is functioning according to immutable and established laws. The Quran has placed great emphasis on the study of nature and on observing the working of the universe, it calls this the means by which to meet Allah (face to face):

> *...that you may believe with certainty in the meeting with your Sustainer. (13:2)*

---

[20] It should be clear that when the term 'reaction' is used in relation to Allah, then the meaning of this is definitely not like the meaning of a human reaction. In most situations, human reaction is based on emotions, whereas the Divine Self is beyond emotions.

[21] *Sunnat-Ullah* – translated as the practice of Allah, the way that the Divine laws are established and are immutable. (Ed)

This means that through the study of nature, those Divine laws become unveiled and apparent before man which deal with the operation and functioning of the universe. This is the reason that the Quran declares the study of nature and observation of the universe as being one of the means to have *Eimaan* in Allah.[22]

1.11   Man and Obedience of Laws

In the external universe the Divine laws are continuing to work automatically, and everything is obliged to follow them. None among these things has the power in any way whatsoever to contravene these laws - they are all prostrate before them:

> *Whatever beings there are in the heavens and the earth, do prostrate themselves to Allah... (13:15)*

Whatever is in the highs and lows of the universe, it is all prostrate before the Divine laws; but since man has been endowed with a self and the fundamental trait of a self is freedom, therefore man has not been created to be forced to obey these laws. He has been given this choice that if he wishes he can obey them, and if he wishes he can go against them:

> *...let him who will, believe (have Eimaan), and let him who will, reject (have Kufr)...* *(18:29)*

If he obeys these laws then his self will develop, and if he does not then his self will remain undeveloped, and this is a fact:

> *Truly he succeeds that purifies it, And he fails that corrupts it. (91:9-10)*

The individual whose self becomes developed becomes successful and accomplished, and the one whose self remains stifled, is ruined and destroyed. From this, two or three things become apparent to us:

(1) Obedience of the Divine laws is not like the forced obedience of orders which are imposed externally but is obedience of the constraints imposed by the human self on itself. This is why the Quran has used the word *'Ata'at'* to describe this, which means the carrying out of a task willingly with the full participation of the heart. When a task is carried out under duress, never mind a self undergoing development, it becomes instead suppressed and stifled. By voluntary, wholehearted obedience of Allah's laws (*Ata'at*), the ability of the freedom to choose and intention of the human self expands. The Quran states:

---

[22] Details of this can be found in my book titled *What is Islam*, Chapter 14, *Man and the External Universe*.

On no self does Allah place a burden greater than it can bear …(2:286)

(2) Since these Divine laws are the manifestation of the Divine attributes, obedience of them is obedience of the higher standard of the human self itself i.e. the desire and effort to colour oneself in their colour and to adopt this pattern. In other words, the demands of the human self are satisfied through these. For example, just as in the physical world if an individual is thirsty and is told by another to drink water, this will not be the obedience of an 'order' rather it will be the satisfaction of the physical demand of his own body.

(3) By obeying these laws, on the one hand there is strengthening of the human self and he sees through his own evidence-based vision that his status is higher than the whole of the outer universe, and on the other hand the eminence and greatness of the Divine Self (in comparison to 'own' self) emerges and becomes apparent. As a result, this fact becomes evident that, whereas he is higher and superior to the whole of the universe, his status is far lower when compared to his greatest criterion (the Divine Self). [In *Salat*, *Qayaam* (standing posture) and *Sajda* (prostration) are representations of these very two states. In *Qayaam* the objective is the affirmation of the human self and its superiority compared to the whole universe, and in *Ruku* (bowing) and *Sajud* (prostration), the willing obedience and subservient status of the human self when compared to the Divine Self].

(4) From this it also becomes clear that there can be nothing in the universe like unto man, because in the universe the only possessor of personality is man. Because the Western materialist considers himself (like other things of the universe) to be a product of matter, he can therefore become absorbed in this world of colour and fragrance, but the one who holds *Eimaan* in the Quranic concept of life finds himself to be unique in this physical universe. His companion can be another possessor of a self, i.e. one human being can be the companion of another at an equal level, and at a higher level the companion of man can be Allah Himself. This is the reason that Rasul-ullah has called Allah '*Al-Rafiqul-Aala*' (Companion of a higher status).

1.12   Companion of Allah

The subject of companionship with Allah leads us towards another important aspect of reality. We observe that in the outer universe the results of the Divine laws manifest themselves in a tangible form in front of us, some rapidly, others far later. For example, the seed of any tree contains the potential that if it is nourished according to the Divine law then one day it will become a tall and sturdy tree for all to see. This outcome can come to fruition in front of us during our own lifespan. But there are some schemes of nature which are such that their results become established after many thousands of years. For example, for the first life cell to reach to the human form, after traversing different evolutionary stages, occurred after millions of years.

But we also observe that if man joins hands with that of nature, then not only is there a significant reduction in this time period within which some act had to bear a result (solely according to the laws of nature), but there is also a manifold increase in its beauty and attraction, utility and benefit. That same plant which under normal circumstances blossomed with flowers after six months and that, too, in only one colour, in the laboratories of Europe can bear multicoloured flowers within twenty-four hours. This means that when man becomes the companion of the Divine laws, then swiftness is added to the creative programme of Allah and beauty is created in its outcome.

The form in which the Divine laws, as bearers of results, exists in the outer universe is also that same form which exists in the human world. For example, the Quran declares:

Nay, We hurl the truth against falsehood, and it knocks out its brain, and behold, falsehood does perish! (21:18)

This principle is functioning in the universe that there is a continuous battle between *Haqq* (truth) and *Batil* (falsehood) in it, and in this clash *Haqq* smashes the head of *Batil* and thus *Batil* ultimately becomes destroyed and eradicated. In other words, constructive forces ultimately overcome destructive forces and in this way the universe keeps advancing forward while traversing through its evolutionary stages. As the Quran has stated, this is the law of nature:

...Verily a day in the sight of your Sustainer is like a thousand years of your reckoning. (22:47)

...in a Day, the measure whereof is (as) fifty thousand years. (70:4)

But if human companionship is united in this then this victory of *Haqq* can materialize in a few days. But this companionship can only materialise from those men who have a solid conviction in the truth of the Divine laws, and who are busy making efforts and taking actions for the development of their self according to these (this is what is called *Eimaan* and righteous deeds). A group of such individuals is called a *Jamaat e Momineen* or *Hizbullah*[23]. As a result of the efforts and actions of this *Jamaat* such a society comes into existence in which the Divine laws

---

[23] *Hizbullah* – this means the party of Allah i.e. those who follow His laws. (Ed)

continue to become effective and manifest results within the minimum of time, and in this way the development of the members of the society continues to take place.

1.13   Individual and Society

The Quran has stated in very clear terms that development of the human self cannot take place as a lone individual, this can only take place within a *Jamaat* (a Quranic society). Addressing the individual, it states:

Enter you, then, among my servants! Yes, enter you My heaven. (89:29-30)

If you wish to enter paradise then enter the *Jamaat* of the men of Allah. In another verse it is stated:

...and be with those who are true (in word and deed). (9:119)

This is the reason that the Quran has declared the solitary cloisters of monasteries and the places of worship of mystics as a concoction of the human mind (57:27) which is contrary to the Deen defined and presented by Allah. The Deen of Allah becomes established within a society. Deen provides the principles and values for the mutual relations of mankind. If some individual goes to a jungle where there is no other human being, then he needs neither Deen nor *Eimaan*, nor can development of his self take place, nor is there any form of evolution of human life. In fact, he cannot even live life at a human level. Therefore, Deen demands collectivism, and the development of the self of an individual is only possible within a society.

1.14   Formulation of a Nation

Now let us take another step forward. When any two human beings in the world set the aim of their life as being only one i.e. there is only one objective and destination in front of them, and the pattern according to which they wish to mould their life is also the same, then the creation of mutual harmony in their outlook and vision is a natural outcome – this is what is called unity of thought and vision, or the sharing of *Eimaan*.

This is that unity of thought and vision which the Quran declares as being the reason for the coming together of people i.e. no matter where two persons of the world live, whatever may be their colour, language, race or nationality, if they place the Divine attributes in front of them as external criteria and are engrossed in efforts to develop their self according to these, then both these human beings (despite having differentiations of colour, race, language or nationality) will be members of one *Jamaat* and will be citizens of one nation. The Quran has stated this to be the very criterion for the formulation of nationality. The unity which is produced among men in this way is far stronger and longer lasting than the bonds of blood, colour, language and the relationships of nationality. If this unity keeps spreading, and ever greater numbers of human beings in the world harmonise together in this way and become of one 'colour', then through this the whole of mankind will become one universal brotherhood. It is obvious from this that the necessary outcome of *Tauheed* of Allah (i.e. keeping His Self as a criterion in front) is the oneness of humanity. Apart from this there is no other basis for the oneness of humanity. The aim and objective of the Quran is that gradually all human beings, by making the *Tauheed* of Allah as the practical model of their life, become one universal brotherhood, and in this way all those differences due to which today the world is turning into a den of beasts, are eliminated.

1.15   *Eimaan* in Allah

From the above explanations this reality becomes apparent to us as to what the concept of Allah is according to the Quran, and what it means to have *Eimaan* in Allah. After this it also becomes clear why the Quran makes this demand from all the human beings of the world that they should have *Eimaan* in that Allah Whose concept the Quran has presented. Leaving aside a few atheists in the world, every person, every tribe, every nation is convinced of the existence of God in some form or another. But the Quran declares that your belief in God in this way is not, in truth, the acceptance of God; this amounts to recognition of that God whose concept is coined by you or other men like you. For example, an individual says that I believe that gold is a good metal, its colour is white, humid air causes it to rust, and striking it against a hard material shatters it into pieces, and since it is the lightest metal in the world, it is therefore commonly used in the construction of airplanes. It is obvious that the individual who becomes convinced of the existence of the metal holding these characteristics by calling it 'gold', is in fact denying the existence of (real) gold. Only that person who is convinced of its correct and true characteristics will be acknowledged as accepting the existence of gold. Hence, the belief in God of the individual who may be convinced about God but is not aware of the correct concept of His attributes, is equivalent to denial of the true God. Therefore, *Eimaan* in Allah will be accepted[24] only from the individual who has conviction in that Allah Whose attributes are detailed by the Quran; and those attributes are not noted anywhere other than in the Quran.

---

[24] Acceptance here means that the human self must have the correct concept in mind in order to benefit from this for the development of the self. It may appear harsh, but this is something we experience in our daily life as well. Though we may genuinely believe something to be true this will not make it a fact, thus we may be holding on to something which is false that will affect our subsequent thought process. (Ed)

1.16   Characteristics of Quranic *Eimaan*

Not only is it the case that the concept of Allah which the Quran presents is not available anywhere else, but the concept of the relationship which the Quran details between Allah and man also cannot be found anywhere else. As we have seen, the Quran tells us that:

(1) Allah has control and power over the whole of the universe, but He uses His sovereignty according to His Own laws made by Him, and there is never any change in these laws. In other words, this whole system of the universe is busily functioning within these defined and established laws which are operational and immutable. These very laws are also functioning in the human world which means that every deed of man produces a defined effect and there is never any exception in this. Though every man has a choice in doing whatever deed he wishes, it cannot happen that he performs a deed of one kind but creates the effect of some other. Whatever kind of deed it is, the same kind of outcome will result. These results are established according to the laws defined by Allah.

(2) Excepting those attributes which are purely related to the omnipotence and omniscience of Allah (e.g. that none has created Him, nor has He come into existence from nothing), the fundamental attributes of the human self are the same as the attributes of the Divine Self, with this difference that these attributes of the human self are finite and in a constrained form, and are also undeveloped. Their development can only take place provided that man keeps the Divine attributes as a standard in front of him. This is the fundamental relationship between a human being and Allah. That which is termed as obedience of the Divine laws is not the obedience of the orders of (Allah forbid) a tyrant or absolute dictator, but instead is obedience of the guidance through which development of the human self takes place. By obeying these instructions, the demands of this human self are satisfied.

It is also clear from this that when we mention the Divine attributes (*Asma-al-Husna*), then it is also in fact a reference to the attributes (finite and in a constrained form) of our own self. This is why it is stated in the Quran:

We have revealed for you (O men!) a Book in which is a message for you...
(21:10)

Surely, We have sent a Book in your direction in which is your *Zikr*. (The meanings of *Zikr* are eminence and importance and also to mention).

In the words of Iqbal[25]:

Muhammad is Yours, so is Gabriel, and the Quran too,
But this sweet Word, is it Your representation or mine?

(3) As the human self keeps developing, he continues to become a participant in the creative programme of Allah. In this way the relation of Allah and man becomes one of companionship in which Allah is, however, the Companion with the higher status.

This relationship between Allah and man will not be found anywhere else other than in the Quran. Among the followers of religion in the east the relationship of man with God is only this much that man worships God because this is the command of God, which man has to obey whether willingly or unwillingly. If an individual does not obey His command, then God becomes angry. In order to appease Him it is necessary to make offerings to Him, or to gain intercession through someone 'closer' to Him. When He becomes pleased in this way, the wishes of man are met, and if He remains angry, then man becomes stuck in misfortune.

Contrary to this, according to the philosophers and thinkers of the West, the relevance of God is only related to the outer universe in which His laws (in the form of natural laws) are operating. It is the task of man to study these laws, and by employing them, harness the forces of nature and bring them into his use. As for the human world, in this men will need to resolve their matters through the use of their own intellect and wisdom; for these there are no immutable principles and laws.

Another concept of the relationship with God is that of those people who have faith in 'spiritualism'. They claim that they have a direct contact with God. They talk to God, hold meetings with Him, get the supplications of people accepted from Him, He discloses hidden matters to them etc., etc. The concept of these kinds of connections is also against Quranic teaching. Whatever Allah wished to impart to mankind is conveyed in a complete form for the last time in His Book (the Quran). The only means of contact now with Allah for human beings is by following His Book.

From this, this reality will have become evident to you, why the Quran has proclaimed to the 'God worshippers' of the world:

So if they have Eimaan as you have Eimaan, they are indeed on the right path...
(2:137)

---

[25] Sir Dr. Muhammad Iqbal – Poet of the East.

If these people accept *Eimaan* in the way that you (*Jamaat e Momineen*) have accepted it, only then can you acknowledge that they have found the correct path of life. If they do not accept *Eimaan* like this and continue to believe in God according to their own concepts, then in the register of Allah they will not be counted among those who have '*Eimaan* in Allah' i.e. according to the Quran this will not be called *Eimaan* in Allah. Furthermore, this much should also be fully understood, that the practical concept of having '*Eimaan* in Allah' means to obey His commands and laws. The Quran does not count that individual who accepts Allah in words yet obeys the commands of non-Allah (other than Allah), as being among the followers of Allah:

...if any do fail to judge by (the light of) what Allah has revealed, they are (no better than) Unbelievers. (5:44)

Those people who do not make decisions according to the Book of Allah are the ones who are called *Kafir*[26].

1.17 *Asma-al-Husna* (Balanced Attributes)

Not only has the Quran mentioned the Divine attributes in general terms but by declaring these as *Al-Asma-al-Husna*, has drawn attention towards another fact. *Husna* is derived from *Husn*, and this is the name of precise proportion. If the proportion of a thing is even slightly disturbed, its *Husn* no longer remains. This is why historians have said that 'if Cleopatra had had a slightly flatter nose, the map of history would have been something else'. The meaning of *Asma-al-Husna* is that, whereas these attributes of Allah are most supreme and most complete, infinite proportion is also found in them. The fact is that correct (and constructive) results can only be derived from attributes and traits when there is precise proportion and balance present in these attributes and traits. No prescription can be effective until there is precise proportion in the weight of its constituent medicinal ingredients. Taking this concept further, this reality will become evident that, for example, water is life-giving but only in that situation when there is a correct proportion of it in the human body. If there is even the slightest decrease or increase in its proportion, then human health is adversely affected; not only does health deteriorate, but if its proportion exceeds a limit (as happens in the case of drowning) then this can result in immediate death. Another example is of

---

[26] *Kafir* - this term is used for those who do not accept the Quran as a revelation from Allah. The word is normally translated as non-believer. Its root *Kufr* (K-F-R) has many facets which include to knowingly deny truth, to prevent, to defy Divine laws. Basically, it means to cover or conceal. It means open denial, not hypocrisy (which is concealed). It also means withholding the means of subsistence which Allah has created for the benefit of the whole of humanity. (Ed)

arsenic, which is a killer chemical, but if it is given in a correct dose it promotes life and sustains strength.

Moving away from the physical world, let us enter the domain of ethics in which this same reality can be seen to be working. For example, being gentle is a pleasant trait but if it exceeds a certain limit, then this becomes disgrace. Forgiveness and overlooking something are good traits within limits, but if these limits are exceeded then it becomes cowardice. Spending wealth is necessary for life, but if it deviates towards excess it becomes wastefulness, and if it is held back then it becomes miserliness. Therefore, attributes and traits only produce pleasant effects when their proportion is correct. In other words, in order to establish correct results it is absolutely essential that there is balance in the attributes.

1.18   Apparently Contradictory Attributes

In the same way that there are Divine attributes in the Divine Self, similarly when there is development in the human self, there is a need for its attributes also to have balance. You will see that the whole teaching of the Quran revolves around this central point. It is stated clearly in it which attribute should manifest itself on what occasion, and to what extent this manifestation should be. Allah gives both life and death (23:80). He is also the giver of severe punishment (2:165) and the One Who returns with mercy (2:160). To the superficial gaze there appears to be a contradiction in these attributes, but for the visionary who descends from the surface and reaches down into the depths of reality, he can say with full surety and certainty based on evidence that there is no contradiction in understanding and stating it as such - that water can both promote life as well as end life. This was the superficiality of vision as a result of which Christianity stated that God is Mercy and that salvation is only through His Grace, not through deeds. And on the other hand, Hinduism created the philosophy of '*Karm-yog*', according to which there is no escape whatsoever from the punishment resulting from a wrong deed (big or small). (The doctrine of reincarnation is based on this assumption). In opposition to both these beliefs, the Quran informs us for example, that:

(1) Arsenic, if used in appropriate measure, is useful.
(2) If it exceeds this proportion slightly, then its harmful effects will ensue.
(3) And if it greatly exceeds a certain limit then it becomes fatal.

Point (3) is that condition where the Law of Requital will be declared as being a severe punishment (*Azaab*) i.e. holder of fatal consequences. But under point (2) it is obvious that by taking suitable actions the dangerous effects of arsenic can be removed. This is called *Tawwabiyyat* (returning). This reality is expressed by the Quran in these words:

...For those things that are good, remove those that are evil...(11:114)

This is called *Afw* in Quranic terms. The proper place for these matters will come later, where explanations will be provided of Allah's various attributes in detail. We thought it necessary to illustrate it briefly at this stage so that this reality becomes clear:

a. What the true meaning of the apparently opposing attributes of the Self of Allah is.

b. What the significance of the attributes being proportionate and balanced is.

c. When these attributes become reflected in the self of an individual with correct proportion and balance, he will be declared as the holder of a balanced personality; and the degree to which a balanced personality epitomises true contentment and real peace and happiness, there is no need to say anything further about that.

d. And it is obvious how balanced that society itself will be which consists of such individuals whose personalities are balanced; and the level of peace and tranquility in which humanity will live because of the establishment of such a society, there is no need to elaborate further on that either.

In relation to the Divine attributes, these matters will also not be available anywhere other than in the Quran. This fact will also become apparent from these details later, with what beauty and finesse the ethical values become defined, and with what ease the clash between good and evil becomes resolved which has perturbed and muddled the intellectual world from the beginning till today. (Further discussion regarding this point will come a little later on).

1.19   The Infinite Attributes of Allah

At this stage this much further clarification is necessary that some of Allah's attributes are such that their precise definition (like the form and reality of the Divine Self) is beyond the cognitive limits of our intellect. For example, it is stated in the Quran that *'He is the First and the Last'* (57:3). We have already previously stated that the concept of such a time which has no beginning anywhere can never even enter our mind, nor can we even conceive of the concept of a space which has no limits.

When we state about Allah that He is the First, we simply cannot truly and correctly comprehend His infinitude. Our mind will of a certainty make its beginning from some point or other. Similarly, when we state about Him that He is the Last, then our mind cannot conceive of this either - it will definitely come to a standstill at some point or other. Hence, we cannot make a true estimate of

Allah's being the First and the Last. The most we can say is that 'when there was nothing, there was Allah - and if there had been nothing, there would be Allah'.

The Quran does not, in any case, demand anything more than this from us.

1.20   Permanent Values

Leaving aside such few attributes, the rest of the Divine attributes are those which in modern terminology are called ethical attributes. For example, *Rabubiyat, Razzaqiyat, Rehmaniyat* etc.[27] These are those attributes which are called the Permanent Values. In the Quranic system of life these values have great significance, in fact we can say that the whole structure of this system (*Ad-Deen*) is raised on these foundations.

From this the question arises, why does man need these Permanent Values. He should solve his problems through the use of his intellect and reasoning. There is no doubt in this that man has been endowed with the ability of intellect and reasoning, and this is that trait which differentiates him from other animals. This is why the Quran places great emphasis on the use of intellect and reasoning, and knowledge and vision. According to the Quran, those people who do not make use of intellect and reasoning are:

For the worst of beasts in the sight of Allah are the deaf and the dumb – those who understand not (do not use intellect). (8:22)

And

Many are the Jinns (nomadic inhabitants) and men, We have made for hell: they have hearts wherewith they understand not, eyes wherewith they see not, and ears wherewith they hear not. They are like cattle – no, more misguided: for they are heedless (of warning). (7:179)

Through the use of knowledge and intellect, by studying the things of the universe, man harnesses the undiscovered forces of nature, and in this way becomes eligible for the 'prostration' of the angels (universal forces) before him.

1.21   Battle of Wits

But whereas in the outer universe human intellect becomes so useful in reaping beneficial results, when this same intellect is applied to the human world, then here

---

[27] *Rabubiyat* – means sustenance, *Razzaqyiat* – means nourishment, *Rehmaniyat* – means development. These are discussed in detail later in the book. (Ed)

it plays a strange game; or we can say that so long as the issue remains confined to controlling the forces of nature, human intellect continues to work without conflict and resistance. But as soon as the question of the use of these forces arises, this very same intellect becomes the cause for mutual clash and upheaval among men. For example, in the research for nuclear power, scientists all over the world are busy working in great peace and calmness in their respective laboratories. But once the nuclear bomb is ready, then conflicts erupt among the nations of the world over its use, and these clashes ultimately take on the shape of war, in which these same forces of nature which were to become the cause for the development of humanity, become instead the cause for the destruction of mankind. Why does this happen? This is because the demand of the intellect of every individual, every group and every nation is that it should protect itself, its own tribe and its own nation. It has no interest in the protection of the interests of any other individual, group or nation i.e. human intellect only sees its own interest - it has no concern about the welfare of others. Hence, when there is a clash of interests between different individuals or nations, then a battle of wits commences in their intellects. In other words, it can be understood that the sentiments of benefitting oneself and avoiding harm to oneself are included within the animal instincts of man.

The task of the intellect is to fulfil the demands of the human emotions. For example, there is a beautiful painting in the keeping of an individual and we desire to obtain it (this is the demand of our emotions). However, that individual does not wish to part with this painting (from this point conflict arises in our emotions). Now our intellect moves forward and informs us of various trickeries on how to acquire this painting. Contrary to this, the intellect of the opponent tells him what steps should be taken for the protection of this painting (this can be called the battle of wits). Now it is obvious that the one whose intellect is sharper will be the one who is successful. After this, the opposing party will be on the lookout for an opportunity to take revenge on him – this is, in fact, what is called disorder. This means that the intellect of man follows on behind his emotions, just like the paws of a dog follow its nose (the smell of its prey).[28]

1.22   Decisions Through Laws

For the eradication or solution of these conflicts, a human society devises certain principles which are implemented equally on all the people who live within this society. These principles are called laws. This means that the various citizens of this society accept this fact that in the case of conflicting matters, instead of following their own desires and their own intellects, they will make decisions according to these accepted principles. The individual who does not decide according to these principles is forced by the society to abide by them. It is obvious

---

[28] At this stage these pointers are considered enough. Further details of these issues are available in my other books *Iblees O Adam*, *Insan Nay Kia Socha* and *What is Islam?*.

that these principles (laws) have great significance in the social life of man. The demand of this requirement is:

(1) In the formulation of these principles there should be no intrusion of the emotions of any particular individual, any particular party, or any particular nation.

(2) And these principles should not be such that whenever it is wished these can be changed.

1.23 Immutable Laws

The Quran states that the formulation of these kinds of principles is not within the capacity of human intellect. This is because (in human matters) the intellect can never be free from emotions. Therefore, these principles should be obtained from such a place which is high above human emotions, and for Whom all human beings (not just men of one nation or one era but all of mankind) are equal. Obviously, such a status cannot be of anyone other than that of the Self of Allah.

Permanent Values are those immutable and unchangeable principles which have been received from Allah for the guidance of the whole of mankind so that they can make their decisions in accordance to them. For the practical application of these principles, human society will work out bye-laws and sub-clauses according to the requirements of its own era, but there will be no authority to make any changes or modifications, or any deletions or additions in these principles. As has already been written, these immutable principles or Permanent Values are those Divine attributes which are termed as (with a view to comprehension) 'ethical principles.

1.24 Understanding the Quranic Principles

We have stated above that the formulation of these immutable principles (Permanent Values) is not within the capability of the human intellect. This does not mean that in order to understand these principles, and after understanding them to reach this conclusion that these are indeed true in their claims and do fulfil their aim, is also outwith the scope of the intellect - not at all. The intellect can understand them but there is an essential condition for this, which is that just as a scientist carries out observation and study of the outer universe using his intellect and vision in an objective manner, and does not allow his emotions and biases to influence them, if in the same way attention and analysis is applied to the Quranic principles, then their truth emerges and becomes evident. The Quran itself has informed us of the technique by which to verify the truth of its claims. In Surah *Yunus* it is stated:

No, they charge with falsehood that whose knowledge they cannot compass, even before the elucidation thereof has reached them: thus did those before them make charges of falsehood: But see what was the end of those who did wrong! (10:39)

The first thing which is stated here is that denial of the Quranic proclamations is done by those people who do not comprehend its factual realities based on knowledge (27:84) i.e. it is essential that in order to understand the Quranic facts the level of knowledge up to which human knowledge has reached within a particular era should remain in front of man. 'Up to the level of knowledge of this era' is said because, as the level of human knowledge continues to rise, the Quranic truths keep on becoming uncovered to the same extent.

The second thing it has said is that it is essential that the thinker who is pondering on the Quranic facts should study world history and become aware of the circumstances and conditions of previous nations. He will see what the outcome was of the nation which lived its life according to the principles of the Quran, and what were the consequences for the one that went against them. It is for this purpose that the Quran has repeatedly placed great weight on the study of history.

And the third technique is this, that a society should be allowed to be shaped according to the Quranic principles. The outcomes of this society will themselves reveal whether or not these principles are based on truth and fact. This is called the pragmatic test.

When thinking and reasoning about the facts of the Quran is performed in this way, then its truths will become uncovered one by one. But (as already noted) the condition is that this thinking and reasoning should not be allowed to become contaminated by emotions. As long as human emotions are not kept within the guidance of *Wahi*, the truth can never reveal itself before us. The Quran states:

…And who is more astray than one who follows his own lusts, devoid of guidance from Allah? For Allah guides not people given to wrongdoing. (28:50)

1.25   Problem of Good and Evil

In any event, this reality has also become evident to us that those Permanent Values or immutable principles according to which a human society should be shaped are indeed based on the Divine attributes. From this the significance of having the Divine attributes in front of us in an accurate manner can also be estimated.

We have already stated that through the correct concept of the Divine attributes and by their being balanced attributes (*Asma-al-Husna*) as per the explanation of

43

the Quran, this most complicated problem of good and evil becomes automatically resolved. Briefly, it can be understood as follows: that the deed which is the cause for development, strength and integration of the human self is a good deed (and it is obvious that these can only be those deeds which are in accordance with the Permanent Values or the Divine attributes), and the deed which produces weakness and disintegration in the human self is evil (and it is obvious that these can only be those deeds which are contrary to the Permanent Values). This is the only criterion in the world for good and evil. From this it can also be judged what the relationship is between the Divine attributes and the human self, and what their importance is.

1.26   Comprehensiveness of Divine Attributes

From the above explanations this reality becomes evident that there is no corner of the outer universe and no area of the human world which is such that it is not connected to the Divine attributes. Whether it is the life of an individual in the human world, or the collective life of mankind, the correct shaping and accomplishment of all is on the pattern of the Divine attributes. These same attributes become the higher standard for the development of the self of an individual. And it is from these very attributes that those immutable principles are shaped, and it is by acting according to them that human society becomes a model of paradise. It is to these that the present successes as well as the future ascension of a human being are linked. By remaining dissociated from these, life can never reach the human level and instead remains stagnant at the animal level (indeed, sunk even lower than this).

It is evident from this what the importance is of the correct concept and knowledge of the Divine attributes in human life. This is the reason that the Quran has placed so much emphasis on *Eimaan* in Allah. (The very meaning of *Eimaan* in Allah is to have concrete conviction in the Divine attributes). This is that very basis on which the whole edifice of human life is raised – this is that very seed from which the 'virtuous' tree of righteous deeds bears fruit. In the words of Iqbal:

Life is built by deeds, Paradise as well as Hell.

Therefore, *Eimaan* in Allah is essentially that focal point around which the whole universe of man revolves, and this is the reason that the Quran has explained the Divine attributes with such detailed clarification and exposition. Since this is not available anywhere in the worlds of religions and philosophies, therefore the teaching of the Quran is without parallel or example. And because a complete concept of these attributes is given within it, there remains no need therefore for any other book (this also means any *Nabi* or Rasul)[29] after this.

In the following pages, the Quranic explanations of these Divine attributes will appear before you.

---

[29] *Nabi* – the recipient of *Wahi* (the Divine revelation) from Allah. *Rasul* - the role as a messenger to pass this *Wahi* on to mankind. Both are the roles assigned to the same individual. (Ed)

2. *Ilaah* (god)

2.1 Linguistic Meaning

According to the dictionary, *Ali'ha, Ilay'hi, Ya'lahu* means to seek refuge from someone after becoming fearful, or to become awestruck; and *A'laha, Ya'lohu* means to give protection to someone, or to take them into peace and security. In relation to these meanings, *Ila'hun* will mean such a being from whom protection can be sought when in danger, to whom supplication can be made for the removal of difficulties, and from the perception of whose greatness and immensity man becomes awestruck. Some consider that this word is derived from *La'ha, Ya'lehu,* which means to hold high status and to be hidden from sight.

Some say that *A'laha* means that that person has become a slave, and *Alla'hahu* means that he has made him his slave. From this viewpoint, *Ila'hun* will mean such a being whose supremacy and sovereignty should be accepted, whose law should be obeyed, and whose rule should be adhered to.

Note how the traits noted above can be found in some form or another among the various concepts which the human mind has established about 'god'. Their being supreme and great, hidden from sight, becoming awestruck by its perception, turning to it for help in times of anxiety caused by troubles, prostrating before it with lowliness and humbleness and obeying its orders - in other words, *Ila'hun* is that comprehensive term which encompasses every kind of concept of 'God'.

The Quran has used the word Allah for the Divine Self (details will be given in the next chapter) i.e. Allah is the name of the Self of God, the description of Whose attributes is spread throughout the pages of the Quran like sparkling pearls. For example, we say that Allah is *Raheem*, Allah is *Kareem* – so *Raheemi* and *Kareemi* are attributes of Allah. The view of most about this word (Allah) is that it is in fact a combination of *Al-Ila'hun*. Through frequent usage the word has gradually evolved to become Allah from *Al-Ila'hun*. In the Arabic language, by prefixing *Al*, a common noun becomes a proper noun. From this perspective the meaning of Allah will be that particular *Ilaah* Whose concept the Quran has put forward.

The focal point of Quranic teaching is *La-Ilaha-i-Lallah*[30] i.e. there is no such being, no such power in the universe which can be acknowledged as *Ilaah* – such a being is only the One Who is called Allah by the Quran. In other words, this then means that it is only the law of Allah which is such Whose obedience should be adhered to in the universe; from Whom means of protection should be sought; Who

---

[30] *La-Ilaha-i-Lallah* – traditionally translated as '*There is no god but Allah*'. (Ed)

should be made a shield for all troubles and difficulties. This law of His is so great and high, and master of so much power and supremacy, that man becomes lost in awe at the thought of His greatness and omnipotence. Looking at it from this angle, *Ilaah* brings forward the concept of Allah as a Being, and from another angle it is also His attribute. It is for this reason that we have commenced our illumination from the term *Ilaah*, so that after this the name of His Being (Allah) comes before us, and then the attributes of this Self, one by one, keep on becoming a source for the shining light of the heart and vision.

We have stated above that the fundamental point of Quranic teaching is *La-Ilaha-i-Lallah*. This proclamation has two parts. One ideological i.e. assurance of this matter and acceptance of this fact that there is no such power in the world before which one should prostrate, which should be obeyed, which should be accepted as master, and which should be considered as the focus of attention to meet one's needs – this is a negative aspect. This is a passive part of this teaching i.e. whatever is in the mind about 'subjugation' should be forgotten, and when in this way the land is cleared, then a new structure should be erected over it. This is a positive aspect i.e. after rejecting all powers, acceptance of this fact that there is one and only one such power whose obedience is essential and prostrating in front of which is appropriate i.e. Allah. Removing all powers from the path in this way and creating a direct connection of man with Allah is the fundamental teaching of the Quran. And since the principal teaching of the Quran is not a new teaching but is the same message which is coming from Allah right from the beginning, therefore every messenger would renew this very same message.

2.2 Teaching of Different *Anbiya*[31]

For example, the Quran states about Noah:

We sent Noah to his people: He said: 'O my people! Obey Allah, you have no other Ilaah[32] (god) but Him...' (23:23) See also (7:59)

Regarding a messenger who came after Noah:

And We sent to them a messenger from among themselves (saying): 'Obey Allah! you have no other Ilaah but Him. Will you not fear Him (the consequences of not following Him)?' (23:32)

Regarding the messenger Hud:

---

[31] *Anbiya* – plural of *Nabi*. (Ed)
[32] We have seen earlier that *Ilaah* is a comprehensive word which cannot be translated by any single word. Therefore, we will not translate *Ilaah* in these verses, but in its place will simply write it as such.

...He said: 'O my people! Obey Allah, you have no other Ilaah but Him...' (7:65)

About the messenger Saleh:

...He said: 'O my people! Obey Allah, you have no other Ilaah (god) but Him...'
(7:73) also see (11:61)

And the messenger Shoaib:

...He said: 'O my people! Obey Allah, you have no other Ilaah but Him...' (7:85)
See also (11:84)

About the messenger Ilyas:

Will you call upon Bal[33] (Ilaah) and forsake the Best of Creators – Allah, your
Sustainer and Cherisher, And the Sustainer and Cherisher of your fathers of old?
(37:125-126)

Towards the end of his life Jacob also took this pledge from his offspring. The Quran states:

Were you witnesses when death appeared before Jacob? Behold, he said to his sons:
'What will you follow after me? They said: 'We shall follow your Ilaah and the Ilaah
of your fathers - of Abraham, Ismail and Isaac – the one (True) Ilaah to Him we bow
(in Islam)'. (2:133)

And about the messenger *Dhu al Nun* (Jonah of the fish):

And remember Dhu al Nun when he departed in wrath: he imagined that We had no
power over him! But he cried through the depths of darkness: 'There is no Ilaah but
You: Glory to You: I was indeed wrong!' (21:87)

Moses also said the same to his people when they petitioned him for an idol to be carved for them for worship:

He said: 'Shall I seek for you an Ilaah other than the (true) Allah, when it is Allah
Who has endowed you with gifts above other nations?' (7:140)

This was because at the Divine Station of *Tur* he (Moses) was entrusted with this same commandment:

---

[33] *Bal* – this was the name of a deity. (Ed)

'Verily, I am Allah: There is no Ilaah but I: So serve you Me (only) and establish Salat to celebrate My message. (20:14)

This was also the teaching of Jesus which he will affirm in front of Allah:

And behold! Allah will say: 'O Jesus the son of Mary! Did you say unto men, ' Follow me and my mother as Ilaahs in derogation of Allah?' He will say: 'Glory to You! Never could I say what I had no right (to say). Had I said such a thing, You would indeed have known it…For You know in full all that is hidden'. (5:116)

2.3 The Teaching of the Quran

This same teaching, protected and preserved in complete form, was passed on to the whole of mankind via Rasul-ullah[34]. The Quran states:

…'Can you possibly bear witness that besides Allah there is another Ilaah?' Say: 'No, I cannot bear witness!' Say: 'But in truth He is the Ilaah, and I truly am innocent of (your shirk of) joining others with Him. (6:19)

In Surah *At-Tauba* it is stated:

But if they turn away, say: 'Allah suffices me; there is no Ilaah but He, on Him is my trust. He is the Sustainer of the Throne Supreme'. (9:129)

In Surah *Ra'ad*:

…Say: 'He is my Sustainer! There is no Ilaah but Him! On Him is my trust, and to Him do I return!' (13:30)

This teaching was revealed via *Wahi* (revelation):

Say: 'What has come to me by Wahi is that, your Ilaah is one Ilaah: Will you therefore bow to His Will (follow His laws)?' (21:108)

The same *Wahi* is referred to in another verse as follows:

Say you: 'I am but a man like you: It is revealed to me by inspiration (through Wahi), that your Ilaah is one Ilaah…' (41:6)

Then it is stated:

---

[34] Rasul-ullah – the last messenger o Allah, Muhammad (PBUH). (Ed)

49

Say: 'Truly am I a warner, no Ilaah is there but the one Allah, Supreme and Irresistible'. (38:65)

Emphasis is placed on this same teaching by the following words:

Know, therefore, that there is no Ilaah but Allah...(47:19)

In another verse it is stated:

Allah! There is no Ilaah but He: and on Allah, therefore, let the Momineen (believers) put their trust. (64:13)

This was mention of the messengers individually. Collectively, it is stated:

Not a messenger did We send before you without this Wahi sent by Us to him: that there is no Ilaah but I: therefore follow and serve Me. (21:25)

This is that teaching whose source is the Divine guidance. Whatever errors occurred in this teaching, they were all the created machinations of the human mind. Allah Himself is a witness on the established evidence-based truth of this teaching, His angels (forces) are a witness, and those learned scholars are a witness who establish a system of justice in the world:

There is no Ilaah but He: that is the witness of Allah, His Malaika and those endued with knowledge, standing firm on justice. There is no Ilaah but He the exalted in Power, the Wise. (3:18)

The pristine concept of the true *Ilaah* is found within the Quran:

And your Ilaah is One Ilaah: there is no Ilaah but He, Rehman and Raheem[35]. (2:163)

That *Ilaah* about Whom it is declared:

Allah is He, other than Whom there is no Ilaah, Who knows (all things) both secret and open, He is Rehman and Raheem. Allah is He, other than Whom there is no Ilaah, the Sovereign, the Quddus[36], the source of peace (and perfection), the Provider

---

[35] *Rehman and Raheem* – both these terms have a common root *Rehm* (R-H-M) which has basic meanings of softness, provision of means of protection and cover. It is related to sources of sustenance and nourishment. *Rehm* also means a mother's womb which provides nourishment without any recompense to a child. For further details see *Lughat-ul-Quran*, Vol. 1, p. 548. (Ed)

[36] *Quddus* – means someone being free from all kinds of faults and blemishes; an attribute of Allah. The root is *Q-D-S*. See *Lughat-ul-Quran*, Vol. 2, p 337. (Ed)

of peace, the Preserver of safety, the Exalted in might, the Irresistible, the Supreme. Glory to Allah! Beyond is He above the partners they ascribe to Him. He is Allah, the Creator, the Evolver, the Bestower of Forms, to Him belong the most balanced attributes, whatever is in the heavens and the earth do follow His laws and He is the exalted in might, the Wise. (59:22-24)

He is that *Ilaah* whose attributes are the following:

Allah! There is no Ilaah but he – the Living, the Self-subsisting, Eternal. No slumber can seize Him nor sleep. His are all things in the heavens and on earth. Who is there that can intercede in His presence except as he permits (as per His Law)? He knows what (appears to His creatures as) before or after or behind them. Nor shall they compass aught of His knowledge except as He wills (per His Law). His Knowledge and Sovereignty extends over the heavens and the earth, and He feels no fatigue in guarding and preserving them. For He is the Most High, the Supreme. (2:255)

Man makes as his god the one whom he believes to be the possessor of some authority and power. And the Quran uproots from its foundation even the very concept of this, that other than Allah anyone else possesses any authority and power at a fundamental level. Therefore, when no-one else other than Allah even possesses any authority and power, then how can there be any god (*Ilaah*) other than Him? The Quran states:

Say: 'Think you, if Allah took away your hearing and your sight, and sealed up your hearts, who – an Ilaah other than Allah – could restore them to you?' See how We explain the signs by various symbols, yet they turn aside. (6:46)

At this point in time we have only briefly mentioned a few attributes of the true *Ilaah*. Since detailed explanations of all the attributes of Allah will be given in the following pages, it is therefore not necessary to go into these details in this chapter. At this stage it is also essential to make this much clear, that the true *Ilaah* of the Quran is the *Ilaah* of the whole of mankind:

The Ilaah of mankind. (114:3)

He is the One Allah of everyone, irrespective of colour, race, nation, country, and when there is only one *Ilaah*, then the whole of mankind is one brotherhood in which racial or national differentiation can have no place. This concept of universal brotherhood and unity of mankind takes birth from the concept of the *Ilaah* of the Quran. The Quran has also informed us of this fact that the creation of the whole of mankind originated from a single cell (39:6) and all human beings are part of one universal brotherhood, among whom the common value connecting them is the Oneness of Allah. (Details of these matters will be found at their respective places).

2.4 Addressing Intellect and Reasoning

It is not the way of the Quran to make someone accept a belief contrary to intellect and reasoning; it always appeals to a true intellect and a good heart. When it extended an invitation towards one *Ilaah*, it was not because (Allah forbid) it could not bear to watch the 'gods' of other religions or other nations being worshipped, but was because it is a fact that there can only be one *Ilaah*:

If there were, in the heavens and the earth, other Ilaahs besides Allah, there would have been confusion in both! But glory to Allah, the Rabb of the Throne, (high is He) above what they attribute to Him! (21:22)

Details of this aspect are stated in another verse as:

No progeny did Allah beget[37]*, nor is there any Ilaah along with Him: (if there were many Ilaahs), behold, each Ilaah would have taken away what he had created, and some would have lorded it over others! Glory to Allah! (He is free) from the (sort of) things they attribute to Him. (23:91)*

Though this is merely a short sentence, from the viewpoint of meaning there is a world of realities concealed within it. By reflecting on the coordination and harmony of the system of the universe, this reality will become evident that this great and mighty scheme is following a special programme, and that there is a precise synchronization and mutual relationship in the constituents of this machinery which mesmerizes the intellect. This amazing complex cannot function with this degree of order and precision unless the authority controlling it is not one. In the presence of two forces possessing different intentions this system cannot function for even one moment. In the movement and revolution of the sun, if there is even a difference of one thousandth of a second, the solar system will disintegrate within a moment. Discoveries of science have made this reality clear that those things of the universe which seem apparently independent, isolated and unrelated, are in fact also mutually dependent upon each other and interrelated. From this it is clear that if there are two, or more than two, permanent beings possessing powers of freedom to choose in arranging the affairs of the

---

[37] This is a statement of fact which requires our profound attention. Whatever we as human beings acquire as we live our life becomes a part of our self, which we cannot pass on to our children e.g. our experiences, education, training, knowledge etc. Allah's Self is infinitely developed, and He is non-physical as we understand our body; hence there is no question of even having any thought of progeny of Allah. According to the Quran, there is nothing in the universe like Him and He is beyond the ability of human imagination and conception. (Ed)

universe, then the consequence will be a dichotomy of outcomes! The Quran has used one word, *La-Fasadata*, for this consequence in which the true picture of 'dichotomous outcomes' or anarchy is present. When every link in the chain of some system is working correctly in its own place, then that system is functioning optimally, and not being in a state of optimum is called *Fasad*, in which that system becomes disturbed and dispersed, and becomes non-functional, and the mutual coordination and synchronization between its constituents disappears. This *Fasad* is created as a result of commands from more than one authority. If there are two fully autonomous drivers inside an engine, then by imagining the consequences which will ensue from the implementation of their own individual intentions, the detailed meaning of *La-Fasadata* can be comprehended. The concept of different gods (whether these are permanent entities like *Aharman o Yazdan*[38] or different disciples of one *Brahma* like a goddess or god, or manifestations of his different powers e.g. *Shiv, Vishnu* etc.) is a remnant of the infantile intellectual period of the human mind, when it used to be thought that there is no coordination and harmonization between the different parts of the system of the universe, instead, they function separately from each other. Winds blow by their own force, therefore there is a need for the god *Dayo*. Rain happens with its own force, therefore there is a need for the god *Inder*. Birth, life and death – there is a need for a separate god for each and all. But when human intellect, having reached its adulthood, witnessed this state of the universe through observations and experiences that '*split the heart of a particle, and blood will drip from the sun*'[39], then where is the possibility for such a belief that the system of the universe is functioning under more than one authority?

The Quran, which assesses realities on the anvil of knowledge and intellect and erases superstition and ignorance, has stated that that Being is the possessor of infinite powers and limitless authority. And He is not in need of this - that various agents and workers should become His hands and arms and assist Him by being in charge of various departments in order to manage and organise the universe.

Turning away from the physical universe, if we look at the social, public and cultural life of man, there too the modern era is the best (or worst) model of the *Fasad* (confusion and conflict) which is produced by the belief in many 'gods'. The fire of these troubles and conflicts, dissatisfaction and absence of tranquility is raging because men have kept separate 'gods' carved out, and the 'god' of one is engaged in battle with another. (Details of these gods will be given later). In place of all these different 'gods', make one real *Ilaah* the centre and then see if all this chaos converts into peace or not. This chaos exists only because the human mind has created more than one *Ilaah*. The '*Ilaah*' of one nation does not allow another nation to exist. The 'god' of one nation is devouring up the people of another

---

[38] *Aharman o Yazdan* – two gods in ancient Persian belief system. (Ed)
[39] A quote from M. Iqbal, philosopher and poet. (Ed)

nation. Every '*Ilaah*', taking its own 'subjects' and its own party with it, is overpowering the other. Everywhere there is conflict, there is not a vestige of equilibrium to be found anywhere. The solution of the universal ideology for which man is searching will be found only in this doctrine, that the God of all countries and nations i.e. the whole of mankind, is only one Allah and also that the whole world should follow only His laws. This is the reason why the Quran has opposed *Shirk*[40] so severely because no system can remain in its correct state through *Shirk*. Warning after warning is given not to propose any other *Ilaah* with Allah:

> *And make not another Ilaah an object of obedience along with Allah: I am from Him a warner to you, clear and open! (51:51)*

This is because everything of the universe is changing and heading towards an end, therefore no entity among these is capable of running the system of the universe permanently on one pattern:

> *And call not, besides Allah, on another Ilaah. There is no Ilaah but He. Everything that exists will perish except His own Face.*[41] *To Him belongs the command, and to Him will you be brought back. (28:88)*

There is no power in the world which is such that it is capable of sharing in His sovereignty and power. His is the only Law which is operational in the universe:

> *Or have they an Ilaah, other than Allah? Exalted is Allah far above the things they associate with Him! (52:43)*

2.5 Incredulity at the Belief of *Tauheed* (Oneness)

Since the concept of focusing all forces into one Self was based on the reality of an organised world and mutually harmonised universe and this fact appeared to be a novel thing to the human mind, when this concept was presented to them, they therefore expressed extreme astonishment. (And what kind of truth has there been which knowledge and reasoning presented before man, and to which ignorance and superstition did not object?) They stated with disbelief:

---

[40] *Shirk* – associating others with Allah and following other laws along with Quranic laws i.e. mixing man-made laws with Quranic laws, establishing and following a system other than Deen as revealed in the Quran. The Quran declares that this practice will lead to ruin in this life as well as the next e.g. see verse (2:85). This has been dealt in the author's book titled *Islam: A Challenge to Religion* p. 36 (Ed)

[41] Other than His Self, everything is changing. Sovereignty belongs only to Him and everything is heading to Him. This meaning is taken from the Urdu book by the author. (Ed)

Has he made the gods (all) into one Ilaah? Truly this is a strange thing! (38:5)

And taking this concept to be (Allah forbid) a meaningless thing, they would disparage it with mocking laughter:

For they, when they were told that there is no Ilaah except Allah, would puff themselves up with pride. (37:35)

And would call the one presenting it (Allah forgive) insane:

And say: 'What! Shall we give up our gods for the sake of a poet possessed?' (37:36)

But the Quran took no notice of this rebuff and evasion because it had full certainty that following the progression and advance in knowledge and intellect, when the secrets of the universe open up before man, he would be automatically obliged to accept this truth that there can only be the Will of One Being working behind this system. In order for the universe to function with such equilibrium and discipline, unity of law is indispensable:

Those who adopt, with Allah, another Ilaah: but soon will they come to know (what the truth is). (15:96)

This is why it is a proclamation of the Quran that those people who have conviction in more than one god have no evidence with them in support of this claim:

Or have they taken for obedience other Ilaahs besides Him? Say: 'Bring your convincing proof'...(21:24)

In this verse *Burhan* (proof, evidence) has been demanded, but as noted in another verse, this is merely a way to state that they do not possess any *Burhan* in any case:

If anyone invokes, besides Allah, any other Ilaah, he has no authority for this...23:117)

Furthermore, it has also been declared that since the claimants of these beliefs have no logic or evidence, on the discovery and disclosure of the facts they will come to realise in how great an error they were trapped, and the state in which they will find themselves from this humiliating defeat does not require further elucidation.

2.6 Humiliation and Ruin of Man Through *Shirk*

The true reality of *Shirk* only becomes revealed to man when he becomes aware of the worth of his own eminence and personalised self. He comes to know at that moment how worthless he had made his own self as a result of making these lowly things as his gods. This is why it is stated:

Take not with Allah another object of obedience; or you (O man!) will sit in disgrace and destitution. (17:22)

In another verse:

...Take not, with Allah, another Ilaah (object of obedience) lest you should be thrown into hell, blameworthy and rejected. (17:39)

In Surah *Shu'ara* it is stated:

So call not on any other Ilaah with Allah, Or you will be among those under the penalty. (26:213)

In Surah *Qaf* it is stated:

...Who set up another Ilaah beside Allah: throw him into a severe penalty. (50:26)

The servants of Allah (*Ibaad-ur-Rehman*) never bow down before anyone else because they are cognisant of the eminence of their self:

Those who invoke not, with Allah, any other Ilaah...(25:68)

2.7 Tyrannical Forces

Among the example of these servants of Allah, the companions of the cave are quoted who had made a resolve to not bow down before anyone other than Allah.[42] How could tyranny tolerate seeing such a purpose flourish and how could the religious elite bear this kind of rebellious slogan against their 'gods'? Therefore, it is obvious what kind of dangers and difficulties they would have had to face. Ultimately, the consequence was that they were obliged to leave their settlement and take refuge in a cave[43]:

---

[42] The narrative of the companions of the cave is detailed in Surah *18, Al-Kahf*. The Quran does not specify the number of companions. (Ed)

[43] For further details see the Urdu book *Shola-e-Mustoor* by the author.

We provided strength to their hearts: Behold, they stood up and said: 'Our Sustainer is the Rabb of the heavens and of the earth: never shall we call upon any Ilaah other than Him: if we did, we should indeed have uttered an enormity! These our people have taken for obedience Ilaahs other than Him: why do they not bring forward an authority clear (and convincing) for what they do? Who does more wrong than such as invent a falsehood against Allah?' (18:14-15)

And notwithstanding the era of the companions of the cave, those who wish themselves to be considered as a 'god' have always utilised tyranny. Pharaoh had said the same to Moses:

He said: 'If you do put forward any Ilaah other than me, I will certainly put you in prison!' (26:29)

And intoxicated by power and authority, he mocked:

Pharaoh said: 'O Chiefs! No Ilaah do I know for you but myself: therefore, O Haman! Light me a kiln out of clay, and build me a lofty palace, that I may mount up to the Ilaah of Moses: but as far as I am concerned I think he is a liar'. (28:38)

In another verse it is stated:

Pharaoh said: 'O Haman! build me a lofty tower, that I may attain the ways and means of reaching the heavens, and that I may mount up to the Ilaah of Moses: but as far as I am concerned, I think Moses is a liar!' Thus was made alluring in Pharaoh's eyes, the evil of his deeds, and he was hindered from the path; and the plot of Pharaoh led to nothing but perdition (for him). (40:36-37)

But the end that resulted for Pharaoh also portrays to us that when a *Mushrik*[44] makes a claim without presenting proof and evidence, to what extent this is based on truth. When his helplessness became apparent to him then this reality became clear to him that, in truth, there can only be One *Ilaah*:

...At length, when overwhelmed with the flood, he said: 'I believe that there is no Ilaah except Him whom the children of Israel believe in: I am of those who submit (to Allah in Islam). (10:90)

'Pharaoh said, there is no *Ilaah* other than me' – from this the meanings of *Ilaah* becomes clear. The invitation of Moses was that, having freed them from the slavery of Pharaoh, Bani Israel should be settled in an environment of freedom

---

[44] *Mushrik* – the one who commits *Shirk*. (Ed)

where they could purely follow the laws of Allah. The claim of Pharaoh was that in his country obedience and submission could only be to him, therefore Bani Israel could not be given permission to adopt obedience to the laws of someone else. From this it is obvious that *Shirk* is not only that man prostrates before idols made of stones, but a far bigger *Shirk* than this is that man obeys the man-made laws of men in place of the Divine laws.

2.8 Shirk of Zoroastrians

The Magi (Parsees, who call themselves followers of Zoroaster) believe in two permanent gods – one a god of virtue and one of evil; one a god of light and one a god of darkness. The Quran has repudiated this dogma as well:

Allah has said: 'Take not for obedience two Ilaahs': For He is just One Ilaah: then fear Me (and Me Alone). (16:51)

2.9 Trinity

Christians believe in three gods: Father, Son, Holy Spirit. This dogma is also false:

They do blaspheme (do Kufr) who say: Allah is one of three in a Trinity: for there is no god except One Ilaah...(5:73)

The Greek belief of Triad which became the Hindu belief based on spirit, matter and God, is also included in this.[45]

2.10 *Ahbaar* and *Ruhbaan* (Religious Scholars and Priests)

The people of the Book had made priests and religious scholars associates of Allah. Through the path of reverence, shrouded in the veil of human holiness and saintliness, this belief becomes embedded in the mind, and in this manner makes its home in the depths of the heart in such a way that its eradication becomes extremely difficult:

They take their priests and their anchorites to be their sustainers in derogation of Allah, and Christ, the son of Mary; yet they were commanded to follow but one Ilaah: there is no Ilaah but He...(9:31)

---

[45] The belief of Hindus is also like that of the Trinity. Believing from ancient times in Brahma (God), *Prakarti* (matter), and *Atma* (spirit/soul), they hold a conviction in 'one in three and three in one'. The famous theologian and philosopher, Ramanuja, was a proponent of this belief and it this very belief which is found in his philosophy.

These people of the Book were told that making a god out of the *Anbiya* and messengers, priests and religious scholars, is not a teaching from Allah, rather it is the consequence of your own deliberate concoctions:

> *...There is no Ilaah except Allah; and Allah is indeed the Exalted in Power, the Wise.*
> *(3:62)*

2.11   Invisible Faces of *Shirk*

Other than these tangible faces of *Shirk*, the Quran describes such an aspect of *Shirk* which the human eye cannot perceive. Describing this indiscernible thing as *Shirk* is only possible by that Allah the All Knowing, All Seeing, Who is acquainted with even the thoughts which pass through the depths of the heart. He states:

> *Do you see such a one who takes for his Ilaah his own passion? Could you be a disposer of his affairs for him? (25:43)*

In another verse:

> *Then see you such a one as takes as his Ilaah his own vain desire? Allah has, knowing (him as such) left him astray, and sealed his hearing and his heart, (and understanding), and put a cover on his sight. Who, then, will guide him after Allah? Will you not then understand? (45:23)*

Keep these Divine verses in front and then cast your eyes on any part of the current day civilised world, and then sometimes peep and search into the most delicate corners of your heart, and then see how many worlds of facts and realities are concealed within this one verse. We have already seen that the Quran declares that chaos arises through accepting more than one *Ilaah*. Just ponder, is the reason for this chaos and mayhem that is erupting from all sides today not simply this, that every human heart is becoming an abode for idols? Every group and every nation has made their own desires into their gods and under the influence and control of these 'gods of desires and emotions', no distinction between right and wrong is retained. Right is that through which an aim is achieved (according to Lenin and Machiavelli) and wrong is that which obstructs the achievement of aims. These are those idols which have turned the world into hell. These idols are not carved at the home of some sculptor but are in fact continually moulded in the factory of the human mind. Their abode is not some temple but the human heart. The idol of possessions and progeny, the idol of prestige and status, the idol of wealth and prosperity, the idol of regime and government, the idol of nation and race - and Allah knows[46] what kind of *Laat* and *Manat* and what kind of *Habl* and *Uzza*[47] are concocted in the human mind at every moment.

This is that frightening and terrifying cliff edge of *Shirk* from which, having slipped, man falls straight into the dreadful destruction and ruin of hell. The Quran has stated that these are those people who go astray despite knowledge. Knowledge differentiates between *Haqq* and *Batil*, but once emotions overwhelm the intellect and desires overpower the mind then knowledge and intellect are never able to show the right path. Having reached this stage, man's ears become deaf to the bells of danger, veils descend over his eyes, his heart becomes rusty and he cannot see the consequences of the results of his deeds. According to George Bernard Shaw, 'Europe is flowing along on a river of emotions and does not consider what kind of an ocean of ruins its end is'[48]. There is no dearth of knowledge in Europe, but all the knowledge is being used in this endeavour, to find what kinds of techniques can be most effective and implemented most rapidly for its own supremacy and for the slaughter of others. The very cause for Allah's earth being so constricted for mankind today is the fact that this knowledge is functioning in submission to the emotions. Man has made his own desires into his deity. If knowledge works globally according to the true *Ilaah* and His laws, then this same hell will become a paradise. Knowledge will, at this time too, still think of making guns and ammunition, but after the gun is made, its direction will not be decided according to the vested interests of men. The decision whether the gun will be used to halt the evil of a tyrant, or whether its target will be the home of weak and feeble nations, will not be made by the manufacturer of the gun but will be made by another power. This is that very point where man is in need of heavenly guidance and *Wahi*. When man uses the outcome of his knowledge according to the laws of Allah, then this same knowledge which today is the destroyer of humanity will become a blessing for humanity. And then the true meaning of '*There is no Ilaah, but Allah*'[49] will be comprehended.

Cast an eye one more time on the attributes of the real *Ilaah* which have been presented to you in the previous pages and see if there is any such aspect of life omitted for which there is the need to seek another '*Ilaah*':

a) Who gives life
b) Provider of nourishment
c) Provider of sustenance
d) Who bestows peace and security

---

[46] This means that if we use the light of the Quran then we, too, can identify all of these man-made idols. (Ed)
[47] *Laat, Manat, Habl, Uzza* - these are idols of the era when the Quran was revealed. (Ed)
[48] Bernard Shaw uttered these words prior to the war in Europe (1939). This war made it clear what that ocean of destruction was in which Europe drowned through its own hands. For further details see *Insaan Ney Kiya Socha* (What Did Man think).
[49] *La-Ilaha-il-Lallah* – this is the Arabic as already noted earlier. (Ed)

e) Who is always watching
f) Who solves problems
g) Who sets things right in all matters
h) In Whom complete trust can be placed
i) Who is called out to in times of hopelessness
j) Who has control of benefit and harm
k) Who has knowledge of both the visible and the unseen
l) Who has power over all
m) Who is Owner of supremacy
n) Who is beyond any fault
o) Master of masters
p) The True Sovereign
q) For Whose life there is no end
r) To Whom all turn for help

Can there be another being other than this Being Who is capable of having obedience to Him accepted, Whose sovereignty should be acknowledged and before Whose laws man should bow? After this, think, what is the meaning of *La-Ilaha?*

But not only *La*, after this *Illa* as well i.e. after the negative comes the positive, the affirmation; construction after destruction; acceptance after refusal; after *La-Ilaha - il-Lallah*. Let us now go to *Illa* after this *La* because just as acknowledgement of the true Allah is impossible until every non-divine force has not been rejected, in this same way mere rejection is also anarchy and chaos until there has not been acceptance of Allah. *La-Ilaha-il-Lallah* – this is the complete Eimaan.

3 Allah

As has already been stated under the previous topic, the personal name of God according to the Quran is Allah which is a combination of *Al* and *Ilaah* i.e. that One *Ilaah* Whose concept is presented by the Quran, and Whose attributes have been explained in it in such great detail.

3.1 Grasping the Reality of the Self

What is Allah? What kind of Being is He? What is the form and reality of His Self? Where did He come from? These are those questions whose answers are outwith the scope of human intellect. Intellect is, in actuality, the name of those collective outcomes which man achieves through his knowledge and observations, and it is obvious that the means through which man obtains knowledge are finite. So when those means are finite, then the product of those means will also be finite, and how can the finite conceive the infinite? What can that man who so far has not even been able to determine what he himself is, determine as to what Allah is? How can that individual who is restricted in reaching the reality of a machine encompass the form and reality of the creator of the machine? Knowledge of the composition of the Divine Self is beyond the scope of human vision. This is the reason that the Quran does not demand visual recognition of Allah – it demands acceptance of *Eimaan* (in Allah).

3.2 *Eimaan* and *Irfaan* (Recognition)

The second method by which to evaluate something which man is not able to comprehend directly is to appraise something which is similar to it; however, that Being (Self of Allah) has no example like it and is invisible:

> *…there is nothing whatever like unto Him…(42:11)*

Therefore, how can the form of Allah be envisioned by the human mind?

Habituated to perceiving things via his senses, man always desires that even the most abstract realities should display before him in the physical form, or at least that this metaphysical reality should be interpreted in such a way that it can form a tangible concept in his mind. This was that fundamental error as a result of which man adopted the worship of idols. Since Islam is a Deen of intellect and reasoning, it therefore closed all those doors through which the paths of this kind of superstition could enter the human mind. It has not mentioned any such example about the Divine Self which may, as a consequence, cause the human mind to drift towards some concrete and visible form of Allah. The Quran wishes to preserve reality as reality; it does not wish to convert the Divine Self into a sculpture in order to fulfil a demand of the human mind.

3.3 Divine Attributes

As has already been written, the reality and form of the Divine Self are beyond the boundaries of perception. However, no-one (barring a few atheists) denies the existence of God. This denial by atheists is also not really a denial but merely a twisting of words. According to believers the power which is maintaining direction and order in the universe is God, and according to non-believers it is nature. Their minds can neither encompass the form of the Divine Self nor can they express the reality of nature. The human mind can determine the process of cause and effect up to the extent of the physical world but cannot reach the truth of the first cause.

The things by which the concept of Allah is imprinted on the mind are His attributes i.e. what powers Allah is Master of, what are the various ways in which His laws operate in the system of the universe etc., etc. Through the correct concept of the Divine attributes, the correct *Eimaan* about the real Allah takes birth in the human heart, whereas through the incorrect interpretation of these attributes, man becomes a follower of falsehood. The Quran has explained the Divine attributes in such detail and with such precision that man is enabled to establish the correct concept of Allah according to these. No religion among all the religions of the world is such that it can state with surety and certainty that its heavenly book is free from any tampering and additions and pure from contamination by the human mind. Leaving aside the claiming of this with certainty and surety, they admit and agree that they do not even possess the book of the founder of their religion in its original form.[50]

3.4 God As Invented by the Human Mind

So it is obvious now that the kind of concept which the human mind will manufacture about god according to these books which have been tampered with, will only be a prototype of those human ideas themselves i.e. the attributes of god will merely be an extended form of human attributes themselves. For example, man has two hands and god will be given four hands. Man can pick up a stone, so god will be able to lift a mountain. Man has a height of around five or six feet, so god will have a height of fifty or sixty feet. The gods and goddesses of India and the statues of Greek idols are manifestations of this very belief. Outwith man himself and the signs of nature, the human mind is not capable of constructing any other concept of god, and the greatest inherent proof of this fact is that other Divine books have been adulterated by the human mind.

---

[50] Details of these matters will be available in my book titled, *Mazahab-e-Aalim ki Asmaani Kitabein.*

3.4.1   Concept of God in *Vedas*[51]

For example, according to the heavenly book claimed by Hindus, *Vedas, Rig Vedas 10*, Hymn 90, Mantra 12-13 and *Rig Vedas 31*, Mantra 11-12 has the following:

The Brahman was born from his mouth, and from both his arms the Kashtri caste of people were born. The ones who are the Vaish were born from his thighs, and from both feet of Parmeshwar the poor Shudar were born. The moon was born from his mouth and from his eyes the sun was born; the goddesses Inder and Agni were born from his mouth, and from his breath the air was born!

Or, for example, in *Rig Veda 31*, Mantra 13 contains the following:

The middle class was given birth from the navel of Parmeshwar (god), and the upper class was given birth from his head. The two ears of Parmeshwar bore the Earth, and the planets and astral bodies were born from his ears.

In *Atharvaveda, Kanda 11*, Hymn 2, Mantra 5-6, God's form is described as follows:

O Lord of our life! The supreme Soul! Greetings to your face. Greetings to your eyes also, your skin, your limbs, and greetings to you and your belly, greetings to your tongue. Greetings to your face, and to your teeth, and greetings to the smell of your teeth.

3.4.2   Worship of Snakes

In *Yajurveda*, Hymn 13, Mantra 6-8:

Prostration to the earth-dwelling snakes, and our prostration to those snakes that are in the wind or heavens. And our prostration to those snakes who either come with arrows or are in the crops, or those snakes that are in their holes. And let our prostrations be accepted by those snakes that live in the rays of the sun or live in waters.

3.4.3   Prostration to a Razor

In *Yajurveda*, Hymn 3, Mantra 63:

O razor! You are the doer of all things and are made of good iron. Prostration to you that you do not harm this child.

---

[51] The quotes as detailed from this are translated from the Urdu version by the author. (Ed)

3.4.4   Prostration to Fever

In *Atharvaveda*, *Kanda 1*, Hymn 25, Mantra 4:

May prostration to the winter fever be accepted and I also prostrate to the summer fever known as Roru. May my prostration to the fever that occurs daily, every second and third day be accepted!

It is obvious that the concepts of things considered worthy of worship as mentioned above are the creation of the limited thinking of man. Kant has written that whatever type of god a nation adopts for its worship, that god is a reflection of the culture and civilisation of that nation, because it is a requirement of the holiness and status of this god that man should present it in the best attire. Therefore, the god proposed by any nation i.e. that god which is a product of the human mind, will make evident the endpoint of the state of intellectual evolution of that nation.[52]

3.4.5   The Belief of Avatar[53]

The belief of avatar is also a reflection of this same inclination of man. Whenever man observed any trait in a human being which was less commonly found among the general masses, that human being was immediately considered as being superhuman and conceptualised as a god in the shape of man. By adopting this very belief of avatar, Christianity moulded it into the doctrine of the divinity of Christ. In his book '*Researches in Oriental History*', Dr. Brown[54] has proven with prodigious research and effort that the divinity of Christ is simply an echo of this belief of avatar. Apart from this, many Christian researchers have reached the conclusion that most of the current teaching of Christianity is taken from the ancient teaching of Buddhism. This is why the famous historian Max Muller writes in his book '*Science of Religion*':

The language of Buddha and his pupils and the language of Christ and his companions are found to have strange similarities. It appears to be as if many tales and metaphors of Buddhism are drawn from the time of the Bible, although it is obvious that these existed in the world well before the start of the Christian calendar (A.D.).[55]

---

[52] This is a very powerful statement of fact which can be verified through evidence by examining the state of the human world up till now. (Ed)

[53] Avatar - a manifestation of a deity or released soul in bodily form on earth; an incarnate divine teacher. (Oxford Dictionary)

[54] Dr George W. Brown, *Researches in Oriental History*.

[55] This is translated from Urdu as quoted in the book by the author. (Ed)

Ernst von Bunsen writes in his book '*Angel-Messiah of Buddhists, Essenes and Christians*':

It is a strange fact that whatever is seen about the life and teaching of Buddha in the oldest records which are available regarding Buddhism, is noted to be glaringly similar to those narrations about Christ which are found in the Bible. It is not possible that this should be called pure coincidence, and this surprising thing increases further when it is seen that these narrations are found only in Pauline Epistles and the Fourth Book. There is no mention of these in the books before these.[56]

Our purpose in mentioning this is that when man devises a god using his own mind, then god becomes merely a man. From the attributes which the Quran has detailed about Allah, the Supreme and Omnipotent, it becomes clear how great the difference is between human thoughts and this teaching of the Quran, the source of which is beyond the reach of the human mind.

3.5 He is One

A detailed description of each of the Divine attributes in turn will be covered in subsequent chapters. But there are four attributes among them which are such that they are mentioned by the Quran in a short Surah in such a way as if these are the fundamental attributes of Allah. This Surah is as follows:

Say: He is Allah, the One and Only; Allah the Eternal, Absolute (As-Samad); He begets not, nor is He begotten; and there is none like unto Him. (112:1-4)

Before moving on to other attributes, we wish to discuss these four attributes under this topic. The fundamental attribute of the Divine Self is *Ahdeat* (Oneness). Though *Ahad* and *Wahed* generally mean one i.e. one with whom there is no other, in *Ahdeat* the aspect of uniqueness is predominant. The fundamental character of a self (personality) is that it is unique in itself. No self can share in another self. This is called its individuality. Therefore, the Self of Allah is *Ahad* (alone) and none shares in it. It is unique and no-one else can be included in it.

3.5.1 *Batil*[57] of the Belief of Magians

By virtue of the self being *Ahad* (one), firstly this belief of the Magians that *Ahrman* and *Yazdan* are two permanent entities as gods is falsified:

---

[56] This is also translated from Urdu as quoted by the author in the book. (Ed)
[57] *Batil* – falsehood. It is the opposite of *Haqq* which means truth. (Ed)

Allah has said: 'Take not (for obedience) two Ilaahs; for He is just One Ilaah: Then fear Me (and Me alone)'. (16:51)

3.5.2 Rejection of the Belief of Trinity

And secondly, the Christian belief of Trinity that Father, Son, Holy Spirit are three in one and one in three gods, is refuted:

O People of the Book! Commit no excesses in your Deen: nor say of Allah aught but the truth. Jesus the son of Mary was (no more than) a messenger of Allah, and His Word, which He bestowed on Mary, and a Spirit proceeding from Him; so, have Eimaan in Allah and His messengers. Say not 'Trinity': desist, it will be better for you, for Allah is One Ilaah: glory be to Him, (far exalted is He) above having a son. To Him belong all things in the heavens and on earth. And enough is Allah as a Disposer of affairs. (4:171)

In another verse it is stated:

Surely, they do Kufr who say Allah is one of three in a Trinity. For there is no Ilaah except one Ilaah. If they desist not from their word, verily a grievous penalty will befall the deniers among them. (5:73)

3.5.3 Gods and Goddesses

One form of *Shirk* is that others be declared as partners in the Divine Self i.e. more than one god should be accepted. Another form is that other powers should be considered as sharing in His tasks, commands and Will. According to the belief system of Hindus, Brahma is the one who creates, Vishnu is the one who sustains, and Shiv is the one who confers death. Aside from these, there are hundreds of goddesses and gods who are regulators of the various departments of fate and destiny. But the Quran declares that:

...They have no protector, other than Him; nor does He share His command with anyone whatsoever. (18:26)

When none can share in His command and Will, then how can he become a disposer of affairs:

Say: 'Shall I take for my protector any other than Allah, the Maker of the heavens and the earth? And He it is that feeds but is not fed'. Say: 'Nay! but I am commanded to be the first of those who bow to Allah (in Islam), and be not you of the company of those who join gods with Allah'. (6:14)

3.5.4 Worship of the Messengers

After gods and goddesses, man made the messengers of Allah into gods and no followers of any religion in the world escaped from this. So much so, that the condition of the followers of Buddhism and Jainism, in whose teachings there is not even the concept of a god, also became such that worship of Buddha and Mahavir was instigated a short time after their deaths. Confucius had condemned the worship of gods but worship of Confucius himself began to then take place in the temples of China. The other religion of the people of China is Taoism whose founder was Lao-Tze. He also did not teach worship of idols, but despite this worship of his statue is also taking place for the last two thousand years.[58] In Japan, along with the statues of Buddha, the manifestations of their 'god' i.e. the sword and the mirror are also worshipped, which according to their ancient religion of Shinto the goddess of the Sun had placed into the keeping of her grandson i.e. the first King of kings of Japan.

3.5.5 Statues of the Founders of Religion

In Christianity, along with the divinity of Christ, statues of Jesus and Mary are worshipped. The belief of avatar among the Hindus is also a reflection of this worship of messengers. Or, as has been noted earlier, worship of the messenger by the Christians is a replica of the avatar belief of Hindus. The Quran has closed the door to worship of the messengers so firmly that no reverent belief of the human mind can open it.[59] Only one verse is quoted here in this regard:

> *It is not (possible) that a man, to whom is given the Book, and wisdom, and messenger-hood, should say to people: 'Be you my followers rather than Allah's'. On the contrary (he would say): 'Be you followers of Him Who is truly the Sustainer of all; for you have taught the Book and you have studied it earnestly'. (3:79)*

In other words, those people who have begun the worshipping of the messengers, this is their own invented path. No messenger of Allah directed them to do this. The messengers of Allah used to come to teach obedience of Allah, not to have themselves worshipped. But what is the cure for the human mind that did not desist from making Allah's messengers as god!

---

[58] Socialism is now becoming normal in China according to which no *Eimaan* remains in any type of god. Therefore, for them worship of 'gods' has either become tales of the distant past or will only exist among those conservative fundamentalists who will not have been affected by the atheistic beliefs of socialism. Such people will, however, be rare there.

[59] Details of this aspect will be available in my book *Iblees O Adam*.

3.5.6 Worship of the Religious Clergy

After the messengers, the turn comes of the religious scholars and saints i.e. the religious clergy, who are initially considered to be the means of reaching God, and subsequently are themselves made into gods. The Magi of Magians, the Brahman of Hindus, the Lama of Buddhists, the priest of Christians - worship of all of these takes place. The Quran locked these windows as well, stating:

> *Yet there are men who take (for obedience) others besides Allah. As equal (with Allah) they love them as they should love Allah, but those with Eimaan are overflowing in their love[60] for Allah. If only the unrighteous could see, behold, they would see the punishment: that to Allah belongs all power, and Allah will strongly enforce the punishment[61]. (2:165)*

3.5.7 Invitation to the People of the Book[62] to *Tauheed*[63]

In relation to this aspect of *Shirk*, the Quran has also invited the people of the Book to *Tauheed*, stating:

> *Say: 'O People of the Book! come to common terms as between us and you: that we follow none but Allah; that we associate no partners with Him; that we erect not, from among ourselves, lords and patrons other than Allah'. If then they turn back, say you: 'Bear witness that we (at least) are Muslims (bowing to Allah's Will)'. (3:64)*

3.6 Beliefs of Materialism

This is the devising of god out of tangible things, but the Quran does not treat the symptoms of disease, instead it addresses the root cause of the disease. Its sight is directed on the finest of finest non-tangible causes and effects on the foundation of which the structure of tangibles arises. We see clearly that the system of nature works on the principle of cause and effect. Effects are established as a result of the accumulation of causes. Man, accustomed to physical forms, considers these effects as existing in themselves, in other words he thinks that these characteristics are intrinsic within these things. This is that idea which is the basis of materialism. An individual observes that the one who consumes arsenic dies after a short interval. He thinks that this property is intrinsically present within arsenic that it is life severing. He sees that if seeds are sown after making the land level and soft,

---

[60] 'Love' as referred to here means to follow Allah's laws as revealed in the Quran. (Ed)
[61] This is the consequence, based on the Law of Requital, of going against the Divine laws. (Ed)
[62] Those who are known to have received Allah's revelation i.e. Christians and Jews. (Ed)
[63] *Tauheed* – oneness of Allah, sometimes translated as monotheism. In practical terms it means following the Permanent Values of the Quran. (Ed)

and if it is watered at suitable times, then crops will sprout from it. He thinks that these potentials are intrinsically present within these things, and when outcomes are what are known as the accumulation of these causes, then no need remains for an 'external' power.

Man, in his infancy, used to consider those things from which benefits were accrued as being worthy of respect, and used to be frightened of those things from which loss was incurred. Therefore, he used to prostrate before them. By worshipping them, he wished to keep them happy. The cow, the Ganges, the tulsi plant, the poplar tree; or on the other hand, snake, thunder, earthquake, all were declared as being worthy of worship under the influence of these very sentiments. When man progressed a little further, though he gave up worship of these things, he now began the worship of those human beings through whose hands these things were being received. Having abandoned the worship of the tulsi plant itself, he began worshipping the Jogi who was handing out these same leaves from his lap. Whether this worship is of the leaves or of the one who hands out the leaves, it happened according to the same sentiment i.e. it was thought that these properties - that they can result in profit or cause harm - are intrinsically present in these things or people. Though this era of worship no longer remains today, the sentiment due to which this worship used to take place still endures. Even now, when he recovers from a disease, although he does not thank the bottle of medicine which became the means for his recovery, he certainly considers the doctor who prescribed the medicine as the bestower of healing. This is the second stage of human intellect. When this same intellect achieves maturity, then at that stage, in the same way that men of today consider thanking the bottle of medicine itself as being contrary to intellect, he will also stop thinking that a man like himself has the power to provide healing. At that time his eyes will accept this truth that in the universe the effect of every deed is manifested according to the established laws of Allah. By operating according to this law, we gain health and strength, and by disobeying it disease and ultimately death occurs. The status of experts on different subjects is no more than this, that they possess knowledge of the Divine laws. They absolutely do not possess the authority or control to change these laws or to establish effects contrary to these laws. This is that truth which the Quran has noted as follows (via the lips of Abraham):

'Who created me, and it is He Who guides me; Who gives me food and drink. And when I am ill it is He Who cures me; Who will cause me to die and then to live (again)'. (26:78-81)

In other words every event manifests itself here according to the law of Allah.

3.7 Human Jurisdiction

And then not only is it that the Quran defines this concept merely about 'things' and not about human beings, considering things to have intrinsic effectiveness is definitely ignorance, but not as dangerous as considering human beings to be absolute sovereigns. The reason for tyranny and cruelty in the world and oppression is because this thing has been imprinted in the minds of subjugated human beings that powerful human beings are masters and owners of all powers. They can confer sustenance and can also snatch it away; they can kill and can grant life also. It is according to these beliefs that human beings who are masters of power and authority force others to become their slaves, and these are those same *Arbab-un-min-doon-Allah* (gods other than Allah) whose 'worship' has been done in every era till now. The Quran teaches *Tauheed* in this matter as well – it declares that the Master of all powers is solely the law of Allah, therefore no human being has this right that he should impose his rule on other human beings. Yusuf (Joseph) says to his companions in the prison:

'O my two companions of the prison! (I ask you) Are many lords differing among themselves better, or Allah, the One, Supreme and Irresistible? If not Him, you follow nothing but names which you have named[64] *- you and your fathers - for which Allah has sent down no authority; the command is for none but Allah: He has commanded that you follow none but Him: that is the right Deen, but most men understand not.'*
(12:39-40)

3.7.1   Fear Disappears Due to *Eimaan*

Just imagine that if *Eimaan* in this type of *Tauheed* becomes established in the heart of man, then does any power remain in the world from which man will be fearful? If he is ever fearful, it will be due to going against the Divine laws, apart from this he will not be fearful of anyone. This is the reason that the Quran has stated the attribute of *Momineen* as being:

...there is no fear, nor shall they grieve. (10:62)

---

[64] The Quran has pointed to a great truth here where human beings give a certain name or title to something and suddenly it assumes some great significance e.g. a name given to a stone such as a diamond, and suddenly it becomes very precious. Another example is where an ordinary human being is termed as His Royal Highness – yet he is only a mortal like any other man in the street. (Ed)

3.8 *Samdeat*

The second verse of Surah *Ikhlas* whose first verse has been noted in Section 3.5, is:

Allah As-Samad. (112:2)

The word *Samad-un* has appeared in the Quran only once, but this word contains within it such a comprehensive meaning that its explanation can be challenging. It is commonly translated as 'Allah is least concerned' and the meaning taken from this is that he is very disinterested. From this 'disinterestedness' the mind immediately thinks of a sovereign, autocrat, king (dictator) who does not care about any rule or law and carries on doing whatever comes to his mind, regardless of whatever the consequences may be, and that in this same way (Allah forbid) Allah does not care. There is no doubt in this that He is the Supreme Being and Ruler of all rulers and is Sovereign Himself, but this is not the meaning of His being 'unconcerned'. The meanings of *Samad* are such a One Who is not dependent on anyone else for any of His affairs; such a leader towards whom one should turn in difficulties and during campaigns; such a high and mighty rock that, when the spectre of floodwater encircles all around, then He is the only source of protection and rescue for the aid of man. From *Samdeat* the meaning is that Allah is not reliant on anyone in any of His matters. This is the fundamental attribute of a developed personality that it does not owe its being, survival and strength on external supports.[65] It remains alive and established due to its own inner strength. And since the Self of Allah is the most complete Being, in His case one cannot therefore even imagine the need for any external support. Contrary to this, every other thing which wishes to exist is in need of His support for its existence. This is the meaning of *Allah As-Samad*.

3.9 Belief in Progeny of God[66]

The third verse of Surah *Ikhlas* states:

He begets not, nor is He begotten. (112:3)

The belief in progeny of God is a very old one. As has been written earlier, because man used to base the god created by his own mind on his own form, that is why he would combine all the human characteristics in this god. For man, children are

---

[65] This is the reason that the Quran repeatedly emphasises to create a self based on *Eimaan* and righteous deeds so that it is not influenced by the outer human world in anyway. (Ed)

[66] The word 'God' has been used here as this is a non-Quranic belief, and not related to Allah. (Ed)

the greatest of blessings and a big support, therefore why would he keep his 'god' deprived of this? And in any case, when he observed that the process of reproduction is only operational through conception and birth, then it could not enter his mind that any being, even if it is God, can be free from this. According to Zoroastrians their most ancient god *Mithra* is regarded as the son of the god *Ahura Mazda*. This same belief, according to Clement Wood and Dr. Brown, having reached Rome, became the belief of Christ as being the son of God. Among Hindus, over and above progeny, gods were also considered to have wives. The wife of *Sheva* is *Parvati* and their son is *Ganesh*. The daughter of Brahma, who is the highest of all gods, is called *Sarswati*. In Ragved Mandal No. 1, Sowkat No. 22, Mantra No. 12 it is stated:

'In this task, I call upon Indra's wife and Waran's wife Agni, to drink sowm, and for my well-being'.[67]

3.9.1 Origin of the Creation of the Universe According to Hinduism

In ancient Hindu religion, the system of the birth of creation is the same one that could be conceived during the era of infancy of the human mind. We present one example here with apologies to the refined feelings of our readers, from *Shatpath Brahmin* and also *Brahdar Neik Upnashid*, according to which:

'Parmeshwar could not copulate due to the fact of being alone. Therefore, he desired a wife for himself and grew as big as a man and woman are when copulating. Then this Ishwar cut himself up in two parts and became a wife from one half and a man from the other. Then the wife hid, and kept changing into a cow, a mare, a she-donkey, an ewe etc. And Parmeshwar kept changing into a bull, a horse, a donkey and a ram etc. From this mating cows, horses, donkeys, single-hoofed animals, sheep etc. were produced.[68]

The need to quote these things is only to illustrate this point, how along with establishing the correct concept of Allah, the Quran also continues to contradict all the wrong and false beliefs in the world. He did not produce anyone through copulation – not only does this contradict Christ and *Uzair* as being sons (of God), but it also contradicts every one of those beliefs according to which the beginning of the birth of creation is accepted to be via the process of fathering and reproduction from God. All of the aspects of the Quran cannot become clearly evident until the different beliefs of the different religions of the universe are not in front of us. The pattern of the Quran is this, that after contradicting all wrong beliefs, it etches the correct concept in the mind. In order to demonstrate these

---

[67] Translation by Prof. Raja Ram Shastri.
[68] *Swami Atmanand* in *Vedarth Prakash*, pp. 83-84.

wrong beliefs we occasionally have to quote those excerpts which may be unpleasant to our aesthetic sense.

3.9.2   Procreation and Creation

Although the meanings of both procreation and creation are to create, as far as the concept of the self is concerned, there is a difference of heaven and earth between them. In procreation (i.e. birth through copulation), a part of the creator transfers and becomes part of the one being created. This matter is against the concept of the self (personality). The self is an indivisible entity, no part of which can be separated from it, neither can any part of one self become the cause for the creation of another self. Therefore, in relation to the self, the very concept of procreation is false. Contrary to this, in creation no part of the creator separates from him, nor does that part become part of the creation. Therefore, from the aspect of the self an act of creation will take place, not an act of procreation. Procreation is a trait of the animalistic level of life. Creation is an attribute of the self – at a fundamental level of the Divine Self, and following from that, of the human self.

Therefore, those religions which have associated the process of procreation with God, are clueless about this fundamental concept of the self. You can see how all these superstitions are contradicted from all sorts of directions and aspects in the Quran. The Quran states:

> *They say: 'Allah has begotten a son': Glory be to Him – Nay, to Him belongs all that is in the heavens and on earth; everything follows His commands. To Him is due the primal origin of the heavens and the earth: When he decrees a matter, He says to it: 'Be, and it is'.*[69] *(2:116-117)*

3.9.3   Creator of Everything

This means that He brought this system of the universe into existence from nothing in such a way that whatever thing He initiated an intention about, it came into existence. How pure and pristine this concept is, and to what an extent He, the True Allah, is master of powers! The Quran states:

> *He to Whom belongs the dominion of the heavens and the earth: no son has He begotten, nor has He a partner in His dominion: it is He Who created all things, and ordered them in due proportions. (25:2)*

---

[69] This does not mean that things are created immediately in their final form. It means things commence being created according to the Divine laws as discussed in Chapter 4. (Ed)

In Surah *Maryam*:

It is not befitting to (the majesty of) Allah that He should beget a son. Glory be to Him! When He determines a matter, He only says to it, 'Be, and it is'. (19:35) See also (4:171, 10:68-69, 23:91)

The belief of the progeny of Allah is so wrong and baseless that no-one can provide any evidence for it. This is the reason that today the followers of those religions among whom this belief is prevalent produce such strange and bizarre interpretations and make efforts that it should be understood that these things are merely metaphorical – it does not mean real progeny.

3.9.4   Acceptance of Reality by Christians

This acceptance by the followers of these religions is in itself proof of the truth of the Quran. Some time ago the Lord Bishop of Canterbury had constituted a commission to investigate to what extent the existing Gospels are trustworthy and to what extent their teaching can be called Divine. In the report of this commission, inter alia, this is also written, that whatever is found in the Gospels regarding Christ being the son of God has no more reality than the status of fiction and that it is an intolerable slander on the Divine Self.

3.9.5   Consorts of Gods

Regarding the belief in Hinduism of a wife of god, this has already been mentioned. In the religion of ancient Babylon, the goddess of agriculture *Ashter's* marriage with the spirit of the date *Tummuz* used to be professed. In the Egyptian religion the marriage of the goddess of the oasis (*Isis*) with the god of the Nile, *Osiris*, used to be avowed. The concept of a consort of god is present in the mythologies of Greece and the religious tales of Rome. *Ops* is the wife of the Greek god *Chronos*, and *Hera* the wife of *Zeus*, *Rhea* is the wife of the Roman god *Saturn*, and *Juno* the wife of *Jupiter*. One of the reasons for the belief in the progeny of god and relatives was probably this, that in the mutual fights of tribal life, the members of one family would be supporters of one another (this is why in this regard there is mention of mutual fights in the tales of Hinduism and the Greek gods). Therefore, they may have thought that these gods should also have near and dear ones who can be helpers, but the true Allah is not in need of help from anyone:

Say: 'Praise be to Allah, Who begets no son, and has no partner in (His) dominion: nor needs He any to protect Him from humiliation: Yes, magnify Him for His greatness and glory!' (17:111)

The reality of belief in the progeny of God is this much, that the mind of earlier man shaped god in his own form, and this belief subsequently continued in generation after generation due to the blind following in the footsteps of the forefathers. No-one evaluated it critically using knowledge and intellect:

> *Further, that He may warn those (also) who say, 'Allah has begotten a son': No knowledge have they of such a thing, nor had their fathers. It is a grievous thing that issues from their mouths as a saying. What they say is nothing but falsehood! (18:4-5)*

After the arrival of knowledge, claimants of these beliefs are themselves embarrassed from these and attempt to hide these under the guise of metaphors and similes.

3.9.6   Belief of Daughters of God

Not only sons but daughters also were attributed to god. And this belief existed among those people who, if a daughter was born into their own house, would be sunk in mourning. In the social structure of Hinduism the extent to which a girl is a recipient of 'respect and value' is well known! But with Brahma a daughter is accepted. This belief was also prevalent among Arabs that angels are the daughters of god, and their own state was such that they used to bury their daughters alive. The Quran states:

> *And they assign daughters for Allah! – Glory be to Him! – And for themselves (sons – the issue) they desire! When news is brought to one of them, of (the birth of) a female (child), his face darkens, and he is filled with inward grief! (16:57-58)*

A similar belief to the one among Hindus of gods and goddesses existed among Arabs about angels i.e. that they have been put in charge of the duties of death and fate and are masters of various departments of the system of the universe. In this regard, relations used to be assumed between them and God: they were made goddesses and declared as being the daughters of God. The Quran states:

> *Yet they attribute to some of His servants a share with Him! Truly is man a blasphemous ingrate avowed! What! Has He taken daughters out of what He Himself creates, and granted to you sons for choice? When news is brought to one of them of (the birth of) what he sets up as a likeness to Allah Most Gracious, his face darkens, and he is filled with inward grief! (43:15-17) See also (21:26-27, 16:57, 43:19)*

3.9.7   Erroneous Belief of the Relationship of Jinns with God

During the era of man's ignorance, belief in Jinn was commonplace i.e. non-perceptible (invisible) forces which were believed to interfere in human matters and influence them. Like other nations, this belief was commonplace among Arabs as well.[70] In any case, the belief among Arabs was that Jinns also maintained relationships with God:

And they have invented a relationship between Him and the Jinns (the universal invisible forces): but the Jinns know that they (have indeed) to appear before His Judgement Seat! (37:158)

3.10   Last Verse of Surah *Ikhlas*

The last verse states:

And there is none like unto Him. (112:4)

The word *Kufu-wun* used in this verse has also only appeared in one place in the Quran. Its meanings include similar, equal, equivalent and incomparable. Its meaning is clear i.e. that unparalleled and incomparable Being Who has no-one sharing in His Self and attributes. No-one is equal to Him, is similar to Him, or is comparable to Him:

…there is nothing whatever like unto Him…(42:11)

Therefore, there remains not the slightest possibility even for a belief such as avatar or *Ilaah* (god).

This is that concept of *Tauheed* which the Quran presents about Allah, and regarding that God who is 'incomprehensible', it expounds those things from which the correct *Eimaan* about this Absolute Self can be engraved on the human heart. Be aware that the word Allah has been mentioned in the Quran about seven hundred times and quoting all of these verses is problematic, therefore it has been noted briefly under this topic. Detailed explanation about the Divine attributes will be found under other topics.

3.11   Clarification of One Important Point

Before moving forward, it appears essential to clarify one point. Since the Quran is the revelation of Allah, therefore the attributes of Allah which have been explained in it are based on truth, they are not the guesswork of human intellect. In other words, these attributes do not mean that man, for the satisfaction of his yearning to worship, established the concept of some deity in the workshop of his

---

[70] In the Arabic language the meaning of Jinn is literally 'being hidden from the eyes'. Details about what the reality is about Jinn according to the Quran are covered at length in my book *Iblees O Adam*.

mind, and then attributed various traits and allocated different names to this conjectured god according to the world of his own concepts. In the same way that (without using a metaphor) accepting this reality that the sun is a mighty stellar body which having risen in the morning provides light and heat is not merely a 'conjectured' belief, but is the acknowledgement of a proven fact, similarly *Eimaan* in the Divine Self and *Eimaan* in His attributes according to the Quran is not a conjectural belief but is acknowledgement of a fact. But the question is this, by acknowledging this fact, what is the benefit to man? Why is acceptance of this essential? The first thing is actually this, that acceptance of reality is in itself proof of human eminence. You can say that the sun does not provide light and heat but provides darkness and coldness instead. Your intellect and reasoning will be ridiculed, and suspicion will arise about your sanity. But *Eimaan* in the attributes of Allah is not only essential on the basis of acknowledging fact but is also the holder of very high and important objectives. We have already discussed these aims in Chapter 1 but because this point is very important, and together with the fact that it is off the beaten track of the worlds of intellect and beliefs, therefore we think that to bring it to our attention repeatedly is not without advantage. We realise that repetition is a flaw in a book but if in order to elaborate and explain some very important reality some particular point is presented more than once, then this cannot be considered to be a meaningless repetition. In this book repetition at some places has been allowed because of this need. (Even the Quran itself presents different aspects repeatedly in order to expound the truth).

The essential aim of *Eimaan* in Allah which has been mentioned above is that the aim of the life of man according to the Quran is to establish the kingdom of Allah on this earth. Man has been created superior to all creation and for all the forces of nature together to serve him. His responsibility in life is to bring everything in the universe under his control while remaining himself under the obedience of the laws of Allah, and by producing strength in his self in this way, to implement the laws of Allah in the whole world. That *Jamaat* which accomplishes this responsibility towards humanity is called a *Jamaat e Momineen* i.e. that *Jamaat* which has *Eimaan* in the Divine Self and Divine attributes according to Quranic teaching. Because this is a supreme responsibility which this *Jamaat* carries out, it is essential that, within the confines of human limitation, the reflection of the Divine attributes radiates in the members of this *Jamaat* with the immensity of their fullest possible potentials.[71] The image of His light should reflect in the mirror of his heart; this unparalleled and incomparable, this 'beyond the limits of imagination,

---

[71] The Quran has not defined the limits of human potentials for the purpose of development of the self. This process continues in the next life as well, therefore a *Momin* should never for a moment think that the development of his self has an upper limit – his goal in life should be to resolutely follow the righteous path under the guidance of Allah i.e. according to the Quran. The higher the level of development of his self, the greater is his capacity to get increased responsibility from Allah (2:286). The ultimate sacrifice in this life is to lay down one's life in the cause of Allah (9:111). (Ed)

idea, thought, guess, presumption' outline of these shining attributes of Allah the Supreme should be seen imprinted on the face of the earth in the visible personas of these highly realised selfs[72] of this *Jamaat*. The apparel of the hearts and minds of the selfs of this *Jamaat* should be 'coloured' in the beautiful and brilliant colours of the Innovator of ever new and unique creations:

The Colour of Allah: and who can colour better than Allah? And it is He Whom we follow. (2:138)

Hence, having *Eimaan* in the Divine attributes means that a *Momin* should, according to the expanse of human constraints, by obedience of the Quran, try to create these attributes within himself and in this way, by achieving 'Divine closeness', keep progressing forward by treading through the stages of the process of evolution of humanity. A *Jamaat* of these kinds of *Momineen* is responsible for establishing and sustaining the kingdom of Allah in this world and their Allah is *Rabb-il-Alameen*. By giving birth to the brilliance of *Rabubiyat* within their own selfs, they also administer sustenance and nourishment of others. Allah is *Razzaq* (Sustainer) – in them, too, there should be the brilliance of *Razzaqiyat*. He is *Raheem* and *Kareem* - the pearls of their rain bearing cloud of generosity and blessings should also be distributed for all. He is *Jabbar* and *Qahhar* – they, too, should possess this much power through which, by curing every rebellious and tyrannical Pharaoh-like human being, they can reform the whole world, and so forth. This is the true purpose of *Eimaan* and conviction in the Divine attributes, otherwise Allah is Allah, whether someone accepts Him or does not. If the whole world closes its eyes, even then the sun will continue to be the source of light and heat, as it is today. Even when nothing was there, Allah was Allah, and at the time when nothing else is left, even then Allah will remain.

3.12   Outcome of Conviction in *Tauheed*

Now let us look at the short verses of Surah *Ikhlas* in which four Divine attributes are noted, what their practical effect on human life is. What is the practical outcome of having *Eimaan* in these attributes?

By having *Eimaan* in one Allah, man becomes free from the slavery of all the false 'gods' of the world. By becoming the follower of One only, he becomes the ruler of the whole universe. He bows at His door, and the world bows in front of him.[73] He becomes His, and the whole universe becomes his.

---

[72] The author uses the word '*Qudsi*' to describe the self. The root of this word is *Q-D-S* which comprises the following meanings: free from all kinds of faults and blemishes, to remove all faults, to strive to the utmost. See *Lughat-ul-Quran*, Vol 2, p. 337

[73] It should be kept in mind that the Quran forbids the bowing of any human being before another human being. This statement refers to the forces of nature. (Ed)

And when this *Jamaat* has *Eimaan* in this reality that their Allah is One, then its essential consequence is that this *Jamaat* will be as one as well. A *Jamaat* accepting the Oneness of Allah should be one nation; if believing in two gods is *Shirk*, then the division of this *Jamaat* into two factions is also *Shirk* (never mind dividing into hundreds of sects). This is why the Quran states:

...and be not you among those who join gods (Shirk) with Allah – those who split up their Deen and become (mere) sects – each party rejoicing in that which is with itself!
(30:31-32)

It is a practical *Shirk* for the Muslim Ummah to be divided into sects and parties: this is because the practical proof of the belief of *Tauheed* of a nation which has *Eimaan* in One Allah is to become and remain as one nation. The foundation of the oneness of a nation is based on this great truth that all the individuals of this nation should follow only one law; the aim of their life should be one. The practical manifestation of having *Eimaan* in One Allah is obedience of His law. Therefore, *Tauheed* of Allah means the oneness of His Law and the practical consequence of oneness of the law means oneness of the nation. The scope of this oneness will keep expanding and the oneness of mankind will manifest. Hence, the final outcome of *Tauheed-e-Allah* is the oneness of humanity, and the practical means of attaining this is the establishment of this system in which the Divine law is followed. There should be no obedience of the commands and laws of any other than this; this system is called an Islamic Government.

3.13 Effect of the Attribute of *Samad* [74]

Hence, when a *Momin* makes this proclamation that His Allah is *Samad*, along with this he also makes an effort to create the attribute of *Samdeat* within his own self. *Samdeat* means that Allah, the One and only, does not require the help of anyone else for the accomplishments of His intentions, rather the whole of the universe requires His help in its difficulties and challenges. The condition of the nation which has *Eimaan* in Allah-*Samad* should also be the same, that it should not be dependent on others for the fulfilment of its plans, rather it should be the possessor of such vast powers that the whole world should turn towards it in their troubles. The utterance of Allah-*As-Samad* repeatedly on the tongue, while the practical state is that of being dependent on others for every need, cannot be the way of the Muslim Ummah. And today the state of our dependency has become such that not only are we dependent on others for meeting our material needs but have also borrowed the ideas and concepts of others.[75] Neither is any ideology our

---

[74] *Samad* – absolutely independent.
[75] This state is the result of failing to comprehend the truth and significance of the Quranic guidance. (Ed)

own, nor any principle, neither is our heart our own, nor our mind. The curse of this apish mentality has overwhelmed us to such an extent that we consider imitation of the way of life of others to be a matter of immense pride. The Quran states:

When in their insolence they transgressed (all) prohibitions, We said to them: 'Be you apes, despised and rejected'. (7:166)

That nation which was given the reins of duty to lead the world is today lagging behind the whole world. What, is this the conduct of life that a nation which has *Eimaan* in Allah-*As-Samad* should have had?

Then the nation which possesses this *Eimaan* that its Allah bears no relation of blood and race to anyone, that He is *Rabb-il-Alameen* and the only way any relation with Him can be established is on the basis of obedience and *Taqwa*, is it possible that that nation will declare the criteria for the division of humanity to be based on colour and blood, race and tribe? Being separated into nations and castes on the basis of race and colour and being divided into tribes and parties are the infantile concepts of the era of ignorance for the eradication of which Islam arrived. Islam came to create such a paradise that the moment an individual proclaims *La-Ilaha-i-Lallah* he enters this paradise like a drop merges with the ocean, such that even if all the forces of the world came together and tried, they would not be able to differentiate this drop from the ocean. One by one, Islam destroyed the self-erected walls of colour, race, language and geographical boundaries (nations), and in this way placed the heavenly message of the unity of mankind in front of the world. According to it there is one and only one criterion for the division of mankind i.e. *Eimaan* and *Kufr*. All those on planet earth who have accepted *Eimaan* belong to one *Millat*[76] and those who deny this fact belong to another nation.[77]

And when a *Momin* accepts this fact that there is no associate or partner with his Allah, then with this he also announces this truth that the nation establishing the government of Allah (without sharing in His Rule) should also be without associates in the human world.[78] This is the reason why the Quran has called the *Jamaat* of *Momineen* as being superior and above all others (3:139).

Reflect closely on these four short verses of Surah *Akhlaas*, and see how by acceptance of the attributes of Allah what supreme principles are held within them

---

[76] *Millat* – people of one ideology. (Ed)

[77] It should be borne in mind that this division is based on ideology, while keeping the whole of mankind as one community on the basis of physical needs. (Ed)

[78] This is in order to avoid compromising Allah's laws by mixing them with non-Quranic laws, as this will not lead to the benefits which are only achieved by following the Quran alone. (Ed)

for the practical life of the *Jamaat e Momineen*.

(1) The one nation of Islam, in which there should be no infiltration of any kind of sectarianism or division into parties; one centre and the focal point of this centre one *Jamaat*; one flame and circling around it those selfless ones who are willing to lay down their lives.

(2) Such a nation which is not dependent on anyone else for the accomplishment of its aims and the establishment of its plans, instead the whole world should look to it for help and assistance.

(3) And then differentiation in this nation based on race and blood should be considered a false distinction – the criterion for differentiation among mankind should be *Eimaan* and *Taqwa* and nothing else.

(4) No nation in the world could equal this one *Millat*, this should be the most supreme and in front of everyone.[79]

In light of these facts, one recitation of Surah *Ikhlas* should in practical terms produce this effect. But just reflect on what our state is today? These sanctified verses of Surah *Ikhlas* are read in those same words even today, in which the Muslims of the era of Rasul-ullah recited them, but is it the case that the same outcome is also produced today which was established in that great time? Consider after all, why is there this difference? It is because today there are only Quranic words remaining in front of us, their spirit has vanished from our vision.

---

[79] Thus serving as a model of earthly paradise for the whole of humanity. (Ed)

4   *Khalq and Amr* (Creating and Directing)

One fundamental trait of the personality is creation i.e. every developed self has an attribute that it should create.[80] But consider, what are the stages of creation? An engineer wishes to construct a house. Its first stage is this that he forms the intention in his heart to construct a house, then he prepares a map in his mind, then he draws this map on a sheet of paper, then he constructs the house according to this map. The house appears before people at that point when it takes the form of a building made of bricks or stones.

4.1 Two Stages of Creation

But it is obvious that before coming into this concrete form, the map of the house was in the mind of the engineer and even before the map came into the mind, its intention was in his heart. Therefore, in the process of the construction of the house, one stage was that when that house was in the intention and knowledge of the engineer and the second stage was that when it came into concrete and visible form in front of the eyes. Though both these stages are continuous links in the construction of the house, it is apparent that from the viewpoint of its state and its nature there is a big difference between the two of them. The Western philosopher, Pringle Pattison, has complained that in the English language there is only one word i.e. creation for these two stages whereas in the Arabic language there are separate words for each one of these two stages.[81] The Quran has used these different words for the manifestation of these two stages. The first stage (when that thing to be created is formed in the stage of intention and knowledge, or you could say, when it does not yet appear in a tangible and visible form before our eyes) is called the domain of *Amr*. And the second stage (when that thing becomes visible in tangible form) is the sphere of *Khalq*. The Quran states:

> *...Is it not His to create and to govern (Khalq and Amr)? (7:54)*

By stating this, these two stages have been related to Allah i.e. everything from its initial stage to the last stage comes into shape and is formed according to His law.

4.2 Literal Meaning

Al-Amara-to is the term used for those small stones which are placed in plains and deserts so that the limits of an area or the signs of a path can be determined from these. From this it is evident that in the word *Amr-un* the aspect of a sign, pointer or direction is prominent. In other words, we can say from this that before 'being',

---

[80] The difference between creation and procreation has been discussed in the previous chapter.

[81] Quoted by M. Iqbal in his lectures titled *The Reconstruction of Religious Thought in Islam*.

everything is moving in the direction of 'becoming'[82] i.e. that thing which has not yet come into being but is progressing towards that direction in which, having advanced further, it will adopt a specific shape and existence. This stage (when it is proceeding in the direction of becoming) is called the domain of *Amr*. Starting from the knowledge and intention of Allah all those stages are included in this up to when it is still in a formless state. This is one meaning of *Amr*.

4.3 *Amr* and Law

An engineer imagines the idea of some machine. The meaning of this conception is that he makes a sketch in his mind that if the parts of this machine are like this, and if this kind of arrangement is put into it, then if it is put into motion with this type of power then that machine will begin to function, and from that these kinds of results will be achieved. It is obvious that in this creative action one item is that machine which exists in front of us in a solid shape and the second is that plan or law according to which this machine remains in operation. This plan or stage of this law is hidden from our eyes though we can estimate or find information about this machine through intellect and reasoning.

The situation which is that of a machine is the same state of all the things of the universe. In the existing system of the universe everything has been created according to a specific plan and is functioning according to a specific law. This part which is related to a plan or law is linked to the domain of *Amr*. At this point it is essential to further understand that we can comprehend this much as to under which law a certain thing moves and is effective, but we cannot say why only that law was made for it and why another law was not devised. This is called the *Mashe'at* of Allah i.e. keeping in view the whole of the universe, Allah made whatever type of law was deemed suitable. Our concern is with the 'how' of this, not with the 'why'. This is the reason why in some verses the word *Amr* also contains the meaning of order or decision. In other words, Allah's decision was like this, His command was like this. He made this law according to His decision, in the matter of which He possesses complete sovereignty. It is obvious from this that that part of the domain of *Amr* where laws are formed for the things of the universe is outside the sphere of limits of our intellect, although where this *Amr* manifests in the form of physical laws, we can determine these through our observation, study and reasoning. These are called the laws of nature. In order to understand this, we can say that the 'pre-natural' stage of the laws under which the things of the universe function, is called the laws of *Mashe'at*, and the stage after this, the laws of nature.

---

[82] In English it will be said 'in the process of becoming'.

Just as in the outer universe there are Divine laws functioning, similarly in the human world every action produces its effect according to a specific law. Mankind receives these laws through *Wahi*, therefore the word *Amr* is sometimes also used for *Wahi*. This means that *Wahi* determines that direction, travelling according to which, the caravan of humanity can reach its intended destination.

Keeping these different meanings of *Amr* before you, reflect on the relevant verses of the Quran and the truth will become apparent.

4.4 Be! and It Is (*Kun-Fa-Ya'koon*)

Let us first of all take the creative stage of 'pre-nature'. In many places of the Quran it is stated:

> *Verily, when He intends a thing, His command is, 'Be', and it is! (36:82)*

There are two issues here which require to be understood; one is that, after forming an intention Allah does not in actual fact say the word *Kun* (like us) – its meaning is that immediately along with His intention the process of creation commences. The second is that *Fa-Ya'koon* does not mean that the moment Allah said *Kun* that that thing came into existence in its final form. In many places of the Quran this reality has been made clear that the evolutionary process is continuing in the universe and the schemes of Allah take a period of thousands and thousands of years from their starting point to reach the state of completion. Hence, *Kun-Fa-Ya'koon* means that together with the intention of Allah the creative programme of this thing commences, and its completion takes place later at its own time. What we have said about 'by saying *Kun* the creative act of this thing commences and its completion takes place later in its own time' is stated according to the human concept of time in which there is a past, a present and a future time. With Allah these differentiations in time means nothing; in front of Him there is always an eternal now, therefore with Him there is no time differential between *Kun* and *Fa-Ya'koon*.

After creation, let us now come to the law. We have already stated that one stage of the Divine law is that where these laws are determined, and we can know nothing about this stage nor why these laws are of this type. The second stage is that in which these physical laws are implemented and actioned in the universe. The Quran has called this *Amr* also. In other words, the physical laws of the universe are also called the '*Amr* of Allah'. In Surah *Al-A'raf* it is stated:

Your Sustainer is Allah, Who created the heavens and the earth in six stages[83] (which occurred in succession one after the other), then He established Himself on the (Throne) of authority: He draws the night as a veil over the day, each seeking the other in rapid succession: He created the sun, the moon, and the stars, (all) governed by laws under His command (His Amr). Is it not His to create and govern? (Khalq and Amr). Blessed be Allah, the Cherisher and Sustainer of the worlds! (7:54) See also (16:12)

In Surah *Ar-Rum*:

And among His signs is this, that heaven and earth stand by His command (Amr)... (30:25)

4.5 Allah's *Amr* in the Heavens and the Earth

Not only are the earth and various planets established as a result of His *Amr* but He has instilled these properties in them so that they continue to carry out the tasks assigned to them according to a defined procedure:

So He completed them as seven firmaments in two stages and He assigned to each heaven its duty (Wahi) and command (Amr)...(41:12)

All the manifestations of nature are busy in the deliverance of their duty according to this very *Amr*. Ships float about on the surface of the oceans according to this same system (22:65). Winds blow all around according to it so that they can assist these vessels in travelling hither and thither (30:46, 45:12).

4.6 Management of Affairs

Once He had created these characteristics in all things, that Sovereign of '*Khalq* and *Amr*' has not (Allah forbid) sat back and suspended His creative activity, but even after the creation of the universe the 'management of affairs' continues unabated, and this process is being accomplished from the same centre of power and authority (throne of supreme power). The Quran declares, ask them:

Say: ...and Who is it that rules and regulates all affairs?... (10:31)

And replies:

---

[83] The word used here is *Yaum*, the literal meaning of which is a day, but also means a long period, duration, stage etc. (Ed)

Verily your Sustainer is Allah, Who created the heavens and the earth in six stages, then He established Himself on the throne (of authority), regulating and governing things...(10:3) See also (13:2, 65:12)

The creative stages of the universe are mentioned in these two verses of Surah *Al-Sajda* in such a beautiful and balanced way that even the scientific discoveries of the modern time are enthralled by this. First it is stated that 'Allah passed this universe through six different stages to give it the present form' (32:4) and after this stated that Allah's pattern of creation is that in the domain of *Mashe'at* a scheme emerges. He begins the scheme of this *Mashe'at* from its lowest level; after this, traversing through various phases according to His '*Amr*', it continues to rise and progress towards its point of completion (35:10). The duration of these evolutionary stages is of thousands and thousands of years according to your calculation and estimate (32:5). (In fact, according to some schemes, fifty thousands of years (70:4)).

4.7 The *Amr* of Allah Always Returns to Him

Because all the concealed secrets of the 'system of *Amr*' are within the sphere of knowledge of that same Master of *Amr* and *Khalq*, therefore all the total affairs of the universe, having gained maturation under those beneficial schemes, are gradually advancing towards that intended destination which has been determined for them:

To Allah do belong the unseen (secrets) of the heavens and the earth, and to Him goes back every affair (for decision)...(11:123)

In the system of the universe, the sequence of events and occurrences is established on this very pattern that every scheme reaches its destination stage by stage. The Quran states:

...that Allah might accomplish a matter already enacted. For to Allah do all questions go back (Amr). (8:44).

So that Allah may complete this *Amr* which is about to happen and all matters (after gaining maturation) return towards Allah's defined objective. See also (57:5). And then these matters are not such that a scheme was begun and then abandoned on the way and another thing was started, or that in some matters ultimate success was achieved and in some others failure. Such things occur in human endeavours; the status of Allah is above and beyond this, His *Amr* is absolute, and His every scheme is assuredly successful:

...For Allah will surely accomplish His purpose (Amr): verily, for all things has Allah appointed a due proportion. (65:3)

...and Allah's Amr (command) must be fulfilled. (33:37) See also (4:47)

Indeed, Allah assuredly takes His *Amr* (scheme) to its final end; He has fixed a scale for everything because His every *Amr* is always accomplished.

Every *Amr* has to reach its objective (54:3). After traversing through various stages and objectives it has to realise a certain status at a defined place. To take these determined scales to their objectives all causes and effects are created, some of which can be grasped by the human intellect whereas some are beyond his understanding:

...And Allah has full power and control over His affairs; but most among mankind know it not. (12:21)

4.8 Allah's Chastisement is also Related to His *Amr*

In the same way that Allah's *Amr* (Divine law) is operating in the outer world, similarly the outcome of deeds is established in the human world according to His law (*Amr*) - the results of the deeds of individuals as well as those of nations. That which is commonly called reward and punishment is another name for the consequences of deeds according to the Law of Requital. When destruction falls upon nations as a result of going against the Divine law, this is also termed as the *Amr* of Allah i.e. this too takes place according to Allah's Law of Requital. The Quran has described the destruction and obliteration of past nations in these very words.[84] At this point, a few examples are given as illustrations. For example, in relation to the flood of Noah his nation was told:

Say: 'O my people! Do whatever you can: I will do (my part): but soon will you know – who it is to whom comes a penalty of ignominy, and on whom descends a penalty that abides.' (39:39-40)

...then when comes Our command (Amr), and fountains of the earth gush forth... (23:27)

When the son of Noah said to his father that I will go to some mountain and take refuge, his father informed him:

---

[84] For details see my books *Jooy e Noor, Barq e Toor* and *Shola e Mastoor*.

The son replied: *'I will betake myself to some mountain: it will save me from the water'. Noah said: 'This day nothing can save from the command (Amr) of Allah, any but those on whom He has mercy'...(11:43)*

And when the time came for the cessation of this destructive flood, it was commanded:

...And the water abated and the Amr (command) was ended...(11:44)

In relation to the destruction of the nation of *Ad* it was stated:

So when Our decree issued (Amr arrived)...(11:58)

The same was also stated about the people of *Thamud*:

When Our Amr came...(11:66)

Lot was provided with knowledge about this *Amr*:

And We made known this decree (Amr) to him, that the last remnants of those (criminals) should be cut off by tomorrow. (15:66)

The punishment which overwhelmed the nation of Shoaib was also called Allah's *Amr*:

When Our Amr was issued...(11:94)

When Bani Israel commenced worshipping of the calf in the absence of Moses, he said on his return:

...did you make haste to bring on the judgment (Amr) of your Sustainer? (7:150)

Regarding the hypocrites of the time of Rasul-ullah, it is stated:

...perhaps Allah will give victory, or a decision according to His Will (Amr). Then they will repent of the thoughts which they secretly harboured in their hearts. (5:52)

About the people of the Book, it is stated:

...But forgive and overlook, till Allah accomplishes His purpose (Allah's Amr arrives): for Allah has power over all things. (2:109)

Allah's law is that whatever kind of tree the seed is of, that same tree will grow from it, and from this tree those same type of flowers and fruit will appear. It is obvious that to make the seed grow into a tree and for the tree to bear its fruit, many forces of nature are functioning through mutual cooperation. Man has acquired knowledge of many forces among these, while some are such towards which his human mind has not yet reached. It may be that there are some effects among them whose reality and form are beyond the limits of the comprehension of man. Those forces which cause the Divine law to be productive are called *Malaika*[85] in Quranic terminology.

4.9 *Malaika*[86] and Allah's *Amr*

The Quran has stated about the *Malaika* that they carry out every task according to the *Amr* of Allah.

> *…and they act (in all things) by His command (Amr). (21:27)*

And:

> *…they guard him by command (Amr) of Allah…(13:11)*

They descend by His *Amr*:

> *We descend not but by command (Amr) of your Sustainer…(19:64)*

And they are the custodians and messengers of Allah's *Wahi*:

> *He does[87] send down His angels (forces) with inspiration of His command (Amr)…*
> *(16:2)*

4.10 *Wahi* is also Allah's *Amr*

Wahi which is sent is also through Allah's *Amr*:

> *…By His command (Amr) does he send[88] Wahi to any of His servants…(40:15)*

Regarding the Book of Moses, it is stated:

---

[85] Details of this are given in my book *Iblees O Adam*.
[86] *Malaika* – commonly translated as 'angels', this term denotes the forces of nature in the universe, both discovered and undiscovered to date. See root *M-L-K* in *Lughat ul Quran*, Vol 2, pp 535-538. (Ed)
[87] Used to send down, because the process of *Wahi* ended after the demise of Rasul-ullah.
[88] Used to send.

You (O Rasul) were not on the Western side when We sent Amr to Moses…
(28:44)

Here *Amr* means the *Wahi* of Allah. In another verse it is stated:

And We granted them clear signs in Amr…(45:17)

And We provided clear signs to Bani Israel of *Amr*. Here, the purpose of *Amr* is also Allah's *Wahi* or Sharia commands for Moses. In the next verse it is stated:

Then We put you on the path of Sharia[89]: so follow you that and follow not the desires of those who know not. (45:18)

4.11   *Amr* Meaning Deen

In these verses, by *Amr* is meant Deen, and Deen and *Wahi* are one and the same thing. This is why the Quran and its commandments are also called the *Amr* of Allah in another verse. In Surah *At-Talaq* in relation to commands regarding woman, it is stated:

That is the command (Amr) of Allah, which He has sent down to you…(65:5)

In other words, those laws which are given through *Wahi* so that human society can be shaped according to them.

4.12   Allah's *Amr* and *Laila-tul-Qadr*[90]

Differentiation in affairs took place that night in which the revelation of the Quran commenced (difference between *Haqq* and *Batil*):

In that (night) is made distinct every affair of wisdom. By command, from Our presence…(44:4-5)

That very night which is called *Laila-tul-Qadr:*

Therein come down Malaika and Ar-Ruh by the law of their Rabb, carrying every Amr. (97:4)

---

[89] Sharia – this refers to the path of Deen. (Ed)

[90] *Laila-tul-Qadr* - the literal meaning is 'Night of Criteria/Standards/Scales'. Metaphorically it could mean the dark period in human history when mankind was lost due to the absence of Allah's guidance. (Ed)

4.13   *Ar-Ruh*[91] is Allah's *Amr*

And *Ar-Ruh* is also Allah's *Amr*:

(O Rasul!) They question you regarding Ar-Ruh. Say: 'Ar-Ruh (comes) by command of my Sustainer: of knowledge (of Allah's affairs) it is only a little that is communicated to you. (O men!) (17:85)

Here, by *Ar-Ruh* is meant the *Wahi* of Allah. Further details of this will be available in the book *Iblees O Adam*.

4.14   *Amr* Meaning Command

In some places *Amr* has also been used to mean command e.g. the *Anbiya* used to provide guidance according to Allah's *Amr* (command of Allah):

We made them leaders, guiding (men) by Our command (Amr)…(21:73)

In another verse the word *Izn* is used for this. It is stated about Rasul-ullah:

And as one who invites to Allah by His Izn and as a Lamp spreading Light. (33:46)

The Imams of Bani Israel also used to provide guidance according to Allah's *Amr*:

And We appointed, from among them, leaders, giving guidance under Our command (Amr)…(32:24)

Here, *Amr* can mean the Divine laws and also the Deen of Moses because as we have seen above the meaning of *Amr* is Deen and also the Divine laws. In these verses too, the meaning of *Amr* will be the Divine laws. The reality is that as far as the outer world or human society is concerned, by command or *Izn* or *Amr* is meant the Divine laws, according to which all these affairs are conducted.

4.15   *Izn* and *Amr*

In Surah *Al-Saba* there is mention of those 'Jinns' who used to serve Solomon. While mentioning them, the synonymous words *Izn* and *Amr* are quoted in one verse:

…And there were Jinns who worked in front of him, by the Izn of His Sustainer, and if any of them turned aside from Our Amr…(34:12)

---

[91] *Ar-Ruh* – this means the *Wahi* of Allah. (Ed)

By 'Jinns' is meant those uncivilised tribes who used to carry out various tasks in the kingdom of Solomon. (Details will be available in my book *Iblees 0 Adam*).

5   *Khalqiyat* (Creation)

It has been noted under the previous topic that according to the programme of Allah there are two phases of creation. The first phase is of the domain of *Amr* in which the thing to be created is in its non-visible and non-perceptible form. The second phase is of creation in which that thing comes before us in a visible form. This is an arbitrary division as the term *Khalq* can otherwise be used at every stage.

5.1 Linguistic Meaning

The linguistic meaning of *Khalq* is to measure something, to estimate it, to make something according to some other thing, to set aright the proportion and balance of something. From these meanings the essence of *Khalq* will be to make something according to a specific standard and estimate by creating proportion and balance between various elements. Seen from this aspect *Takhleeq* will also have two steps. One is to bring different elements into existence from nothing, for which the Quran has used the words *Badee* and *Fatir* (their explanation will come later), and the second step is to keep producing ever new things from these created elements by employing different formulations. In this it could also be that when a thing (according to a specific order and scale) has been created once, it can be repeated in the same way i.e. it continues to be made over and over according to the same pattern, and it can also be that new additions keep taking place in the created things. The Quran has mentioned both these aspects.

5.2 Beginning and Repeating

A question is posed about the first phase:

> ...*Who originates creation, then repeats (Yu-eedu-hu) it...(27:64)*

And a response is given:

> *It is Allah Who begins creation; then repeats (Yu-eedu-hu) it; and your every step moves towards His defined stages. (30:11)*

A few verses later, the Quran states:

> *It is He Who begins creation; then repeats (Yu-eedu-hu) it; and for Him it is most easy... (30:27) See also (29:19, 10:34)*

94

The meaning of *Yu-eedu-hu* is not merely 'repeating', it also means to give rotation.[92] This means that following the commencement of its creation, by giving it rotation and passing it through different revolutionary stages in this way He (Allah) takes it to its point of completion. This process of the passing of things of the universe through various stages and phases to their point of completion can be comprehended by man, and now it has also become apparent as a scientific fact (according to the modern theory of evolution), but the start of the creation i.e. the process of its coming into existence from nothing cannot come within the grasp of the human intellect. This is why the Quran has not gone into the details of this. By saying only this much it has moved forward, that Allah:

To Him is due the primal origin of the heavens and the earth...(2:117)

Say: 'Shall I take for my protector any other than Allah, the Creator of the heavens and the earth (from nothing)? (6:14)

Being *Badee* or *Fatir* in this way is the same as that which is expressed through the words 'Be! and it is'. The meaning of 'Be! and it is' has been explained in Chapter 4. At that point this was made clear that from this it is not meant that everything sprouts out from somewhere just like that. In the system of the universe the creation of everything comes into being according to a specific Divine law. For the seed to become a tree, and for the drop of water to become a pearl, many stages have to be traversed. Regarding all these matters it is noted in the Quran that by passing through different stages, different phases and different levels, these acquire their final and complete form. This is why from 'Be! and it is' is meant that for the commencement of something Allah does not require any materials and causes, their beginning is according to His command and intention, and then according to His Own determined laws those things adopt their final form by passing through various stages.

5.3 Heavens and Earth

This is a fact that Allah Alone has created the entire system of the universe, but the Quranic technique is that it explains in numerous ways that reality which it wishes to engrave more profoundly on the heart. For example, it is stated as a question:

Or, who has created the heavens and the earth...(27:60)

---

[92] The term used means passing something through various stages of development and testing e.g. the creation of the earth went through many stages before it was possible to make it habitable for human beings. (Ed)

Who is it that has created the heavens and the earth? And another time this fact is brought forward by this method, declaring that even if these people who oppose the Quran in this way are asked, who is the creator of the heavens and the earth, they too will acknowledge this fact that the creator of the system of the universe and the earth is indeed Allah. For example:

If you were to question them, 'Who created the heavens and the earth?' They would be sure to reply, 'These were created by Him, the exalted in Power, full of Knowledge'. (43:9) See also (29:61, 31:25, 39:38)

At some places this same truth is explained in this way that whatever is in the physical world, its Creator is that same true Allah, however, if you accept a god other than Him, then specify what did this god create? After mentioning the creations of the heavens and the earth in Surah *Luqman*, the Quran states:

Such is the creation of Allah: now show Me what is there that others besides Him have created; nay, but the transgressors are in manifest error. (31:11)

Then He gives answers to these questions Himself, that this is their omission that they are making gods of others. All this is created by Him and He is the Creator of all:

All Hamd[93] is for Allah Who created the heavens and the earth and Who made the darkness and the light…(6:1)

Along with this the Quran also made this reality clear that Allah did not create this system of the universe futilely and pointlessly, without purpose and meaning, without aim and need, but created it with infinite wisdom. There is a specific purpose for its creation. Since materialists are not convinced of the existence of a metaphysical force behind this system, their belief is that all things of creation have come into existence via blind nature, just like that without any purpose, need, aim and reason, and will end in the same way. Repudiation of this belief is done in the Quran using different means and techniques. It states:

Not without purpose did We create heaven and earth and all between! That were the thought of Kafirs! But woe to Kafirs because of the fire (consequences of denial)! (38:27)

---

[93] *Hamd* – usually translated as 'praise', here it means that both the visible and non-visible creation, including man himself, present enough evidence that Allah is the Creator of everything, and the expression of this appreciation is included in *Hamd*. (Ed)

5.4 Knowledge of Things and Islam

This is why it is said that the task of the *Jamaat* of *Momineen* should be this, that they should take the things of the universe one by one, and after lifelong experimentation and observation and a period of research and investigation, prove this that Allah has not created anything uselessly and without purpose. Today the West expresses pride on this aspect that they have made great progress in the physical sciences. There is no doubt that this is in fact a reason for pride and acclaim. When the Quran stated that Adam deserves the prostration of angels to him and the system of the universe has been subjugated to man, then those individuals or nations who harness the forces of nature, fulfill this aim. But fourteen hundred years ago, the Quran had stated about the *Jamaat e Momineen*:

Behold! In the creation of the heavens and the earth, and the alternation of night and day – there are indeed signs for men of understanding. Men who reflect (Zikr) in the Laws of Allah, standing, sitting, and lying down on their sides and contemplate the (wonders of) creation in the heavens and the earth. (thus reaching this conclusion) 'Our Sustainer! Not for naught have You created this! Glory to You! Give us freedom from the penalty of the fire'. (3:190-191)

From this it also became clear what is meant by '*Zikr*' of Allah i.e. reaching this truth through observation and study of nature that this system is functioning according to Divine laws, and nothing in the universe is created futilely and without purpose. But the difference between a *Momin* thinker and a Western thinker will be that, after discovering the things of nature, the Western thinker will wander around in the valleys of conjecture and speculation to determine their purpose and need. Though he will determine the properties and characteristics of the different 'constituents of the universe', he will declare the sum total of these individual constituents i.e. the whole of the universe, as being purposeless and meaningless. He will search for the benefits and advantages of 'creation' (created things) in microscopic detail, but regarding the Creator of this beneficial and advantageous creation, he will hold the belief that He is (Allah forbid) a 'blind nature' which is devoid of aim, intent and wisdom. In other words, he will term each individual part of a machine as being useful but will declare the sum total of these parts, i.e. the machine, to be purposeless, and will consider the Creator of this machine (Allah forbid) as being 'intellectually blind'.

You can now conclude yourself whether this is the following of intellect or the death of intellect! Contrary to this, a wise *Momin* will prove from these very same discoveries, that the creation of the universe is not the work of a 'blind nature' but is the act of such a Being Who is Wise, Knowledgeable, All-Seeing and All-Knowing. From the usefulness of its parts, he will prove that the whole machine is beneficial and advantageous, and from the usefulness of the whole machine, that the Creator of the machine is knowledgeable and wise, and from this he will reach the conclusion that this system of the universe has not come into existence without necessity and purpose, instead it has been brought into existence for the achievement of a grand and splendid purpose under the auspices of the infinite wisdom of Allah, All-Wise and All-Seeing. In other words, a wise *Momin* will keep strengthening this *Eimaan* of his, which was based on the 'unseen', in the light of the dynamic and lively results of tangible and evidence-based experiments and experiences, with vision and knowledge, and in this way will prove that:

> *...I do invite unto Allah – on evidence clear as the seeing with one's own eyes...*
> *(12:108)*

5.5 Science and Muslims

The style of a Muslim is that standing, sitting, walking about, he should keep reflecting and pondering on everything which is present in the universe. When moving, he is invited to the attraction of the pleasantness and beauty of the lilies and poppies; and when he sits, he can visualize millions of suns concealed within each and every particle of sand; and when he lies down, the star studded ceiling of the heaven discloses its long concealed secrets of astronomy to him; and in this way, by pondering on each and everything, he should prove that:

> *...Not for naught have You created this universe...(3:191)*

What a display of shutting the eyes to reality it is to allege about such a Deen that it is against knowledge of the sciences. But how can we complain about others, when Muslims themselves demonstrate by their own conduct that these alive and perennial verses of Allah, the Ever-Living and Established, are for the purpose of reciting for mere '*Sawab*[94]' and by 'Allah's *Zikr*' is meant the counting of rosary beads. And then by proclaiming that this system of the universe is not false, pointed towards another fact. The doctrine of some philosophers is that there is no existence of the things which we see all around us anywhere outside of the human mind; these are just manifestations of our thoughts, nothing exists in itself outside of this. This type of belief is also to be found among Hindus, according to which they call this universe *Maya* (mirage) i.e. which does not exist in itself, rather is merely the name of the self-deception of the human mind. Discussion of the philosophical aspect of this belief will be carried out at another place but by conceiving the universe to be an illusion and mirage, the deadly effects which this has on the practical life of man do not require further explanation. This is why the Quran made it clear that this system of the universe is not *Batil* (false) but is *Haqq*

---

[94] *Sawab* – this term is used for the concept of obtaining some unseen reward in the hereafter. For further details see *The Life in the Hereafter* by the author. (Ed)

(truth). Its creation is *bil-Haqq* and holds a purpose. Furthermore, the meaning of *bil-Haqq* is for the establishment of constructive effects:

> *See you not that Allah created the heavens and the earth bil-Haqq? If He so will, He can remove you and put (in your place) a new creation! (14:19) See also (16:3)*

5.6 The Universe Has Been Created *bil-Haqq*

Bil-Haqq also means that everything is created with a view to a specific purpose. Wherever it has been placed in this grand machinery, it fits precisely, and it is busy working to fulfil that purpose for which it has been created. By this the mind shifts to this fact that the power which is running this system is not some blind nature but is a knowledgeable and wise Being Who Himself is *Haqq* and whatever He has created is also *Haqq*. In other words, by the very fact of this system of the universe being *Haqq*, this provides evidence of the Creator of the universe being *Haqq*. These are those verses, those signs from which the heart of a *Momin* achieves the paradise of contentment and assurance:

> *Allah created the heavens and the earth Bil-Haqq: verily in this are signs for Momineen. (29:44) See also (30:8)*

This system of the universe being *bil-Haqq* is an established fact. There is never the slightest discrepancy within the system under which it is unwaveringly functioning. If it had come into existence purely by chance, it would have been scattered and dispersed long ago. Do you not see that whenever there is the slightest error in the functioning of a system of railways i.e. it moves away slightly from 'Haqq', then how much devastation results in it. Hence, this subjugation of the sun and the moon, this alternation of the night and day, this process of everything carrying out its assigned tasks according to its own respective measures according to precise time and defined scales, does it not point to this fact that all this is the consequence of the infinite wisdom of a Wise and All-Knowing Being:

> *He created the heavens and the earth bil-Haqq: He makes the night overlap the day, and the day overlap the night: He has subjected the sun and the moon (to His law) so each one follows a course for a time appointed. Is He not the Exalted in Power – He Who protects as per His laws. (39:5)*

From these verses we come to know that this system of the universe is not created by chance without purpose and necessity:

We created not the heavens and the earth and all between them, merely in (idle) sport (Laa'ebeen[95])! (21:16) See also (44:38-40)

Where by the use of one word *Laa'ebeen* (sport), the Quran points to the creation of the universe being *bil-Haqq*, it also invalidates a false belief by this. It is a belief of Hindus that *Parthwi* (earth) and *Akaash* (sky) is the *Laila* (playmate) of *Ishwar* (God). In other words, by the creation of the earth and heavens, God is playing a sport (Allah forbid) and is entertaining himself. When he becomes bored with the sport then, just as children demolish their sandcastles themselves, he, too, will scatter and disperse this system. Related to this, the name of one God (Shevjee) among them, *Natrajan* i.e. a Raja of players, is a very big player. This is the reason why the Quran did not consider it sufficient to merely declare it as *Batil* (false) but by adding the word *Laa'ebeen* to it, contradicted this belief with forcefulness. Clearly, fourteen centuries ago no one in Arabia would have known that this kind of belief even existed in the world.

5.7 Reflection in the System of the Universe

Then, since this scheme of the universe is created in truth (*bil-Haqq*), that is why it has been repeatedly emphasised to reflect and ponder on it. That thing which has come into form by chance without any purpose and need, or which has been made merely for sport, who gives an invitation to ponder and reflect on it? The question of reflection and reasoning only arises when some system is working under some special wisdom. At one place it is stated:

Do they see nothing in the government of the heavens and the earth and all that Allah has created? (7:185)

And at another place that there are signs for people of wisdom and intellect in the manifestations of nature:

Among His Signs is this that He created you from dust; and then - behold, you are men scattered (far and wide)! And among His Signs is this, that He created for you mates from among yourselves, that you may dwell in tranquility with them, and He has put love and mercy between your (hearts); verily in that are signs for those who reflect. And among His Signs is the creation of the heavens and the earth, and the variations in your languages and your colours: verily in that are signs for those who know. And among His Signs is the sleep that you take by night and by day, and the

---

[95] *Laa'ebeen* – the root of the word is L-Ain-B. It means work which is useless but from which one can derive pleasure; to be non-serious about a thing; movement without a result; useless deed. This is about those who think that life is merely a plaything or a joke, they do not take life seriously. See *Lughat-ul-Quran,* Vol 2, pp 471-2. (Ed)

quest that you (make for livelihood) out of His Bounty: verily in that are signs for those who hearken. And among His Signs, He shows you the lightning, by way both of fear and of hope, and He sends down rain from the sky and with it gives life to the earth after it is dead: verily in that are Signs for those who are wise. (30: 20-24)

5.8 The Beauty of Creation

And not only this, but an invitation is extended to reflect and ponder on this system of nature and witness whether in such a grand system of the universe which astounds the intellect, is there any fault, any error, any omission, any disorder, any unsuitability, any lack of proportion, any mistake, any crease visible anywhere? Is there any chance to point the finger at anything?

He Who created the numerous heavens one above another: no want of proportion will you witness in the creation of Ar-Rehman. So turn your vision again: see you any flaw? Again, turn your vision a second time: your vision will come back to you dull and discomfited, in a state of worn out. (67:3-4)

To the superficial glance no order and connection, no proportion and balance is visible in this system of the universe. But as human knowledge and experience keep expanding, his research takes him towards this absolute conclusion that there is no crease in the Divine creation, no wrinkle in the blanket of lunar light.

5.9 Increase or Decrease in Creation is According to Allah's Will

Then, if this system of the universe had somehow come into existence by chance, then whatever was made initially would have remained as such. Those who accept soul and matter to be from the past hold this very belief. They say that whatever number of souls have been created, there can be no decrease or increase in it nor can matter decrease or increase; only forms change now, alterations keep taking place in the moulds; or on the other hand, the doctrine of the materialists of Europe that, 'what is life but the appearance of arrangements of elements, what is death but the disintegration of these elements'. According to them, the system of the universe is the name given to the various stages of the process of evolution, otherwise nothing here can increase or decrease.

But the universe created by Allah, the Wise and All-Knowing, is not of this type that after creating it He sat back (Allah forbid) as if He had become a useless limb. European philosophers think that the system of the universe is like a clock which once wound up, keeps running automatically. This doctrine is also a product of the human mind, it is not based on fact. To think that the Being which possesses this capability that He can bring the universe into existence from nothing and formulate such laws according to which this functions with balance and synchronisation, that after doing so much, His powers became suspended and He sat back idle, is not knowledge but ignorance. The Possessor of such great powers - and idle! Does your intellect concede this? What, does evidence and observation also demonstrate this? Suspension emerges at that time when all energies end and life changes into death. The living One, and living with powers, and along with this established, He can never die. Leaving aside death, He cannot even doze off:

…No slumber can seize Him nor sleep…(2:255)

Therefore, the doctrine of suspension i.e. Allah sitting back idle, is a sign of shutting the eyes to facts. In the veins and arteries of the system of the universe, His Wisdom and Will is continuously functioning and working. He creates, then according to the law of *Mashe'at*, He has knowledge about the reality of what is not meant to remain any longer and He removes it, and that which has the ability to remain, He retains it:

Allah does blot out or confirm what He Wills: with Him is the mother of the Book (Divine laws). (13:39)

Having created, He has not now become oblivious of His creation:

And We have made, above you, many tracts; and We are never unmindful of creation. (23:17)

Not only beauty and adornments but keeps creating ever new creations:

…He adds to His creation as per His Will…(35:1)

Up till now there was mention of various aspects of creation. But the Quran has summed up all details and specifics into one sentence when it stated:

…the Creator of all things…(6:102) See also (39:62, 40:62)

This was the general aspect i.e. this proclamation that He is the Creator of everything. But to instill the truth in the mind in an unambiguous way, the Quran has made it clear by illustration with an example, that none other than Him has ever created anything:

Say: 'Have you seen partners of yours whom you call upon besides Allah? Show me what it is they have created in the earth. Or have they a share in the heavens?' (35:40) See also (46:4)

At one place this same question is asked in the form of a negative question:

O mankind! call to mind the grace of Allah unto you! Is there a Creator, other than Allah, to give you sustenance from heaven or earth? There is no Ilaah but He: how then are you deluded away from the truth? (35:3)

5.10　False Gods are Themselves a Creation

Those whom you worship (whether they are human beings or signs of nature) are themselves creations of Allah:

Those whom they invoke besides Allah create nothing and themselves created. (16:20)
See also (52:35-36)

These false gods are not only idols of clay and stones but are also living gods whose worship is carried out during their life or after their death. It is stated about their helplessness:

Yet they have taken, besides Him, gods that can create nothing but are themselves created; that have no control of hurt or good to themselves; nor can they control death nor life nor resurrection. (25:3)

At another place it is stated that if there had been another creator other than Allah, and if the creations of both had mingled together, then there could also be this doubt that there may be another creator. But when this is not the case, then how can one be deceived:

...or do they assign to Allah partners who have created (anything) as He has created, so that the creation seemed to them similar? Say: 'Allah is the Creator of all things: He is the one, Supreme and Irresistible.' (13:16)

Leaving aside some big thing, other than Allah no-one can create even the smallest of things[96] (22:73-74). When all these things which the erroneous vision of man converts into gods are created by Allah, then the Creator certainly knows what potentials there are in His Creation for various tasks. Hence, when He (the Creator) says that no-one possesses the capability to create anything in My creation, then this is a statement of the state of reality:

Should He not know – He that created? And He is the One that understands the finest details and is well acquainted with them. (67:14)

---

[96] This is in reference to Allah's ability to create from nothing. This point is elaborated later by the author. (Ed)

He is fully aware what potentials are hidden in His creation and where the limits of their potentials come to an end:

...for He is well-versed in every kind of creation. (36:79)

It should be made clear that wherever in these verses it is stated that no god other than Allah has the power to create, by this is meant to bring into existence something from nothing. Otherwise, the other meaning of creation i.e. producing something by a new arrangement of different elements is that act of creation[97] for which man possesses the ability. When the Quran declares Allah as being the best of Creators (23:14, 37:125), there is a reference in this to the fact that there can be creators other than Allah. But He is the best of Creators i.e. that ultimate beauty and adornment, complete balance and proportion which is found in the creation of Allah cannot be found in the creation of others.

In the light of this discussion, reflect that when a *Jamaat* consists of those individuals whose selfs are becoming developed (i.e. the attributes of Allah are manifesting in their selfs), then the first trait of this *Jamaat* will be that it should become a partner in the creative programme of Allah. The fundamental trait of a *Momin* is creation, and creation also of such a type that, just as an attribute of Allah is that when He makes an intent about something then that thing becomes manifest and emerges, the state of a *Momin* should also be such that (within the constraints of being human) when he intends to do something then this intent should assuredly reach its completion. In the same way that his Allah is not dependent on an outsider for the completion of His intents, similarly the state of the *Jamaat* of *Momineen* should be such that in the attainment of their aims they are not reliant on outsiders. This *Jamaat* will be the cause for the creation of ever new aims, lively objectives, and bright and sustainable wishes in the world.

When their Allah is not a static Being of inertia and an idol of stone but instead is a Creator and Maker, then does it suit them to spend a life that is static and suspended like stones? They should also be creators and makers (within the confines of being human). They should be the creator of their own world and in the creation of this new world, no-one should be their equal or comparable – this is the very secret of being a *Momin*, this is the essence of his being, and this is the very proclamation of the Quran.

---

[97] Whatever man creates is through the use of those potentials and intellect which are bestowed by Allah. Here, the Quran draws our attention to this matter, to relate all creation to His Self. (Ed)

6   *Rabubiyat* (Sustenance)

After creation (*Takhleeq*), the first stage is *Rabubiyat*. This has already been explained that by *Kun-Fa-Yakoon* (Be! and it is) does not mean that by Allah saying '*Kun*' (Be), that thing at once comes into existence in its completed form. By this is meant that the process of its creation commences and by gradually going through evolutionary stages, it reaches its point of completion. Taking something from its point of initiation gradually towards its stage of completion and providing complete guidance for this is called *Rabubiyat*, and the one Who does this is called *Rabb*. The general meaning of this will be the One who provides 'nourishment' i.e. *Rabubiyat* will mean that in order for something to be taken through all of its stages from its beginning until its completion; to oversee and supervise; provide nourishment; make it grow and enable it to reach its completion; from a water drop till it becomes a pearl; till a seed becomes a tree; till water and clay turns to the form of a man; whatever kind of stages arise en route to be watchful and to accommodate them, providing those means which are sufficient for its requirements and on which its life depends.

6.1 Displays of *Rabubiyat*

This arrangement that along with the birth of a child fountains of milk should gush forth for its nourishment, was not a matter within the control of a human; this is a manifestation of the marvel of *Rabubiyat* of that Creator of the Universe. Then also reflect on these links in this process of *Rabubiyat* that, following the birth of a child and up to a period of two to two and a half years, how changes occur automatically in this diet of his according to the demands of his nutrition. Because in the beginning the stomach of a child is fragile, therefore at the beginning the composition of the milk contains proportionately more water and less fat. As the child grows its stomach continues to develop the ability to digest a stronger diet and along with this ability, stage by stage, the proportion of water in the milk reduces and fat composition increases, although the milk producing 'machinery' is still the same and the constituents from which the milk is produced in the mother also remain unchanged, so much so that when the child develops the strength and ability to digest other food, then these springs of milk dry up. For those children who are placed on artificial feeding, charts are prepared for their diet which detail how the proportion of water and milk will decrease and increase in relation to age. The principle of this proportion is defined on this process of nature which it keeps in view in relation to the child's diet. From this one system it can be understood whether this arrangement is that of a 'blind nature' i.e. could the inventor of this process from which man, who possesses so much intelligence and understanding, knowledge and experience, obtains guidance to prepare food for the child, be a 'blind nature'? This is just an example, otherwise you will see that whichever thing you cast your eye on in this wide and expansive system of the universe, whatever means of sustenance are needed are all present from the direction of nature from the beginning to the end at every stage for its survival and strength. For human life air, water, light and food are indispensable constituents. The state of air is such that wherever man is, whether travelling or not, low or high, day or night, ample air remains automatically around him and he is not even aware at what moment he takes a breath; so much so, that even during sleep this action continues to function automatically. This is the same situation with light. By reflecting on the system of 'water supply' which Allah's system of *Rabubiyat* has made for water to reach every place, the intellect and vision become lost in amazement. The rays of the sun take clean and distilled water from the brackish water of the oceans by evaporation to the heights of the atmosphere and leave contaminations behind. This freshwater floats around hither and thither in the vessels of the clouds, and wherever it is needed, the mouth of this vessel is opened. Whatever is beyond necessity is kept stored in the reservoirs of snow on the tops of the mountains which during the days of summer gradually keeps flowing to the plains. Whatever proportion of water is required on the plains is used, and the remainder flows forward and again joins the ocean, and some by being absorbed into the earth, remains stored in the form of underground wells and springs. Could this system even be imagined by a 'blind nature'? Could all this organisation and arrangement have just happened to come into existence? Just look at food, what is there which is not produced in the land, and all this is provided without any cost! There is no tax or restriction on anything. Perhaps it could be said that it appears from the kinds of troubles that man has to bear in order to sustain his life and for the sake of his body and soul, that he is subject to cruelty from every direction. But by looking at it a bit more closely you will yourself reach the right conclusion. *'My Saki blessed me with transparent wine, devoid of intoxication. Whatever colours you see belong to my goblet'.*[98]

6.2 Non-Divine Economic System

The system of Allah, *Rabb-il-Alameen*, was indeed the possessor of conveniences and comforts, but when man took it into his grasp and began the distribution of Allah's bestowed resources for his own ends and objectives, then clouds of troubles appeared over mankind. These troubles and difficulties are self-created by man. If the means of nourishment are distributed according to the Divine laws, then see how man will spend a life of paradise. What an irony it is that an ant and a sparrow should live its life in peace and tranquility whereas the life of man, the 'most superior among the creation', should be worse than hell! While a child remains in the care of nature, no deprivation or difficulty reaches it (if it does come then it is as a consequence of man's self-created system), but the moment he gives

---

[98] The author does not give a reference for this quote. It may be a couplet by Iqbal. (Ed)

up his mother's milk and enters the world of the human system, then mountains of problems begin to descend on him. The aim of the Quran is that that system of life which man having taken into his own hands has turned this earthly paradise into hell, should be established on those lines which Allah, *Rabb-il-Alameen*, has fixed for the universal *Rabubiyat* of mankind. These laws are preserved in the pages of the Quran whose beginning is with this verse:

Every type of Hamd is for Allah who is the Sustainer of whole of the universe. (1:2)

6.3 *Rabb-il-Alameen* (The Sustainer of All Worlds)

In other words, the attribute of Allah which is mentioned foremost in the Quran is that of *Rabubiyat* and this *Rabubiyat* is not for any particular species, any particular group, any particular nation, rather is the *Rabubiyat* for the whole world – the *Rabubiyat* for the whole system of the universe. The word *Rabb-il-Alameen* has been reiterated nearly forty times in the Quran so that the significance of this comprehensive system of *Rabubiyat* becomes firmly engraved on the human heart. To explain this, it is stated in another place:

Pharaoh said: 'And what is the 'Sustainer and Cherisher of the worlds'? (Moses) replied: 'The Sustainer and Cherisher of the heavens and the earth, and all between - if you want to be quite sure.' (26:23-24)

This reality of the *Rabubiyat* of the universe has been repeated at nearly fifteen different places in the Quran in varying ways. At some places the *Rabubiyat* of mankind is referred to:

Say: I seek the protection (of the laws) of the Sustainer and Cherisher of Mankind. (114:1)

Say! I wish to come within the protection of the laws of the Sustainer of mankind. Or at another place by condensing all these details, summarised it in one line, stating that He is the *Rabb* of 'all things':

Say! 'Shall I seek for my Sustainer other than Allah, when He is the Sustainer of all things?'...(6:164)

He is also the Creator of everything and the Sustainer of everything too. In this amazing system of the universe, from the finest particle to the massive stellar bodies, and beyond even these only Allah knows to where, from the beginning to the ultimate end of everything, in every phase of life, providing all sustenance to it and keeping an eye on everything, is a trait pertaining only to the majesty of Allah, *Rabb-il-Alameen*. For example, it is stated in the Quran:

...the Sustainer of the Throne of Honour (Arsh-e-Kareem)[99]. (23:116)

In other words, the master of that centre of forces from where this whole system of the universe is functioning in such a beautiful and balanced way is only Allah. The creation of all that exists, *Rabubiyat* and administration and management, is solely within His grip and hold. Regarding the different departments and the various aspects of the system of nature also, it is stated in various verses that Allah is the owner and controller of it all:

He is the Rabb of Sirius[100] (the Mighty Star). (53:49)

In Surah *Ar-Rehman* it is stated:

Rabb of the two Easts and Rabb of the two Wests. (55:17)

At another place He is called *Rabb ul Mashariq[101]* (37:5). *Rabb ul Masharaq* and *Al-Magharib[102]* (70:40) in Surah *Al-Maarij*, and at one place as *Rabb ul Falaq[103]* (113:1). Similarly, He has been called the *Rabb* of Makkah, the centre of Islam (27:91) and also *Rabb ul Izzat[104]* (37:180) i.e. possessor of sovereignty and power.

As has been noted above, if the economic and social system of the world is managed according to the Divine laws, then man will never have to face any difficulty or hindrance about the resources of life. This is what is meant by accepting Allah as our *Rabb* i.e. shaping our society according to His system of *Rabubiyat*. This is indeed the aim and manner of life of the *Jamaat e Momineen*. The proclamation of this very matter was made through these words which were stated by Rasul-ullah:

Say! 'Shall I seek for my Sustainer other than Allah, when He is the Sustainer of all things'? ...(6:164)

No other is a shareholder with Him in this *Rabubiyat*:

(That Quran) Which gives guidance to the straight path, and we have Eimaan therein: we do not associate any with our Rabb. (72:2)

---

[99] This is repeated about six times.
[100] This can also mean intellect and consciousness.
[101] *Mashariq* is the plural of *Mashraq* which means East.
[102] *Magharib* is the plural of *Maghrib* which means West.
[103] *Falaq* means dawn.
[104] *Izzat* means power.

This means that the system of our society will be purely according to Allah's law of *Rabubiyat* – not this, that some parts are taken from these laws and some from human ideas, and in this way through their amalgamation to formulate a code of laws. This is a blatant *Shirk* for which there is absolutely no permission in Islam. Man as a *Momin* cannot associate anyone else in Allah's system of *Rabubiyat*. Hence, an example is mentioned in Surah *Al-Kahf* of a *Momin* man who states:

> *But for my part that He is Allah, My Rabb, and none shall I associate with my Sustainer. (18:38)*

This doctrine, that creation is in the hands of another god (*Brahma*) and *Rabubiyat* is in the hands of another god (*Vishnu*), is a sign of ignorance about the reality of Allah. Everything is created by this One Allah, and only He is the One Who by taking everything through the stages of life conveys them to their completion:

> *Say: Is it that you deny Him Who created the earth in two Days (stages)? And do you join equals with Him? He is Rabb of the Worlds. (41:9)*

Rabubiyat is neither in the hands of some god or goddess nor in the hand of any man. This fact is not in need of any explanation that a man only bows before another man when he thinks that my needs of life are in the control of another. The blessing of Allah has spread the means of sustenance on the vast and wide face of the earth for the whole of mankind without expectation of any remuneration or return (41:10) (equally for every needy person). But the usurping powers commandeer these resources into their own possession, and after this they get done whatever they wish from the hungry masses of humanity. Pharaoh, in proof of his claim of being 'god', had declared this very thing:

> *I am your sustainer, most high. (79:24)*

And this is not only related to the one Pharaoh of Moses, the pharaohs of every era do all of this to maintain the strength of their 'godliness'. The Quran came to eliminate tyranny from the world. Hence, it has reiterated this truth in various ways nearly nine hundred and fifty times that your *Rabb* is Allah alone – *Rabubiyat* is not in the control of any other. That which you think - that the means of sustenance of life are in the hands and control of tyrannical forces - this will only be like this till that time that you think like this. When you stop thinking like this and acquire *Eimaan* in this that the ownership of *Rabubiyat* is only with that Being of Allah, then a revolutionary change will take birth in you, your viewpoint will transform, and when such a change occurs in your psychological state, then no power of the world will be able to make you accept their 'godliness'. The state of those who accept Allah as *Rabb* is indeed unique:

In the case of those who say, 'Our Rabb is Allah', and, further, stand straight and steadfast, the universal forces descend on them: 'Fear you not!', nor grieve! but receive the Glad Tidings of Jannat, the which you are promised! (41:30)

In Surah *Al-Ahqaf* it is stated:

Verily those who say, 'Our Rabb is Allah,' and remain firm (on that Path), on them shall be no fear, nor shall they grieve. (46:13)

6.4 True Freedom

When the human heart becomes home to such a strong *Eimaan*, then man never bows before anyone other than Allah. Other than at His door, he does not supplicate before any other portal, and he does not remain the servant of any other than Him. This is itself the declaration of the true *Rabb* Himself:

Your Rabb has decreed that you follow none but Him ...(17:23)

Hence, the meaning of having *Eimaan* in Allah's *Rabubiyat* is that, other than Allah, the sovereignty of no-one else should be accepted. Bowing before every possessor of power in the world by believing it to be a master, tendering your begging bowl in front of whichever high edifice is sighted, is humiliation of the human self and is the stripping of humanity. This is exactly what Yusuf had told his jailhouse companions:

O my two companions of the prison! Are many gods differing among themselves better, or the One Allah, Supreme and Irresistible? (12:39)

6.5 Chains of Slavery

But, of course, man does not confine his means and sources of imprisonment and bondage to one place only – he purchases the chains of slavery from various nooks and crannies. If one chain is placed on him forcibly, he puts on ten more chains voluntarily. These are those chains which find their way through the paths of reverence and adoration to become installed in his heart and mind. The Quran has mentioned in numerous places those people who were told in clear terms to accept one *Rabb* as their Allah, but derogating Allah, they declared the *Anbiya* and the angels themselves as their *Rabb*:

Nor would he (a man of Rabb) instruct you to take angels and Anbiya for gods and patrons. What! would he bid you to Kufr after you have bowed your will to Islam? (3:80)

They went even further than this and accepted their scholars and their elders as their masters:

They take their priests and their anchorites to be their gods in derogation of Allah ...
(9:31)

6.6 Obedience of Religious Clergy and Scholars

What is the acceptance of scholars and clergy as being masters other than this – the affirmation of their words without any logic or reasoning, and the acceptance of these as being worthy of obedience in the same way as the *Wahi* descended from Allah, and to declare their deeds as having the status of being beyond criticism, and to believe them to be masters of those hidden powers which are solely attributed to the Being of Allah. But the difficulty is that when we read these verses of the Quran, after saying that these are but the tales of past nations, these have nothing to do with us, we move forward, even though the Quran does not narrate these historical examples in order that this 'story telling' may become the means to help us slumber (Allah forbid). It narrates these events and stories of past peoples and the circumstances and way of life of previous nations in order to infuse life into the Islamic Ummah, and wishes to tell them how former nations, having reached these precipices of destruction and ruin, slipped. So that you too should not slip by reaching these cliffs. But the state in which we are today is apparent - that same Muslim who was told to invite the people of the Book to:

...come to common terms as between us and you: that we follow none but Allah; that we associate no partners with him; that we erect not, from among ourselves, gods and patrons other than Allah...(3:64)

This was the very teaching of the Quran, that obedience of other than Allah should not be adopted. So much so, that even the messengers whose status was the highest after the status of Allah, they also extended invitations towards the obedience of Allah, they never used to teach obedience of their own selves:

It is not (possible) that a man, to whom is given the Book, and Wisdom, and the messenger-hood, should say to people: 'Be you my followers rather than Allah's': on the contrary (He would say) 'Be you followers of Him Who is truly the Cherisher of all: for you have taught the Book and you have studied it earnestly'. (3:79)

But this truth should once again be understood, that the practical meaning of accepting Allah as *Rabb* is that we shape our system in accordance with the Divine laws; other than this there is no other form of acceptance of Allah as *Rabb*. This is that system in which no human being remains at the mercy of another human being and therefore does not accept subjugation to anyone. The *Jamaat* through which this kind of system of *Rabubiyat* is established is called the *Jamaat* of *Rabba'niyeen*. Among them, every individual is concerned about the *Rabubiyat* of others and in this way the development of all the individuals of humanity continues to take place. Within this 'development' their physical sustenance is included as well as the accomplishment of all latent human potentials. The focal point of Islamic teaching is the establishment of this very system of *Rabubiyat*.[105] *Rabubiyat* is an important trait of a developed self and its manifestation takes place automatically through the *Jamaat e Momineen*.

(Since, as has already been noted, the word *Rabb* occurs nine hundred and fifty times in the Quran, this is why it is difficult to note all these verses here. Those verses will appear at other places).

---

[105] Further details are covered in my book titled *The Quranic System of Sustenance*.

7   *Razzaqiyat* (Provision of *Rizq*)

That means of sustenance which is received from some direction as a gift is called *Rizq*. But there is one distinction in its basic meaning and that is that it should be received at the time that it is required. Hence, the meaning of *Rizq* is that means of sustenance which is received freely from Allah according to the need of everything without any effort or repayment. It should be made clear that 'getting *Rizq*' does not mean that ready baked bread is put into the mouth of man. By *Rizq* is meant that all the resources for the physical needs of man are present in the earth which every needy one can obtain. This wide and vast surface of the earth is the banqueting table (*Maida*) for the numerous and diverse favours of that Allah *Razzaq* which is spread out equally for His creation. The One Who has created creation has also made arrangements for its *Rizq* Himself:

> *It is Allah Who has created you: further, He has provided for your sustenance; then He will cause you to die; and again He will give you life. Are there any of your 'Partners' who can do any single one of these things? ...(30:40)*

7.1 *Rizq* from the Heavens and Earth

He has organised the system of the universe in such a way, and it is busy in carrying out its duties in such a manner, that all the means and resources of *Rizq* keep appearing before man:

> *Who has made the earth your couch, and the heavens your canopy; and sent down rain from the heavens; and brought forth therewith fruits for your sustenance...*
> *(2:22)*

Accumulating stores of water in the lofty skies and then producing life-giving *Rizq* from the dead land through these - these are all the amazing displays of His attribute of *Razzaqi*:

> *It is Allah Who has created the heavens and the earth and sends down rain from the skies, and with it brings out fruits wherewith to feed you ...(14:32)*

Rain is both a cause for the production of *Rizq* and is *Rizq* in itself because water is an indispensable part of *Rizq*:

> *...and the fact that Allah sends down sustenance from the sky, and revives therewith the earth after its death...(45:5)*

The initial source of life is also water and the cause for its continuing existence too. The continuous flow of the stream of life is a result of its blessings:

...We made from water every living thing...(21:30) See also (50:9-11)

7.2 System of *Rizq* is in Allah's Hand

This system of *Rizq* is established through the planned execution of the Creator of the heavens and earth and none can dare to deny this fact. Even the materialist who verbally denies the existence of God will also accept this fact that this system is not the handiwork of man. This is another matter that he will give the name of 'laws of Nature' to this system. But who is going to deny this fact that 'laws' can never be implemented without the existence of a deciding power with the freedom to choose - this Being is called Allah:

Say: 'Who is it that sustains you (in life) from the sky and from the earth? or Who is it that has power over hearing and sight? And Who is it that brings out the living from the dead and the dead from the living? and Who is it that rules and regulates all affairs?' They will soon say, 'Allah'...(10:31)

The Quran, with its unique style of reasoning, by presenting the awesome system of the universe to us, directs the human mind to the Oneness of Allah. This is because the overwhelming wonder of the system of the universe draws man to reach this conclusion that the Will of a Being with freedom to choose and possessing intent is working behind this system. And its integrity and harmony points to this fact that the Being possessing free will is 'One' and Alone i.e. in the whole of the universe there only one law is in action:

Or, Who originates creation, then repeats it, and Who gives you sustenance from the heaven and the earth? (can there be another) god besides Allah? Say, 'Bring forth your argument, if you are telling the truth!' (27:64) See also (35:3)

7.3 No-one else Possesses Authority over *Rizq*

This was the general aspect of this belief that only Allah provides *Rizq*. Alongside this, the practical aspect of this is also made evident that other than Him no-one else is the controller of *Rizq*. By combining these two parts the completion of *Eimaan* takes place:

And follow others than Allah, such as have no power of providing them, for sustenance (Rizq), with anything in the heavens or the earth, and cannot possibly have such power? (16:73)

In this short verse the Quran has negated all those 'gods' whose obedience and subjugation is accepted because man (of his own accord) thinks that the provision of *Rizq* is in their control. But the reality is that regardless whether the gods and goddesses are of the era of 'superstition' or are human gods of the era of 'civilisation and enlightenment', *Rizq* is not in anyone's hand, it is only in Allah's hand, and when *Rizq* only comes from His direction, then leaving Him, how can there be slavery and subjugation to someone else?

...The things that you follow besides Allah have no power to give you sustenance: then seek you sustenance from Allah, serve Him, and be grateful to Him: to Him will be your return. (29:17)

If He shuts off the sources of sustenance, then no power can open them:

Or who is there that can provide you with Sustenance if He were to withhold His provision? ...(67:21)

Leaving aside the shutting off of all means of sustenance, if there is even the slightest variation in this system e.g. clean and pure water rising from the sea becomes clouds and all its contaminants (which are responsible for its salinity) remain behind in the sea – if any change occurs in this system and the seawater becomes clouds just as it is and in the same format begins to rain upon the earth, just consider how with even with this minor change what the state of the world will become. Through this balanced system He provides *Rizq* to mankind and desires nothing in return:

...We ask you not to provide sustenance: We provide it for you ...(20:132)

This is the distinction between the true Sustainer and 'false gods'.

7.4 Beneficial *Rizq*

All the things which Allah has created as *Rizq*, those are *Tayyab*[106], pure, beneficial and pleasant, apart from the consumption of those which Allah Himself has forbidden. Hence, those things which Allah has declared to be *Halal* and beneficial, no-one has the right to label them as being *Haram* and detrimental:

Say: Who has forbidden the beautiful (gifts) of Allah, which He has produced for His servants, and the things, clean and pure, (which He has provided) for sustenance? ... (7:32)

---

[106] *Tayyab* – a thing which provides pleasure to the human senses, being and personality, which is pleasing to eat, hear, see and smell. See *Lughat-ul-Quran*, Vol 2, pp 117-118.

In another verse it is stated that Allah has provided for you *Rizq* of pleasant things (16:72).[107] But those things which He has created as *Halal* and beneficial, pure and useful, man makes them *Haram* and harmful through the intervention of his hands. Some examples of turning these from beneficial to injurious, useful to harmful, are glaringly clear. Water is absolutely life-giving but when it overflows and exceeds limits, then this same water becomes a cause for fatalities. Hence, it is also important to keep in view the defined scales in the use of everything. Transgressing the limit of these scales is called *Asraaf* (exceeding the limits) which is destructive. The Quran states:

> *…eat and drink: But waste not by excess …(7:31)*

In another verse it is stated that Allah has produced various kinds of fruits for you, so eat these fruits, and when you harvest the crop, then from that distribute His share as a right as well. The Quran states:

> *…But waste not by excess, for Allah loves not the wasters…(7:31)*

And do not exceed the limits because He does not like those who exceed limits. This is that breaking of laws, the effects and consequences of which manifest intrinsically very quickly.

7.5 Observing the Divine Limits

But certain situations are such where the consequences and effects of breaking the laws do not become apparent immediately, and man does not perceive them discernibly. This is that point where the guidance of a visionary is needed. A kidney stone does not form in a day. It is the consequence of months and sometimes years of a gradual imperceptible process. During this time the patient is not even aware that those things which he is consuming considering them to be extremely beneficial, how harmful these are becoming for him. Here a physician is required, who by diagnosing through symptoms and signs, can say which things are harmful for him. That physician will forbid certain items permanently for him because they do not suit this patient's constitution, and some things he will give permission to be consumed in a specific combination. For the sake of his health this patient will first of all need to have confidence in the expertise of this physician, after this trust he will need to follow his instructions to the letter.[108] If he does not do this, he will not have the fortune to attain good health.

---

[107] See also (40:64).
[108] Merely keeping the prescription safe or just reading it will provide no benefit.

This example is related to physical health. But for man diseases of the physical body are not as harmful as those harmful diseases which result in damage to his self (personality). Through diseases of the body his current life becomes miserable, but through the second type of diseases both his present life as well as the life to come in the hereafter become a continuous hell. Hence, the Quran which is a complete code for the whole life of man provides full instructions like an expert physician and kind doctor. In this respect, certain things are such regarding which the Quran states that these are not suitable for the disposition of humanity; this is why the command was given to not even go near them. Some are those about which the Quran states that these things are intrinsically useful and beneficial but the manner in which they are utilised results in a difference in their effects.

7.6 Prescribing *Halal* and *Haram*

If we pick fruit from our own orchard and eat it then it is beneficial and *Halal*, but if we steal fruit from the orchard of another and eat it, then that same fruit is *Haram* and harmful i.e. both fruits are of the same kind, their properties are similar, if their constituents are analysed there will be no difference in the composition of both. But due to the difference in the 'manner of use' there will be the difference of life and death in their result. A materialist cannot comprehend this distinction. He states that the same kind of things can be purchased with the money from a thief as with the money from a labourer. In order to understand this difference (as explained in the first example), it is essential to have conviction in the expertise of the physician and this is what is called *Eimaan*. This is what is absent in the heart of the materialist and its consequence is that today no 'health' is visible in any aspect of human life. The whole of Europe and as a consequence the whole world is turning into such a hell whose flames are turning humanity into a heap of ash.

It should be made clear that having conviction in the 'expertise of a physician' is initially in the form of '*Eimaan* in the unseen' but after this the results of its treatment will convert this '*Eimaan* in the unseen' into conviction based on evidence.

In any event the Quran, like a compassionate physician, emphasises that whatever is bestowed by Allah as *Rizq*, should be consumed using pure methods and not through *Haram* means i.e. firstly, do not set yourself to make decisions about *Halal* and *Haram* yourself, instead act according to that same decision that your 'expert physician' has made:

Say: 'See you what things Allah has sent down to you for sustenance? Yet you hold forbidden (Haram) some things thereof and some lawful (Halal).' Say: 'Has Allah indeed permitted you, or do you invent (things) to attribute to Allah?' (10:59)

There is another point implicit in the consumption in a 'pure manner' of those things which have been declared as *Halal* by Allah. This means that it is not essential that an individual must eat all the *Halal* things of the world. 'Pure' means that which produces pleasant and positive results. Therefore, from these *Halal* things, that thing which someone does not like and is not according to preference or is unsuitable for health, should not be consumed. The difference which is present in not eating something in this way and in considering something to be *Haram* is obvious.[109]

It has already been stated above that as a result of the method used for obtaining *Rizq*, the nature of *Rizq* and its effects change. If *Rizq* is obtained through legitimate means then this *Rizq* becomes balanced *Rizq*, pure *Rizq* and honourable *Rizq*. This kind of *Rizq* is the portion belonging to those people who have *Eimaan* in Allah and who make efforts under His defined laid down laws.

7.7 Honourable (*Kareem*) *Rizq*

The Quran states:

> *Those who accept Eimaan and work righteousness, for them is protection and a sustenance most honoured (Kareem). (22:50) See also (8:4, 11:88, 24:26)*

The question is, what is it that is known as *Rizq e Kareem* (sustenance with dignity) and how is it obtained? The matter is evidently clear. One society is that in which the means of sustenance are in the grip and control of a few human beings, while the remainder of the population are reliant and dependent on them for their daily bread. They extract work out of these dependent people according to their will; in this way their own dependency forces them into servitude. It is obvious that self-respect and eminence of humanity cannot endure by obtaining sustenance in this way. This is the bread of humiliation and bondage. Contrary to this, an alternative society is one in which the sources of sustenance are not in the ownership of any individual, instead they are the means to fulfil all the needs of the needy, and the people who organise and manage it, administer it in such a way that no individual remains deprived of his needs. In this, no individual is dependent on any other individual nor is he a servant. In this society every individual receives sustenance with respect and dignity.

The teaching of the Quran is that wherever the *Jamaat e Momineen* may be, they should make efforts to establish this kind of Quranic system. If they are successful in this, then that is great. But if they see that the environment there cannot become favourable in any way at all for this type of society, then they should migrate to

---

[109] See also (2:57), (2:172), (5:88), (7:160), (16:114) and (20:81).

such a land which is favourable for such a society (provided that such a land exists somewhere). They are told that they should not give up and by 'cutting off their feet' remain sitting in this unfavourable environment purely under the influence of the fear of dying from hunger if they left this piece of land and moved to another place. They are directed:

O My servants who have Eimaan! truly, spacious is My Earth: therefore, only follow Me! (29:56)

In the terminology of the Quran this is called *Hijrat* (migration). After *Hijrat* the next and final stage is that of *Jihad* and *Qital* (fighting), and it is a fact that among righteous deeds this has the highest status in which a *Momin* presents his greatest and most precious possession, in other words such as his life, in the establishment and strengthening of the Divine system. If the consequence of such a righteous deed is not *Rizq e Kareem* then of what other deed will it be?

Those who have Eimaan, and adopt exile, and fight in the path of Allah as well as those who give (them) asylum and aid, these are (all) in very truth Momineen: for them is the protection and a Kareem Rizq. (8:74) See also (8:26, 10:93)

7.8 Power in the Land and *Rizq* in the Life of the Hereafter

These are those righteous deeds whose consequences are power and statehood, and *Rizq e Kareem* in this world. The life of success and eminence – that life in which man only bows his head before the laws of the One Allah – is the most respectable and steadfast life. However, this *Rizq* does not remain confined to this world only, in the life of the hereafter it is bestowed by Allah as *Rizq eTayyab*. First of all, consider the Mujahideen who lay down their life in the cause of Allah. In return for the spilling of their sanctified blood, when their nation gains power in the land and as a consequence obtains *Rizq e Kareem* (honoured sustenance) in this life, these martyrs are gifted *Rizq* from their *Rabb*:

Think not of those who are slain in Allah's way as dead. Nay, they live, finding their sustenance (Rizq) in the presence of their Rabb...(3:169)

Those migrants who lay down their lives in the cause of Allah are also given glad tidings of *Rizq e Hasna*[110]:

Those who leave their homes in the cause of Allah, and are then slain or die, on them will Allah bestow verily a goodly provision: Truly Allah is He Who bestows the best provision. (22:58)

---

[110] *Rizq e Hasna* – balanced sustenance which helps in self-development. (Ed)

And when they achieve the life of Jannat as a result of *Eimaan* and righteous deeds, then there too *Rizq* will be bestowed by Allah.

It should be made clear that the people residing in that society which is shaped according to the laws of Allah live a life of Jannat both in this world and in the world of the hereafter too. We are aware of the *Rizq e Kareem* of this life, but we can say nothing about what the nature and state of this *Rizq* will be in the life of the hereafter. But this much is evident from this, that development of the human self will continue to take place in the life of the hereafter, the means and resources for which are termed as the *Rizq e Kareem* of that place.

7.9 Oppression and Tyranny

As has been noted above, the most vulnerable need of man is *Rizq*. In this world cruelty and tyranny, brutality and suppression continue only on this basis that powerful men take control of the means of *Rizq*, and after this get done whatever they want from human beings who are under their thumb. No human being is ready to become the slave of another human being willingly, no-one is agreeable to merrily and blithely put on the shackle of slavery from someone around his own neck. The enslavement of a human being is contrary to the eminence of humanity. But weak and feeble, helpless and beleaguered man becomes ready to accept all forms of enslavement when he is told that by not doing so the doors of *Rizq* will be closed to you. The *Azaab* of hunger is such a severe *Azaab* that in order to save himself from it a human being becomes obligated to accept every demand. Tyranny in the world starts from this very point and is kept propped up through this same force. Hence, in order to eradicate tyranny and subjugation from the world and to raise weak and feeble human beings to the level of humanity, it is essential that this erroneous belief is eliminated from their minds that the *Rizq* of another human being is in the hand of a man. And that this truth be unveiled to him that the sources of *Rizq* are open equally to the whole of the creation of Allah. Every individual has the right to take anything from these according to his need and aptitude. Hence, no human being needs to bow down before another man.

7.10   Slavery and Servitude

This is a humiliation for humanity that a human being should remain in the servitude of another human being merely for the sake of his daily bread. Since Pharaonic forces in the world have imposed this belief on the human mind with great intensity and tenacity that we are the masters of *Rizq*, this is why the Quran has, with equal intensity and reiteration, refuted this *Batil* belief, and in lieu has placed this correct *Eimaan* in man's heart that *Rizq* is not in the hands of any human being – it is only in the Hand of Allah. But as has been stated already, by

'*Rizq* being in the Hand of Allah', is meant that the means of sustenance should remain in the ownership of that society which distributes it according to the Divine laws. This is that reality which the Quran has explained by stating that the distribution of *Rizq* and its production and supply is according to the *Mashe'at* of Allah. In the human world the *Mashe'at* of Allah is carried out through the hands of those human beings who assume responsibility to implement His laws. Where the reins of power are not in the hands of these individuals (*Jamaat e Momineen*), the distribution of *Rizq* does not take place according to the laws of *Mashe'at*; it takes place according to the self-created laws and regulations of men, the consequence of which is an agonizing hell for humanity.

7.11   *Rizq* is in Allah's Hand

In light of these points all those verses of the Quran will be understood in which it is stated that the shortage and abundance of *Rizq* is in the natural control of Allah. No human being has been given the right to reduce or increase the *Rizq* of another human being. The Quran states:

> …*It is Allah that gives (you) want or plenty…(2:245)*

> *Allah does enlarge, or grant by measure, the sustenance (which He gives) to whomsoever as per His will*[111]…*(13:26) See also (17:30, 28:82, 29:62)*

And this is that principle within which there are very great signs for those who possess *Eimaan* because:

> *See they not that Allah enlarges the provision and restricts it, to whomsoever He wills*[112]*? Verily in that are signs for those who have Eimaan. (30:37)*

Do they not ponder on this matter that Allah (according to His law of *Mashe'at*) makes sustenance abundant for the one who wishes, and gives to him who wishes according to a defined measure; in this (His law of *Mashe'at*) there are great signs for those who have *Eimaan*.

The keys of *Rizq* in the heavens and earth are only in His possession. He is indeed the Master of all the treasures of *Rizq*:

---

[111] The explanation of this aspect has been covered in detail in my book titled *The Book of Destiny*. There is a specific chapter on sustenance (*Rizq*).

[112] Enlargement and restriction of *Rizq* is related to the man-made system under which man lives, which it is necessary to recognise in order to understand how the system of *Rabubiyat* operates. (Ed)

To Him belong the keys of the heavens and the earth: He enlarges and restricts the sustenance to whom He will: for He knows full well all things. (42:12)

The keys of the treasures of the heavens and earth are with Him. For the one who wishes, He provides more sustenance to him, and for the one who wishes, He gives him measured sustenance, and He has complete knowledge of all matters.

7.12   Evil Resulting from Intoxication of Wealth

We have noted above that when the distribution of sustenance does not take place according to the Divine laws, then the world becomes hell. What happens is that the means of sustenance fall into the hands of a small minority; this group becomes an evil model of arrogance and pride of Pharaonic forces, whose 'principle' is that that which is according to their desire is legitimate and rational, and whatever goes against their desires is evil and false. When this Pharaonic phantom rides the heads of this group, then they force the subjugated human being to prostrate in front of this claim of theirs:

(Pharaoh said to his people) 'I am your sustainer, most high'. (79:24)

These are those Pharaohs and Nimrods who, befuddled by the intoxication of their wealth, oppose every heavenly revolutionary invitation; because one injunction of the heavenly invitation is also this, that the means of sustenance be snatched away from human hands and should be placed in the control of the Divine laws so that the needs of life of every individual of humanity are fulfilled through these without any hesitation and effort, and continue thus through a balanced process. This is that reality towards which the Quran has drawn attention by stating:

Never did We send a warner to a population, but the wealthy ones among them said: 'We believe not in the (Message) with which you have been sent.' They said: 'We have more in wealth and in sons, and we cannot be punished.' Say: 'Verily my Sustainer enlarges and restricts the provision according to His law, but most men understand not.' (34:34-36)

And in whichever habitation We sent some messenger, the prosperous category of freeloaders there always stated this, that we refuse to accept these commandments which have been provided to you. They said that we are greater than you in both progeny and wealth and the punishment which you are warning us about can never grip us. (O Rasul) relate to them that your system in which the distribution of *Rizq* is according to your whims cannot continue here. The distribution of *Rizq* and its provision and restriction should be according to Allah's law of *Mashe'at*.

This very intoxication of indulgence in wealth gives rise to the desire in their hearts to dominate the earth and they wish that they could snatch the reins of the earth and draw them into their grasp, so that they could use the blood of the poor and exploit it for their hedonistic assemblies. Regarding the people of Saba, it is noted in the Quran that Allah had granted them abundant *Rizq* and land but despite this their greed continued to multiply, and they would say:

> ...*Our Sustainer, lengthen the distance between our journeys*[113]...*(34:19)*

When the condition reaches such a level, the throne of rebellion and arrogance is toppled in accordance with the immutable law of Allah, and such a system whose foundations are based on dominating the earth and on gluttonous blood sucking becomes the cause for its own destruction. After the glaring condition of the people of Saba, it is stated:

> ...*so We made them as tales and dispersed them all in scattered fragments...(34:19)*

So we made this nation a tale from the past. And they were scattered like grains of sand.

7.13 Consequences of Transgression

This same immense truth is narrated in the form of a simile in Surah *An-Nahl* in which it is stated that the people of a town used to spend their life in great peace and tranquility. Sustenance was plentiful and there were all kinds of comforts. After this they began to be ungrateful for the favours of Allah, the essential consequence of which was that the hell of hunger and fear engulfed them. After this it is stated:

> *Then eat of what Allah has provided for you (which is) lawful and good. And be grateful for the favour of Allah, if it is (indeed) Him that you obey. (16:114)*

This means that if the system of a society is established according to the Divine laws then an abundancy of sustenance prevails in it, and every individual lives a life of peace and tranquility. But if this system becomes shaped according to self-created human laws, then social imbalance is produced from this, whose consequence is nothing but destruction and ruin. This is why it is stated regarding the previous nations (people of the Book):

---

[113] One interpretation of this could be 'give us more land'. (Ed)

If only they had stood fast by the Law, the Gospel, and all the revelation that was sent to them from their Sustainer, they would have enjoyed happiness from every side...
(5:66)

Contrary to this, spurning these principles becomes the cause for misery and humiliation for man:

But whosoever turns away from My Message, verily for him is a life narrowed down...
(20:124)

By having unwavering *Eimaan* in these Divine laws (the Quran) and acting tirelessly according to them, 'honourable sustenance' is availed:

Those who have Eimaan and work righteousness, for them is protection and a sustenance most honourable. (22:50)

In another verse it is stated that this 'honourable sustenance' is the natural consequence of their *Eimaan* and righteous deeds:

That He may reward those who have Eimaan and work deeds of righteousness: for such is protection and a sustenance most generous. (34:4)

7.14   Quest for Allah's *Fadl* (Blessings)

If efforts are made according to these laws for obtaining sustenance, then it is known as the 'quest for Allah's *Fadl*'. *Fadl* commonly means an increase, but in most places in the Quran it has been used to refer to economic conveniences (the chapter on *Fadl* itself will come later). Since these conveniences are bestowed by Allah without any effort or expectation, therefore it is called '*Fadl Ullah*'. But since these conveniences do not reach man automatically, it is necessary for man to desire and search for these and this is called the 'search for *Fadl Ullah*'. Regarding those who set out looking for this *Fadl Ullah*, the Quran has stated:

...others travelling through the land, seeking of Allah's bounty...(73:20)

In Surah *Al-Jummah* it is stated that, after finishing with *Salat*:

And when the Salat is finished, then may you disperse through the land, and seek of the bounty of Allah...(62:10)

It also states about the *Muhajireen*[114]:

---

[114] *Muhajireen* - those who migrate in the cause of Allah. (Ed)

...to the indigent Muhajirs, those who were expelled from their homes and their property, while seeking Grace from Allah and (His) Good Pleasure...(59:8)

The same was stated about the *Jamaat* of the companions of Rasul-ullah:

...seeking Grace from Allah and (His) Good Pleasure...(48:29)

From these verses it is clear that although Allah's bestowed *Rizq* is present in the earth for the nourishment of mankind, in order to gain it desire, search, effort and struggle is essential - without this no-one gets *Rizq*. Secondly, the meaning of this desire and quest does not mean that every individual (or group) should gather to himself whatever much *Rizq* he can and leave nothing for others. This is wrong – the correct system is that all members of society, according to their own individual ability and capacity, should exert themselves in gaining *Rizq*, and whatever is achieved (under a collective system), they should make it freely available for the nourishment of all individuals. In the terminology of the Quran this is called '*Infaaq Fi Sabeel Ullah*' which you will find emphasised in the Quran from the beginning till the end.

7.15 Making Available in the Cause of Allah

For example, if you turn over the first page of the Quran, the definition of *Muttaqeen* will appear first of all. Along with other attributes one of their glaring traits is stated as being:

...and keep open Rizq (for others) out of what We have provided for them. (2:3)

They keep the *Rizq* bestowed by Allah open to be spent in His cause. Along with this, read the following:

...Verily the most honoured of you in the sight of Allah is (he who is) the most righteous (Muttaqee) of you...(49:13)

From this it will become clear that in the view of Islam, in order to achieve honour and respect, it is necessary to keep available the outcome of our hard work in 'the cause of Allah'. In relation to '*Infaaq Fi Sabeel Ullah*', the following verses also require attention – (2:254, 3:179, 4:37-39, 9:74-76, 13:22, 14:31, 22:35, 28:54, 36:47, 63:10). By keeping these verses in view, the true meaning of this great verse will become apparent to you.

7.16 *Rizq* of all Living Things is the Responsibility of Allah

In one verse of the Quran it is stated:

There is no moving creature on earth, but its sustenance depends on Allah...(11:6)

It is said that if Allah is responsible for the *Rizq* of every living thing, then why does so much of creation die hungry. But while saying this, it is forgotten that the responsibility of Allah is only as long as you keep yourself under His established system. When you go outwith His system and begin to consider yourself to be free from the protection of His system, then at that moment His responsibility will also be removed. Keep yourself within His system and then see how His 'responsibilities' are fulfilled. Imposing a Pharaonic system devised by men over ourselves, and then expecting those outcomes which are specific to the Divine system, if this is not blatant ignorance, then what else is it? What can the outcome be of the one who takes shelter under a ramshackle building during an earthquake other than destruction. If he comes under the impregnable roof of Allah, then see if Allah assumes responsibility for his protection or not:

...whoever rejects evil and has Eimaan in Allah has grasped the most trustworthy hand-hold, that never breaks...(2:256)

This 'dependable support' is that Divine system, after which no need remains for any other support. When the system of Allah was established on this earth, at that time the people had come to understand what the correct meaning is of the verse (11:6). An official from Kufa (a town in Iraq) once came to Medina and found that the Caliph Umer was eating bread made from barley. He said, what, can the leader of the *Momineen* of such a grand state not even consume bread made from wheat? The reply received was that Umer can only eat bread made from wheat when he is sure that every human being within the boundaries of his Caliphate has bread made from wheat available to him. Until this fact is established with certainty, how can Umer consume bread made from wheat? Now just consider, can any human being remain hungry in such a system of government? The commencement of Quranic teaching is with these very words, *Alhamdo Lillah e Rabb-il-Alameen* i.e. all kinds of *Hamd*[115] is for that Allah Who is *Rabb-il-Alameen* – His attribute of *Mahmoodiat*[116] is because He is *Rabb-il-Alameen*; He is the Nourisher and Sustainer of the whole of the universe. Hence, the *Mahmoodiat* of the nation in this world which will be responsible for the establishment of that government, will also be due to its attribute of *Rabubiyat*. It will be deserving of admiration at that point

---

[115] *Hamd* – the feeling of appreciation and admiration that arises in the human heart on seeing a very rare and delightful sight or thing; an appreciation of the creator of any beautiful thing.
[116] *Mahmoodiat* – the attribute which has *Hamd*. See *Lughat-ul-Quran*, Vol 1, pp 369-372.

when it arranges for the nourishment of all those people who have come under the canopy of the Divine system; and the arrangement to also be such that, just as their Allah has proclaimed about Himself:

I do not want from them any Rizq… (51:57)

Similarly, those people in whose hands is the control of the administration and organisation of this society, they should not extract material for their own luxury and comfort from the toil of their 'people', instead they should be concerned about their *Rabubiyat*. Since I have provided details of this system in my book, *The Quranic System of Sustenance*, in great depth, hence, at this point these explanations are considered sufficient.

7.17   Hunger and Poverty are Allah's *Azaab*

At this juncture it is important to reiterate that hunger and poverty are Allah's *Azaab* (punishment). In Surah *An-Nahl* it is quoted as an example that when a population became ungrateful for the favours of Allah, then as a recompense of this crime:

…So Allah made it taste of hunger and fear like a garment for what they had been doing. (16:112)

In other words, fear and hunger is a chastisement from Allah and to remain secure from these things is His blessing. The Quran states:

…Who provides with food against hunger, and with security against fear. (106:4)

This punishment visits that nation which engages in rebellion against His laws. Its beginning arises from the powerful echelon at the top, and the subjugated category (the poor and the general public) becomes criminal for the crime of accepting this Pharaonic system; hence, just as in the higher echelon the fire of absence of tranquility and disappearance of peace is ignited, Allah's *Azaab* takes the shape of the curse of hunger and poverty in the lower class. But, unfortunately, for some time this belief has become embedded in our minds that the life of poverty and destitution, helplessness and feebleness, dependence and deprivation is the life of those who are closer to Allah – this is the sign of those servants who are closer to Him. These beliefs are the consequence of the continuous propaganda of the creation of the *Ajmi*[117] philosophy of life and of 'Christ's preachers', who desire to keep Muslims entrenched in this deception that the 'kingdom of heaven' can only be acquired by the one who is the weakest and most subjugated in the land. We

---

[117] *Ajmi* – the term is used for non-Arab thinking which influenced the early part of the Islamic State and its ideology. (Ed)

have been locked in this deception of monasticism for a long time and do not understand that deprivation and poverty are an *Azaab* of Allah, not a mercy. The natural consequence of *Eimaan* and righteous deeds is power in the land and honourable sustenance. The mark of true *Momineen* is this:

Such in truth are Momineen: they have grades of dignity with their Sustainer and protection, and honoured sustenance. (8:4)

From the above explanations you will have seen that *Razzaqiyat* is an attribute of Allah. In the external universe the manifestation of this attribute occurs automatically but in the human world its *modus operandi* changes. In this, though the means of sustenance are available from Allah free of charge, firstly desire and effort has to be made for the attainment of *Rizq*, and secondly the distribution of *Rizq* has to be carried out according to the Divine laws. All this can only be done by that *Jamaat* whose members manifest this attribute in their selfs. It is obvious that when the economic system is in the hands of this kind of *Jamaat*, then how contented mankind will be from the point of view of the provision of *Rizq*. The fact is that the world has not yet been able to even reach that level from where it could see this reality clearly unveiled before it, how the external revolution following on from the 'revolution within the consciousness' causes this earthly being to become such a being who is worthy of heaven. Currently the world wishes to solve the difficulties of its *Rizq* by employing mechanical techniques such as communism which can never succeed. Once it has seen these techniques and procedures through to the end, then after that it will turn in the direction of the Quranic treatment, and the alleviation of its suffering will also be at that very time. To take 'Allah' out of your world and to then desire for peace - such a thought is impossible and is that of the insane.

8   *Rehmat* (Mercy)

The basic meaning of *Rehm* is gentleness and kindness. (*Rehmun*: the uterus of a woman within which the fetus develops and remains protected from external effects). The meanings of *Rehmat* are that gift which fulfills the apparent and hidden needs of someone, and in this way his nourishment takes place just as the fetus is nourished in the womb of a mother. From this respect Allah's *Rehmat* is also another link in the attributes of *Rabubiyat* and *Razzaqiyat*, with this difference that the aspect of gentleness is predominant in this. It also means to cover something and to ensure the provision of the means of protection. When the word *Rehmat* or *Rehm* is used in mutual relations then its meaning will also be of love, nearness and affection. For example, where it is emphasised that parents should be treated with kindness and compassion, this is referred to as *Rehmat*:

> *And, out of kindness, lower to them the wing of humility (Rehmat)…(17:24)*

Where relations between husband and wife are mentioned, this *Rehmat* includes the sentiments of love combined with kind-heartedness:

> *And among His signs is this, that He created for you mates from among yourselves, that you may dwell in tranquility with them, and He has put love and Rehmat (mercy) between your (hearts): verily in that are signs for those who reflect. (30:21)*

Allah also uses the word *Rehmat* for generous provision and economic prosperity (17:28).

8.1 Allah is *Raheem*

The way in which Allah's attribute of *Rabubiyat* has been mentioned with intensity and reiteration in the Quran, similarly His attribute of *Rehmat* has also been mentioned repeatedly. The beginning of its every verse is with the name of Allah, Who is *Rehman* and *Raheem*. At some places that Allah is *Raheem* and *Wadood*, at other places *Rauf-ur-Raheem*, *Tawwab-ur-Raheem*, *Ghafoor-ur-Raheem*, *Aziz-ur-Raheem* and *Birr-ur-Raheem*. In the Quran such names of Allah have appeared at least one hundred fifty times in which *Rehman* and *Raheem* are present. Other places at which *Rehmat* is mentioned are over and above these. In Christianity too, God has been called *Raheem*, but there He is mercy alone (God is Mercy), nothing other than this. But in the Quran *Rehm* is only one facet of the attributes of Allah. Apart from this He has other attributes as well. Indeed, the concept of Allah in the Quran is so complete that after this God, there remains no need for another 'god'. Contrary to this, the consequence of the limited concept of God in Christianity was this, that Europe had to search for other 'gods' for administration, organisation and justice, and since these gods were carved by the human mind, therefore on lifting the curtain it was learned that these are responsible for 'persistent conflicts and bloodshed'. If Europe had somehow found the 'Allah of the Quran' then its state today would have been something else.

8.2 *Rehman* and *Raheem*

In relation to Allah's attribute of *Rehmat*, the words *Rehman* and *Raheem* have been used many times; though the root of both these words is the same, from the point of view of the rules of lexicon there is an extremely refined distinction between them. *Raheem* means he whose *Rehmat* remains compulsorily operational continuously and according to a specific pattern and procedure. And *Rehman* means the one whose *Rehmat* manifests swiftly with great intensity. In order to understand this difference, it is necessary to examine the law of evolution of the universe. The law of evolution informs us that the things of the universe, while developing and evolving according to a particular pattern and process, reach their completion. But sometimes it also happens that such a rapid revolution emerges in a certain thing that by skipping over many links of evolution, it suddenly becomes something else from what it was. This is known as Emergent Evolution in terminology. The general nourishment of the universe takes place according to Allah's attribute of *Raheemiyat* and this sudden or Emergent Evolution according to His attribute of *Rehmaniyat*. This is the reason why the Quran has noted the attributes of *Rehman* and *Raheem* as being separate entities, though the meaning of both are related to the provider of the means of sustenance and sources of protection with kindness and compassion.

This should also remain clear that the term *Rehman* is only applicable to the Being of Allah, whereas in *Raheem* other 'providers of *Rehmat*' can also be included, for example it was stated about Rasul-ullah that he is *Rauf-un-Raheem* (9:128).

8.3 Wondrous Displays of Allah's *Rehmat* in the Universe

The requirement of Allah's *Rehmat* was that when man was sent to this world, the means for his physical sustenance should be made available automatically. The first and foremost dependence of man's life is on air (as has been already mentioned). Allah has dispersed this around planet earth in such a fashion that wherever man goes air is around him and the process of its inward and outward flow in man is set in such a way that man, engaged in carrying out all sorts of worldly tasks, does not even notice how the respiratory process is continuously functioning automatically (without his intent and effort). Along with air, the arrangement for light also exists on the same pattern. After light, let us look at water. It has been placed everywhere flowing and protected in such a way that no other water supply system in the world can compete with it. After this the question of *Rizq* arises. So, for man's need the process of produce from the land is operating with such order and organisation, that there was no power in any machinery that could make it operate in this way. In the Divine distribution of these things there is no distinction between higher and lower, small or great. It never happens that the first ray of the sun strikes the palace of a Brahmin[118] and the last and fading rays reach the hut of that of a *Shudar* (a lower caste); that the heavy and effective drops of rain pour down on the fields of a *Jaghirdar*[119] and the 'sparse and ineffective' portion on the land of a peasant. All this is received through His *Rehmat* and received without any charge or recompense. Allah has declared these favours as His Own *Rehmat*. The Quran states:

> *Then contemplate the effects of Allah's Rehmat! how He gives life to the earth after its death. Undoubtedly, He is going to give life to the dead…(30:50)*

In another verse it is stated:

> *Among His Signs is this, that He sends the winds, as heralds of glad tidings, giving you a taste of His Rehmat (Mercy), that the ships may sail by His command and that you may seek of His Bounty: in order that you may be grateful. (30:46) See also (7:57)*

Only He can do all this, other than Him, no-one else:

> *Who guides you through the depths of darkness on land and sea, and Who sends the winds as heralds of glad tidings, going before His Mercy? (Can there be another) god besides Allah? High is Allah above what they associate with Him! (27:63)*

The splashes of His bountiful rain pour down at that time when man is completely despairing about the earth reviving to a fresh life:

> *He is the One that sends down rain (even) after (men) have given up all hope and scatters His Rehmat (far and wide). And He is the Protector, Worthy of all Hamd. (42:28)*

For human development, division of day and night was also absolutely necessary, the day to seek a livelihood and the night for the sake of peace; this is also attributed to Allah's *Rehmat*:

> *It is out of His Rehmat that He has made for you Night and Day, that you may rest therein, and that you may seek of his Grace; and in order that you may be grateful. (28:73)*

---

[118] Brahmin - highest caste according to the Hindu religion.
[119] *Jagirdar* - big landowner. (Ed)

8.4 Continuity of Divine Guidance is Allah's *Rehmat*

This was the arrangement for man's physical needs. As far as this part is concerned, animals and man are both equal. But man is not defined by his body alone and his needs are not only physical needs. There is within him another thing other than his body, which is called the human self - and this is that thing which is the reason for his eminence as a human being. Hence, for man the need for the development of his self is also inseparably linked with his physical nourishment.

Development of the human self takes place via that heavenly guidance which is called *Wahi*[120]. Alongside the example of rain, the Quran has also noted this heavenly guidance (30:41-53), and in this respect Rasul-ullah is declared to be a *Rehmat* for mankind from Allah:

We sent you not, but as a Rehmat for all times[121]. (21:107)

8.5 Who is the *Rehmat* of Messenger-hood for?

But just as the blessing of rain can only be profitable to that land which opens up its breast to absorb the drops of *Rehmat*, and is ready to accept its effect, even if heavily laden clouds came a thousand times on barren land, no fragrant grasses or scented herbs will be produced. Similarly, messenger-hood can only be a sign of *Rehmat* for those who are willing to be influenced by this *Rehmat*. The name of this 'acceptance' is *Eimaan*. Hence, it is stated that though it is true that the messenger is *Rehmat* for all times, but:

... this Rehmat is for those of you, who accept Eimaan...(9:61)

This is because, as stated in verses (30:48-53), neither can the message be made to be heard by the dead and deaf, nor can the path be made visible to the blind. By dead, deaf and blind people is meant those people about whom it is stated in another verse:

...They have hearts wherewith they understand not, eyes wherewith they see not, and ears wherewith they hear not. They are like cattle, nay more misguided: for they are heedless. (7:179)

---

[120] Details of this are available in the book titled *Iblees O Adam* under the subject of *Wahi*.
[121] The word used here is *Alameen*, plural of *Alam*, which is translated as world. It could be translated as all the worlds for the whole of mankind for all times. (Ed)

8.6 Messenger-hood is also *Rehmat* for *Nabi* Himself

This was the relationship of messenger-hood to other human beings but for a *Nabi* to receive messenger-hood himself is also due to *Rehmat* from Allah (11:28, 11:63). But no-one receives this *Rehmat* of Allah through his own effort and skill, no human being can become a *Nabi* through his own efforts. Before Rasul-ullah himself received messenger-hood, he had no inkling of this matter that he was going to be selected for this great responsibility (28:86). In another verse it is stated that if Allah had wished, even after revealing the Quran He could have removed it, but it was due to His *Rehmat* that He did not do this (17:86-87).

The decision as to who will be selected for this *Rehmat* of Allah (i.e. messenger-hood) was made under the *Mashe'at* of Allah:

...But Allah will specially choose for His Rehmat whom He will - for Allah is greatest possessor of Fadl. (2:105) See also (3:74, 19:50)

8.7 Books of Revelation are *Rehmat* for Mankind

The aim of messenger-hood and the messenger is to convey the guidance of Allah to the people, and this guidance used to be communicated through these books which used to be revealed to these *Anbiya* (messengers of Allah). Hence, these Divine Books are a *Rehmat* for humanity. Earlier Books were *Rehmat* in their own respective eras. Then, when these were tampered with, that same *Rehmat* was preserved in the Quran in its complete form. Now this very Book is a *Rehmat* of Allah for all mankind and for all times. About the Torah, from among the earlier Books, the Quran states:

And before this (the Quran), was the Book of Moses as a guide and Rehmat...
(46:12) See also (6:154, 7:154, 11:17, 28:43)

8.8 The Quran is *Rehmat*

And now the Quran is a *Rehmat*:

And this is a Book which We have revealed as a blessing: so follow it and be righteous, that you may receive Rehmat. (6:155)

There is guidance in it, hence this is *Rehmat* (12:111). It is such a *Rehmat* which removes those differences which former Ummahs had devised in relation to their religions (27:77-78). Not only is it a remover of differences of previous Ummahs, but the Book which eradicates all differences, and this is the evidence for its being a guidance and a *Rehmat*:

And We sent down the Book to you for the express purpose, that you should make clear to them those things in which they differ, and that it should be a guide and Rehmat to those who have Eimaan. (16:64)

Not only for matters in which there are differences but a *Rehmat* which makes every matter clear:

...and We have sent down to you the Book explaining all things, a Guide, a Rehmat, and Glad Tidings to Muslims. (16:89)

The details in it and the manifestation of these is according to the knowledge of Allah, hence there is no possibility of any error anywhere in it - this is also evidence for its being a *Rehmat*:

For We had certainly sent unto them a Book, based on knowledge, which We explained in detail, a guide and Rehmat to all who have Eimaan. (7:52) See also (10:82, 29:51, 31:2-3)

When this Book is such a *Rehmat* then however much mankind celebrates with joy at this gift of *Rehmat*, it is not enough:

O mankind! there has come to you a direction from your Rabb and a healing for your hearts, and for those who have Eimaan, a guidance and Rehmat. Say: 'In the bounty of Allah. And in His Rehmat, in that let them rejoice': that is better than all that they hoard[122]. (10:57-58)

But as has been noted earlier, in order to benefit from this *Rehmat* it is essential to make ourselves willing to accept its effect. Hence, it is stated about the Quran that though it has guidance and warning for the whole of mankind, it will only become a *Rehmat* for those who will maintain conviction in its truths:

These are clear evidences to men and a Guidance and Rehmat to those who have Eimaan. (45:20) See also (7:203-204)

Whoever becomes associated with this source of guidance, Allah will bless him with His *Rehmats*:

O mankind! verily there has come to you a convincing proof from your Rabb: For We have sent unto you a light (that is) manifest. Then those who have Eimaan in Allah,

---

[122] This refers to the human trait of accumulation and hoarding. The Quran instructs us to move away from this towards the establishment of Deen by attending to the needs of fellow human beings. (Ed)

and hold fast to Him, soon will He admit them to Rehmat and Grace from Himself
and guide them to Himself by a straight way. (4:174-175)

8.9 *Siraat-e-Mustaqeem*[123] is *Rehmat*

Examine closely the latter part of the above quoted verse in which it is stated that finding a straight and balanced path in the journey of life is a *Rehmat* of Allah. The forces of *Iblees*[124] are always busily engaged in these efforts that man, leaving this path, should adopt other ways. Remaining protected from these evil efforts is also a *Rehmat* of Allah. Hence, it is noted about Rasul-ullah himself:

But for the Grace of Allah to you and His Rehmat, a party of them would certainly
have plotted to lead you astray…(4:113)

Aside from external influences, remaining protected from the hedonism fuelled whisperings of one's own heart, is also a *Rehmat* of Allah. In the narrative of Yusuf, the wife of the Aziz stated:

'Nor do I absolve my own self (of blame): the (human) self is certainly prone to evil,
unless my Rabb do bestow His Rehmat: but surely my Rabb is Protecting, Raheem.'
(12:53) See also (4:83)

This fact should once again be brought to mind that when it is said that one cannot be protected from these whisperings etc. without Allah's *Rehmat*, this does not mean that for this purpose man himself cannot do anything, that this occurs only through Allah's 'mercy and compassion'. This concept is against the teaching of the Quran.[125] When it is stated that this can only happen through Allah's *Rehmat*, it means that it can only happen in that situation when man follows Allah's *Wahi*, because (as we have seen earlier) the meaning of Divine *Rehmat* is Divine *Wahi* which is now preserved in the Quran. Hence, the only way to remain protected from the intrigues of *Iblees* and the whisperings of the heart is that man should obey the Quran and make use of his emotions under its guidance.

---

[123] *Siraat-e-Mustaqeem — Siraat* means straight, while *Mustaqeem* means a path which is well established and clearly defined. (Ed)

[124] Further details are discussed in my book *Iblees O Adam*.

[125] This is against the Law of Requital as stated in (45:22) where each self is held accountable for his or her deeds. The Quranic guidance acts as an external criterion by which to recognise emotions and to counter these by taking actions according to the Permanent Values. (Ed)

8.10   Leniences in *Shariat*[126] are *Rehmat*

To receive such leniences in *Shariat* due to which it becomes possible to implement the laws is a *Rehmat* of Allah. For example, in relation to the *Law of Qisas*, the recompense for murder is murder, but together with this it is stated:

> ...*But if any remission is made by the brother of the slain, then grant any reasonable demand, and compensate him with handsome gratitude, this is a concession*[127] *and Rehmat from your Rabb...(2:178) See also (24:10)*

But this concession and *Rehmat* can only be received via the law of Allah, not as a result of the personal sentiment of sympathy of some individual. The implementation of the Divine laws is the responsibility of the Islamic system, and personal sentiments of sympathy should never intervene in their implementation. For example:

> *The woman and the man guilty of adultery or fornication, flog each of them with a hundred stripes: Let not compassion move you in their case, in a matter prescribed by Allah, if you have Eimaan in Allah and the Hereafter Day...(24:2)*

8.11   The Law of Requital is a *Rehmat*

This is because it is the Law of Requital itself on which the foundation of the system of the universe is based and this is also a *Rehmat* of Allah:

> *If they accuse you of falsehood, say: 'Your Rabb is full of Rehmat all-embracing, but from criminal people never will His wrath be turned back'. (6:147)*

This is because if there is no recompense for evil deeds, then people will continue to exceed in their rebellion, and life on earth will become intolerable for those who are decent:

> *If We had Rehmat on them and removed the distress which is on them, they would obstinately persist in their transgression, wandering in distraction to and fro. (23:75)*

---

[126] *Shariat* – here this means that which is revealed in the Quran. This is a code of Permanent Values put forward by the Quran as guidance for the establishment of the system of Deen. It is completely at variance with the current religious meaning accorded it by the different sectarian religions of Islam. (Ed)

[127] It should be made clear that compensation is only for accidental manslaughter, there is no compensation for premeditated murder (4:92-93).

The Law of Requital is not confined to individuals only, the rise and fall of nations also occurs according to it:

To all are degrees (or ranks) according to their deeds: for your Rabb is not unmindful of anything that they do. Your Rabb is self-sufficient, full of Rehmat: if it were His will, He could destroy you (as per His law), and in your place appoint whom He will as your successors, even as He raised you up from the posterity of other people.
(6:132-133)

8.12   Period of Respite is also a *Rehmat*

An interval has been kept between the commission of a deed and the manifestation of its result so that those who commit an error in ignorance can make amends during this time, and this is called the period of respite and is Divine *Rehmat*:

But your Rabb is Most protecting, full of Rehmat. If He were to call them (at once) to account for what they have earned, then surely, He would have hastened their punishment: but they have their appointed time, beyond which they will find no refuge. (18:58)

If an individual or nation realises that it has taken a step in the wrong direction, then it is necessary for it to immediately turn around and return to the point from where the step in the wrong direction was taken, following which it should step in the right direction. Turning back from the wrong path is called *Taba* and stepping in the right direction after this is called *Aslaha*. By doing this an individual becomes protected from the harmful effects which were incurred as a result of going in the wrong direction, this is called *Maghfirat*. Keeping the provision of these matters within the 'Law of Requital' is Allah's *Rehmat*.

8.13   Acceptance of *Tauba* is also a *Rehmat*

The Quran states:

Say: 'O my Servants who have transgressed against their selfs! Despair not of the Rehmat of Allah: for Allah provides protection (as per His law) from all ill effects: for He is Protecting, Raheem. (39:53)

Provided this error has occurred inadvertently, and is not deliberate and due to arrogance, and after this amends have also been made:

When those come to you who have Eimaan in Our signs, Say: 'Peace be on you: Your Rabb has inscribed for Himself Rehmat: verily, if any of you did evil in ignorance, and thereafter repented, and amend (his conduct), lo! He is Protecting (from ill effects as per law), Raheem. (6:54)

But if after this man again adopts rebellion, then he will have to suffer the consequences for this i.e. a one-off repentance cannot be a permanent permit of protection:

It may be that your Rabb may show Rehmat unto you; but if you revert, We shall (also) revert: And we have made hell a prison for those who reject Eimaan. (17:8)

According to the Law of Requital the natural consequence of wrong deeds is called *Azaab* which is the opposite of *Rehmat* i.e. development of the human self takes place under *Rehmat* whereas under *Azaab* its development halts and he becomes deprived of human eminence. This is why the Quran has referred to *Azaab* as the antonym to *Rehmat*:

He punishes as per His law, and He grants Rehmat as per His law, and towards Him are you turned. (29:21)

In another verse *Rehmat* is mentioned as opposite to destruction (67:28); this is because what greater punishment can there be other than destruction and annihilation? Remaining protected from dangers is also called *Rehmat* by the Quran (36:44). Similarly, to be kept protected from the troubles which come as a deluge with wars is also a *Rehmat* (48:25).

8.14   Getting Freedom from *Azaab* is *Rehmat*

Certain blunders of nations are such that they fall into the pit of degradation forever as a result and from which they cannot escape. But there are certain errors which are such that recovery can be possible from their effects (punishment). This is called obtaining '*Najaat* after *Azaab*'. This too, has been termed as *Rehmat* of Allah i.e. instead of some nation being deprived of the sweetnesses of life forever, the possibility of recovery remaining in them is *Rehmat*. Hence, when Bani Israel achieved their escape from the tyranny of Pharaoh, it was declared to be Allah's *Rehmat*:

They said: 'In Allah do we put out trust. Our Rabb! make us not a trial for those who practice oppression; And deliver us by Your Rehmat from those who reject (You).'
(10:85-86)

When the nation of Noah was surrounded on all sides by the *Azaab* of destruction, Noah said:

...This day nothing can save, from the command of Allah, any but those on whom He has Rehmat...(11:43)

Similarly, when *Azaab* overwhelmed other errant nations, then whichever righteous people were saved from among these was also called Allah's *Rehmat* (7:72, 11:58, 11:66, 11:94, 21:74-75).

8.15 Being Protected from the *Azaab* of the Hereafter is also a *Rehmat*

This was regarding *Azaab* as related to this world. The same is stated regarding *Azaab* of the hereafter: remaining protected from this is also Allah's *Rehmat*:

On that day, if the penalty is averted from any, it is due to Allah's Rehmat; and that would be a manifest achievement. (6:16) See also (3:116, 40:9, 44:41-42, 76:31)

8.16 Jannat is *Rehmat*

The people of *A'raf* (those at the heights) will say to the inhabitants of hell, look, those same people are in Jannat about whom you used to swear that Allah will not have *Rehmat* on them. Just see, they were the very ones told to enter Jannat, there is neither any fear for you and nor will you be sorrowful:

Behold! are these not the men whom you swore that Allah with His Rehmat would never bless? Enter you the Garden: no fear shall be on you, nor shall you grieve. (7:49)

Glad tidings for this very Jannat are given based on *Eimaan* and righteous deeds (9:21-22). This is evident achievement i.e. a great triumph:

Then, as to those who believed and did righteous deeds, their Sustainer will admit them to His Rehmat that will be the achievement for all to see. (45:30)

8.17 Righteous Progeny

Now observe the great blessings of heavenly *Rehmat* on worldly life. Being bestowed with righteous progeny is by His *Rehmat*. Abraham had become hopeless about having children during his old age. At that time, Allah with His *Rehmat* fulfilled his heartfelt wish with the desired pearl. Hence, when the messengers sent by Allah gave both him and his wife the glad tidings of offspring, she became amazed. Upon that, they responded:

…Do you wonder at Allah's decree? The grace of Allah and His blessings on you, O you people of the house! for He is indeed worthy of all praise, full of all glory! (11:73)

Similarly, regarding the birth of Yahya it is stated:

A recital of Rehmat of your Rabb to His servant Zakariya. (19:2)

After this, the birth of Yahya is mentioned.

8.18 Continuing Resolution of Matters

For human matters to be resolved into a pleasant outcome is also Allah's *Rehmat*. Regarding the people of the Cave, it is stated:

…betake yourselves to the cave: Your Rabb will shower His Rehmat on you and will dispose of your affair towards comfort and ease. (18:16)

8.19 Finding a Righteous Companion

Finding an excellent and supportive companion in the world is also Divine *Rehmat*. It is declared about Aaron in the Quran:

And, out of Our Rehmat, We gave him (Moses) his brother Aaron, a Nabi. (19:53)

To be included in the *Jamaat* of the righteous is such a great *Rehmat* for which the famous *Anbiya* would pray. Solomon, while passing through the Valley of *Namal*, had entreated:

…And admit me, by Your Grace, to the ranks of Your righteous servants. (27:19)

8.20 Power and Authority

This is because through this that great *Rehmat* is attained in this world which is the mark of distinction of the *Jamaat e Momineen* i.e. by becoming established on the land, a nation state and government is acquired. When Yusuf was bestowed with this distinct *Rehmat*, it was stated:

Thus, did We give established power to Yusuf in the land, to take possession therein as, when, or where he pleased. We bestow of our Rehmat as per Our law, and We suffer not, to be lost, the reward of those who do righteous deeds. (12:56)

Before proceeding, let us also examine how this *Rehmat* is gained. The Quran states:

Allah has promised, to those among you who have Eimaan and work righteous deeds, that He will, of a surety, grant them in the land, inheritance (of power), as He granted it to those before them; that He will establish in authority their Deen - the one which He has chosen for them; and that He will change (their state), after the fear in which they (lived)[128]*, to one of security and peace: They will obey Me (alone) and not associate aught with Me. If any do reject Eimaan after this, they are rebellious and wicked. So establish Salat and establish Zakat; and obey the Messenger; so that you may receive Rehmat. (24:55-56)*

Though further details about this illustrious verse will come in their own place, this much is evident here, that in order to become eligible for this *Rehmat* of Allah, the indispensable conditions which require to be fulfilled are as follows:

(1) *Eimaan*
(2) Righteous deeds
(3) Obedience of Allah alone
(4) Not to make anyone other than Allah as sovereign and ruler
(5) Establishment of *Salat*
(6) Establishing the dispensing of *Zakat*
(7) Obedience of Rasul-ullah[129]

In other words, the strengthening of *Jamaat* by establishing *Salat*, leading to *Imamat*[130] and organisation; consolidation of the central authority and arranging the provision of the means of sustenance of mankind through the dispensing of *Zakat*; and all of this to be achieved by following the Divine system.

8.21 Elimination of Differences

Since this is the natural consequence of establishment in the land and righteous deeds, hence it endures as such as long as this nation remains firm on *Eimaan* and righteous deeds, and for this the foremost condition is that it does not become captive to the curse of sectarianism and the rivalries of parties. For the Ummah to remain as one Ummah is a *Rehmat* of Allah:

---

[128] Without the system of Deen, fear and uncertainty will always exist in the human world. (Ed)
[129] This means following the Quran as Rasul-ullah followed the Quran (as noted in the Quran). (Ed)
[130] *Imamat* – leadership within the system of Deen. (Ed)

If Your Rabb had so willed, He could have made mankind one people[131]: but they will not cease to dispute. Except those on whom Your Rabb has bestowed His Rehmat...
(11:118-119)

In other words, the nation on which there is Allah's *Rehmat* becomes a united Ummah by avoiding differences, and the Quran has been revealed for this very purpose that differences become eradicated:

And We sent down the Book to you for the express purpose, that you should make clear to them those things in which they differ, and that it should be a guide and Rehmat to those who have Eimaan. (16:64)

After this perspicuous Book, differences and sectarianism, distancing from Allah's *Rehmat* and the practical denying of *Tauheed* is (in Quranic terms) the path of *Shirk*:

...and be not you among those who join gods with Allah (Shirk), Those who split up their Deen, and become (mere) Sects, each party rejoicing in that which is with itself!
(30:31-32)

The practical meaning of *Tauheed* is mutual harmony and unity in outlook. One Allah, one Rasul, one Book, one straight path and one Ummah treading on this path - then what reason is there for any difference? Unity in thought and deeds is indeed Allah's *Rehmat*, and this is that very conduct of the *Jamaat e Momineen*:

Muhammad is the messenger of Allah; and those who are with him are strong against Kuffar, (but) compassionate amongst each other...(48:29)

8.22   Means of Power and Defence Are *a Rehmat*

This was about the internal organisation for strengthening of the government and state, the revolution of hearts and vision. Regarding the external organisation, it is stated that provision of the means of defence against dangers from enemies is also a *Rehmat*. The barricade created by *Dhul-Qarnain*[132] which was like a dam built to halt the overflowing flood of invaders, was a *Rehmat* of Allah:

Thus, were they made powerless to scale it or to dig through it. He said: This is Rehmat from my Rabb... (18:97-98)

---

[131] This is an important point to which the Quran has drawn our attention i.e. this is a natural consequence of giving the freedom to choose to Adam, and it is now man's choice to follow the revelation and be united, or to choose not to accept it and remain disunited, which leads to fear and uncertainty in the world. Indeed, the powerful elite aims to 'divide and rule' and promote 'might is right' as a value to exploit fellow human beings. (Ed)
[132] *Dhul-Qarnain* – a righteous character referred to in the Quran (18:83-98). (Ed)

Here, another point requires attention i.e. the accomplishment of Deen can only occur with both aspects: there should be *Rehmat* and compassion in their hearts and along with this, there should be such force available that they can counter the opponents. Contrary to this, the Quran states about Christian monasticism (and they themselves claim this as well) that they only have compassion, no force:

...and We ordained in the hearts of those who followed him Compassion and Rehmat. But the Monasticism which they invented for themselves, We did not prescribe for them...(57:27)

In other words, they only had one component so Deen was not complete. This is why in the beginning, due to the absence of power, they abandoned worldly affairs and adopted a life of monasticism. But when statehood fell into their hands, for the completion of the second part they have had to become purely worldly, and due to not being able to create a blend between compassion and power they became completely secular. If Europe had gained complete Deen by both these aspects, then it would not have adopted this rebellion in such a way.[133]

8.23   Hopelessness of *Rehmat* of Allah is *Kufr*

This was that method through which the *Rehmat* of Allah remains in action, but if this *Rehmat* slips away due to the misdeeds of a nation and statehood and government transforms into slavery and subjugation, even then one should not become hopeless about Allah's *Rehmat*. Such hopelessness is *Kufr* because this will be a practical affirmation that the law of Allah does not possess this potential that by living life according to it, the greatness which has slipped away can be restored, and this is what *Kufr* is:

Those who reject (display Kufr) the signs of Allah and the meeting with Him[134], it is they who shall despair of My Rehmat: it is they who will (suffer) a most grievous Penalty. (29:23)

---

[133] The author has commented in this way in some of his other writings as well. However, Europe knowingly adopted the path of secularism, and even during the eras of religious rule they deliberately followed a path different from Christian values. As the Quran has stated e.g. (12:106), most people will commit *Shirk* deliberately as they do not see any benefit in following the revelation wholeheartedly since it is contrary to their own desires. In today's world, it is becoming abundantly clear that despite the availability of plenty of literature on the Quran, the rich and powerful elites are following the path of their desires, thus ignoring the Law of Requital. They do not hold themselves accountable for their deeds, and do not consider that they can be held accountable for all the wrongs which they are deliberately inflicting on their fellow human beings across the globe. (Ed)

[134] 'Meeting with Him' – this is usually translated as meeting in the hereafter. However, Allah is everywhere and not confined to one place or space e.g. (57:4), and we do not go and meet Him

This is losing one's way. Abraham stated:

> *...And who despairs of Rehmat of His Rabb, but such as go astray. (15:56)*

This is why Allah stated about His 'Own' servants:

> *Say: O my Servants who have transgressed against their selfs! Despair not of Rehmat of Allah: for Allah provides protection against all excesses: for He is All Protecting, Raheem. (39:53)*

That Allah Who gives direction to the rain clouds at that time when the whole world has given up all hope of rain:

> *He is the One that sends down rain (even) after (men) have given up all hope and scatters His Rehmat (far and wide). And He is the Protector, Worthy of all Hamd. (42:28)*

8.24   Infinite Vastness of Means of *Rehmat*

The treasures of Allah's *Rehmat* can never become empty; this is the short-sightedness of man that he measures them according to his own scales:

> *Say: If you had control of the Treasures of the Rehmat of my Rabb, behold, you would keep them back, for fear of spending them: for man is niggardly! (17:100)*

His *Rehmat* encompasses everything:

> *...Our Rabb! Your Reach is over all things, in Rehmat and Knowledge...(40:7)*

This is why when His law of *Rehmat* wishes to extend its hand of beneficence, who can stop Him?

> *Say: Who is it that can screen you from Allah if (as per His Law of Requital) it be His wish to give you punishment or to give you Rehmat...(33:17) See also (35:2, 39:38)*

8.25   Conditions for Deserving *Rehmat*

But His *Rehmat* is always conditional, when these conditions are fulfilled then this *Rehmat* is conferred. For example, when Moses prayed that his Ummah be blessed

---

anywhere. Here, it means that the consequences of not following the Divine laws are tantamount to 'meeting Him' as His presence is everywhere. (Ed)

with *Rehmats* (till end times), it was stated in response that, following the revelation of the Quran, this *Rehmat* will become conditional on obedience of the Quran[135]:

> *...but My Rehmat extends to all things. That (Rehmat) I shall ordain for those who do right, and practice Zakat, and those who have Eimaan in Our signs; Those who follow Rasul, the unlettered Nabi, whom they find mentioned in their own (scriptures), in the law and the Gospel; for he commands them what is just and forbids them what is evil; he allows them as lawful what is good (and pure) and prohibits them from what is bad (and impure); He releases them from their heavy burdens and from the yokes that are upon them. So it is those who have Eimaan in him, honour him, help him, and follow the light which is sent down with him, it is they who will prosper. (7:156-157)*

And My *Rehmat* encompasses all things. So I will write *Rehmat* for those people who will act righteously, and will dispense *Zakat*, and will establish *Eimaan* in Our laws. This means those people who will follow this *Nabi* whose coming these people find noted in their Torah and Gospel. He will command them to righteousness, forbid evil, and will declare *Halal* for them that which is pure. He will declare *Haram* that which is impure, and will distance their burdens, chains and impediments from them. Only those people who have *Eimaan* on this (*Nabi*) and will provide strength to him and will help him, and will follow this Light which will be sent with him, will be successful.

And the practical sign of obedience of Allah and Rasul is this - that Muslims become the arms and hands of each other (9:71) and after this make their life absolutely challenging, as the *Rehmats* of Allah are with those people who live a life of continuous Jihad and tenacious efforts in this world of trials and tribulations for the sake of the establishment of Divine sovereignty, and when the time comes they are willing to give up every dearest thing. *Hijrat*[136] is in fact the name given to this motive, departing from your land is one part of this, and these are the people who can become candidates for the *Rehmat* of Allah:

> *Those who accepted Eimaan and those who suffered exile and fought (and strove and struggled) in the path of Allah, they have the hope of the Mercy of Allah: And Allah is All-Protecting, Raheem. (2:218)*

Not those people who are sitting idly doing nothing and simply waiting for tomorrow. How can you compare those who are 'sitting to those who are racing'?

---

[135] 'Quran' here refers to the Divine revelation of the time received by Moses i.e. Torah. (Ed)
[136] *Hijrat* - usually translated as migration, it has wider connotations. It also means to give up something or to move away. (Ed)

Not equal are those Momineen who sit and receive no hurt and those who strive and fight in the cause of Allah with their possessions and their persons...(4:95-96)

And all of this is not to be carried out on the basis of impulsive or momentary sentiments, but should be performed with determination and solid resolve, because only a rock which is standing firm and balanced on its foundation can face perils, unlike particles of sand which are ever willing to flow away with every roll of a wave. This resoluteness, steadfastness, and not losing heart is what the Quranic terminology calls *Sabr* and the *Rehmats* of Allah are with the *Sabireen* (plural of *Sabir*):

And (remember) Isma'il, Idris, and Dhul-Kifl, all (men) of constancy and patience; We admitted them to Our Rehmat: for they were of the righteous ones. (21:85-86)

This is that attribute which the Quran has explained in clear words:

Be sure we shall test you with something of fear and hunger, some loss in goods or lives or the fruits (of your toil), but give glad tidings to those who patiently persevere, Who say, when afflicted with calamity: 'To Allah We belong, and to Him is our return': they are those on whom (descend) blessings from Allah, and Rehmat, and they are the ones that receive guidance. (2:155-157)

8.26 Regaining Lost Greatness is *Rehmat*

When the state of *Eimaan* and deeds becomes such, then the *Rehmats* of Allah themselves seek out such men; lost wealth, stolen eminences and buried treasures are once again achieved. In the case of the narrative relating to Moses, when those orphan children were given their buried treasure, Allah called this His *Rehmat*:

...So, your Rabb desired that they should attain their age of full strength and get out their treasure - Rehmat from your Rabb...(18:82)

And the recompense for the *Sabr* of Ayub was given in this way, that his lost home and possessions and a lot more together with this were restored:

So, We listened to him: We removed the distress that was on him, and We restored his people to him, and doubled their number, as Rehmat from Ourselves, and a thing for commemoration, for all who serve Us. (21:84)

As a result of *Eimaan* and *Taqwa* a double share of *Rehmats* are awarded, and such a glowing light comes into their hands in the brightness of which the whole world can be led:

O you who have Eimaan! fear Allah, and have Eimaan in His Messenger, and He will bestow on you a double portion of His Rehmat: He will provide for you a Light by which you shall walk (straight in your path), and He will provide means of protection: for Allah is All Protecting, Raheem. (57:28)

This is the technique for not becoming hopeless of gaining *Rehmat*.

8.27   Man's Strange Response

But man is a strange creature; Allah showers His *Rehmat* on him and he adopts transgression, thinking that all this is obtained through his own skills. What Allah? And what *Rehmat* of His? And when these *Rehmats* slip away from him then he becomes as hopeless as if there is no support left for him:

When we give him a taste of some Rehmat from Ourselves, after some adversity has touched him, he is sure to say, this was to happen like this for me ...(41:50)

And:

...And truly, when We give man a taste of Rehmat from Ourselves, he does exult thereat, but when some ill happens to him, on account of the deeds which his hands have sent forth, truly then man displays Kufr! (42:48)

Even though what should have happened was that when the means of sustenance were plentiful and human abilities were freely available (i.e. *Rehmats* of Allah), these should have been utilised according to the laws of Allah (this is what *Shukr*[137] means i.e. being grateful to Allah). And when, as a consequence of his adopting the wrong path, man becomes deprived of these *Rehmats,* then if adherence to the Divine laws is established more so than before so that the ill effects of the wrong path are erased, then following this these *Rehmats* can be obtained again due to the constructive results of these deeds.

8.28   Supplications for *Rehmat*

Remember! these *Rehmats* are so vital to human life that even Allah's great *Anbiya* used to pray for them (7:151, 27:19); and those big leaders of people as well, who are turned into gods by their followers as a result of their piety and eminence, also remain supplicators for Allah's *Rehmat*.

---

[137] *Shukr* - to fill up and express, obedience and the performance of duties which must be done, expression of thankfulness, to give much in return for little. The human efforts to produce full results. See *Lughat-ul-Quran*, Vol 1, pp 767-770. (Ed)

Those whom they call upon do desire (for themselves) means of access to their Rabb, even those who are nearest: they hope for His Rehmat and fear His Wrath…(17:57)

This same supplication was taught to the *Millat e Islamia* (Muslims) via Rasul-ullah:

And say: 'O my Sustainer! grant Your protection and Rehmat for You are the Best of those who show Rehmat!' (23:118)

Then the way in which the servants of Allah wish for *Rehmat* is reiterated in various places. In the last verse of Surah *Al-Baqra* the comprehensive supplication which is taught is 'and have *Rehmat* on us' (2:286) and at the start of Surah *Al e Imran* it is stated 'and bestow *Rehmat* from Your presence' (3:7, 39:9, 23:109). These are the characteristics of the servants of that Allah who is Himself the best of those Who bestow *Rehmat* and Whose Rasul is a *Rehmat* himself for all the worlds for all time. Hence, that *Jamaat e Momineen* will also be a possessor of *Rehmat*, a cause of *Rehmat* for the whole world, bequeathing the means of sustenance to the whole of mankind and the one that becomes a cause for the development and realisation of their nascent potentials. This is because the attributes of *Rehmaniyat* and *Raheemiyat* of Allah will be sparkling with their full brilliance within them.

Before proceeding further, it is essential to understand one important point. The fundamental belief of Christians is that God is mercy and the Quran also states that Allah is *Raheem* and *Rahman*. But there is a very important and fundamental distinction between these two. The belief of Christians is that every human child is born with the burden of sin of his first parents (Adam and Eve) and this burden cannot be removed through the efforts and deeds of man; this can only be removed through the mercy of God and its practical procedure is to have belief in the atonement of Jesus.

The Quran revoked this fundamental doctrine of Christianity. It stated that contrary to this, a human child is born with a clean slate devoid of any former burden and he possesses the freedom of this action that whatever path he wishes, he can adopt. Whatever kind of path he adopts, the consequences of this will become apparent in front of him according to the Law of Requital of Allah.

But if it ever happens that man makes some unwitting error and on realising this he repents over it and makes amends immediately, then an allowance has also been kept in the Law of Requital of Allah for this, so that in this way he can remain protected from the harmful consequences of his error. The inclusion of this provision in the Law of Requital is defined as the *Rehm* of Allah. As an example, you can understand it like this, that it is Allah's law that the person who puts his hand into fire will burn his hand and as a result he will suffer severe pain. But the Allah Who has created the property of burning in fire has, along with this, also created such medicines the use of which provide relief from the resultant burning and pain. The creation of these medicines is *Rehm*.

9 *In'aam (Naimat, Nu'ama)*[138]

The word *In'aam* originates from *Na'mun* which means a thing or scene possessing such a state due to which the eyes are soothed. *Taneem'atun* is a plant whose leaves are extremely soft and delicate, and green and fresh. The northerly breeze which is very clement is called *Nu'aama*, and along with this a very high star is also called *An-Nuamatu*. From these meanings it is evident that every aspect of human social life being pleasant, spacious, gentle, prosperous, joyful and elevated is a *Naimat*. The attribute of Allah is that He is the giver of these kinds of bounties to man.

9.1 The Path of Those People with *In'aam*

The Quran has taught that the greatest thing of all to be desired is *Siraat e Mustaqeem*:

> *(O Allah!) Show us the balanced straight path. (1:6)*

Siraat e Mustaqeem is the straight path which leads to the intended destination. But because *Siraat e Mustaqeem* was an intangible concept, it is made clear in this manner that it is the path of those righteous beings on whom Allah has bestowed His *In'aam*:

> *The path of those on whom You have bestowed Your In'aam…(1:7)*

The description of these righteous beings is done by stating that these are the *Anbiya*, the truthful ones, the martyrs, and the doers of righteous deeds:

> *All who obey Allah and the messenger are in the company of those on whom is the Grace of Allah, of Anbiya, the sincere (lovers of Truth), the witnesses (who testify), and the righteous (who do good): Ah! what a beautiful fellowship! (4:69)*

But this still remained a general statement, so details and explanations were given about Allah's *In'aam* in numerous verses under various topics and in various contexts, so that the difference between *Naimat* (bounty) and *It'aab* (punishment) becomes apparent, and so that no individual or nation remains stuck in any error of judgment, or in a state of complacency regarding the evaluation of the consequences of their deeds.

---

[138] Generally translated as bounty, grace etc. (Ed)

9.2 The Path of Guidance

First of all the great *Naimat* which has been referred to is *Siraat e Mustaqeem* i.e. the path of guidance which has been mentioned above (1:5-6). In other words, righteousness and guidance are *Fadl* of Allah and His *Naimat* (49:7-8). Contrary to this, misguidance, being astray and debased are His wrath and punishment. This is not the path of those on whom Allah's *In'aamat* (rewards) are showered:

The way of those on whom You have bestowed Your Grace, those whose (portion) is not wrath, and who go not astray. (1:7)

9.3 *Naima*[139] of Deen and the World

Islam is that Deen which encompasses both 'religion' and 'world'. It teaches neither the materialism of the West nor the *Sanyas* and Monasticism of the East. Instead it provides guidance for that kind of life whose aura comprises a blend of the two; hence the bounties of Allah will encompass both Deen and *Duniya* (the world), the soul and matter, today and tomorrow. Let us first look at details of the 'bounties of Deen'.

9.4 Bounties of Deen

The advent of *Anbiya* in a nation used to be a *Naimat* of Allah:

Remember Moses said to his people: 'O my people! Call in remembrance the favour of Allah unto you, when He produced Anbiya among you'...(5:20)

To the Muslims themselves it was stated that the nomination of the *Kaaba*[140] has been done so that the bounties may be completed on you, and so that you follow the path of guidance (2:150-151). Similarly, receiving the *Shariat* which gives guidance in the problems of life is also Allah's *Naimat*. Hence, while explaining matters related to divorce it is stated:

...But remind yourselves with Allah's Naimat on you, and the fact that He sent down to you the Book and wisdom, for your instruction...(2:231)

9.5 Messenger-hood is Itself a *Naimat*

Messenger-hood (*Nabuwwat*) is in itself a *Naimat* of Allah, hence, after mentioning various *Anbiya* it is stated:

---

[139] *Naima* – the plural of *Naimat*. (Ed)
[140] *Kaaba* i.e. Makkah as a symbol. (Ed)

Those were some of the Anbiya on whom Allah did bestow His Naimat, of the posterity of Adam...(19:58)

Pointing towards the manifest victory, protection and guidance of the straight path, it was stated to Rasul-ullah that all *Naima* were completed on him:

Verily We have granted you a manifest Victory: That Allah may protect you from all false accusations of the past and which may come later; fulfil His favour on you; and guide you to the Straight Path. (48:1-2)

In another verse, after reference to Rasul-ullah's earlier circumstances, there is a reminder of the protection provided to him during his orphan state. When you were in search of truth *(Haqq)*[141] then the light of guidance was bestowed on you, and you were not left dependent on anyone else for the necessities of life. These are the bounties of Allah, the communication of which is commanded:

Did He not find you an orphan and give you shelter (and care)? And He found you looking for guidance, and He gave you guidance. And He found you in need, and made you independent... So as for the bounty of your Rabb - rehearse and proclaim. (93:6-8, 11)

And then the bestowing of the Deen of Islam and its completion was declared as the completion of *Naimat*:

...This day have I completed your Deen for you, completed My favour upon you, and have chosen for you Islam as your Deen...(5:3)

And in the remembrance of Allah's *Naima*, obedience of Rasul-ullah, and as a consequence of this obedience, adherence to the covenant and commitment which was made with Allah for the protection of Deen, is emphasised for Muslims:

And call in remembrance the favour of Allah unto you, and His covenant, which He ratified with you, when you said: 'we hear and we obey'...(5:7)

Now let us look at the other side of the picture i.e. a discussion of worldly *Naima*.

9.6 Preference[142] over Nations of the World

Achieving superiority and supremacy above all the nations of the world is Allah's

---

[141] This is an important fact which is noted here i.e. guidance comes to those who seek it. (Ed)
[142] Here supremacy means that the system is to be based on the values of the revelation and not according to man-made laws. (Ed)

Naimat, hence, Bani Israel are repeatedly reminded about this:

O Children of Israel! call to mind My Naimat which I bestowed upon you, and that I provided you supremacy over all other nations. (2:47)

Becoming free from the tyranny of Pharaoh, the provision of shade from clouds, abundance of sustenance, blessings of *Mann*[143] and *Salwa*[144] - all of these were *Naima* of Allah (2:57). The means of sustenance, dwellings and animals from which man meets the needs of his life, construction of fortified castles on hilltops and in underground caves, attire for daily needs, iron mail for protection in the battlefield - all of these are *Naima*:

It is Allah Who made your habitations homes of rest and quiet for you; and made for you, out of the skins of animals, (tents for) dwellings, which you find so light (and handy) when you travel and when you stop (in your travels); and out of their wool, and their soft fibres (between wool and hair), and their hair, rich stuff and articles of convenience (to serve you) for a time. It is Allah Who made out of the things He created, some things to give you shade; of the hills He made some for your shelter; He made you garments to protect you from heat, and coats of mail to protect you from your (mutual) violence. Thus, does He complete His Naimat on you, that you may follow His laws. But if they turn away, your duty is only to pass the clear Message. They recognise the favours of Allah; then they deny them; and most of them are ungrateful. (16:80-83)

Similarly land, canals and springs, rain and production through rain, animals of burden on the back of the earth, ships on the surface of the oceans (31:31) - all of these are assigned under the control of man so that he keeps the *Naima* of Allah in mind (43:10-13). Through purity and cleanliness together with abundance of economic means in social life, *Naimat* is completed:

...Allah does not wish to place you in a difficulty, but to make you clean, and to complete his Naimat on you, so that you may be grateful. (5:6)

Purification of the heart and vision is also implicit in this aside from physical cleanliness.

9.7 Power in the Land is Allah's *Naimat*

This section was about the individual life. Now let us cast the eye on the collective

---

[143] *Mann* - to receive beneficence from Allah with no major effort. It also means favours. See *Lughat-ul-Quran*, Vol, pp 542-544. (Ed)

[144] *Salwa* – anything which provides consolation and reassurance. This refers to both physical and psychological needs of human beings. See *Lughat-ul-Quran*, Vol 1, p 701. (Ed)

life. The fundamental principle which was laid down was that the nation which has the *Naima* of Allah will achieve superiority over other nations of the world.

O Bani Israel! Call to mind the favour which I bestowed on you, and that I preferred you to all others. (2:47)

Hence, where Bani Israel were reminded of many other *Naima*, they were specifically told that *Anbiya* were sent among them; they were bestowed with power in the land; and such other things were conferred on them which no-one else was given[145]:

Remember Moses said to his people: 'O my people! Call in remembrance the favour of Allah unto you, when He produced Anbiya among you, made you kings, and gave you what He had not given to any other among the peoples'. (5:20)

9.8 Power is *Naimat*

Hence establishment of rule in the land, power and authority, are all *Naima* of Allah:

...call in remembrance that He made you inheritors after the people of Noah and gave you a stature tall among the nations. Call in remembrance the benefits (you have received) from Allah: that so you may prosper. (7:69)

Similarly, beautiful palaces and fortified castles are also *Naima* of Allah (7:74).

9.9 Increase in Numbers is a *Naimat*

An increase in numbers in a *Jamaat* is also a *Naimat* of Allah:

...But remember how you were little, and He gave you increase...(7:86)

9.10 Victory and Triumph is a *Naimat*

Victory, success and triumph in the battlefield is a *Naimat* of Allah (3:173). To be protected from the clutches of attacking enemies is also a *Naimat*.

O you who have Eimaan! Call in remembrance the favour of Allah unto you when certain men formed the design to stretch out their hands against you, but (Allah) held

---

[145] The bounties which are obtained through Deen cannot be obtained outwith the Quranic values. (Ed)

back their hands from you: so fear (the consequences of the laws of) Allah. And on Allah let Momineen put (all) their trust. (5:11)

9.11   Becoming Free from Slavery is a *Naimat*

During the initial period of Islam, many such events occurred in which Muslims were encircled within very difficult situations due to their opponents. Bringing them out protected and safe and returning them victorious and successful, is called a *Naimat* of Allah (33:9). In the same way, compare with the situation of *Bani Israel*: achieving release from the tyranny and subjugation of Pharaoh and receiving freedom from the curse of slavery was called a *Naimat* of Allah for them:

Remember! Moses said to his people: 'Call to mind the favour of Allah to you when He delivered you from the people of Pharaoh'...(14:6)

9.12   Revitalizing a Dead Nation with the Blood of Life

For a nation to achieve life again after death, and for it to be once again numbered amongst living nations, is Allah's *Fadl* (2:242). But we have not yet mentioned that greatest *Naimat* of all as a result of which these *Naima* are achieved. The Quran declares:

And hold fast, all together, by the rope which Allah (stretches out for you) and be not divided among yourselves; and remember with gratitude Allah's favour on you; for you were enemies and He joined your hearts in love, so that by His Grace, you became brethren; and you were on the brink of the pit of fire[146], and He saved you from it. Thus, does Allah make His Signs clear to you: That you may be guided. (3:103)

In other words, mutual unity: for the Islamic nation to become one Ummah, not to be divided into sects and factions, is that *Naimat* of Allah which became the line of distinction between the era of ignorance and the Islamic period. Subjugation of the universal forces by man is a *Naimat*:

Do you not see that Allah has subjected to you all things in the heavens and on earth, and has made his bounties flow to you in exceeding measure, (both) seen and unseen...(31:20)

All this is made subject to control by man so that man remains bowed before the

---

[146] When human emotions, desires and intellect function outwith the guidance of *Wahi*, they only consider their own good. Here, the Quran states that without its guidance you would have remained divided both within your own self and among yourselves, and inner division can never lead to outer unity. (Ed)

laws of Allah:

...Thus does He complete His favours on you, that you may bow to His Will (laws).
(16:81)

This is that path of guidance (2:150) which was revealed through Rasul-ullah (2:151). And this is what is called Islam which is a complete Deen, and by reaching which all the *Naima* of Allah are achieved:

...This day have I completed your Deen for you, accomplished My favours upon you, and have chosen for you Islam as your Deen...(5:3)

9.13 How *Naima* are Multiplied

Following the achievement of all these *Naima*, and after this for increase and development in them, this principle is established that whoever does *Shukr* for his *Naima*, his *Naima* will continue to multiply, and whoever does *Kufr* of these *Naima*, his *Naima* will be snatched from him. For *Shukr e Naimat* see the topic under '*Shukr*'. Here it will be sufficient to state briefly that to utilise the *Naima* of Allah according to the correct Divine laws is *Shukr e Naimat*, and to obtain advantage wrongly from them, employing them in unjust ways, is *Kufr*. For example, when the Muslims were bestowed with the *Naimat* of government and state, it was with this purpose:

Those who, if We establish them in the land, establish Salat and organise Zakat, enjoin the right and forbid wrong...(22:41)

As long as they kept fulfilling this purpose the state kept on expanding, and when they turned *Shukr e Naimat* into *Kufran e Naimat* i.e. started taking illegitimate advantage of this great bounty of Allah, the state turned from the 'kingdom of Allah' into a dictatorship, and gradually that *Naimat* was snatched away and then they became bound up in the painful chastisement of humiliation and ruin.

To keep in mind this same purpose, Bani Israel were also instructed: Remember! all these *Naima* have been made available cheaply for you; as long as you continue to display *Shukr* for these, these will continue to multiply, but if you do *Kufr e Naimat* then you will be bound in a severe punishment:

And remember! your Sustainer caused to be declared (publicly): 'If you are grateful, I will add more (favours) unto you; But if you show ingratitude, truly My punishment is terrible indeed.' (14:7)

9.14   Submission to Other than Allah is *Kufr* of *Naimat*

The fundamental and intrinsic form of being grateful for *Naima* is to have *Eimaan* in One Allah and to have *Eimaan* in Allah means to completely deny 'non-Allah' (which the Quran calls *Batil*). Other than Allah, no other rebellious power should be followed nor should any other law be accepted other than His. If this disobedience is done, it will be *Kufr* of *Naimat*:

And Allah has made for you mates (and companions) of your own nature, and made for you, out of them, sons and daughters and grandchildren, and provided for you sustenance of the best: will they then believe in vain things, and be ungrateful for Allah's favours? And obey others than Allah, such as have no power of providing them, for sustenance, with anything in heavens or earth, and cannot possibly have such power? (16:72-73)

This is because man achieves all *Naima* by obeying the laws of Allah. To relate these to some other power is to declare *Shirk* in opposition to *Tauheed*, and is *Kufr* in opposition to *Shukr* (16:53-55). This reality is explained as follows by an example:

Allah sets forth a parable: a city enjoying security and quiet, abundantly supplied with sustenance from every place: Yet was it ungrateful for the favours of Allah: so Allah made it taste of hunger and terror like a garment (from every side), because of the (evil) which (its people) wrought. And there came to them a Messenger from among themselves, but they falsely rejected him; so the wrath seized them even in the midst of their iniquities. So eat of the sustenance which Allah has provided for you, lawful and good; and be grateful for the favours of Allah, if it is He Whom you follow. (16:112-114)

9.15   Kufr of *Naima* by the Leaders of a Nation

According to the teaching of the Quran this *Kufr* and *Shukr* are not confined to individuals only; from the point of view of the collective, its effect is very profound. It is apparent therefore that this *Kufr* will commence from the higher echelons who are called national leaders. The consequence of their *Kufr* is that they fall into the pits of hell, taking the whole nation along with them. The Quran states:

Have you not turned your vision to those who have changed the favour of Allah into blasphemy and caused their people to descend to the house of perdition? Into Hell? They will burn therein, an evil place to stay in! (14:28-29)

The reality is that the nation which, like a herd of buffalo, becomes habitual in following behind men with eyes shut without looking around, meets this same sorry end. Contrary to this, the Divine law saves and removes those people who make use of their heart and mind, intellect and vision, and do not let go of their hold on *Shukr e Naimat* from the encirclement of hell. So, when the nation of Lot was engulfed from all sides by the exemplary hell of destruction and obliteration, then Allah saved those individuals among them who practiced *Shukr* because of their being grateful:

> *We sent against them a violent tornado with showers of stones, except Lot's household; them we delivered by early dawn as a Grace from Us. Thus do we reward those who are grateful. (54:34-35)*

This is why it is instructed to always entreat Allah for the ability to perform *Shukr e Naimat* (46:15).

9.16 Psyche of Man

But as has been noted in the previous chapter, man happens to be a strange creature. When Allah showers His *Naima* on him, he contravenes His laws, avoids them and sidesteps them. But when these *Naima* begin to be snatched from him as a consequence of his *Kufr*, then he becomes hopeless and despondent:

> *Yet when We bestow Our favours on man, he turns away and becomes remote on his side, and when evil seizes him he gives himself up to despair! (17:83)*

In this appalling environment of deprivation and despair he then returns to the Divine laws, and then in recompense for his being on the right path, he achieves his seized *Naima* and lost treasures again. But after this he again forgets them, and associating these *Naima* to others, begins to do *Shirk*:

> *...but when He bestows a favour upon him as from Himself, (man) does forget what he cried and prayed for before, and he does set up rivals unto Allah...(39:8)*

9.17 Egotistic Attitude

And at other times he exceeds even this, and the menace of egotism embeds itself in his mind, and he starts declaring that I have received all this as a result of my own planning and my own knowledge and skill. What Allah! And what laws of His!

> *Now when trouble touches man, he cries to Us: But when We bestow a favour upon him as from Ourselves, he says, 'This has been given to me because of a certain knowledge (I have)!' Nay, but thinking like this is the cause for destruction, but most of them understand not! (39:49)*

At this point it is important to understand this much that whatever man receives, it is as a consequence of his effort and action. But the question is what part of this endeavour is due to his own effort and what part due to those potentials which he has received automatically. If an individual possesses a higher level of intellect, then he has not purchased this brain himself, he has received it without any effort and payment. This individual earns more compared to the individual who has not received a good brain and declaring it to be the result purely of his own skill, he does not consider anyone else to have a share in it. The Quran declares that the relatively higher earnings of this individual is the consequence of those intellectual potentials of his which were bestowed on him free. Hence by calling this part of his income his own skill, he should not become the sole owner, instead this should be allocated for the common sustenance of mankind according to the Divine law.[147] This is also the condition of man that he never holds himself responsible for his trouble and worry. Firstly, he tries to hold someone else responsible for this and if this is not possible, then he states that God has unjustly humiliated me, I was not in any way at fault:

Now, as for man, when his Rabb tries him (as per law), giving him honour and gifts, then says he, (puffed up), 'My Rabb has honoured me.' But when He tries him, restricting his subsistence for him, then says he (in despair), 'My Rabb has humiliated me!' (89:15-16)

This is not the truth – no-one receives *Naima* without any reason, nor are those which have been gained then snatched away without any cause. For this there is an established immutable law of Allah and this law is that in the (good or bad) state of any nation no change occurs till the time that that nation does not produce a change within itself. Changes in the external world are in fact manifested according to changes in the internal psychology of this nation.

9.18   Immutable Law

The Quran states:

Because Allah will never change the grace which He has bestowed on a people until they change what is in their (own) selfs: and verily Allah is He Who hears and knows (all things). (8:53)

A severe chastisement becomes imposed on that nation which changes the *Naima* of Allah itself in this way:

---

[147] Details of this are covered in my book titled *The Quranic System of Sustenance.*

Ask the Children of Israel how many clear (Signs) We have sent them. But if any one, after Allah's favour has come to him, substitutes (something else), Allah is strict in punishment. (2:211)

Hence, for this purpose that the significance of being grateful does not remain concealed from the eyes, it is emphasised that *Naima* be displayed. Bani Israel were repeatedly reminded to always keep the *Naima* of Allah in front of them:

O Children of Israel! call to mind the (special) favour which I bestowed upon you... (2:40) See also (2:122)

Then, addressing the whole of mankind, it was instructed not to let Allah's *Naima* disappear out of sight:

O mankind! Call to mind the favours of Allah unto you...(35:3)

So much so, that even Rasul-ullah was told to display the *Naima* of his *Rabb*:

But the bounty of your Rabb - rehearse and proclaim! (93:11)

For the same warning it is stated that on the Day of Judgment there will be a question regarding every *Naimat*, about how did you spend and utilise it:

Then, shall you be questioned that Day about the favours. (102:8)

9.19   Let us Recap

From the above discussion this reality has become apparent to us that finding the path of guidance is a *Naimat* of Allah, and that is why messenger-hood and revelation, the Book and wisdom are bounties of Allah which are bestowed on a nation. By walking on this path of guidance the successes, eminences, triumphs and accomplishments of the world are attained. Wealth and prosperity, authority and rule, home and hearth, wife and children, grand palaces, fortified castles, increase in *Jamaat*, supremacy and power over enemies, all of these are *Naima* of Allah. Contrary to this, the snatching away of these *Naima* and the overshadowing of some nation by humiliation and ruin is Allah's punishment. Gratitude for these *Naima* is that these should only be used for those purposes which have been defined by the Divine laws. As a consequence of this gratitude these *Naima* will continue to increase and will keep multiplying, and the roots of a nation will continue to become sturdier. Contrary to this, if a wrong advantage is taken from these, then this is *Kufr* (denial) of these *Naima* and as a result these *Naima* are snatched away; these begin to transform into decline; and since the life of nations is counted not in days but is reckoned in centuries, these *Naima* are therefore snatched away gradually in such an imperceptive way that a superficial glance does not perceive any discernable difference in the state of this nation. This is why man often falls into the trap of thinking that no accountability whatsoever is being taken of the injustices of this nation. So much so that even the nation itself ridicules the immutability of the Law of Requital, mocks it, and in the intoxication of wealth and power does not understand that it is standing at the foot of a mountain containing a volcano within which a silent fire is unceasingly multiplying, until this volcano erupts and the unleashed storm of wave after wave of molten lava engulfs them in its fold, and then no possibility of salvation, no route of escape remains for them, and in its place only their tales remain.

There are thousands of worlds of wisdom and vision, lesson and instruction implicit in the law which the Quran has explained regarding being deprived of *Naima* (the snatching of *Naima*) i.e.:

Because Allah will never change the favour which He has bestowed on a people until they change what is in their (own) selfs: and verily Allah is He Who hears and knows (all things). (8:53)

In relation to the rise and fall of nations this is a great law. As the explanation of this law will be found at another place, a brief summary will suffice here. First of all this reality has been exposed in it that though Allah is definitely Omnipotent, His status is not like that of our worldly rulers who, when they are pleased, bestow a full treasure chest and when they are vexed, snatch it away. The laws of His Will are fixed, and this system of the universe is functioning due to these same laws. The conduct and organisation of human life also function according to this same code. Furthermore, reward or punishment of Allah is not something which is imposed on man ready made from outside, rather it is the natural consequence of the inner change within man. This is an important point which will be easier to understand through a tangible example. For example, it is the property of water that it is liquid, it flows down a slope, it takes on the shape of whatever container it is poured into. But when this same water, by absorbing cold within it, creates such a change within itself that it turns into a slab of ice, then it remains neither liquid nor does it flow down a slope, nor can it adopt the shape of every container i.e. it is the same water but due to an internal change it has now become the follower of some other clause of the law of nature. Now it is not a liquid but has turned into a solid and the properties of this state have now been created in it. Now if this water wished that it could retrieve its snatched traits then it will have to produce changes within itself i.e. it will need to become liquid again through heat. Following this change, its former properties will automatically return. Or looking at another aspect, when this same water absorbs more heat then it will change from liquid into gas. Now it will turn into another form and the law governing this form will become applicable to it. Instead of flowing down a slope, it will now rise up, will become lighter than air; if it now wished to retrieve its snatched properties, then it will have to produce a change within itself as a result of which the same properties will return.

Now just reflect on this state of affairs that every Muslim prays numerous times to Allah:

Show us the straight path, the path of those on whom You have bestowed Your favours...(1:6-7)

But does not grasp that if despite this, his condition is not like those people on whom Allah has bestowed His favours and bounties, then what is its secret? The secret is that same one which has been mentioned above. On the one hand he prays, and on the other hand Allah tells him that a reward can only be bestowed on you once you create the potential for it within yourself - the result will manifest itself. Therefore, we should look at what the change was which those people who benefitted from Allah's bounties had created within themselves, and when those bounties have been gradually snatched away, then which change was it that resulted in this. And today, if there is the desire to retrieve these same snatched *Naima*, then what kind of change is required to be created within us in order to achieve this. Maintaining our state fixedly as a solid slab of ice yet cherishing the desire for the property of a liquid - if this is not self-deception then what else is it? Remember! the way that the law of Allah is immutable regarding changing the states of water, it is similarly immutable regarding the life and death of nations of the world (35:43). The law of Allah is a living reality and nothing becomes made from mere sacred desires and beautiful wishes. '*So long as your glance is not on the realities of life, your glass will not be able to compete with the rock*'[148].

9.20   A Doubt

It is stated that when a Muslim prays to Allah to help him to tread on the path of those people who have received Allah's *Naima* (1:7) and the characteristics of these people who achieved these *Naimas* is that they are righteous, truthful, martyrs and *Anbiya*, then:

All who obey Allah and the messenger are in the company of those on whom is the Grace of Allah, of Anbiya, the Truthful, the Martyrs, and the Righteous: Ah! what a beautiful companionship! (4:69)

From this it is then deduced that a Muslim, while following the path of a *Nabi*, can himself become a *Nabi* and as a result of this logic some people offer proof of the

---

[148] This may be a couplet by M. Iqbal. (Ed)

features of messenger-hood. This line of argument is based on absolute ignorance of the teaching of the Quran.[149]

9.21   Another Doubt

It is often said that all those amenities and prosperities which the Quran has called the *Naima* of Allah are available to Western nations. From this aspect they will be declared as nations possessing bounties, although they deny even the existence of God and also do not accept His defined human values – what is the answer to this?

The response to this is that there are two parts of the laws of Allah. One is those laws which are related to the material universe, these are called natural laws. Whichever nation harnesses the forces of nature according to these laws will achieve prosperities and successes and in this there is no distinction between a *Kafir* and a *Momin*.

But the second part of the laws of Allah is that one which is related to human life. The nation which harnesses the forces of nature but does not bring these into use according to these laws will neither itself find internal peace and tranquility, nor will the rest of mankind live in contentment and peace in relation to them just as is happening today. But for the nation which utilises the outcome of the forces of nature according to human values, the development of their own self will keep taking place, and the rest of the world will also live in peace and tranquility under its shadow. Such a nation is called a *Jamaat e Momineen*. On this basis all the nations of the world will be divided into three categories:

(1) That nation which, having harnessed the forces of nature, utilises these according to the Permanent Values of humanity will be called a *Jamaat e Momineen*.
(2) That nation which, having subjugated the forces of nature, utilises these according to their own desires and interests will be a *Jamaat of Kuffar*.
(3) And that nation which does not even harness the forces of nature will not even reach the status of humanity; it will live life at an animal level.

---

[149] Details of this will be available in the book titled *Mairaaj e Insaniyat* under the chapter on the finality of messenger-hood.

10   *Fadl* (Abundance)

In the Arabic language the word *Fadl* is taken as being the opposite of 'scarcity' i.e. something being plentiful and not scarce, greater than need. Generally, this word is used for economic conveniences, but it can also be used for superiority, higher rank, hierarchy etc. Indeed, also for rewards and gifts, favours, acts of generosity and donations i.e. giving beyond what is someone's due or to give as a favour without expecting anything in return. For example, in Surah *Al-Baqra* it is stated:

> *...And do not forget liberality between yourselves...(2:237)*

The Bestower of these kinds of rewards and favours, raining down such bounties, is Allah, the greatest giver of *Fadl* (3:174). And the one who is showered with the *Fadls* of Allah is the possessor of *Fadl* i.e. '*Ulul Fadl*'. In Surah *An-Nur*, after the incident of *Ifk* (slandering), it is stated:

> *Let not those among you who are endued with grace and amplitude of means resolve by oath against helping their kinsmen, those in want, and those who have left their homes in Allah's cause...(24:22)*

10.1   Messenger-hood is a *Fadl* of Allah

As with *Naima*, Allah's *Fadl* too can be divided into each of the two categories of Deen and *Duniya* (world). Let us first consider the department of Deen.

Nabuwwat is Divine *Fadl*, and receiving it is dependent on the Will of Allah, not on the skill and endeavour of someone. A brief mention has been made of it in the previous chapter on *In'aam*. The people of the Book, in particular the Jews, used to say that whoever does not follow our Deen and is not from among the Bani Israel, how can he be a *Nabi*? In response it is stated:

> *...Say: 'All bounties are in the hand of Allah: He grants them to whom He wishes: And Allah cares for all, and He knows all things'. (3:73)*

In the same connection, at another place it is stated:

> *... But Allah will choose for His Special Mercy whom He will - for Allah is Possessor of abounding Fadl. (2:105) See also (2:90, 17:86-87)*

10.2 The Quran is Allah's *Fadl*

Nabuwwat was meant to be the *Wahi* of Allah which is now preserved within the Quran, hence the Quran is also Allah's *Fadl* and *Rehmat*. For mankind to receive it is also Allah's *Fadl*, and as a consequence of this, whatever the universe of humanity achieves is also His *Fadl* and *Rehmat*:

O mankind! verily there has come to you a convincing proof from your Rabb: For We have sent unto you a light (that is) manifest. Then those who have Eimaan in Allah, and hold fast to Him, soon will He admit them to mercy and grace from Himself and guide them to Himself by a straight path. (4:175-176)

Hence, the Quran is such a supreme bounty and highest favour that no matter how much happiness is displayed by mankind on receipt of it, it will be insufficient:

O mankind! Surely, there has come to you a direction from your Rabb and a healing for the diseases in your hearts – and a guidance and Rehmat for the Momineen. Say: ' In the bounty of Allah and in His Rehmat – in that let them rejoice'; that is better than all that they hold. (10:57-58).

Along with the Quran, the conduit for the Quran, Rasul-ullah himself, was also a great *Naimat* for humanity and this was also a *Fadl* and *Ihsan* of Allah:

O Nabi! Truly We have sent you as a witness, a bearer of glad tidings, and warner, and as one who invites to Allah's (grace) by His leave, and as a lamp spreading light. Then give the glad tidings to Momineen, that they shall have from Allah a very great bounty. (33:45-47) See also (62:2-9)

10.3 Inheriting the Quran is a Great *Fadl*

This Book, the teaching of which was provided by Rasul-ullah, was received by the Muslim Ummah as an inheritance. This inheritance is in itself a supreme *Fadl*:

Then We have given the Book for inheritance to such of Our servants as We have chosen: but there are among them some who wrong their own selves; some who follow a middle course; and some who are, by Allah's leave, foremost in good deeds; that is the highest Grace. (35:32)

(It is possible that in this verse being 'foremost in righteous deeds' is defined as the supreme *Fadl*. Even then it is the same, because by inheritance of the Quran the aim is for the *Momineen* to keep progressing in righteous deeds).

10.4   Practicable *Shariat* is Divine *Fadl*

The uniqueness of this Book is that the *Shariat* in it is not such a burden which when you lift it, it cannot be lifted, rather it is such an easy code which can be followed with ease. It is not some kind of chain as a result of which the human capacity to reason and to act becomes a captive, nor any kind of commandment which is impracticable. The receiving of such a *Shariat* is also a *Fadl* of Allah:

> *Say: 'See you what things Allah has sent down to you for sustenance? Yet you hold forbidden some things whereof and some things lawful'. Say: 'Has Allah indeed permitted you, or do you invent things to attribute to Allah?' And what think those who invent lies against the Day of Judgment? Verily Allah is full of bounties to mankind, but most of them do not do Shukr. (10:59-60).*

Support of this is given in Surah *An-Nur*, where it is stated that those people who accuse righteous women with some slander will have to bring forth four witnesses to support their claim, and if they cannot do this then they will be punished. This is because to try and stain the chastity of someone is not any ordinary crime. But along with this it is also stated that if some man accuses his wife and cannot obtain a witness, then he should take an oath as proof of his claim. This exception has made the law easier. This allowance is declared to be a *Fadl* of Allah:

> *If it were not for Allah's grace and mercy on you, and that Allah is Oft-Returning, full of Wisdom. (24:10)*

10.5   Righteousness and Guidance are a *Fadl* of Allah

Therefore, getting guidance and righteousness from the Quran and treading on this straight path is Allah's *Fadl* (49:7-8). The former *Anbiya* also used to proclaim receiving guidance and righteousness as Allah's *Fadl*. Hence, in his sermon in the prison Yusuf states:

> *'And I follow the ways of my fathers, Abraham, Isaac, and Jacob; and never could we attribute any partners whatever to Allah: that (comes) of the grace of Allah to us and to mankind: yet most men are not grateful'. (12:38)*

10.6   Saving Oneself from Being Misguided is Allah's *Fadl*

But evil forces are always busy in the effort to divert people from the path of righteousness and guidance. About Rasul-ullah himself it is stated:

> *But for the grace of Allah to you and His mercy, a party of them would certainly have plotted to lead you astray. But (in fact) they will only lead their own selves astray, and*

to you they can do no harm in the least. For Allah has sent down to you the Book and wisdom and taught you what you knew not (before): And great is the grace of Allah unto you. (4:113)

This is why the *Momineen* are directed to not follow the whisperings[150] of Satan by leaving Allah's guidance. This is also a great *Fadl* of Allah and it is from this that the development of the human self takes place (24:21). Details of the effects which are established in the worldly life as a result of this human self-development will be covered later.

10.7   The Blessing of the Hereafter is a *Fadl*

To be successful in the life of the hereafter is also a Divine *Fadl*. Hence, at numerous places the rewards and favours of Jannat have been declared as *Fadl* e.g. (35:34-35, 44:51-57, 57:21). This supreme *Fadl* is intrinsically linked to righteous deeds:

… But those who have Eimaan and work righteous deeds will be in the luxuriant meads of the gardens: they shall have, before their Rabb, all that they wish for. That will indeed be the magnificent Fadl (of Allah). (42:22)

This is that same *Fadl* and blessing with which the martyrs laying down their life in the path of Allah are rewarded (3:168-170). And achieving companionship of these very people is considered to be a *Fadl* of Allah:

All who obey Allah and the messenger are in the company of those on whom is the Grace of Allah, of the Anbiya, the Truthful, the Martyrs, and the Righteous: Ah! what a beautiful fellowship! Such is the bounty from Allah: And sufficient is it that Allah knows all. (4:69-70)

10.8   Divine *Fadl* in Worldly Matters

Now see the amazing display of Allah's *Fadl* in worldly matters – this system of the universe in which, on the one hand, such a vast arena has been left open for the struggles and endeavours of life, and on the other hand so many means have been made available for comfort and pleasure - this is *Fadl* for mankind:

It is Allah Who has made the night for you, that you may rest therein, and the day as

---

[150] The root of the word used here is W-S-W-S, which means the passing of bad thoughts through the mind i.e. the thoughts of self-interest which emotions create in the heart (or mind), or which mischievous people incite in someone's mind (7:20, 114:4-5). See *Lughat-ul-Quran*, Vol 2, pp 715-716. (Ed)

that which helps to see. Verily Allah is full of Grace and Bounty to men: yet most men give no thanks. (40:61)

10.9   The Life of Eminence is a Divine *Fadl*

This was a reference to the general favours in the system of nature. Now let us consider the rewards of *Eimaan* and righteous deeds. The Quran has explained one thing as a basis and foundation, and that is that by following Deen man achieves a life of distinction, and that not even a common or average level of life, never mind a life of humiliation and deprivation. And a life of eminence is a *Fadl* of Allah:

> *O you who have Eimaan! if you keep in view the laws of Allah, He will grant you a criterion (to judge between right and wrong), remove from you (all) evil (that may afflict) you, and protect you: for Allah is the Possessor of Fadl unbounded. (8:29)*

Such a nation should always be counted among the nations which are alive. For a dead nation to get life is also a *Fadl* of Allah:

> *Did you not turn your vision to those who abandoned their homes, though they were in thousands (in number), for fear of death? Allah said to them: 'Die': Then He restored them to life. For Allah is full of bounty to mankind, but most of them are ungrateful. (2:243)*

10.10   Achieving Powers is a *Fadl*

Similarly, obtaining positive powers is also a *Fadl* of Allah. In the story of Solomon, when it is noted that the Queen of Saba (Sheba) becomes obedient and a follower, Solomon, after witnessing these astounding forces, exclaimed:

> *...he said: 'This is by the grace of my Rabb! to test me whether I am grateful or ungrateful'...(27:40)*

At another place it is noted that Solomon had a grand army which was mostly based on horse cavalry and that Solomon had full knowledge of the rules and principles regarding these contingents. This is also called the *Fadl* of Allah (27:16). Dawood (David) had expertise in the technique of producing iron mail armour; this has also been called Divine *Fadl* (34:10-11).

10.11   Victory and Triumph is Allah's *Fadl*

Gaining victory and success against an enemy and returning from the battlefield successful and triumphant is also a *Fadl* of Allah (3:172-173). At another place the word 'Fadl' is mentioned as the opposite of 'trouble' in the battlefield from which its meanings are further elucidated (4:72-73). Leaving aside the battlefield, what instance is there in this world of challenges when we are not faced by some obstacle; life itself is the name of persistent struggle, continuous effort, and Jihad without end. Hence, success in the Jihad of life is a *Fadl* of Allah. Contrary to this, if some trick of an enemy becomes effective, some stratagem of his overwhelms, or by becoming entangled in some deception of his, such a step is taken which goes against the interest of the *Millat*, then this is obedience of Satan. Remaining protected from this is also a *Fadl* of Allah (4:83).

10.12   Divine *Fadl* By Spending in the Path of Allah

This is because by trapping him in their deceptive net, Satanic doubts (the sentiments of human self-interest) try to divert him from the path of guidance. For example, the requirement of the Quranic system of sustenance is that whatever is beyond one's needs should be passed on to the societal system so that the requirements of others who are in need are met from this. But the individual self-interests of man scare him by telling him that if you gave all this to 'others' then what will be left for 'yourself'? You will die of hunger. Even though the truth is that what is apparently considered as giving to others is, in reality, giving to your 'own self'. This is because watering the roots of a tree is for the sake of growth and blossoming of the branches and leaves. Growth of the collective life of a *Millat* is the cause for the success and prosperity of individuals. The Quran has stated this fact in the following words after giving the command for *Infaaq*[151]:

The Evil one threatens you with poverty and bids you to conduct unseemly. Allah promises you His protection and bounties. And Allah cares for all and He knows all things. (2:268)

10.13   Establishment of Peace is Divine *Fadl*

The greatest desire and yearning of man is that he should live in peace and tranquility. But those people who (somehow) acquire power and authority snatch away the peace of others and unleash chaos in the society. But in opposition to them another *Jamaat* is caused to stand up, which halts these transgressors from their excesses and in this way establishes peace in the society. This is also termed as the *Fadl* of Allah:

...And did not Allah check one set of people by means of another, the earth would indeed be full of mischief: But Allah is full of bounty to all the worlds. (2:251)

---

[151] *Infaaq* – to keep wealth and the means of sustenance available for all. (Ed)

Those people who acquire power in the world think that they can now do whatever their hearts desire, there is no-one around to question us. If it is in truth like this, then there will be unbridled chaos in the world. But it is not like this. Here, the Law of Requital of Allah is functioning according to which the result of every deed (including even the thoughts passing through the mind) is of a surety established. This law, and its functioning without any favour, and its implementation is in itself Allah's *Fadl*:

Those who reject Eimaan will suffer from that rejection: and those who work righteousness will spread their couch (of repose) for themselves: that He may reward those who have Eimaan and work righteous deeds, out of His Bounty. For He loves not those who are Kafireen. (30:44-45)

10.14 Who Attains *Fadl*

We have seen what the different forms of Divine *Fadl* are and in what varying manners and techniques it is operating. The question now is, who receives this *Fadl* and how is it obtained? For this it is stated in very clear words that this *Fadl* of Allah is obtained by the one who deserves it and the conditions to deserve it are that man should continuously assess his own self on the highway of life, to see whether his step has gone in the wrong direction? If he realises that he has stepped on to the wrong path, then at some point he should return to that point from where he had taken a step in the wrong direction (this is called *Tauba*), and after this he should tread on that path which the Divine law (the Quran) has specified for him. As a consequence of this, that traveller becomes deserving of Allah's *Fadl*. In a nutshell, only he attains *Fadl* who deserves it:

Seek you the protection of your Rabb, and return to Him; that He may grant you enjoyment, good (and true), for a term appointed, and bestow His abounding grace on all who abound in merit...(11:3)

And after this 'return' (*Tauba*), not only is the loss compensated but far more than the heart's desire is received (42:25-26).

10.15 Getting Respite is also *Fadl*

The Law of Requital of Allah is an established fact according to which every deed produces its own effect. But there is a time interval between the time that a deed is done and for its consequence to manifest tangibly before us (just as there is an interval between the sowing of a seed in the soil and the ripening of the crop). If during this interval man, abandoning the wrong path, adopts the right path, and carries out such deeds whose constructive results are far weightier, then due to this the destructive effects of his former wrong conduct are eradicated. This is called 'receiving forgiveness'. In other words, his righteous deeds secure him from the ill effects of his former unpleasant deeds. This is called '*Maghfirat*'. Therefore, this time of respite (in which recovery is possible) is a *Fadl* of Allah. Attention has been drawn to this fact in various places in the Quran e.g. (2:64, 27:71-73). In the battle of *Uhd*[152] when a tactical error was committed by a *Jamaat* of Muslims and because of this they had to withdraw, then after this they were 'accorded forgiveness' because of their '*Tauba*' i.e. when they produced unity again within their dispersed forces and stood up against the enemy with courage and fortitude, their defeat turned into victory. This is also termed as a *Fadl* of Allah (3:151). Similarly, in the incident of *Ifk* it is stated that when those people who made a mistake accepted their error, and in this way turned back from their wrong path, the punishment of destruction on the nation was averted from them (24:12-14). This is also called Allah's *Fadl*.

10.16   Reward Exceeding Effort

This was the state of errors and mistakes. As far as righteous deeds are concerned the reward received for these is far greater than human calculation and this is also called Allah's *Fadl* (4:32, 4:173, 24:38, 35:29-30). The word *Fadl* has been used in numerous places in relation to economic conveniences. For example, in Surah *Al-Jummah* it is stated:

And when the Salat is finished, then may you disperse through the land, and seek of the bounty of Allah…(62:10)

This was the *Fadl* which Rasul-ullah and the *Jamaat e Momineen* used to search for:

… seeking grace from Allah and (His) Good Pleasure…(48:29)

At another place it is stated about the *Muhajireen*[153]:

…while seeking grace from Allah and (His) Good Pleasure…(59:8)

10.17   How Does This Occur?

The Quran has specified in very clear terms that wealth and authority, triumph and success, the joys of life, and abundance of sustenance - so much so that all that which is known as '*Fadl*' - are achieved by following Deen. If Muslims forsake their Deen, then Allah will confer all this on some other nation. It is stated in Surah *Al-Maida*:

---

[152] The second battle fought between the Muslims and the Quraish of Makkah in 624 AD. (Ed)
[153] *Muhajireen* – group of Muslims who migrated from Makkah to Medina in the time of Rasul-ullah due to various reasons. (Ed)

O you who have Eimaan! if any from among you turn back from his Eimaan, soon will Allah produce a people whom He will love as they will love Him, lowly with the Momineen, mighty against the Kafireen, fighting in the way of Allah, and never afraid of the reproaches of such as find fault. That is the grace of Allah, which He will bestow on whom He pleases. And Allah encompasses all, and He knows all things.
(5:54)

10.18 In Summary

We have seen that the Self of Allah is *Dul Fadl al-Azeem* (which is the most complete and supreme Self) i.e. master of every kind of *Fadl* (i.e. highest *Fadl*). He bestows *Fadl* on the whole of mankind (according to His law).

From this it is evident that the society which is based on those individuals whose self has become developed will have all these favours and bounties available to it, and it will make these freely available for the *Rabubiyat* of the whole of mankind. Therefore, in order to determine if some society has been shaped according to the Divine laws (Allah's Deen) or not, it will have to be seen whether that society has the conveniences of life available to it in ample abundance or not (this is called *Fadl*), and then whether these conveniences have been made freely available to mankind or not. That nation which is itself weak and deprived or is keeping the forces of nature and the means of sustenance confined to some special group (nation or country), and does not consider every child of Adam as an equal partner in it, such a nation has nothing to do with the system of life (*Ad-Deen*) defined by Allah. You can consider that the selfs of the individuals of this nation have not been realised.[154]

---

[154] This is an extremely profound statement – according to the Quran, the human self is created by each individual him or herself by living life voluntarily within the Permanent Values. This is called acquisition of *Eimaan* (2:177), as a consequence of which an individual performs righteous deeds which lead to development of the self, which will then work for the establishment of Deen for the good of all mankind. Immortality in the life of the hereafter is for this type of self according to the Quran. (Ed)

11   *Munn*[155] (Munificence)

In relation to *Fadl, Rehmat,* and *In'aam,* the Quran has also mentioned another attribute which it has defined by the word *Munn*[156]. The meaning of *Munn* is to give someone something without any effort or hardship, or any charge or expectation of any return, just as the means of sustenance (air, light, water, *Rizq* from the land) have been provided to all of mankind without any charge or expectation of any return. This is an attribute of Allah, the manifestation of which should also be manifested in 'His servants'.

But if an individual, after giving someone something without any charge, then reminds him of this favour for the rest of his life, then this *Munn* becomes a burden. In these situations, the word *Munn* will not be an attribute, rather it will be a flaw.

With respect to *Munn* being free of any charge, it is stated in the Quran regarding those prisoners of war from the enemy side who fall into your hands during a battle that:

> *...thereafter either leave them with generosity or after taking ransom*[157]*...(47:4)*

At another place it is noted that if you give something to someone without any charge, then do not give it with the intention that you will get something more in return:

> *Nor expect, in giving, any increase (for your own self). (74:6)*

Regarding the meaning of 'becoming a burden', it is stated in Surah *Al-Baqra*:

> *Those who spend their substance in the cause of Allah and follow not up their gifts with reminders of their generosity or with injury, for them their reward is with their Rabb: on them shall be no fear, nor shall they grieve. (2:262)*

A little later in another verse it is stated:

---

[155] Since the word *Ihsan* is prevalent among us for this attribute, therefore the translation of *Munn* will be with this word whereas the reality of the meaning of *Ihsan* is quite different from this.

[156] *Munn* is the name given to a weight which is heavier than a *Ratl.* The *Munn* prevalent among us (*Maund*) also refers to this weight.

[157] The Quran stated this value at a time when slavery was widespread thus emphasising the significance of human freedom and respect. (Ed)

O you who have Eimaan! cancel not your assistance by reminders of your generosity or by injury...(2:264)

From this it becomes clear as to what the correct meaning of *Munn* is. Now let us see in what forms *Munn* manifests itself from Allah.

11.1 *Nabuwwat* is a Favour of Allah

Nabuwwat is conferred free of charge. When the people of previous nations said to their *Anbiya* that you are human beings exactly like us, how can you be messengers, in response to this they replied that this is true:

...True, we are human like yourselves, but Allah does grant His grace to such of his servants as He pleases...(14:11)

The appearance of a *Nabi* among a nation is also Allah's *Munn*:

Allah did confer a great favour on Momineen when He sent among them a messenger from among themselves, rehearsing unto them the Signs of Allah, sanctifying them, and instructing them in Scripture and Wisdom, while, before that, they had been in manifest error. (3:164)

11.2 Receiving Guidance is Allah's Favour

This is why this matter was further clarified and explained:

They impress on you as a favour that they have embraced Islam. Say, 'Count not your Islam as a favour upon me: Nay, Allah has conferred a favour upon you that He has guided you to Eimaan', if you are true and sincere. (49:17)

This is because messenger-hood was not a commerce (Allah forbid) for the promotion of which the 'shopkeeper' has to be embarrassingly obliged for the favour of a customer.

11.3 Getting Wealth and Authority is Allah's *Munn*

Subjugation and enslavement are Allah's punishment. For a nation to achieve freedom from this chastisement and to become endowed with prosperity and authority is Allah's *Munn*. When Bani Israel were repressed under the tyranny of Pharaoh and Allah wished to transform their lowliness into supremacy, then it was stated:

And We wished to be gracious to those who were being depressed in the land, to make them leaders (in Eimaan) and make them heirs. To establish a firm place for them in the land, and to show Pharaoh, Haman, and their hosts, at their hands, the very things against which they were taking precautions. (28:5-6)

This is the real *Munn* which ensues from the direction of Allah. Contrary to this, another type of *Munn* is that one which comes from those 'gods' that man himself makes as his deities. And that *Munn* is of the kind of compassion that a butcher displays towards his goat by raising it. When Pharaoh stated to Moses that 'you are very ungrateful, just remember how many favours we granted you and now how you are returning that favour', in reply, using a few brief words with a single stroke Moses described that reality as a result of which Pharaonic politics stood exposed. Moses stated:

And this is the favour with which you do reproach me, that you have enslaved the Children of Israel. (26:22)

Yes, you are recounting those favours to me in return for which you have enslaved *Bani Israel* like this.

11.4   Gaining Freedom from Slavery is *Munn*

This 'favour and blessing' was that from which gaining freedom was in itself *Munn* and the real favour which came from Allah was this:

And surely, We bestowed Our favour on Moses and Aaron. And We delivered them and their people from (their) great calamity. (37:114-115)

But this *Munn* had indeed commenced from that very time when Moses was saved in his childhood from the clutches of Pharaoh. The Quran states:

And indeed We conferred a favour on you (Moses) another time (before). 'Behold! We sent to your mother, by inspiration, the message'. (20:37-38)

Following this comes the narrative about floating Moses (in a casket) onto the river. Hence, protection from the clutches of someone's cruelty is also Allah's *Munn*.

When a cruel human being or some tyrannical nation becomes ensnared in punishment due to the consequences of their crimes, then those people who are kept protected from this punishment have the *Munn* of Allah on them. When Qarun was encircled by his arrogance, and the burden of his worship of capitalism buried him in the 'depths of the earth', then those people who used to gaze at his wealth and say how unjust it is that we are not able to get these riches, the next day they prostrated in gratitude and said:

> *...had it not been that Allah was gracious to us, He could have caused the earth to swallow us up! Ah! those who reject Allah will assuredly never prosper. (28:82)*

Now this secret became evident to them that the mere attainment of riches is not true success and fortune, it is essential to have the correct system along with this. In the beginning it was generally the poor who accepted *Eimaan* in Rasul-ullah. In this new society (which was established according to the Divine laws) the status of these poor people was higher even than the biggest leaders of the Quraysh. Seeing this, these leaders used to be infuriated and burn with resentment as to how much honour and respect is being given to these 'lowly' people. This psyche of theirs is described in the following words:

> *Thus did We try some of them by comparison with others, that they should say: 'Is it these then that Allah has favoured from amongst us?' Does not Allah know best those who are grateful? (6:53)*

From these verses it is clear that Allah provides the means of sustenance and guidance free of charge to mankind, and following this, does not remind anyone of this favour. In the society in which the selfs of individuals develop (according to the Divine laws), the need of every needy one is fulfilled free of charge and then there is no reminder of this favour to them. One sign of a developed self is that it gives to the needy free of charge and even the thought of any return does not arise. In explicit words they tell those whose needs they fulfil that:

> *We feed you for the sake of Allah alone: no reward do we desire from you, nor thanks. (76:9)*

12 *Ghadab* and *It'aab* (Recompense)

It has been noted in the first chapter that among the Divine attributes there are also those attributes which seem to be contradictory e.g. He is *Raheem* (Merciful), and also *Qahhar* (Vanquisher). But if we look into this more deeply, then it will become plain that the question of these attributes being contradictory does not even arise. If you support someone who has been wronged, then this will be a display of your sentiments of mercy and sympathy but for the support of a wronged person it is necessary for you to prevent an oppressor from cruelty. For this you may also need to use force (according to need). From this it will be said that on the one hand you are extremely merciful and on the other hand extremely stern. But by paying close attention it will become evident that both attributes are indeed two sides of the same coin. Sympathy with the victim and sternness against the oppressor is a requirement of justice. Since the Divine attributes are complete in all aspects, it is essential that if He is *Ghafur ur Raheem* then He should also be *Shadeed ul Aqaab*. But together with this, it is also necessary that to whatever extent an attribute needs to be manifested at any particular time, only that proportion of the attribute should be displayed. This is known as the Divine attributes being balanced (*Asma-al-Husna*) i.e. for there to be complete equilibrium and proportion in these attributes.

Under the previous topics we have seen how the Divine attributes (*Rehmat, Ina'am, Fadl* etc) manifest themselves. Now the other side of the picture comes before us which shows us how His other types of attributes e.g. *Ghadab, La'nat* etc. are displayed on which occasions. From this, this fact will also become evident that these types of (apparently) opposite attributes will also be demonstrated by the individual whose self is developed. Such individuals will on the one hand be merciful among themselves, and on the other hand will be very stern towards the *Kuffar*. But these attributes will comprise very precise proportion, and because of this the self of this person will itself be balanced, which is called a Balanced Personality. And for the nation which is based on such individuals, the society of that nation will also be balanced, and a guarantor of world peace and security.

12.1 Meaning of *Ghadab*

First let us look at the Divine attribute of '*Ghadab*'. We generally take the meaning of *Ghadab* as that of being angry, and when a word of anger is uttered then the mind immediately submits to such a sentiment under the influence of which man, having lost his mental balance, becomes fiery and in this state of insanity he does all that which he himself later rues. But when this word is related towards Allah, then its meaning will not be that of anger, rather this *Ghadab* will, in actuality, be another name for the Law of Requital. The purpose of this is a recompense for crimes. When the people of the Book used to criticise the Muslims, saying why do you have *Eimaan* in the Quran, then in response it was stated:

> *Say, 'Shall I inform you of (what is) worse than that as penalty (as per the Law of Requital) from Allah? (It is that of) those who incurred the curse of Allah and His Wrath...' (5:60)*

In other words, *La'nat* and *Ghadab* are two different states of punishment for deeds. Similarly, when Bani Israel adopted worship of the calf, they were told:

> *Indeed, those who took the calf (for worship) will obtain wrath from their Rabb and humiliation in the life of this world, and thus do We recompense the inventors (of falsehood). (7:152)*

From this it becomes evident that Allah's *Ghadab* is another term for the punishment of deeds. In this there is not even an iota of that emotional psyche which is found in human *Ghadab* i.e. anger. It is people themselves who invite this *Ghadab* of Allah by their own deeds and become deserving of it. Addressing Bani Israel, it is stated:

> *(Saying), 'Eat of the good things We have provided for your sustenance but commit no excess therein, lest My Wrath should justly descend on you: and those on whom descends My Wrath (Ghadab) do perish indeed.' (20:81)*

But when, having fallen into the trap of Samri[158] they adopted worship of the calf, Moses, witnessing this on his return, stated in anger:

> *...He said, 'O my people, did your Rabb not make you a good promise? Then, was the time (of its fulfillment) too long for you, or did you wish that wrath from your Rabb descend upon you, so you broke your promise to me?' (20:86)*

12.2   Who are Deserving of Allah's *Ghadab*?

The Quran has noted those deeds due to which Allah's *Ghadab* descends from the circumstances and conditions of past nations, and what the state of these nations becomes as a result of this. When the nation of Ad was invited by the messenger Hud towards the Oneness of Allah, they rejected it because of their rebellion, and began to say that the path on which our forefathers have been treading is right for us. At this Hud stated:

> *...punishment and wrath have already come upon you from your Rabb... (7:71)*

---

[158] *Samri* may have been an individual among the Bani Israel or may be a symbolic reference. (Ed)

And this *Ghadab* came down in such a form that:

> *...And We cut off the roots of those who rejected Our Signs... (7:72)*

Even the roots of this nation were severed. How are the roots of nations severed? When the penalty of the *Ghadab* of Allah falls on them, what does their state become? Regarding this, the Quran has explained it in very clear terms so that every nation can see for itself whether it is from among these condemned people or not. For example, when the collective crimes of Bani Israel increased beyond an extreme limit and there was no possibility remaining of their improving, and the time for the manifestation of the results of their deeds arrived, it was stated about them:

> *Shame is pitched over them (like a tent) wherever they are found, except when under a covenant (of protection) from Allah and from men; they draw on themselves wrath from Allah, and pitched over them is (the tent of) destitution...(3:112) See also (5:80, 2:61, 7:152)*

12.3   Allah's *Ghadab* due to Rejection of the Quran

Following the revelation of the Quran, this *Ghadab* descends because of rejection of the Quran, because the path on which man needs to tread to reach the intended destination can only be found through obedience of the Quran. Other than this, Allah's guidance is nowhere else. So those people who adopt other paths by leaving this guidance will surely head towards ruin and destruction – this is called Allah's *Ghadab*. It is stated about these people:

> *Miserable is the price for which they have sold their selfs, in that they deny (the revelation) which Allah has sent down, in insolent envy that Allah of His Grace should send it to any of His servants He pleases: thus have they drawn on themselves wrath upon wrath. And humiliating is the punishment of those who reject Eimaan. (2:90)*

This is because rejecting the Quran is in fact like disputing with Allah as to why He has declared only this to be the straight path (*Sirat e Mustaqueem*) which has been preserved in the Quran. Now it is apparent that the consequence of this kind of attitude of these people will be the same as that of the opponents of truth and reality. It is about these very people that it is stated:

> *But those who dispute concerning Allah after He has been accepted, futile is their dispute in the sight of their Rabb: on them will be a penalty terrible. (42:16)*

12.4 Recipients of Allah's *Ghadab* Omit the Duty of Forbidding Evil

The state of the nation which deserves Allah's *Ghadab* is such that they see each other immersed in evils but no-one forbids anyone from this. Promoting good and forbidding evil is a very vital duty. But when evils become so common in a nation that the society does not even consider evils to be evils, no-one even prohibits anyone, or moral courage becomes so weak that no-one can even pick up the courage to prohibit it, or hypocrisy increases to such an extent that in order to be popular (to be liked by all) man keeps agreeing with everyone, then at that time Allah's chastisement encircles that nation. When Allah's *Ghadab* descended on the Bani Israel, this had become their very condition. The Quran states:

Nor did they (usually) forbid one another the iniquities which they committed: evil indeed were the deeds which they did. (5:79)

12.5 Mutual Enmity

Not only this, but mutual enmity takes birth in this nation; they become thirsty for each other's blood. Due to their mutual differences, they resort to war and murder. All of this was done by Bani Israel and it is towards this that the attention of the Muslim Ummah is drawn by the Quran, that remember:

If a man kills a Momin intentionally, his recompense is hell, to abide therein (forever): And the wrath and the curse of Allah are upon him, and a dreadful penalty is prepared for him. (4:93)

12.6 Absconding from the Battlefield

It is not sufficient to merely be united and in agreement with one another, it is also essential to remain resolute and steadfast against the enemy. The nation which loses courage in the battlefield and takes flight is encompassed by Allah's punishment from all directions. This is the reason why the *Jamaat e Momineen* is told:

O you who have Eimaan! when you meet the Unbelievers in hostile array, never turn your backs to them. If any do turn his back to them on such a day - unless it be in a stratagem of war, or to retreat to a troop (of his own)- he draws on himself the wrath of Allah, and his abode is hell - an evil refuge (indeed)! (8:15-16)

This is because at such a time there is the fear of the entire nation being imprisoned in the *La'nat* (curse) of enslavement by others due to their cowardliness, and subjugation and enslavement is a very great *Ghadab* of Allah. Hence, when the

Momineen were given the glad tidings of victory in Makkah, then regarding those hypocrites and *Mushrikeen* of Makkah who were about to become subjects, the Quran stated:

And that He may punish the hypocrites, men and women, and the polytheists men and women, who imagine an evil opinion of Allah. On them is a round of evil: the wrath of Allah is on them: He has cursed them and got hell ready for them: and evil is it for a destination. (48:6)

The *Ghadab* of Allah is about to be manifested on them i.e. humiliation and disgrace is going to descend on them due to their deeds.

12.7   Friendship with the Condemned

Leaving aside being caught oneself in the wrath of Allah, even companionship with the condemned is dangerous. This is because just as by going near someone with leprosy there is the chance of being infected by germs, in the same way by befriending those people on whom the wrath of Allah has descended the human heart and mind becomes inclined to accept their infectious diseases. And those virtuous and pure abodes of the hearts which had the potential to house the *Rehmat* of Allah become graveyards of rotten and repulsive bones over which vultures hover and shriek. The Quran states:

O you who have Eimaan! Turn not (for friendship) to people on whom is the Wrath of Allah...(60:13) See also (58:14)

12.8   Rejecting Islam after Accepting It (*Irt'daad*)[159]

This was about friendship with those who are condemned and the *Kuffar*. But whoever having once treaded on the right path then leaves it, and adopts wrong paths, his end is absolutely clear. It is stated about them in Surah *An-Nahl*:

Anyone who, after accepting Eimaan in Allah, displays Kufr, except under compulsion, his heart remaining firm in Eimaan - but such as open their breast to Kufr, on them is wrath from Allah, and theirs will be a dreadful penalty. (16:106)

It is generally understood that only he adopts *Kufr* after *Eimaan* i.e. only he becomes a *Murtad* who openly announces his departure from Islam and adopts some other religion. Undoubtedly this is *Irt'daad*. But *Irt'daad* is not only confined to this. The Quran also tells us of those forms where an individual calling himself a Muslim becomes a *Mushrik*. Details of this will be found under the topic of

---

[159] *Irt'daad* - apostacy (47:25) (Ed)

Eimaan and *Shirk*. Here it is sufficient to say only this much, that we should not remain complacent thinking that since we call ourselves Muslims therefore Allah's *Ghadab* (wrath) cannot manifest on us no matter what we may do, because the ones who invite *Ghadab* are only those people who, leaving this religion, adopt some another religion. Remember! a *Momin* is only the one who lives his whole life precisely in accordance to the laws of Allah. The consequence of this kind of life is so clearly evident that there is no difficulty in distinguishing between these people and those who adopt some other path. Who is not aware of what the prosperities and deprivations of life are?

12.9   Life of a *Momin* and One Condemned Cannot be the Same

This is why it is stated that the lives of both of these cannot be alike:

Is the man who follows the good pleasure of Allah like the man who draws on himself the wrath of Allah, and whose abode is in hell? A woeful refuge! (3:162)

When these two cannot be the same, then it does not become difficult either to judge between them as to who is a *Momin* in the real sense and on whom is the wrath of Allah; who is favoured with His bounties and who has the wrath of Allah on him; who is on the straight path and who has lost his way. The life of a *Momin* is a life of distinction.

Every day we offer prayers in every *Rakat* of *Namaz* that O Allah! may we not tread on the path of those people who became deserving of Your wrath and condemnation. But we never pay attention to this fact as to whether our life is like those people who were showered with the favours and blessings of Allah, or is it like those who became engulfed in His wrath? The Quran has detailed the distinctive outlines of both kinds of life with such clarity that there is no difficulty in differentiating between the two. Hence, it is not at all difficult to determine this matter either, as to whether our life is the life of a favoured nation, or that of a condemned one.

To live life like that of a condemned nation while harbouring the desire for the successes and prosperities of a favoured nation, if this is not self-deception then what else is it? These are the kinds of prayers which are returned and thrown back in the face of the supplicant.

From the above discussion this truth becomes apparent to us that regarding the nation in which the selfs of the individuals have become developed i.e. the Divine attributes are manifesting in it:

1. The life of this nation will never be like those on whom the 'wrath of Allah' has descended.

2. That nation will be the possessor of such powers that it will be able to present with evidence the destructive effects of their deeds to those nations who are treading on the wrong path i.e. it will be able to punish them for their crimes, and in this way demonstrate the system of justice and fairness by its practical establishment in the world. This is called the establishment of the sovereignty of Allah and this is the system which is responsible for worldly peace.

13   *La'nat* (Deprivation from Allah's Bounty)

In the previous topic we mentioned the *Ghadab* of Allah as opposed to *In'aam*. This topic cannot be completed until *La'nat* as opposed to *Rehmat* is also not explained. A misunderstanding of the meaning of the word *La'nat* has created a great misconception among us. Non-Muslims complain that the Quran (Allah forbid) is full of profanity – 'the God of the Muslims tosses *La'nat* at *Kuffar*'. This misconception is based on the fact that we attribute the same meaning to the word *La'nat* as the one prevalent among us. Otherwise, if the correct meaning of this word is before us, then this matter cannot be a cause for complaint for anyone.[160]

The meaning of *La'nat* is to remove, to keep something afar - its meaning is absolutely clear. The individual whose self becomes developed, and the nation which lives its life according to the laws of Allah, benefit from the prosperities (Divine bounties) of life. Whoever lives life contrary to these laws remains far from these prosperities and becomes deprived of these; this is called the *La'nat* of Allah i.e. absence from His blessings and eminences, remoteness from His *Rehmat* and *Naimat*. And since being deprived of Allah's *Rehmat* is a very great misfortune, therefore in this respect *La'nat* is a curse.[161] Hence, when the word *La'nat* is used with reference to Allah, its meaning will be deprivation from His bounties, and when it is uttered from the direction of other than Allah, then its meaning will be of such a curse in which the meaning of misfortune and deprivation will be implied. Therefore, wherever in the Quran words synonymous to *La'nat* have been used, in them also there is the connotation of being afar and of deprivation. For example, it is stated about the people of Madyan:

As if they had never dwelt and flourished there! Ah! Behold! How the Madyan were removed (from sight) as were removed the Thamud! (11:95)

13.1   Being Denied Allah's *Na'ima*

Here the word used for annihilation is *Bo'd* which means being kept away from and deprived i.e. whoever has moved away from the *Rehmat* of Allah, his destruction is assured. About Satan the Quran states:

(The Pagans), leaving Him, call but upon female deities: They call but upon Satan the persistent rebel! Allah did curse him...(4:117-118)

---

[160] And this is not only confined to non-Muslims, some Muslims also ironically present this reason to justify their profanity.

[161] Here the word curse does not refer to a profanity but to an adverse outcome. (Ed)

184

The word *Mara'da* means being deprived, being without, therefore the meanings of Satan as *Mareed'un* designates the one who is deprived of goodness and obedience, just as barren sand is described as being devoid of vegetation because there is no sign of any greenery in it, and this is why its meaning is also to be without flora. *Shaja'ra Amra'do* means that tree on which there is no leaf. Hence, in the Quran the tree of *Zaqum* has also been called the tree of *Mal'un* i.e. the tree on which there is *La'nat* (17:60). And *Shaitan e Mal'un* has also been called *Shaitan e Rajeem* (15:34-35, 38:77). The meanings of *Rajeem* are also to be condemned and kept at a distance. That weapon which is thrown at a distance is also described as *Rajeem*. Hence, a catapult by which a stone is hurled at a great distance is called *Marjam*. In the same way the word *Soh'qa*[162] has been used in the meaning of *La'nat* (67:11). The meaning of the word *Soh'aq* is also that of a distance. The term *Makan e Saheeq*, which means a place far far away, has been used in the Quran.

From these explanations you will have seen that the meanings of the word *La'nat* and its synonyms are of being kept far away i.e. of causing to be deprived. And its meaning is clear i.e. those on whom there will be Allah's *La'nat* will be kept far from His bounties, in other words, will be kept deprived. From this you can judge what iota of hate or enmity or profanity is there in the use of this word? The difficulty here is that many words are used in their original language for some other meaning whereas in a different language some other sense is taken from them. In order to establish the correct meanings of the words of the Quran, one should look at the original Arabic language and the Quran itself, not the words of one's own language and their usage. (I have established the meanings of all the synonymous words of the Quran in this way in my *Lughat-ul-Quran*).

13.2   *La'nat* Occurs Due to the Law of Requital

As we have seen under the subject of *Ghadab*, Allah's *La'nat* does not rain down without a cause, rather it is a natural consequence of the wrong deeds of man i.e. this is a part of the Law of Requital itself. When the people of the Book used to criticise the Muslims about what this thing is which they have accepted as *Eimaan*, in response it was stated:

> Say: 'Shall I point out to you something much worse than this, (as judged) by the treatment it received from Allah'? Those who incurred the curse of Allah and His wrath...(5:60)

Thus Allah's *La'nat* is indeed another name for the punishment of deeds. In Surah *Al-Araf*, following the decisions on the Day of Judgment, there is mention of a

---

[162] The word *Soh'aq* also means far away. The word *Makan e Saheeq* has appeared in the Quran which means a place very far away.

dialogue between the denizens of hell and the inhabitants of paradise. In this, a crier addressing the denizens of hell, will proclaim:

> ...*The La'nat of Allah is on the wrong-doers; Those who would hinder (men) from the path of Allah and would seek in it something crooked: they were those who denied the Hereafter. (7:44-45)*

Almost identical words are quoted in (11:18-19). This means the *La'nat* of hell will be received in return for adopting a crooked path and hindering others from the straight path.

13.3   On Which Nations Does *La'nat* Rain Down?

By describing the state of affairs of past nations, the Quran has presented this reality before us as to the consequences of which crimes the *La'nat* of this world and the hereafter descended on these nations; and then also made this clear what is called *La'nat* of this world and what the *La'nat* of the hereafter will be. Referring to when the nation of Ad was destroyed by the *Azaab* (punishment) of Allah, the Quran states:

> *Such were the Ad People: they rejected the Signs of their Rabb; disobeyed His messengers; And followed the command of every powerful, obstinate transgressor. And they were pursued by a curse in this life, and on the Day of Judgment. Ah! Behold! for the Ad rejected their Rabb! Ah! Behold! removed (from sight) were Ad the people of Hud! (11:59-60)*

As with the people of Thamud, *La'nat* on the people of *Madyan* has been mentioned earlier (11:95). These same words have been used in verse (11:68) regarding the Thamud. The people of Pharaoh also had *La'nat* both in this world and in the hereafter (11:99, 28:42). It is stated about Bani Israel that:

> *But because of their breach of their covenant, We cursed them, and made their hearts grow hard...(5:13)*

After this a list of their crimes is detailed (5:13) and this was not just confined to Bani Israel - whichever nation breaks the covenant will receive this same punishment. Having a covenant with Allah means that once you have accepted *Eimaan* in Allah, then you made this pledge with Him that you will keep your life under the obedience of His laws. If, after this, you freed your life from His obedience, then this is breaking the covenant with Allah and practical disobedience of the covenant even if you keep claiming a thousand times with your tongue that you accept it. Bani Israel also never made this proclamation that we deny the existence of Allah:

But those who break the covenant of Allah, after having plighted their word thereto, and cut asunder those things which Allah has commanded to be joined, and work mischief in the land; on them is the curse; for them is the terrible abode. (13:25)

Another severe accusation has also been levelled against Bani Israel because of which they were made deserving of *La'nat* i.e.:

Nor did they forbid one another the iniquities which they committed: evil indeed were the deeds which they did. (5:79)

13.4   Mutual Distrust and Enmity is Allah's *La'nat*

Now let us examine what the details are of the *La'nat* mentioned above. The Quran states:

...Amongst them We[163] have placed enmity and hatred till the Day of Judgment... (5:64)

It was not only that the Jews had merely adopted a rebellious and mutinous attitude, they had converted Allah's Deen into a children's play park. There was no respect and value for it in their eyes; they used to ridicule it and mock it, and it is obvious that when some nation's scale of *Eimaan* and conduct sinks to such a depth, then how can they cultivate higher moral sentiments in their hearts? (4:46)

It is apparent that the pleasantries of life can be obtained by practically following the correct system of life, and the correct system of life cannot be found anywhere other than the Quran. Therefore, the nation which refuses to accept the truth of this system, or merely accepts it verbally but does not adopt it practically, remains deprived of these pleasantries. This fact has been brought forth in various places in the Quran (2:88-89, 4:47, 33:64-65).

Not only is it that the nation which completely avoids this system remains deprived of its pleasant effects, but even that nation which after having adopted it then abandons it will also face the same consequence (as is happening to us). Hence, it is stated in Surah *Al e Imran*:

How shall Allah Guide those who reject Eimaan after they accepted it and bore witness that the messenger was true and that clear signs had come unto them? but Allah guides not a people unjust. Of such the reward is that on them (rests) the curse of Allah, of His forces (angels), and of all mankind. (3:86-87)

---

[163] Here, Allah has related it to Himself – it means as per His laws. If a people do wrong, then they suffer these effects as a consequence. (Ed)

Allah's *La'nat* means to be deprived of those pleasures and prosperities which were attained through living life under the Divine system. After this the second form of living is that man, using intellect and reasoning alone, harnesses the forces of nature and in this way benefits from the conveniences of life for a while. But the nation treading on the path of a 'wrong religion' declares the world as being worthy of loathing and in this way remains deprived of the forces of nature as well, and this is the *La'nat* of *Malaika*. After this the third form is that even if there is no supremacy over the other nations of the world, then at least there should be equality with them, so that they can take advantage of those benefits which are generally available to mankind. But no-one respects this kind of humiliated and disgraced nation, and in this way they remain deprived even of those advantages which were available to them as ordinary human beings – this is the '*La'nat* of human beings'.

This is the outcome of that nation which having once treaded on the correct path of Deen, again adopts the wrong path. You may be searching for the signs of such a nation in the pages of history, but you do not require any quest or effort for this; just place a mirror in front and look into it and see your face - it will become evidently clear which nation it is that the Quran has referred to in these words.

After this the question which will surely arise is whether this deprivation and misery of ours will remain forever, or is there any possibility of escape from it? The Quran states that there is no reason to become despondent; if even now you abandon this wrong path and adopt the correct path of the Quran, then you can once again benefit from the bounties of life in this way:

> *Except for those that repent after that and make amends; for verily Allah is All Protecting, Raheem. (3:89)*

This means that when you bring about a change in your state, then Allah's other attribute will manifest itself. (Have you perceived what this means for apparently opposing attributes being present in the Divine Self?).

13.5 *La'nat* due to Denial of Truth

La'nat is not only the consequence of denial of truth, whoever buries reality, hides the truth, also remains deprived of bounties (2:159). According to the Quran, the meanings of *Eimaan* are that man, after having achieved conviction in the truth of the laws of Allah, should live his life under that system which is responsible for the implementation of these laws.[164] Obedience of this system is 'obedience of

---

[164] This is called the system of Allah which was first of all established by Rasul-ullah.

Allah and Rasul'. It is apparent from this that any action by members of this society which is the origin for any trouble (or damage) within the society, will be a very great crime. The Quran has termed this as wronging 'Allah and Rasul' and the consequence of this is stated to be deprivation of those bounties which were achieved through association with this system. The Quran states:

Those who annoy Allah and His Messenger - Allah has cursed them in this World and in the hereafter and has prepared for them a humiliating punishment. And those who annoy Momin men and women without any cause, bear (on themselves) a calumny and a glaring crime. (33:57-58)

13.6   *La'nat* for Killing a Momin

When *La'nat* is deserved for hurting the *Momineen*, then a severe crime such as the killing of a *Momin* can never remain without any consequences:

If a man kills a Momin intentionally, his recompense is hell, to abide therein (forever): And the wrath and the curse of Allah are upon him, and a dreadful penalty is prepared for him. (4:93)

This is because all of these are matters due to which turmoil is unleashed in the system of a nation, conflicts arise, and chaos is that evil for the eradication of which the Quran is revealed. This is that very accusation which is levelled against the *Kuffar* (47:22-23).

13.7   Slavery is a *La'nat*

In the previous topics it has been seen that power and authority are among the bounties of Allah. Hence, a life of subjugation and deprivation is Allah's *La'nat*. This is the reason why the Quran has declared the words '*Maghlub*'[165] and '*Mal'un*'[166] to have synonymous meanings (33:60-62). For example, when the Muslims were given the glad tidings of victory in Makkah, then regarding those *Kafireen* who were going to be subjugated, the Quran declared:

...On them is a round of evil: the wrath of Allah is on them...(48:6)

Not only a life of deprivation and misery in this world but a life of hell in the hereafter also, which is a life of *La'nat* in its own right (9:68, 40:52).

---

[165] *Maghlub* – means under the subjugation of another. (Ed)
[166] *Mal'un* – on whom is *La'nat*. (Ed)

13.8   Blind Obedience is a Cause for *La'nat*

After explaining these crimes (as a result of which there is deprivation from bounties), the Quran has drawn attention to that basic and fundamental crime which is the true root cause of all these crimes, and that crime is the practice of following behind others blindly instead of making use of one's own intellect and reasoning. Hence, the Quran has outlined the state of those nations entering hell in these words:

> He will say: 'Enter you in the company of the people who passed away before you - men and jinn - into the fire'. Every time a new people enters, it curses its sister-people (that went before), until they follow each other, all into the fire. Says the last about the first: 'Our Rabb! it is these that misled us: so give them a double penalty in the fire'. He will say: 'Doubled for all': but this you do not understand. Then the first will say to the last: 'See then! No advantage have you over us; so taste you of the penalty for all that you did'. (7:38-39)

This was that very matter which Abraham asserted in response to his people:

> And he said: 'For you, you have taken idols besides Allah, out of mutual love and regard between yourselves in this life; but on the Day of Judgment you shall disown each other and curse each other: and your abode will be the fire, and you shall have none to help you'. (29:25)

This means that this wrong path is not as a consequence of the use of intellect and reasoning, instead, you have only adopted it because you are friends of one another, and what one does, the other blindly begins to do. And this blind obedience takes root from this, that man begins to consider some people as lords in his mind, accepts them as his leaders, and then whatever he hears from them or whatever is passed to him in relation to them, he starts following with eyes closed. This conduct is a cause for the humiliation of humanity and when the truth becomes evident, then man himself accepts how misleading this conduct is. The intensity and emphasis with which the Quran has explained this will be detailed at another place. Here, consider only this much, how this conduct becomes deserving of Allah's *La'nat*. Another aspect of the life of the denizens of hell is presented in the Quran as follows:

> And they would say: 'Our Rabb! We obeyed our chiefs and our great ones, and they misled us as to the (right) Path. Our Rabb! Give them double penalty and curse them with a very great curse'! (33:67-68)

13.9   *La'nat* as a Result of Not Reflecting on the Quran

But by understanding this, do not satisfy yourself that these are the narratives of past nations – that these have nothing to do with us. The Quran has stated in very clear terms that those people who do not make use of intellect and reasoning in the Quran, and blindly follow the path on which a nation is treading, they remain deprived of those bounties which were acquired by following (the Quran) with the use of reasoning and comprehension:

> *Such are the men whom Allah has cursed for He has made them deaf and blinded their sight. Do they not then earnestly seek to understand the Quran, or are their hearts locked up by them? (47:23-24)*

Not reflecting on the Quran and not making use of one's eyes in its light - if this is not Allah's *La'nat* then what else is it? What! is there still any need to ask why we are disgraced?

14 *Qahhar*[167](Omnipotence)

Since the word *Qahar*[168] is also used in relation to the meanings of anger and rage, it was considered suitable therefore to include it in the same vein as *Ghadab* and *It'aab*. The meaning of *Qahar* is not anger and rage but is supremacy and authority. When the courtiers of Pharaoh complained that leaving Moses and his people free like this will result in them fomenting revolution, Pharaoh told them not to worry, I will deal with them:

Said the chiefs of Pharaoh's people: 'Will you leave Moses and his people, to spread mischief in the land, and to abandon you and your gods?' He said: 'Their male children will we slay; their females will we save alive; and we have over them complete power and authority.' (7:127)

From this it is apparent that the meaning of *Qahar* is supremacy, authority, power and control. But in order to understand the correct meaning of Allah's *Qahar* (and *Jabar*), it is important to show how these words were used among the Arabs. When a bone is broken then pieces of wood are placed above and below it and bound tightly, as a result the bone fuses after some days. This method of treatment is called *Jabar* i.e. that kind of power and force by the application of which (joined bones are not broken but) broken bones are joined together.

On the other hand, *Lahm un Maqhur'un* is the name of that meat which is softened by placing it over fire and in this way making it edible i.e. turning its hardness into softness through heat, so that it can be brought into correct usage. It is obvious that there is an element of both power and force in *Jabar* and *Qahar*. But ordinary men will use this force for conflict, therefore from their side *Jabar* and *Qahar* will be evil. But when this same force (*Jabar* and *Qahar*) is used from the direction of Allah (or from the direction of His system which will be responsible for the implementation of the Divine laws), its aim will be to make it better. Briefly, it can be understood that the meaning of *Qahar* (and *Jabar*) here will be to keep the rebellious forces within the grip of the laws. From this the meaning of *Qahiro*[169] (6:18) will be easily comprehended. The complete verse is as follows:

If Allah touches you with affliction (as per His laws), none can remove it but He; if He touches you with happiness (as per His laws), He has defined scales for everything. He is Supreme watching all His servants; and He is the Wise, acquainted with all things. (6:17-18)

---

[167] *Qahhar* – this is an attribute of Allah.
[168] This is the root of *Qahar* which means omnipotence. See *Lughat ul Quran*, Vol 2, pp 388-389. (Ed)
[169] *Qahiro* means the one who does *Qahar*.

Remember! there is no other possibility for man to counter the harm which reaches him through disobedience of the laws of Allah except by returning to His laws. This is the same condition for seeking good. This is because the scales of good and bad are established according to His laws, over which He has complete control. No individual can go outwith the grip of His laws; these encompass everything. But this supremacy of His is not that of tyranny and corruption - He is aware of every issue and His every decision is based on wisdom.

The matter is absolutely clear. The system of the universe is not functioning under blind forces; the effect of every deed in it is established according to His laws. If adversity falls on someone, then that too comes in recompense of his deeds according to the Law of Requital of Allah. And if the pleasantries of life are obtained, then their condition is also the same. Allah has established scales (laws) for these matters, and not only has He established laws, but He is so Sovereign and Omnipotent that His laws continuously carry on establishing their own respective results. Nothing in the universe is outwith the grip of these laws. If there was no law here or the grip of these laws was weak, then this system of the universe would turn upside down. Similarly, the law of Allah is functioning within the world of human beings, and He has established such forces which continue establishing the consequences of human deeds:

He is Omnipotent keeping watch over His servants, and He sets guardians over you...
(6:61)

Hence, the meanings of *Qahir* and *Qahhar* are being the Possessor of Supremacy and Authority, Owner of Absolute Sovereignty, above everyone, the One Who has no-one outwith His grip, and no law of another works other than His. This is why Yusuf had stated to his companions in the prison:

...are many gods differing among themselves better, or the One Allah, Supreme and Omnipotent? (12:39)

14.1   Owner of All Kinds of Authorities

This is because when every kind of control and authority belongs to Him, then how can there be different and separate 'gods'? In Surah *Ar-Ra'd* it is stated:

Say: 'Who is the Rabb of the heavens and the earth?' Say: '(It is) Allah'. Say: 'Do you then take protectors other than Him, such as have no power either for good or for harm to themselves? Say: 'Are the blind equal with those who see? Or the depths of darkness equal with light?' Or do they assign to Allah partners who have created as He has created, so that the creation seemed to them similar? Say: 'Allah is the Creator of all things'...(13:16)

O Rasul! ask these people Who is the Sustainer of the heavens and the earth? They say it is Allah: other than Him there is no other god. Then say to them, when He is the Sustainer, then why is it that you have created others as your god besides Him, who (leaving aside the provision of profit or loss to others) do not possess any authority to provide profit or loss to their own self. Say to them (when this is the state of affairs, then think for yourselves) can the one who sees and the one who is blind be the same? Can this be the case that darkness and light become equal, or is it that the gods professed by these people have also produced similar creations in the same way that Allah has created them, and in this way the matter became doubtful for them (i.e. that not only Allah but others can also become gods)? After these explanations the Quran states:

... Say! 'He is the One, the Supreme and Omnipotent'. (13:16)

In Surah *Al-Zumar* it is stated that Allah does not need progeny to help Him because He is Self-Sustaining (39:4) and alone and exercises control and authority over every matter. He has no need for any companion or supporter. In the verse after this it is stated that following the creation of the heavens and the earth, He set the system of the universe into motion on an exact scale. The alternations of day and night, the predetermined fate of the moon and the sun all manifest according to His authority and direction because He is Allah the Omnipotent and All-Preserving (39:5) and the provider of protection. In the same strain it is also stated in Surah *Sa'ad* that He is All-Powerful and Omnipotent and protecting (38:65-66). Dynamisms in the universe occur according to His law:

One day the Earth will be changed to a different Earth. And so will be heavens, and (men) will be marshalled forth, before Allah, the One Irresistible. (14:48)

In Surah *Al-Momin* it is stated:

The day whereon they will (all) come forth: not a single thing concerning them is hidden from Allah. Whose will be the dominion that Day? That of Allah, the One the Irresistible! (40:16)

This is the correct meaning of *Qahhar*, not the one which is commonly understood among us which leads the human mind immediately towards associating it with tyranny and oppression, brutality and cruelty. Allah is beyond this as stated by the Quran:

> *...the Rabb of Honour and Power! He is free from what they ascribe to Him.*
> *(37:180)*

From the above explanations it is evident that in a developed personality where on the one hand there are attributes of affinity and love, on the other hand there are also attributes of power and control, so that through them rebellious forces can be checked from causing upheaval. The system of justice in the world can be established through the hands of these kinds of nations.

This is that reality which Iqbal[170] has expressed in these words:

> *Firm, protective, visionary and mending,*
> *These four elements together make a Muslim.*

---

[170] M. Iqbal - *Zarb e Kaleem*, p53.

15   *Al-Jabbar ul Mutakabbir*[171]

As with *Qahhar*, the correct meaning of *Jabbar* is not generally comprehended among us. From this also the mind moves towards the meaning of the use of force and coaxing. And this is because the correct meanings of these words are hidden from our eyes. As has been explained under the previous topic, the meaning of *Jabbar* is to fix some problematic issue in such a way that force is made use of. For example, when a bone is broken it is tied suitably between two wooden splints as a result of which it knits together. This method of treatment is called *Jabbar*. Hence, that wood by which this bone is tied in this way is called *Jibbara-tun* and the bandage with which it is tied is called *Jabeera*. Therefore, *Jabbar* means that Being Who has tied up all the system of the universe within the power of His laws in such a way that nothing can move even an inch from its defined position, and in this grip there is not an iota of injustice or duress, rather it is completely based on wisdom and understanding and it is in order to make the system of the universe function on a pattern of balance. Hence, *Jabbar* also means that Being Who puts right every disorder; in this technique of treatment and reformation, control and authority is also included. When man lives life according to a wrong pattern then conflict will surely arise in his life. If he now wishes his own reformation, then he will have to tie himself up within the chains of the laws of Allah. He will have to bring the stream of life within the concrete shores of the confines and limits of Allah. After this his 'broken bones' will join together; his conflicted state will be reformed. This is the correct meaning of *Jabbar*. In the Quran this term has appeared only once for Allah (59:23).

15.1   Human Attribute of *Jabbariat*

But when this same attribute is referred to human beings who will use it to enact cruelty on the weak and subjugated, then this will be a flaw, because no human being has this right that he should make another human being his subject and submissive to him on the basis of power and might. Whoever does this will be called cruel and tyrannical and will be rebelling against the Divine law. Anyone adopting such a path will remain in loss and condemned. In Surah *Ibrahim* it is stated:

> *...and frustration was the lot of every powerful obstinate transgressor. (14:15)*

In Surah *Al-Momin* it is stated:

---

[171] The Exalted in ight Who puts things in order e.g. using a force to join and heal broken bones.

...Thus, does Allah, seal up every heart - of arrogant and obstinate transgressors.
(40:35)

But when these very same forces will be used to establish a system of justice and reform in the world, then these will become a model of the Divine attributes. This is the difference between the manifestation of power by a developed self and the use of force at an animal level.

15.2   *Al-Mutakabbir*

In the verse quoted above the word *Mutakabbir* has also appeared along with *Jabbar-un*. When this word is used for ordinary human beings then its meaning will be those people who, merely intoxicated by power and authority, consider themselves to be superior to other human beings, and in this way declare it to be their right to rule others. But when this same attribute is referred to Allah, then its meaning will be supremacy and sovereignty, and authority and greatness. The word *Al-Mutakabbir* has also appeared only once (with *Al-Jabbar-un*) in the Quran (59:23). It is stated in Surah *An-Nisa*:

For Allah is Most High, Great. (4:34)

In Surah *Al-Jathiyah* it is stated:

To Him be Greatness in the heavens and the earth: and He is Exalted in Power, Wise!
(45:37)

This is the greatness which will be apportioned to that *Jamaat* (Hizbullah) which will be responsible for the establishment of the system of Allah in the world, and in the personalities of whose members the Divine attributes will be reflected. This type of greatness will suit them, because the kind of greatness which the Quran has declared as flawed is that greatness which is devoid of truth. In Surah *Al-A'raf* it is stated:

Those who behave arrogantly on the earth in defiance of truth...(7:146)

Similarly, in Surah *Ha-Mim* (*Fussilat*) it is stated:

Now the Ad behaved arrogantly through the land, against truth and reason... (41:15)

Hence, the expression of greatness which is based on truth is not bad; this is the fundamental trait of that self in which there is the reflection of the Divine attributes. This greatness will be achieved as a result of producing constructive results in connection with benefits to mankind and this is the pattern of those individuals whose self has been developed.

16 *Al-Muntaqim – Zun-tiqaam*

In relation to the Divine attributes, from the point of view of the prevalent understanding among us of those words which lead to wrong meanings, one word among them is also '*Intiqaam*'. One attribute of Allah is *Zun-tiqaam* which is commonly translated as the 'revengeful one' and because of the prevalent meanings of being revengeful, the mind immediately thinks of anger and rage. This is because among us a shade of rage is definitely included in '*Intiqaam*' (revenge). But as we have noted under the topic of '*Ghadab*', Allah is far above the sentiments of anger and rage which are found among human beings. *Naqmun* means the middle part of a path. Hence, the meaning of *Intiqaam* will be that those animals which scatter away from the path should be gathered together and brought into the centre of the path again, so that they can tread in the right direction. It is apparent this also means that this is the consequence of wrong deeds according to the Law of Requital. Hence, when it is stated that Allah is *Zun-tiqaam* then this will mean that He punishes criminals for their deeds according to the Law of Requital.

16.1   The Law of Requital

After mentioning the rebellion and transgression of Pharaoh's people, it is stated:

> *So, We exacted retribution from them: We drowned them in the sea, because they rejected Our Signs and failed to take warning from them. (7:136) See also (43:55)*

In connection with the evil deeds of the criminals of past nations it is noted:

> *So We exacted retribution from them: now see what was the end of those who falsified! (43:25) See also (3:137)*

In another verse it is stated:

> *And who does more wrong than one to whom are recited the signs of his Rabb, and who then turns away therefrom? Verily from criminals We shall exact Retribution. (32:22)*

About the liars and deniers too of the era of Rasul-ullah it is stated:

> *...We shall be sure to exact retribution from them. (43:41)*

When the Law of Requital of Allah seizes then no-one can escape from its grip. This is the retribution of Allah:

> *One day We shall seize you with a mighty onslaught: We will indeed (then) exact Retribution! (44:16)*

He warns the criminals, but they do not take any advantage of this warning and remain rooted in their obstinacy and rebelliousness. After this, the penalty of their deeds confronts them and then no-one can free them from this grip of Allah's hell:

> *Truly strong is the grip of Your Rabb. (85:12)*

About the people of Lot it is stated:

> *And (Lot) did warn them of Our punishment, but they disputed about the warning. (54:36)*

This is the meaning of Allah's *Intiqaam*, and because of this very *Intiqaam* He is *Zun-tiqaam*:

> *Never think that Allah would fail his messengers in His promise: for Allah is Exalted in power - Allah is powerful in exacting retribution. (14:47) See also (3:4, 39:33-37)*

From these explanations it is clear that the meaning of Allah's *Intiqaam* is the destructive consequence of evil deeds according to the Law of Requital. This will also be the meaning of '*Intiqaam*' by the *Jamaat e Momineen* who will implement Allah's laws. Their *Intiqaam* will not be based on some personal grievance or enmity; instead their love and opposition will both be for the sake of 'Allah'. And the reality is that what is commonly called enmity will also carry the element of reformation among them. Amputating a gangrenous finger and throwing it away appears to be hard-hearted, but to the one whose eyes are on the good of the whole body, he knows that in this amputation and truncation the sentiment of kindness and compassion is also present. Details of these matters will be available under the topics of 'War and Jihad'[172]. Here, the aim is only to state that the *Intiqaam* of the servants of Allah, who reflect the Divine attributes within themselves, will also be to reform the system of humanity. In this there will be no personal sentiment of revenge and enmity hidden beneath it. This is because the nation establishing the Divine laws will, in truth, become the means of implementing 'Allah's *Intiqaam*' within human limits, and will not seek personal revenge. The power to forbid evil and to seize is the fundamental attribute of a developed self and this is its '*Intiqaam*'.

---

[172] See the chapter on War and Jihad in the book *Mairaj e Insaaniyat* by the author. (Ed)

17 Allah's Knowledge

If Allah is uninformed about the matters of His Own creation, then what sort of Allah can He be? This is why the description of Allah's knowledge is given in great detail and with great emphasis in the Quran. And the reality is that the coordination and harmonization, organisation and management of this system of the universe which leaves intellects awestruck, can be done only by this Being Who has complete and full knowledge of everything from a drop of water to the ocean, and from a tiny particle to the sun; such knowledge in which there is not an iota of guesswork or conjecture, speculation or doubt, sure knowledge and complete knowledge. Just as Allah's Self is the most complete, in the same way His knowledge is also the completest.

17.1   Knowledge of Everything of the Universe

The Quran has stated the comprehensiveness of Allah's knowledge in three words in such an all-inclusive way, that as the human intellect continues to ponder on it, it becomes entranced i.e.:

> *...and of all things He has complete knowledge.[173] (2:29)*

Sustainability and continuity are contained in the word *Aleem-un* i.e. not this, that sometimes He has knowledge and at other times He does not - rather, He has knowledge of everything at all times. These words are constantly repeated at various places in relation to different subjects with the aim of engraving them on man's heart; and in such a way that, if you cross reference these words in their respective verses in relation to different contexts, then this fact will automatically become evident as to how much the reiteration and emphasis of these was required. For example, see verses (2:231, 2:282, 21:81). In Surah *Al-Hadid* it is stated:

> *He is the First and the Last, the Evident and the Immanent: and He has full knowledge of all things. (57:3)*

This same fact is stated in alternative words as follows:

> *...My Rabb comprehends[174] in His knowledge all things...(6:80)*

---

[173] The three words in Arabic are (*Wa Ho'wa*) *BaeKullay Shay'an Aleem*. (Ed)
[174] The word used here is '*Wa'siya*' which includes the concept of vastness, abundance, power, encompassing everything. See *Lughat ul Quran*, Vol 2, pp 711-712. (Ed)

These words are also repeated in different ways at various places e.g. (7:89, 20:98, 40:7). The word *Wa'siya* (as used in the above verse 6:80) is explained in another verse in the following way:

> *... and that Allah comprehends, all things in (His) Knowledge. (65:12)*

At another place it is stated:

> *...and takes account of every single thing. (72:28)*

17.2 Knowledge of Every Atom in the Heavens and Earth

This was an overview. Details of this will be found in various places in the Quran. In Surah *Al e Imran* it is stated:

> *From Allah, verily nothing is hidden on earth or in the heavens. (3:5)*

The same has been reiterated in (14:38, 29:52, 35:38). At another place the Quran states:

> *... Who knows all the secrets in the heavens and the earth...(25:6) See also (5:97, 10:61, 34:3, 49:1)*

There is no living thing about whose affairs He is not aware:

> *...He knows the time and place of its definite abode and its temporary deposit: All is in a clear Book (of Allah's Knowledge). (11:6)*

17.3 Knowledge of the Manifestations of Nature

The changes which continually manifest in natural phenomena, and the manner in which every part of the system of the universe is engaged in carrying out its assigned duties - He has knowledge of it all:

> *He knows all that goes into the earth, and all that comes out thereof; all that comes down from the sky and all that ascends thereto, and He is Raheem and Ghafoor. (34:2)*

In Surah *Al-An'am* it is stated:

> *With Him are the keys of the unseen, the treasures that none knows but He. He knows whatever there is on the earth and in the sea. Not a leaf does fall but with His knowledge: there is not a grain in the darkness (or depths) of the earth, nor anything*

fresh or dry (green or withered) but is (inscribed) in a clear Book (of Allah's Knowledge). (6:59) See also (57:4)

17.4 *Eimaan* in Allah's Knowledge Has an Effect on Human Deeds

As has been already written, correct *Eimaan* in the Divine attributes specifically influences the practical life of man. For example, Allah is All-Knowing; He knows everything. Even if all human beings accept *Eimaan* in this Divine attribute, He will still be All-Knowing and All-Aware just as in that situation where not a single individual accepts *Eimaan* in this fact. He was even All-Knowing and All-Aware at that time when no human being existed. Hence, the *Eimaan* of a human being has no effect whatsoever on Allah's attributes, from this it is his own life which is reformed, his own point of view is transformed and a change occurs in his mentality.

If it is a strong conviction of some individual that, leaving aside the tangible deeds of life, Allah is cognisant of even the inner intentions of his heart, and together with this he also has *Eimaan* in this fact that no deed can remain without a consequence, then imagine to what extent his life will be under the obedience of the Divine laws. What a respectable and useful member of the community of humanity he will be; and if such an *Eimaan*, instead of being in a single individual, emerges in the heart of a *Jamaat*, and then moving forward from a *Jamaat*, the majority of mankind comes towards this, then this world which today has become an absolute hell due to a dearth of this *Eimaan*, will transform into such a paradise in which there will be an environment of peace and tranquility from every direction. This is that objective for which the Quran repeatedly brings Allah's attributes to our attention with so much repetition and clarity, and emphasises so greatly in having a strong *Eimaan* in them.

17.5 Knower of All Hidden and Manifest Deeds of Life

Regarding human deeds, the Quran informs us that whatever you hide and whatever you manifest, Allah is acquainted with all these matters:

Say: Whether you hide what is in your hearts or reveal it, Allah knows it all: He knows what is in the heavens, and what is on earth. And Allah has power over all things. (3:29)

In Surah *Al-Maida* it is stated:

...But Allah knows all that you reveal, and you conceal. (5:99)

In Surah *Al-Inaam* it is stated:

...He knows what you hide, and what you reveal, and He knows the (recompense) which you earn (by your deeds). (6:3) See also (24:29)

At another place it is stated:

...and knows what you hide and what you reveal. (27:25) See also (36:76)

In Surah *An-Nahl* it is stated:

And Allah does know what you conceal, and what you reveal. (16:19) See also (16:23)

In Surah *Taha* it is stated:

If you pronounce the word aloud, (it makes no difference): for verily He knows what is secret and what is yet more hidden. (20:7)

In Surah *An-Naml* it is stated:

And verily your Rabb knows all that their hearts do hide. As well as all that they reveal. (27:74) See also (28:69)

At another place it is stated:

...For He knows what is manifest and what is hidden. (87:7) See also (2:284, 21:110, 33:54, 43:80, 47:26)

17.6   Self-Deception of Hypocrites

When Allah's knowledge encompasses everything that is current and hidden, manifest and secret in this way then it is obvious how much self-deception those people are ensnared in who consider that they can say one thing with their tongues while concealing another thing in their hearts, and that no-one can have any knowledge of it. It is about these very ones that it is stated:

Know they not that Allah knows what they conceal and what they reveal? (2:77) See also (4:63, 5:61)

This is because Allah is aware of the secrets of the bosom and confidences of the hearts:

...Allah knows well all the secrets of the heart. (3:119) See also (5:7, 11:5, 29:10, 31:23, 39:7, 64:4))

And informed us in very clear words:

He knows of the tricks that deceive with the eyes, and all that the hearts conceal. (40:19) See also (50:16)

When He is cognisant of even the thoughts passing through the depths of the hearts, then how can the whisperings and secret trickeries of people be concealed from Him. The Quran states:

See you not that Allah does know (all) that is in the heavens and on earth? There is not a secret consultation between three, but He makes the fourth among them, nor between five but He makes the sixth, nor between fewer nor more, but He is in their midst, wheresoever they be: in the end will He tell them the truth of their conduct, on the Day of Judgment. For Allah has full knowledge of all things. (58:7)

Nothing can be concealed from Allah:

But Allah has full knowledge of what they secrete. (84:23)

17.7   Knowledge of Past and Future

This is not the place for a philosophical discussion about time. Here, it is sufficient to understand this much that since man's knowledge is finite, he has therefore divided the infinite system of time into past, present and future parts. But Allah's knowledge is infinite, hence for Him the question of past, present and future does not even arise. Before Him, (in the words of Iqbal[175]) 'there is an eternal now', hence:

...He knows what (appears to His creatures as) before or after or behind them... (2:255) See also (20:110, 21:28, 22:76)

This infinite knowledge of His is not only about existing human beings, but is also about all those human beings who have passed away, and of those who have yet to come:

To Us are known those of you who hasten forward, and those who lag behind.[176] (15:24)

---

[175] M. Iqbal, *The Reconstruction of Religious Thought in Islam.* (Ed)
[176] This verse is more related to those who advance in the path of Allah, and those who remain behind. (Ed)

As with time, the state of space is also such that some things are present in front of man (which he can see) and some are unseen, but in the 'eyes of Allah' there can be no difference between seen or unseen (present or absent), everything is in front of Him at all times. This fact is explained by the Quran in these three words[177]:

He knows the unseen as well as that which is manifest. (6:73) See also (23:92, 32:6, 39:46, 59:22, 62:8)

This is termed as knowing all in full (5:116, 9:78) i.e.:

...And He is witness to all things. (34:47)

17.8   Knowledge of the Unseen is Only for Allah

Allah possesses knowledge of the unseen and this knowledge is confined to His Being. Other than Allah, no-one else (on their own) possesses knowledge of the unseen. Rasul-ullah was told:

...The unseen is only for Allah...(10:20)

In another verse it is stated:

Say: None in the heavens or on earth, except Allah, knows what is hidden...(27:65)

After this, this is made clear that man is not aware of the knowledge of the unseen. In Surah *Maryam* it is stated, have you also seen that individual who denies our law and categorically declares that he will receive progeny and wealth:

Has he penetrated to the unseen, or has he taken a contract with (Allah) Most Gracious? (19:78)

Regarding the deniers, liars and objectors of the messenger-hood of Rasul-ullah, along with other matters the Quran also states this:

Or that the unseen is in their hands, and they write it down? (52:41) See also (53:35, 68:47)

Even the messengers themselves do not have knowledge of the unseen. Noah said to his people:

---

[177] The All-Knowing, the Unseen, the Witness. (Ed)

I tell you not that with me are the treasures of Allah, nor do I know what is hidden…
(11:31)

When the people of Hud demanded that you bring forward the punishment about which you are frightening us, he stated:

He said: the knowledge (of when it will come) is only with Allah…(46:23)

Rasul-ullah himself accepted that knowledge of the unseen is not with anyone except Allah:

Say: I tell you not that with me are the treasures of Allah, nor do I know what is hidden…(6:50)

In another verse it is stated:

They ask you about the (final) hour - when will be its appointed time? Say: The knowledge thereof is with my Rabb (alone)…(7:187)

Hypocrites were those people who had one thing in their heart and something different on their lips. They used to remain intermingled with the Muslims and used to also come into the presence of Rasul-ullah. The Quran states about them:

Or do those in whose hearts is a disease, think that Allah will not bring to light all their rancour? Had We so willed, We could have shown them up to you, and you would have known them by their marks: but surely you will know them by the tone of their speech! And Allah knows all that you do. (47:29-30)

The Quran states, not only about Rasul-ullah, but also about all the *Anbiya*:

One day will Allah gather the messengers together, and ask: 'What was the response you received (from men to your teaching)?' They will say: 'We have no knowledge: it is You Who knows in full all that is hidden.' (5:109)

17.9   *Wahi* is Related to the Unseen

The lack of knowledge of the messengers of Allah about the unseen was due to their status as human beings. The revelation which was received from Allah was based on unseen knowledge i.e. no human being could know these facts based on his personal knowledge. This is that unseen (*Wahi*) about which the Quran states:

He (alone) knows the unseen, nor does He make any one acquainted with His mysteries, except a messenger whom He has chosen: and then He makes a band of watchers march before him and behind him (to safeguard His revelation). (72:26-27) See also (3:179)

From this it is clear that knowledge of the unseen of the messenger is a part of the *Wahi* which is sent to him and is not outwith it. On this basis, whatever was given to Rasul-ullah in relation to unseen knowledge is preserved within the Quran.

The narratives of past nations and details of the messengers of Allah from the past which are noted in the Quran are based on this unseen knowledge. For example, in relation to the narrative of Maryam, it is stated:

This is part of the tidings of the things unseen, which We reveal unto you by inspiration...(3:44)

After detailing the story of Noah, it is stated:

Such are some of the stories of the unseen, which We have revealed unto you: before this, neither you nor your people knew them...(11:49)

The same is stated in the narrative of Yusuf that 'this is from among the facts of the unseen which are being revealed upon you' (12:102).

17.10   False Gods Have no Knowledge of the Unseen

Other than through *Wahi* no-one possesses knowledge of the unseen, whether they are ordinary human beings or 'gods' created by men. In fact, regarding these false gods[178] it is specifically stated that they have no knowledge about anything, even though people worship them and make them their intermediaries because (in their assumption) they possess knowledge of the unseen due to their 'status of being courtiers in the Divine court':

They serve, besides Allah, things that hurt them not nor profit them, and they say: 'These are our intercessors with Allah.' Say: 'Do you indeed inform Allah of something He knows not, in the heavens or on earth?' Glory to Him! and far is He above the partners they ascribe (to Him)! (10:18) See also (13:33)

Their status is actually such that they do not even know this much as to when they are going to be resurrected after death:

---

[178] Other than Allah, every god is false (*Batil*).

Say: None in the heavens or on earth, except Allah, knows what is hidden: nor can they perceive when they shall be raised up. (27:65)

Among these 'false gods' are included all those *Pirs*, *Fakirs*, holy men, saints etc. about whom their devotees state (we do not worship them but) that they possess knowledge of the unseen, not only during their lifetimes but even after their death – this belief is against the Quran. We have seen in previous pages that, according to the Quran:

(1) Other than Allah no-one else possesses knowledge of the unseen and;
(2) Whatever amount of knowledge about the unseen Allah needed to pass on to mankind, He passed it on through *Wahi* via the messengers.

This process of *Wahi* ended on Rasul-ullah, hence, no individual can possess knowledge of the unseen (no matter how near to Allah he may be considered to be). Whoever claims this, is in reality claiming messenger-hood (receiving *Wahi* from Allah), regardless what name he gives to it e.g. *Kashf, Alhaam, Muhaddassiat, Basharaat* etc.[179] Whoever holds this belief that a certain elderly saint has knowledge of the unseen, is accepting the continuation of messenger-hood after its cessation, which is a blatant opposition of the Quran. The state of man is such that he cannot even say with certainty whether the consequence of some matter will be favourable for him or a loss. Hence, in this connection the Quran states:

...But it is possible that you dislike a thing which is good for you, and that you love a thing which is bad for you. But Allah knows, and you know not. (2:216)

This is because man has been given very little knowledge as compared to the knowledge of Allah:

... of knowledge it is only a little that is communicated to you (O men!). (17:85)

At this point it is important to comprehend another reality also. This system of the universe is functioning according to the laws established by Allah. One part of these are known as the laws of nature. Man can obtain knowledge about these laws, and it is now apparent that:

(1) If some matter has to be according to some procedure and law and;
(2) If some person has knowledge of this law,

then he can tell in advance how some event will turn out. It is obvious that this cannot be called knowledge of the unseen - it will be called knowledge of the law e.g. experts on the laws governing the sun, moon and rotation of the earth can tell

---

[179] These are the various methods claimed by which to obtain knowledge of the unseen. (Ed)

hundreds of years in advance when there will be an eclipse of the sun, moon or earth; how big this will be and how long it will last. And in this 'forecast' of theirs there will not be the slightest variation. This will not be called knowledge of the unseen but will be called a consequence of the knowledge of the laws governing the solar system.

But this type of 'forecasting' will be able to be carried out about those things of the universe which have not been given any kind of freedom to choose and intent. Such a claim can never be made about something which has the freedom to choose e.g. a scientist will forecast when there will be a solar eclipse, but even if there are ten such scientists gathered all together, they will not be able to tell where a fly sitting in front of them on a table is going to land again.

And when they cannot even forecast this small matter about the future of a fly, then who can forecast anything about the future of a possessor of freedom to choose and intent, such as a human being? The knowledge of this cannot belong to anyone other than Allah.

But in some places in the Quran such a technique of expression has been employed by which a superficially thinking individual can harbour a passing doubt in his heart that Allah does not possess knowledge (Allah forbid) of the true state of affairs. These are those places where it is stated that We have done this in this way so that We can know (*Lae-Nalama*) what each among you is like.

On similar lines in which it is stated that We have done it like this, *Lae Nablu'wannakum* (which is commonly translated as) so that We test you, from this the thought also arises, does Allah not know the truth of the matter that He wishes to test man?

This is, in reality, another way to state that 'Allah did it like this so that this reality can emerge as to what will be your reaction, how much strength has been acquired within you, how much development has taken place in your potentials, how much your self has been realised'.

'*Ibtala*' means to manifest the real state of something. The purpose of human life is for the self of a human being to become developed. In the world different situations appear before man. At these junctures man can see to what extent his self has become developed. The level to which his self has become developed will be the same extent to which he will be able to confront these situations. This is what the Quran has called *Lae-Nalama* at some places and *Lae Nablu-wanna-kum* etc. at other places. The correct meaning of these words is: 'so that this truth becomes evident that…'. From this the matter becomes unequivocally clear that by 'testing' this does not mean that Allah is not knowledgeable of their deeds; He knows full well their deeds. The purpose of this is that the reality becomes evident both to them and to others about how much strength and perseverance is in them.

17.11   Meaning of *Lae-Nalama*

From the above explanations this reality has become apparent to us that Allah possesses knowledge of both the seen and unseen. He is acquainted with even the thoughts which pass through the depths of the heart. There is not an atom in this universe about which He does not have complete knowledge. Hence, the verses in which words such as *Lae-Nalama* appear do not mean that Allah wishes to gain knowledge about these matters. The purpose of these is to make reality clear and manifest. For example, it is stated in Surah *Saba*:

But (Iblees[180]) had no authority over them, except that We might differentiate the man who has Eimaan in the Hereafter from him who is in doubt concerning it: and your Rabb does watch over all things. (34:21)

The meaning of '*Lae-Nalama*' is so that We can differentiate, inform by separating, so that this fact becomes evident as to who has *Eimaan* in the hereafter and who doubts it. With these meanings the aim becomes completely clear. When the command was given regarding possession of the *Qibla* (Makkah), the purpose for this was given as:

... and We appointed the Qibla to which you are used, only to test those who followed the Messenger from those who would turn on their heels...(2:143)

In order to stop tyranny and subjugation and for the establishment of the Divine order, it was stated in relation to the wars which the Muslims were obliged to fight, that even if you face defeat somewhere, this is not something to fear:

...Such days (of varying fortunes) We give to men and men by turns: that Allah may know those that have Eimaan, and that He may take to Himself from your ranks witnesses (to Truth). And Allah loves not those that do wrong. (3:140)

In Surah *At-Tauba* it is stated:

Or think you that you shall be abandoned, as though Allah did not know those among you who strive with might and main, and take none for friends and protectors except Allah, His Messenger, and the Momineen? But Allah is well-acquainted with (all) that you do. (9:16)

---

[180] *Iblees* – human desires and emotions which prevent him from coming towards the Quranic guidance. For more details see *Lughat ul Quran*, Vol. I, pp 182-184.

The last part of this verse is telling us clearly that the purpose of providing such opportunities is to manifest the strength of *Eimaan* of these people, otherwise what matter is there that Allah is not aware of? In a verse of Surah *Muhammad* this fact is further clarified:

And We shall provide such opportunities until it becomes clear to those among you who strive their utmost and persevere in patience; and We shall surely make your real state manifestly clear. (47:31)

The verse which comes before this states '…and Allah is completely aware of your deeds' (47:30). In Surah *Al-Hadid* it is stated that We have sent the messenger, Books, and sharp-edged swords along with them, so that:

*…that Allah may test who it is that will help, unseen, Him and His messengers…
(57:25)*

As a result of this the hypocrisy of the hypocrites becomes openly manifest. *Momin* and hypocrite become separated and differentiated (3:166-167). The truthful one and the liar become recognisable (29:11). This is the purpose of defining the limits of Allah and the differentiation between *Halal* and *Haram* (5:95).

From this it is clear what the true meaning of this part is, that 'Allah can know what each among you is like'. Elucidation of this will be found in this verse of Surah *Anfal* in which it is stated about the prisoners of war that if you prove by your behaviour that you are no longer inclined to create trouble, but instead desire peace and reconciliation, then no kind of danger will reach you - instead you will have much to gain:

O Nabi! say to those who are captives in your hands: 'If Allah finds any good in your hearts, He will give you something better than what has been taken from you, and He will provide protection…(8:70)

Here also the aim is to say this, that if you can prove by your conduct that your intention is pure, then you will receive all kinds of protection and amenities, although Allah knows all. He knows who is hiding what in his heart:

…Well does He know what you are intent upon…(24:64)

He also knows who the denier is (69:49), who is the troublemaker, and who is righteous (2:220). He has knowledge of who is following His guidance and who is misguided:

Your Rabb knows best who strays from His way: He knows best who they are that receive His guidance. (6:117) See also (53:30-32, 68:7).

17.12   Omniscient, All-Knowing, All-Seeing and All-Hearing

As has been written previously, *Eimaan* in the knowledge of Allah exerts a great influence on our deeds. Allah also has knowledge of those things regarding which we are certain that no-one else in the world is aware of other than ourselves; this is because He is Omniscient. He is also aware of those deeds and circumstances of ours which we do not tell anyone else about - this is because he is All-Knowing. He is also watching us at those times when we think that no-one is watching us - this is because He is All-Seeing. He also listens to those secret whispers of ours about which we have self-satisfaction that no-one hears them - because He is All-Hearing. Wherever we may be, He is with us:

...And He is with you wheresoever you may be[181]. And Allah sees well all that you do. (57:4)

Whatever righteous deed you do, Allah is aware of it (2:197). And whatever you spend in His path, openly or secretly, He has full knowledge of it (2:215, 2:270-271, 2:273, 3:92). He is aware of not only righteous deeds but every kind of deed:

...For Allah is not unmindful of what you do. (2:85) See also (35:8, 2:95, 16:91, 42:25, 13:42, 29:45, 47:30)

It has been noted repeatedly in the Quran that Allah is *Aleem*; this has been mentioned nearly one hundred and twelve times. Similarly, His being All-Seeing is referred to at many places:

...and know that Allah sees well what you do. (2:233) See also (2:96, 2:237, 2:265, 3:163, 11:112, 41:40, 49:18, 57:4)

This is an error of judgment on the part of man that he thinks that no-one is watching him:

Thinks he that none beholds him? (90:7)

What, does man think that no-one is watching him, though the reality is that Allah watches all his servants (3:20). This fact has been mentioned at nearly forty places. At some places this same fact has been noted using the word *Khabeer* (being aware):

---

[181] We have to ensure that we are with Him i.e. through the Quran i.e. being conscious of this fact all the time. (Ed)

> *...And Allah is well acquainted with what you do. (2:234) See also (2:271, 3:153, 11:111, 27:88, 58:13)*

This has been reiterated about thirty-six times.

Then, in the same way that He watches everything, He also listens to every word, no matter in what solitude it is uttered:

> *Say: 'My Rabb knows (every) word (spoken) in the heavens and on earth: He is the One that hears and knows (all things).' (21:4)*

He is All-Hearing and All-Seeing (58:1, 22:61). This has been reiterated at least forty-two times.

17.13   The Law of Requital

When this is the state of the expanse of Allah's knowledge, then which matter can be concealed from Him? As far as man is concerned, the meaning of Allah being Omniscient and All-Hearing is that there can be no kind of omission and error in the working of the Law of Requital. The consequence of every good and bad deed (no matter how miniscule it may be) will appear before man:

> *Then shall anyone who has done an atom's weight of good, see it! And anyone who has done an atom's weight of evil, shall see it. (99:7-8)*

This is the truth and state of knowledge of the most complete Being (Allah). In the same way that that Being is infinite, similarly, His knowledge is also infinite. It is evident now that the knowledge of that individual who develops his self according to the criteria set by the attributes of Allah will also keep multiplying along with the development of his self. This is the reason that the Quran has declared the *Momineen* to be holders of knowledge and vision, and possessors of intellect and foresight. On the other hand, it has declared in clear terms that those people who do not make use of knowledge and intellect are inhabitants of hell. They live life at the animal level - they are the worst of creation (8:22). This is because the fundamental difference between man and animals is only that of the self. Hence, those human beings whose self remains dormant and undeveloped never even rise to the level of being human.

It is evident from this how knowledgeable, visionary, hearing and perceptive that society will be which takes on the responsibility for the establishment of the Divine system. This was that fact towards which that old lady inhabiting an area of Syria had drawn the attention of the Caliph Umer, when in reply to his question as to whether she had passed the information of her problems on to the Caliph, she replied that if the Caliph cannot make arrangements to remain aware of the circumstances of every member of his state, then he has no right to establish rule in the name of Allah the Omniscient.

By Caliph (or *Ameer ul Momineen*) is meant that member of the *Jamaat e Momineen* whose self has attained the highest development among them. The *Jamaat e Momineen* itself consists of those individuals who are 'coloured in the colours of the attributes of Allah' i.e. who are (within human limits) *Aleem, Khabeer, Samee* and *Baseer*.[182]

---

[182] *Aleem* -All-Knowing, *Khabeer* - All-Aware, *Samee* - All-Hearing, *Baseer* - All-Seeing. (Ed)

18   *Qudrat*

Qadrun means to make an estimate. In general terms, estimation and the application of scales is called procedure and law. This means that the management and organisation of the universe is being conducted according to those laws which have been established by Allah. A law is not the name of some tangible force. It is a principle or formula according to which a scheme functions and leads to some outcome. It is obvious that in order to make some law or principle lead to a consequence there is need for a force. If there is no implementing power behind a law, then that law possesses no meaning. The balance and perfection with which the Divine laws are in operation in the universe makes it clear that the force which is working behind them is complete and exalted. This Divine power is termed force at some places and *Qudrat* at other places. The word *Qudrat* points to this reality that the power of Allah (Allah forbid) is not the power of a tyrannical dictator which works blindly but is the power of One Who has absolute wisdom which is utilised in making His laws produce results. In Surah *Ad-Dariyat* it is stated:

For Allah is He Who gives (all) Sustenance, Possessor of Power, Steadfast. (51:58)

This is why the Quran enjoins not to associate anyone with Him[183] because since every kind of power is with Him alone, then how can anyone be an associate and share with Him?

Yet there are men who take others besides Allah, as equal (with Allah): They love[184] them as they should love Allah. But those of Eimaan are overflowing in their love for Allah. If only the unrighteous could see, behold, they would see the penalty: that to Allah belongs all power, and Allah (His Law) is strict in punishment. (2:165)

Here, it is stated that all power belongs to Allah alone. In Surah *Al-Kahf* it is stated:

...There is no power but with Allah...(18:39)

---

[183] The Quran places repeated emphasis on this important matter of knowing the truth and then having *Eimaan* in it. It is an important issue of the human belief system that we must not believe in something which is not true, no matter how much we are convinced of its being the 'truth' – if we fail to do this, then our self will not be the same as the one created through *Eimaan* as per the Quran e.g. (2:177). For example, the concept of Allah put forward by the Quran is evidence-based fact, and *Eimaan* in this is not the same as belief in the concept of gods prevalent among various religions as discussed earlier in this book. (Ed)

[184] The meaning of love here means obedience.

18.1   Omnipotent (Possessing Absolute Power)

At other places the word *Qadirun* appears:

See they (who deny the hereafter as noted in 17:98) not that Allah, Who created the heavens and the earth, has power to create the like of them? ... (17:99)

In Surah *Ya-sin* it is stated:

Is not He Who created the heavens and the earth able to create the like thereof? Yea, indeed! for He is the Creator Supreme, of Skill and Knowledge! (36:81)

It is not that He has become weary following the creation of the heavens and the earth that He cannot recreate these things, or that after their death He cannot bring human beings back to life again:

See they not that Allah, Who created the heavens and the earth, and never wearied with their creation, is able to give life to the dead? Yea, verily He has power over all things. (46:33)

18.2   Power to Give Life Again

For the All-Powerful One Who has brought the system of the universe into existence from nothing, how can it be difficult for Him to give life again? He possesses power over every matter:

Say: Travel through the earth and see how Allah did originate creation; so will Allah produce a later creation: for Allah has power over all things. (29:20)

In Surah *Al-Qiyamah* it is stated that the Allah Who created man from an infinitesimal thing:

Has not He the power to give life to the dead? (75:40)

In Surah *At-Tariq* it is stated:

Surely (Allah) is able to bring him back (to life)! (86:8)

So *Qadir* that if He wished, every atom of the human body will be brought back:

Nay, We are able to put together in perfect order the very tips of his fingers. (75:4)

If He desires, He can erase mankind from the face of the earth and bring another creation in their place:

If it were His will, He could destroy you, O mankind, and create another race; for He has power to do this. (4:133)

After rejecting the belief of the divinity of Christ, it is stated:

In blasphemy indeed are those that say Allah is Christ the son of Mary. Say: Who then has the least power against Allah, if His will were to destroy Christ the son of Mary, his mother, and all - everyone that is on the earth? For to Allah belongs the dominion of the heavens and the earth, and all that is between. He creates as per His Mashe'at. For Allah has power over all things. (5:17)

18.3   Control Over the Source of Life

And this is very easy. We do not need to go far – just take water for instance on which life is so dependent. If He changes the nature and property of water or changes its existing process, then see how in place of life, death ensues everywhere!

And We send down water from the sky according to (due) measure, and We cause it to soak in the soil; and We certainly are able to drain it off (with ease). (23:18)

This is because the system of the heavens and the earth is functioning under His *Amr*, the laws of nature are the manifestation of His Will:

Allah is He Who created seven (numerous) firmaments and of the earth a similar number. Through the midst of them (all) descends His command: that you may know that Allah has power over all things, and that Allah comprehends, all things in (His) Knowledge. (65:12)

18.4   Control Over the Replacing of Nations

In the same way that His law of life in the manifestation of nature is functioning and continuing, similar laws are also functioning in the fate of nations and countries. The rise and fall of nations, their life and death, and their change and replacement, all takes place under the domain of these very laws:

… We can certainly substitute for them better (men) than they; And We are not to be defeated (in Our Plan). (70:40-41)

Because the laws according to which all this takes place were established according to the *Mashe'at* of Allah, this is why it is stated at another place that acquiring government or losing it is based on Allah's *Mashe'at*. In other words, all this happens as a result of those laws which He has put in place according to His *Mashe'at*.

Say: O Allah! Lord of Power (And Rule), You give power to whom You Will (as per Your law) and You take away power from whom You Will. You bestow with honour whom You Will and You bring down whom You Will (as per Your Mashe'at). In Your hand is all command. Verily, over all things You have power. (3:26)

O Allah, You are the Only Sovereign and authority of the universe. The acquisition and loss of government, receiving power or humiliation, all takes place according to Your law of *Mashe'at*. The source of every kind of authority is in Your Hand; nothing lies outwith Your sovereignty.

He possesses power over that nation which defies His established laws to bring destruction on it from 'above and below' according to His Law of Requital:

Say: He has power to send calamities on you, from above and below, or to cover you with confusion in party strife, giving you a taste of mutual vengeance - each from the other. See how We explain the signs by various (symbols); that they may understand. (6:65)

It was this type of hell of destruction and ruin which descended on the opponents of Islam (the Quraysh of Makkah) through the hands of Rasul-ullah and his *Jamaat*. Regarding this, the messenger was told:

And We are certainly able to show you (in fulfilment) that against which they are warned. (23:95) See also (43:42)

This was that 'sign of Allah' for which these people were becoming so desperate and anxious:

They say: 'Why is not a sign sent down to him from his Rabb?' Say: Allah has certainly power to send down a sign: but most of them understand not. (6:37)

This is the very law for the rise and fall of nations. This was the law of falsifying the signs of Allah under which the destruction of previous nations happened and even today, under this same law, the stars of fortune of worldly nations are formed and destroyed. According to this law, when the effects and consequences of its deeds of life descend on some nation, then no power in the world can save them from their effects. This is because the grip of Allah is the grip of a Being Who possesses power and authority, not the grip of one who is weak and frail from which one is able to escape:

The (people) rejected all Our Signs; but We seized them with such penalty (as comes) from One Exalted in Power, able to carry out His Will. (54:42)

In contrast to those who deny, there are blessings of His mercies for the righteous from this same All-Powerful Allah:

As to the righteous, they will be in the midst of gardens and rivers, In an assembly of truth, in the presence of a Sovereign Omnipotent. (54:54-55)

Therefore, obtaining blessings and favours, or these being snatched away, is according to the law of this same Omnipotent Allah:

...it is (only) Allah who prevails over all things. (18:45)

18.5   Correct Meaning of *Ila'ae*

In the Quran, the word *Ila'ae* has also been used for the manifestations and displays of nature by Allah, which is commonly translated as a '*Naimat*' (bounty). Hence in Surah *Ar-Rehman* the translation which will be commonly found is, for example:

Then which of the favours of your Rabb will you deny? (55:13)

There is no doubt that this word is also used for favours, but in the Arabic language *Ila'ae* is also used in the meaning of *Qudrat*. Hence, Ibne Jareer Tabri has written its meaning as *Qudrat*.[185] And regarding the verse on the birth of Jinns from fire, Imam Razi has written that *Ila'ae* means *Qudrat*.[186] Therefore, at other places in the Quran where this word has also appeared, apart from Surah *Ar-Rehman*, its meaning as *Qudrat* rather than *Naimat* (favour) appears more suitable. In Surah *Al-Araf*, where the messenger Hud stated to his people that Allah has made them heirs after the people of Noah and provided strength and prosperity to their generation, after this the Quran states:

...Call in remembrance the power from Allah: so that you may prosper. (7:69)

A little further on, when the messenger Saleh addressed his people to remind them about the time Allah made them heirs after the people of Ad and settled them in this land in such a way that you construct palaces in the meadows and make castles by carving the mountains, after this it is again stated:

...so bring to remembrance the power from Allah...(7:74)

---

[185] *Tafseer Ibne Jareer*, Vol. 27
[186] *Tafseer Kabeer*, Vol. 8

In Surah *An-Najm*, in connection with the destruction and ruin of former nations, it is mentioned that Allah overturned their habitations rising above the face of the earth, and His punishment encircled these dwellings:

> *Then which of the powers of your Rabb, (O man,) will you dispute about? This is a warner, of the (series of) warners of old. (53:55-56)*

It is also clear from these verses that there is a need here to mention the power of Allah, not a reference to the favours of Allah.

From the above explanations we have seen that a complete Self possesses complete power. Hence, the degree to which a human self keeps developing will result in a corresponding increase in its powers. The manifestation of a self is through power but these powers of his are not that of a sandstorm or a hurricane which carry on causing destruction blindly. These forces remain confined within the bounds of law and procedure and are employed in the development of humanity. To mete out punishment to criminals for their crimes is also one aspect of the development of humanity. This is because if destructive forces are not checked in the world then development becomes impossible. The Quran wishes to establish such a society in which the selfs of all individuals are developing, and their energies are utilised for the welfare and growth of mankind. These are the ones whom it proclaims as the balanced Ummah and the righteous Ummah. Due to the absence of this Ummah, the world today is becoming an abode of hell.

18.6 *Taqdeer* (Destiny)

The root of the word *Taqdeer* is also from *Q-D-R* from which the word *Qudrat* is derived. In this respect, I had originally included a chapter on *Taqdeer* in the first edition of this book. Later, I felt that the subject of *Taqdeer* is so big and the problem is so complicated that it cannot be explained in any book cursorily, for this it needs a book in its own right. Consequently, I wrote a book on the problem of *Taqdeer* which is published under the title '*Kitab ul Taqdeer*' (The Book of Destiny). Due to the existence of this book, there is no need now for this chapter whose connection was with the issue of *Taqdeer* and *Mashe'at*. Because of this, it has been deleted from this book. Those readers who are interested in the problem of *Taqdeer* and desire to understand it in detail should read this book i.e. *Kitab ul Taqdeer*.

19   *Arsh* and *Kursi* (Throne and Sovereignty)

To express the sovereignty and supremacy, control and authority of Allah, the word *Arsh* also appears in the Quran. The literal meaning of *Arsh* is a roof:

How many populations have We destroyed, which were given to wrong doing? They tumbled down on their roofs (Arsh). And how many wells are lying idle and neglected, and castles lofty and well-built? (22:45)

This word is also used in relation to every lofty building or railing etc. built around the rooftops of tall buildings:

And your Rabb taught bee to build its cells in hills, on trees, and in (men's) habitations (Arsh). (16:68)

This word is also generally used to mean the seat of government. In the story of Yusuf, it is stated that when his parents arrived:

And he raised his parents high on the throne…(12:100)

Mention of the throne of government of the Queen of Saba has appeared in the Quran in these words:

…and she has a magnificent throne. (27:23) See also (27:38-41)

Hence the word *Arsh* is used for control, authority, government etc. In modern times, its meaning can be interpreted suitably through the word 'control', all this is encompassed in 'control'.

The other word is *Kursi*. Its meaning is reality and foundation, but it is also used to mean supremacy and authority, as well as knowledge.

19.1   Meaning of Allah's *Arsh* (Throne)

Both of these words have been used in reference to Allah's control and sovereignty, and vastness of knowledge. For example, in Surah *Al-Mominoon* it is stated, do you think I have created you useless without any purpose? After this it is stated:

Therefore exalted be Allah, the Master, the Reality: there is no god but He, the Rabb of the Throne of Honour. (23:116)

In another verse it is explained in these words:

Say: 'Who is the Rabb of the seven heavens, and the Rabb of the Throne (of Glory) Supreme?' They will say, (They belong) to Allah. Say: 'Will you not then be filled with awe?' Say: 'Who is it in whose hands is the governance of all things, who protects (all), but is not protected?' If you know. (23:86-88)

19.2   Government of the Universe

In other words, the explanation of 'the Possessor of the Throne of Greatness' is done by stating that everything is in His grip, control and power. It is stated in Surah *Bani Israel*:

Say: If there had been (other) gods with Him, as they say, behold, they would certainly have sought out a way to the Lord of the Throne! Glory to Him! He is high above all that they say! Exalted and Great (beyond measure)! (17:42-43)

At another place this 'elevated high status' is referred to as 'highly raised level':

Raised high above ranks (or degrees), (He is) the Lord of the Throne (of Authority) ...(40:15)

By stating that along with Being the 'Possessor of *Arsh*', We do whatever We wish, He has referred to His sole rule and control:

Lord of the Throne of Glory, Doer of all that He intends. (85:15-16)

This is because if there was someone else sharing in His sovereignty and control, intent and authority, then there would have been chaos in the system of the universe :

If there were, in the heavens and the earth, other gods besides Allah, there would have been confusion in both! but glory to Allah, the Rabb of the Throne: (High is He) above what they attribute to Him! (21:22)

Because other than Him, there is no other being who is capable of becoming *Ilaah*. Greatness and government, resplendence and balanced authority, belong only to Him. The central control of the universe is in His hand alone:

Allah! There is no god but He! Rabb of the Throne Supreme! (27:26)

Since the whole system of the universe operates according to His laws (this is the meaning of control), therefore any individual (or group) who follows His laws will not remain in need of any other crutch:

> ...*Say: Allah suffices me: there is no god but He: On Him is my trust, He the Rabb of the Throne Supreme! (9:129)*

It is His control and authority which is in the heavens and earth:

> *Glory to the Rabb of the heavens and the earth, the Rabb of the Throne (of Authority)! (He is) far above those things which they attribute to Him (due to ignorance). (43:82)*

19.3   *Istwa alal Arsh* (Established on Throne)

The first phase was the creation of the universe, the second was the organisation and management of the world. This planning of affairs, management and organisation, establishment and control, and pragmatism and dealing with the world is declared by the Quran as being *Istwa alal Arsh*, by which is meant the central control of the universe. The meaning of *Istwa* is to maintain an established and sustainable posture. In the tale of Noah, it is stated:

> *And when you have embarked on the Ark (Istwaita) - you and those with you, say: 'Hamd be to Allah, Who has saved us from the people who do wrong.' (23:28)*

And when that vessel, having saved itself from the blows of the violent storm, banked at Judi, it was stated about it:

> *...The Ark rested on Mount Judi...(11:44)*

This word is also used for the firm and stable way in which one sits on the back of animals:

> *In order that you may sit firm and square on their backs...(43:13)*

When man progresses from childhood and adolescence and becomes an adult, his body parts and energies become mature and attain strength. This state is also described using the word *Istwa*. Regarding Moses it is stated:

> *When he reached full age, and was firmly established (Istwa), We bestowed on him wisdom and knowledge: for thus do We reward those who do good. (28:14) See also (53:6)*

In this same way, when a tiny sapling becomes a sturdy tree and reaches strength and maturity, this state is also described using this same word:

...it then becomes thick, and it stands on its own stem... (48:29)

And when this word comes together with *Ila*, then its meaning will be to draw attention, such as:

It is He Who has created for you all things that are on earth; then He turned to the heaven, and made them into seven (numerous) firmaments; and of all things He has perfect knowledge. (2:29)

At another place it is stated that He created the earth in two 'days' (periods):

Then He paid attention to the design of the heaven... (41:11)

From these explanations it becomes known that the meaning of *Istwa* is to maintain control and authority based on an established process (or to be directed to create improvement and strength in something); hence, the meaning of *Istwa alal Arsh* will be to maintain control and authority over the organisation and management of the universe. This is that authority and supremacy through which the running of the affairs of the system of the universe is carried out i.e. the way in which everything of the system of the universe is seen to be busily carrying out its assigned duties is the obedience of the implemented commands by Allah's throne of power:

Allah is He Who raised the heavens without any pillars that you can see; is firmly established on the throne (of authority); He has subjected the sun and the moon (to His law)! Each one runs (its course) for a term appointed. He does regulate all affairs...(13:2)

19.4 Regulation of Affairs

This has been mentioned in Surah *Al-Araf* also (see 7:54). In Surah *Yunus*, after mention of the creation of the heavens and the earth, it is stated:

...and is firmly established on the throne (of authority), regulating and governing all affairs...(10:3)

This 'regulation of affairs' is explained at another place in this way:

It is Allah Who has created the heavens and the earth, and all between them, in six days[187], and is firmly established on the Throne (of Authority): you have none, besides Him, to protect or intercede (for you): will you not then receive admonition? He rules (all) affairs from the heavens to the earth: in the end will (all affairs) go up to Him, on a day, the space whereof will be (as) a thousand years of your reckoning. (32:4-5)

The explanation of these matters will be found at their own place. Here, take note of just this much that *'Istwa alal Arsh'* has been referred to regarding those regulations of affairs as a result of which the system of the universe is established; and under the command of which the manifestations of nature are busily engaged in performing their respective duties. In Surah *Al-Hadid* it is stated:

He it is Who created the heavens and the earth in six days and is moreover firmly established on the Throne (of Authority). He knows what enters within the earth and what comes forth out of it, what comes down from heaven and what mounts up to it. And He is with you wheresoever you may be. And Allah sees well all that you do. To Him belongs the dominion of the heavens and the earth: and all affairs are referred back to Allah. (57:4-5)

19.5 The Basis of the System of the Universe is on *Rehmat*

The foundation of the organisation and management of the universe is on *Rehmat* i.e. all things of the universe obtain their means of sustenance from the direction of Allah. This is why it is stated:

(Allah) Rehman (i.e. Provider of sustenance) is firmly established on the throne (of authority). To Him belongs what is in the heavens and on earth, and all between them, and all beneath the soil. (20:5-6)

In Surah *Hud*:

He it is Who created the heavens and the earth in six days - and His Throne was over the waters - that He might provide you opportunities, (so that you find out about yourself that) which of you is best in conduct...(11:7)

19.6 Allah's *Arsh* is on Water!

This does not mean that His *Arsh* is floating around on water. As has been stated above, the meanings of *Arsh* are of control and authority, sovereignty and rule. Water is specifically referred to because water is in fact the fountain of life:

---

[187] A day here means a period, as explained in the later part of the verse. (Ed)

> *…We made from water every living thing…(21:30)*

It is a fact (which is also supported by the discoveries of science) that the beginning of life occurred from water and its survival is based on it too. Hence, by 'His *Arsh* being on water' is meant that His is the only control and authority on the source of life. Furthermore, this point is also worthy of attention that after mentioning '*Arsh* on water' here, reference has been made to *Ibtela*[188]. At another place the aim of life and death is also stated to be testing and accountability through deeds. It is stated:

> *He Who created Death and Life, that He may provide opportunities to you to see which of you is best in deed…(67:2)*

In other words, this means that the *Tafseer* (interpretation) of 'His *Arsh* is on water' is implicit in the words 'death and life' and the meaning is clear from this that He is also the Master of the source of life. This interpretation is present in many places in the Quran that death and life are in His control and authority alone e.g.:

> *How can you reject Eimaan in Allah? Seeing that you were without life, and He gave you life; then will He cause you to die, and will again bring you to life; and again to Him will you return. (2:28)*

19.7   Holders of *Arsh*

How the organisation and administration of this astounding and great system of the universe functions, how the orders from the centre of governance of this Allah of the universe descend and are executed - encompassing these matters is outwith the intellect and understanding of man. The nature and reality of the works of Allah, the implementation of which is ongoing in this universe, cannot come within the comprehension of man. At the most, he has been provided access to knowledge of things (knowledge of nature); beyond the knowledge of physics, he has no reach. Hence, the verses relating to those matters which are about metaphysics are in Quranic metaphors i.e. those realities which are expounded via allegories. In the same context, there is a verse about the 'holders of *Arsh*':

> *Those who sustain the Throne (of Allah) and those around it remain busy in performing defined programme of their Rabb…(40:7)*

On the Day of Judgment, *Malaika* (angels) will also be around the '*Arsh*':

---

[188] *Ibtela* - this has two meanings, one is to obtain information about one's welfare or to acquire information about him; the second meaning is for the condition of something to become known, whether good or bad. See *Lughat ul Quran*, Vol 1, pp 186-188. (Ed)

And you will see the angels surrounding the Throne (Divine) on all sides, carrying out the defined tasks assigned from their Rabb...(39:75)

At another place it is stated:

And the angels will be on its sides, and eight will, that Day, bear the Throne of your Rabb above them. (69:17)

19.8   Ascertaining Dimension and Direction

It has been noted that Allah's *Arsh* is not the name of some material thing which is kept at some specific place. The 'carrying' of it is also not like the carrying of a material throne, rather from this is meant the obedience or the establishment of Allah's laws. The Quran has explained these matters metaphorically, otherwise to assign some solid throne to Allah, to fix it at some specified place, and to actually assign some angels to carry it, is to wrongly assess the concept of Allah. His Being is above and beyond the definitions of dimension, direction and space. When Pharaoh mockingly told Haman, come build a high structure for me so that I can climb it and see where the *Rabb* of Moses sits, the Quran stated that he has diverted from the right path: what knowledge does he have about that Who is called Allah (40:36-37). Hence, attribution of dimension and space about the Being of Allah is based on a wrong perception about Him. His grandeur is such that:

...He is with you wherever you are...(57:4)

Similarly, the state of His Throne of governance is such that it encompasses the expanse of the heavens and earth:

...His control does extend over the heavens and the earth...(2:255)

This is the Quranic concept of *Arsh Ilahi* (Allah's throne). Whichever *Jamaat* of the *Momineen* becomes responsible for the establishment of Allah's sovereignty in this world, and how it will be known to be the holder of Allah's *Arsh*, is a separate subject for discussion, which is not pertinent at this point. Simply observe this much at this point, that when the state of that Allah Whose power and control, authority and intent, supremacy and reign, sovereignty and dominion is this, then how boundless and unchained will be the powers of those people in whom these attributes reflect. Weakness and powerlessness, helplessness and hopelessness, inability and feebleness, subjugation and slavery will not be able to get anywhere near them. They will themselves be the possessors of power, and will be the providers of protection and nourishment for all those who are weak and deprived in the world. Since they will be the living manifestation of the powers of Sovereign Allah in this world, therefore control over the sources of life will be theirs alone.

Their throne of rule will be spread to every corner and their seat of authority established everywhere. This is the very nature of the magnificence of the men of Allah in the world, and it can be determined from this to what extent His attributes are reflected in them. Having their heads buried in the lap of dust cannot be the conduct of the men of *Rabb Al-Arsh Al-Azeem*. What is the status of the powers of Allah's men? According to Iqbal:

Can anyone estimate His powers?
Fates are transformed by the glance of a Momin.

But a developed self manifests both the attributes of majesty and eminence.

The one in whose bosom there is the dew of tranquility,
The hearts of rivers quake in the face of that storm.[189]

---

[189] This is also from Iqbal. (Ed)

20   *Mala'kut* (Power)

The control and authority, power and supremacy of Allah which are mentioned in the previous chapters have also been expressed using the word *Malak*. This word also essentially means sovereignty and authority and from this viewpoint it is taken to mean government and kingship. By kingship is not meant for an individual to be a king but to be a holder of authority. When the laws in the universe are of that same Allah, then it will be declared that it is His rule alone in the whole kingdom:

Unto Allah belongs the dominion of the heavens and the earth. He gives life and He takes it. Except for Him you have no protector nor helper. (9:116)

This has been reiterated at various places so that this established fact can become very clearly embedded in the mind (see 2:107, 7:158, 57:2). From the context and perspective of these verses it will become known how the attentions of man, removing them from all other directions, have been concentrated on this focal point that sovereignty and rule in the heavens and earth is His alone, because He has brought the universe into existence, created the universe and the earth from nothing. And after this, He creates whatever He wishes according to His Divine laws. This is why it is His authority which is over the whole of creation, and it is His laws which are operational in it:

...For to Allah belongs the dominion of the heavens and the earth, and all that is between. He creates what He wishes. For Allah has power over all things. (5:17) See also (42:49)

20.1   Rule over the System of the Universe

His authority and rule are not just confined to the creation of the universe; after this the whole system of the universe is functioning according to His command. His control is over every manifestation of nature and not a single thing can go against His law. This is what is called right rule and kingship:

See you not that it is Allah Whose established programme all beings in the heavens and on earth do follow, and the birds with wings outspread? Each one knows its own (mode of) duties. And Allah knows well all that they do. Yea, to Allah belongs the dominion of the heavens and the earth; and to Allah is the final goal (of all). See you not that Allah makes the clouds move gently, then joins them together, then makes them into a heap (layer upon layer)? Then will you see rain issue forth from their midst. And He sends down from the sky mountain masses (of clouds) wherein is hail: He strikes therewith whom He wills (as per His law) and He turns it away from whom He wills, the vivid flash of His lightning well-nigh blinds the sight. It is Allah

Who alternates the night and the day: verily in these things (displays of nature) is an instructive example for those who have vision. (24:41-44) See also (39:5)

It was following the observation of this awe-inspiring organisation and arrangement of the manifestations of nature that Abraham reached this conclusion, that the Being managing this great system of the universe is definitely such that it is not under the obedience of anyone, and the whole of the universe is under His command:

So also did We show Abraham the power and the laws of the heavens and the earth, that he might (with understanding) have certitude. (6:75)

20.2   No Other Has a Share in the Rule of the Universe

Such a sovereignty in which He has no associate or partner:

He to whom belongs the dominion of the heavens and the earth: no son has He begotten, nor has He a partner in His dominion: it is He who created all things and ordered them in due proportions. (25:2)

It is stated in Surah *Bani Israel*:

Say: Hamd be to Allah, who begets no son, and has no partner in (His) dominion: Nor He needs any assistance due to any weakness: magnify Him for His greatness and glory! (17:111)

This is because just as nothing in the universe is outwith His control, similarly no tiny atom is outside the sphere of His knowledge. Everything is in front of His 'eyes', everything is under His watch:

Him to Whom belongs the dominion of the heavens and the earth! And Allah is witness to all things. (85:9)

Hence, to contemplate someone else partaking in His rule and sovereignty is ignorance because an associate and partner can only be that one who possesses some inherent control or authority. But when the fact is that no single thing of the universe possesses any intrinsic power (all is bestowed by Allah), then which entity will be a sharer and partner in His Divinity and dominion. Therefore, it is stated:

What! Do they take for intercessors others besides Allah? Say: 'Even if they have no power whatever and no intelligence?' Say: 'To Allah belongs exclusively (the right to grant) intercession[190]: to Him belongs the dominion of the heavens and the earth: In the end, it is to Him that you shall be brought back.' (39:43-44)

At another place it is stated:

And blessed is He to Whom belongs the dominion of the heavens and the earth, and all between them: with Him is the knowledge of the Hour of Judgment, and to Him shall you be brought back. And those whom they invoke besides Allah have no power of intercession – only he who bears witness to the truth, and they know.
(43:85-86)

Those who are declared as gods by people other than this King of kings (Allah), do not have the authority equivalent to even an atom in the vast expanse of the universe:

...Such is Allah your Rabb: to Him belongs all dominion. And those whom you invoke besides Him have not the least power. (35:13)

20.3   Allah's Sovereignty in the Life of the Hereafter

The domain of sovereignty of Allah is not confined to this world only, the life in the hereafter is also within the boundaries of His sovereignty. This is because the differentiations between 'today and tomorrow' are the creation of our observations. In His 'vision' past, present and future have no difference. Just as He is the sole Sovereign from the lowest point to the highest, without any limits of 'space', similarly He is the Master of all from the beginning till the end, without any constraints of 'time'. Hence, if it is His rule today, then tomorrow will be His rule also. When it is asked:

... Whose will be the dominion that Day? (40:16)

The reply is:

...His will be the dominion the day the trumpet will be blown...(6:73)

In Surah *Al-Hajj*:

On that Day, dominion will be that of Allah...(22:56) See also (25:26)

In another verse it is stated:

---

[190] The meaning of this will be explained at another place.

To Allah belongs the dominion of the heavens and the earth, and the day that the hour of judgment is established, that day will the dealers in falsehood perish! (45:27)

Hence, the verdicts of punishment and protection will be according to the laws of this Ruler of rulers:

Do you not Know that to Allah (alone) belongs the dominion of the heavens and the earth? He punishes as per His law, and He provides protection as per His law: and Allah has power over all things. (5:40) See also (3:189), (5:18), (5:120), (48:14)[191]

20.4   Dominion Over the Earth and the Heavens

It is apparent from the previous explanations that sovereignty in the universe belongs to Allah, the control of authority is in His hand alone. The Quran states:

…Who is it in Whose hands is the governance of all things…(23:88)

Then it states:

So glory to Him in Whose hands is the dominion of all things: and to Him will you all be brought back.[192] *(36:83) See also (67:1)*

This is why one attribute of Allah among His balanced attributes is also that of '*Malik ul Quddus*' (59:23, 62:1). The true King, pure from all faults, above and beyond all weaknesses:

Therefore, exalted be Allah, the King, the Reality: there is no god but He, the Rabb of the Throne of Honour. (23:116) See also (20:114)

In the external universe Allah's governance is continuously ongoing directly, but in the human world organisation and functioning occurs via human hands. This is called government and authority, and Allah has put laws in place for the receipt and loss of the power of government and authority. From this it is clear that when all this is received and lost according to His laws, then it will be absolutely correct to state that He is indeed the Ruler of rulers, even though in the human world, according to His Divine law, He passes on the organisation and running to those people who have this ability, and when they no longer retain this ability then He snatches it away from them:

---

[191] Details of these verses is not the place here.
[192] Verses like this mean that every step man takes is in His direction regardless. (Ed)

...Lord of Power (And Rule), you give power to whom You will (as per the law), and You strip off power from whom You will (as per the law) ...(3:26)

This is because everything is in His ownership:

To Him belongs all that is in the heavens and on earth...(22:64)

And when the ownership is His, then He is also the real King:

Whatever is in the heavens and on earth, are busy carrying out completion of His programme: to Him belongs dominion, and to Him belongs Hamd: and He has power over all things. (64:1)

20.5   Splendour of Greatness

In the whole of the universe the governance is His, then who can be greater than Him. Hence, greatness in the universe is also His:

To Him be glory throughout the heavens and the earth...(45:37)

This is that Allah to whose obedience the Quran extends an invitation:

...Such is Allah your Rabb: to Him belongs all Dominion...(35:13)

(This subject has been confined to Allah's general control and governance. How His rule becomes established in this world is a separate topic which will be dealt with at its own place).

The fundamental trait of a complete self is to become the possessor of the freedom to choose and make decisions. Therefore, the scope of responsibilities will be in direct proportion to the extent to which the human self becomes developed. The truth is that to judge to what extent a self is developed, it should be observed to what extent it is the possessor of freedom to choose and make decisions; it should be seen to what extent it makes its own choices and decisions. If an individual does not make decisions on his own behalf but follows behind the decisions of others (whether ritually or under duress), then consider that his self is not developing. Obedience can only be of the laws of Allah, and that too with full conviction of the heart and mind. Within the confines of these laws, man should be fully autonomous in making his own choices and decisions - this is how a developed self is identified.

That *Jamaat* in which the selfs of its members become developed like this will be the possessor of the freedom to choose and make decisions. It will be the one which will have the right to govern, but its government will not be to make individuals obey its orders, instead it will be for the obedience of Allah's laws so that in this way their own selfs can also become developed.

21   *Ah'ya* (Life) and *Ima'tat* (Death)

The scope of Allah's power and authority is so wide that death and life is also in His hand alone. What is the source of life? This is that question which continues to be unfathomable by those who are thinkers and researchers (regardless of whether they are philosophers from the past or scientists of the modern era). The maximum to which investigations of science have so far reached is how life appeared on the face of this earth. But they can say nothing about where life actually came from. The Quran informs us that Allah is *Al-Hayyu* i.e. He Himself is alive[193] and life in the universe is a creation of His. In other words, just as matter is a creation of His, similarly, life is also a creation of His. And this is that thing which is not in the control of any other (i.e. creating life is not possible by anyone else), though He has established laws for the strengthening (and weakening) of life, according to which it can be strengthened and can also be destroyed. Therefore, since its ultimate destruction (called death) occurs according to His established laws, He has stated the same about death as with life, that it is within His control. This is the meaning of those verses of the Quran in which it is stated 'He is the One Who gives life, He is the One Who gives death', for example:

Unto Allah belongs the dominion of the heavens and the earth. He gives life and He takes it. Except for Him you have no protector nor helper. (9:116)

In Surah *Al-Hadid* it is stated:

To Him belongs the dominion of the heavens and the earth: It is He Who gives Life and Death; and He has Power over all things. (57:2)

In Surah *Yunus*:

It is He Who gives life and Who gives death, and your every step goes towards Him. (10:56)

This reality has been repeated at different places in the Quran. By reflecting on these verses, it will become evident how miraculous this style of expression of the Quran is in the way that it presents one principle many times through cross reference of verses, and at every place it seems as if this matter is being narrated for the first time. Through this repetition and emphasis, the principle in view becomes embedded in the mind with all its splendour and brilliance. For 'He is the One Who gives life and death', keep the following verses in view and then see

---

[193] He is life and no-one gave Him this life. This is an important point to understand as acquisition of *Eimaan* and reflection on these Divine attributes and acquiring them (within human limits) will give us life. (Ed)

to what extent the above style happens to appeal to the heart (15:23, 23:80, 40:68, 44:8, 50:43, 53:44).

21.1 Evidence from Nature

To those people who deny the existence of Allah, life and death is presented as an evidence in front of them. It is stated:

How can you reject Eimaan in Allah? Seeing that you were without life, and He gave you life; then will He cause you to die, and will again bring you to life; and your every step goes towards Him. (2:28)

In Surah *Al-Hajj*:

It is He Who gave you life, will cause you to die, and will again give you life. But truly man is a most ungrateful creature. (22:66)

21.2 Negative Aspect

This was the positive side of this subject i.e. that Allah alone is the master of death and life. Together with this, its negative aspect is also explained so that the truth becomes well engrained in the heart. It is stated:

Yet have they taken, besides him, gods that can create nothing but are themselves created; that have no control of hurt or good to themselves; nor can they control death nor life nor resurrection. (25:3)

21.3 The Materialist

Among European scientists there exists a group whose belief is that when a particular arrangement is created among the elements of matter, then life becomes automatically created within them merely by chance, and then when this arrangement becomes disturbed due to (physical) perturbations of the environment, then death takes place. This group is not a product of the modern era; references to their existence are given from the times of the Greek philosophers. At the time of the revelation of the Quran this also existed; it is to them that the Quran refers when it states:

And they say: 'What is there but our life in this world? We shall die and we live, and nothing but time can destroy us.' But of that they have no knowledge: they merely conjecture. (45:24)

Did you notice what the final outcome of this atheistic (materialistic) doctrine is? It is this, that life is the name of this physical life only, which ends with dying. After this, there is no life. The Quran gives surety of the continuity of life, and those who have conviction in the Quran have *Eimaan* in this. Hence, after noting this doctrine of atheism, the Quran has declared in clear words that the truth is not that which these people profess; the truth is this:

Say: 'It is Allah Who gives you life, then gives you death; then He will gather you together for the Day of Judgment about which there is no doubt': But most men do not understand. (45:26)

To what extent the ideology of the materialists regarding death and life is merely conjectural and speculative and does not meet the criteria of factual knowledge - in fact, how people are arising from among them who are contradicting the doctrine of death and life of their previous scientists - this is not the place for this discussion.[194] At this point note only this much, how the Quran, after rejecting every false doctrine, has clarified this fact that not only is life created by Allah but death also occurs according to His law. Hence, there is no difficulty for Him that after death He bestows life again, and this decree is based on knowledge, not on conjecture and speculation.

Let us see the practical consequence of this *Eimaan*. For man, the biggest arena of danger for his mistake is the risk of death. Man continues to do anything in order to save his life[195], for this, he bows his head to the ground before every possessor of power and authority.

But when a *Momin* creates the conviction within himself that a human being does not end through death, rather life continues to go forward, then the electrifying energies of courage and boldness, bravery and initiative, race through his heart and veins. He does not fear any human being and proceeds forward in the arena of life with head held high, clothed as in a shroud, fully intoxicated by the conviction of *Eimaan*, to lay down his life for the truth. There is no chain of the world which can imprison his freedoms, no tyrannical power which can become an impediment in his path of *Eimaan*. These are those men of high self-awareness, and followers of Allah, due to whose valours the system of truth and justice is established in the world, and whose *Eimaan*, like the light emitted by a lofty lighthouse in the stormy waves of events, serve as a torch of guidance. A developed self is able to recognise this fact. Just consider to what extent the system of a society which is shaped through the hands of such individuals will be willing to lay down its life for the sake of consolidating the Permanent Values.

---

[194] This has been covered in the book titled *The Life in the Hereafter: What does the Quran say?*
[195] We can only prolong our physical life and delay our inevitable physical death up to a point. (Ed)

22 *Tawakkul* (Conviction)

Have you seen an airman jumping from an aircraft? The aircraft is flying at a height of fifteen to twenty thousand feet with a speed of three hundred to four hundred miles per hour. From it, an airman jumps out with great calmness and comes to land on the ground with great comfort and ease. Have you ever pondered why this airman jumps out with such calm and ease? This is because he has a parachute which deploys with the slightest touch and is so strong that despite such a weight and such speed its string does not break, nor does its fabric tear. With the help of this parachute, the airman descends. It is merely this strong trust in this parachute which persuades this airman to jump from such a height. If he does not have such confidence and trust in it, then never mind jumping, he will not even dare to look down from the aircraft. In the Arabic language this kind of trust and conviction is called *Tawakkul*.

We have seen in the previous pages that Allah's immutable laws are working in both the outer universe and the human world. Since the effects of these laws present themselves in a tangible form in the outer world, this is why it is easy to have certainty and trust in them. But as far as the human world is concerned, firstly, their effects are non-perceptible, and secondly, these effects manifest over a very long period of time (evolutionary pace). These effects will manifest according to the scales of human calculation at that time when these laws become implemented through the hands of a *Jamaat e Momineen*. It is obvious that when this *Jamaat* rises up with these laws, at that time their effects will not be in front of this *Jamaat*. The question is, what is the nature of that power on the basis of which this *Jamaat* will become prepared for such a life-threatening and patience testing campaign. That force cannot be any other than this, that they have complete trust and conviction in the strength and immutability of the Divine laws. Without this they will not be able to take even one step. This is why it is stated that:

For, Momineen are those who, when Allah is mentioned, feel a tremor in their hearts, and when they hear His signs rehearsed, find their Eimaan strengthened, and put (all) their trust in their Rabb; Who establish Salat and make it available (for mankind) what We have given them for sustenance: such in truth are the Momineen: they have grades of dignity with their Rabb, and protection, and honourable sustenance. (8:2-4)

The *Tawakkul* of a *Jamaat e Momineen* is not merely a theoretical belief; they have complete conviction in this matter that whichever individual (or group) has trust in the laws of Allah, he no longer remains in need of any other support or crutch. These laws are sufficient to achieve his aim. They also have full conviction in this fact that every scheme of Allah assuredly reaches its point of completion. It never happens that it breaks somewhere in the middle or that it ultimately proves to be a failure. This is because:

> ... *And if any one puts his trust in Allah, sufficient is (Allah) for him. For Allah will surely accomplish his purpose: verily, for all things has Allah appointed a due proportion. (65:3)*

22.1 *Tawakkul* of *Anbiya*

When *Tawakkul* is among the traits of *Eimaan* of the *Momineen*, then it is obvious how much stronger and unwavering will be the *Tawakkul* of the *Anbiya* on Allah. The reality is that when the *Anbiya* used to proclaim the truth, according to the common worldly standard they were usually helpless and weak, devoid of resources and without friends and support; and the first reaction to their invitation was that every rebellious and unruly force would rise up with its full might to oppose them. In this horde of unfavourable circumstances and difficulties, this was the tremendous power of *Tawakkul* on Allah which did not allow any tremor in their resolve, or any falter in their firm footedness. The whole world would be against them but in their glittering eyes there were no signs of fear, and no crease of worry could be seen on their glowing foreheads. Noah is encircled by the rebels, opposing forces are bent upon causing all types of harm, but with *Tawakkul al* Allah, he proclaims with heightened fortitude that:

> ...*O my people, if it be hard on your (mind) that I should stay (with you) and commemorate the signs of Allah, yet I put my trust in Allah. Get you then an agreement about your plan and among your partners, so your plan be on to you dark and dubious. Then pass your sentence on me and give me no respite. (10:71)*

In other words, do all of this and then wait and and see whether it is your treacheries, your partners in crime, and your companions in this planning that are more powerful, or that law of Allah in which I have reposed my trust! How superb is this challenge and with what courage and certainty it is being presented? The proclamation of this 'weak and feeble' servant of Allah was heard by the world, and after that its consequence was also witnessed, how the rebellious and disobedient opponents were destroyed all together. It was in similar circumstances that Hud stated to his people:

> ...*so scheme against me, all of you, and give me no respite. I put my trust in Allah, My Rabb and your Rabb! There is not a moving creature, but He has grasp of its fore-lock. Verily, it is my Rabb that is on a straight path. (11:55-56)*

The messenger Shoaib also stated the same:

...I only desire (your) betterment to the best of my power; and my success (in my task) can only come from Allah. In Him I trust, and unto Him I look. (11:88) See also (7:89)

The foremost symbol of the Islamic system, Abraham, a model of righteousness, also gave such an earth-shattering and tremor causing challenge to his people, and stated:

...We are clear of you and of whatever you follow besides Allah: we have rejected you, and there has arisen, between us and you, enmity and detestation forever, unless you have Eimaan in Allah and Him alone...Our Rabb! in You do we trust, and to You do we turn in repentance: to You is (our) final goal. (60:4)

Other than these individual examples, it is generally noted regarding all of the *Anbiya* that when their people rejected and falsified them and turned against them in opposition, then they in turn responded thus:

...True, we are human like yourselves, but Allah does grant His grace to such of his servants as He wills. It is not for us to bring you an authority except as Allah permits. And on Allah let all men of Eimaan put their trust. No reason have we why we should not put our trust on Allah. Indeed, He Has guided us to the Ways we (follow). We shall certainly bear with patience all the hurt you may cause us. It is only Allah in whom those who wish to put their trust, should put their trust. (14:11-12)

In the early period of Rasul-ullah's invitation towards *Haqq*, the way that the flame of Lahab[196] remained in conflict with the light of Mustafa[197] is such a glaring example of rebellion and unruliness on one side, and conviction and determination on the other side, to which the world is a witness. In this torrent of opposition, the way that the dignified being of Rasul-ullah manifested unwavering *Tawakkul* on Allah is the best model for every claimant of *Eimaan*. Alone and isolated, surrounded from every side by enemies, yet his proclamation is:

... Say: 'See you then? the things that you invoke besides Allah, can they, if Allah wills some penalty for me, remove His penalty? Or if He wills some grace for me, can they keep back His grace?' Say: 'Sufficient is Allah for me! In Him trust those who put their trust.' Say: 'O my People! Do whatever you can: I will do (my part): but soon will you know - who it is to whom comes a penalty of ignominy, and on whom descends a penalty that abides.' (39:38-40)

How unfavourable the circumstances are, yet how strong is the trust in the laws.

---

[196] Historically, Abu Lahab was the uncle of the last messenger who opposed his messenger-hood vehemently until his death. (Ed)
[197] Another name by which the last messenger is known. (Ed)

This is the hallmark of *Tawakkul* (trust and conviction). Human beings usually endeavour that if relations spoil with strangers to allow it, but to not spoil relations with near and dear ones, because in times of trouble the support of near and ones can be trusted as compared to outsiders. But for the one who stands up to raise the voice of *Haqq*, the criteria for 'dear ones' and 'outsiders' is totally different. The near one is the one who says yes to the invitation towards *Haqq*, the outsider is the one who evades it. This is why the claimant of *Haqq* does not care whether relationships with near and dear ones remain on good terms or turn sour. He does not even think of counting on their support and companionship, so how can he be afraid of spoiling his relationship with them? The Quran states:

And admonish your nearest kinsmen and lower your wing to Momineen who follow you. Then if they disobey you, say: 'I am free (of responsibility) for what you do!' And put your trust on the Exalted in Might, the Raheem. (26:214-217)

Surah *At-Tauba* was a proclamation of war against all the rejectors of the laws of Allah. After this proclamation it is stated:

But if they turn away, say: 'Allah suffices me: there is no god but He: On Him is my trust, He the Rabb of Al-Arsh, Supreme!' (9:129) See also (13:30, 67:29)

22.2   Only the *Tawakkul* of the One on *Haqq* is Genuine

Amongst those who were engaged in rebellion and transgression, the Jews participated the most in this opposition. It was instructed, do not be apprehensive of their opposition, Allah's Law of Requital will very soon make a decision as to what the end result is of those who transgress from the righteous path, you should continue giving the invitation with resolve and fortitude, and after that:

So put your trust in Allah: for you are on (the path of) manifest Truth. (27:79)

Apart from those who were openly rebellious, there was also a group of hypocrites who would whisper in secret. It was stated, what do you care about their intrigues either - your trust is on that Allah who is aware of every matter, both seen and unseen:

They have 'obedience' on their lips; but when they leave you, a section of them meditate all night on things very different from what you tell them. But Allah records their nightly (plots): so keep clear of them, and put your trust in Allah, and enough is Allah as a disposer of affairs. (4:81) See also (58:10)

You should not be fearful of the negative maneuverings from the open opposition of these *Kuffar*, and the unceasing covert intrigues of the hypocrites; keep following

Allah's laws, Allah's support and blessing will be like a shadow covering you at all times:

O Nabi! Fear Allah, and hearken not to the Unbelievers and the Hypocrites: verily Allah is full of Knowledge and Wisdom. But follow that which comes to you by inspiration from your Rabb: for Allah is well acquainted with (all) that you do. And put your trust in Allah, and enough is Allah as a disposer of affairs. (33:1-3) See also (33:48)

22.3   *Wakil* (Disposer of Affairs)

Tawakkul means trust and confidence, therefore the meaning of *Wakil-un* will be the one who can be trusted and confided in, the one to whom one's affairs can be assigned – this is the practical demonstration of trust and confidence. Whatever thing is given into the keeping of this individual in whom there is trust and confidence, he supervises and protects it fully. Hence, all these traits are included in the term *Wakil-un* and it is on this basis that Allah is proclaimed as *Wakil-un*:

That is Allah, your Rabb! there is no god but He, the Creator of all things: then obey Him: and He has power to dispose of all affairs. (6:102) See also (11:12, 39:62)

Creator of the universe, Sustainer of everything, overseeing all - then from who else above Him will problem solving and resourcefulness, protection and supervision be available:

Yea, unto Allah belong all things in the heavens and on earth, and enough is Allah to carry through all affairs. (4:132)

This is why it is stated that in the journey of life, when you ask for protection, ask for His alone; when you raise your eyes for companionship and help, then only look towards Him; and when you place trust and confidence, then do it only in Him:

(He is) Rabb of the east and the west: there is no god but He: take Him therefore for (your) Disposer of Affairs. (73:9)

Do not take any other than Him as a guardian, do not trust in the protection of anyone else. This was the command given to Bani Israel in the Torah:

We gave Moses the Book and made it a guide to the Children of Israel, (commanding): Take not other than Me as disposer of (your) affairs. (17:2)

And whoever places his trust in someone else as a result of doubt in the heart, feebleness of *Eimaan*, and due to the whispering of *Iblees*, then he will ultimately see all his supports to be flimsy, all his aids hot air, and all his guardians turn out to be weak and helpless. The truth is that if man abandons Allah's laws and places his trust on some other constitution and code, then this can never ever protect him. In other words, whoever does not make the laws of Allah his *Wakil*, can have no other *Wakil* in the world, or that no power which is contrary to the laws of Allah can provide supervision and protection. Hence, it is announced to Rasul-ullah:

If it were Our Will, We could take away that which We have sent you by inspiration: then you will not find any to plead your affair in that matter as against Us, except for mercy from your Rabb: for his bounty is to you (indeed) great. (17:86-87)

22.4   Non-Quranic and Quranic *Tawakkul*

This is the Quranic meaning of *Tawakkul*. Contrary to this, let us see what meaning is perceived amongst us of *Tawakkul*. Amongst us, the state is such that when an individual does not work, sits idle at one place, abandons all means and resources, does not make any effort or struggle to achieve anything, lays his head down on the hard work of others, then it is said about him that he is sitting having '*Tawakkul* on Allah', that he is very *Mutawakkul*. And this thing is counted among virtuousness and saintliness, 'praiseworthiness and religiosity'. The more he continues to increase in such *Tawakkul*, the more he is considered as being worthy of respect. However, can you imagine such a thought that this could be the teaching of Islam? That Islam which is the doctrine of a life of persistent endeavour, continuous struggle, ceaseless effort and hard work, action upon action, Jihad and wholehearted Jihad. Can it comprise such an instruction due to which all the practical powers of man are paralysed and all his lively energies become stunted? What, will this be the only meaning of *Tawakkul* in Islam - 'seal on lips, ears deaf, eyes shut' - to become static and lifeless with hands idle in laps, and remain a burden on the shoulders of humanity like a corpse?

Islamic teaching can never teach this. This is absolutely a non-Islamic doctrine and is the consequence of non-Quranic concepts of life i.e. those concepts which declare the eminence of humanity to be the desertion of intellect, abandonment of desires, and dereliction of resourcefulness. These are those non-Quranic beliefs which have turned the electric being of a 'Muslim' into a heap of ash, and that same *Tawakkul* which was once displayed in the form of a lightning sword in the hands of those who were prepared to sacrifice their lives in the path of Allah, has become a chain wrapped around his ankles.

Quranic *Tawakkul* teaches us that when a matter confronts us, firstly see which of Allah's laws are applicable to it, then through consultation with your companions, deliberate on its constituents and implications. In this way, when you arrive at a firm decision, then pursue it with a concrete resolve, and have full trust and confidence in this Divine law according to which you acted. This was the teaching which was given to Rasul-ullah (and through him to the Muslim Ummah). Thus, it was stated to him:

...and consult them in affairs. Then, when you have taken a decision put your trust in Allah. For Allah keeps them as friends those who put their trust (in Him). (3:159)

The correct meaning of *Tawakkul* has been presented in very clear terms in the narrative of Bani Israel. Moses told his people:

O my people! Enter the holy land which Allah has assigned unto you, and turn not back ignominiously, for then will you be overthrown, to your own ruin. (5:21)

Take note that it is stated here that 'this land which Allah has written for you, made it your destiny, has come to be your share according to Divine distribution, rise and occupy it'. But:

They said: 'O Moses! In this land are a people of exceeding strength: Never shall we enter it until they leave it: if (once) they leave, then shall we enter.' (5:22)

This was that nation whose practical abilities had become debilitated, whose efforts had weakened and whose courage had become demoralized. It did not wish to rise of its own accord but wished this instead, that all of these tasks could be accomplished automatically and that the rewards of these could fall into their laps while they sat doing nothing. This was that kind of '*Tawakkul*' which is prevalent nowadays among us. But within this same nation those people who had understood the correct meaning of *Tawakkul* said:

(But) among (their) Allah-fearing men were two on whom Allah had bestowed His grace: They said: 'Assault them at the (proper) gate: when once you are in, victory will be yours; But on Allah put your trust if you are Momineen'. (5:23)

From this it has become evident what the correct meaning of *Tawakkul* is i.e. when you rise with determined resolve for the achievement of an aim then the support of the Divine law will be by your side. But Bani Israel did not accept this true meaning of *Tawakkul*. They were convinced of that meaning of *Tawakkul* which is prevalent among us today. They said that when that particular land has been destined for us, then what need is there for us to exert any effort? Whatever is written in our fate will surely eventually be received by us automatically. It was because of this wrong belief that they had reconciled to live this slavish easy-going life of humiliation and failure:

They said: 'O Moses! while they remain there, never shall we be able to enter, to the end of time. Go you, and your Rabb, and fight you two, while we sit here (and watch).' (5:24)

What, is this not the same reply which the proponent of 'non-Quranic *Tawakkul*' also demonstrates wherever he is, through his conduct at every stage in the struggle of life today? The question is, whether with this kind of '*Tawakkul*' did they get that land which had become the destiny of Bani Israel? How could they get it? As a consequence, the command was given that when their condition is such:

Allah said: therefore, will the land be out of their reach for forty years: In distraction will they wander through the land: But sorrow you not over these rebellious people. (5:26)

After forty years of wandering through the desert and living in the wild, the previous generation faded away in the plains of Sinai and a new generation took birth, which developed according to the revelation of Allah in the free environment of the wild. It arose, grew, and with full efforts and endeavours occupied that land which had been destined for Bani Israel.

It has become apparent from this what the correct meaning of *Tawakkul* is and what the incorrect meaning is. This was why Moses had emphatically instructed his people to learn to trust correctly in Allah because it is only through this that you will be able to achieve *Najaat* from the hell of slavery and subjugation:

Moses said: 'O my people! If you do have Eimaan in Allah, then in Him put your trust if you submit (your will to His)'. They said: 'In Allah do we put our trust. Our Rabb! make us not a trial for those who practice oppression; And deliver us by Your Mercy from those who reject (You)'. (10:84-86)

This was the same supplication of Moses and Aaron and in reply it was stated:

Allah said: 'Accepted is your prayer (O Moses and Aaron)! So stand you straight, and follow not the path of those who know not. (10:89)

By *Tawakkul* and the acceptance of supplication is meant that whatever campaign you have made a resolve on, stand firm on it and adopt that technique which is according to the Divine law, success will be assured.

When Noah said to his people, do whatever comes into your minds, my *Tawakkul* is on my Allah, did he then sit down after this with hands clasped doing nothing? Not at all! With full determination and hard work, he constructed a boat under the guidance of the revelation of Allah, and when the deluge of the flood arrived, he launched the boat into the wild torrent, stating, O Allah! whatever preparation I could make in order to be saved from the destruction of this storm, I did following Your command. Now this boat is at Your disposal, if there is support from Your law then this will reach the shore. So the world observed that in this storm, which did not allow any sign of rebelliousness and disobedience to remain, if anything survived it was that same ark which this sincere servant of Allah had made with his gentle hands, and which was handed over to the mercy of the waves with trust in the Divine law.

22.5 Muslims of the Earlier Era and *Tawakkul*

After mentioning these stories of former Ummahs, let us now return to that era in which the deeds of life of the sincere devotees of Allah were the practical interpretations of the Quranic principles of life. Let us see what the meaning of *Tawakkul* was during that era. In Surah *Al-Anfal*:

Against them make ready your strength to the utmost of your power, including steeds of war, to strike terror into (the hearts of) the enemies, of Allah and your enemies, and others besides, whom you may not know, but whom Allah does know. Whatever you shall spend in the cause of Allah, shall be repaid unto you, and you shall not be treated unjustly. But if the enemy incline towards peace, do you (also) incline towards peace, and trust in Allah: for He is One that hears and knows (all things). Should they intend to deceive you - verily Allah suffices you: He it is that has strengthened you with His aid and with Momineen; And (moreover) He has put affection between their hearts: not if you had spent all that is in the earth, could you have produced that affection, but Allah has done it: for He is Exalted in might, Wise. O Nabi! sufficient unto you is Allah, and unto Momineen who follow you. (8:60-64)

Reflect on these great verses and see what kind of system has been established by the Quran for *Tawakkul* on Allah, victory from Allah, success and prosperity, Divine protection, abundance from Allah. Let us see what the different links of this process are: the system will automatically become evident:

(1) The presence of the messenger (and after the messenger, the successor of the messenger i.e. the living centre of the system)
(2) A *Jamaat e Momineen* to carry out the obedience of the righteous central authority
(3) That *Jamaat* in the hearts of whose members one outlook and mutual attachment has been created through mutual love and affection.

(4) Such material power should exist in this *Jamaat* which, visible and invisible, is sufficient to counter all enemies, and as a consequence of which fear is instilled in the hearts of the enemies.

(5) At the time of need, everything is sacrificed for this great aim.

(6) With this manifestation of power, the state of morality is such that as soon as the enemy yields for peace, they also immediately agree.

(7) If the enemy deceives, let it deceive, but they themselves will never deceive. They are transparent in all matters.

(8) Equipped with all these resources and wherewithal, and with the wealth of this high character (*Taqwa*), maintain *Tawakkul* in Allah and remain desirous of His aid and companionship.

When this system takes birth, then the consequence of having *Tawakkul* in Allah will be:

...If there are twenty amongst you, patient and persevering, they will vanquish two hundred: if a hundred, they will vanquish a thousand of the Unbelievers: for these are a people without understanding. (8:65)

These were the Mujahideen, bound as a pearl necklace with this system, the state of whose hearts was such that when they were informed that the enemy is preparing to oppose them in great numbers and laden with weapons, instead of being fearful they become even more courageous, and would assert with the complete conviction of their hearts: 'So what! if the enemy is powerful, the One on Whom we trust is Omnipotent':

Men said to them: 'A great army is gathering against you': And frightened them: But it (only) increased their Eimaan: They said: 'For us Allah suffices, and He is the best disposer of affairs'. (3:173)

What was the outcome of this unwavering and lofty *Tawakkul*?

And they returned with grace and bounty from Allah: no harm ever touched them: For they followed the good pleasure of Allah: And Allah is the Rabb of bounties unbounded. (3:174)

These were those results through the reminder of which *Taqwa* and *Tawakkul* were emphasised. It is stated:

O you who have Eimaan! Call in remembrance the favour of Allah unto you when certain men formed the design to stretch out their hands against you, but (Allah) held back their hands from you: So, fear Allah. And on Allah let Momineen put (all) their trust. (5:11)

It was the immense force of *Taqwa* and *Tawakkul* which, despite the lower numbers and relatively fewer material resources, bestowed such resolve, steadfastness and extreme courage on the Muslims that they were never fearful even of the greatest battles. The opponents could not fathom this secret. They would concoct the strangest of fables in the interpretation of this, and not only they, but the European historian who is ignorant of the powers of *Eimaan* and *Taqwa*, has not been able to understand even to the present time what the secret was behind these unparalleled powers of the Muslims. And when, due to his lack of vision and perception, he cannot reach the truth, then he begins to fabricate exaggerated fictional tales. This was the same state of the hypocrites. Although their tongues were familiar with the words *Taqwa* and *Tawakkul*, their hearts were strangers to the spirit of these words. This is why they would say sarcastically, look how arrogant the intoxication of their Deen has made them, the *Jamaat* is only a handful yet is aiming to conquer the earth and the heavens:

Lo! the hypocrites say, and those in whose hearts is a disease: 'These people, their Deen has misled them'. But if any trust in Allah, behold! Allah is Exalted in might, Wise. (8:49)

But along with this, this reality was made clear to the Muslims that Allah's victory is dependent on this: that you do not lose courage; do not demonstrate cowardice; the practical proof of *Tawakkul* is that you remain firm footed. Consequently, its example was illustrated in the Battle of Uhad. It was those same Muslims who had come out into the battlefield for the sake of truth and *Haqq*, but right from the beginning two groups became disheartened at the instigation of the hypocrites, and in this way the spirit of *Sabr* (firmness of heart) and *Tawakkul* (unwavering trust in Allah's laws) became weakened. Consequently, that same enemy which only yesterday was defeated by a small *Jamaat* of only three hundred and thirteen men in the Battle of Badr, overpowered them in the battlefield of Uhad:

Remember two of your parties meditated cowardice; but Allah was their protector, and in Allah should the Momineen put their trust. (3:122)

22.6   Migration and *Tawakkul*

Only that environment can be congenial for a *Momin* in which life can be spent according to the laws of Allah; other than this every other environment is unsuitable for him. If the environment in some place is unfavourable, then the duty falls on him to make it suitable. But if, despite his efforts, it cannot be made favourable, then the other alternative is that, rather than breathing in this poison laden atmosphere, he should move to some such place where either a suitable environment already exists, or the possibilities to make it favourable are greater.

This is what is known as *Hijrat* (migration).[198] Such a situation demands great courage. Man has an affinity for his surroundings, the attraction of relationships also ties one down; then, over and above everything else, the sources of income are well established and their forms are defined. To abandon all of these and move to a 'new world' demands great *Sabr* (perseverance) and supreme *Tawakkul* (trust in Allah). These are the attributes which are declared to be invaluable character traits. It is stated:

To those who leave their homes in the cause of Allah, after suffering oppression, We will assuredly give a goodly home in this world; but truly the reward of the hereafter will be greater. If they only realised (this)! (They are) those who persevere in patience and put their trust on their Rabb. (16:41-42)

Details of this aspect are cited in Surah *Al-Ankabut* in these words:

O My servants who have Eimaan! truly, spacious is My earth: therefore, only follow My commands! Every self shall have a taste of death, in the end to Us shall you be brought back. But those who have Eimaan and work deeds of righteousness - to them shall We give a home in heaven, lofty mansions beneath which flow rivers, to dwell therein for aye; an excellent reward for those who do (good)! Those who persevere in patience and put their trust in their Rabb. How many are the creatures that carry not their own sustenance? It is Allah who feeds (both) them and you: for He hears and knows (all things). (29:56-60)

How migrants and trustees obtain *Rizq* and what the conditions are for its attainment, has already been discussed under the topics of *Razzaqiyat* and *Fadl*. At this point it only needs to be seen that *Sabr* and *Tawakkul* are those forces on the basis of which a *Momin* progresses forward, avoiding all those thorny bushes on the way which impede his path. These were those factors which were hindering the *Kuffar* from acceptance of *Haqq*:

They say: 'If we were to follow the guidance with you, we should be snatched away from our land'. Have We not established for them a secure sanctuary, to which are brought as tribute fruits of all kinds, a provision from Ourselves? but most of them understand not. And how many populations We destroyed, which exulted in their life (of ease and plenty)! now those habitations of theirs, after them, are deserted, all but a (miserable) few! and We are their heirs! (28:57-58)

This was because they considered their skills and expertise to be sufficient in themselves and opted for rebellion against the laws of Allah. They depended on those ideals which were not enduring. They chose to hold on to those supports

---

[198] Details of this will be found in the book titled *Mairaj e Insaniyat*.

which were themselves going to end one day. If man is going to trust, it should be in the One Who is alive and will remain alive for eternity. Only the law of this living and sustaining Allah is such in which man should put his trust:

And put your trust in Him Who lives and dies not...(25:58)

Only this Being is worthy of trust, and complete trust can be placed only in Him:

...such is Allah my Rabb: In Him I trust, and to Him I turn. (42:10)

This is the *Eimaan* of a *Momin* and his way of life i.e. complete trust and confidence in the laws of Allah. It is also clear from this that the individual whose self is developed and in whom the Divine attributes are reflected in this way, that individual and the *Jamaat* consisting of such individuals and their established system will possess this great character trait that complete trust and full confidence can be placed in every matter of theirs. They will not deceive anyone and will not cheat and betray anyone. Their every commitment and agreement will be firm. Whenever they say anything to anyone, he will be assured that it will happen like this. The world will trust them with the same certainty and assurance that they themselves trust the firmness of Allah's laws. Just think how much peace and tranquility will result due to this kind of *Jamaat* in the world and the existence of such a system. The Quran wishes to create these kinds of individuals and this type of system.

23   *Willayat* (Companionship)

The basic meaning of *Al-Waliyu* is to be close and near to someone. We have seen in the previous chapters that the relationship between Allah and man is of mutual companionship. From this aspect they are declared to be *Wali* of each other. But it is essential for this companionship that man obeys the laws of Allah. In this regard, when it is said about man that he is 'Allah's *Wali*', then from this will be meant that by having the status of being obedient to Allah's laws, he is a companion in the creative programme of Allah; and when it is said about Allah that He is the *Wali* of man, then from this will be meant that He becomes the companion of whoever obeys His laws. In this regard (that the laws of Allah are obeyed), *Willayat* also means sovereignty and authority, government and supremacy, and protection and supervision. But when it is said about two human beings they are *Wali* of one another, then from this will be meant equality of companionship and friendship e.g.:

> *The Momineen, men and women, are protectors one of another...(9:71)*

In Surah *Al-Kahf* there is the example of two owners of orchards. One of them is so intoxicated by his prosperity that He even denied the supremacy and authority of Allah, and began to think that everything was being attained purely as a result of his own skill and expertise, no part is played in it by the laws of Allah. The consequence was that all his prosperity was ground into dust. After quoting this example, the Quran states:

> *There, the (only) protection comes from Allah, the true One. He is the best to reward, and the best to give success. (18:44)*

Here, the meaning of *Willayat* is of guidance and of finding a solution, and this is specific for the Being of Allah, the obedience of Whose laws is essential. It is stated in Surah *Al-Anfal* in relation to the mention of the *Momineen* and *Muhajireen* (those who migrated):

> *...As to those who accepted Eimaan but came not into exile, you owe no duty of protection to them until they come into exile...(8:72)*

Here, the meaning of *Willayat* is that of companionship and friendship, and this is that relationship which is specific to Islamic unity and affection within a *Millat*.

23.1   Only Allah is *Wali*

A *Momin* who has a firm conviction that in the stages of life true victory and support can only be achieved through the obedience of Allah's laws, who has *Eimaan* from the depths of his heart in this great truth that trust and certainty can only be placed in His laws, will assuredly search for real peace and tranquility only in the protection and guidance of Allah by turning his face away from 'non-Allah' forces. In Surah *Al-Baqra* it is stated:

Let there be no compulsion in Deen[199]: Truth stands out clear from error: whoever rejects evil and has Eimaan in Allah has grasped the most trustworthy hand-hold, that never breaks. And Allah hears and knows all things. Allah is the protector of those who have Eimaan: from the depths of darkness[200] He will lead them forth into light. Of those who accept Kufr their patrons are the evil ones: from light they will lead them forth into the depths of darkness. They will be companions of the fire, to dwell therein forever. (2:256-257)

The support of Allah's companionship and supervision is so strong that it can never break. Other than this, of all the other supports none is such which can provide security and protection for man in the struggle of life:

The parable of those who take protectors other than Allah is that of the spider, who builds (to itself) an abode; but truly the flimsiest of houses is the spider's house; if they but knew. (29:41)

This is because it is His Being which is the sole source of all power, He is Master of death and life, All-Powerful over all things:

What! Have they taken protectors besides Him? But it is Allah, He is the protector, and it is He Who gives life to the dead: It is He Who has power over all things. (42:9)

Who other than such a Being, Master of such powers, can be so capable and be made master and chief, guardian and organiser, and whose laws and commands should be obeyed?

---

[199] Through this verse the Quran dispels all claims of the use of force to compel anyone to its guidance. *Eimaan* is acceptance of Quranic guidance willingly after convincing the human intellect, based on evidence, that there is great benefit in acceptance of what is given in the Quran. It is absolutely voluntary and is our choice. This is covered in detail in the book *What is Islam* by the author. (Ed)

[200] There is no inner guidance within human beings. As a consequence, we all tend to follow our personal desires. We use our intellect to fulfill our desires which then creates conflicts in the world. The Quran offers its guidance to eliminate these conflicts. (Ed)

Say: 'Shall I take for my protector any other than Allah, the Maker of the heavens and the earth? And He it is that feeds but is not fed'. Say: 'Nay! but I am commanded to be the first of those who bow to Allah (in Islam)' and be not you of the company of those who join gods with Allah. (6:14)

From this the reality becomes clear that the meaning of making Allah a *Wali* is that obedience should only be of His laws - this is Islam, this is the practice of a *Wali* of Allah. In another verse it is stated:

Say: 'Who is Rabb of the heavens and the earth?' Say: (It is) Allah. Say: 'Do you then take protectors other than Him, such as have no power either for good or for harm to themselves'? ...(13:16)

What will you gain from having one who has no control over his own profit and loss as a companion and helper? (It should be borne in mind that profit and loss i.e. the consequence of human deeds, only manifest according to the laws of Allah. Hence, stating that no individual is in control of his gains and losses is a manifestation of a fact). This is why support and companionship can only be of Allah according to Whose laws the entire system of life is busily in action:

Unto Allah belongs the dominion of the heavens and the earth. He gives life and He takes it. Except for Him you have no protector nor helper. (9:116) See also (2:107, 32:4)

Such a Patron Who does not need another's patronage, Who is not dependent on the aid of another:

Say: 'Hamd be to Allah, who begets no son, and has no partner in (His) dominion: Nor (needs) He any to protect Him from weakness (free from all this)'. Magnify Him for His deserving greatness[201]. (17:111)

Man searches for some support and pursues a patron at that time when the tempest of hopelessness and despair engulfs him from every direction, and it is evident that in the dark clouds of futility and bleakness, the ray of light of true hope can only appear via the sparkling Divine laws. It is He Who brings life to the parched land, Who gives rise to the joyous spring of success and jubilation after anguish and desolation:

He is the One that sends down rain (even) after (men) have given up all hope and scatters His mercy (far and wide). And He is the Protector, worthy of all admiration. (42:28)

---

[201] Since Allah with His attributes serves as a higher model for human self-development, hence recognising and understanding His attributes and their significance is essential. (Ed)

Those who, having abandoned Allah, make others their masters and patrons i.e. begin to obey the self-created laws of men, will learn in a very short period of time indeed what the true status of these 'gods of wax' was and what a self-deception it was to rely on them:

They call on such deities, besides Allah, as can neither hurt nor profit them: that is straying far indeed! They call on one whose hurt is nearer than his profit: evil, indeed, is the patron, and evil the companion! (22:12-13)

This is because the end is obvious of the individual who places on sand the foundation of his castle which he has for his protection. These are those ends and consequences toward which attention is drawn through historical evidences:

Do they not travel through the earth, and see what was the end of those before them? Allah brought utter destruction on them, and similar end awaits those who reject Allah. That is because Allah is the protector of those who have Eimaan, but those who reject Allah have no protector. (47:10-11)

23.2   The *Kuffar* and Unjust Have No *Wali*

The entities which those who turn their faces away from Allah make as their patrons and masters, protectors and guardians, are themselves dependent for help and support on others. Hence, when the time comes all the veils of deception are lifted and this fact becomes manifest to them, that:

...and the wrong doers will have no protector nor helper. (42:8)

What can be the end of such people other than destruction and annihilation?

Verily Allah has cursed Kafireen and prepared for them a blazing fire, To dwell therein forever: no protector will they find, nor helper. (33:64-65) See also (45:10)

Ultimately, this was the evident failure and ruin towards which the attention of those who spurned *Haqq* was drawn, and they were warned about the consequences of their evil path, that remember:

...Whoever, forsaking Allah, takes Satan for a friend, has of a surety suffered a loss that is manifest. Satan makes them promises and creates in them false desires; but Satan's promises are nothing but deception. (4:119-120)

23.3 *Willayat* of Satans

As has been explained in great detail in my book titled *Iblees O Adam*, by Satan is meant:

(i) Those emotions of man himself which provoke him to rebel against the obedience of Allah's laws, and furthermore;

(ii) Those rebellious forces which cause people to obey them instead of the laws of Allah.

The pattern of every force of evil is that they try to appease their hangers-on and close affiliates with toys and keep their expectations of hope alive with false promises. This is why obedience of such forces and trust in their friendship ultimately takes them down into the pit of destruction and ruin. It was this very fact that Abraham had pointed to when he said to his father:

'O my father! serve not Satan: for Satan is a rebel against (Allah) Most Gracious'. 'O my father! I fear lest a penalty afflict you from (Allah) Most Gracious, so that you become to Satan a friend'. (19:44-45)

Association with, and obedience of those who choose to rebel against Allah, takes man into their class. It was against this that the progeny of Adam was warned, but as with gold plating, there is such a glitter and fascination in falsehood and deception, that at the slightest glance diverted away from *Haqq*, man becomes ensnared in the trap of *Batil*:

Behold! We said to the angels, 'Bow down to Adam': They bowed down except Iblees. He was one of the Jinns, and he broke the command of his Rabb. Will you then take him and his progeny as protectors rather than Me? And they are enemies to you! Evil would be the exchange for the wrong doers! (18:50)

The forces of *Iblees* and the disciples of Satan are incessantly busy in the pursuit of suppressing the voice of *Haqq*. This is why they continually secretly advise their followers that wherever they see an invitation to *Haqq* and truth, to initiate opposition to it:

...But the evil ones ever inspire their friends to contend with you...(6:121)

Those people become entrapped in the nets of deception of these satans who are in actuality not on the right path but consider in themselves that they are on the guided path:

Some He has guided: others have (by their choice) deserved the loss of their way; in that they took the evil ones, in preference to Allah, for their friends and protectors, and think that they receive guidance. (7:30)

These satans persist in continuously making the wrong path of life attractive in the eyes of these people, so that they can never come to the right path. The end of such people is obvious:

By Allah, We (also) sent (Our messengers) to peoples before you; but Satan made, (to the wicked), their own acts seem alluring: he is also their patron today, but they shall have a most grievous penalty. (16:63)

These are those people who consider their own wishes and delusional desires to be reality, and considering realities to be nothing but playthings, never reflect seriously on them, and never confine the storm laden tides of their desires within the shores of Allah's commands in order to take the stream of life on to the right course. It is about them that it is stated:

Leave alone those who take their Deen to be mere play and amusement and are deceived by the life of this world. But proclaim (to them) this (truth): that every self delivers itself to ruin by its own acts[202]: it will find for itself no protector or intercessor except Allah...(6:70)

Who can save from destruction the one who has withdrawn himself from the protection of Allah?

23.4   *Willayat* and Obedience

As has been written earlier, the meaning of having *Eimaan* on Allah's *Willayat* is that nothing else should be obeyed other than His laws, no-one else should be declared worthy of obedience. If you are to bow, it is to be only before His commands; if servitude is to be adopted it should only be to this true Patron. This is a glaring aspect of the practical demonstration of *Eimaan* in Allah's *Willayat*. It is stated in Surah *Al-Kahf*:

...with Him is (the knowledge of) the secrets of the heavens and the earth: how clearly He sees, how finely He hears (everything)! They have no protector other than Him; nor does He share His command with any one whatsoever. (18:26)

---

[202] A very important fact is stated here which requires profound reflection. It is a law that fire burns regardless of whether one is aware of its property to burn or not, and whoever puts his finger into it in ignorance of this, will still end up with his finger burnt. Similarly, the Divine Law of Requital is working within us, and whether we are aware of it or not, it impacts on our inner self. (Ed)

His *Willayat* is such in which no-one else's command can operate. In His sovereignty the currency of someone else cannot function. Obedience is purely to Him:

Is it not to Allah that sincere devotion is due? But those who take for protectors other than Allah (say): 'We only serve them in order that they may bring us nearer to Allah'. Truly Allah will judge between them in that wherein they differ. But Allah guides not such as are false and ungrateful. (39:3)

Obedience can only be of Allah's laws, other than this, obedience of anything else is not legitimate.[203] This is what is known as guidance of Allah, apart from which there is no other guidance which is deserving of being called guidance, no matter in what shape it presents, in what garb it is clothed, in what form it is concealed, and by what name it is called. Rasul-ullah was told:

Never will the Jews or the Christians be satisfied with you unless you follow their form of creed. Say: 'The Guidance of Allah, that is the (only) Guidance'. Were you to follow their desires after the knowledge which has reached you, then would you find neither protector nor helper against Allah. (2:120)

This guidance of Allah is within the Quran and its obedience is the obedience of Allah, and from this the *Willayat* of Allah can be achieved:

Thus, have We revealed it to be a judgment of authority in Arabic. Were you to follow their desires after the knowledge which has reached you, then would you find neither protector nor defender against Allah. (13:37)

In matters of life this code of laws is the true path of guidance, it is what is known as the *Shariat* of Allah, and by the obedience of this Allah becomes the *Wali* of human beings:

Then We put you on the (right) path: so follow you that (Way), and follow not the desires of those who know not. They will be of no use to you in the sight of Allah: it is only wrong-doers (that stand as) protectors, one to another: but Allah is the protector of the righteous. These are clear evidences to men and a guidance and Rehmat to those of assured Eimaan. (45:18-20)

It is stated to those who accept the Quran as a code of life:

---

[203] The point to consider here is that these laws exist as an external standard and do not require human acceptance in order to function. It is up to each one of us to recognise their existence and then use our free volition to accept or reject them and subsequently live with the consequences of our decision. (Ed)

And Allah gave them a reward in this world, and the excellent reward of the hereafter. For Allah loves those who do good. O you who have Eimaan! If you obey those who do Kufr, they will drive you back on your heels, and you will turn back (from Eimaan) to your own loss. Nay, Allah is your Protector, and He is the best of Helpers. (3:149-150) See also (11:113)

It is only obedience of the Quran which is legitimate, other than this obedience of anything else cannot be called guidance:

Follow (O men!) the revelation given unto you from your Rabb, and follow not, as friends or protectors, other than Him. Little it is you remember of admonition. (7:3)

Whoever, leaving the Quran, begins to follow other doctrines of life, cannot have any share in Allah's *Willayat* and guidance:

…He whom Allah guides is rightly guided; but he whom Allah leaves to stray, for him will you find no protector to lead him to the right path. (18:17) See also (17:97, 42:44)

23.5   Allah's Companions (*Auliya*[204] *Allah*)

Obedience and servitude solely of Allah, i.e. obedience of the Quran and other than this not to consider anyone else worthy of obedience and submission, are the traits of the companions of Allah. The natural consequence of this is that these people cannot have any kind of fear and grief:

Behold! verily on the companions (obedient servants) of Allah there is no fear, nor shall they grieve. (10:62)

This is because:

Those who have Eimaan and (constantly) guard against evil; for them are glad tidings, in the life of the present and in the hereafter; no change can there be in the words of Allah. This is indeed the supreme felicity. (10:63-64)

Turning the abode of the human heart into peace and tranquility is a very great blessing, but not that mirage-like peace and tranquility which is gained through the giving up of desires and the monasticism of shunning contact with the world, rather that peace and tranquility which is the natural consequence of accomplishments in this world and successes of the hereafter. And this is achieved through correct *Eimaan* and deeds:

---

[204] *Auliya* – plural of *Wali* which means companion. (Ed)

In the case of those who say, 'Our Rabb is Allah', and, further, stand straight and steadfast, the cosmic forces (Malaika) descend on them: (these state) 'Fear you not!', 'nor grieve! but receive the glad tidings of the garden (of Bliss), the which you were promised!' We are your protectors in this life and in the Hereafter: therein shall you have all that your self shall desire; therein shall you have all that you ask for! (41:30-31)

Bring this fact once more to mind that this condition of the companions of Allah (obedient men of Allah), that they do not have any kind of fear and grief, is the consequence of obedience of the laws of Allah. Hence, the individual who becomes a follower of the laws of Allah will be included in the category of the companions of Allah (*Auliya* Allah). There is no separate group as such of *Auliya* Allah, no separate *Jamaat*. There are no special signs for their recognition. All Muslims are *Auliya* Allah, provided that they live their life under the obedience of the Quran, and the essential consequence of this obedience is establishment on the earth. Thus, *Auliya* Allah is actually another name for *Millat e Islamia*, the Islamic State, which is responsible for the dissemination and interpretation of the commands of Allah and the implementation of the laws of Allah in the world. Among them there is nothing secret, no concealed knowledge, no hidden way of life. The clear and manifest teaching of the Quran, the clear results of this teaching, the clear objective, and the clear methods to achieve this objective - this is the straight path of the Quran (*Sirat e Mustaqeem*). It is declared that this is the glaring trait of *Auliya* Allah that they will have no kind of fear and grief. At the time of the 'creation of Adam', addressing mankind, it was stated that you will spend your life in such a world where at every step the rebellious forces of transgression and mutual enmity will have spread their nets. Only the one who continues to obey the guidance of Allah will remain protected from this conflict and confrontation. The Quran states:

...and if, as is sure, there comes to you guidance from Me, whosoever follows My guidance, on them shall be no fear, nor shall they grieve. (2:38)

It has been made clear here that the procedure through which to remain protected from fear and grief is that the guidance of Allah be followed. And since it is stated about the *Auliya* Allah that they will not have any kind of fear and grief, it can therefore be deductively known from this that *Auliya* Allah is the name of those who follow the guidance of Allah i.e. all *Momineen* are *Auliya* Allah. This belief or concept which is prevalent among us that there is a special group of '*Auliya* Allah' who are possessors of 'spirituality', is not a Quranic concept. According to the Quran, when the Islamic State establishes its system according to the laws of Allah, then this state is the one which will be called *Auliya* Allah i.e. that nation which, through obedience of the laws of Allah, will become the companion of Allah in making the creative programme of Allah and the system of *Rabubiyat* universal.

According to the division put forward by the Quran, two distinct groups have emerged in front of us. One is that which obeys the laws of Allah, and other than Him, do not bow down before anyone else. This group is of the *Auliya* Allah. This will be called *Hizb ul Momineen* or *Millat e Islamia*. In opposition to this the other group is that which, instead of obeying *Wahi* and the guidance of Allah, declares as doctrine and procedure the path of life defined by human beings. This group is *Auliya* Satan, the *Jamaat* of deniers. Now it is obvious that between these two groups no kind of relationship of the heart, no reason for any togetherness, no commonality of outlook, no mutual harmony, no compatibility, no understanding will be possible.

23.6   Relations of Friendship with Outsiders

Both have different ideologies, both have a separate *Kaaba* - how can there be compatibility of hearts between them? This is why the former (*Jamaat e Momineen*) are informed in very clear and unambiguous words that:

Let not Momineen take for friends or helpers Kafir rather than Momineen: if any do that, in nothing will there be help from Allah: except by way of precaution, that you may guard yourselves from them. But Allah cautions you (to remember) Himself; for the final goal is to Allah. (3:28)

In Surah *An-Nisa* it is stated:

O you who have Eimaan! Take not for friends Kafir rather than Momineen: Do you wish to offer Allah an open proof against yourselves? (4:144)

This is because, as noted earlier, the *Momineen* are companions and helpers of one another, and the *Kuffar* are friends of one another. Where is the possibility for oneness between Islam and *Kufr*?

Those who have Eimaan, and adopted exile, and fought for Eimaan, with their property and their persons, in the cause of Allah, as well as those who gave (them) asylum and aid, these are (all) friends and protectors, one of another. As to those who accepted Eimaan but came not into exile, you owe no duty of protection to them until they come into exile; but if they seek your aid in Deen, it is your duty to help them, except against a people with whom you have a treaty of mutual alliance. And (remember) Allah sees all that you do. Those who practice Kufr are protectors of one another: Unless you do this, (protect each other), there would be tumult and oppression on earth, and great mischief. (8:72-73)

261

It is stated in Surah *At-Tauba*:

> *The Momineen, men and women, are protectors one of another: they enjoin what is just, and forbid what is evil: they establish Salat, practice Zakat, and obey Allah and His Messenger. On them will Allah pour His mercy: for Allah is Exalted in power, Wise. (9:71)*

About the Jews and Christians it is stated:

> *O you who have Eimaan! take not the Jews and the Christians for your friends and protectors: They are but friends and protectors to each other. And he amongst you that turns to them (for friendship) is of them. Verily Allah guides not a people unjust. (5:51)*

Reflect carefully how this reality is unveiled in clear words that whichever group an individual maintains a friendship with, he will be considered to be one of them, because friendship is another name for relationships based on the affinity of hearts. Wherever an individual's heart is, he will be counted there, particularly those people who ridicule your Deen, who view these immutable truths with scorn, criticise and belittle them, even the slightest inclination of the heart towards them is enough to take one towards the pit of hell:

> *O you who have Eimaan! take not for friends and protectors those who take your Deen for a mockery or sport, whether among those who received the Scripture before you, or among those who are Kuffar; but fear you Allah, if you have Eimaan (indeed). (5:57)*

This is because:

> *Your (real) friends are (no less than) Allah, His Messenger, and the (fellowship of) Momineen, those who establish Salat and organise Zakat, and they bow down before Allah's laws. (5:55)*

23.7 Friendship with Hypocrites

In the above lines there is mention of no friendship with those people who openly reject *Eimaan*, who are obviously distinct from the *Jamaat e Momineen* and have a different path of life. But there is also such a group which, despite claiming to have *Eimaan*, is not part of the group of those who have *Eimaan*. Their *Eimaan* never goes further than the level of their throat, they display their connection to the Islamic system for the sake of their vested interests and aims, but in truth their only interest is their own advantage and objectives. Regarding this masked, cloak and dagger *Jamaat* of hypocrites, it is stated that:

They but wish that you should reject Eimaan, as they do, and thus be on the same footing (as they): But take not friends from their ranks until they migrate in the way of Allah (leaving behind enemies). But if they turn renegades, slay them and fight them wherever you find them; and take no friends or helpers from their ranks. (4:89)

Details of the hypocrites will be given at its own place; here it is essential to state this much that like the *Kuffar*, there is no separate group of hypocrites. This is only a name for a *Jamaat* of those who claim Islam, their Islam is limited to their tongues only, no evidence of this is obtained from their conduct. These people seem to apparently be with us but in their hearts are with others. They are equal partners in the benefits from the system but will never support it in times of difficulty. The search for false power is their way of life and the pursuit of wrong status is their aim; wherever they can get power, no matter how it is obtained, they will grab it without hesitation. It is about them that it is stated:

To the Hypocrites give the glad tidings that there is for them (but) a grievous penalty; Yea, to those who take for friends Kafireen rather than Momineen: is it power they seek among them? Nay, all power is with Allah. (4:138-139)

23.8   Who Are Our 'Own'

And let us proceed and see how the Quran wishes to keep an obvious demarcation and very clear difference between *Kufr* and *Eimaan*. In Surah *At-Tauba* it is stated:

O you who have Eimaan! take not for protectors your fathers and your brothers if they love infidelity above Eimaan: if any of you do so, they do wrong. Say: If it be that your fathers, your sons, your brothers, your mates, or your kindred; the wealth that you have gained; the commerce in which you fear a decline: or the dwellings in which you delight - are dearer to you than Allah, and His Messenger, and the striving in His cause; then wait until Allah brings about His decision (as per law): and Allah guides not (as per His law) the rebellious. (9:23-24)

The one who is an enemy of the system of Allah is an ill-wisher of that *Jamaat* which rises for the establishment of this system, what relationship can they have with those who exist for this supreme aim and die for its sake. The relationship of friendship can never exist between these two:

O you who have Eimaan! Take not my enemies and yours as friends (or protectors), offering them (your) love, even though they have rejected the Truth that has come to you, and have (on the contrary) driven out the Messenger and yourselves (from your

*homes), (simply) because you have Eimaan in Allah your Rabb! If you have come out
to strive in My Way and to seek My good pleasure, (take them not as friends),
holding secret converse of love (and friendship) with them: for I know full well all
that you conceal and all that you reveal. And any of you that does this has strayed
from the straight path. (60:1)*

A couple of verses after this verse it is stated that in this matter the pattern of life
of the first leader Abraham and his companions is the best model for you 'when
they told their people that we are disgusted with you, and from all of those whom
you obey after having rejected Allah'. The Quran states:

*There is for you an excellent model to follow in Abraham and those with him, when
they said to their people: 'We are clear of you and of whatever you follow besides
Allah: we have rejected you, and there has arisen, between us and you, enmity and
hatred for ever, unless you have Eimaan in Allah and Him alone… (60:4)*

The reality is that Islam establishes the criteria for relations, affection, unity and
love differently from the rest of the world. Those who, after accepting *Eimaan* in
Allah and His messenger, live their life according to His code of laws, are all
members of one brotherhood and members of one nation; and those who are
outwith this system are members of another *Jamaat*, no matter if they are the
closest of relations or the dearest of friends. The relation of father and son (Noah
and his son), the relation of son and father (Abraham and his father), the relation
of husband and wife (Lot and his wife), all relations of near and dear ones (Rasul-
ullah and the Quraysh tribe, Bani Hashem), all break up if the connection of Islam
is not shared among them. And those who become associated in this connection
become members of one brotherhood, even if previously no kind of reason for
commonality is shared according to worldly standards, such as race, language,
nationality, tribalism and relatives. This is because the foundation for their mutual
association and companionship is based on this supreme truth that they all have
one *Wali* and *Maula*. About the Jews it is stated:

*If only they had Eimaan in Allah, in Nabi, and in what has been revealed to him, never
would they have taken them for friends and protectors, but most of them are
rebellious wrong-doers. (5:81)*

This is because, after accepting *Eimaan*, these people would have become
members of a new community, they would have accepted Allah as their *Wali* and
Maula, and then there would have been no relationship left with the *Kuffar* because
the *Wali* and *Maula* of *Kuffar* are satans:

…We made the evil ones friends (only) to those without Eimaan. (7:27)

The difference between a *Momin* and a *Kafir* is indeed this - that a *Momin* only accepts the sovereignty of Allah, only adopts obedience and submission to Him. But a *Kafir* lives his life under the system devised by men; rejecting Allah, he obeys men and thus by accepting them as masters, he places his trust in their supremacy and companionship. What can be the consequence of this other than hell:

Do those who do Kufr think that they can take My servants as protectors besides Me? Verily We have prepared hell for Kafireen for (their) entertainment. (18:102)

These same people have also been called wrong doers because they do not maintain companionship (*Willayat*) and obedience at their correct place. They all become members of one brotherhood no matter what name it may have, and in opposition to *Haqq* they are companions of one another, regardless of how numerous their mutual individual differences may be:

...it is only wrong-doers (that stand as) protectors, one to another: but Allah is the protector of the righteous. (45:19)

23.9   Opportunities for *Willayat* of Allah

When there are these two categories whose aims of life are mutually exclusive and whose paths of life are mutually opposing, then it is obvious that conflict and confrontation between them is inevitable. The forces of *Batil* will always remain engaged in this pursuit that the voice of *Haqq* is never able to be raised, and for this they will use every tyrannical tactic of theirs. This is that point where the *Willayat* of Allah becomes a shield for the *Jamaat* supporting the protection of *Haqq*. In the early life of the Muslims when they were given permission to engage in battle, it was stated:

And why should you not fight in the cause of Allah and of those who, being weak, are ill-treated (and oppressed)? Men, women, and children, whose cry is: 'Our Rabb! Rescue us from this town, whose people are oppressors; and raise for us from You one who will protect; and raise for us from You one who will help!' (4:75)

Hence, on one side the supplications of the oppressed and indigent arose fervently from their hearts, and on the other side the *Willayat* of Allah sprang forth in the shape of the armies and soldiers of the *Auliya* Allah (companions of Allah). The command was issued:

Those who have Eimaan fight in the cause of Allah, and those who do Kufr fight in the cause of evil: so fight you against the friends of Satan: feeble indeed is the cunning of Satan. (4:76)

In other words, rebellious forces will appear to be fearsome and menacing, but really will be very weak and unstable because their trust is completely dependent on the *Willayat* (i.e. companionship, support, protection, friendship, obedience and supervision) of *Batil* and deception; and the trust of the *Jamaat e Momineen* is on the *Willayat* of Allah. Hence, the *Jamaat* whose *Wali* (planner, guardian, protector and watcher) is stronger is the one which will ultimately be successful and prosperous. Allah states:

> *O Nabi! strive hard against the unbelievers and the hypocrites and be firm against them. Their abode is hell, an evil refuge indeed. They swear by Allah that they said nothing (evil), but indeed they uttered blasphemy, and they did it after accepting Islam; and they meditated a plot which they were unable to carry out: this revenge of theirs was (their) only return for the bounty with which Allah and His Messenger had enriched them! If they repent, it will be best for them; but if they turn back (to their evil ways), Allah will punish them with a grievous penalty in this life and in the hereafter. They shall have none on earth to protect or help them. (9:73-74)*

It was said to these *Kuffar* and hypocrites i.e. the ones who were rebellious and shunned *Haqq*, on what false pretences are you so arrogant? You cannot escape from the grasp of the Law of Requital, no helper and guardian can make you free from the grip of this law:

> *Not on earth nor in heaven will you be able (fleeing) to frustrate (His Plan), nor have you, besides Allah, any protector and helper. (29:22) See also (11:20, 42:31)*

The grip of the Divine law is not such that you can obstruct it in any way whatsoever or find any such protector and guardian in opposition to it who can save you from the consequences of your deeds. There is only one way to do this, that you should acknowledge His invitation and obey His laws, and in this way come under the shadow of His protection. Then you will not have any kind of fear and grief. If you will not accept His invitation, then no-one can be your helper:

> *If any does not hearken to the one who invites (us) to Allah, he cannot frustrate (Allah's Plan) on earth, and no protectors can he have besides Allah: such men (wander) in manifest error. (46:32)*

23.10 The Immutable Law of Nature

And this is not some new thing or a chance *Amr* (event) that the righteous will reap success and victory in their opposition to the *Kuffar*, rather it is one law from among the absolute laws of nature, and one rule from its unable to be changed immutable rules. Just as it is an immutable law of nature that with the arrival of light darkness can no longer remain, similarly this is also an immutable law that

266

Batil in opposition to *Haqq*, the *Kuffar* in opposition to the *Momineen* - these can never succeed:

> *If those who do Kufr should fight you, they would certainly turn their backs; then would they find neither protector nor helper. (Such has been) the practice (approved) of Allah already in the past: no change will you find in the practice (approved) of Allah. (48:22-23)*

Hence, there is no reason to be afraid or fearful of these people:

> *And strive in His cause as you ought to strive. He has chosen you and has imposed no difficulties on you in Deen; it is the way of your father Abraham. It is He Who has named you Muslims, both before and in this (Revelation); that the Messenger may be a witness for you, and you be witnesses for mankind! So, establish Salat, establish Zakat and hold fast to Allah! He is your protector - the best to protect and the best to help. (22:78)*

In Surah *Al-Anfal* it is stated:

> *And fight them on until there is no more tumult and oppression, and there completely prevail Deen of Allah and everywhere; but if they cease, verily Allah does see all that they do. If they refuse, be sure that Allah is your protector - the best to protect and the best to help. (8:39-40)*

When the reality is such, then loss of courage by the righteous in the battle between *Haqq* and *Batil* will be an indication of this *Amr* that they lost sight of this immutable law of Allah (even if momentarily). Hence, in the battle of *Uhad* when two groups showed signs of slight weakness, then it was stated regarding this:

> *Remember two of your parties meditated cowardice; but Allah was their protector, and in Allah should the Momineen put their trust. (3:122)*

The Pharaonic forces of *Batil* provoke such qualms so that fear of their power entrenches in the hearts of the righteous but those who have full trust in the *Willayat* of Allah have nothing to fear:

> *It is only the evil one that suggests to you the fear of his votaries: be you not be afraid of them, but fear Me, if you are Momineen. (3:175)*

23.11 Recognising Allah's *Wali*

The shining attribute of a *Momin* is that he should not fear any power which is other than Allah and should enter the arena fully prepared to oppose *Batil*. For him, death is a sport. The one who fears death is the one who considers life to be only the life of this world. For the one for whom the process of life also continues after death, in fact life traverses its further evolutionary stages in that phase, what reason can there be to fear death. His state is such that *'as death arrives, a smile appears on his lips'*. This is why it is stated:

Say: 'O you that stand on Judaism! If you think that you are friends to Allah, to the exclusion of (other) men, then express your desire for death, if you are truthful!' But never will they express their desire (for death), because of the (deeds) their hands have sent on before them; and Allah knows well those that do wrong. (62:6-7)

This is because they are aware that no matter how many claims they might make with their tongues, there will be no helper and protector other than Allah at the time of the manifestation of results. (6:51, 42:46). At that point the *Maula* of the *Kuffar* will be hell (57:15), and no friend (*Maula*) will be of any use to any other friend (*Maula*) (44:41). Regarding those people who make others their *Maula* and patron other than Allah, Allah is overseeing their deeds (42:6). There, each and every atom of good and evil will become manifest.

A *Momin* has this *Eimaan* that his *Wali* (guardian and caretaker) is Allah. This is the correct relationship between a human being and Allah. Hence, Rasul-ullah was informed:

...Allah is your Protector...(66:2)

And the *Momineen* are taught these supplications, that:

...You are our protector; help us in victory against those who are Kafir. (2:286)

23.12 Whose *Wali* Does Allah Become

But the question is, how can this *Willayat* of Allah be attained? Whose *Wali* does Allah become and how? Regarding this, the Quran has informed us in absolutely clear terms that, remember, the people who are successful are:

...He will be their friend, because of their deeds. (6:127)

Allah becomes a *Wali* as a consequence of deeds; His *Willayat* is only for the righteous:

'For my protector is Allah, Who revealed the Book, and He will choose and befriend the righteous'. (7:196)

There is one and only one way to make Allah one's *Wali*, and to be His *Wali*, and that is that righteous deeds should be according to His revealed Book; other than this there is no other suitable means. The mere wishes and desires of someone will not bear results. It is a clear decision of Allah that:

Not your desires, nor those of the people of the Book (can prevail): whoever works evil, will be requited accordingly. Nor will he find, besides Allah, any protector or helper. (4:123) See also (4:173)

The human self develops through the obedience of the laws of Allah (which are preserved in the Quran), which means that man continues to become a reflection of the Divine attributes (within human limits). In this way, Allah becomes the *Wali* of man and man becomes the *Wali* of Allah, and this is the correct relationship between man and Allah.

The Ummah which takes shape by the coming together of these kinds of individuals is called the *Jamaat* of *Auliya* Allah. Whatever it becomes the protector and guardian of in this world, that then becomes secure and protected from all kinds of danger. This protection and security is an essential consequence of this Divine system which is shaped through the hands of the *Jamaat e Momineen*.

24 *Durr e Manthoor*[205]

24.1 Miscellaneous Attributes of Allah

Other than the attributes of Allah which have been mentioned in the previous pages, there are many other attributes which have also been noted in the Quran. If all of these attributes were to be explained in detail, then there would be a requirement for many volumes for this. Hence, we will confine ourselves to only a brief summary of the remaining attributes. If you study the Quran in the light of these brief introductions, then the details will become apparent to you themselves. If you wish to understand their wider meanings, then refer to my work titled *Lughat-ul-Quran* for this.

24.2 *Al-Hakeem* (The Wise)

The reins of a horse are called *Al-Hakamahto*. The task of a rein is to not allow the animal to become out of control and unruly, but to make it go at the correct speed on the right path. Hence, *Al-Hikmahto* means to retain matters within the correct boundaries and to not allow any among them to go here and there. That person is called *Hakeem-un* who, with correct proportion and balance, keeping its every requirement in view, makes everything with great beauty and precision, in fact, accomplishes all matters in this way. In the light of these connotations, this reality will become clear that when Allah is called *Al-Hakeem*, what the meaning of this will be. Since this Divine attribute is very fundamental and important, it is therefore mentioned in the Quran at many places e.g. *Hakeem-in-Khabeer* (11:1), *Hakeem-un-Aleemun* (6:139) etc.

From this it is evident how every matter will be based on wisdom in a society which consists of those individuals whose self is a holder of the Divine attributes.

24.3 *Al-Haleem* (The Forbearing)

The person whose nerves are weak becomes provoked at the slightest thing; his emotions are inflamed by the most minor of criticisms. Contrary to this, in the individual whose energy is developed there is calm in his temperament, his nerves and limbs are strong, he is rightly trained, he is mature, stable, reflective and serious. He does not become provoked by every small issue, pays serious attention to matters, reaches decisions with pragmatism and care, and then stands firmly resolved on this decision. Such an individual is called *Haleem-un*. The meaning of

---

[205] *Durr e Manthoor* – literally 'scattered pearls'. These are some Divine attributes which the author has grouped together in this chapter. (Ed)

Allah as *Haleem-un* is that His Law of Requital does not become 'inflamed', rather it takes deeds towards their results according to rules and laws. And if, during this period, reformation is carried out in these deeds, then it provides a means of protection from their ill effects. See how the Quran has expressed this fact, in Surah *Al-Baqra* it is stated:

> *Allah will not call you to account for thoughtlessness in your oaths, but for the intention in your hearts; and He is all Protecting, Most Forbearing. (2:225) See also (2:235)*

In the battle of *Uhad*, a small blunder was made by some of the Mujahideen, as a result of which victory turned into a temporary setback. In relation to this event it is stated:

> *Those of you who turned back on the day the two hosts met, it was Satan who caused them to fail, because of some mistake they had done. But Allah Has blotted out (their fault): For Allah is Protecting, Haleem (Most Forbearing). (3:155)*

In order to understand the Quranic meaning of *Haleem*, these two verses are sufficient in themselves. Apart from these verses, this word has also been used at some seven or eight other places e.g. (2:263, 4:12, 5:101, 17:44, 22:59, 33:51, 35:41, 64:17).

24.3 *Al-Ghafoor, Al-Ghaffar, Al-Afuwwo*[206]

When there is an outbreak of an epidemic disease in some place, most of the population usually becomes its victim, but despite this some people remain protected from this attack. These are the people in whom there is a greater immunity. This strength of theirs keeps individuals protected by countering the harmful effects of the disease. This is called *Maghfirat.*[207] According to Allah's Law of Requital every deed establishes its own effect. If the weight of the deeds producing constructive effects of some individual or nation are greater, then it remains protected against the destructive effects of these deeds (harmful effects), which are made by it in error or omission. This is called the attribute of *Ghaffari* and *Ghafuri* (2:281). This attribute has also been mentioned at numerous places. *Affuwan Ghafur-un* (22:60) is also mentioned at a few places i.e. the One Who instead of taking notice, moves forward (the One Who overlooks) – the meaning of this is the same as that of *Maghfirat*. The meaning of *Maghfirat* is not that of 'forgiveness' merely for the sake of it.

---

[206] All these terms are related to providing protection (Ed)
[207] *Maghfirat* – this is covered in detail in Chapter 6 of the author's book titled *The Life in the Hereafter: What does the Quran say?* (Ed)

24.4 *At-Tawwab* (Returning)

You may be travelling somewhere and on the way you take a wrong turn at a crossroads. After travelling some distance, you come to realise (or someone else informs you) that you have gone in the wrong direction. From here, in order to go in the correct direction, it is necessary that you come back to that same place from where you had stepped in the wrong direction. This kind of 'return' is called *Tauba*. We have seen that, according to Allah's Law of Requital, there is an interval between a deed and the manifestation of its result. If during this period, man abandons this wrong path and adopts the right path, and then does such righteous deeds as a consequence of which protection is obtained from the harmful effects of the previous error, then that individual is saved from destruction and ruin. This Divine attribute is called *Tawwabiyat*:

> *...For He is Oft-Returning. (110:3)*

Man is *At-Ta'eb* (the one who returns) and Allah is *At-Tawwabo* (the One Who returns to this man swiftly).

24.5 *Rauf-un*[208]

The words *Rehmat* and *Raft* are almost synonymous with this difference that the word *Rehmat* means to bestow means of nourishment, and the meaning of *Raft* is to remove those impediments which are obstructing the path of an individual's development. This is the reason why the attributes of *Rauf-un* and *Raheem* are generally mentioned in the Quran together:

> *Were it not for the grace and mercy of Allah on you, and that Allah is full of kindness and mercy, (you would be ruined indeed). (24:20)*

In Surah *At-Tauba* it is stated:

> *...but He turned to them (also): for He is unto them Rauf-un, Raheem. (9:117) See also (2:143, 16:7, 16:47, 22:65; 57:9, 59:10)*

At one place in Surah *At-Tauba* one attribute of Rasul-ullah is also cited as *Rauf-un Raheem-un* (9:128). This will be the same state of those followers of Rasul-ullah in whose self the Divine attributes are reflected.

24.6 *Al-Wadud (Love and Mercy)*

---

[208] *Rauf-un* - to eliminate impediments from the path of nourishment. (Ed)

Mo'addat and *Rehmat* are also two branches of the same tree. In Surah *Ar-Rum* it is stated:

And among His Signs is this, that He created for you mates from among yourselves, that you may dwell in tranquility with them, and He has put love and mercy between your (hearts): verily in that are signs for those who reflect. (30:21)

This is why in one place in the Quran *Wadud* appears alongside *Raheem*, and with *Ghafur* at another place. The messenger Shoaib stated to his people:

But ask protection of your Rabb and turn unto Him: for my Rabb is indeed full of Mercy and Loving-Kindness. (11:90)

In Surah *Al-Buruj*, after mentioning reward and punishment, it is stated:

And He is all Protecting, full of Loving-Kindness. (85:14)

It should be made clear that the blessings of the rain bearing clouds of Allah's *Rehmat, Maghfirat*, love etc. are according to His special laws, and in order to benefit from these blessings, we have to make ourselves deserving of them. How will that land which is barren benefit from this? Regarding Allah's love it is stated:

*O you who have Eimaan! if any from among you turn back from his Eimaan, soon will Allah produce a people whom He will love as they will love Him, lowly with Momineen, mighty against Kuffar, fighting in the way of Allah, and never afraid of the reproaches of such as find fault. That is the grace of Allah, which He will bestow **on** whom as per His Mashe'at (law). And Allah encompasses all, and He knows all things. (5:54)*

These are the conditions for Allah's love and *Mo'addat*, by fulfilling which we can make ourselves worthy of them!

24.7 *Al-Kareem (Eminent)*

Among the Arabs, the word *Kareem* had wide ranging meanings. You can understand it as follows, that they would use the term *Al-Kareem* for the one about whom they wished to assert that he encompasses all the lofty traits and pleasant attributes of humanity. The possessor of all kinds of status and respect, deserving of all types of dignity and admiration, holder of boundless generosity, large-heartedness and philanthropy, kindness and compassion - a developed self is a mirror image of all of these balanced attributes. From this it is evident what its aim and meaning will be when this word is used for Allah. In Surah *An-Naml* it is stated:

... And if any is grateful, truly his gratitude is for his own self; but if any is ungrateful, truly my Rabb is free of all needs, Supreme in Honour! (27:40)

This means that He is not in need of anyone's *Shukr* (gratitude) nor can the *Kufr* of anyone do any harm to Him, rather His *Fadl* and blessings will rain down upon the one who displays *Shukr* (gratitude). In Surah *Al-Infitar* it is stated:

O man! What has seduced you from your Rabb Al-Kareem? Him Who created you. Fashioned (passing through various stages) you in due proportion and provided you with a just balance. (82:6-7)

In other words, the creation of man and then his balanced status is all due to the *Fadl* and *Karam* of Allah. Here, Allah is called *Kareem* but at another place He is called *Akram*:

Proclaim! And your Rabb is Akram (Most Bountiful), He Who taught (the writing knowledge through) the pen, taught man all that which he knew not. (96:3-5)

At the time of the creation and balancing of man, He is *Rabb-e-Kareem*; and at the time of the education of man He is *Rabb-e-Akram*. The distinction between *Kareem* and *Akram* is the same as that between creation and education. Creation and balancing are also due to His *Karam*, as well as education. But compared to creation, education is a greater *Karam*. That is why the word *Akram* (Bestower of extremely great *Karam*) has been used for this.

24.8 *Al-Burro* (Infinitely Righteous)

The meaning of *Al-Burro* is Master of boundless expanses, Creator of vastness in the path of life. This attribute has also appeared alongside *Raheem*. It is stated about the inhabitants of paradise that they will say:

But Allah has been good to us and has delivered us from the penalty of the scorching wind. Truly, we did call unto Him from of old: truly it is He, Al-Burro, Al-Raheem! (52:27-28)

24.9 *Al-Hafeez²⁰⁹, Ar-Raqeeb²¹⁰, Al-Mohaiman²¹¹, Al-Hayyu²¹², Al-Qayyum²¹³, Al-Muqeet²¹⁴*

When Allah is the Creator, Sustainer and Nourisher of the whole of the universe; He possesses knowledge of everything, is the Knower and the Aware, then it is obvious that He is also the custodian of everything:

> *...and your Rabb does watch over all things. (34:21) See also (11:57)*

In another verse it is stated:

> *...and Allah does watch over all things. (33:52) See also (4:1)*

When the sons of Yaqub (Jacob) requested their father to send the younger brother of Yusuf along with them, promising to protect him, Jacob responded, what protection can you offer:

> *...But Allah is the best to take care (of him) ...(12:64)*

During the reign of Solomon, it is stated about the 'Jinns' who used to be busy in carrying out tasks:

> *... and it was We Who guarded them. (21:82)*

In Surah *Al-Hashr* the term *Al-Mohaiman* also appears with the same meanings (59:23). In Surah *Al-Baqra* it is stated that the supervision and protection of the universe does not weary Allah, because neither is sleep for His eyes nor dozing for His mind. He is Alive in such a way that for His Life there is no end or decline. Everything is established according to His command and He is not dependent on anyone for His existence:

> *Allah! There is no god but He, the Living, the Self-subsisting, Eternal. No slumber can seize Him nor sleep... and He feels no fatigue in guarding and preserving them...*
> *(2:255) See also (3:1, 20:111, 40:65)*

He is Guardian over everything:

---

²⁰⁹ *Al-Hafeez* – the Protector
²¹⁰ *Ar-Raqeeb* – the Guardian
²¹¹ *Al-Mohaiman* – the Custodian
²¹² *Al-Hayyu* – the Living One and the Giver of Life
²¹³ *Al-Qayyum* – the Established One
²¹⁴ *Al-Muqeet* – the Caretaker

…And Allah has power over all things. (4:85)

Al-Hayyu is a supreme attribute of Allah. The most important thing in the universe is life, not only is it important, but is spellbinding for the intellects as well. This is because (as noted under the subject of 'Life and Death') human research has not yet been able to determine the answer to this secret as to what the origin of life is. The Quran has stated that Allah's Self is *Al-Hayyu* i.e. He is alive in Himself and is the Bestower of life on others. It is obvious that when this attribute becomes reflected in the human self, what its own state will become, and how beneficial its outcomes will be. Its own state will be such that it will not be able to die even with death, it will become the possessor of immortal life, and the state of its attributes will be such that it will provide the means of nourishment of life to others. And that society which will consist of such individuals, and the system which will take shape through their hands, will contain the means of sustenance of life in abundance for every single individual of humanity - not only for physical life, but for human life also i.e it will contain the means of nourishment for the development of the selfs of all individuals.

24.10   *Awwal O Aakhir* (The First and The Last)

Allah is above and beyond the limits of time and space. When there was nothing, He was present. When there will be nothing, He will be present:

He is the First and the Last, the Evident and the Immanent …(57:3)

He is present and a witness everywhere:

…for Allah is witness of all things. (22:17)

These are those attributes which specifically belong to the Self of Allah and no-one else can be associated in them.

24.11   *Qareeb-un* (Nearness)

When He is present everywhere then it is also erroneous to think that He is residing at some specific place. Allah states:

When My servants ask you concerning Me, I am indeed close (to them): I listen to the supplication of every suppliant when he calls on Me…(2:186)

In Surah *Hud* it is stated:

…certainly, for my Rabb is near, ready to answer (supplication). (11:61)

276

In Surah *Al-Saba* it is stated:

> *... it is He Who hears all things and is near. (34:50)*

Even closer than the jugular vein:

> *...for We are nearer to him than his jugular vein. (50:16) See also (56:85)*

We cannot comprehend anything about how Allah's Being is present everywhere and is closer to us than our jugular vein.[215] But as has been already noted, our relationship with Allah is linked via His laws. Hence, we should recognise that His Law of Requital is all-encompassing in such a way that wherever we are and in whatever state we may be, we cannot hide from the eyes of His law; even the fleeting thoughts passing through our heart and the stealthy glances of our eyes cannot remain outwith the domain of its grasp. In other words, our every deed, thought and intention will of a surety establish its effect according to Allah's law.

This will be the state of that society which becomes shaped according to the Divine laws. In it, too, every deed will of a surety manifest its effect; neither anyone's hard work will go wasted, nor will a criminal be able to escape the consequences of his deed.

24.12 *Al-Lateef* (The Intangible)

But despite being so close, so *Lateef* that He cannot be seen:

> *No vision can grasp Him, but His grasp is over all vision: He is above all comprehension yet is acquainted with all things. (6:103) See also (22:63, 31:16, 33:34, 67:14,)*

Lateef also means the dispenser of kindness:

> *Gracious is Allah to His servants...(42:19)*

Allah deals with His servants (in providing guidance) compassionately. In another verse it is stated:

> *... Verily my Rabb does treat with leniency according to His Mashe'at (law) ...(12:100)*

---

[215] The concept of Allah given in the Quran points to the fact that He has to be everywhere to create the universe, to be able to add to His creation on a continual basis, to cause it to function according to His laws and for the effective functioning of the Law of Requital. (45:22). (Ed)

24.13 *Ash-Shaheed* (Present and Watchful)

So *Lateef* that He is not visible to the eyes, but so near that He is present and watching everywhere, and is a witness to all things:

> *...for Allah is witness to all things. (58:6) See also (4:33, 5:117, 22:17, 33:55, 34:47)*

No matter how secret a deed may apparently seem, it cannot hide from Allah's knowledge because He is a witness to every deed:

> *...when Allah is Himself witness to all you do? (3:98) See also (11:46)*

When some such matter is presented for which no witness can be found, Allah is a witness to that too. After mentioning the decision in a case involving Dawood and Solomon, it is stated:

> *...We did witness their judgment. (21:78)*

And We were a witness on their decision, and not only a witness to this one verdict, wherever there is *Haqq*, Allah is a witness to it. Just reflect! when a messenger comes and proclaims that whatever I say is not from myself, but this is a message which has been revealed for you from your Allah, obviously this is a very great proclamation, and for the verification of its truth there is a need for a very great witness. Who is this witness? The Quran states:

> *But Allah bears witness that what He has sent unto you He has sent from His own knowledge, and Malaika bear witness: But enough is Allah for a witness. (4:166) See also (3:18)*

Witnessing the messenger-hood of Rasul-ullah:

> *...and We have sent you as a messenger to mankind. And enough is Allah for a witness. (4:79)*

Such a messenger whose message of guidance and righteousness is going to overpower every constitution and way of life in the world:

> *It is He Who has sent His messenger with guidance and Deen of Haqq, to proclaim it over all Deen (man-made systems): and enough is Allah for a witness. (48:28)*

Let us examine the various links of the process of guidance and righteousness. The first pronouncement of the proclaimer of *Haqq* appears to be that of an apparently helpless and isolated individual. People falsify it due to mischief and enmity and in this way a battle commences between *Haqq* and *Batil*. All the apparently visible means of support seem to be with the forces of *Batil*, and *Haqq* is envisioned as being in a state of helplessness and powerlessness. At this juncture, no-one who is merely looking at worldly means and causes will forecast that *Haqq* will emerge victorious from this battle. But there is also such a witness present who makes an unequivocal proclamation that ultimately the victory will be of *Haqq*, and then the results will show what a supreme truth this evidence was based on. The Quran states:

Say: 'What thing is most weighty in evidence?' Say: 'Allah is witness between me and you; This Quran has been revealed to me by inspiration, that I may warn you and all whom it reaches. Can you possibly bear witness that besides Allah there is another god?' Say: 'Nay! I cannot bear witness!' Say: 'But in truth He is the one Allah, and I truly am innocent of (your blasphemy of) joining others with Him. (6:19) See also (10:29, 17:96, 29:52, 46:8)

The meaning of Allah being a witness in these matters means that when reflection and reasoning is applied to the Quran in the light of knowledge and vision, then it will become a witness itself of being from Allah. And when you will reason and reflect on the system of the universe, from there, too, this fact will become evident to you how resolutely the laws of Allah remain in operation, and how constructive their results are; this will be the evidence of the *Malaika*.[216] Similarly, when the results of the Quranic system will manifest themselves, from them too, evidence of the Quran being *Haqq* will become available. Moving on from this, the life of a *Momin* and the conduct of the *Jamaat e Momineen* will itself be an evidence of this fact that these people are flagbearers of *Haqq*. The fact is that every developed self is a witness of *Haqq*.

24.14 *Al-Haseeb* (The Reckoner)

When He is a witness on every deed, then it is apparent that He is also the One keeping account of all deeds and actions. Not a single atom can be outwith the sphere of His Law of Requital. In front of His knowledge both the hidden and the manifest are the same, therefore no deed can venture outwith the limits of accountability:

...whether you show what is in your minds or conceal it, Allah calls you to account for it ...(2:284) See also (15:92-93)

---

[216] The Quran has called the forces of nature *Malaika*. For further details see the book by the author titled *Iblees O Adam*.

And He does not need any helper or companion for this, He is sufficient in Himself to take account:

> *… But all-sufficient is Allah in taking account. (4:6) See also (4:86, 33:39)*

Every single atom comes within the grip of accountability:

> *We shall set up scales of justice for the day of judgment (the day of manifestation of consequences), so that not a self will be dealt with unjustly in the least, and if there be (no more than) the weight of a mustard seed, We will bring it (to account): and enough are We to take account. (21:47)*

And this 'accountability' will not only be on the 'Day of Judgment', rather this process begins right here. According to His Law of Requital and law of respite, some results have a delayed appearance and others a more rapid one, but accountability commences immediately in any case. This means that the effect of every deed begins to establish itself along with the time that it is committed; the fact that its tangible and visible result becomes apparent to us following an interval of time is another matter. Regarding this, it is stated that:

> *… He is swift in calling to account. (13:41)*

Hence, it is stated regarding the consequences of denial and defiance against which the *Kuffar* of Makkah used to be warned:

> *Whether We shall show you (within your life-time) part of what we promised them or take to Ourselves your self (before it is all accomplished), your duty is to make (the message) reach them: it is our part to call them to account. (13:40) See also (24:39, 40:17)*

His accountability is very strict and the outcome of His accountability is extremely well executed:

> *How many populations that insolently opposed the command of their Rabb and of His messengers, did We not then call to account - to severe account? and We imposed on them (as a consequence of their deeds) an exemplary punishment. (65:8)*

Details about how this accountability takes place, and how these results manifest will be covered in some future volumes.[217] Here, it is sufficient to say that these things do not come from somewhere outside, rather this accountability continually imprints within the human self itself, though it all takes place according to Allah's Law of Requital:

---

[217] See '*The Life in the Hereafter: What Does the Quran Say?*' (Ed)

Every man's fate We have fastened around his own neck: on the day of judgment We shall bring out for him a scroll, which he will see spread open. (It will be said to him:) 'Read your (own) record: sufficient is your self this day to make out an account against you'. (17:13-14)

This has also been stated in different words as: the responsibility for the accountability of every individual resides with Allah:

For to Us will be their return; then it will be for Us to call them to account. (88:25-26)

When the formation of a human society is through the hands of those individuals whose selfs reflect the attributes of Allah, then accountability for the deeds of every individual continually takes place in it; neither the good deed of anyone remains without a recompense, nor can any crime hide. In this, no-one is let off the hook, nor is any injustice done to anyone - the scales of justice are present and the deeds of the life of the people.

24.15   *Ash-Shakir, Ash-Shakoor*

The fundamental meaning of *Shukr* is the fullest results of deeds. Therefore, *Ash-Shakir* and *Ash-Shakoor* mean the Provider of the fullest recompense for human deeds:

What can Allah gain by your punishment, if you are grateful and you have Eimaan? Nay, it is Allah that recognises (all good), and knows all things. (4:147) See also (2:158)

He is such an appreciator of good that whatever you spend in the path of Allah (for the establishment of the Divine system), He gives recompense for it far beyond its worth:

If you loan to Allah, a balanced loan, He will double it to your (credit), and He will grant you protection: for Allah is most ready to appreciate (service), Most Forbearing. (64:17)

In Surah *Fatir* it is stated that those people who establish the system of *Salat* and organise *Zakat* in obedience of the Book of Allah invest their possessions in such a commerce in which there can never be any loss. Allah has set up this type of commerce for this very purpose:

For He will pay them their meed, nay, He will give them (even) more out of His Bounty: for He surely provides means of protection, most ready to recompense for deeds. (35:30)

When these people enter paradise their proclamation there will be nothing but this:

And they will say: 'Hamd to Allah, Who has removed from us (all) sorrow: for our Rabb is indeed All Protecting ready to appreciate deeds'. (35:34)

24.16 *As-Salaam, Al-Momin*

The Quran has described the ultimate successes of human life with one comprehensive word and that word is *Salaam*. Just consider! what is the aim of all human endeavours and the meaning of all human struggles and challenges other than that he should attain security, a life of peace and tranquility, a life of contentment and security. That life in which there is no fear and grief, no kind of sadness or sorrow; in which there is complete serenity and calmness, but not that deceptive peace which is achieved by the extinguishing of wishes and the giving up of desires; rather, that tranquility of heart which is attained after harnessing the universal forces and utilising the outcome according to the Divine values. This is because *As-Salaam, Al-Momin* are also Allah's attributes (the Bestower of peace and security):

...the Source of Peace, the Guardian of Eimaan ...(59:23)

It should be clarified that the meaning of *Salaam*, other than that of peace and security, is also to make something complete (*Mussallam*). The Self of Allah is the most complete. The self of the individual who obeys His laws also becomes complete. This is that *Salaam* (to become complete) towards which the system of Allah invites us:

But Allah does invite to the home of peace: He does guide (whosoever wishes) as per His Law of Mashe'at to a way that is straight. (10:25)

Allah extends an invitation to the abode of peace through the Quran:

... There has come to you from Allah a (new) light and a perspicuous Book. Wherewith Allah guides all who seek His good pleasure to ways of peace and safety, and leads them out of darkness, by His will (as per law), unto the light, guides them to a path that is straight. (5:15-16)

This is because the abode of security with Allah is for those who acquire *Eimaan* on His perspicuous Book and tread on the straight path:

This is the way of your Rabb, leading straight: We have detailed the signs for those who receive admonition. For them will be a home of peace in the presence of their Rabb: He will be their friend, because of what they practiced (righteousness). (6:126-127)

This is that righteous path in which there is security for those who tread on it:

...and peace and security to all who follow guidance! (20:47)

And Allah's guidance is now nowhere other than in the Quran, therefore it is proclaimed about that blessed night[218] in which the revelation of the message of security and peace commenced:

Peace and security in all matters (in this blessed night), this until the rise of morning![219] (97:5)

The Quran is the centre for the education of the mind and heart for Muslims, hence it is a source of peace and security from the beginning to the end. The political centre of the Islamic nation is the *Kaaba*[220] therefore it is also the holder of peace and tranquility:

...whoever enters (its confines) it attains security...(3:97)

Reflect how dire the need is for the world to have such a piece of land which no tyrant's evil hands have the power to reach; where man, having once arrived, can breathe in a completely free and dynamic environment; where there is no kind of fear and grief; where everything he possesses is safe and protected. This centre of peace and refuge is the *Kaaba* because it is the centre of Allah's Rule in the world, and it is obvious that the domain of the centre of that system which is the source of peace and security will automatically be as the inherent provider of peace and tranquility.

---

[218] Or in the era of darkness.

[219] The dark era of ignorance (the night) in which the light of the Quran descended to guide man to the light of the dawn. This is metaphorical and does not refer to a specific 'night'. (Ed)

[220] The Quran uses the word '*Bakka*' to imply an abode of security (3:95). The *Kaaba* was the first such abode. (Ed)

24.16.1 Glad Tidings of Peace to Righteous People

The *Anbiya*, whose beings were the cause for Divine favours, were blessed with glad tidings of peace and security. It is stated about Noah and his followers:

The word came: O Noah! Come down (from the Ark) with peace from Us, and blessing on you and also on peoples who are in your company ...(11:48) See also (37:79)

It is stated about Abraham:

Peace and salutation to Abraham! (37:109)

About Moses and Aaron it is stated:

Peace and salutation to Moses and Aaron! (37:120)

Similarly, about the messenger Ilyas it is stated:

Peace and salutation to such as Elias! (37:130)

About Yahya it is proclaimed:

So peace is on him the day he was born, the day that he died, and the day that he shall be raised up to life! (19:15)

Similarly, it is stated about Jesus:

So peace is on me the day I was born, the day that I die, and the day that I shall be raised up to life! (19:33)

It is stated about all the messengers:

And Peace and security on the messengers! (37:181)

About all the righteous people it is proclaimed:

Say: Hamd be to Allah, and peace and security on his servants whom He has chosen. (Who) is better? Allah or the false gods they associate (with Him)? (27:59)

All these people are those in whose selfs is the reflection of the attributes of Allah, hence, for them there is peace and security.

24.16.2 Peace and Security in Paradise

The society which is formed via the hands of such individuals whose self, having become developed, is a model of the attributes of Allah, is like a mirror in this world of the life of paradise. And when these people will go to the next life after this world, they will have the reward of a life of paradise there.[221] Paradise of the hereafter is defined by evolutionary stages of life and only those individuals will be able to tread these stages whose self has been developed. It is stated about these individuals:

> *The righteous will undoubtedly be (in comfort) amid gardens and springs. (Their greeting will be): 'Enter you here in peace and security'. (15:45-46) See also (50:34)*

In Surah *Ad-Dukhan* it is stated:

> *As to the righteous (they will be) in a position of security. (44:51)*

There will be no disagreeable talk there, salutations of peace and security will reach their hearing from all directions[222]:

> *They will not there hear any vain discourse, but only salutations of peace: And they will have therein their sustenance, morning and evening. (19:62) See also (56:26)*

In that life no vain talk will fall on their ears, whatever they hear will be greetings of peace and security. All the supplications and speech of the inhabitants of paradise will be for peace and tranquility:

> *(This will be) their exclamation therein: 'Glory to You, O Allah!' And 'Peace' will be their greeting therein! and the close of their call will be: 'Hamd be to Allah, the Cherisher and Sustainer of the worlds!' (10:10)*

The inhabitants of *A'raf* will send this gift of peace (*Salaam*) to those in paradise:

---

[221] Human life is one continuous spectrum which carries on beyond physical death. The state of development which our self has reached at the point of death is the same state which then has to continue beyond physical death albeit on a different plane of existence. This aspect is covered in detail in the book by the author *The Life in the Hereafter: What Does the Quran say?*. (Ed)

[222] This is one of the signs of achieving righteousness in this life as well, where the *Momineen* dislike vain talk and lies such as are broadcasted via the media everywhere. However, these are required to be heard and analysed as part of accountability as per the Law of Requital. Being saved from this in the hereafter will be a recompense for their efforts in this life during the process of their endeavours in establishing the Islamic system. (Ed)

...they will call out to the companions of the paradise, 'peace on you'...(7:46)

The *Malaika* will come and extend greetings of felicitations to the companions of paradise:

...and Malaika shall enter unto them from every gate (with the salutation): 'Peace unto you for that you persevered in patience! Now how excellent is the final home!' (13:23-24) See also (16:32, 39:73)

24.16.3 *Salaam* in the Islamic Society

The *Momineen* have been directed to follow the style of greetings and communication which will be in paradise in this life as well. Or, in other words, it can be said that the form of mutual supplications and greetings which has been defined for the existing social interaction of Muslims will be the same in the life of paradise too. Just consider, that if life becomes shaped on Islamic lines, then how, right here in this world, a paradise of peace and security will come into existence! About the social life of Muslims, it is proclaimed:

O you who have Eimaan! enter not houses other than your own, until you have asked permission and saluted those in them: that is best for you, in order that you may always heed this (your mutual relation is of peace and tranquility). (24:27)

Not only in strangers' houses, but also when you enter your own dwellings, present greetings of peace and tranquility to your own household:

...But if you enter houses, salute each other - a greeting of blessing and purity as from Allah ...(24:61)

Just imagine how much that society, whose members have this state that when they encounter one another they shower blossoms of peace and serenity over one another, will be like that of the life of paradise. When Muslims were cognisant of the truth of the teaching of the Quran and were following it in the truest sense, then this same *Salaam* which has become merely a lifeless ritual, was a lively manifestation of their mutual discipline and cooperation, and harmony of hearts. Today, this *Salaam* is the sum total of two words which appear mechanically on the tongue superficially from the level of the throat, these do not have any link with the heart, even though the aim of the Quran was that words should be the means of expression of the sentiments of your heart, and should be a mirror of your deeds. If there is no mutual harmony between the heart and the tongue, words and deeds, then these words can have no weight in the Quranic scales.

Rather, this is that hypocrisy which is deserving of the worst kind of condemnation from Allah:

Grievously odious is it in the sight of Allah that you say that which you do not. (61:3)

This is why in the Islamic social system '*Assalaam-o-Alaikum*' is not merely the sum of two words but is a demonstration of the relationships of the hearts of the members of the society, those relationships which are established on the foundations of mutual respect and love, welfare and promotion of tranquility. In this society when one person meets another person, he says to him that I desire that you live in peace and security from every respect. Its first meaning is this, that you remain assured that no kind of hurt will come to you from my direction. In reply, the other person, whilst also expressing this desire, says '*Wa-Alaikum-Salaam*' i.e. both these individuals make this avowal that we do not envisage any threat from one another, instead we have full and complete assurance that we will live in mutual peace and harmony. This was the meaning of '*Assalaam-o-Alaikum*' in Islamic society.

Now let us also consider another aspect of this mode of social life. Today, our state is such that an individual who considers himself superior in some way expects that others will say *Salaam* to him. He considers it demeaning to do it first himself. But let us see what teaching the Quran gives us in this regard. Among mankind, who can have a higher status than Rasul-ullah. The elevated status and dignity of that eminent being on whom having *Eimaan* is compulsory cannot be encompassed! But the Quran states:

When those come to you who have Eimaan in Our signs, Say: 'Salaam be on you':
Your Rabb has inscribed for Himself Rehmat ...(6:54)

This means that the desire for peace and security for the members of the Ummah, and the institution of a practical programme for the accomplishment of these desires should stem from the centre of the system itself.

The root of Islam is *S-L-M*. Amongst us the general meaning of Islam is taken to be the 'Religion of Peace and Security'. This is also correct that Islam is a Deen of peace and security, but peace and security is a passive state i.e. absence of conflict and disorder - there is no active aspect in this.

But when we pay attention to the other meaning of *S-L-M*, then the active aspect emerges and becomes apparent to us. That other meaning is to become complete, to complete the self of an individual by addressing a deficiency. If we view it from this aspect, then Islam is the name of that system in which every individual resides in peace and security, and his human potentials and the latent abilities of his self are also continuously becoming complete. In this way Islam becomes a beautiful mix of both passive and active aspects.

24.17 *Al-A'la*[223], *Al-Azeem*[224], *Al-Ali'yu*[225], *Al-Mut'aal*[226]

On the face of the earth, man is the holder of the highest status of all, and in the scales of humanity, the individual whose personality is the most developed is considered as holding the highest status. The Self of Allah is the completest, hence, His status is also the highest. Man cannot even imagine the greatness and supremacy of which He is the possessor:

> ...*for He is the Most High, the Supreme (in glory).* *(2:255) See also (42:4)*

In another verse:

> *He knows the unseen and that which is manifest: He is the Great, the Most High.*
> *(13:9)*

Holder of the highest status and along with this, also Wise:

> ...*and He is Most High, Most Great. (42:51)*

Undoubtedly, He is the holder of wisdom and authority:

> ... *high in dignity, full of wisdom. (43:4)*

Following on from knowledge and wisdom, for human beings the criteria for high status is sovereignty and supremacy. However prodigious the possession of power, accordingly great is the possession of stature. But the Quran does not accept the sovereignty of anyone other than Allah. Hence, if sovereignty belongs to Him, then supremacy and authority are also only suitable for Him:

> ... *the command is with Allah, Most High, Most Great! (40:12)*

No-one is included in this sovereignty of His:

> *That is because Allah - He is the Reality; and those besides Him whom they invoke,*
> *they are but vain falsehood: verily Allah is He, Most High, Most Great. (22:62) See*
> *also (31:30, 34:23)*

---

[223] *Al-A'la* – The One above everyone
[224] *Al-Azeem* – The One possessing greatness
[225] *Al-Ali'yu* – The Most Superior
[226] *Al-Mut'aal* – The Holder of the highest status

He is the true Ruler:

> *High above all is Allah, the King, the Truth…(20:114) See also (23:116)*

Therefore, all types of greatness are for Allah, He is the true master of the universe. It is only appropriate for man that, by virtue of being the highest in the whole world, he should bow down before this holder of the highest status (Allah). Everything in the universe should be serving man, but he in turn should remain active in completing the defined and declared programme of the true King of kings:

> *Then establish the supremacy and greatness of your Rabb in the world! (56:74) See also (56:96)*

In another verse:

> *Glorify the name of your Guardian Rabb, Most High. (87:1)*

This is because no one can claim to have equality with Him, He is far beyond this:

> *…and far is He above having the partners they ascribe unto Him! (16:1)*

His Being is pure and beyond *Shirk*, pure and above all those things which the human mind associates towards Him:

> *…Praise and glory be to Him! (for He is) above what they attribute to Him! (6:100)*

Free from all those attributions which are asserted about Him due to ignorance:

> *Glory to Him! He is high above all that they say! Exalted and Great! (17:43)*

24.17.1 Exalted Servants of Allah

It is apparent that if Allah the Exalted and Highest is the holder of such an elevated status, then at what heights the men establishing His rule in the world will be, at such heights that no other nation can even come close to. It is declared about them:

> *So lose not heart, nor fall into despair: for you must gain mastery if you are true in Eimaan. (3:139) See also (47:35)*

In the same way that in the whole universe their Allah is alone and without any associates due to His exalted stature and illustrious supremacy, similarly, no-one from amongst the whole of mankind can be a competitor of this *Jamaat* of His servants. But this loftiness and eminence of theirs will be neither the product of rebellion and arrogance, nor the source of its creation. One kind of 'higher stature' is Pharaoh, who had declared:

...I am your Lord, Most High. (79:24)

But his proclamation was based on self-deception. Arrogance and transgression can never be true superiority. Superiority is only that which is achieved by obeying the Divine laws, only that can be considered to be established which includes prostration to these. True greatness was never the share of Pharaoh, it was the share of Moses. When the confrontation with the magicians of Pharaoh took place and Moses feared that the people may be influenced by the tricks of the magicians, it was stated:

We said: fear not! for you will have the upper hand. (20:68)

This is because truth is essential for true supremacy and the truth was only with Moses, not with the people of Pharaoh. This is why it is stated that the plans of the opponents of *Haqq* and truth are always defeated, and Allah's command reigns supreme:

...and humbled to the depths the word of Kafireen. But the word of Allah is exalted to the heights: for Allah is Exalted in might, Wise. (9:40)

Therefore, every kind of greatness and majesty is for Allah, for the Deen of Allah, and for that nation which is the cause of establishment of Deen in the world.

24.18 *Al-Mateen* (The Powerful), *Al-Aziz* (The Omnipotent)

Izzat also means power but such a power which also comprises dominance. Hence, the meaning of *Aziz* will be a possessor of supremacy. In *Matanat* too, the meaning of power is implied but such a power in which there is no slack and no deficiency. Therefore, a *Mateen* will be that kind of possessor of power whose planning and implementation is strong and firm. The Quran states:

Those who reject Our signs, We shall gradually visit with punishment, in ways they perceive not; respite will I grant unto them: for My scheme is strong (and unfailing). (7:182-183) See also (68:45)

This is because Allah is the Master of all forces, and is *Mateen* and supreme:

For Allah is He Who provides Sustenance, possessing power, Al-Mateen. (51:58)

The word *Aziz* has been used for Allah in numerous places in the Quran. In some places He is *Aziz-un Hakeem* (2:240) i.e. that Being Whose supremacy is not based on blind power (Allah forbid) but is based entirely on wisdom and righteousness. In some places He is *Aziz-un Zuntiqaam* (3:4) i.e. His supremacy is in order to administer reward and punishment for deeds in full accordance with the procedure of the Law of Requital. Under the rule of the weak, neither the deserving receive their due nor the criminals their recompense. This is why in order for there to be justice, established supremacy and sustainable control is needed. It is because of this that He is also mentioned as being *Qawwayun Aziz* (22:40) i.e. His control has not come into action purely by chance but is the result of His infinite powers. When the people of Pharaoh became gripped by the consequences of their crimes, it was stated:

...but We seized them with such penalty (as comes) from One Exalted in Power, able to carry out His Will. (54:42) See also (37:180)

Whoever is looking for *Izzat* (power) will have to obey His laws because real power cannot be found anywhere else:

If any do seek for glory and power, to Allah belong all glory and power ...(35:10)

He bestows power to those who are in search of power, but how?

...To Him mount up (all) words of purity: It is He Who exalts each deed of righteousness ...(35:10)

In this way this power comes into the share of His righteous servants:

...But power and glory belong to Allah and His Messenger, and to Momineen; but the hypocrites know not. (63:8)

Hypocrites are seekers of power associated with others, what a deceptive vision and omission of the heart this is:

To the hypocrites give the glad tidings that there is for them (but) a grievous penalty; yea, to those who take for friends Kafireen rather than Momineen: is it power they seek among them? Nay, all power is with Allah. (4:138-139)

291

All *Izzat* is for Allah, and (bestowed by Him) for His messenger and the *Jamaat e Momineen* because they are the heirs and followers of this Book which is *Aziz* in itself:

> *...And indeed, it is a Book of exalted power. (41:41)*

There is no doubt in this that it appears to us as if the deniers of this Book are also possessors of power and glory, but their power is like the adornment of fake gems which in appearance may dazzle the eyes, but can never satisfy the test of a true measure:

> *But the state of Kafireen is such that they are lost in self-glory and separatism. (38:2)*

But the state of the deniers of truth is such that they are stubbornly fixed to the assumed lie of their false pride. These are the people whose state is such that:

> *When it is said to him, 'fear the consequences of going against the laws of Allah', he is led by arrogance to (more) crime. Enough for him is hell; an evil bed indeed. (2:206)*

That hell where they will have to spend a life of extreme humiliation. And it will be said to them about this punishment:

> *Taste you (this)! Truly were you mighty, honourable! (44:49)*

And all of this because these people had deceived themselves by setting false standards for power and respect. The criterion for power is only this:

> *...But power and honour belong to Allah, and His Messenger, and to Momineen ...*
> *(63:8)*

In other words, true *Izzat* and *Takreem* is achieved by the elevation of character, not through deception and injustice.

When the Quran declared that established and sustainable *Izzat* and *Takreem* is for the *Jamaat e Momineen*, and such an *Izzat* too in which no other nation could be their equal, then it is clear from this that we existing Muslims, who (unfortunately) are counted amongst the lowest of nations, cannot call ourselves *Momin*. A *Momin* and a life of humiliation are two contradictory entities.

24.19 *Al-Baari, Al-Musawwar* (The Creator)

It is stated in Surah *Al-Hashr*:

> *He is Allah, the Creator, the Evolver, the Bestower of Forms ...(59:24) See also (2:54)*

The fundamental trait of a developed self is that of creation. We have written in detail about Allah's attribute of creation at the start. *Al-Baari* and *Al-Musawwar* are also in fact about the phases of the process of creation. Creation means to make a new thing by creating a particular proportion and order among different elements. In this new order the extraneous and superfluous bits are separated, this is the trait of *Baari*. Following this, giving it a particular form is the attribute of sculpturing (shaping and mapping). It is these phases of creation and balancing which have been explained at another place in these words:

> *Him Who created you. Fashioned you in due proportion and gave you a just bias; In whatever form He willed, did He put you together. (82:7-8)*

The first phase is creation, after this producing proportion and symmetry by trimming and shaving, balancing and harmonising, and plotting the correct map by adjusting all the finer points, as a result of which all the glittering adornments of beauty and display come together to become a lively miracle of tapestry:

> *And you have a sense of pride and beauty in them...(16:6)*

This last phase is of giving form and shape:

> *He it is Who shapes you in the wombs as He pleases (as per His law) ...(3:6)*

Such a multifaceted creation that the map of one does not match that of another, and of such beautiful proportion that - if the 'instruments' of sight, smell and breathing were only as unsymmetrical parts and devoid of any kind of proportion, even then these would have met physical needs in this way - these became thousands of attractions of beauty and splendour:

> *...and has given you form, and made your forms balanced and beautiful ...(64:3)*

Can this be called conjuring by some 'blind' nature (Allah forbid)? If the allure and uniqueness of some entrancing painting by an artist can be considered as being the verbal testimony of his artistic expertise, then why can the beauty and display of the rainbow colours and *Attar* of this gallery of the universe not be taken as evidence of the unparalleled creativity of its Creator? Creator, and together with being the Creator, also *Baari* and *Musawwar.*

> *...So blessed be Allah, the Best of Creators! (23:14)*

In addition, *Al-Musawwar* not only means the One who devises outlines and shapes, it also means the One Who bestows form as well, and this is an important fundamental attribute. Students of philosophy know that, according to Aristotle, the existence of something is another name for its form. In other words, (he states) when something adopts a certain form then at that time we say that it has come into existence. In the perceptible world there is no existence for a formless thing. Hence, when the Quran declares Allah as *Al-Musawwar*, then by this is also meant that He brings every one of those things into existence by giving it a special form.

24.20 *Al-Waase (Without Limits)*

Experts in astronomy tell us that when they study any one system of the galaxies, they are left amazed and bewildered on beholding its infinite expanses, at how far the limits and boundaries of this universe are spread out! This is the state of a small portion of one department of the system of the universe; just try and imagine, what this whole and spectacular universe will be like? But from where can that imagination be obtained in which even the outline of these infinite expanses can be encompassed. And if this is the state for the universe, then how can the expanses of the Creator Himself be accommodated in someone's sphere of conception, imagination, perception and assumption! The Possessor of such infinite unparalleled expanses, boundless spans and depths – to attribute time and space to such an Allah?

Praise and glory be to Him! (for He is) above what they attribute to Him! (6:100)

The truth is that association of time and space can be declared to be appropriate for physical entities, but personality is far above these references:

To Allah belong the east and the west: withersoever you turn, there is the presence of Allah. For Allah is All-Embracing, All-Knowing. (2:115)

Allah's attribute of *Waase-un* generally appears in the Quran along with the attribute of *Aleem-un* (2:247, 2:268, 3:73, 5:54). Hence, this expanse is in reality the expanse of His knowledge and wisdom. Since this expanse is infinite our limited mind cannot therefore conceptualise it, although even we are aware of this much that in comparison to the body, how much wider the world of the human self is. The world of the self is certainly very eminent, but the world of the human intellect is also immensely expansive. To what extremities our concepts and thoughts reach cannot even begun to be imagined.

By descending from the vastness of Allah's knowledge, if we wish to observe how He is *Al-Waase* in our economic and social world, then by establishing a social system according to His laws we can see how in this every single grain converts into seven hundred grains:

The parable of those who spend their substance in the way of Allah is that of a grain of corn: it grows seven ears, and each ear has a hundred grains. Allah gives manifold increase as per His law of Mashe'at: And Allah possesses great expanse and He knows all things. (2:261)

This is why it is stated that when you are obedient to Allah's commands then this concern as to where sustenance will be obtained from should never grip you. Organise the social and economic system on the lines of Allah's laws and then see how His boundlessness bestows without measure (4:130, 24:32). Details have been covered under the subject of *Rizq*.

24.21   *Al-Wahab* (Giver of Free Bounties)

Mohbat is stated to be that gift which is given neither for any expectation of any return nor as remuneration for work. Whatever kind of sustenance is available in the universe for the nourishment of humanity is all of it this kind of gift from Allah. This is why another attribute of Allah is also *Al-Wahab*. For the nourishment of humanity, other than the means of sustenance, the guidance of *Wahi* holds very great significance. This is also bestowed by Allah as a *Mohbat*. In this, there is neither any question of a return by the Giver (Allah), nor any skill and effort expended by the receiver (*Nabi*). This is that guidance which every traveller in the journey of life needs all the time, this is why the supplication of the *Jamaat e Momineen* is:

Our Rabb! (they say), 'Let not our hearts deviate now after You have guided us, but grant us mercy from Your own presence; for You are the Grantor of Bounties without measure'. (3:8)

About those who reject this guidance, it is stated:

Or have they the treasures of the mercy of Your Rabb, the Exalted in Power, the Grantor of Bounties without measure? (38:9)

The treasures of *Rehmat* (blessings) of Allah (*Al-Wahab*) are only with Him, hence the whole world is dependent on Him whereas He is free from all. In the human world the state of those individuals whose self reflects this attribute of Allah will also be this, that they will gift the means of sustenance to the rest of humanity without expecting anything in return. This is what is known as the system of *Rabubiyat* which is shaped through the hands of the *Jamaat e Momineen*.

24.22 *Al-Ghani* (Free of All Needs)

When man coined[227] an idol from his own mind and moulded it in his own form, he determined those same traits for this idol which his mind was able to devise. At the most, he was able to accord it the status of a worldly monarch. For him, there could be no greater status than this. After that, when he observed that worldly monarchs have their orders obeyed by their subjects and teach them obedience to the monarchy, all this happens in this way so that no disturbance arises in the kingship of these monarchs, and the degree to which the subjects are obedient and compliant is the same degree to which the rule of this king will be strong and his kingdom will be enduring. If this king receives dues from his subjects and accepts taxes, this will also be so that his rule becomes strengthened. Therefore, in all these matters that king will be reliant on his subjects. Even though he may not say this out loud and he hides this dependency of his behind the screen of the law, the truth will remain that he is dependent on his people. This is why when man gave the status of a god to the idol devised by his own mind, together with this he also assumed it to be essential that God is dependent on the worship of his servants - He is in need of their offerings and gifts in the same way that worldly kings are in need of them. But when the Quran introduced the real Allah to the world, it also made this fact clear that obedience of the laws of Allah is in the interest of human beings themselves. There is no 'personal interest' of Allah hidden in this. This is why He does not have any need for the worship and 'offerings' of men; He is free from these things; He is *Mustaghni*; this is all for our own benefit. If some patient acts on the instructions of a doctor, then in this there is benefit to the patient himself, the doctor is free from this (*Mustaghni*). If some student obeys the instructions of his concerned teacher, his own advantage is in this, the teacher has no personal need in this. Similarly, Allah is free from the *Kufr* and *Eimaan* of human beings. He does not like *Kufr* because man lands in the destruction of hell as a result of this. He likes *Eimaan* because this becomes the cause for the success of man:

> *If you reject (Allah), truly Allah has no need of you; but He likes not Kufr for His servants (as not advantageous to you): if you are grateful, He will like it for you (i.e. it is to your advantage). No bearer of burdens can bear the burden of another. In the end, to your Rabb is your Return, when He will tell you the truth of all that you did (in this life). For He knows well all that is in hearts. (39:7)*

Pointing towards the consequences and the end of those ungrateful people of former nations, the Quran states:

> *That was because there came to them messengers with clear signs, but they said: 'Shall (mere) human beings direct us?' So they rejected (the Message) and turned away. But*

---

[227] Gods created by human thoughts. (Ed)

Allah can do without (them): and Allah is free of all needs, worthy of all Hamd. (64:6)

Moses told his people:

And Moses said: 'If you show ingratitude, you and all on earth together, yet is Allah free of all wants, worthy of all praise. (14:8) See also (64:6)

Gratitude and *Kufr*, obedience and rejection, all are for the self of man himself:

...Any who is (so) grateful does so to the profit of his own self: but if any is ungrateful, verily Allah is free of all wants, worthy of all Hamd. (31:12) See also (27:40)

Endeavour in the journey of life, and making an effort and taking action, is for the benefit of man himself. Whoever makes efforts in the correct way will benefit from their results himself. Whoever sits down and does not use his arms and legs, will face the consequences of this:

And if any strive (with might and main), they do so for their own selfs: for Allah is free of all needs from all creation. (29:6)

Depending upon the nature of the deeds of an individual, the level of his status will be decided accordingly:

To all are degrees (or ranks) according to their deeds: for your Rabb is not unmindful of anything that they do. Your Rabb is self-sufficient, full of mercy ...(6:132-133)

The 'tasks and prayers' defined by Deen are also for the good of the people themselves, Allah is not in need of these prayers and rites. In relation to Hajj it is stated:

...Hajj thereto is a duty men owe to Allah, those who can afford the journey; but if any do Kufr, Allah stands not in need of any of His creatures. (3:96)

And it became a duty on men from Allah that if they had the ability to reach there, then do 'Hajj' of this house. But whoever rejects this, remember that the Self of Allah is free from the whole world.

The basis of the system of *Rabubiyat* is on *Infaaq* i.e. keeping open the proceeds of one's efforts in order to spend in the cause of Allah. The meaning of this 'cause of Allah' is also the sustenance and nourishment, well-being and welfare of mankind; Allah is not in any need of our possessions and wealth:

O you who have Eimaan! Give of the good things which you have earned, and of the fruits of the earth which We have produced for you, and do not even aim at getting anything which is bad, in order that out of it you may give away something, when you yourselves would not receive it except with closed eyes. And know that Allah is free of all wants, and worthy of all Hamd. (2:267)

As has been noted under the subject of 'the belief in progeny of Allah', because offspring are a support at that time when man becomes in need of help from others, this is why, based on ignorance, people also established the belief in progeny of Allah. But the Quran emphasises how much this idea is *Batil* and based on an ignorance of reality. What possible support does Allah need from someone? Everything in the heavens and earth are in His ownership, He is free from the whole of the universe, why would such an Allah require the support of progeny?

They say: 'Allah has begotten a son!' - Glory be to Him! He is self-sufficient! His are all things in the heavens and on earth! No authority you have for this! say you about Allah what you know not? (10:68) See also (22:64, 31:26)

Everything in the heavens and the earth is His, He is the Master and Creator of the whole of the universe.[228] He is free from, and above and beyond even the slightest possibility of any need and dependency; He is totally free of the need from anything in the universes for all times.[229]

The truth is that (as noted previously) the fundamental characteristics of the self are freedom and independence. A developed self is self-sufficient and free from the need of the support of others. Therefore, how can the Self of Allah be dependent on anyone? This will be the same state of those whose self is a reflection of the Divine attributes. They, too, will not be dependent on others in the world, and that society which will be shaped through their hands will also not require the support of others.

Among us the translation of *Al-Ghani* (or *As-Samad*) is commonly done as 'could not care less', Allah 'does not care'. This phrase is handed down as a tradition in every religious family. But by 'could not care less', such a false concept arises in the mind about Allah, which is not only inappropriate to associate with Him, but is completely contrary to His Eminence. 'Could not care less' means the one who does not take into account any rule and law, does not care about any principle and code of conduct. He does whatever comes to his mind, and whatever he wishes,

---

[228] And even of multiverses, as modern research indicates that there is the possibility of multiple universes. (Ed)

[229] This fact becomes obvious when one looks at those Divine attributes which are attributable to Him exclusively i.e. He is the First and the Last. (Ed)

he decides accordingly. This concept about Allah is completely against that concept which Allah has provided about Himself in the Quran.

I have also translated *Al-Ghani* in the above noted verse as 'free from needs', though from this respect 'free of all needs' means the one who is not dependent on any single thing. No objection can be raised over this translation, but I think the word *Mustaghni* is more appropriate and comprehensive. The meaning of *Mustaghni* is that though He may have everything, He is not dependent on any one of those things. This is *Istaghna*, which has far wider meanings other than freedom from needs and not being dependent on others. Hence, the Self of Allah is completely *Mustaghni*. *Istaghna* is a fundamental attribute of a developed (human) self.

24.23 *Al-Fattah* (The Differentiator)

The meaning of *Fatah* is to open, to differentiate between *Haqq* and *Batil*. From this it also becomes clear what the correct meaning is of what the Quran calls *Fatah*. According to the Quran, this is an immutable law of nature that *Haqq* will remain dominant and *Batil* will be subdued. At whatever point in whatever confrontation this natural differentiation between *Haqq* and *Batil* openly manifests, it will be declared as *Fatah*. Hence, wherever the Quran mentions *Fatah* for the *Momineen* the meaning of this is not victory but the supremacy of *Haqq*, and because this differentiation of *Haqq* and *Batil* is according to Allah's law, hence Allah is *Fattah* and *Fateh*. In Surah *Al-Araf* this meaning has become clearly evident. Regarding the invitation of the messenger Shoaib and his people's rejection of it, it is stated that Shoaib informed them:

And if there is a party among you who accepts Eimaan in the message with which I have been sent, and a party which does not have Eimaan, hold yourselves in patience until Allah does decide between us: for He is the best to decide. (7:87)

Here, the word *Hakim* has been used for the one making a decision. Two verses after this, this supplication is noted from the lips of Shoaib:

…Our Rabb decide between us and our people in truth, and You are the best of those who give decision. (7:89)

Here, the word *Fateh* has been used for the 'decision maker' i.e. the one who makes the differentiation between *Haqq* and *Batil*. It is stated about Rasul-ullah himself:

Say, 'Our Rabb will bring us together; then He will judge between us in Haqq. And He is the Knowing Judge.' (34:26)

These two groups gathered together at one place, and then after this such a glaringly evident decision was reached among them that every particle of *Badr* and *Hunain*[230] is a witness on this. Such a verdict that after this no question remained of the mixing of *Haqq* and *Batil*. Both became distinctly separate, and established such a criterion till the Day of Judgment that no doubt could remain for anyone in the differentiation of *Haqq* and *Batil*. In Quranic *Lughat* (language) this is indeed the very meaning of *Fateh*. Now you can understand that when words like *Fateh* and victorious are used for a *Momin*, what the correct meaning of these words will be i.e. the one who differentiates between *Haqq* and *Batil* according to the Divine laws. This is that delicate but extremely important difference between a worldly *Fateh* and a Quranic *Fateh*, by overlooking which the superficial glance cannot differentiate between Hulagu Khan[231] and Umer Farooq, even though in front of one there was a desire for personal supremacy, while in front of the other was the differentiation between *Haqq* and *Batil* as a result of the manifestation of Allah's attribute of *Fattah* - that differentiation which is carried out according to *Haqq* and knowledge. This is because Allah is such a *Fattah* Who is *Haqq* and Omniscient. In the human system of life these decisions of Allah take place according to the Quran, because the Quran is the proclaimer of decisions:

Indeed, the Quran is a decisive statement, and not a meaningless thing. (86:13-14)

In other words, a proven reality in itself and the maker of fully clear decisions between *Haqq* and *Batil*. Hence, this is that Book of the code of laws for Allah's court and the implementation and execution of this code will be the manifestation of Allah's authority and decision making.

When the Quran states about the *Jamaat e Momineen* that they achieved *Fatah,* then the aim from this is not only that their enemies were defeated and that they overcame them, by this is also meant that because of this those impediments were removed which were an obstruction in the path of their advancement, and in this way the 'doors opened' before them to ever expanding avenues in their life. Therefore, every *Fatah* of the *Jamaat e Momineen* is a new chapter for further growth, and this process is a limitless one.

24.24 *Al-Haqq* (The Absolute Truth)

Allah is *Haqq,* anyone who is called out to other than Him is *Batil*:

That is because Allah is Haqq, and that which they call upon other than Him is Batil, and that Allah is the Most High, the Grand. (22:62) See also (22:6, 31:30)

---

[230] These are two battle grounds where there was a fight between Muslims and the *Kuffar* in the era of Rasul-ullah. (Ed)

[231] A Mongol ruler, grandson of Ghengis Khan. Wikipedia. (Ed)

Haqq is that which is established; immutable; cannot be erased; is established in its place; meets all the criteria of reality; proves to be true on every criterion of knowledge and vision; whose outcomes should always be constructive; which should meet every constructive demand of the era. Contrary to this, *Batil* is that which is erasable; which cannot remain; which merely exists in skepticism; speculation and conjecture, in reality has no existence; that which produces destructive effects. Only the Being of Allah is *Haqq*. The forces of *Batil* only appear to be powerful so as long as *Haqq* does not present itself. When *Haqq* appears, then *Batil* becomes destroyed. The foundation of the whole invitation of the Quran is on this great principle alone, that the Being of Allah is the only *Haqq*, anything other than Allah is *Batil*. It appears to be merely a minor issue but as we continue to reflect on it, ever greater realities will keep becoming unveiled. First of all, that the Being of Allah is an established fact; not this, that the desire for worship of the devotees has carved a god from their own mind. The Being of Allah was worthy of submission even then when no forehead was familiar with the pleasure of prostration, and will still be worthy of submission even at that time when no manifestation of servitude and obedience will remain. This is because He is *Haqq*, and a manifest *Haqq*. This is a different matter that someone may deliberately shut his own eyes, but no doubt can arise in *Haqq* being *Haqq* because of this. Today eyes can be shut, but at the time of the manifestation of consequences there will be no possibility to do this:

That day, Allah will pay them in full their deserved recompense, and they will know that it is Allah who is evidently perfect in justice. (24:25)

But becoming aware of this truth at that time will be of no benefit, the time for turning your face away from *Batil* and coming to *Haqq* is now:

For that is Allah, your Rabb, the Haqq. And what can be beyond Haqq except Batil? So how are you averted (away from Haqq)? (10:32)

The meaning of accepting Allah as *Haqq* is to have *Eimaan* on this evident reality that governance and sovereignty is only for Him, it is not legitimate to accept the obedience and rule of anyone other than Him. He is the sole possessor of all greatness and supremacy:

So exalted is Allah, the Sovereign, the Haqq; there is no deity except Him, Rabb of the Noble Throne. And whoever invokes besides Allah another deity for which he has no proof - then his account is only with his Rabb. Indeed, Kafireen will not succeed. (23:116-117) See also (20:114)

Having *Eimaan* in Allah's being *Haqq* means that whatever is from Him should be accepted as *Haqq*. He Himself is *Haqq*, therefore He has created the universe with *Haqq*:

> *It is He who created the heavens and the earth in true (proportions): the day He says, 'Be,' behold! it is. His word is the truth. His will be the dominion the day the trumpet will be blown. He knows the unseen as well as that which is open. For He is the Wise, well acquainted (with all things). (6:73)*

The universe has been created with *Haqq*, and the Quran has been revealed with *Haqq* for the guidance of the human world:

> *...that it is Haqq from their Rabb ...(2:26)*

Hence, today *Haqq* is within the Quran i.e. in the universe the things of nature are a manifestation of *Haqq*, and in the human world the laws of the Quran are models of *Haqq* - this system is that Deen of *Haqq* which is going to overcome all of the man-made systems of human beings:

> *It is He who has sent His Messenger with guidance and Deen of Haqq to manifest it over all Deens, although they who associate others with Allah detest it. (9:33) See also (48:28, 61:9)*

Allah is *Haqq*; the universe of nature is created with *Haqq*; His messenger is sent with *Haqq*; the Deen brought by him is *Haqq*; and the *Jamaat* is the heir of the Book, the flagbearer of *Haqq*; other than this all the remainder is *Batil*. *Haqq* is that which will remain while *Batil* is the one which will disappear. Only that will remain whose connection is with *Haqq*. This is the only truth, all the rest are fictional tales!

By stating that the universe is created *Bil-Haqq*, the Quran has lifted the curtain on an extremely erroneous perception of the human mind. Plato presented this concept that this visible universe does not possess its own existence, that things with their real existence are in the 'state of metaphors', and that whatever is seen in the universe is a shadow of these things. Going forward, this (*Batil*) concept became *Yog* amongst Hindus and the foundation of mysticism (Sufism) amongst Persians and Muslims. Hindus stated that all the world is *Maya* (deception). Amongst us, mysticism presented the concept of unity of existence, according to which it is said that existence is only of God, other than Him there is no existence of anything else.

By stating this, that the universe is created *Bil-Haqq*, the Quran has uprooted all these *Batil* concepts and beliefs. The universe possesses its own existence and has been locked within the chains of Allah's laws so that man can benefit from it (this is what is meant by conquering the universe).

24.25 *Hameed-un, Majeed-un* (The Praiseworthy, The Majestic)

Keep in view all those attributes which are expounded in the Quran about Allah, and then see which is that attribute of beauty and excellence due to which His Self is exalted, and which is that trait of fault and decay from which His Being is not free. Adorned with all the accoutrements of beauty and resplendence, possessing all majestic excellence, all balanced attributes belong to Him alone (59:24). Every kind of appreciation and praise, and every manner of admiration and respect is for Him alone. This is why the very beginning of the Quran is with this infinite proclamation:

All Hamd for that Allah Who is Rabb of all worlds. (1:2) See also (45:36)

But in the Arabic language the word *Hamd* has a fundamental and supreme feature. You are on vacation in some country. Suddenly, such a view appears in front of you at some location which is very pleasing and worthy of attention, seeing which you spontaneously utter the word 'wow' - this will be defined as *Hamd* i.e. this will be *Hamd* for the creator of that view. Hence, when it is said about Allah that this is *Hamd* for Him, then this will mean that every beautiful corner of the universe is a talking picture of the creative programme of Allah, on seeing which sentiments of appreciation and admiration arise involuntarily from the heart. Note in what kinds of styles the Quran has detailed this reality:

Hamd to Allah, Who created (out of nothing) the heavens and the earth ...(35:1) See also (6:1)

In Surah *Al-Momin* it is stated:

It is Allah Who has made for you the earth as a resting place, and the sky as a canopy, and has given you shape - and made your shapes beautiful, and has provided for you sustenance, of things pure and good; such is Allah your Rabb. So glory to Allah, the Rabb of the worlds! He is the Living (One): There is no god but He: call upon Him, giving Him sincere devotion. Hamd to Allah, Rabb of the worlds! (40:64-65) See also (31:25)

He is the Creator of everything, and after creation, selects these things according to His immutable laws for evolutionary phases, and is managing this system in a beautifully balanced way. Hence, the first and the last *Hamd* is only for Him:

Your Rabb does create and choose as He wills[232]: no choice have they (in the matter):
Glory to Allah! and far is He above the partners they ascribe (to Him)! And your
Rabb knows all that their hearts conceal and all that they reveal. And He is Allah:
There is no god but He. To Him be Hamd, at the first and at the last: for Him is the
command, and to Him shall you (all) be brought back. (28:68-70) See also (34:1,
30:18)

24.25.1 *Khalqiyat, Razzaqiyat, Rabubiyat*

He is the *Khaliq* (Creator) and the *Raziq* (Sustainer and Nourisher) too. Hence, Who other than Him can be deserving of praise and admiration? :

Allah enlarges the sustenance (which He gives) to whichever of His servants He
pleases (as per His Law of Mashe'at); and He (similarly) grants by (strict) measure,
(as per the law)[233]: for Allah has full knowledge of all things. And if indeed you ask
them who it is that sends down rain from the heavens and gives life therewith to the
earth after its death, they will certainly reply, Allah! Say, 'Hamd be to Allah'! But most
of them understand not. (29:62-63)

Khaliq and *Raziq*, and the Bestower of all favours; bestowing in those circumstances when man is overwhelmed by hopelessness as a consequence of visible means and causes:

He is the One that sends down rain (even) after (men) have given up all hope and
scatters His Mercy (far and wide). And He is the Protector, Worthy of all Hamd.
(42:28)

His *Rabubiyat* does not end with material needs only but guidance is also bestowed from Him for the fulfillment of human eminence. This is why, if His dignified benevolence regarding physical needs are a cause for *Hamd* and appreciation of Him, then in the field of guidance and direction His generous mercy is deserving of even greater appreciation and admiration than this:

Hamd be to Allah, Who has sent to His servant the Book, and which is free from all
types of convolutions and complexities. (18:1)

That exalted Book about which it is stated that '*Batil* cannot approach it from any direction, in front or from behind' and which has been sent by:

...One full of Wisdom, Worthy of all Hamd. (41:42)

---

[232] According to His law of *Mashe'at*. (Ed)
[233] In the human world it is human beings who carry out these responsibilities. For details of the system of *Rabubiyat* see the author's book titled *The Quranic System of Sustenance*. (Ed)

When 'knowledge' was bestowed on Dawood and Solomon, they bowed in gratitude in appreciation and *Hamd* of Allah:

We gave (in the past) knowledge to Dawood and Solomon: And they both said: 'Hamd be to Allah, Who has favoured us above many of his Momineen servants!' (27:15)

Rasul-ullah also stated the same in gratitude of the glorious blessings of Islam and the Quran:

Hamd be to Allah …(27:93)

Regarding the attributes of the *Momineen*, it is stated that they are *Hamidun*, all are doers of *Hamd* of Allah (9:112).

24.25.2 The Law of Requital – Reason for *Hamd* and Appreciation

The code of laws (guidance and direction) is received from Allah for this reason that people can be made aware of the Law of Requital. They are to be informed that the essential consequence of obedience to the laws of Allah is success and prosperity, and the natural consequence of disobedience will be annihilation and ruin. When the punishment of destruction and ruin descends on some nation because of their rebellion and transgression, then though it will only seem to be a point at which to learn some lesson, in truth for those possessing vision this will be an opportunity for *Hamd* and appreciation of Allah, because if His Law of Requital is not implemented and executed with such coordination and discipline, then the integrity of the universe will be shattered. Balance and proportion in the world are maintained according to this very law. These are those opportunities in relation to which it is stated:

Before you We sent (messengers) to many nations, and We afflicted the nations with suffering and adversity, that they might learn humility. When the suffering reached them from us, why then did they not learn humility? On the contrary their hearts became hardened, and Satan made their (criminal) acts seem alluring to them. But when they forgot the warning they had received, We opened to them the gates of all (good) things, until, in the midst of their enjoyment of Our gifts, on a sudden, We called them to account. when lo! they were plunged in despair! Of the wrong-doers the last remnant was cut off. Hamd be to Allah, the Sustainer of the worlds. (6:42-45)

When the people of Lot were engulfed in the punishment of Allah because of their deeds, and Lot and his companions remained protected from this punishment, then after narrating this event it is stated:

Say: Hamd be to Allah, and peace on his servants whom He has chosen (for his Message). (Who) is better? Allah or the false gods they associate (with Him)? (27:59)

Similarly, when the people of Noah were engulfed in difficulties due to the flood, and Allah saved Noah and his companions from the tyranny of an unjust and rebellious people, then at this stage it was stated:

And when you have embarked on the Ark - you and those with you, say: 'Hamd be to Allah, Who has saved us from the people who do wrong'. (23:28)

This was only a partial narration of different events. In Surah *Al-Saffat* this very principle is explained as a rule, that in the battles of *Haqq* and *Batil*, Our messengers and forces always remain victorious and supreme and the forces of *Batil* become destroyed and annihilated. After citing this principle, it is stated:

Glory to your Rabb, the Rabb of Power! (He is free) from what they ascribe (to Him)! And Salaam (peace and security) on the messengers! And Hamd to Allah, the Rabb of the Worlds. (37:180-182)

24.25.3 *Muqaam e Mehmud* (Status of Eminence)

Indeed, this was that path by treading on which Rasul-ullah achieved his status of *Mehmud*[234]:

And (O Messenger) spend some time in the small watches of the night: (it would be) an additional task for you: soon will your Rabb raise you to a Station of Hamd! (17:79)

Reaching the status of *Mehmud* is guaranteed by treading on the path of *Hamd* defined by Allah, Who is deserving of all *Hamd*. This is the fulfilment of the eminence of humanity. This is the zenith of life. This is the ultimate aim, and those who are worthy of *Hamd* and appreciation are those righteous ones who achieve this status. These are those people whose developed self is the manifestation of the Divine attributes, and thus become deserving of *Hamd* and appreciation i.e. when the world witnesses those great achievements of theirs which become guarantors for the *Rabubiyat* and prosperities of mankind, then songs of praise and appreciation flow spontaneously from the lips of people.

---

[234] *Mehmud* – from *Hamd*, the one whose character is praiseworthy according to the Permanent Values. (Ed)

24.26 *Tasbeeh*

Everything in the universe has its head bowed before that law according to which it is to live its life, and for which it has been created:

> *...while all creatures in the heavens and on earth have, willing or unwilling, bowed to His Will, and to Him shall they all be brought back. (3:83)*

The things of nature are busy in fulfilling whatever task has been assigned to them, and in this way are prostrating in front of the commands of Allah:

> *Whatever beings there are in the heavens and the earth do prostrate themselves to Allah (acknowledging subjection), with good-will or in spite of themselves ...(13:15)*
> *See also (22:18)*

The interpretation of this *Tasleem* and *Sajud* is explained in Surah *An-Nahl* as follows:

> *And to Allah does obeisance all that is in the heavens and on earth, whether moving (living) creatures or Malaika: for none are arrogant (before their Rabb). They all revere their Rabb, high above them, and they do all that they are commanded. (16:49-50)*

Consider the words *Yafa'loona-ma-Yuma'roon* ('and they do all that they are commanded'), which is the prostration itself of these things. This is in effect their submission (*Aslama*) i.e. they are engrossed in accomplishing whatever task has been assigned to them. Nothing slackens in the slightest in this task, nothing moves even an inch either way from its designated path, and it is on this that the system of the universe is dependent. The words *Aslama* and *Yasjudu* appear in the verses quoted above. In some verses the words *Sabba'ha*, *Yo'sabbiho* (*Tasbeeh*) have been used for the same meaning:

> *The seven (numerous) heavens and the earth, and all beings therein, declare His glory: there is not a thing but celebrates His Hamd; And yet you understand not how they declare His glory! Verily He is Oft-Forbearing, All Protecting! (17:44)*

The meaning of *Sab'hun*[235] is to float, a steed galloping swiftly, i.e. the way in which the arms are stretched out to their maximum whilst swimming; similarly when the horse stretches its legs fully and sprints, this is called *Sab'hun*. This is why the meanings of swiftness and distance (stretching the arms and legs far and wide) are

---

[235] About the stellar bodies it is mentioned in the Quran '...*all (the celestial bodies) are swimming along, each in its rounded course*' (21:33, 36:40). How comprehensive is the use of the word swimming for depicting the movement of these celestial bodies in space.

both contained in this word. Hence, *Sabba'ha-fil-Ard* means 'travelling to far away lands.' The Quran states:

True, there is for you by day prolonged occupation (Sab'han Taweelan) with duties.
(73:7)

Therefore, when it is stated that everything in the universe is immersed in doing *'Tasbeeh'* of Allah, from this it will be meant that these are busy in action with full swiftness in carrying out those duties which have been assigned to them.

24.26.1 *Tasbeeh and Hamd*

Now let us also reflect on another example. You have a machine in front of you whose every part is fitted at its proper place. The whole machine is functioning extremely efficiently, there is no fault anywhere, no lapse, it is solid, strong, durable, established in its proper place, alive results are constantly appearing according to the purpose for which it is constructed. As soon as you observe this machine, you will be profuse in your expression of appreciation and praise of its designer. Words of admiration about him will appear on your lips spontaneously. This machine will be wholly a representation of its designer. Every pleasing picture is a sonnet in praise of the innovation and magical display of its artist. Every marvellous sculpture is a living testimony of the skilful art of its sculptor. When this is the state of only these small things, then is this amazingly vast and awesome machinery of the universe, which is busy in action with such organisation and discipline, beauty and balance, not the fully alive praise and *Hamd* of its unique and unparalleled Creator? Every single atom in it is the walking and talking picture of its superlative beauty and adornment. Are these pictures and their rainbow colours which transfix the eyes not hymns of praise of the brilliance of their Creator (*Al-Musawwar*)? Thus, for the eye that sees, everything which is busy in carrying out its assigned duties is the living evidence of *Hamd* and praise of its own Creator, the Omnipotent *Rabb*. Its persistence in action is the flowing vastness in *Hamd* and admiration of Allah, and its every motion is the perpetual melody of appreciation and applause. Keep these explanations in mind, and then reflect on those verses in which Allah's *Tasbeeh* and *Tahmeed* are referred to, and the meaning will unveil itself and become apparent to you.

24.26.2 *Tasbeeh* by the Manifestations of Nature

The Quran states:

See you not that it is Allah Whose praises (Yo-Sabbiho) all beings in the heavens and on earth do celebrate, and the birds (of the air) with wings outspread? Each one knows its own (mode of) Salat and Tasbeeh. And Allah knows well all that they do. (24:41)

Dawood and Solomon, who were bestowed with a great realm and abundance of knowledge and wisdom, used to remain busy in singing praises in Allah's *Tasbeeh*, and along with them, other things of nature also:

> *... it was Our power that made the hills and the birds celebrate Our praises, with Dawood: it was We Who did (all these things). (21:79) See also (34:10, 38:18)*

Thunder from the clouds which excites dread and fright in the hearts is in reality fulfilling its duty and responding in obedience to commands, proclaiming the greatness and power of Allah, and is the drumming forebearer of the blessings of the rain to follow:

> *Nay, thunder pronounces His praises, and so do Malaika, with awe ...(13:13)*

There is mention of '*Tasbeeh*' by the manifestations of nature at many places:

> *Whatever is in the heavens and on earth, let it declare the praises and glory of Allah ...(57:1) See also (59:1, 61:1, 62:1)*

It has been explained at the beginning about the *Malaika* that they remain bowed down in front of the Divine commands, and 'only do that for which they are given a command.' This is indeed their *Tasbeeh* and *Taqdees*[236]. This was what the *Malaika* had said in the story of Adam:

> *...whilst we do celebrate Your praises and glorify You ...(2:30)*

At another place it is stated:

> *Even those who are in His (very) presence are not too proud to serve Him, nor are they (ever) weary (of His service): They celebrate His praises night and day, nor do they ever flag or intermit. (21:19-20) See also (7:206, 41:38, 42:5)*

These can also be taken to mean *Malaika*. Obedience is implicit in their nature, hence they remain in perpetual obedience and do not become fatigued by it, because this is a trait of their nature.[237]

24.26.3 *Tasbeeh* by Human Beings

This was the *Tasbeeh* and *Hamd* of those things of nature and of those who carry out Allah's designated tasks. Now let us examine the *Tasbeeh* and *Taqdees* of human

---

[236] *Taqdees* – to perform a task with great precision, free from all faults and blemishes. (Ed)
[237] The whole life of a river spent in flowing.

beings. The state of the system of nature and *Malaika* is that they are absorbed in the performance of whatever task they have been charged with (16:50). They are busily engaged in fulfilling their duties. They can never adopt rebellion and disobedience against the Divine laws; they do not even possess the ability for defiance and transgression; they do not even have the choice for disobedience. But contrary to this, man has the choice to transgress, he can also rebel against the Divine laws and can also ignore them. So, in the same way that everything in nature is always busily 'performing *Tasbeeh*' (doing obedience), every human being cannot be described as being similarly engaged at every moment in *Tasbeeh* and *Tahmeed*. He will only be considered as being engaged in *Hamd* and praise (*Tasbeeh*) at that time when he is obeying those laws which have been defined as a code of life for him. The extent to which he is immersed in the obedience of these commands is the extent to which he will be considered as being absorbed in *Tasbeeh* and *Hamd* of Allah. The whole life of the *Anbiya* (messengers of Allah) used to be spent in obedience to the Divine laws, therefore their every breath used to be a sacred refrain of *Tasbeeh* and *Tahmeed*. They used to be busy continuously and persistently in Allah's '*Tasbeeh*'. In the early phases of their invitation, the onslaught of difficulties and opposition would encircle them from all four sides. Though the un-favourableness of circumstances used to appear very discouraging, in these difficulties and obstacles they were directed to not be fearful of the hostile circumstances and to remain busy in the accomplishment of your duty with determination and fortitude. The greater the opposition is, the greater you should become busy in the obedience of Allah's commands, ultimately success will certainly be yours:

Therefore, expound openly what you are commanded, and turn away from those who associate gods with Allah. For sufficient are We unto you against those who scoff, those who adopt, with Allah, another god: but soon will they come to know. We do indeed know how your heart is distressed at what they say. But remain engaged in 'Tasbeeh and Tahmeed' of your Rabb and be of those who prostrate (Sajda) themselves (in front of Divine laws). And serve your Rabb until there come unto you the hour that is certain[238]. (15:94-99)

Here, the meaning of '*Tasbeeh, Tahmeed* and *Sajda*' is clear i.e. complete obedience of the Divine laws, applying His Rule to yourself and then to the whole of the world in a practical sense, and then to stand firm and steadfast on this. This '*Tasbeeh* and *Tahmeed*' is emphasised at numerous places :

---

[238] As per the Law of Requital, time is required for collective deeds to bear results. Here, the Quran instructs patience and perseverance, as the consequences of evil deeds will finally catch up with those people who persist in wrongdoing. (Ed)

And put your trust in Him Who lives and dies not; and do Tasbeeh with His Hamd;
and enough is He to be acquainted with the errors of His people. (25:58) See also
(20:130, 40:55, 50:39, 52:48, 76:26)

24.26.4 Key Meaning of *Tasbeeh*

In the narrative of Moses, the meaning of *Tasbeeh* becomes clearly apparent when
he received the command for Jihad against the transgression and disobedience of
Pharaoh, and because this campaign was very tough, he prayed to Allah:

(Moses) said: O my Rabb! expand me my chest; ease my task for me; and remove the
impediment from my speech, So they may understand what I say: and give me a
minister from my family, Aaron, my brother; add to my strength through him, and
make him share my task: that we may celebrate Your Hamd without stint, and
remember You without stint: for You are He that (ever) regards us'. (20:25-35)

After this it is described in detail how the supplication of Moses was accepted,
how he received the backing and support of Allah, and how he succeeded in his
campaign. The tyranny and subjugation of Pharaoh was drowned in the destructive
flood, and in his place the throne of Allah's sovereignty was established, and in
this way Allah's '*Tasbeeh* and *Zikr*' became widespread everywhere. In place of
human laws, the sphere of Allah's laws became established – this is the practical
aspect of *Tasbeeh* and *Tahmeed* of Allah. This was the very mission of the *Anbiya*,
and after them, this is the aim of the heirs of the Book of Allah i.e. the *Jamaat e*
Momineen:

Only those have Eimaan in Our signs, who, when they are recited to them, fall down
in prostration, and celebrate the Hamd of their Rabb, nor are they (ever) puffed up
with pride. (32:15) See also (33:42, 48:9)

24.26.5 *Tasbeeh* of a *Momin*

This *Tasbeeh* is the same as that which has already been briefly mentioned in the
narrative of Moses i.e. persistently persevering in efforts for the establishment and
continuation of Allah's rule, dedicating life for the achievement of this supreme
objective - this is the *Tasbeeh* and *Tahmeed* of the *Jamaat e Momineen*:

When comes the help of Allah, and victory, and you do see the people enter Allah's
Deen in crowds, celebrate the Hamd of your Rabb, and seek for His protection: for
He is surely Oft-Returning (in Grace and Mercy). (110:1-3)

This is the *Hamd* of a *Momin* and this is his *Tasbeeh*, that he should live his own life
according to the Divine laws and become the cause for the establishment and

implementation of these laws in the whole world. Now consider that when the Muslims had correctly comprehended what the meanings of *Hamd* and admiration, and *Takbeer* and *Taqdees* were, what the state of their life and the state of the world was then, and after that when Deen remained only the name for the 'counting of rosary beads', what their condition had transformed into. In the words of Iqbal:

Either a continuous Takbeer in the expanse of the heavens,
Or Tasbeeh and ritualised practices in the lap of dust.

That Deen of the one conscious of his own self and in obedience to Allah,
This religion of the mullah, of dead and lifeless things.

24.27 *Subhaan-Allah*

As has already been written, the meaning of 'distance' is also implicit in the meaning of *Sabhun*, hence *Subhaan* means 'far from all kinds of faults', pure and sacred. Therefore, if *Hamd* is a positive attribute (i.e. the presence of all goodness and abilities), then *Tasbeeh* contains within it a negative view (i.e. absent from all kinds of faults and decline, and pure); that same *La* (no) and *Illa* (but) which is glaringly visible in every aspect of the Divine attributes:

They say: 'Allah has begotten a son'. Glory be to Him. Nay, to Him belongs all that is in the heavens and on earth: everything follows His laws. (2:116)

In other words, this means that Allah is far above the false belief that people have established about Him. He is far beyond this, and is free from all of these kinds of faults and pure from all flaws:

No son did Allah beget, nor is there any god along with Him: (if there were many gods), behold, each god would have taken away what he had created, and some would have lorded it over others! Glory to Allah! (He is free) from the (sort of) things they attribute to Him! (23:91)

That Being is pure and above all of these kinds of wrong concepts and false beliefs. In many verses, after referring to the false belief of 'offspring of Allah', it is stated that Allah is far from this, He is free from such utterances. See verses (4:171, 10:68, 16:57, 19:35, 21:26, 39:3, 43:81).

Besides the belief of progeny, other entities are also associated with Allah. He is far above this false belief as well. He is the origin of all powers, the Creator and Master of the entire universe. What need does He have for which He should take partners with Him. If there were more than one god in the universe, then the whole system of the universe would be in chaos:

If there were, in the heavens and the earth, other gods besides Allah, there would have been confusion in both! but glory to Allah, the Rabb of the Throne: (High is He) above what they attribute to Him! (21:22) See also (17:42)

In many verses this great fact has been proclaimed that the Being of Allah is far above and free from this *Shirk* (association of partners with Him) which people do (6:100, 9:31, 10:18, 12:108, 16:1, 28:68, 30:40, 39:67). In Surah *Al-Maida* it is stated that on the Day of Judgment Jesus will be asked:

And behold! Allah will say: 'O Jesus the son of Mary! Did you say unto men, obey me and my mother as gods in derogation of Allah'?' He will say: Glory to You! never could I say what I had no right (to say). Had I said such a thing, You would indeed have known it. You know what is in my heart, though I know not what is in Yours. For You know in full all that is hidden. (5:116)

The *Malaika* will be questioned and they will also give a similar answer (34:41). Even when the righteous devotees of Allah, who have been turned into gods by people without reason, are enquired about this, they too will reply in the same way (25:18).

At some places where greatness and supremacy, and exaltation and sovereignty have appeared, *Subhaan*-Allah has been mentioned, because the meaning of acceptance of His greatness is that it should be acknowledged about Him that He is free and above any faults and decline:

Is not He Who created the heavens and the earth able to create the like thereof? Yea, indeed! for He is the Creator Supreme, of skill and knowledge (infinite)! Verily, when He intends a thing, His command is, 'Be', and it is! So glory to Him in Whose hands is the dominion of all things: and to Him will you be all brought back. (36:81-83)

Other than the above places, this word has also been used in a few other verses with the same meanings e.g. (17:93, 17:108, 21:87, 30:17, 36:36). By reflecting at all these points, this reality will become clear that wherever the Quran has emphasised the greatness and supremacy of Allah through *Hamd* and appreciation, it has highlighted this point through *Tasbeeh* and *Taqdees* that He is free from all flaws, and pure from all kinds of weaknesses and flaws, and He is far above the kind of concepts which the human mind devises.

The only correct concept about His attributes is the one which the Quran defines. Hence, no individual can have a correct *Eimaan* on Allah until that time that he has *Eimaan* in the Quran, and to acknowledge the Quran as being from Allah, it is essential to have *Eimaan* in the messenger-hood of Rasul-ullah:

313

...that is the established Deen: but most among mankind understand not. (30:30)

25   Metaphorical References

At some places in the Quran such words have been used about Allah which refer to human body parts e.g. hand, eye etc. It is obvious that this is merely a metaphorical reference in which these words are used figuratively according to our mode of conversation, otherwise these words cannot be applied to that Being about Whom the proclamation of the Quran itself is, 'there is nothing whatever like unto Him' (42:11), with the meanings with which we use them e.g. in Surah *Al-Qasas* it is stated:

...Everything (that exists) is perishable except His Being (Face) ...(28:88)

The literal meaning of the word *Waj-hun* is face but it is evident that the meaning here cannot be a 'face'. The meaning is apparent from the translation. In another verse it is stated:

All that is on earth will perish: But will abide (forever) the Being (Face) of your Rabb, full of Majesty, Bounty and Honour. (55:26-27)

In Surah *Al-Baqra* it is stated:

To Allah belong the east and the west: whithersoever you turn, there is the presence of Allah. For Allah is All-Embracing, All-Knowing. (2:115)

Here, the meaning becomes even clearer i.e. Allah is present everywhere. Apart from *Waj-hun* the word *Yad-un* (hand) has also been used at a few places. For example, it is stated in Surah *Al e Imran*:

...Say: All bounties are in the hand of Allah: He grants them to whom He pleases (as per His laws) ...(3:73) See also (57:29)

It is obvious that the meaning of *Yad* here is not of a 'hand' but is of control and authority. It also means this in our own language. Regarding Ibrahim (Abraham), Ishaq (Isaac) and Yaqoob (Jacob), it is stated in the Quran:

And commemorate Our servants Abraham, Isaac, and Jacob, possessors of power and vision. (38:45)

The meanings are evident that they were possessors of power and vision. Therefore, the meanings of *Yad-un* are of authority and control, power and influence. In Surah *Ad-Dhariyat* it is stated:

With power and skill did We construct the firmament: for it is We Who create the vastness of space. (51:47)

At the location of Hudaibiya[239], when the followers of *Tauheed* (the Oneness of Allah) presented all their possessions of life in the path of Allah and made a covenant to sacrifice all for the sake of the proclamation of *Haqq*, it was stated:

Verily those who plight their fealty to you do no less than plight their fealty to Allah: the hand of Allah is over their hands …(48:10)

In other words, these people are selling their possessions and their lives into the hands of Allah, they are the sellers and Allah is the purchaser. Here, too, the meaning of *Yad* (hand) is clear. In Surah *Az-Zumar* it is stated:

…On the Day of Judgment, the whole of the earth will be but His handful, and the heavens will be rolled up in His right hand: Glory to Him! High is He above the partners they attribute to Him! (39:67)

Here also the meaning of hand is of control and authority. In the story of Noah, it is stated that Allah said to him:

But construct an ark under Our eyes and Our inspiration …(11:37)

Obviously, the meaning of 'under Our eyes' means construct an ark under Our supervision. From these verses it is clear that these words are used purely metaphorically and this style of expression is prevalent in every language, otherwise such a concept cannot even be considered about the Being of Allah, Who is present everywhere and is All-Seeing and All-Knowing, and is free and pure from every kind of material reference, that He possesses a body like that of human beings. Leaving aside possession of a body, no glance can find Him:

No vision can grasp Him, but His grasp is over all vision: He is above all comprehension yet is acquainted with all things. (6:103)

There was no great need to provide an explanation on this subject because after everything that is noted in the Quran about the Divine attributes, and all that has been written in the previous pages, there remains not the slightest need to tell any man possessing vision that the Being of Allah is free and beyond all tangible references. But at the same time the need for these pointers was felt necessary so that no doubt should linger in any heart about these verses of the Quran, and so that this fact becomes clearly evident that wherever in the Quran such words are

---

[239] This is in reference to the historical pact which was agreed between the Quraish of Makkah and Rasul-ullah at this place which was located en route to Makkah (around A.D. March 628). (Ed)

used metaphorically about Allah which refer to human body parts, what their true meaning is. It is a clear proclamation by the Quran about the Being of Allah:

...there is nothing whatever like unto Him ...(42:11)

And under this topic this is the final word and decisive declaration. The truth is that He is the Being of Allah; even the self of man himself is far removed from references to the body and its parts. Personality simply cannot be in a tangible form, it can only be recognised through its attributes.

26   *Zalikum-Allah* (This is Allah)

It is proclaimed in the Quran:

> *...such is Allah, your Rabb: to Him belongs (all) dominion. There is no god but He: then how are you turned away? (39:6)*

The foundation of Quranic teaching is:

> *...there is no god except Allah ...(37:35)*

Although it is a short sentence of four words, if you examine it closely, all four corners of the universe have been enfolded in it. 'There is no such being whose laws should be obeyed – but yes, there is the One Being of Allah'.

Whatever has been written in the previous pages (and other than this, whatever supreme attributes are noted in the Quran), are the high edifice of this established foundation, the encircling sphere of this focal point, and the flourishing and evergreen interpretations of this truth. Take each single pristine attribute of Allah and keep putting it in place of an *Ilaah*, one by one every aspect of the Quranic teaching will keep becoming complete – other than Him no one possesses the authority of *Rabubiyat*; other than Him there is no Creator; other than Him no-one has any power; the fountains of *Rizq* are solely in His control; other than Him, governance belongs to no-one; serving anyone other than Him is not legitimate; and so on and so forth.

Reflect once again on this foundation of Quranic teaching, and just consider that when a believing *Momin*, with full knowledge and conviction, and with vision based on evidence, proclaims from the depths of his heart that *'there is no god except Allah'*, then to what an extent this revolutionary proclamation of his becomes the cause for dynamic and seismic movement in the arena of the world. Rejection of every non-Allah power in the world, rebellion against every man-made system of human beings, revolt against every code of life which is anti-humanitarian, not because there is some prejudice or arrogance against them, but for the proclamation of this sublime reality that man simply cannot devise such a system of life in which the growth and development of the human self can take place.[240] Only that Being can do this Who has bestowed personality on man.

To journey through all four corners of the whole world in a focused manner with head held high, not because of arrogance and pride, but for the demonstration of

---

[240] This is how the best can emerge from the human self and man can truly discover the higher purpose of his life. (Ed)

this supreme truth that no man is in possession of this right that he should make another man prostrate before him. If there is any prostration, then it should only be in front of the laws of that Allah in front of Whom there is a right to prostrate. If there is any obedience, then it is only of the commands of this One Being, in the obedience of Whom the secret of human eminence lies. Prostration before any of the manifestations of nature, denial of the eminence of humanity and bowing your head before a human being like yourself, is an extreme humiliation of the self:

...if anyone assigns partners to Allah, is as if he had fallen from heaven and been snatched up by birds, or the wind had swooped (like a bird on its prey) and thrown him into a far-distant place. (22:31)

This is why Shirk has been declared to be the greatest of injustices (31:13) and there is nothing more unjust than this. This is denial of one's own self and acceptance of the divinity of those who are at the most men just like us:

Verily those whom you call upon besides Allah are men like unto you ...(7:194)

That individual who has handed over an invaluable entity such as human eminence and dignity of the self to others, then after this what can still be remaining behind about which he can have any kind of reticence or hesitation whatsoever to sell? Such a human being is the slave of his own hedonistic desires. In comparison to the code of laws of Allah, any human system of life whether it is devised by oneself or by someone else is subservience to other than Allah, the essential consequence of which is humiliation and ruin; and is such a hell of absence of peace and dearth of tranquility, the life invading and worldwide blaze of which engulf every corner of human life. Contrary to this, the individual who has *Eimaan* in the immutability of Allah's laws, confines all worldly and intellectual forces within the shores of this great and supreme code, takes the ark of life steadily towards that paradise where there is no kind of fear and grief:

In the case of those who say, 'Our Rabb is Allah', and, further, stand straight and steadfast, Malaika descend on them: 'Fear you not!' (they say), 'nor grieve! but receive the glad tidings of the paradise, the which you were promised!' (41:30)

Having *Eimaan* in Allah and denying every power other than Allah, this is the secret of life, this is the true life:

... Whoever rejects evil and has Eimaan in Allah has grasped the most trustworthy handhold, that never breaks. And Allah hears and knows all things. (2:256)

But *Eimaan* is only that *Eimaan* whose origin is conviction of the heart and whose manifestation is individual purity of character and conduct, and which is a collective system of life, not that which remains limited merely to the movement of the tongue, while the practical life of man is falsifying it. What is the value of a body which is so soul-less?

As has already been written at the start, the definition of the Being of Allah is beyond the cognitive perception of man. Whatever knowledge He wished to pass to man, He gave it via His attributes which are expounded in the Quran.[241] Hence, whatever we can learn about Allah is only that much which the Quran notes. Other than this, there is no other means by which we can recognise the Being of Allah or can obtain knowledge about Him. For a *Momin* this is the final point of knowledge and the last boundary of appraisal. We can neither advance beyond this, nor can the effort to go beyond this bear results. Islam is a simple and straightforward, clean and transparent syllabus of teaching and code of action. It contains neither aimless philosophical arguments, nor meaningless conjectures about the idea of the world. The meaning of Islam is *Eimaan* in Allah according to the Quran revealed on Rasul-ullah, which should be the focus of all aspects of intellect and reason, and to continue to reflect the Divine attributes within oneself within human limitations and covering all aspects of actions in life. The *Jamaat* possessing this *Eimaan* and such deeds is called the Muslim Ummah, and their natural outcome is establishment in the land i.e. implementation of this system on this earth whose practical formation was done by the last messenger of Allah and his companions – this is Islam. Other than this, all the rest are inventions and conjectures of the human mind which have no connection with the truth. Whatever people say about Allah (from conjectures and their minds), He is far above and beyond it. Whatever is said about Allah outwith the Quran is a conjecture of the human mind. The True Allah is He about Whom the Quran has declared:

> *...Such is Allah your Rabb: to Him belongs all dominion. And those whom you invoke besides Him have not the least power (not even equivalent of an atom).*
> *(35:13)*

When the consciousness of man opened its eyes, he remained wandering in search of that point on reaching which he could then say with full conviction and assurance, that this is Allah. This was the ultimate end of his curiosity and the eminence of his humanity. In search of this ultimate aim, for eons he wandered and searched through deserts and jungles, but the human mind alone could not find the secret of this objective anywhere, neither in the schools of Greece, nor in the firehouses of Persia, nor in the temples of India, nor in the cloisters of Rome. Whenever, and wherever any sound of the eternal melody of Allah's *Wahi* reached the ear, signs of vivacity in his eyes and of illumination on his forehead began to

---

[241] The Quran is a complete Book of guidance from an infinitely developed Being which, if viewed and studied in this way, will clearly reveal its significance. (Ed)

sparkle. But as soon as that sound vanished, he again became lost in that same valley of bewilderment. This continued to happen until that time that these eternal melodies of these scattered songs became enfolded into such a real instrument which became the guiding voice of the caravan of humanity. The name of this truth-bearing instrument is the *Quran-ul-Azeem* (the Exalted Quran).

For the first time, the Quran informed man that *Eimaan* in Allah is the foundation for *Eimaan* of man in his own self, and the meaning of *Eimaan* of man in his own self is *Eimaan* in this fact:

(1) Man is not just the name for his physical body; other than the body, he also possesses another entity which is called the human personality.

(2) If suitable development of the human self takes place, then those attributes continue to come alive, within the confines of human limits, which in relation to Allah are called the Balanced Attributes[242]. A self which is developed in such a way remains alive after the death of the physical body, and in order to traverse further evolutionary stages sets out on the journey of the world of the hereafter.

(3) This kind of development of the human self takes place within that society which is shaped according to the Divine laws (the Quranic system of life). This society is responsible for ensuring the provision of all necessary means for the nourishment of the body and self of all individuals of humanity.

(4) Without this kind of system of society, man lives a life of hell both in this world and in the life of the hereafter also.

Rasul-ullah demonstrated this by establishing this type of Quranic society and transforming the world into a paradise; and today the hell of this world can only be changed in this way into a paradise when this kind of society is once again established in the world. Other than this, there is no other way for success and emancipation of the world. This is the aim of having *Eimaan* in Allah according to the Quran.

Let us recap this reality once again:

1. There are certain attributes of Allah which are specifically for Him alone, and no-one else can be a partner in them e.g. He is the First and the Last etc. The remainder of His attributes can be manifested through the human self but only within human limits. The proportion to which these attributes manifest in an individual will be the same extent to which he will be called a possessor of righteousness and character.

---

[242] The Quran calls these *Al-Asma-al-Husna*.

2. The Divine attributes which are noted in the Quran are that external criterion by which every man can assess whether development of his self is taking place or not, and if it is taking place, then to what extent. If this external criterion is not in front of us, then man ails from this self-deception that he simply assumes that he is progressing forward in 'spirituality'. Remember! 'Quranic spirituality' is another name for balanced righteousness and character.

3. The non-Quranic concept of 'spirituality' which is called mysticism is purely an individual sentiment; this is why when these claimants of spirituality are asked what proof do they have that they are traversing the stages of spirituality, they have no other answer to this than – 'the state of intoxication can only be understood by the one who himself drinks wine'. This state cannot be made comprehensible to others. This is complete self-deception. According to the Quran, development of the human self emerges naturally through the character and righteousness of an individual. As has already been stated, the extent to which the character and righteousness of an individual (within human limits) will be a reflection of the attributes of Allah will be the same extent to which his self will have become developed.

4. When we have stated that the manifestation of the development of the human self occurs through the righteousness and character of an individual, then it becomes clear from this that it is not that kind of an intoxication the effects of which can only be enjoyed by the one who is drinking an intoxicant himself. The display of the talents of a developed self is in the collective life of human beings, because character and behaviour can only be known at that time when one man has to deal with another man.

5. We have also seen that aside from being numerous and different, at certain places the Divine attributes are also mutually opposing. For example, He is *Raheem* and *Kareem*, and also *Jabbar* and *Qahhar*. The meanings of character are that wherever any kind of manifestation is necessary for an attribute, that attribute should be exhibited. If in place of *Adl* the attributes of *Afw*, and in place of *Rehm* the attributes of *Qahhariat* are displayed, then disorder can emerge in the system of the world from this. The question is, how can it be ascertained as to which attribute should manifest in which situation. You will see that generally in the Quran at the end of its verses some attribute of Allah will be noted. If you delve deeper into these verses, then this fact will become evident that whatever kind of issues and details are noted in these verses, then in that situation this attribute should be exhibited which appears at the end of these verses. By reflecting and reasoning on the Quran on these lines, this ability develops in man where he can ascertain as to what kind of Divine attribute was manifested in what kinds of events and occasions. In such situations, this same kind of

attribute should be manifested by him – *Afw* in the situation of *Afw*, *Adl* in the situation of *Adl*.

6. You will observe that the greatest amount of destruction in the world has not occurred through the hands of those who were deniers of God; the majority of destruction happened via the hands of those who were God worshippers, who by taking one of the attributes of God, kept exceeding it in intensity and extremeness. For example, *Rehm* is one attribute of God. Christianity created such an extreme position in this attribute, that in their religion the concept of *Adl* and the Law of Requital simply did not remain. The consequence of this was that a flood of sins appeared amongst them and crimes spread like an epidemic. 'Confessions and pardoning' started to sell in the bazaar like fruits and vegetables, and the 'representatives of God' started selling paradise for pennies. This was that belief of transgression and excessiveness in the Divine attributes, in order to stop which, the Quran stated that all the Divine attributes carrying their complete balance (beauty) are concentrated in the Being of Allah. While maintaining the balance of these attributes, call on Allah:

> *The most beautiful attributes belong to Allah: so call on him by them; but stay away from such who transgress in His attributes: for what they do, they will soon be requited. (7:180)*

Cut off your relations from those people who take some of these attributes and run off in one direction. Their belief is taking them towards misguidance. You should stay away from them, soon they will find out how laden with destructive consequences their belief and path were.

The right path is solely this, that at whatever place whatever kind of Divine attribute's manifestation is required, this attribute should manifest there, and in whatever proportion it is required at this point. Among the Divine attributes there is neither such an attribute which should be abandoned, nor is there such a one in which transgression and excessiveness should be adopted. All His attributes possess the best results at their own places. It is on this basis that His attributes are proclaimed with the definition of *Al-Husna*. These attributes with this beauty and balance will not be found in any of the religions of the world. These are noted only in the Quran and this is why *Eimaan* in this Allah can be called *Eimaan Billah*, which is introduced by the Quran. This is the reason why the Quran also demands *Eimaan Billah* from those people who have *Eimaan* in God according to their own idea and concept. From this, this fact also emerges in front of us as to what the practical meaning of *Eimaan Billah* is. The practical meaning of this is that His attributes are declared to be an external criterion to assess this fact as to whether the self of an individual is or is not developing, and if it is developing, then to what extent. From this it is clear that *Eimaan* in Allah serves as the foundation for man to have *Eimaan* in his own self.

Remember! the individual who is in denial of his own self (i.e. considers himself as the possessor of life based only on his physical body and that's it), he cannot have *Eimaan* in Allah. This is because for the individual who becomes a 'denier of the existence of his self', the question of his being a '*Momin* of Allah' simply does not arise. But it can be expected about the individual who accepts the existence of 'his self' that one day he may become a '*Momin* of Allah'.

And this is only possible by having *Eimaan* in the Quran.

Before We Are Born

Essentials of Embryology
and Birth Defects

Before We Are Born

Essentials of Embryology and Birth Defects

5th Edition

Keith L. Moore, PhD, FIAC, FRSM
Professor Emeritus of Anatomy and Cell Biology
Faculty of Medicine, University of Toronto
Toronto, Ontario, Canada

Professor of Human Anatomy and Cell Science
Department of Anatomy, Faculty of Medicine
University of Manitoba
Winnipeg, Manitoba, Canada

T.V.N. Persaud, MD, PhD, DSc, FRCPath (Lond.)
Professor and Former Head
Department of Human Anatomy and Cell Science
Professor of Pediatrics and Child Health
Professor of Obstetrics, Gynecology, and Reproductive Sciences
University of Manitoba, Faculty of Medicine

Consultant in Pathology and Clinical Genetics
Health Sciences Centre
Winnipeg, Manitoba, Canada

W.B. Saunders Company
A Division of Harcourt Brace & Company
Philadelphia   London   Toronto   Montreal   Sydney   Tokyo

W.B. SAUNDERS COMPANY
A Division of Harcourt Brace & Company

The Curtis Center
Independence Square West
Philadelphia, Pennsylvania 19106

Library of Congress Cataloging-in-Publication Data

Moore, Keith L.
Before we are born:essentials of embryology and birth defects/
  Keith L. Moore, T.V.N. Persaud.—5th ed.

p. cm.

Includes bibliographical references and index.

ISBN 0–7216–7377–5

1. Embryology, Human. 2. Abnormalities, Human. I. Persaud, T.V.N.
  II. Title.

[DNLM: 1. Embryology. 2. Abnormalities. QS 604 M822b 1998]

QM601.M757 1998   612.6′4—dc21

DNLM/DLC   97–50318

BEFORE WE ARE BORN: ESSENTIALS OF EMBRYOLOGY AND BIRTH DEFECTS   ISBN 0-7216-7377-5

Last digit is the print number: 9   8   7   6   5   4   3   2   1

To our wives, Marion and Gisela,

our children, and our grandchildren—

especially the two latest grandchildren—

Courtney Michaella (KLM)

and Brian (TVNP)

Preface

■ The fifth edition of *Before We Are Born* presents the essentials of human embryology (normal development) and teratology (abnormal development). This synoptic volume contains the basic facts and concepts of development that are essential for students of medicine and the associated health sciences. This work is a digest of our larger book, *The Developing Human: Clinically Oriented Embryology,* 6th edition. Therefore, persons wishing more information on any of the subjects should consult the more comprehensive text.

An important feature of this book is the *Clinically Oriented Questions* that appear at the end of each chapter. Over the years we have been asked these and other questions by students and lay people. Because of misconceptions derived from newspaper articles and discussions on television and radio, we have done our best to give answers that are supported by current research and medical practice.

The fifth edition of *Before We Are Born* contains more clinically oriented material than previous editions. These sections are highlighted in color to set them apart from the rest of the text. This edition also contains numerous color photographs of embryos (normal and abnormal). Many of the illustrations have been improved using *three-dimensional renderings* and more effective use of colors. There are also additional diagnostic images (ultrasound and MRI) of embryos and fetuses, and scanning electron micrographs to illustrate three-dimensional aspects of embryos.

The teratology content has increased because the study of abnormal development is so helpful in understanding risk estimation, the causes of anomalies, and how malformations may be prevented. Molecular aspects of developmental biology have been highlighted throughout the book, especially in those areas that appear promising for clinical medicine and future research. Successful completion of national board examinations now requires knowledge of this aspect of development.

We have continued our attempts to give an *easy-to-read account of human development before birth.* Every chapter has been thoroughly revised to reflect new findings in research and their clinical significance. The chapters are organized to present a systematic and logical approach that explains how embryos and fetuses develop. In addition to being updated, the material includes more information that is useful in clinical practice and will be most helpful to those taking problem-solving courses.

Many of our colleagues (listed alphabetically) have helped with the preparation of this edition; it is a pleasure to record our indebtedness to them: *Dr. Albert E. Chudley,* Professor of Pediatrics and Child Health, Director of Clinical Genetics, Health Sciences Centre, University of Manitoba, Winnipeg, Manitoba, Canada; *Dr. Angelika J. Dawson,* Director, Cytogenetics Laboratory, Health Sciences Centre and Department of Pediatrics and Child Health, University of Manitoba, Winnipeg, Manitoba, Canada; *Dr. Raymond Gasser,* Louisiana State University School of Medicine, New Orleans, Louisiana; *Dr. Christopher R. Harman,* Department of Obstetrics, Gynecology, and Reproductive Sciences, Women's Hospital and University of Manitoba, Winnipeg, Manitoba, Canada; *Dr. Elizabeth Hay,* Pfeifer Professor of Embryology, Department of Cell Biology, Harvard Medical School, Boston, Massachusetts; *Professor K. Hinrichsen,* Rühr-Universität, Medizinische Fakultät, Institut für Anatomie, Bochum, Germany; *Dr. Dagmar K. Kalousek,* Program Head, Cytogenetics/Embryopathology Laboratory and Professor of Pathology, University of British Columbia, Vancouver, British Columbia, Canada; *Dr. Peeyush K. Lala,* Professor of Anatomy and Cell Biology, Faculty of Medicine, University of Western Ontario, London, Ontario, Canada; *Dr. Bernard Liebgott,* Professor of Anatomy and Cell Biology, Faculty of Medicine and Department of Biological Sciences, Faculty of Dentistry, University of Toronto, Toronto, Ontario, Canada; *Dr. Edward A. Lyons,* Professor of Radiology and Obstetrics and Gynecology, Health Sciences Centre, University of Manitoba, Winnipeg, Manitoba, Canada; *Dr. Kohei Shiota,* Professor and Chairman of the Department of Anatomy and Developmental Biology and Director of the Congenital Anomaly Research Center, Faculty of Medicine, Kyoto University, Kyoto, Japan; *Dr. Gerald S. Smyser,* Altru Health System, Grand Forks, North Dakota; and *Dr. Michael Wiley,* Associate Professor, Department of Anatomy and Cell Biology, Faculty of Medicine, University of Toronto, Toronto, Ontario, Canada.

Persons who have contributed photographs are individually acknowledged in the figure legends. The new illustrations were prepared by Hans Neuhart, President of the Electronic Illustrators Group in Fountain Hills, Arizona. Marion Moore in Toronto did the word processing and helped with review of the manuscript, as did Gisela Persaud in Winnipeg. William Schmitt, Medical Editor, Laurie Sander, Production Manager, and Agnes Byrne, Project Manager, W.B. Saunders Company, and their colleagues have been most helpful with our work. To all these people, we extend our sincere thanks. Last, but not least, we thank our wives, Marion and Gisela, for their continued understanding and support.

KEITH L. MOORE
T.V.N. PERSAUD

Contents

11. The Pharyngeal (Branchial) Apparatus 197

12. The Respiratory System 241

13. The Digestive System 255

14. The Urogenital System 289

15. The Cardiovascular System 329

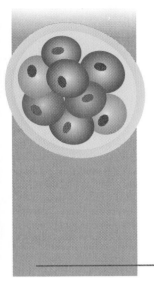

Introduction To Human Embryology

1

▧ Human development is a continuous process that begins when an **oocyte** (ovum) from a female is fertilized by a **sperm** (spermatozoon) from a male. Development involves many changes that transform a single cell, the **zygote** (fertilized ovum), into a multicellular human being. Most developmental changes occur before birth, but important changes also occur during the later periods of development: infancy, childhood, adolescence, and adulthood.

Human embryology is the science concerned with the origin and development of a human being from a zygote to the birth of an infant. The study of embryology bridges the gap between prenatal development and obstetrics, perinatal medicine, pediatrics, and clinical anatomy.

STAGES OF HUMAN DEVELOPMENT

Although human development is usually divided into *prenatal* (before birth) and *postnatal* (after birth) periods, development is a continuum that begins at fertilization (conception). Birth is a dramatic event during development, resulting in a change in environment. *Development does not stop at birth*; important developmental changes occur after birth — development of teeth and female breasts, for example. Most developmental changes are completed by the age of 25. The stages of development that occur before birth are illustrated in the *Timetables of Human Prenatal Development* (Figs. 1 – 1 and 1 – 2). The following list explains the terms used in these timetables and in subsequent discussions.

Embryological Terminology

Most embryological terms have Latin (L.) or Greek (Gr.) origins. An understanding of the origin of terms often serves as a memory key. The term *zygote*, for example, is derived from the Greek word *zygōtos,* meaning yoked, which indicates that the sperm and oocyte unite to form a new cell, the zygote.

Oocyte (L. *ovum,* **egg).** This term refers to the female germ or sex cell produced in the *ovaries.* When mature, the oocyte is called a *secondary oocyte,* or mature ovum. A *blighted ovum* refers to an early embryo whose development has ceased. Although the embryo is dead, the other products of conception, the chorionic (gestational) sac, for example, may survive for several weeks.

Sperm (spermatozoon). This term refers to the male germ or sex cell produced in the *testes* (testi-

cles). Sperms (spermatozoa) are expelled from the male urethra during ejaculation.

Zygote. This cell, formed by the union of an oocyte and a sperm, is the beginning of a new human being (i.e., an embryo). The expression *fertilized ovum* refers to a secondary oocyte (ovum) that is impregnated by a sperm; when fertilization is complete, the oocyte becomes a zygote.

Fertilization or Conception Age. It is difficult to determine exactly when fertilization (conception) occurs because the process cannot be observed in vivo (within the living body). Physicians calculate the age of the embryo or fetus from the first day of the last normal menstrual period (LNMP). This is the *gestational age*, which is about 2 weeks longer than the *fertilization age* because the oocyte is not fertilized until about 2 weeks after the preceding menstruation (Fig. 1 – 1). Consequently, when a physician gives the age of an embryo or fetus, 2 weeks must be deducted to determine the actual or fertilization age of the developing human.

Cleavage. Mitotic cell division, or cleavage of the zygote, forms embryonic cells called *blastomeres.* The size of the early embryo remains the same because the blastomeres become smaller at each succeeding cell division.

Morula. When 12 or more blastomeres have formed, the ball of cells resulting from cleavage of the zygote is called a *morula* and resembles the berry-like fruit known as the mulberry (L. *morus).* The morula stage is reached about 3 to 4 days after fertilization, just as the developing human enters the uterus from the uterine tube (fallopian tube).

Blastocyst. After the morula passes from the uterine tube to the uterus, a fluid-filled cavity — *the blastocyst cavity* — forms inside it. This change converts the morula into a blastocyst, which contains an *inner cell mass* or embryoblast that will form the embryo.

Embryo. This term refers to the developing human during its early stages of development. The *embryonic period* extends to the end of the eighth week, by which time the beginnings of all major structures are present. Only the heart and circulation are functioning. The size of embryos is given as crown-rump length (CRL), which is measured from the vertex of the skull (crown of the head) to the rump (buttocks).

Conceptus. This term refers to the embryo and its membranes (i.e., the *products of conception* or *fertil-*

ization). The term refers to all structures that develop from the zygote, both embryonic and extraembryonic; hence it includes the embryo as well as its associated membranes — the amnion, chorionic (gestational) sac, and yolk sac (see Chapter 8).

Primordium. This term refers to the beginning or first discernible indication of an organ or structure (i.e., its earliest stage of development). The term *anlage* has a similar meaning. The primordium or anlage of an upper limb appears as a limb bud on day 26 (Fig. 1 – 1).

Fetus. After the embryonic period (8 weeks), the developing human is called a fetus. During the *fetal period* (ninth week to birth), differentiation and growth of the tissues and organs formed during the embryonic period occur. Although developmental changes are not so dramatic as those happening during the embryonic period, they are very important because they make it possible for the tissues and organs to function. The rate of body growth is remarkable, especially during the third and the fourth months (see Fig. 1 – 2), and weight gain is phenomenal during the terminal months.

Trimester. This is a period of *3 calendar months*. Obstetricians commonly divide the 9-month period of gestation into three trimesters. The most critical stages of development occur during the first trimester, when embryonic and early fetal development is occurring.

Abortion (L. *aboriri*, to miscarry). This term means a premature stoppage in development and refers to the birth of an embryo or fetus before it is *viable* — mature enough to survive outside the uterus. The main types of abortion are:

- *Threatened abortion* is a common complication in about 25% of pregnancies. Despite every effort to prevent a spontaneous abortion, about half of these pregnancies ultimately abort (Filly, 1994). All terminations of pregnancy that occur naturally or are induced before 20 weeks are abortions.
- *Spontaneous abortion.* About 15% of recognized pregnancies end in spontaneous abortion (i.e., they occur naturally), usually during the first 12 weeks.
- *Legally induced abortions*, or *elective abortions*, are usually produced by drugs or suction curettage (evacuation of the embryo and its membranes by suction from the uterus). Some abortions are induced because of the mother's poor health (mental or physical) or to prevent the birth of a se-

verely malformed child (e.g., one without most of its brain).
- A *missed abortion* is the retention of a conceptus in the uterus after death of the embryo or fetus. An *abortus* refers to the products of an abortion (i.e., the embryo/fetus and its associated membranes, such as the amnion and chorionic sac).
- An *abortus* refers to an embryo or nonviable fetus and its membranes weighing less than 500 gm that are expelled from the uterus.
- *Miscarriage* refers to a spontaneous abortion of a fetus and its membranes before the middle of the second trimester.

IMPORTANCE OF EMBRYOLOGY

The study of prenatal stages of development, especially those occurring during the embryonic period, helps us to understand the normal relationships of adult body structures and the causes of congenital anomalies. *Embryology illuminates anatomy* and explains how abnormalities develop. The embryo is vulnerable to large amounts of radiation, viruses, and certain drugs during the third to eighth weeks (see Chapter 9).

The knowledge physicians have regarding normal development and the causes of congenital anomalies aids in giving the embryo the best possible chance of developing normally. Much of the modern practice of obstetrics involves what could be called applied or **clinical embryology**. Because some of their patients may have disorders resulting from maldevelopment such as spina bifida and congenital heart disease, the significance of embryology is readily apparent to pediatricians. Progress in surgery, especially in the prenatal and pediatric age groups, has made knowledge of human development more clinically significant. Understanding and correcting most congenital anomalies (e.g., cleft palate and cardiac defects) depend on an understanding of normal development and the deviations that have occurred.

HISTORICAL HIGHLIGHTS

Greek scholars made many important contributions to the science of embryology (Horder et al., 1986; Dunstan, 1990). The first recorded embryologic studies are in the books of **Hippocrates of Cos** (Fig. 1 – 3), the famous Greek physician of the fifth century B.C. In the fourth century B.C., **Aristotle of Stagira**, a philosopher and scientist, wrote the first known account of embryology, in which he described development of chick and other embryos. **Claudius Galen** (second century A.D.), a Greek physician and medical scientist in Rome, wrote a book entitled *On the Formation of*

Text continued on page 8

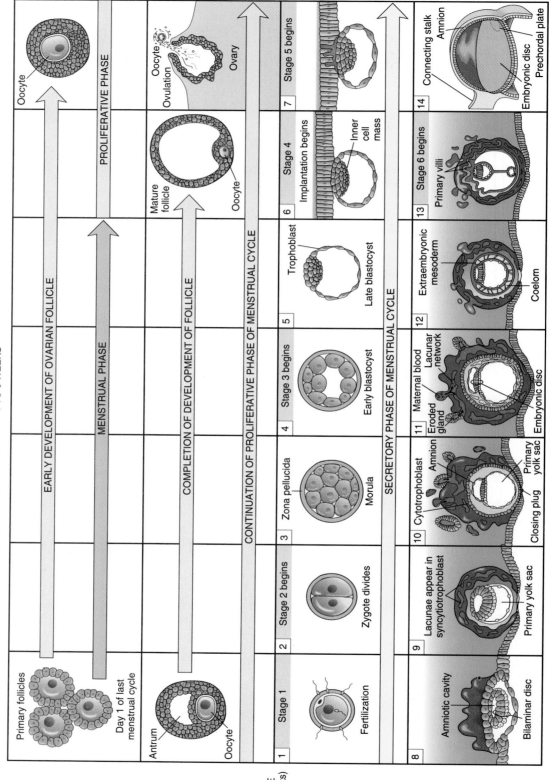

TIMETABLE OF HUMAN PRENATAL DEVELOPMENT
1 TO 6 WEEKS

EARLY DEVELOPMENT OF OVARIAN FOLLICLE

PROLIFERATIVE PHASE

MENSTRUAL PHASE

COMPLETION OF DEVELOPMENT OF FOLLICLE

CONTINUATION OF PROLIFERATIVE PHASE OF MENSTRUAL CYCLE

SECRETORY PHASE OF MENSTRUAL CYCLE

Primary follicles

Day 1 of last menstrual cycle

Antrum

Oocyte

Oocyte

Oocyte
Ovulation
Ovary

Mature follicle
Oocyte

AGE (weeks)

1

1	2 Stage 2 begins	3 Zona pellucida	4 Stage 3 begins	5	6	7
Stage 1						Stage 5 begins
Fertilization	Zygote divides	Morula	Early blastocyst	Trophoblast	Stage 4	
				Late blastocyst	Implantation begins	
					Inner cell mass	

2

8 Amniotic cavity	9 Lacunae appear in syncytiotrophoblast	10 Cytotrophoblast	11	12 Extraembryonic mesoderm	13 Stage 6 begins	14
Bilaminar disc	Primary yolk sac	Amnion	Maternal blood	Coelom	Primary villi	Connecting stalk
		Closing plug	Lacunar network			Amnion
		Primary yolk sac	Eroded gland			Embryonic disc
			Embryonic disc			Prechordal plate

4

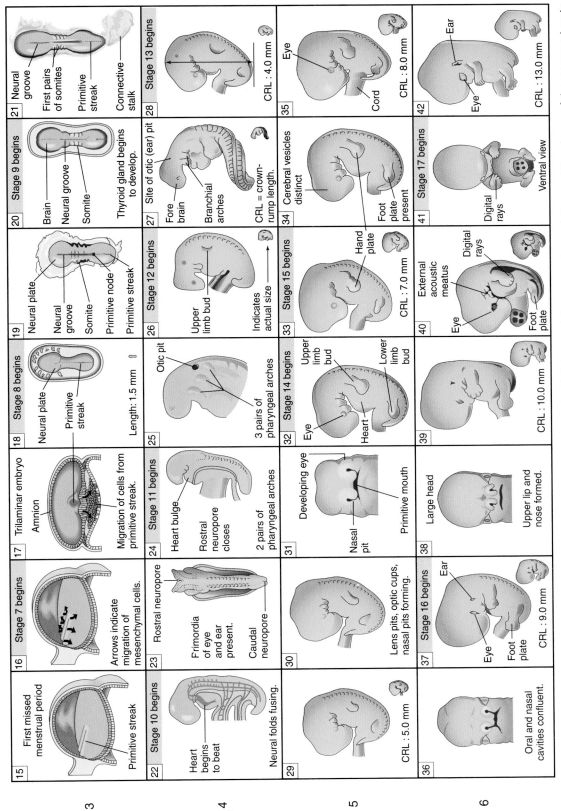

■ **Figure 1–1.** Early stages of embryonic development. Development of an ovarian follicle containing an oocyte, ovulation, and the phases of the menstrual cycle are illustrated. Human development begins at fertilization, about 14 days after the onset of the last menstruation. Cleavage of the zygote in the uterine tube, implantation of the blastocyst, and early development of the embryo are also shown. For a full discussion of embryonic development, see Chapter 6. Beginning students should make no attempt to memorize these tables or the stages (e.g., that Stage 3 begins on day 4 and Stage 5 on day 7).

5

TIMETABLE OF HUMAN PRENATAL DEVELOPMENT
7 to 38 weeks

AGE (weeks)

7

43 — Actual size — CRL: 16 mm

44 — Stage 18 begins — Eyelids beginning

45 — Head large but chin poorly formed. Grooves between digital rays indicate fingers.

46 — Wall of uterus — Uterine cavity — Amniotic sac — Smooth chorion

47 — Genital tubercle — Urogenital membrane — Anal membrane — ♀ or ♂

48 — Stage 19 begins — Eyelid — External ear — Wrist, fingers fused

49 — Actual size — CRL: 18 mm

8

50 — Upper limbs longer and bent at elbows. Fingers distinct but webbed.

51 — Ear — Eye — Nose — Fingers — Toes

52 — Stage 21 begins — Large forehead

53 — Stage 21 — External genitalia still in sexless state but have begun to differentiate.

54 — Stage 22 begins — Genital tubercle — Urethral groove — Anus — ♀ or ♂

55 — Ear — Elbow — Eye — Wrist — Knee — Toes

56 — Stage 23 — CRL: 30 mm

9

57 — Beginning of fetal period.

58 — Ear — Elbow — Eye — Wrist — Knee — Toes

59 — Placenta

60 — Genitalia — Phallus — Urogenital fold — Labioscrotal fold — Perineum — ♀

61 — CRL: 45 mm

62 — Genitalia — Phallus — Urogenital fold — Labioscrotal fold — Perineum — ♂

63 — CRL: 50 mm

10

64 — Face has human profile. Note growth of chin compared to day 44.

65 — Ears still lower than normal.

66 — Ears still lower than normal.

67 — Clitoris — Labium minus — Urogenital groove — Labium majus — ♀

68 — Genitalia have ♀ or ♂ characteristics but still not fully formed.

69 — Glans penis — Urethral groove — Scrotum — ♂

70 — CRL: 61 mm

6

Eleventh Week to Full Term

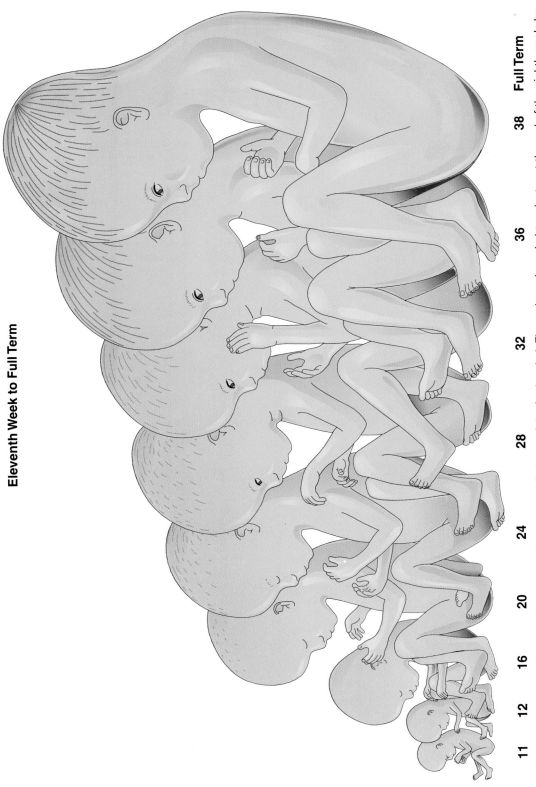

11   12   16   20   24   28   32   36   38   Full Term

■ **Figure 1–2.** Conclusion of embryonic development and features of the fetal period. The embryonic period terminates at the end of the eighth week; by this time, the beginnings of all essential structures are present. The fetal period, extending from the ninth week to birth, is characterized by growth and elaboration of structures. Sex is clearly distinguishable by 12 weeks. Fetuses are viable 22 weeks after fertilization, but their chances of survival are not good until they are several weeks older. These 11- to 38-week fetuses are shown at about half their actual sizes. For more information, see Chapter 7.

■ **Figure 1–3.** Drawing of Hippocrates, "the Father of Medicine" (460–377 B.C.). He placed medicine on a scientific foundation. In addition to the Hippocratic oath attributed to him, he wrote several books on anatomy, including one on embryology.

the Foetus, in which he described the development and nutrition of fetuses.

Growth of science was slow in the middle ages (A.D. 1000–1400). The composition and sequential development of the embryo in relation to the planets and each month of pregnancy were described by **Constantinus Africanus** during the 11th century. In the 15th century, **Leonardo da Vinci** made accurate drawings

of dissections of the pregnant uterus and associated fetal membranes (Fig. 1–4).

William Harvey (Fig. 1–5) studied chick embryos in 1651 with simple lenses and made new observations. He believed the sperm, after entering the womb, changed into an egglike substance, which then developed into an embryo. He also studied the development of the fallow deer; however, when he was unable to observe early stages, he concluded that embryos were secreted by the uterus.

Early microscopes were simple, but they opened a new field of observation. In 1672 **de Graaf** observed little chambers (undoubtedly what we now call blastocysts) in the rabbit's uterus and concluded that they came from organs he called *ovaries*. **Marcello Malpighi,** studying what he believed were unfertilized hen's eggs in 1675, observed early embryos. As a result, he thought the egg contained a miniature chick. Despite this, his observations on the developing chick were good.

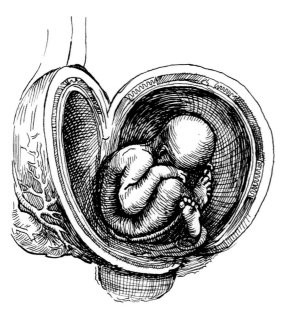

■ **Figure 1–4.** Reproduction of Leonardo da Vinci's drawing made in the 15th century, showing a fetus in a uterus that has been incised and opened.

■ **Figure 1–5.** William Harvey (1578–1657), discoverer of the circulation of blood, carried out comparative studies in embryology. (From Sabiston DC Jr, Lyerly HK: *Essentials of Surgery.* Philadelphia, WB Saunders, 1997.)

Hamm and Leeuwenhoek first observed human sperms using an improved microscope in 1677 (Fig. 1-6), but they did not understand the sperm's role in fertilization. They thought that the sperm contained a miniature preformed human being (Fig. 1-7). **Spallanzani** showed in 1775 that both the ovum and sperm are necessary for the initiation of a new individual. From his experiments, Spallanzani concluded that the sperm is the fertilizing agent that initiated development.

Great advances were made in embryology when the *cell theory* was established in 1830 by **Schleiden** and **Schwann**. The concept that the body was composed of cells and cell products soon led to the realization that the embryo developed from a single cell called the zygote. They discovered and demonstrated the cellular nature of tissues. Great progress was made in our understanding of prenatal development through the improved techniques for fixing, sectioning, and staining of tissues and reconstruction of human embryos developed by **Wilhelm His** (1831-1904). His method of graphic reconstruction paved the way for producing current three-dimensional, computer-generated images of human embryos.

Hans Spemann received the Nobel Prize in 1935 for discovering the phenomenon of primary induction —how one tissue determines the fate of another.

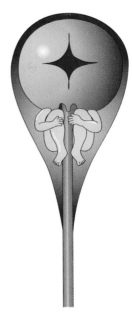

■ **Figure 1-7.** Copy of a 17th-century drawing of a sperm by Hartsoeker. The miniature human being within it was thought to enlarge after the sperm entered an ovum. Other embryologists at that time thought that the oocyte contained a miniature human being that enlarged when stimulated by a sperm.

Edwards and **Steptoe** pioneered the technique of human *in vitro fertilization,* which led to the birth of the first "test tube baby" in 1978.

The *principles of heredity* were developed in 1865 by an Austrian monk named **Gregor Mendel,** but medical biologists did not understand the significance of these principles in the study of mammalian development for many years. **Flemming** observed chromosomes in 1878 and suggested their probable role in fertilization. The first significant observations on human chromosomes were made by **von Winiwarter** in 1912. In 1923, **Painter** concluded that there were 48 chromosomes. This number was accepted until 1956, when **Tjio** and **Levan** reported finding 46 chromosomes. It is now firmly established that humans have only 46 chromosomes.

Recent advances in the field of molecular biology have led to the application of sophisticated techniques (e.g., *recombinant DNA technology*, chimeric models, and transgenic mice) and are now widely used in research laboratories to address such diverse problems as the genetic regulation of morphogenesis, the temporal and regional expression of specific genes, and how cells are committed to form the various parts of the embryo. For the first time we are beginning to understand how, when, and where selected genes are activated and expressed in the embryo during normal

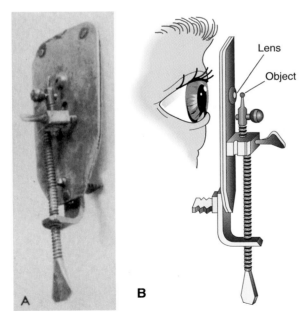

■ **Figure 1-6.** *A,* Photograph of a 1673 Leeuwenhoek microscope. *B,* Drawing of a lateral view illustrating the use of this primitive microscope. The object was held in front of the lens on the point of the short rod, and the screw arrangement was used to adjust the object under the lens.

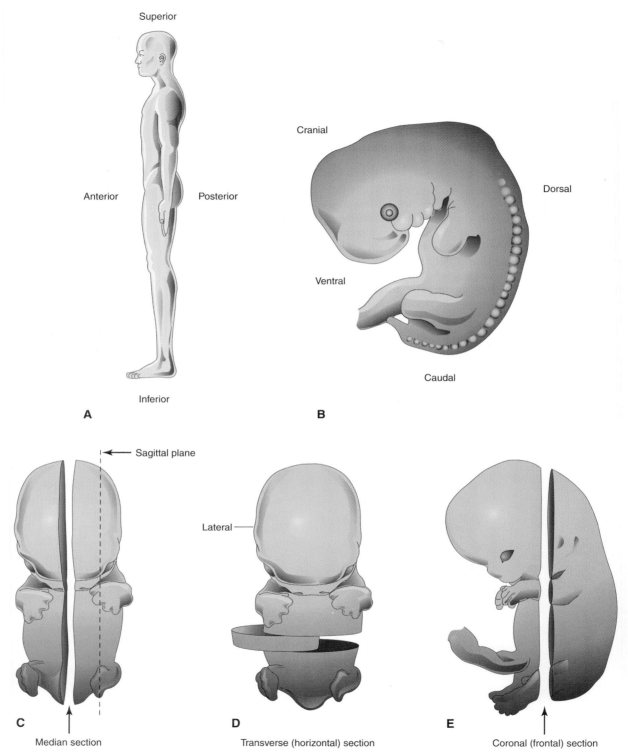

Labels in image A: Superior, Anterior, Posterior, Inferior

Labels in image B: Cranial, Dorsal, Ventral, Caudal

Labels in images C, D, E: Sagittal plane, Lateral, Median section, Transverse (horizontal) section, Coronal (frontal) section

A

B

C

D

E

■ **Figure 1–8.** Drawings illustrating descriptive terms of position, direction, and planes of the body. *A,* Lateral view of an adult in the anatomic position. *B,* Lateral view of a 5-week embryo. *C* and *D,* Ventral views of 6-week embryos. *E,* Lateral view of a 7-week embryo. In describing development, it is necessary to use words denoting the position of one part to another, or to the body as a whole. For example, the vertebral column (backbone) develops in the dorsal part of the embryo, and the sternum (breast bone) develops ventral to it in the ventral part of the embryo.

and abnormal development (Goodwin, 1988; Rossant and Joyner, 1989; Rusconi, 1991; Smith, 1996). *Endogenous retinoic acid* has been identified as an important regulatory substance in embryonic development. Apparently, it acts as a transcriptional activator for specific genes that are involved in embryonic patterning (Eichele, 1989; Giguere, 1994).

Homeobox-containing (HOX) genes now appear to be important in controlling pattern formation during embryonic development (Muragaki et al, 1996). *The Nobel prize for physiology or medicine* was awarded in 1995 to Edward B. **Lewis**, Christiane **Nüsslein-Volhard**, and Eric F. **Wieschaus** for their discovery of genes that control embryonic development. These discoveries are helping us to understand the causes of spontaneous abortion and congenital anomalies.

DESCRIPTIVE TERMS

In anatomy and embryology several terms of position and direction are used, and various planes of the body are referred to in sections. All descriptions of the adult are based on the assumption that the body is erect, with the upper limbs by the sides and the palms directed anteriorly (Fig. 1–8*A*). This is the **anatomic position**. The terms *anterior* or *ventral* and *posterior* or *dorsal* are used to describe the front and back, respectively, of the body or limbs and the relations of structures within the body to one another. When describing embryos, *dorsal* and *ventral* are always used (Fig. 1–8*B*).

Superior or *cranial* (cephalic) and *inferior* or *caudal* are used to indicate the relative levels of different structures. In embryos, *cranial* and *caudal* are used to denote relationships to the head and tail, respectively. Distances from the source of attachment of a structure are designated as *proximal* or *distal*. In the lower limb, for example, the knee is proximal to the ankle and the ankle is distal to the knee.

The *median plane* is an imaginary vertical plane of section that passes longitudinally through the body, dividing it into right and left halves (Fig. 1–8*C*). The terms *lateral* and *medial* refer to structures that are respectively farther from or nearer to the median plane of the body. A *sagittal plane* is any vertical plane passing through the body that is parallel to the median plane (Fig. 1–8*C*). The sagittal planes are named after the sagittal suture of the skull (see Chapter 16), to which they are parallel.

A *transverse (horizontal) plane* refers to any plane that is at right angles to both the median and coronal planes (see Fig. 1–8*D*). A *coronal (frontal) plane* is any vertical plane that intersects the median plane at a right angle and divides the body into front (anterior or ventral) and back (posterior or dorsal) parts (see Fig. 1–8*E*). The coronal planes are named after the coronal suture of the skull (see Chapter 16), to which they are parallel.

Clinically Oriented Questions

1. Should I be able to reproduce the timetables of human development and know the characteristics of each stage?

2. What is the difference between the terms *conceptus* and *embryo*? What are the products of conception?

3. Why do we have to study human embryology? Does it have any practical value in medicine and other health sciences?

4. I have heard that animal and human embryos look alike. Is this true?

5. Physicians date a pregnancy from the first day of the LNMP, but the embryo does not start to develop until about 2 weeks later. Why do they do this?

6. Is the zygote a human being? When does human development begin?

The answers to these questions are given at the back of the book.

REFERENCES AND SUGGESTED READING*

Allen GE: Inducers and "organizers": Hans Spemann and experimental embryology. *Pubbl Stn Zool Napoli* 15:229, 1993.

Beller FK, Zlatnik GP: The beginning of human life. *J Assist Reprod Genet* 12:477, 1995.

Churchill FB: The rise of classical descriptive embryology. *Dev Biol* (NY) 7:1, 1991.

Dunstan GR (ed): *The Human Embryo. Aristotle and the Arabic and European Traditions.* Exeter, University of Exeter Press, 1990.

Eichele G: Retinoids and vertebrate limb pattern formation. *Trends Genet* 5:246, 1989.

Filly RA: Ultrasound evaluation during the first trimester. *In* Callen PW (ed): *Ultrasonography in Obstetrics and Gynecology.* Philadelphia, WB Saunders, 1994.

Gasser R: *Atlas of Human Embryos.* Hagerstown, MD, Harper & Row, 1975.

Giguere V: Retinoic acid receptors and cellular retinoid binding proteins: Complex interplay in retinoid signaling. *Endocr Rev* 5:61, 1994.

Gilbert SF: *Developmental Biology,* 5th ed. Sunderland, Sinauer Associates, 1997.

Goodwin BC: Problems and prospects in morphogenesis. *Experientia* 44:633, 1988.

*In this and other chapters, the references include not only those cited in the text, but ones that are classic (e.g., Streeter, 1942) and others that will be helpful to those wishing more details about embryology and related subjects.

Horder TJ, Witkowski JA, Wylie CC (eds): *A History of Embryology*. Cambridge, Cambridge University Press, 1986.

Muragaki Y, Mundlos S, Upton J, Olsen BR: Altered growth and branching patterns in synpolydactyly caused by mutations of HOXD 13. *Science* 272:548, 1996.

Nathanielsz PW: *Life Before Birth. The Challenges of Fetal Development*. New York, WH Freeman and Company, 1996.

Persaud TVN: *Problems of Birth Defects: From Hippocrates to Thalidomide and After*. Baltimore, University Park Press, 1977.

Persaud TVN: *A History of Anatomy: The Post-Vesalian Era*. Springfield, IL, Charles C Thomas, 1997.

Persaud TVN, Chudley AE, Skalk RG: *Basic Concepts in Teratology*. New York, Alan R. Liss, 1985.

Rossant J, Joyner AL: Towards a molecular-genetic analysis of mammalian development. *Trends Genet* 5:277, 1989.

Roush W: "Smart" genes use many cues to set cell fate. *Science* 272: 652, 1996.

Rusconi S: Transgenic regulation in laboratory animals. *Experientia* 47:866, 1991.

Smith J: How to tell a cell where it is. *Nature* 381:367, 1996.

Streeter GL: Developmental horizons in human embryos. Description of age group XI, 13 to 20 somites, and age group XII, 21 to 29 somites. *Contrib Embryol Carnegie Inst* 30:217, 1942.

Thompson MW, McInnes RR, Willard HF: *Thompson and Thompson's Genetics in Medicine*, 5th ed. Philadelphia, WB Saunders, 1991.

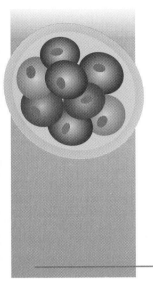

Human Reproduction

2

■ For humans to survive, a mechanism must exist for the production of new individuals. Human reproduction, like that of most animals, involves the union of sex cells or gametes — an **oocyte** (ovum) from the female and a **sperm** (spermatozoon) from the male. Each cell brings a half share of genetic information to the union so that the new cell, a **zygote**, receives the genetic information required for directing the development of a new human being. The reproductive system in both sexes is designed to ensure the successful union of the sperm and oocyte — **fertilization**.

Before puberty (prior to development of secondary sex characteristics), male and female children are not strikingly different except for their genitalia. The sexual maturation that normally occurs during puberty results in considerable differences in appearance, so that the sexually mature male is distinctly masculine and the female is unmistakably feminine. Puberty encompasses the period during which the child, who is incapable of reproduction, is transformed into a person who is capable of reproduction. These changes involve the gross appearance, as well as alternations in the reproductive organs and psyche. The time period of puberty varies between the sexes, as does the age of onset.

Puberty is the period, usually between the ages of 12 and 15 years in females and 13 and 16 years in males, when the capability of sexual reproduction is attained. *Puberty begins when secondary sex characteristics first appear* (pubic hair, for example). Although the most obvious changes are in the reproductive system, puberty affects the whole body (e.g., an increase in the growth rate — the **pubertal growth spurt**). Girls are often taller and heavier than boys of the same age during early puberty. **Menarche** (first menstruation) often occurs in 8- to 11-year-old girls. Puberty ends with the first menstrual cycle (period). *Puberty in males* begins later (13 to 16 years); however, signs of sexual maturity may appear in 12-year-old boys. Puberty ends when mature sperms are formed.

REPRODUCTIVE ORGANS

Each sex has reproductive or *sex organs*, which produce and transport gametes from the *sex glands*, or gonads, to the site of fertilization in the uterine tube (Fig. 2-1). The penis, the sex organ in the male, deposits sperms (spermatozoa) produced by the *testes* in the vagina of the female genital tract during sexual intercourse.

Female Reproductive Organs

The **vagina** (Fig. 2-1A) serves as the excretory passage for menstrual fluid, receives the penis during sex-ual intercourse, and forms the inferior part of the birth canal. The vagina communicates superiorly with the cavity of the cervix (L. neck) of the uterus and inferiorly with the *vestibule of the vagina*, the space between the labia minora (plural of L. *labium minus*). The size and appearance of the **vaginal orifice** vary with the condition of the *hymen*, a thin fold of mucous membrane that surrounds the vaginal orifice (Fig. 2-3).

Oocytes are produced by two oval-shaped **ovaries** located in the superolateral part of the pelvic cavity, one on each side of the uterus (Fig. 2-1A). When released from the ovary at *ovulation*, the secondary oocyte or ovum passes into one of two trumpet-shaped *uterine tubes* (fallopian tubes, oviducts). These tubes open into the *uterus* (L. womb), which protects and nourishes the embryo and fetus until birth.

UTERUS

The uterus is a thick-walled, pear-shaped organ (Fig. 2-2). It varies considerably in size but is usually 7 to 8 cm in length, 5 to 7 cm in width at its superior part, and 2 to 3 cm in thickness.

The uterus consists of two main parts:

- **Body**, the expanded superior two thirds
- **Cervix**, the cylindrical inferior third

The **fundus** is the rounded part of the body superior to the orifices of the uterine tubes. The body of the uterus narrows from the fundus to the **isthmus**, the 1-cm-long constricted region between the body and cervix. The lumen of the cervix, the **cervical canal**, has a constricted opening or os at each end. The **internal os** (ostium) communicates with the cavity of the body of the uterus, and the **external os** communicates with the vagina.

The walls of the body of the uterus consist of three layers:

- **Perimetrium**, the thin external layer of peritoneum
- **Myometrium**, the thick smooth muscle layer
- **Endometrium**, the thin internal mucous membrane

At the peak of its development, the endometrium is 4 to 5 mm thick. During the secretory phase of the menstrual cycle (see Fig. 2-9), *three layers of the endometrium* can be distinguished microscopically (Fig. 2-2C):

- **Compact layer**, consisting of densely packed connective tissue around the neck of the uterine glands
- **Spongy layer**, composed of edematous connec-

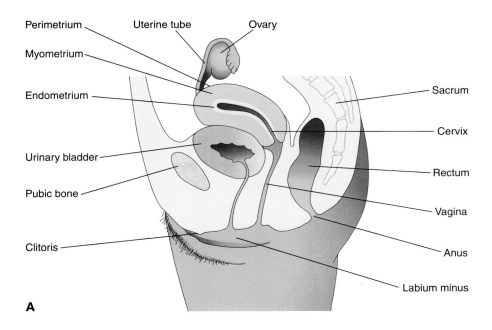

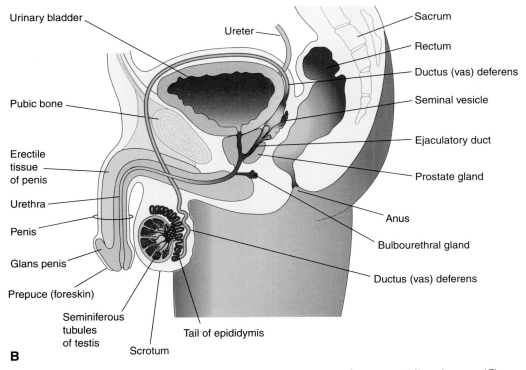

■ **Figure 2–1.** Schematic sagittal sections of the pelvic regions of a woman (A) and a man (B).

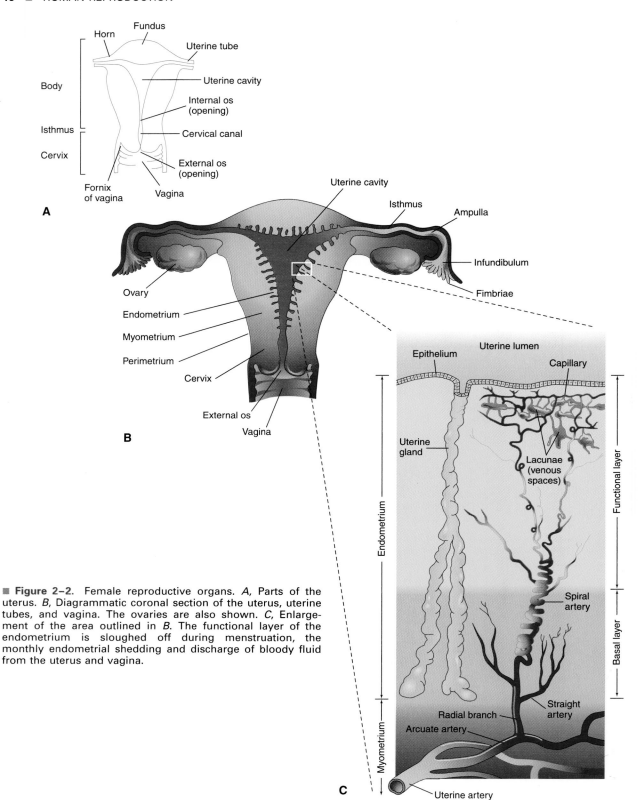

■ **Figure 2–2.** Female reproductive organs. *A*, Parts of the uterus. *B*, Diagrammatic coronal section of the uterus, uterine tubes, and vagina. The ovaries are also shown. *C*, Enlargement of the area outlined in *B*. The functional layer of the endometrium is sloughed off during menstruation, the monthly endometrial shedding and discharge of bloody fluid from the uterus and vagina.

tive tissue containing the dilated, tortuous bodies of the uterine glands
- **Basal layer**, containing the blind ends of the uterine glands

The basal layer of the endometrium has its own blood supply and is not cast off during menstruation. The compact and spongy layers, known collectively as the *functional layer*, disintegrate and are shed at menstruation and after parturition (delivery of a baby).

UTERINE TUBES

The uterine tubes (fallopian tubes, oviducts), 10 to 12 cm long and 1 cm in diameter, extend laterally from the **horns** (L. *cornua*) of the uterus (Fig. 2–2*A*). The tubes carry oocytes from the ovaries and sperms entering from the uterus to reach the fertilization site in the **ampulla of the uterine tube** (Fig. 2–2*B*). The uterine tube also conveys the dividing zygote to the uterine cavity. Each tube opens at its proximal end into a horn of the uterus and into the peritoneal cavity at its distal end. For descriptive purposes, the uterine tube is divided into four parts:

- Infundibulum
- Ampulla
- Isthmus
- Uterine part

OVARIES

The ovaries are almond-shaped reproductive glands located close to the lateral pelvic walls on each side of the uterus (Fig. 2–2*B*). The ovaries produce estrogen and progesterone, the hormones responsible for the development of secondary sex characteristics and regulation of pregnancy. The ovaries are also responsible for producing and maintaining oocytes.

FEMALE EXTERNAL SEX ORGANS

The external genitalia, or female external sex organs, are known collectively as the **vulva**, or pudendum (Fig. 2–3). The **labia majora** (major labia), fatty external folds of skin, conceal the vaginal orifice, the opening of the vagina. Inside these labia are two smaller folds of mucous membrane, the **labia minora** (minor labia). The **clitoris**, a small erectile organ, is at the superior junction of these folds. The clitoris, the morphologic equivalent of the penis, is very important in the sexual excitement of a female. The vagina and urethra open into a cavity, the **vestibule of the vagina** (cleft between labia minora).

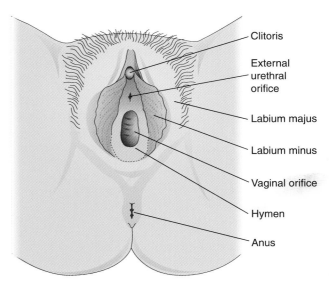

■ **Figure 2–3.** External female genitalia. The labia are spread apart to show the external urethral and vaginal orifices.

Labels: Clitoris; External urethral orifice; Labium majus; Labium minus; Vaginal orifice; Hymen; Anus

Male Reproductive Organs

The parts of the male reproductive system (Fig. 2–1*B*) include the testes, epididymis, ductus deferens (vas deferens), prostate, seminal vesicles, bulbourethral glands, ejaculatory ducts, and urethra. The *sperms* are produced in the *testes*, two oval-shaped glands (gonads) that are suspended in the scrotum, a loose pouch of rugose (wrinkled) skin.

Each **testis** consists of many highly coiled seminiferous tubules that produce the sperms. The sperms pass from the testis into a single, complexly coiled tube, the **epididymis**, where they are stored. The sperms are not mature (i.e., capable of fertilizing oocytes) when they leave the testes. It takes days for the sperms to mature in the epididymis. From the inferior end of the epididymis, a long straight tube, the **ductus deferens** carries the sperms from the epididymis to the ejaculatory duct. The ductus deferens passes from the scrotum through the inguinal canal into the abdominal cavity. The ductus then descends into the pelvis, where it fuses with the duct of the seminal vesicle to form the **ejaculatory duct**, which enters the urethra.

The **urethra** is a tube leading from the urinary bladder to the outside of the body; its spongy part runs through the **penis** (Fig. 2–1*B*). Within the penis the urethra is surrounded by three columns of spongy **erectile tissue**. During sexual excitement this tissue fills with blood under increased pressure. This causes the penis to become erect and thus able to enter the vagina during sexual intercourse. Ejaculation of *semen* — sperms mixed with seminal fluid produced by the following glands: **seminal vesicles, bulboure-thral glands**, and **prostate** — occurs when the penis is further stimulated. Consequently, the urethra transports both urine and semen but not at the same time.

GAMETOGENESIS

The *sperm and oocyte are highly specialized sex cells* (Fig. 2-4). They contain half the number of chromosomes (i.e., 23 instead of 46). The number of chromosomes is reduced during a special type of cell division called **meiosis**. This type of cell division occurs during the formation of gametes — **spermatogenesis** in males and **oogenesis** (ovogenesis) in females.

Gametogenesis (gamete formation) is the process of formation and development of specialized generative cells called **gametes**, or germ cells — oocytes in females and sperms in males (Fig. 2-5). This process, which involves the chromosomes and cytoplasm of the gametes, prepares these specialized sex cells for *fertilization* (union of male and female gametes). During gametogenesis, the chromosome number is reduced by half and the shape of the cells is altered, especially the male sex cells.

Meiosis

Meiosis consists of two meiotic cell divisions (Fig. 2-6), during which the chromosome number of the germ cells is reduced to half (23, the *haploid* number) the number present in other cells in the body (46, the *diploid* number).

The **first meiotic division** is a *reduction division* because the chromosome member is reduced from diploid (Gr. double) to haploid (Gr. single). *Homologous chromosomes* (one from each parent) pair during prophase and then separate during anaphase, with one representative of each pair going to each pole. Homologous chromosomes, or homologs, are pairs of chromosomes of one type, one inherited from each parent. At this stage, they are *double chromatid chromosomes*. The X and Y chromosomes are not homologs, but they have homologous segments at the tips of their short arms. They pair in these regions only. By the end of the first meiotic division, each new cell formed (secondary spermatocyte or secondary oocyte) has the *haploid chromosome number* (double chromatid chromosomes), that is, half the number of chromosomes of the preceding cell (primary spermatocyte or primary oocyte). This separation or disjunction of paired homologous chromosomes is the *physical basis of segregation* — the separation of allelic genes during meiosis.

The **second meiotic division** follows the first division without a normal interphase (i.e., without an intervening step of DNA replication). Each chromosome divides and each half, or *chromatid*, is drawn to a different pole; thus, the haploid number of chromosomes (23) is retained, and each daughter cell formed

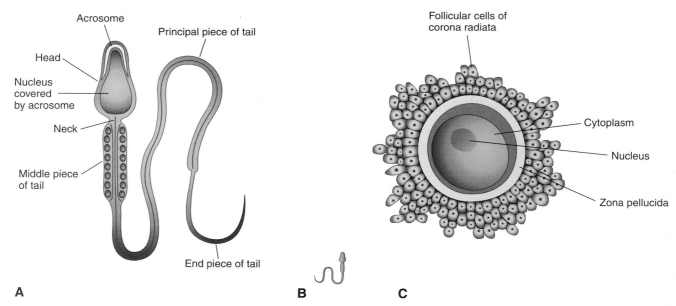

A　　　　　　　　　　　　　**B**　　**C**

■ **Figure 2-4.** Male and female gametes (sexual cells). *A*, Drawing showing the parts of a human sperm (×1250). The head, composed mostly of the nucleus, is partly covered by the acrosome, an organelle containing enzymes. The tail of the sperm consists of three regions: middle piece, principal piece, and end piece. *B*, Sperm drawn to about the same scale as the oocyte. *C*, Drawing of a human secondary oocyte or ovum (×200), surrounded by the zona pellucida and corona radiata.

NORMAL GAMETOGENESIS

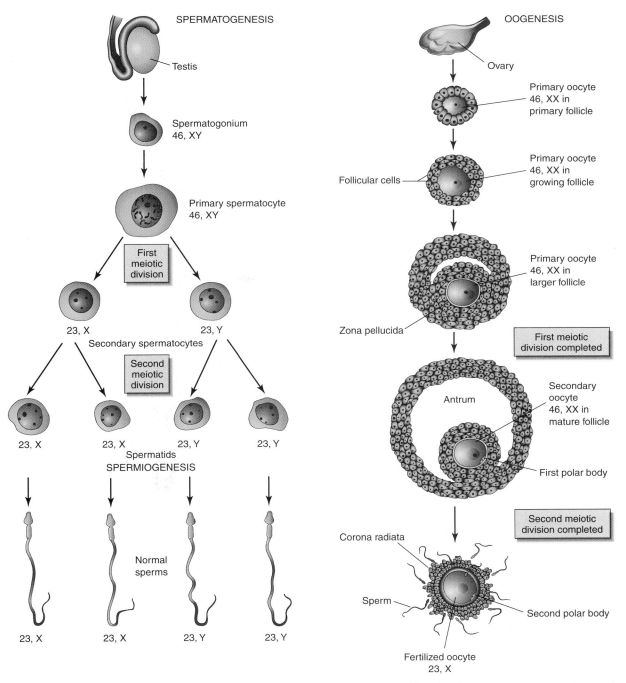

■ **Figure 2–5.** Normal Gametogenesis—conversion of germ cells into gametes. The drawings compare spermatogenesis and oogenesis. Oogonia are not shown in this figure because they differentiate into primary oocytes before birth. The chromosome complement of the germ cells is shown at each stage. The number designates the total number of chromosomes, including the sex chromosome(s) shown after the comma. *Note*: (1) Following the two meiotic divisions, the diploid number of chromosomes, 46, is reduced to the haploid number, 23; (2) four sperms form from one primary spermatocyte, whereas only one mature oocyte results from maturation of a primary oocyte; (3) the cytoplasm is conserved during oogenesis to form one large cell, the mature oocyte, or ovum. The polar bodies are small nonfunctional cells that eventually degenerate.

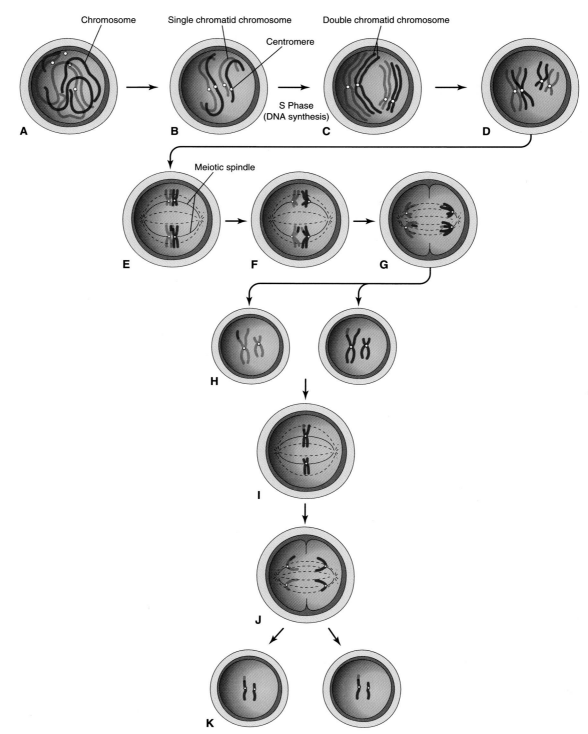

■ **Figure 2–6.** Diagrammatic representation of meiosis. Two chromosome pairs are shown. *A* to *D*, Stages of prophase of the first meiotic division. The homologous chromosomes approach each other and pair; each member of the pair consists of two chromatids. Observe the single crossover in one pair of chromosomes, resulting in the interchange of chromatid segments. *E*, Metaphase. The two members of each pair become oriented on the meiotic spindle. *F*, Anaphase. *G*, Telophase. The chromosomes migrate to opposite poles. *H*, Distribution of parental chromosome pairs at the end of the first meiotic division. *I* to *K*, Second meiotic division. It is similar to mitosis except that the cells are haploid.

by meiosis has the reduced haploid number of chromosomes, with one representative of each chromosome pair (now a single chromatid chromosome). The second meiotic division is similar to ordinary mitosis except that the chromosome number of the cell entering the second meiotic division is haploid. For more details about meiosis, see Thompson et al (1991).

IMPORTANCE OF MEIOSIS

Meiosis is significant in several ways:

- It provides for *constancy of the chromosome number* from generation to generation by reducing the chromosome number from diploid to haploid, thereby producing haploid gametes.
- It allows random *assortment of maternal and paternal chromosomes* between the gametes.
- It relocates segments of maternal and paternal chromosomes by *crossing over of chromosome segments*, which "shuffles" the genes and produces a recombination of genetic material.

SPERMATOGENESIS

Spermatogenesis refers to the entire sequence of events by which primitive germ cells — **spermatogonia** — are transformed into mature germ cells, or sperms. This maturation process begins at *puberty* (13 to 16 years) and continues into old age (Fig. 2-5).

These spermatogonia have been dormant in the seminiferous tubules of the testes since the late fetal period. They begin to increase in number at puberty. After several mitotic divisions, the spermatogonia grow and undergo gradual changes that transform them into **primary spermatocytes**, the largest germ cells in the seminiferous tubules. Each primary spermatocyte subsequently undergoes a reduction division — the *first meiotic division* — to form two haploid **secondary spermatocytes**, which are about half the size of primary spermatocytes. Subsequently the secondary spermatocytes undergo a *second meiotic division* to form four haploid **spermatids**, which are about half the size of secondary spermatocytes. During this division, no further reduction occurs in the number of chromosomes. The spermatids are gradually transformed into four mature sperms by a process known as **spermiogenesis** (Fig. 2-7). During this metamorphosis (change in form), the nucleus condenses, the acrosome forms, and most of the cytoplasm is shed. Spermatogenesis, including spermiogenesis, requires about 2 months for completion and normally continues throughout the reproductive life of a male. When spermiogenesis is complete, the sperms enter the lumina of the seminiferous tubules. The sperms move to the **epididymis** (Fig. 2-1B), where they are stored and become functionally mature.

The **mature sperm** is a free-swimming, actively motile cell consisting of a head and tail (Fig. 2-4A). The *neck of the sperm* is the junction between the head and tail. The **head of the sperm**, forming most of the bulk of the sperm, contains the nucleus of the cell, which has 23 chromosomes. The anterior two thirds of the head is covered by the **acrosome** (acrosomal cap), an organelle containing enzymes (Fig. 2-7) that facilitate sperm penetration during fertilization (see Chapter 3). The **tail of the sperm** consists of three segments: the *middle piece, principal piece,* and *end piece*. The tail provides the motility of the sperm, assisting with its transport to the site of fertilization in the ampulla of the uterine tube. The *middle piece of the tail* contains the energy-producing cytoplasmic and

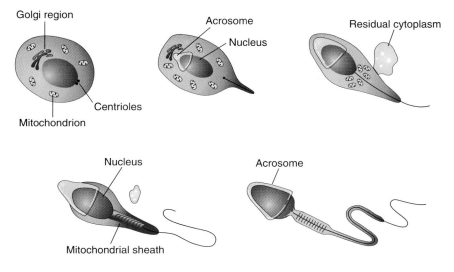

■ **Figure 2–7.** Drawings illustrating the last phase of spermatogenesis — spermiogenesis. During this process the rounded spermatid is transformed into an elongated sperm. Note the loss of cytoplasm, development of the tail, and formation of the acrosome. The acrosome, derived from the Golgi region of the spermatid, contains enzymes that are released at the beginning of the fertilization process to assist the sperm in penetrating the corona radiata and zona pellucida surrounding the secondary oocyte. The mitochondria arrange themselves end to end in the form of a tight helix, forming a collarlike mitochondrial sheath. Note that the excess cytoplasm is shed during spermiogenesis.

mitochondrial apparatus, which produces the lashing movements of the tail.

OOGENESIS

Oogenesis (ovogenesis) refers to the sequence of events by which **oogonia** are transformed into **oocytes** (Fig. 2-5). This maturation process begins during the fetal period but is not completed until after *puberty* (12 to 15 years). Oogenesis, a recurring process, is part of the **ovarian cycle** (see Fig. 2-9). Except during pregnancy, these cycles occur monthly during the reproductive life of females. During early fetal life, primitive ova — *oogonia* — proliferate by mitotic division. These oogonia enlarge to form **primary oocytes** before birth. By the time of birth, all primary oocytes have completed the prophase of the first meiotic division. These oocytes remain in prophase until puberty. Shortly before ovulation, a primary oocyte completes the *first meiotic division* (Fig. 2-5).

Unlike the corresponding stage of spermatogenesis, however, the division of cytoplasm is unequal. The **secondary oocyte** receives almost all the cytoplasm, and the *first polar body* receives very little; this small nonfunctional cell soon degenerates. At ovulation the nucleus of the secondary oocyte begins the *second meiotic division* but progresses only to metaphase, where division is arrested.

If the secondary oocyte is fertilized by a sperm, the second meiotic division is completed. Again, most cytoplasm is retained by one cell, the *mature oocyte* or *fertilized oocyte* (Fig. 2-5). The other nonfunctional cell, the *second polar body*, is very small and soon degenerates. The secondary oocyte released at ovulation is surrounded by a covering of amorphous material known as the *zona pellucida* and a layer of follicular cells called the *corona radiata* (Fig. 2-4C). Compared with ordinary cells, the secondary oocyte is large and just visible to the unaided eye as a tiny speck. Up to 2 million primary oocytes are usually present in the ovaries of a newborn female infant. Most of these oocytes regress during childhood so that by puberty no more than 40,000 remain. Of these, only about 400 mature and are expelled at ovulation during the reproductive period. The number of oocytes that ovulate is greatly reduced in women who take *contraceptive pills* because the hormones in the pills prevent ovulation from occurring.

COMPARISON OF MALE AND FEMALE GAMETES

The sperm and secondary oocyte (ovum) are dissimilar in several ways because of their adaptation for specialized roles in reproduction. Compared with the sperm, the oocyte is massive and immotile (Fig. 2-4), whereas the microscopic sperm is highly motile. The mature oocyte also has an abundance of cytoplasm, whereas the sperm has very little. The sperm bears little resemblance to an oocyte or any other cell because of its sparse cytoplasm and specialization for motility.

With respect to their sex chromosome constitution, **there are two kinds of normal sperm** (Fig. 2-5): 22 autosomes plus an X chromosome (i.e., 23, X); and 23 autosomes plus a Y chromosome (23, Y). **There is only one kind of normal ovum**: 22 autosomes plus an X chromosome (i.e, 23, X). *The difference in sex chromosome complement forms the basis of primary sex determination.*

Abnormal Gametogenesis

Disturbances of meiosis during gametogenesis, such as nondisjunction (Fig. 2-8), result in the formation of chromosomally abnormal gametes. If involved in fertilization, these gametes with numerical chromosome abnormalities cause abnormal development such as occurs in infants with **Down syndrome** (see Chapter 9).

The ideal maternal age for reproduction is generally considered to be from 18 to 35 years of age. The likelihood of chromosomal abnormalities in the embryo increases significantly after age 35. In older mothers, there is an appreciable risk of *Down syndrome* or some other form of trisomy in the infant (see Chapter 9). The likelihood of a fresh *gene mutation* (change in DNA) also increases with age. The older the parents are at the time of conception, the more likely they are to have accumulated mutations that the embryo might inherit. For fathers of children with fresh mutations, such as the one causing *achondroplasia* (a form of dwarfism), this age relationship has continually been demonstrated (Stoll et al, 1982). This does not hold for all dominant mutations and is not an important consideration in older mothers. For a discussion of *gene mutations*, see Chapter 9 and Thompson et al (1991).

During meiosis, homologous chromosomes sometimes fail to separate and go to opposite poles of the germ cell. As a result of this error of cell division — **nondisjunction** — some gametes have 24 chromosomes and others only 22 (Fig. 2-8). If a gamete with 24 chromosomes unites with a normal one with 23 chromosomes during fertilization, a zygote with 47 chromosomes forms (see Fig. 9-1). This condition is called **trisomy** because of the presence of three representatives of a particular chromosome instead of the usual two. If a gamete with only 22 chromosomes unites with a normal one, a zygote with 45 chromosomes forms. This condition is known as **monosomy** because only one representative of the particular chro-

Continued on page 25

ABNORMAL GAMETOGENESIS

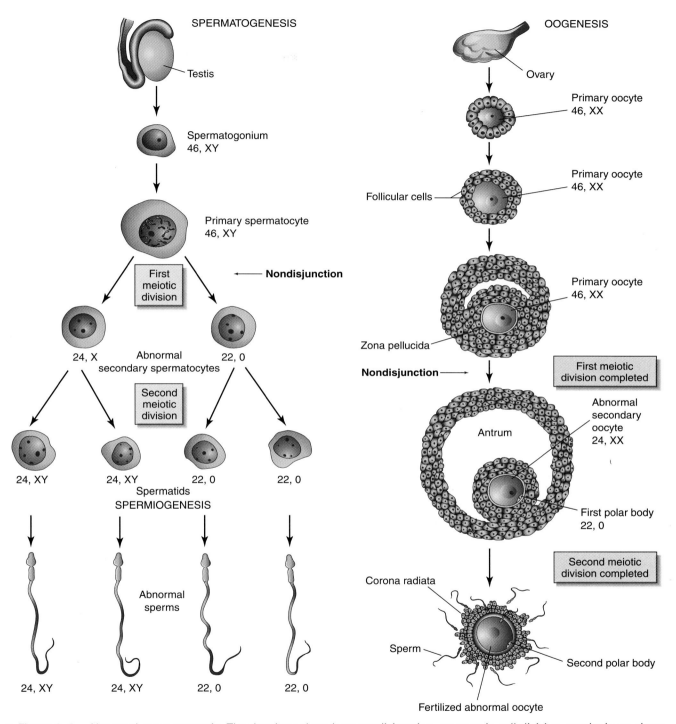

■ **Figure 2–8.** Abnormal gametogenesis. The drawings show how nondisjunction, an error in cell division, results in an abnormal chromosome distribution in germ cells. Although nondisjunction of sex chromosomes is illustrated, a similar defect may occur during the division of autosomes. When nondisjunction occurs during the first meiotic division of spermatogenesis, one secondary spermatocyte contains 22 autosomes plus an X and a Y chromosome, and the other one contains 22 autosomes and no sex chromosome. Similarly, nondisjunction during oogenesis may give rise to an oocyte with 22 autosomes and two X chromosomes (as shown) or may result in one with 22 autosomes and no sex chromosome.

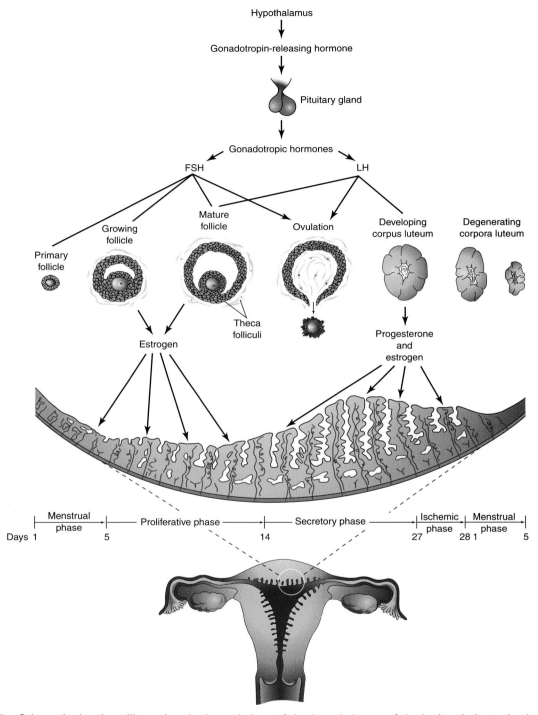

■ **Figure 2–9.** Schematic drawings illustrating the interrelations of the hypothalamus of the brain, pituitary gland, ovaries, and endometrium. One complete menstrual cycle and the beginning of another are shown. Changes in the ovaries—the *ovarian cycle*—are induced by the gonadotropic hormones (follicle-stimulating hormone [FSH] and luteinizing hormone [LH]). Hormones from the ovaries (estrogens and progesterone) then promote cyclic changes in the structure and function of the endometrium—the *menstrual cycle*. Thus, the cyclic activity of the ovary is intimately linked with changes in the uterus. The ovarian cycles are under the rhythmic endocrine control of the adenohypophysis of the pituitary gland, which in turn is controlled by gonadotropin-releasing hormone (GnRH), produced by neurosecretory cells in the hypothalamus of the brain.

mosome pair is present. For a description of the clinical conditions associated with numerical disorders of chromosomes, see Chapter 9.

Up to 10% of sperms in an ejaculate may be grossly abnormal (e.g., with two heads), but it is generally believed that these abnormal sperms do not fertilize oocytes owing to their lack of normal motility. Most morphologically abnormal sperms are unable to pass through the mucus in the cervical canal. Measurement of forward progression is a subjective assessment of the quality of sperm movement. X-rays, severe allergic reactions, and certain antispermatogenic agents have been reported to increase the percentage of abnormally shaped sperms. Such sperms are not believed to affect fertility unless their number exceeds 20%.

Although some oocytes have two or three nuclei, these cells die before they reach maturity. Similarly, some ovarian follicles contain two or more oocytes, but this phenomenon is infrequent. Although compound follicles could result in multiple births, it is believed that most of them never mature and expel the oocytes at ovulation.

FEMALE REPRODUCTIVE CYCLES

Commencing at puberty and normally continuing throughout the reproductive years, human females undergo monthly reproductive cycles (sexual cycles), involving activities of the **hypothalamus** of the brain, **pituitary gland**, **ovaries, uterus**, uterine tubes, vagina, and mammary glands (Fig. 2–9). These monthly cycles prepare the reproductive system for pregnancy.

A *gonadotropin-releasing hormone* (GnRH) is synthesized by neurosecretory cells in the hypothalamus and is carried by the *hypophyseal portal system* to the anterior lobe of the pituitary gland. GnRH stimulates the release of two hormones produced by this gland, which act on the ovaries:

- *Follicle-stimulating hormone* (FSH) stimulates the development of ovarian follicles and the production of **estrogen** by its follicular cells.
- *Luteinizing hormone* (LH) serves as the "trigger" for ovulation (release of secondary oocyte) and stimulates the follicular cells and corpus luteum to produce **progesterone**.

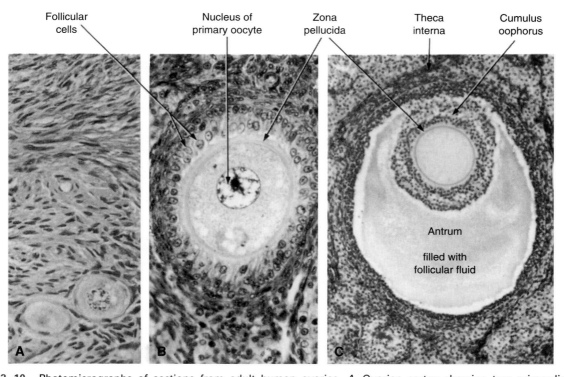

■ **Figure 2–10.** Photomicrographs of sections from adult human ovaries. *A*, Ovarian cortex showing two primordial follicles containing primary oocytes (×250). *B*, Growing follicle containing a primary oocyte, surrounded by the zona pellucida and a stratified layer of follicular cells (×250). *C*, An almost mature follicle with a large antrum. The oocyte, embedded in the cumulus oophorus, does not show a nucleus because it has been sectioned tangentially (×100). (From Leeson CR, Leeson TS: *Histology*, 3rd ed. Philadelphia, WB Saunders, 1976.)

These hormones also produce growth of the ovarian follicles and endometrium.

Ovarian Cycle

FSH and LH produce cyclic changes in the ovaries (development of follicles, ovulation, and corpus luteum formation) — the **ovarian cycle**. During each cycle, FSH promotes growth of several primary follicles (Fig. 2-9); however only one of them usually develops into a mature follicle and ruptures through the surface of the ovary, expelling its oocyte (see Fig. 2-11). Hence, 4 to 11 follicles degenerate each month.

FOLLICULAR DEVELOPMENT

Development of an ovarian follicle (Figs. 2-9 and 2-10) is characterized by:

- Growth and differentiation of a primary oocyte
- Proliferation of follicular cells
- Formation of zona pellucida
- Development of a connective tissue capsule, the theca folliculi (Gr. *theke*, box)

The **theca folliculi** differentiates into two layers, an internal vascular and glandular layer — the *theca interna* — and a capsulelike layer — the *theca externa*. Thecal cells are thought to produce an *angiogenesis factor* that promotes growth of blood vessels in the theca interna (Fig. 2-10C), which provide nutritive support for follicular development.

OVULATION

The follicular cells divide actively, producing a stratified layer around the oocyte (Fig. 2-10). The ovarian follicle soon becomes oval and the oocyte eccentric in position because proliferation of the follicular cells occurs more rapidly on one side. Subsequently, fluid-filled spaces appear around the cells; these spaces coalesce to form a single large cavity, the **antrum**, containing **follicular fluid** (Fig. 2-10C). After the antrum forms, the ovarian follicle is called a vesicular or **secondary follicle**. The primary oocyte is pushed to one side of the follicle, where it is surrounded by a mound of follicular cells, the **cumulus oophorus**, that projects into the enlarged antrum. The follicle continues to enlarge until it reaches maturity and forms a bulge on the surface of the ovary (Fig. 2-11A). It is now a **mature ovarian follicle**.

Around midcycle (14 days in an average 28-day menstrual cycle), the ovarian follicle under the influence of FSH and LH (Balasch et al, 1995), undergoes a sudden *growth spurt*, producing a cystic swelling or bulge on the surface of the ovary. A small oval avascular spot, the **stigma**, soon appears on this swelling (Fig. 2-11A). Prior to ovulation, the secondary oocyte and

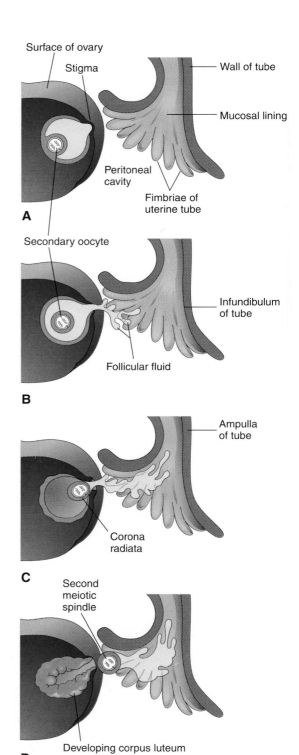

■ **Figure 2–11.** Diagrams (*A* to *D*) illustrating ovulation. The stigma ruptures, and the secondary oocyte is expelled from the ovarian follicle with the follicular fluid. After ovulation, the wall of the follicle collapses and is thrown into folds. The follicular wall is transformed into a glandular structure, the corpus luteum.

some cells of the cumulus oophorus detach from the interior of the distended follicle (Fig. 2–11*B*).

Ovulation is triggered by a surge of LH production (Fig. 2–12). Ovulation usually follows the LH peak by 12 to 24 hours. The **LH surge**, elicited by the high estrogen level in the blood (see Fig. 2–13), appears to cause the stigma to balloon out, forming a vesicle. The stigma then ruptures, expelling the secondary oocyte with the follicular fluid (Fig. 2–11*D*). Expulsion of the oocyte is the result of intrafollicular pressure and possibly contraction of smooth muscle in the theca externa owing to stimulation by prostaglandins. *Enzymatic digestion of the follicular wall* seems to be one of the principal mechanisms leading to ovulation (Oehninger and Hodgen, 1993).

The expelled secondary oocyte is surrounded by the zona pellucida and one or more layers of follicular cells, which are radially arranged to form the **corona radiata** and cumulus oophorus (Figs. 2–10*C* and 2–11*C*), which form the oocyte-cumulus complex (Talbot, 1985). The LH surge also seems to induce resumption of the first meiotic division of the primary oocyte. Hence, mature ovarian follicles contain secondary oocytes (Fig. 2–11*A* and *B*).

Mittelschmerz and Ovulation

A variable amount of abdominal pain called mittelschmerz (Ger. *mittel*, mid; *schmerz*, pain), accompanies ovulation in some women. In these cases ovulation results in slight bleeding into the peritoneal cavity, which results in sudden constant inferolateral pain in the abdomen. Mittelschmerz may be used as a symptom of ovulation; however, there are better ones, such as the *basal body temperature*, which usually shows a slight drop followed by a sustained rise after ovulation.

Anovulation and Hormones

Some women do not ovulate because of an inadequate release of gonadotropins; as a result, they are unable to become pregnant in the usual way. In some of these women, *ovulation can be induced* by the administration of gonadotropins or an ovulatory agent,

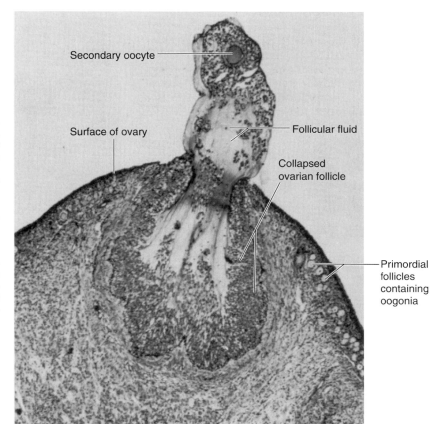

■ **Figure 2–12.** Photomicrograph of a section of an ovary taken just after rupture of an ovarian follicle during ovulation. The secondary oocyte, previously torn away from the cumulus oophorus (Fig. 2–11*D*), has been carried with the gelatinous follicular fluid out of the follicle and the ovary into the peritoneal cavity. The follicular cells adhering to the secondary oocyte constitute the corona radiata. Ovulation occurs through a small opening that develops when the stigma ruptures (Fig. 2–11*B*). Extrusion takes 1 to 2 seconds and is not an explosive process as once thought. (From Page EW, Villee CA, Villee DB: *Human Reproduction: Essentials of Reproductive and Perinatal Medicine*, 3rd ed. Philadelphia, WB Saunders, 1981. Courtesy of Dr. Richard J. Blandau.)

Secondary oocyte

Surface of ovary

Follicular fluid

Collapsed ovarian follicle

Primordial follicles containing oogonia

such as *clomiphene citrate*. This drug stimulates the release of pituitary gonadotropins (FSH and LH), resulting in maturation of several ovarian follicles and multiple ovulations. The incidence of multiple pregnancy increases up to 10-fold when ovulation is induced. Apparently, the fine control of FSH output is not present and multiple ovulations occur, leading to multiple pregnancies and abortions, because there is no chance that seven or more embryos can survive.

CORPUS LUTEUM

Shortly after ovulation, the walls of the ovarian follicle and theca folliculi collapse and are thrown into folds (Fig. 2–11D). Under LH influence they develop into a glandular structure, the **corpus luteum**, which secretes *progesterone* but some estrogen as well. These hormones, particularly progesterone, cause the endometrial glands to secrete and prepare the endometrium for implantation of the blastocyst.

If the oocyte is fertilized, the corpus luteum enlarges to form a *corpus luteum of pregnancy* and increases its hormone production. When pregnancy occurs, degeneration of the corpus luteum is prevented by *human chorionic gonadotropin* (hCG), a hormone secreted by the syncytiotrophoblast of the chorion (see Chapter 3), which is rich in LH. The corpus luteum of pregnancy remains functionally active throughout the first 20 weeks of pregnancy. By this time the placenta has assumed the production of the estrogen and progesterone that is necessary for the maintenance of pregnancy (see Chapter 8).

If the oocyte is not fertilized, the corpus luteum begins to involute and degenerate about 10 to 12 days after ovulation. It is then called a *corpus luteum of menstruation*. The corpus luteum is subsequently transformed into white scar tissue in the ovary, forming *corpus albicans* (atretic or degenerating corpus luteum). Except during pregnancy, ovarian cycles normally persist throughout the reproductive life of women and terminate at **menopause** — permanent cessation of menstruation.

Menstrual Cycle

The menstrual cycle is the period during which the oocyte matures, is ovulated, and enters the uterine tube (Fig. 2–13). The hormones produced by the ovarian follicles and corpus luteum (estrogen and progesterone) produce cyclic changes in the endometrium of the uterus. These monthly changes in the uterine lining constitute the **menstrual** or **endometrial cycle**, commonly referred to as the menstrual

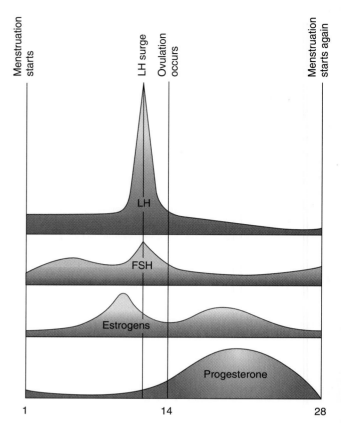

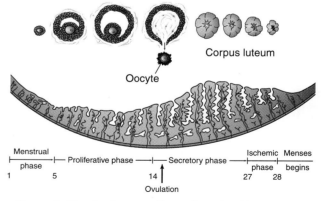

■ **Figure 2–13.** A diagram illustrating the blood levels of various hormones during the menstrual cycle. Follicle-stimulating hormone (FSH) stimulates the ovarian follicles to develop and produce estrogens. The level of estrogens rises to a peak just before the luteinizing hormone (LH) surge induces ovulation. Ovulation normally occurs 24 to 36 hours after the LH surge. If fertilization does not occur, the blood levels of circulating estrogens and progesterone fall. This hormone withdrawal causes the endometrium to regress and menstruation to start again.

cycle, or period, because *menstruation* (flow of blood from uterus) is an obvious event. *The normal endometrium is a mirror of the ovarian cycle* because it responds in a consistent manner to the fluctuating concentrations of ovarian hormones. The average menstrual cycle is 28 days, with day 1 of the cycle designated as that day on which menstrual flow begins. Menstrual cycles can vary in length by several days in normal women. In 90% of women, the length of the cycles ranges between 23 and 35 days. Almost all these variations result from alterations in the duration of the proliferative phase of the cycle.

Anovulatory Menstrual Cycles

The typical reproductive cycle illustrated in Figure 2–13 is not always realized because the ovary may not produce a mature follicle and ovulation does not occur. In *anovulatory cycles*, the endometrial changes are minimal; the proliferative endometrium develops as usual, but no ovulation occurs and no corpus luteum forms. Consequently, the endometrium does not progress to the secretory phase; it remains in the proliferative phase until menstruation begins. Anovulatory cycles may result from *ovarian hypofunction*, but they are commonly produced by self-administered sex hormones. The estrogen, with or without progesterone, in *birth control pills* acts on the hypothalamus and pituitary gland, resulting in inhibition of secretion of GnRH, FSH, and LH, the secretion of which is essential for ovulation to occur. *Suppression of ovulation is the basis for the success of birth control pills.* In most cases, when no other method of contraception is used, the interval between cessation of *oral contraception* and the occurrence of pregnancy is 12 months; however, conception can occur after 1 month in some cases.

PHASES OF MENSTRUAL CYCLE

Changes in the estrogen and progesterone levels cause cyclic changes in the structure of the female reproductive tract, notably the endometrium. Although the menstrual cycle is divided into three phases for descriptive purposes (Fig. 2–13), *the menstrual cycle is a continuous process*; each phase gradually passes into the next one.

Menstrual Phase. The first day of menstruation is the beginning of the menstrual cycle. The functional layer of the uterine wall is sloughed off and discarded with the menstrual flow (L. *menses*, months), which usually lasts 4 to 5 days. The menstrual flow, or **menses,** discharged through the vagina consists of varying amounts of blood combined with small pieces of endometrial tissue. After menstruation, the eroded endometrium is thin.

Proliferative Phase. The proliferative phase, lasting about 9 days, coincides with growth of ovarian follicles and is controlled by estrogen secreted by these follicles. There is a two- to threefold increase in the thickness of the endometrium and in its water content during this *phase of repair and proliferation*. Early during this phase the surface epithelium reforms and covers the endometrium. The glands increase in number and length and the spiral arteries elongate.

Secretory Phase. The secretory phase, lasting about 13 days, coincides with the formation, functioning, and growth of the corpus luteum. The progesterone produced by the corpus luteum stimulates the glandular epithelium to secrete a glycogen-rich material. The glands become wide, tortuous, and saccular, and the endometrium thickens because of the influence of progesterone and estrogen from the corpus luteum and the increase in fluid in the connective tissue. As the spiral arteries grow into the superficial compact layer, they become increasingly coiled (Fig. 2–2C). The venous network becomes complex and shows large *lacunae* (venous spaces). *Direct arteriovenous anastomoses* are prominent features of this stage.

If fertilization occurs:

- Cleavage of the zygote and blastogenesis (formation of the blastocyst) occur.
- The blastocyst begins to implant in the endometrium on about the sixth day of the secretory phase (day 20 of a 28-day cycle).
- Human chorionic gonadotropin (hCG), a hormone produced by the syncytiotrophoblast of the chorion (see Chapter 4), keeps the corpus luteum secreting estrogens and progesterone.
- The secretory phase continues and menstruation does not occur.

If fertilization does not occur:

- The corpus luteum degenerates.
- Estrogen and progesterone levels fall, and the secretory endometrium enters an *ischemic phase* during the last day of the secretory phase.
- Menstruation occurs.

Ischemia (reduced blood supply) occurs as the spiral arteries constrict, giving the endometrium a pale appearance. This constriction results from the decreasing secretion of hormones, primarily progesterone, by the degenerating corpus luteum. In addition to vascular changes, the hormone withdrawal results in the stoppage of glandular secretion, a loss of interstitial fluid, and a marked shrinking of the endometrium. Toward the end of the ischemic phase, the spiral arteries become constricted for longer periods. This results in *venous stasis* and patchy ischemic necrosis (death) in the superficial tissues. Eventually, rupture of damaged vessel walls follows, and blood seeps into the surrounding connective tissue. Small pools of blood form and break through the endometrial surface, resulting in bleeding into the uterine lumen and from the vagina.

As small pieces of the endometrium detach and pass into the uterine cavity, the torn ends of the arteries bleed into the uterine cavity, resulting in a loss of 20 to 80 ml of blood. Eventually, over 3 to 5 days, the entire compact layer and most of the spongy layer of the endometrium are discarded in the *menses*. Remnants of the spongy and basal layers remain to undergo regeneration during the subsequent proliferative phase of the endometrium. It is obvious from the previous descriptions that the cyclic hormonal activity of the ovary is intimately linked with cyclic histological changes in the endometrium.

If pregnancy occurs, the menstrual cycles cease and the endometrium passes into a *pregnancy phase*. With the termination of pregnancy, the ovarian and menstrual cycles resume after a variable period (usually 6 to 10 weeks if the woman is not breastfeeding her baby). If pregnancy does not occur, the reproductive cycles normally continue until the end of a woman's reproductive life — *menopause*, the permanent cessation of the menses — usually between the ages of 48 and 55. The syndrome of endocrine, somatic (body), and psychic changes occurring at the termination of the reproductive period are called the *climacteric* (climacterium).

TRANSPORTATION OF GAMETES

Transportation of the gametes refers to the way the oocyte and sperm meet each other in the ampulla of the uterine tube, the usual site of fertilization.

Oocyte Transport

The secondary oocyte is expelled at ovulation from the ovarian follicle in the ovary with the escaping follicular fluid (Fig. 2-11*D*). During ovulation, the fimbriated end of the uterine tube becomes closely applied to the ovary. The fingerlike processes of the tube, the *fimbriae*, move back and forth over the ovary (Fig. 2-14). The sweeping action of the fimbriae and fluid currents produced by the cilia of the mucosal cells of the fimbriae "sweep" the secondary oocyte into the funnel-shaped infundibulum of the uterine tube. The oocyte then passes into the ampulla of the tube, mainly resulting from *waves of peristalsis* — movements of the wall of the tube characterized by alternate contraction and relaxation — that pass toward the uterus. The nature of oocyte transport through the rest of the uterine tube is extremely complex and involves many factors that are poorly understood (Egarter, 1990; Beer, 1991).

Sperm Transport

From their storage site in the epididymis, mainly in its tail, the sperms are rapidly transported to the urethra by peristaltic contractions of the thick muscular coat of the ductus deferens (Fig. 2-15). As the sperms pass by the accessory sex glands — *seminal vesicles, prostate*, and *bulbourethral glands* — secretions from them are added to sperm-containing fluid in the ductus def-

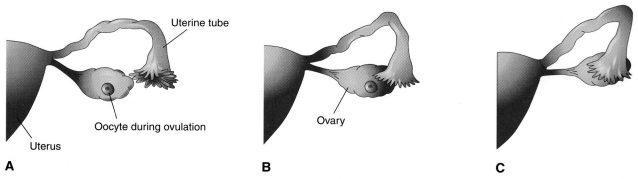

A **B** **C**

■ **Figure 2-14.** Drawings (*A* to *C*) illustrating the movement of the uterine tube that occurs during ovulation. Note that the fimbriated infundibulum of the tube becomes closely applied to the ovary. Its fingerlike fimbriae move back and forth over the ovary and "sweep" the secondary oocyte into the infundibulum as soon as it is expelled from the ovarian follicle and ovary during ovulation (see Fig. 2-11).

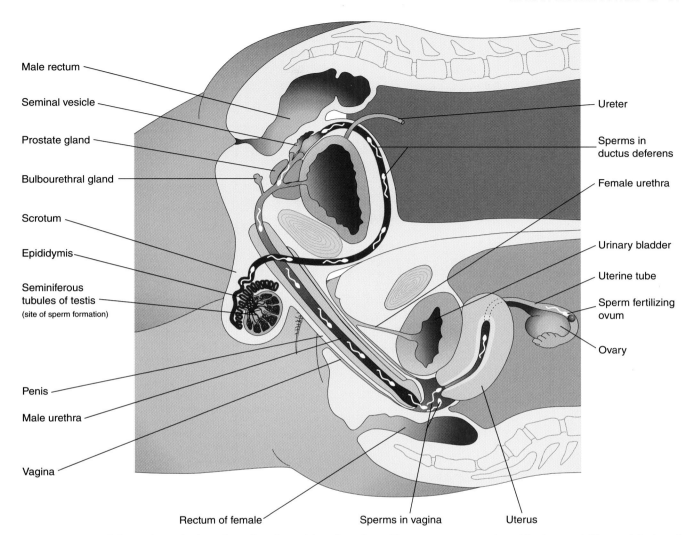

Male rectum

Seminal vesicle

Prostate gland

Bulbourethral gland

Scrotum

Epididymis

Seminiferous
tubules of testis
(site of sperm formation)

Penis

Male urethra

Vagina

Rectum of female

Sperms in vagina

Uterus

Ureter

Sperms in
ductus deferens

Female urethra

Urinary bladder

Uterine tube

Sperm fertilizing
ovum

Ovary

■ **Figure 2–15.** Schematic sagittal section of male and female pelves. The sperms are produced in the seminiferous tubules of the testis and stored in the epididymis. During ejaculation the sperms pass along the ductus deferens and ejaculatory duct and enter the urethra, where they mix with secretions from the seminal vesicles, prostate, and bulbourethral glands. This mixture—semen—is deposited in the superior portion of the vagina close to the external os of the uterus. The sperms pass through the cervix and the cavity of the uterus into the uterine tubes, where fertilization usually occurs.

erens and urethra. From 200 to 600 million sperms are deposited around the external os of the cervix and in the fornix of the vagina during sexual intercourse. The sperms pass slowly by movements of their tails through the cervical canal. The enzyme *vesiculase*, produced by the seminal vesicles, coagulates some of the *semen* (seminal fluid containing sperms) and forms a vaginal plug that may prevent the backflow of semen into the vagina. At the time of ovulation, the cervical mucus increases in amount and becomes less viscid, making it more favorable for sperm transport.

The reflex ejaculation of sperms may be divided into two phases (Moore and Agur, 1995):

- *Emission* — semen is delivered to the prostatic part of the urethra through the ejaculatory ducts after peristalsis of the ductus deferentes (plural of ductus deferens) and seminal vesicles; emission is a sympathetic response.
- *Ejaculation* — semen is expelled from the urethra through the external urethral orifice; this results from closure of the vesical sphincter at the neck

of the bladder, contraction of urethral muscle, and contraction of the bulbospongiosus muscles.

Passage of sperms through the uterus and uterine tubes results mainly from muscular contractions of the walls of these organs. *Prostaglandins* in the semen are thought to stimulate uterine motility at the time of intercourse and assist in the movement of sperms through the uterus and tubes to the site of fertilization in the ampulla of the tube. *Fructose* in the semen, secreted by the seminal vesicles, is an energy source for the sperms (Barratt and Cooke, 1991).

The **ejaculate** (sperms suspended in secretions from accessory sex glands) averages 3.5 ml, with a range of 2 to 6 ml. The sperms move 2 to 3 mm per minute, but the speed varies with the pH of the environment. They are nonmotile during storage in the epididymis but become motile in the ejaculate. They move slowly in the acid environment of the vagina but move more rapidly in the alkaline environment of the uterus. It is not known how long it takes sperms to reach the fertilization site, but the time of transport is probably short. Settlage et al (1973) found a few motile sperms in the ampulla of the uterine tube 5 minutes after their deposition near the external uterine os. Some sperms, however, took up to 45 minutes to complete the journey. Only about 200 sperms reach the fertilization site. Most sperms degenerate and are resorbed by the female genital tract.

MATURATION OF SPERMS

Freshly ejaculated sperms are unable to fertilize oocytes. They must undergo a *period of conditioning* — **capacitation** — lasting about 7 hours. During this period a glycoprotein coat and seminal proteins are removed from the surface of the sperm's acrosome. The membrane cholesterol-phospholipid ratios, as well as the membrane potential, become altered. Capacitated sperms show no morphologic changes, but they are more active. Sperms are usually capacitated in the uterus or uterine tubes by substances secreted by these parts of the female genital tract. During *in vitro fertilization*, a process whereby several oocytes are placed in a medium to which sperms are added for fertilization (see Fig. 3–3), capacitation is induced by incubating the sperms in a defined medium for several hours. Completion of capacitation permits the acrosome reaction to occur (Acosta, 1994).

Angiotensin-converting enzyme (ACE) present in the acrosome of the sperm is probably involved in inducing the **acrosome reaction** and the fertilization process. The acrosome reaction of sperms must be completed before the sperm can fuse with the oocyte (Allen and Green, 1997). When capacitated sperms come into contact with the corona radiata surrounding a secondary oocyte, they undergo changes that result in the development of perforations in the acrosome (see Fig. 3–1). Multiple point fusions of the plasma membrane of the sperm and the external acrosomal membrane occur. Breakdown of the membranes at these sites produces apertures. The changes induced by the acrosome reaction are associated with the release from the acrosome of enzymes, including *hyaluronidase* and *acrosin*, that facilitate fertilization.

Sperm Counts

During evaluation of male fertility, an analysis of semen is made. Sperms account for less than 10% of the semen. The remainder of the ejaculate consists of the secretions of the accessory sex glands: seminal vesicles (60%), prostate (30%), and bulbourethral glands (10%). In the ejaculate of normal males there are usually more than 100 million sperms per milliliter of semen. Although there is much variation in individual cases, men whose semen contains 20 million sperms per milliliter, or 50 million in the total specimen, are probably fertile (Comhaire et al, 1992). A man with less than 10 million sperms per milliliter of semen is likely to be sterile, especially when the specimen contains immotile and abnormal sperms. Thus, in assessing fertility potential, the total number and motility of sperms in the ejaculate are taken into consideration. For potential fertility, at least 40% of sperms should be motile after 2 hours and some should be motile after 24 hours. It is believed that male infertility is the cause of one third to one half of unintentionally childless marriages. Male infertility may result from endocrine disorders, abnormal spermatogenesis, or obstruction of a genital duct (e.g., ductus deferens).

Deferentectomy or Vasectomy

The most effective method of contraception in the male is *deferentectomy* (excision of a segment of the ductus deferens). This surgical procedure, called **vasectomy**, is reversible in at least 50% of cases. Following deferentectomy there are no sperms in the ejaculate, but the amount of seminal fluid is the same.

VIABILITY OF GAMETES

Studies on early stages of development indicate that *human oocytes are usually fertilized within 12 hours after extrusion from the ovaries at ovulation.* In vitro observations have shown that the oocyte cannot be fertilized after 24 hours and that it degenerates shortly thereafter. *Most human sperms probably do not survive for more than 48 hours in the female genital tract.* Some sperms are stored in folds of the mucosa of the cervix and are gradually released into the cervical canal and pass from the uterus into the uterine tubes. The short-term storage of sperms in the cervix provides a gradual release of sperms and thereby increases the chances of fertilization. After being frozen to low temperatures, semen may be kept for many years. Children have been born to women who have been artificially inseminated with semen stored for several years.

SUMMARY OF REPRODUCTION

Fertilization (conception) involves the union of an oocyte from a female and sperm from a male. The reproductive system in both sexes is designed to produce gametes and ensure their union. The secondary oocyte develops in the ovary and is expelled from it at ovulation. It is carried into the infundibulum of the uterine tube by sweeping motions of the fimbriae of the tube. Peristaltic waves in the tube move the oocyte to the fertilization site in the ampulla of the tube.

The sperms are produced in the seminiferous tubules of the testis and stored in the epididymis. During ejaculation, usually occurring during sexual intercourse, the semen is deposited in the vagina. Although there are several million sperms in the semen, only a few thousand pass through the cervical canal and uterine cavity and along the uterine tube. Only about 200 sperms reach the ampulla where fertilization occurs if a secondary oocyte is present.

Clinically Oriented Questions

1. Does a ruptured hymen indicate that a woman is not a virgin?
2. I have heard that a woman can have an erection. Is this true?
3. I know of a woman who claimed that she menstruated throughout her pregnancy. How could this happen?
4. If a woman forgets to take a birth control pill and then takes two, is she likely to become pregnant?
5. What is coitus interruptus? I have heard that it is a safe method of birth control. Is this true?
6. What is the difference between spermatogenesis and spermiogenesis?
7. I have heard that an IUD (intrauterine device) is a contraceptive. Is this correct?
8. I was told that a 5-year-old child had a baby. Is this possible?
9. What is the difference between the terms *menopause* and *climacteric*?

The answers to these questions are given at the back of the book.

REFERENCES AND SUGGESTED READING

Acosta AA: Process of fertilization in the human and its abnormalities: Diagnostic and therapeutic possibilities. *Obstet Gynecol Surv* 49:567, 1994.

Allen CA, Green DPL: The mammalian acrosome reaction: Gateway to sperm fusion with the oocyte. *Bioessays* 19:241, 1997.

Angell R: Mechanism of chromosome nondisjunction in human oocytes. *Prog Clin Biol Res* 393:13, 1995.

Balasch J, Miro F, Burzaco I, et al: The role of luteinizing hormone in human follicle development and oocyte fertility: Evidence from in vitro fertilization in a woman with long-standing hypogonadotrophic hypogonadism and using recombinant human follicle stimulating hormone. *Hum Reprod* 10:1678, 1995.

Barratt CLR, Cooke ID: Sperm transport in the human female reproductive tract — a dynamic interaction. *Int J Androl* 14:394, 1991.

Beer E: Egg transport through the oviduct. *Am J Obstet Gynecol* 165:483, 1991.

Carr DH, Gedeon M: Population cytogenetics of human abortuses. *In* Hook EB, Porter IH (eds): *Population Cytogenetics: Studies in Humans.* New York, Academic Press, 1977.

Comhaire FH, Huysse S, Hinting A, et al: Objective semen analysis: Has the target been reached? *Hum Reprod* 7:237, 1992.

Cumming DC, Cumming CE, Kieren DK: Menstrual mythology and sources of information about menstruation. *Am J Obstet Gynecol* 164:472, 1991.

Dooley M, Lim-Howe D, Savros M, Studd JWW: Early experience with gamete intrafallopian transfer (GIFT) and direct intraperitoneal insemination (DIPT). *J R Soc Med* 81:637, 1988.

Edwards RG, Brody SA: *Principles and Practice of Assisted Human Reproduction.* Philadelphia, WB Saunders, 1995.

Egarter C: The complex nature of egg transport through the oviduct. *Am J Obstet Gynecol* 163:687, 1990.

Gilbert SF: *Developmental Biology,* 5th ed. Sunderland, Sinauer Associates, 1997.

Kierszenbaum AL: Mammalian spermatogenesis in vivo and in vitro: A partnership of spermatogenic and somatic cell lineages. *Endocr Rev* 15:116, 1994.

Moore KL, Agur AMR: *Essential Clinical Anatomy.* Baltimore, Williams & Wilkins, 1995.

Oehninger S, Hodgen GD: Hypothalamic-pituitary-ovary-uterine axis. *In* Copeland LJ: *Textbook of Gynecology.* Philadelphia, WB Saunders, 1993.

Poyser NL: The control of prostaglandin production by the endometrium in relation to luteolysis and menstruation. *Prostaglandins Leukot Essent Fatty Acids* 53:147, 1995.

Rosenbusch BE: Cytogenetics of human spermatozoa: What about the reproductive relevance of structural chromosomal aberrations? *J Assist Reprod Genet* 12:375, 1995.

Settlage DSF, Motoshima M, Tredway DR: Sperm transport from the external cervical os to the fallopian tubes in women. *Fertil Steril* 24:655, 1973.

Steptoe PC, Edwards RG: Birth after implantation of a human embryo. *Lancet* 2:36, 1978.

Stoll C, Roth MP, Bigel P: A re-examination of paternal age effect on the occurrence of new mutants for achondroplasia. *Prog Clin Biol Res* 104:419, 1982.

Talbot P: Sperm penetration through oocyte investments in mammals. *Am J Anat* 174:331, 1985.

Thompson MW, McInnes RR, Willard HF: *Thompson and Thompson Genetics in Medicine*, 5th ed. Philadelphia, WB Saunders, 1991.

Zaneveld LJD: Capacitation of spermatozoa. *In* Ludwig H, Tauber PF (eds): *Human Fertilization*. Stuttgart, Georg Thieme Publishers, 1978.

The First Week of Human Development

3

■ *Human development begins at fertilization*, the process during which a male gamete or sperm (spermatozoon) unites with a female gamete or oocyte (ovum) to form a single cell, the **zygote**. This highly specialized, totipotent cell is the beginning of embryonic development. The zygote, just visible to the unaided eye as a tiny speck, contains chromosomes and genes (units of genetic information) that are derived from the mother and father. The unicellular organism, or zygote, divides many times and becomes progressively transformed into a multicellular human being through cell division, migration, growth, and differentiation (Gilbert, 1997). Although development begins at fertilization, the stages and duration of pregnancy described in clinical medicine are calculated from the commencement of the mother's *last normal menstrual period* (LNMP), which is about 14 days before conception occurs (see Fig. 1–1). This is the *gestational age*, which overestimates the actual fertilization or embryonic age by 2 weeks.

FERTILIZATION

The usual site of fertilization is the ampulla of the uterine tube, its longest and widest part (see Fig. 2–2B). If the oocyte is not fertilized here, it slowly passes along the tube to the uterus, where it degenerates and is resorbed. Although fertilization may occur in other parts of the tube, it does not occur in the uterus.

Fertilization is a complex sequence of "coordinated molecular events" (for details see Acosta, 1994) that begins with contact between a sperm and an oocyte (Fig. 3–1) and ends with the intermingling of maternal and paternal chromosomes at metaphase of the first mitotic division of the **zygote**, a unicellular embryo (see Fig. 3–2E). Defects at any stage in the sequence of these events may cause the zygote to die. Carbohydrate-binding molecules on the surface of the gametes are possibly involved in the process of fertilization through gamete recognition and union of the cells (Boldt et al, 1989).

Phases of Fertilization

The phases of fertilization are (Figs. 3–1 and 3–2):

- **Passage of sperm through corona radiata surrounding zona pellucida of an oocyte**. Dispersal of the follicular cells of the corona radiata surrounding the oocyte and zona pellucida appears to result mainly from the action of the enzyme *hyaluronidase,* released from the acrosome of the sperm. *Tubal mucosal enzymes* also appear to assist hyaluronidase. Movements of the tail of the sperm are also important in its penetration of the corona radiata.

- **Penetration of zona pellucida surrounding the oocyte**. This is the important phase in the initiation of fertilization. The formation of a pathway for the sperm through the zona results from the action of enzymes released from the acrosome (Allen and Green, 1997). The enzymes—*esterases, acrosin,* and *neuraminidase*—appear to cause lysis (Gr. dissolution or loosening) of the zona pellucida, thereby forming a path for the sperm to follow to the oocyte. The most important of these enzymes is *acrosin*, a proteolytic enzyme (Carlson, 1994). Once the sperm penetrates the zona pellucida, a **zona reaction**—a change in its properties—occurs in this amorphous layer that makes it impermeable to other sperms. The composition of this extracellular glycoprotein coat changes after fertilization (Moos et al, 1995). The zona reaction is believed to result from the action of lysosomal enzymes released by cortical granules near the plasma membrane of the oocyte. The contents of these granules, which are released into the perivitelline space (Fig. 3–1A), also cause changes in the plasma membrane of the oocyte that make it impermeable to sperms (Bercegeay et al, 1995).

- **Fusion of plasma membranes of the oocyte and sperm**. The plasma or cell membranes of the oocyte and sperm fuse and break down at the area of fusion. The head and tail of the sperm enter the cytoplasm of the oocyte, but the sperm's plasma membrane remains behind (Fig. 3–1B).

- **Completion of second meiotic division of the oocyte and formation of female pronucleus**. After entry of the sperm, the oocyte, which has been arrested in metaphase of the second meiotic division, completes the division and forms a mature oocyte and a second polar body (Fig. 3–2B). Following decondensation of the maternal chromosomes, the nucleus of the mature oocyte becomes the female pronucleus.

- **Formation of male pronucleus**. Within the cytoplasm of the oocyte, the nucleus of the sperm enlarges to form the male pronucleus, and the tail of the sperm degenerates (Fig. 3–2C). Morphologically the male and female pronuclei are indistinguishable. During growth of the pronuclei, they replicate their DNA—1 n (haploid), 2 c (two chromatids).

- **Membranes of pronuclei break down, the chromosomes condense and become arranged for mitotic cell division**—the first cleavage division (see Fig. 3–4A). The fertilized oocyte, or zygote, is a unicellular embryo (Fig. 3–2E). The combination of 23 chromosomes in each pronucleus results in a zygote with 46 chromosomes.

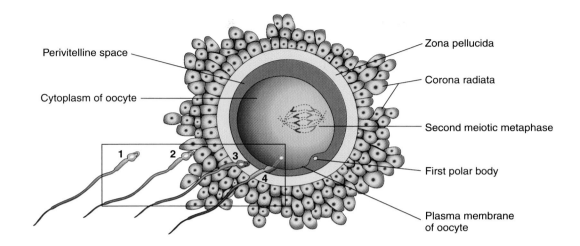

Perivitelline space

Cytoplasm of oocyte

Zona pellucida

Corona radiata

Second meiotic metaphase

First polar body

Plasma membrane
of oocyte

A

Sperm nucleus
containing
chromosomes

Acrosome
containing
enzymes

Plasma
membrane
of sperm

Perforations in
acrosome wall

Enzymes are
breaking down
zona pellucida

Sperm in cytoplasm
of oocyte without its
plasma membrane

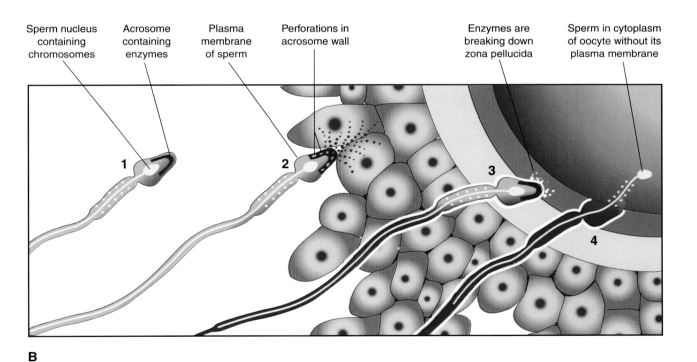

B

■ **Figure 3–1.** Diagrams illustrating the acrosome reaction and a sperm penetrating an oocyte. The detail of the area outlined in *A* is given in *B*. 1, Sperm during capacitation, a period of conditioning that occurs in the female reproductive tract. 2, Sperm undergoing the acrosome reaction, during which perforations form in the acrosome. 3, Sperm digesting a path through the zona pellucida by the action of enzymes released from the acrosome. 4, Sperm after entering the cytoplasm of the oocyte. Note that the plasma membranes of the sperm and oocyte have fused and that the head and tail of the sperm enter the oocyte, leaving the sperm's plasma membrane attached to the oocyte's plasma membrane.

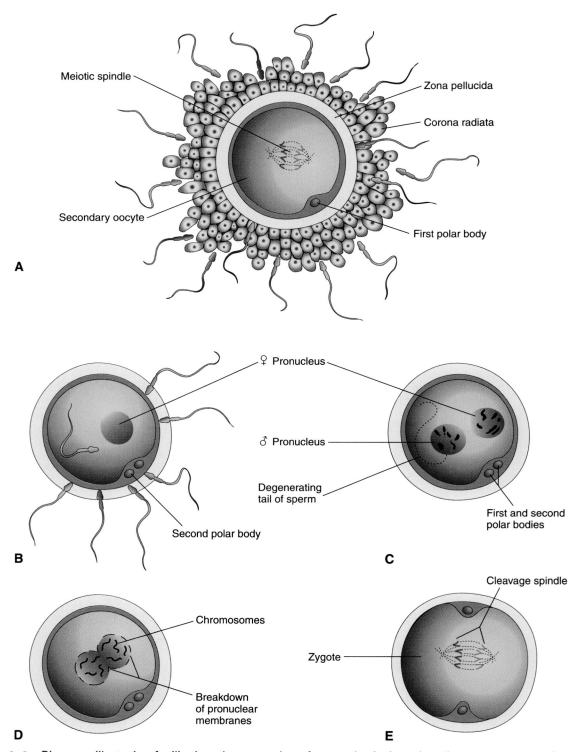

Labels in figure:
- Meiotic spindle
- Zona pellucida
- Corona radiata
- Secondary oocyte
- First polar body

A

- ♀ Pronucleus
- ♂ Pronucleus
- Degenerating tail of sperm
- Second polar body
- First and second polar bodies

B

C

- Chromosomes
- Breakdown of pronuclear membranes
- Cleavage spindle
- Zygote

D

E

■ **Figure 3–2.** Diagrams illustrating fertilization, the procession of events beginning when the sperm contacts the secondary oocyte's plasma membrane and ending with the intermingling of maternal and paternal chromosomes at metaphase of the first mitotic division of the zygote. *A*, Secondary oocyte surrounded by several sperms. (Only four of the 23 chromosome pairs are shown.) *B*, The corona radiata has disappeared; a sperm has entered the oocyte, and the second meiotic division has occurred, forming a mature oocyte. The nucleus of the ovum is now the female pronucleus. *C*, The sperm head has enlarged to form the male pronucleus. *D*, The pronuclei are fusing. *E*, The zygote has formed; it contains 46 chromosomes, the diploid number.

Fertilization is completed within 24 hours of ovulation. An immunosuppressant protein—the *early pregnancy factor* (EPF)—is secreted by the trophoblastic cells and appears in the maternal serum within 24 to 48 hours after fertilization. EPF forms the basis of a pregnancy test during the first 10 days of development (Nahhas and Barnea, 1990).

Dispermy and Triploidy

Although several sperms begin to penetrate the zona pellucida, usually only one sperm enters the oocyte and fertilizes it. Two sperms may participate in fertilization during an abnormal process known as *dispermy*, resulting in an extra set of chromosomes. Triploid conceptions account for about 20% of chromosomally abnormal abortions (Crane, 1994). The resulting **triploid embryos** (69 chromosomes) appear quite normal, but they nearly always abort. Aborted fetuses with triploidy have severe *intrauterine growth retardation* with a disproportionately small trunk and many other anomalies (e.g., of the central nervous system). A few triploid infants have been born, but they all died shortly after birth (Carr, 1971). Livebirths are uncommon, occurring in fewer than 1 in 2500 pregnancies.

Results of Fertilization

Fertilization

- Stimulates the secondary oocyte to complete the second meiotic division, producing the second polar body.
- Restores the normal diploid number of chromosomes (46) in the zygote.
- Results in variation of the human species through mingling of maternal and paternal chromosomes.
- Determines the chromosomal sex of the embryo; an X-bearing sperm produces a female embryo and a Y-bearing sperm produces a male embryo.
- Causes metabolic activation of the oocyte which initiates cleavage (cell division of zygote).

The zygote is genetically unique because half of its chromosomes come from the mother and half from the father. The zygote contains a new combination of chromosomes that is different from that in the cells of either of the parents. *This mechanism forms the basis of biparental inheritance and variation of the human species.* Meiosis allows independent assortment of maternal and paternal chromosomes among the germ cells (see Fig. 2–6). *Crossing over of chromosomes*, by relocating segments of the maternal and paternal chromosomes, "shuffles" the genes, thereby producing a recombination of genetic material.

In Vitro Fertilization and Embryo Transfer

In vitro fertilization (IVF) of oocytes and transfer of the dividing zygotes (cleaving embryos) into the uterus have provided an opportunity for many women who are sterile (e.g., because of tubal occlusion) to bear children. The first of these IVF babies was born in 1978 (Steptoe and Edwards, 1978).

The steps involved during IVF and embryo transfer are the following (Fig. 3–3):

- Ovarian follicles are stimulated to grow and mature by the administration of gonadotropins.
- Several mature oocytes are aspirated from mature ovarian follicles during *laparoscopy*—viewing of ovaries with a laparoscope. Oocytes can also be removed by an ultrasound-guided large-gauge needle inserted through the vagina into the ovarian follicles (Ritchie, 1994).
- The oocytes are placed in a Petri dish containing a special culture medium and capacitated sperms.
- Fertilization of the oocytes and cleavage of the zygotes are monitored microscopically.
- Dividing zygotes (cleaving embryos) during the four- to eight-cell stage are transferred to the uterus by introducing a catheter through the vagina and cervical canal into the uterus; the probability of a successful pregnancy is enhanced by inserting up to three embryos.
- The patient remains in the supine position (face upward) for several hours.

Obviously, the chances of multiple pregnancies are higher than when pregnancy results from normal ovulation and passage of the morula into the uterus via the uterine tube. The incidence of spontaneous abortion of transferred embryos is also higher than normal. This may result from the high incidence of chromosomal and other cellular abnormalities present in conceptuses fertilized in vitro (Winston, 1996).

Cryopreservation of Embryos

For a discussion of cryopreservation of embryos, intracytoplasmic sperm injection, and assisted in vivo fertilization, see Edwards and Brody (1995) and Moore and Persaud (1998).

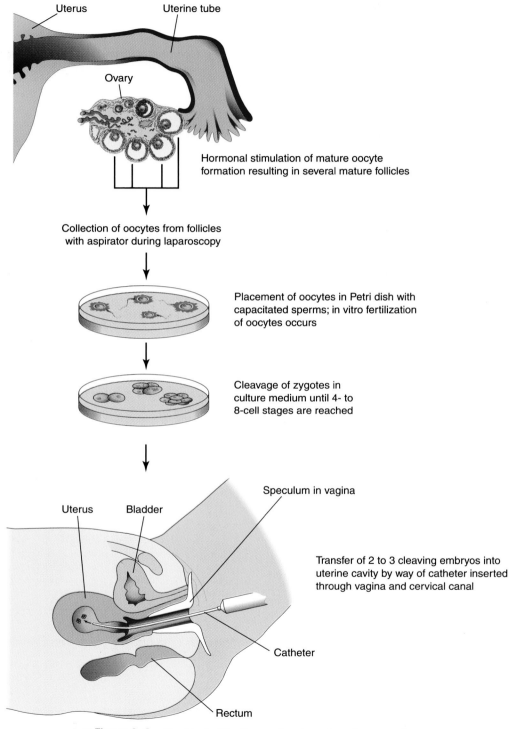

Uterus

Uterine tube

Ovary

Hormonal stimulation of mature oocyte formation resulting in several mature follicles

Collection of oocytes from follicles with aspirator during laparoscopy

Placement of oocytes in Petri dish with capacitated sperms; in vitro fertilization of oocytes occurs

Cleavage of zygotes in culture medium until 4- to 8-cell stages are reached

Speculum in vagina

Uterus   Bladder

Transfer of 2 to 3 cleaving embryos into uterine cavity by way of catheter inserted through vagina and cervical canal

Catheter

Rectum

■ **Figure 3–3.** In vitro fertilization and embryo transfer procedures.

CLEAVAGE OF ZYGOTE

Cleavage consists of repeated mitotic divisions of the zygote, resulting in a rapid increase in the number of cells. These cells — **blastomeres** — become smaller with each cleavage division (Fig. 3 - 4). First the zygote divides into two blastomeres; these cells then divide into four blastomeres, eight blastomeres, and so on. Cleavage normally occurs as the zygote passes through the uterine tube toward the uterus (see Fig. 3 - 6). During cleavage, the zygote is still contained within the rather thick, jelly-like *zona pellucida* (pellucid zone), which is translucent under the light microscope. Division of the zygote into blastomeres begins about 30 hours after fertilization. Subsequent divisions follow, forming progressively smaller blastomeres (Fig. 3 - 4).

After the nine-cell stage, the blastomeres change their shape and tightly align themselves against each other to form a compact ball of cells. This phenomenon, known as **compaction**, is probably mediated by cell surface adhesion glycoproteins (Gilbert, 1997). Compaction permits greater cell-to-cell interaction and is a prerequisite for segregation of the internal cells that form the inner cell mass (embryoblast) of the blastocyst (Fig. 3 - 4E). When there are 12 to 15 blastomeres, the developing human is called a **morula** (L. *morus*, mulberry) because of its resemblance to the fruit of the mulberry tree. The internal cells of the morula — **inner cell mass** — are surrounded by a layer of flattened cells that form the outer cell layer, or **trophoblast**. The spherical morula forms 3 days after fertilization, about which time it enters the cavity of the uterus.

FORMATION OF BLASTOCYST

Shortly after the morula enters the uterus (about 4 days after fertilization), fluid passes from the uterine cavity through the zona pellucida to form a fluid-filled space — the **blastocyst cavity** — inside the morula (Fig. 3 - 4E). As fluid increases in the blastocyst cavity, the blastomeres are separated into two parts:

- The **trophoblast** (Gr. *trophe*, nutrition), a thin, outer cell layer that gives rise to the embryonic part of the placenta.
- The **inner cell mass**, a group of centrally located blastomeres that gives rise to the embryo; because it is the primordium of the embryo, the inner cell mass is also called the **embryoblast**.

At this stage of development, the conceptus is called a **blastocyst**. The inner cell mass now projects into the blastocyst cavity, and the trophoblast forms the wall of the blastocyst (Fig. 3 - 4F). After the blastocyst has floated in the uterine secretions for about 2 days, the zona pellucida degenerates and disappears. *Shedding of the zona pellucida* or "hatching of the blastocyst" has been observed in vitro (Veeck, 1991). Shedding of the zona pellucida permits the blastocyst to increase rapidly in size. While floating freely in the uterine cavity, the embryo derives nourishment from secretions of the uterine glands.

About 6 days after fertilization (day 20 of a 28-day menstrual cycle), the blastocyst attaches to the endometrial epithelium, usually adjacent to the inner cell mass (Fig. 3 - 5A). As soon as it attaches to the endometrial epithelium, the trophoblast starts to proliferate rapidly and differentiate into two layers (Fig. 3 - 5B):

- **Cytotrophoblast** (cellular trophoblast), the inner layer of cells
- **Syncytiotrophoblast** (syncytial trophoblast), the outer syncytial layer consisting of a multinucleate protoplasmic mass formed by the fusion of cells; no cell boundaries can be observed in the syncytiotrophoblast.

The fingerlike processes of the syncytiotrophoblast (syntrophoblast) extend through the endometrial epithelium and invade the endometrial connective tissue (stroma). By the end of the first week, the blastocyst is superficially implanted in the compact layer of the endometrium and is deriving its nourishment from the eroded maternal tissues. The highly invasive syncytiotrophoblast expands quickly adjacent to the inner cell mass or *embryonic pole*. The syncytiotrophoblast produces proteolytic enzymes that erode the maternal tissues, enabling the blastocyst to burrow into the endometrium. *At about 7 days*, a cuboidal layer of cells, the **hypoblast** (primary endoderm), appears on the surface of the inner cell mass facing the blastocyst cavity (Fig. 3 - 5B). Comparative embryological data suggest that the hypoblast arises by delamination from the inner cell mass (Carlson, 1994).

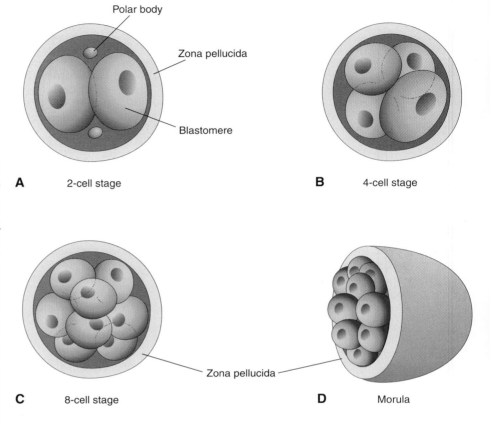

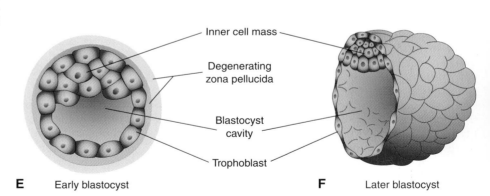

■ Figure 3–4. Drawings illustrating cleavage of the zygote and formation of the blastocyst. *A* to *D* show various stages of cleavage. The period of the morula begins at the 12- to 16-cell stage and ends when the blastocyst forms. *E* and *F* are sections of blastocysts. The zona pellucida has disappeared by the late blastocyst stage (5 days). The polar bodies shown in *A* are small, nonfunctional cells that soon degenerate. Cleavage of the zygote and formation of the morula occur as the dividing zygote passes along the uterine tube. Blastocyst formation normally occurs in the uterus. Although cleavage increases the number of cells, blastomeres, note that each of the daughter cells is smaller than the parent cells. As a result, there is no increase in the size of the developing embryo until the zona pellucida degenerates. The blastocyst then enlarges considerably. The inner cell mass, or embryoblast, gives rise to the tissues and organs of the embryo.

Preimplantation Diagnosis of Genetic Disorders

Using currently available techniques of micromanipulation and DNA application, a dividing zygote known to be at risk for a specific genetic disorder may be diagnosed before implantation (Geber et al, 1995). The sex of the embryo can be determined from a blastomere taken from a six- to eight-cell dividing zygote and analyzed by DNA amplification of sequences from the Y chromosome. This procedure has been used to detect female embryos during IVF in cases in which a male embryo would be at risk for a serious X-linked disorder (Handyside et al, 1990).

Abnormal Embryos and Spontaneous Abortions

Many zygotes, morulas, and blastocysts abort spontaneously. The early implantation stages of the blastocyst

are critical periods of development that may fail to occur because of inadequate production of progesterone and estrogen by the corpus luteum (see Fig. 2–9). Clinicians occasionally see a patient who states that the last menstrual period was delayed by several days and her last menstrual flow was unusually profuse. Very likely such patients have had an early spontaneous abortion; thus, the overall *early spontaneous abor-*

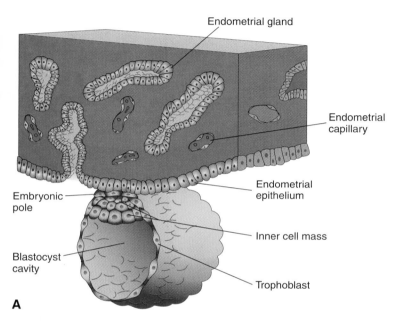

Endometrial gland

Endometrial capillary

Endometrial epithelium

Embryonic pole

Inner cell mass

Blastocyst cavity

Trophoblast

A

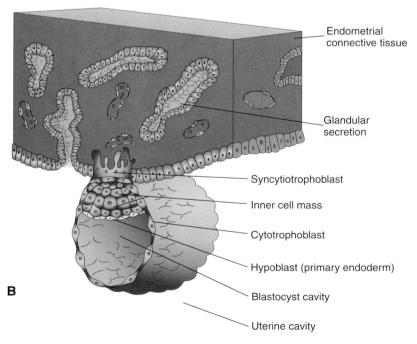

Endometrial connective tissue

Glandular secretion

Syncytiotrophoblast

Inner cell mass

Cytotrophoblast

Hypoblast (primary endoderm)

Blastocyst cavity

B

Uterine cavity

■ **Figure 3–5.** Drawings of sections illustrating the attachment of the blastocyst to the endometrial epithelium and the early stages of its implantation. *A*, Six days; the trophoblast is attached to the endometrial epithelium at the embryonic pole of the blastocyst. *B*, Seven days; the syncytiotrophoblast has penetrated the epithelium and has started to invade the endometrial stroma (framework of connective tissue). Some students have difficulty interpreting illustrations such as these because in histological studies it is conventional to draw the endometrial epithelium upward, whereas in embryological studies the embryo is usually shown with its dorsal surface upward. Because the embryo implants on its future dorsal surface, it would appear upside-down if the histological convention were followed. In this book, the histological convention is followed when the endometrium is the dominant consideration, and the embryological convention is used when the embryo is the center of interest, as in these illustrations.

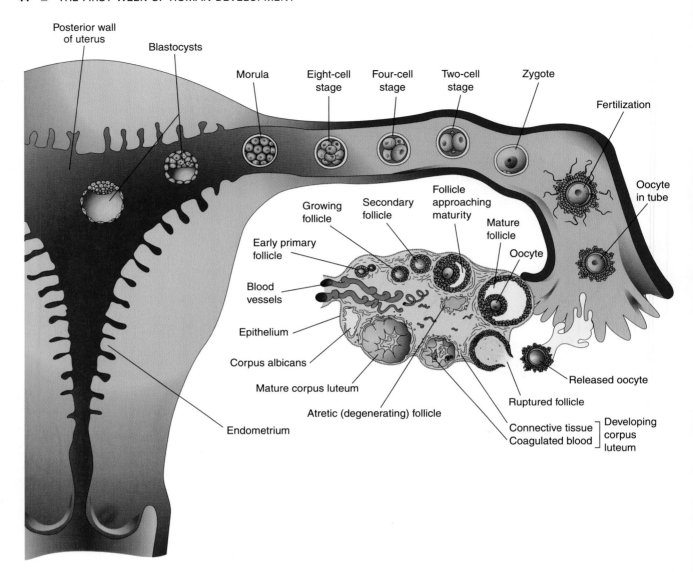

■ **Figure 3-6.** Diagrammatic summary of the ovarian cycle, fertilization, and human development during the first week. Stage 1 of development begins with fertilization in the uterine tube and ends when the zygote forms. Stage 2 (days 2 to 3) comprises the early stages of cleavage (from 2 to about 16 cells—morula). Stage 3 (days 4 to 5) consists of the free unattached blastocyst. Stage 4 (days 5 to 6) is represented by the blastocyst attaching to the posterior wall of the uterus, the usual site of implantation. The blastocysts have been sectioned to show their structure.

tion rate is thought to be about 45% (Rubin and Farber, 1988).

Early spontaneous abortions occur for a variety of reasons, an important one being the presence of **chromosomal abnormalities** in the zygote. Carr and Gedeon (1977) estimated that about 50% of all known spontaneous abortions occur because of chromosomal abnormalities. Hertig and associates (1959) examined blastocysts recovered from early pregnancies and ob-

served several clearly defective dividing zygotes and early blastocysts. Some were so abnormal that survival would not have been likely. The early loss of embryos—*pregnancy wastage*—appears to represent the disposal of abnormal conceptuses that could not have developed normally. It appears that there is a natural screening of embryos, without which about 12% instead of 2 to 3% of infants would likely be congenitally malformed (Warkany, 1981).

SUMMARY OF FIRST WEEK OF DEVELOPMENT

Human development begins at fertilization. When an **oocyte** is contacted by a **sperm**, it completes the second meiotic division. As a result, a mature oocyte and a *female pronucleus* are formed. After the sperm enters the oocyte, the head of the sperm separates from the tail and enlarges to become the *male pronucleus*. Fertilization is complete when the pronuclei unite and the maternal and paternal chromosomes intermingle during metaphase of the first mitotic division of the **zygote**, the primordium of a human being. As it passes along the uterine tube toward the uterus, the zygote undergoes *cleavage* (a series of mitotic cell divisions) into smaller cells—**blastomeres** (Fig. 3–6). About 3 days after fertilization, a ball of 12 or more blastomeres, the **morula**, enters the uterus.

A *blastocyst cavity* soon forms in the morula, converting it into a **blastocyst** consisting of

* The *inner cell mass, or embryoblast*, which gives rise to the embryo and some extraembryonic tissues
* A *blastocyst cavity*, a fluid-filled space
* The *trophoblast*, a thin outer layer of cells

The **trophoblast** encloses the inner cell mass and blastocyst cavity and later forms extraembryonic structures and the embryonic part of the placenta. Four to 5 days after fertilization, the zona pellucida is shed and the trophoblast adjacent to the inner cell mass attaches to the endometrial epithelium. The trophoblast adjacent to the embryonic pole differentiates into two layers, an outer **syncytiotrophoblast**—a multinucleated mass without distinct cell boundaries—and an inner **cytotrophoblast**—a mononucleated layer of cells. The syncytiotrophoblast invades the endometrial epithelium and underlying connective tissue. Concurrently, a cuboidal layer of **hypoblast** forms on the deep surface of the inner cell mass. By the end of the first week, the blastocyst is superficially implanted in the endometrium.

Clinically Oriented Questions

1. Women do not commonly become pregnant after they are 48 years old, whereas men can impregnate women when they are very old. Why is this? Is there an increased risk of Down syndrome or other severe congenital anomalies in the child when the father is over 50?

2. Are there contraceptive pills for men? If not, what is the reason?

3. Is a polar body ever fertilized? If so, does the fertilized polar body give rise to a viable embryo?

4. What is the common cause of most spontaneous abortions during the first week of development?

5. I have heard that a woman could have dissimilar twins resulting from one oocyte being fertilized by a sperm from one man and another one being fertilized by a sperm from another man. Is this possible in humans?

6. Are there differences in meaning between the terms *impregnation, conception,* and *fertilization*?

7. Do the terms *cleavage* and *mitosis* of the zygote mean the same thing?

8. How is the dividing zygote (cleaving embryo) nourished during the first week? Do the blastomeres contain yolk?

9. Can one determine the sex of a cleaving embryo developing in vitro? If so, what medical reasons would there be for doing so?

The answers to these questions are given at the back of the book.

REFERENCES AND SUGGESTED READING

Acosta AA: Process of fertilization in the human and its abnormalities: Diagnostic and therapeutic possibilities. *Obstet Gynecol Surv* 49:567, 1994.

Allen CA, Green DPL: The mammalian acrosome reaction: Gateway to sperm fusion with the oocyte? *Bioessays* 19:241, 1997.

Bercegeay S, Jean M, Lucas H, Barriere P: Composition of human zona pellucida as revealed by SDS-PAGE after silver staining. *Mol Reprod Dev* 41:355, 1995.

Boldt J, Howe AM, Parkerson JB, et al: Carbohydrate involvement in sperm-egg fusion in mice. *Biol Reprod* 40:887, 1989.

Bowie J, Boue A, Laza P: Retrospective and prospective epidemiological studies of 1500 karyotyped spontaneous human abortions. *Teratology* 12:11, 1975.

Carlson BM: *Human Embryology and Developmental Biology.* St. Louis, CV Mosby, 1994.

Carr BR, Blackwell RE: *Textbook of Reproductive Medicine.* Norwalk, CT, Appleton & Lange, 1993.

Carr DH: Chromosome studies on selected spontaneous abortions: Polyploidy in man. *J Med Genet* 8:164, 1971.

Carr DH, Gedeon M: Population cytogenetics of human abortuses. *In* Hook EB, Porter IH (eds): *Population Cytogenetics: Studies in Humans.* New York, Academic Press, 1977.

Crane JP: Ultrasound evaluation of fetal chromosome disorders. *In* Callen PW (ed): *Ultrasonography in Obstetrics and Gynecology.* Philadelphia, WB Saunders, 1994.

Edwards RG, Brody SA: *Principles and Practice of Assisted Human Reproduction.* Philadelphia, WB Saunders, 1995.

Geber S, Winston RM, Handyside AH: Proliferation of blastomeres from biopsied cleavage stage human embryos in vitro: An alternative to blastocyst biopsy for preimplantation diagnosis. *Hum Reprod* 10:1492, 1995.

Gilbert SF: *Developmental Biology,* 5th ed. Sunderland, Sinauer Associates, 1997.

Handyside AH, Kontogianni EH, Hardy K, Winston RML: Pregnancies from biopsied human preimplantation embryos sexed by Y-specific DNA amplification. *Nature* 344:768, 1990.

Hertig AT, Rock J, Adams EC, Menkin MC: Thirty-four fertilized human ova, good, bad, and indifferent, recovered from 210 women of known fertility. *Pediatrics* 23:202, 1959.

Moore KL, Persaud TVN: *The Developing Human: Clinically Oriented Embryology,* 6th ed. Philadelphia, WB Saunders, 1998.

Moos J, Faunders D, Kopf GS, Schultz RM: Composition of the human zona pellucida and modifications following fertilization. *Hum Reprod* 10:2467, 1995.

Nahhas F, Barnea E: Human embryonic origin early pregnancy factor before and after implantation. *Am J Reprod Immunol* 22:105, 1990.

Ritchie WGM: Ultrasound evaluation of normal and induced ovulation. *In* Callen PW (ed): *Ultrasonography in Obstetrics and Gynecology.* Philadelphia, WB Saunders, 1994.

Robertson JA: Ethical and legal issues in human embryos donation. *Fertil Steril* 64:885, 1995.

Rubin E, Farber JL: *Pathology.* Philadelphia, JB Lippincott, 1988.

Steptoe PC, Edwards RG: Birth after implantation of a human embryo. *Lancet* 2:36, 1978.

Talbot P: Sperm penetration through oocyte investments in mammals. *Am J Anat* 174:331, 1985.

Veeck LL: *Atlas of Human Oocyte and Early Conceptus,* vol 2. Baltimore, Williams & Wilkins, 1991.

Warkany J: Prevention of congenital malformations. *Teratology* 23: 175, 1981.

Winston NJ: Developmental failure in preimplantation human conceptuses. *Int Rev Cytol* 164:139, 1996.

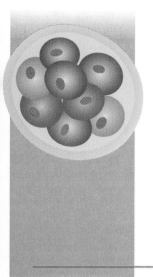

The Second Week of Human Development

4

■ Implantation of the blastocyst is completed during the second week of embryonic development. As this crucial process occurs, morphologic changes occur in the inner cell mass, or embryoblast, that produce a bilaminar embryonic disc composed of two layers, epiblast and hypoblast (Fig. 4-1). The **embryonic disc** gives rise to the germ layers that form all the tissues and organs of the embryo. Extraembryonic structures forming during the second week are the amniotic cavity, amnion, yolk sac, connecting stalk, and chorionic sac.

COMPLETION OF IMPLANTATION AND CONTINUATION OF EMBRYONIC DEVELOPMENT

Implantation of the blastocyst commences at the end of the first week and is completed by the end of the second week. The actively erosive **syncytiotrophoblast** invades the endometrial stroma (connective tissue framework), which supports the capillaries and glands. As this occurs, the blastocyst slowly embeds itself in the endometrium. The blastocyst implants in the endometrial layer at its embryonic pole (site of inner cell mass). Syncytiotrophoblast cells from this region displace endometrial cells in the central part of the implantation site. Proteolytic enzymes produced by the syncytiotrophoblast cells promote *proteolysis*—dissolution of proteins, which facilitates the invasion of the maternal endometrium during implantation. The stromal (connective tissue) cells around the implantation site become loaded with glycogen and lipids and assume a polyhedral appearance. Some of these new cells—**decidual cells**—degenerate adjacent to the penetrating syncytiotrophoblast. The syncytiotrophoblast engulfs these degenerating cells, providing a rich source of *embryonic nutrition*.

As the blastocyst implants, more trophoblast contacts the endometrium and differentiates into two layers (Fig. 4-1A):

- The *cytotrophoblast*, a layer of mononucleated cells that is mitotically active and forms new trophoblast cells that migrate into the increasing mass of the syncytiotrophoblast, where they fuse and lose their cell membranes.
- The *syncytiotrophoblast*, a rapidly expanding, multinucleated mass in which no cell boundaries are discernible.

The syncytiotrophoblast begins to produce a hormone, *human chorionic gonadotropin* (hCG), which enters the maternal blood in the lacunae (L. hollow cavities) in the syncytiotrophoblast (Fig. 4-1C). The hCG maintains the endocrine activity of the corpus luteum in the ovary during pregnancy and forms the basis for *pregnancy tests*. Highly sensitive radioimmunoassays are available for detecting hCG. Enough hCG is produced by the syncytiotrophoblast at the end of the second week to give a positive pregnancy test, even though the woman is probably unaware that she is pregnant.

Formation of Amniotic Cavity, Embryonic Disc, and Yolk Sac

As implantation of the blastocyst progresses, a small cavity appears in the inner cell mass, which is the primordium of the **amniotic cavity** (Fig. 4-1A). Soon amniogenic (amnion-forming) cells called *amnioblasts* separate from the epiblast and organize to form a thin membrane, the **amnion**, which encloses the amniotic cavity (Fig. 4-1B and C). Concurrently, morphologic changes occur in the inner cell mass (embryoblast) that result in the formation of a flattened, almost circular bilaminar plate of cells—the **embryonic disc**—consisting of two layers (Fig. 4-2B):

- **Epiblast**, the thicker layer, consisting of high columnar cells related to the amniotic cavity
- **Hypoblast**, or primordial endoderm, consisting of small cuboidal cells adjacent to the blastocyst cavity

The epiblast forms the floor of the amniotic cavity and is continuous peripherally with the amnion. The hypoblast forms the roof of the **exocoelomic cavity** and is continuous with the thin wall of this cavity (Fig. 4-1B). The cells that migrated from the hypoblast to form the *exocoelomic membrane* surround the blastocyst cavity and line the internal surface of the cytotrophoblast. The blastocyst cavity is now called the *exocoelomic cavity*. The exocoelomic membrane and cavity soon become modified to form the **primary yolk sac**. The embryonic disc then lies between the amniotic cavity and the primary yolk sac (Fig. 4-1C).

Cells from the yolk sac endoderm give rise to a layer of loosely arranged connective tissue, the **extraembryonic mesoderm**, which surrounds the amnion and yolk sac (Bianchi et al, 1993). Extraembryonic mesoderm is later formed by cells that arise from the primitive streak (see Chapter 5). The yolk sac and amniotic cavities make morphogenetic movements of the cells of the embryonic disc possible.

As the amnion, embryonic disc, and primary yolk sac form, isolated cavities called **lacunae** appear in the syncytiotrophoblast (Figs. 4-1C and 4-2). The lacunae soon become filled with a mixture of maternal blood from ruptured endometrial capillaries and secre-

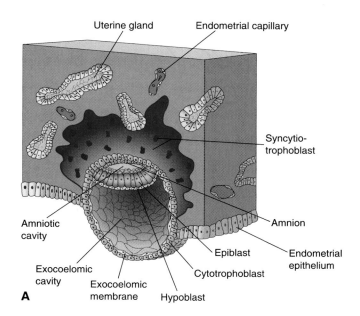

A

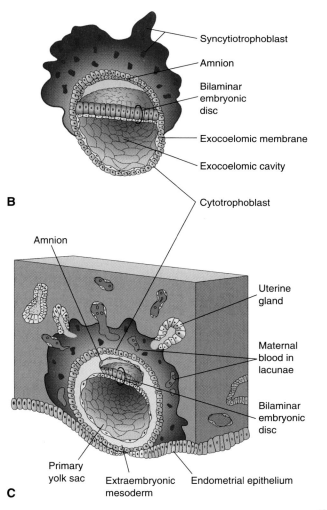

B

C

■ **Figure 4–1.** Drawings illustrating implantation of a blastocyst into the endometrium. The actual size of the conceptus is about 0.1 mm. *A,* Drawing of a section through a blastocyst partially implanted in the endometrium (about 8 days). Note the slitlike amniotic cavity. *B,* An enlarged three-dimensional sketch of a slightly older blastocyst after removal from the endometrium. Note the extensive syncytiotrophoblast at the embryonic pole adjacent to the embryonic disc and the much larger amniotic cavity. *C,* Drawing of a section through a blastocyst of about 9 days implanted in the endometrium. Note the lacunae appearing in the syncytiotrophoblast. The type of implantation illustrated here, in which the blastocyst becomes completely embedded in the endometrium, is called *interstitial implantation.*

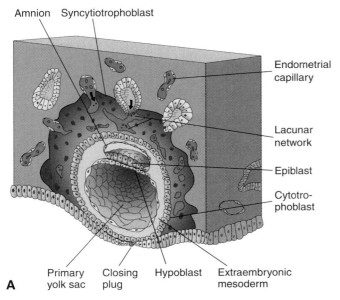

Amnion   Syncytiotrophoblast

Endometrial capillary

Lacunar network

Epiblast

Cytotrophoblast

Primary yolk sac   Closing plug   Hypoblast   Extraembryonic mesoderm

A

Actual size of implanted blastocyst : •

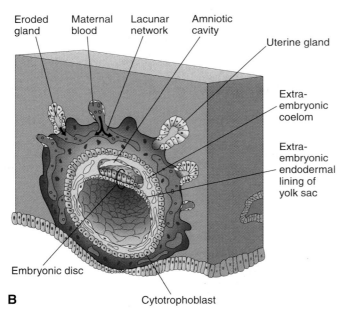

Eroded gland   Maternal blood   Lacunar network   Amniotic cavity

Uterine gland

Extra-embryonic coelom

Extra-embryonic endodermal lining of yolk sac

Embryonic disc

B   Cytotrophoblast

■ **Figure 4–2.** Drawings of sections through two implanted blastocysts. *A*, 10 days; *B*, 12 days. This stage of development is characterized by communication of the blood-filled lacunae. In *B*, note that cavities have appeared in the extraembryonic mesoderm, forming the beginning of the extraembryonic coelom.

tions from eroded uterine glands. The maternal blood also receives hCG produced by the syncytiotrophoblast, which maintains the **corpus luteum**, an endocrine glandular structure that secretes estrogen and progesterone for maintenance of the pregnancy. The fluid in the lacunar spaces, sometimes called *embryotroph* (*Gr. trophe*, nourishment), passes to the embryonic disc by diffusion.

The communication of the eroded uterine vessels with the lacunae represents *the beginning of uteroplacental circulation*. When maternal blood flows into the lacunae, oxygen and nutritive substances become available to the extraembryonic tissues over the large surface of the syncytiotrophoblast. Because both arterial and venous branches of maternal blood vessels communicate with the lacunae, a primitive circulation of blood is established. *Oxygenated blood* passes into the lacunae from the *spiral arteries* in the endometrium, and *deoxygenated blood* is removed from them through endometrial veins (see Chapter 2).

The 10-day human conceptus (embryo and associated membranes) is completely embedded in the endometrium (Fig. 4–2*A*). For about 2 days, there is a defect in the endometrial epithelium that is filled by a **closing plug**, a fibrinous coagulum of blood. By day 12 an almost completely regenerated uterine epithelium covers the closing plug (Fig. 4–2*B*). As the conceptus implants, the endometrium connective tissue cells undergo a transformation known as the **decidual reaction**. After the cells swell because of the accumulation of glycogen and lipid in their cytoplasm, they are known as **decidual cells**. The primary function of the decidual reaction is to provide an immunologically privileged site for the conceptus (Carlson, 1994).

In a 12-day embryo, adjacent syncytiotrophoblastic lacunae have fused to form **lacunar networks** (Fig. 4–2*B*), giving the syncytiotrophoblast a spongelike appearance. The lacunar networks, particularly obvious around the embryonic pole, are the *primordia of the intervillous space of the placenta* (see Chapter 8). The endometrial capillaries around the implanted embryo first become congested and dilated to form *sinusoids* — thin-walled terminal vessels that are larger than ordinary capillaries. The syncytiotrophoblast then erodes the sinusoids and maternal blood flows into the lacunar networks. Maternal blood flows in and out of the networks, establishing the *primitive uteroplacental circulation*. The degenerated endometrial stromal cells and glands, together with the maternal blood, provide a rich source of material for embryonic nutrition. Examination of Figures 4–1 and 4–2 shows that growth of the bilaminar embryonic disc (embryo) is slow compared with growth of the trophoblast.

As changes occur in the trophoblast and endometrium, the extraembryonic mesoderm increases and isolated spaces appear within it (Fig. 4–2). These spaces rapidly fuse to form a large isolated cavity, the **extraembryonic coelom** (Fig. 4–3*A*). This fluid-filled cavity surrounds the amnion and yolk sac, except where they are attached to the chorion by the con-

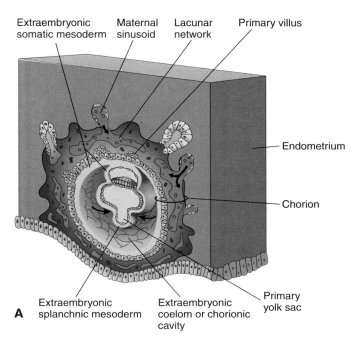

Extraembryonic somatic mesoderm   Maternal sinusoid   Lacunar network   Primary villus

Endometrium

Chorion

A   Extraembryonic splanchnic mesoderm   Extraembryonic coelom or chorionic cavity   Primary yolk sac

■ **Figure 4–3.** Drawings of sections through implanted human embryos, based mainly on Hertig et al (1956). Observe that (1) the defect in the surface epithelium of the endometrium has disappeared; (2) a small secondary yolk sac has formed; (3) a large cavity, the extraembryonic coelom, now surrounds the yolk sac and amnion, except where the amnion is attached to the chorion by the connecting stalk; and (4) the extraembryonic coelom splits the extraembryonic mesoderm into two layers: the extraembryonic somatic mesoderm lining the trophoblast and covering the amnion and the extraembryonic splanchnic mesoderm around the yolk sac. *A*, Thirteen days, illustrating the decrease in relative size of the primary yolk sac and the early appearance of primary chorionic villi. *B*, Fourteen days, showing the newly formed secondary yolk sac and the location of the prechordal plate in its roof. *C*, Detail of the prechordal plate area outlined in *B*.

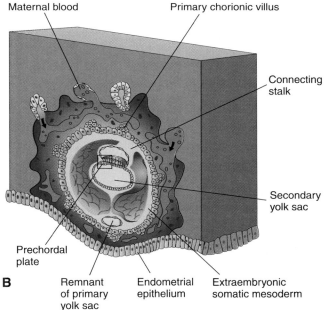

Maternal blood   Primary chorionic villus

Connecting stalk

Secondary yolk sac

Prechordal plate

B   Remnant of primary yolk sac   Endometrial epithelium   Extraembryonic somatic mesoderm

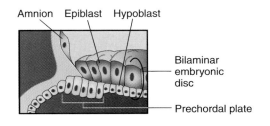

Amnion   Epiblast   Hypoblast

Bilaminar embryonic disc

Prechordal plate

C

necting stalk. As the extraembryonic coelom forms, the primary yolk sac decreases in size and a smaller **secondary (definitive) yolk sac** forms (Fig. 4–3B). This smaller yolk sac is formed by extraembryonic endodermal cells that migrate inside the primary yolk sac from the hypoblast of the embryonic disc (Fig. 4–4). During formation of the secondary yolk sac, a large part of the primary yolk sac is pinched off. The yolk sac contains fluid but no yolk. It may have a role in the selective transfer of nutritive materials to the embryonic disc. The trophoblast absorbs nutritive fluid from the lacunar networks in the syncytiotrophoblast, which is transferred to the embryo.

DEVELOPMENT OF THE CHORIONIC SAC

The end of the second week is characterized by the appearance of **primary chorionic villi** (Figs. 4–3 and 4–5). Proliferation of cytotrophoblast cells produces cellular extensions that grow into the overlying syncytiotrophoblast. The growth of the cytotrophoblastic extensions is thought to be induced by the underlying **extraembryonic somatic mesoderm**. The cellular projections form primary chorionic villi, the first stage in the development of the chorionic villi of the placenta.

The Placenta as an Allograft

Because the chorionic sac forms part of the placenta, the conceptus, which inherits both paternal and maternal genes, can be regarded as an allograft in the uterus with respect to the mother. What protects the placenta from rejection by the mother's immune system? This question has puzzled embryologists and immunologists for a long time and remains an active area of research. Syncytiotrophoblastic cells of the floating chorionic villi, although exposed to maternal immune cells within the blood sinusoids, lack major histocom-

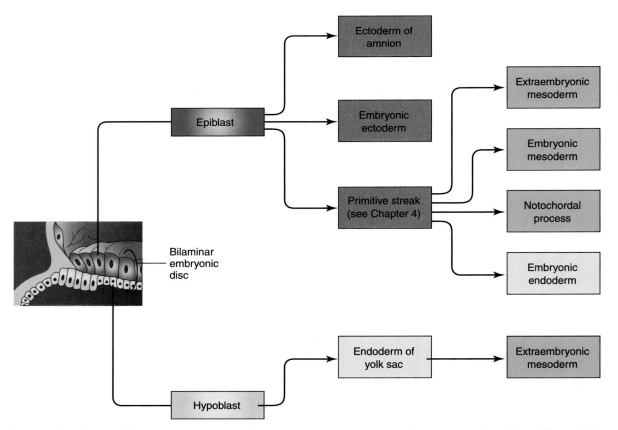

■ **Figure 4–4.** Origin of tissues in the embryo. The colors in the boxes are used in drawings of sections of conceptuses.

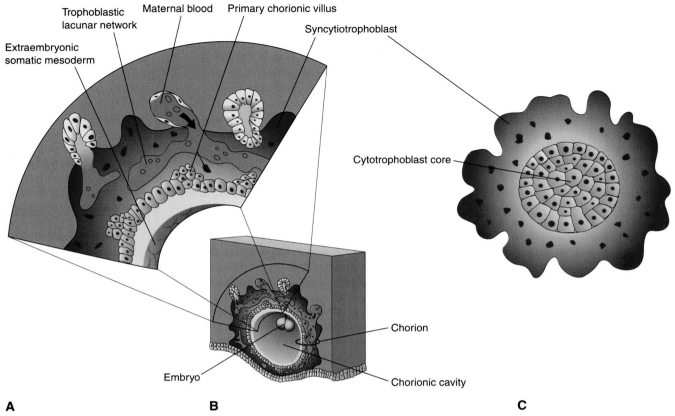

■ **Figure 4–5.** *A,* Detail of the section (outlined in *B*) of the wall of the chorionic sac. *B,* Sketch of a 14-day conceptus illustrating the chorionic sac and the shaggy appearance created by the primary villi (×6). *C,* Drawing of a transverse section through a primary chorionic villus (×400).

patibility (MHC) antigens and thus do not evoke rejection responses (Faulk and Temple, 1976; Lala et al, 1984; Vince and Johnson, 1996). However, extravillous cytotrophoblastic cells, which break out of the anchoring villi and invade uterine decidual tissue, express class I MHC antigens (Sunderland et al, 1981). These cells remain exposed to two types of maternal immune cells within the decidua—T lymphocytes and natural killer (NK) lymphocytes—and therefore are potential targets of immune attack (Lala, 1990). Protection of these cells is believed to be mediated by at least two mechanisms.

First, the unique, nonpolymorphic nature of the class I MHC antigens (HLA-G) expressed by the extravillous trophoblast (Ellis et al, 1986; Kovats et al, 1990) makes these antigens poorly recognizable by T lymphocytes and yet recognizable by NK cells, turning off their killer function (Carosella et al, 1996; Vince and Johnson, 1996; King et al, 1997).

Second, decidual cells produce locally active immunosuppression molecules, such as prostaglandin E_2, which prevent activation of T cells and NK cells within the decidua (Lala et al, 1988; Parhar et al, 1988; Parhar et al, 1989; Lala, 1990). Indeed, the immunoregulatory function of decidual cells is consistent with their life history. It has been shown that uterine endometrial stromal cells that differentiate into decidual cells during pregnancy are derived from progenitor (stem) cells that migrate from the hematopoietic organs such as the fetal liver and bone marrow (Lysiak and Lala, 1992).

The extraembryonic coelom splits the extraembryonic mesoderm into two layers (Fig. *4–3B* and *C*):

- *Extraembryonic somatic mesoderm,* lining the trophoblast and covering the amnion
- *Extraembryonic splanchnic mesoderm,* surrounding the yolk sac

The extraembryonic somatic mesoderm and the two

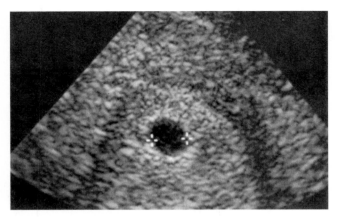

■ **Figure 4–6.** Transverse endovaginal sonogram of an early chorionic (gestational) sac. The mean sac diameter is the distance between the cursors (∗). (From Filly RA: Ultrasound evaluation during the first trimester. *In* Callen PW (ed): *Ultrasonography in Obstetrics and Gynecology*, 3rd ed. Philadelphia, WB Saunders, 1994.)

layers of trophoblast constitute the **chorion**. *The chorion forms the wall of the chorionic sac* (gestational sac), within which the embryo and its amniotic and yolk sacs are suspended by the connecting stalk. The extraembryonic coelom is now called the **chorionic**

cavity. The amniotic sac (with the embryonic epiblast forming its "floor") and the yolk sac (with the embryonic hypoblast forming its "roof") are analogous to two balloons pressed together (site of embryonic disc) and suspended by a cord (connecting stalk) from the inside of a larger balloon (chorionic sac).

Transvaginal ultrasonography is used for measuring chorionic (gestational) sac diameter (Fig. 4–6). This measurement is valuable for evaluating very early embryonic development and pregnancy outcome (Filly, 1994b). The 14-day embryo still has the form of a flat bilaminar embryonic disc, but endodermal cells in a localized area are now columnar and form a thickened circular area called the **prechordal (prochordal) plate** (Fig. 4–3*B* and *C*). This plate indicates the future site of the mouth and *an important organizer of the head region.*

IMPLANTATION SITES OF THE BLASTOCYST

Implantation of the blastocyst begins at the end of the first week and usually occurs in the endometrium of the uterus, usually superiorly in the body of the uterus, slightly more often on the posterior than on the anterior wall. Implantation of a blastocyst can be

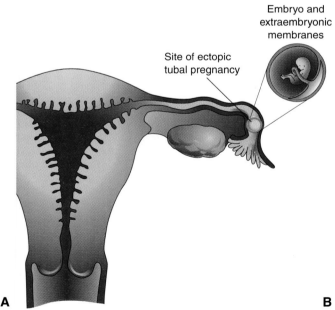

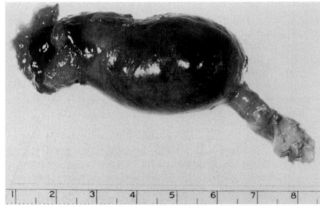

■ **Figure 4–7.** *A*, Coronal section of the uterus and tube illustrating an ectopic tubal pregnancy. *B*, Photograph of an unruptured ectopic tubal pregnancy in the ampulla of the uterine tube. (From Page EW, Villee CA, Villee DB: *Human Reproduction: Essentials of Reproductive and Perinatal Medicine*, 3rd ed. Philadelphia, WB Saunders, 1981.)

detected by ultrasonography and highly sensitive radio-immunoassays of hCG during the second week (Filly, 1994b).

Placenta Previa

Implantation of a blastocyst in the inferior segment of the uterus near the internal os (opening) results in *placenta previa*, a placenta that partially or completely covers the os (see Fig. 4-8). Placenta previa may cause bleeding because of premature separation of the placenta during pregnancy.

Extrauterine Implantation Sites

Blastocysts may implant outside the uterus. Extrauterine implantations result in **ectopic pregnancies** (Filly, 1994a); 95 to 97% of ectopic implantations occur in the uterine tube. *Most ectopic pregnancies are in the ampulla and isthmus of the uterine tube* (Fig. 4-7). Ectopic tubal pregnancy occurs in about 1 in 200 pregnancies in North America. The highest rates of ectopic pregnancy are in women 35 years of age or older and in women who are nonwhite (Rubin, 1983); however, "all women of childbearing age are at risk of harboring an ectopic gestation."

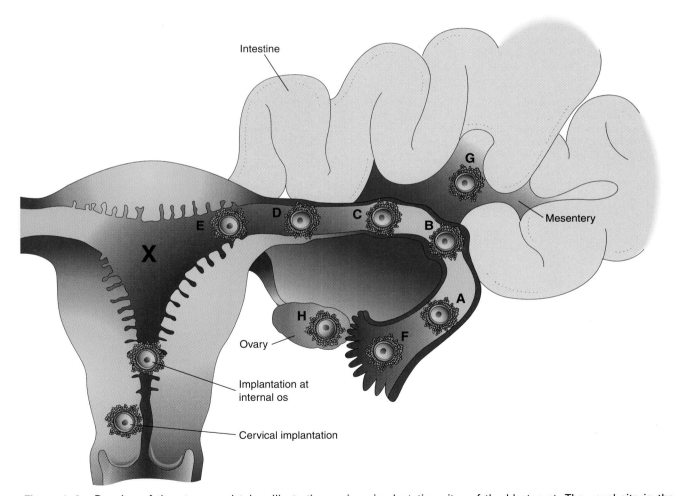

■ **Figure 4-8.** Drawing of the uterus and tubes illustrating various implantation sites of the blastocyst. The usual site in the posterior wall of the uterus is indicated by an X. The approximate order of frequency of ectopic implantations is indicated alphabetically (*A*, most common; *H*, least common). *A* to *F*, Tubal pregnancies. *G*, Abdominal pregnancy. *H*, Ovarian pregnancy. Tubal pregnancies are the most common type of ectopic pregnancy.

A woman with a tubal pregnancy has signs and symptoms of pregnancy (e.g., misses her menstrual period). She may also experience abdominal pain and tenderness because of distention of the uterine tube, abnormal bleeding, and irritation of the pelvic peritoneum. The pain may be confused with *appendicitis* if the pregnancy is in the right uterine tube. Ectopic pregnancies produce hCG at a slower rate than normally implanted pregnancies (Cartwright and DiPietro, 1984); consequently, assays may give false-negative tests if performed too early. *Endovaginal (intravaginal) sonography* is very helpful in the early detection of ectopic pregnancies (Filly, 1994a).

There are *several causes of tubal pregnancy*, but they are often related to factors that delay or prevent transport of the cleaving zygote to the uterus (e.g., by mucosal adhesions or blockage caused by scarring resulting from infection in the abdominopelvic cavity such as *pelvic inflammatory disease*). Ectopic tubal pregnancies usually result in rupture of the uterine tube and hemorrhage into the peritoneal cavity during the first 8 weeks, followed by death of the embryo. Tubal rupture and hemorrhage constitute a threat to the mother's life and so are of major clinical importance. The affected tube and conceptus are usually surgically removed (Fig. 4–7*B*).

Blastocysts that implant in the ampulla or in fimbriae of the uterine tube (Fig. 4–8) are often expelled into the peritoneal cavity, where they commonly implant in the rectouterine pouch, a pouch of peritoneum between the rectum and the uterus (Fig. 4–9). In excep-

tional cases, an **abdominal pregnancy** may continue to full term and the fetus may be delivered alive through an abdominal incision. Usually, however, an abdominal pregnancy creates a serious condition because the placenta attaches to abdominal organs, which causes considerable intraperitoneal bleeding.

Cervical implantations are unusual (Fig. 4–8); some of these pregnancies are not recognized because the conceptus is aborted during early gestation. In other cases, the placenta becomes firmly attached to fibrous and muscular parts of the cervix, often resulting in bleeding and subsequent surgical intervention, such as *hysterectomy* (excision of uterus). For more discussions of the clinical implications of ectopic pregnancy, see Moore and Persaud (1998).

Spontaneous Abortion of Early Embryos

Abortion is commonly defined as the termination of pregnancy before 20 weeks' gestation, before the period of viability of the embryo or fetus. Most abortions of embryos during the first 3 weeks occur spontaneously. *Sporadic* and *recurrent spontaneous abortions* are two of the most common gynecologic problems (Hill, 1995). The frequency of early abortions is diffi-

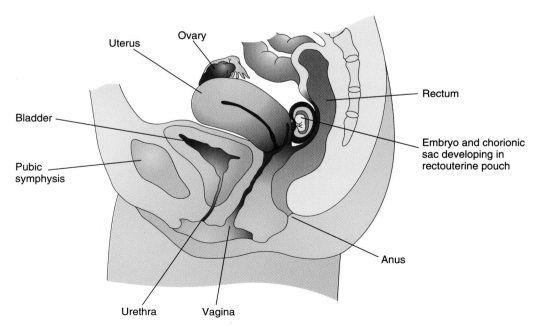

■ **Figure 4–9.** Drawing of a median section of a female pelvis illustrating an abdominal pregnancy. Although a blastocyst expelled from the uterine tube may attach to any organ or to the mesentery of the intestines, it commonly attaches to the peritoneum in the rectouterine pouch.

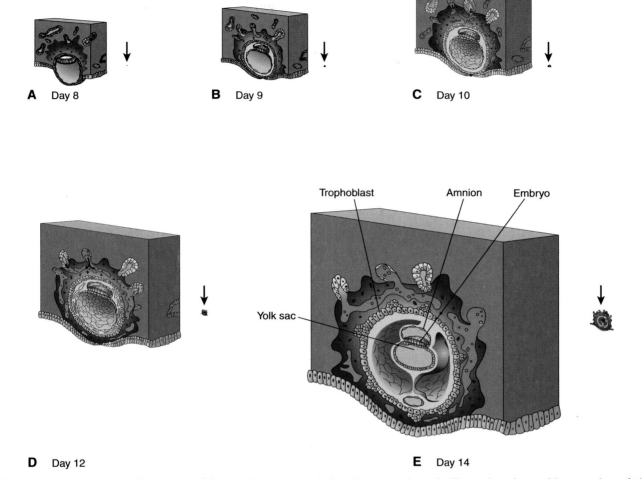

A   Day 8   **B**   Day 9   **C**   Day 10

D   Day 12   **E**   Day 14

■ **Figure 4–10.** Drawings of sections of human blastocysts during the second week, illustrating the rapid expansion of the trophoblast and the relatively minute size of the conceptuses (×25); the sketches indicated by arrows show the actual size of the blastocysts.

cult to establish because they often occur before women are aware that they are pregnant. An abortion occurring just after the first missed period is very likely to be mistaken for a delayed menstruation. Detection of a conceptus in the menses (menstrual blood) is very difficult because of its small size (Fig. 4-10E).

Study of most early spontaneous abortions resulting from medical problems reveal abnormal conceptuses. Hertig et al (1959) studied 34 early embryos recovered from women of known fertility and found 10 of them so abnormal that they probably would have aborted spontaneously by the end of the second week of development. Hertig (1967) estimated that of the 70 to 75% of blastocysts that implant, only 58% survive to the end of the second week. He further estimated that

16% of this latter group would be abnormal and would abort in a week or so. The incidence of chromosomal abnormalities in early spontaneous abortions is about 61% (Boué et al, 1975).

Summarizing the data of several studies, Carr and Gedeon (1977) estimated that 50% of all known spontaneous abortions result from chromosomal abnormalities. The higher incidence of early abortions in older women probably results from the increasing frequency of *nondisjunction of chromosomes* during oogenesis (see Chapter 2). It has been estimated that from one third to one half of all zygotes never become blastocysts and implant. Failure of blastocysts to implant may result from a poorly developed endometrium; however, in many cases lethal chromosomal abnormalities in the zygote probably cause the abortion.

SUMMARY OF IMPLANTATION OF THE BLASTOCYST

Implantation of the blastocyst begins at the end of the first week and is completed by the end of the second week. Implantation may be summarized as follows:

- The zona pellucida surrounding the oocyte degenerates (day 5). Its disappearance results from enlargement of the blastocyst and degeneration caused by enzymatic lysis. The lytic enzymes are released from the acrosomes of the sperms that surround and partially penetrate the zona pellucida.
- The blastocyst adheres to the endometrial epithelium (day 6).
- The trophoblast begins to differentiate into two layers—syncytiotrophoblast and cytotrophoblast (day 7).
- The syncytiotrophoblast erodes endometrial tissues (capillaries, glands, and connective tissue), and the blastocyst starts to embed in the endometrium (day 8).
- Blood-filled lacunae appear in the syncytiotrophoblast (day 9).
- The blastocyst sinks beneath the endometrial epithelium, and the defect in the endometrial epithelium is filled by a closing plug (day 10).
- Lacunar networks form by fusion of adjacent lacunae (days 10 and 11).
- The syncytiotrophoblast erodes endometrial blood vessels, allowing maternal blood to seep in and out of lacunar networks, thereby establishing a *primitive uteroplacental circulation* (days 11 and 12).
- The defect in the endometrial epithelium gradually disappears as the endometrial epithelium is repaired (days 12 and 13).
- Primary chorionic villi develop (days 13 and 14).

Inhibition of Implantation

The administration of relatively large doses of estrogens ("morning-after pills") for several days, beginning shortly after unprotected sexual intercourse, usually does not prevent fertilization but often prevents implantation of the blastocyst. *Diethylstilbestrol* given daily in high dosage may also accelerate passage of the dividing zygote along the uterine tube (Kalant et al, 1990). Normally, the endometrium progresses to the secretory phase of the menstrual cycle as the zygote forms, undergoes cleavage, and enters the uterus. The large amount of estrogen disturbs the normal balance between estrogen and progesterone that is necessary for preparation of the endometrium for implantation of the blastocyst. Postconception administration of hormones to prevent implantation of the blastocyst is sometimes used in cases of sexual assault or leakage of a condom, but this treatment is contraindicated for routine contraceptive use. The "abortion pill" *RU486* also destroys the conceptus by interrupting implantation because of interference with the hormonal environment of the implanting embryo.

An *intrauterine device* (IUD) inserted into the uterus through the vagina and cervix usually interferes with implantation by causing a local inflammatory reaction. Some IUDs contain progesterone that is slowly released and interferes with the development of the endometrium so that implantation does not usually occur.

SUMMARY OF SECOND WEEK OF DEVELOPMENT

Rapid proliferation and differentiation of the trophoblast are important features of the second week (Fig. 4–10). These processes occur as the blastocyst completes its implantation in the endometrium. The various endometrial changes resulting from the adaptation of these tissues to implantation are known as the **decidual reaction**. Concurrently, the *primary yolk sac* forms and extraembryonic mesoderm arises from the endoderm of the yolk sac as well as from the primitive streak. The extraembryonic coelom forms from cavities that develop in the *extraembryonic mesoderm*. The extraembryonic coelom later becomes the **chorionic cavity**. The primary yolk sac becomes smaller and gradually disappears as the secondary or definitive yolk sac develops. As these changes occur,

- The **amniotic cavity** appears as a space between the cytotrophoblast and the inner cell mass, or embryoblast.
- The inner cell mass differentiates into a **bilaminar embryonic disc** consisting of *epiblast*, related to the amniotic cavity, and *hypoblast*, adjacent to the blastocyst cavity.
- The **prechordal plate** develops as a localized thickening of the hypoblast (primordial endoderm), which indicates the future cranial region of the embryo and the future site of the mouth; the prechordal plate is also an important organizer of the head region.

Clinically Oriented Questions

1. What is meant by the term *implantation bleeding*? Is this menses (menstrual fluid)?
2. Can drugs taken during the first 2 weeks of pregnancy cause congenital anomalies of the embryo?

3. Recently I heard the term *interception* used in reference to birth control. What does it mean? Does this method prevent conception?

4. Can an ectopic pregnancy occur in a woman who has an IUD?

5. Can a blastocyst that implants in the abdomen develop into a living, full-term fetus? How would it be delivered?

6. Does combined intrauterine and abdominal pregnancy occur?

The answers to these questions are given at the back of the book.

REFERENCES AND SUGGESTED READING

Bianchi DW, Wilkins-Haug LE, Enders AC, Hay ED: Origin of extraembryonic mesoderm in experimental animals: Relevance to chorionic mosaicism in humans. *Am J Med Genet* 46:542, 1993.

Boué J, Boué A, Lazar P: Retrospective and prospective epidemiological studies of 1500 karyotyped spontaneous abortions. *Teratology* 12:11, 1975.

Carlson BM: *Human Embryology and Developmental Biology*. St. Louis, CV Mosby, 1994.

Carosella ED, Dausset J, Kirszenbaum M: HLA-G revisited. *Immunol Today* 17:404, 1996.

Carr DH, Gedeon M: Population cytogenetics of human abortuses. *In* Hook EB, Porter IH (eds): *Population Cytogenetics: Studies in Humans*. New York, Academic Press, 1977.

Cartwright PS, DiPietro DL: Ectopic pregnancy: Changes in serum human chorionic gonadotropin concentration. *Obstet Gynecol* 63:76, 1984.

Ellis SA, Sargeant IL, Redman CWG, McMichael AJ: Evidence for a novel HLA antigen found on human extravillous trophoblast and a choriocarcinoma cell line. *Immunology* 59:595, 1986.

Faulk WP, Temple A: Distribution of beta-2 microglobulin and HLA in chorionic villi of human placentae. *Nature* 262:799, 1976.

Filly RA: Ectopic pregnancy. *In* Callen PW (ed): *Ultrasonography in Obstetrics and Gynecology*, 3rd ed. Philadelphia, WB Saunders, 1994a.

Filly RA: Ultrasound evaluation during the first trimester. *In* Callen PW (ed): *Ultrasonography in Obstetrics and Gynecology*, 3rd ed. Philadelphia, WB Saunders, 1994b.

Gilbert SF: *Developmental Biology*, 5th ed. Sunderland, Sinauer Associates, 1997.

Hertig AT: The overall problem in man. *In* Benirschke K (ed): *Comparative Aspects of Reproductive Failure*. New York, Springer Verlag, 1967.

Hertig AT, Rock J, Adams EC: A description of 34 human ova within the first seventeen days of development. *Am J Anat* 98:435, 1956.

Hertig AT, Rock J, Adams EC, Menkin MC: Thirty-four fertilized human ova, good, bad and indifferent, recovered from 210 women of known fertility. *Pediatrics* 23:202, 1959.

Hill JA: T-helper 1–type immunity to trophoblast: Evidence for a new immunological mechanism for recurrent abortion in women. *Hum Reprod* 10(suppl 2):114, 1995.

Kalant H, Roschlau WHE, Hickie RA: *Essentials of Medical Pharmacology*. Toronto, BC Decker, 1990.

King A, Loke YW, Chaouat G: NK cells and reproduction. *Immunol Today* 18:64, 1997.

Kovats S, Main EK, Librach C, et al: A class 1 antigen, HLA-G, expressed in human trophoblasts. *Science* 18:220, 1990.

Lala PK: Similarities between immunoregulation in pregnancy and malignancy: The role of prostaglandin E_2 [editorial]. *Am J Reprod Immunol* 20:147, 1990.

Lala PK, Kearns M, Colavincenzo V: Cells of the fetomaternal interface: Their role in the maintenance of viviparous pregnancy. *Am J Anat* 170:501, 1984.

Lala PK, Kennedy TG, Parhar RS: Suppression of lymphocyte alloreactivity by early gestational human decidua. II. Characterization of suppressor mechanisms. *Cell Immunol* 116:411, 1988.

Lysiak JJ, Lala PK: *In situ* localization and characterization of bone marrow–derived cells in the decidua of normal murine pregnancy. *Biol Reprod* 47:603, 1992.

Moore KL: *Clinically Oriented Anatomy*, 3rd ed. Baltimore, Williams & Wilkins, 1992.

Moore KL, Persaud TVN: *The Developing Human: Clinically Oriented Embryology*, 6th ed. Philadelphia, WB Saunders, 1998.

Parhar RS, Kennedy TG, Lala PK: Suppression of lymphocyte alloreactivity by early gestational human decidua. 1. Characterization of suppressor cells and suppressor molecules. *Cell Immunol* 116:392, 1988.

Parhar RS, Yagel S, Lala PK: PGE_2-mediated immunosuppression by first trimester human decidual cells blocks activation of maternal leukocytes in the decidua with potential antitrophoblast activity. *Cell Immunol* 120:61, 1989.

Rubin GL: Ectopic pregnancy in the United States: 1970 through 1978. *JAMA* 249:1725, 1983.

Saji F, Kameda T, Koyama M, et al: Impaired susceptibility of human trophoblast to MHC nonrestricted killer cells: Implication in the maternal-fetal relationship. *Am J Reprod Immunol* 19:108, 1989.

Sunderland CA, Redman CWG, Stirrat GM: HLA-A, B, C antigens are expressed on nonvillous trophoblasts of the early human placenta. *J Immunol* 127:2614, 1981.

Vince GS, Johnson PM: Reproductive immunology, conception, contraception and consequence. *Immunologist* 4:172, 1996.

The Third Week of Human Development

5

■ Rapid development of the embryo from the embryonic disc during the early part of the third week is characterized by

- Appearance of the primitive streak
- Development of the notochord
- Differentiation of three germ layers from which all embryonic tissues and organs develop

The third week of embryonic development occurs during the week following the first missed menstrual period, that is, 5 weeks after the onset of the last normal menstrual period (LNMP).

Cessation of menstruation is the first indication that a woman may be pregnant; however, missing a menstrual period is not always a certain sign of pregnancy; for example, delay of menstruation may result from emotional shock or illness.

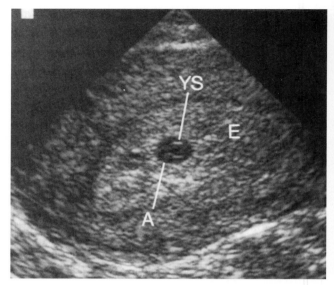

■ **Figure 5–1.** Endovaginal sonogram of a conceptus about 3 weeks after conception, showing the amnion (A) and yolk sac (YS). The endometrium (E) surrounding the conceptus is also visible. (From Filly RA: Ultrasound evaluation during the first trimester. *In* Callen PW (ed): *Ultrasonography in Obstetrics and Gynecology,* 3rd ed. Philadelphia, WB Saunders, 1994.)

Pregnancy Tests

Relatively simple and rapid tests are now available for detecting pregnancy. Most tests depend on the presence of an *early pregnancy factor* (EPF) in the maternal serum and *human chorionic gonadotropin* (hCG), a hormone produced by the syncytiotrophoblast and excreted in the mother's urine. The EPF can be detected 24 to 48 hours after fertilization, and the production of hCG is sufficient to give a positive indication of pregnancy early in the second week of development. About 3 weeks after conception, approximately 5 weeks after the LNMP (Fig. 5–1), a normal pregnancy can be detected with ultrasonography (Filly, 1994).

A frequent symptom of pregnancy is nausea and vomiting, which may occur by the end of the third week; however, the time of onset of these symptoms is variable. Vaginal bleeding at the expected time of menstruation does not rule out pregnancy because there may be a slight loss of blood from the implantation site of the blastocyst. *Implantation bleeding* results from leakage of blood into the uterine cavity from disrupted endometrial lacunae around the implanted blastocyst. When such bleeding is interpreted as menstruation, an error occurs initially in determining the *expected date of confinement* (EDC) and delivery date of the baby.

GASTRULATION: FORMATION OF GERM LAYERS

Gastrulation is the process by which the bilaminar embryonic disc (Fig. 5–2*A*) is converted into a trilaminar embryonic disc. *Gastrulation is the beginning of morphogenesis* (development of body form) and is the significant event occurring during the third week. Gastrulation begins with formation of the **primitive streak** on the surface of the epiblast of the embryonic disc (Fig. 5–2*B*). Each of the three germ layers (ectoderm, mesoderm, and endoderm) gives rise to specific tissues and organs.

- *Ectoderm* gives rise to the epidermis, the central and peripheral nervous systems, the retina of the eye, and various other structures (see Chapter 6).
- *Endoderm* is the source of the epithelial linings of the respiratory passages and gastrointestinal (GI) tract, including the glands opening into the GI tract and the glandular cells of associated organs such as the liver and pancreas.
- Mesoderm gives rise to smooth muscular coats, connective tissues, and vessels associated with the tissues and organs; mesoderm also forms most of the cardiovascular system and is the source of blood cells and bone marrow, the skeleton, striated muscles, and the reproductive and excretory organs.

Formation of the primitive streak, germ layers, prechordal plate, and notochord are the important processes occurring during gastrulation. During this period the embryo is referred to as a *gastrula*.

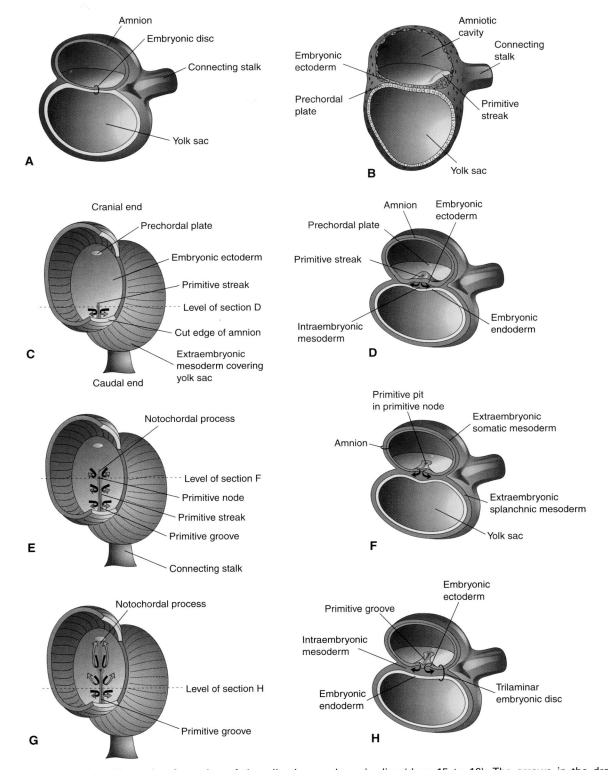

Figure 5–2. Drawings illustrating formation of the trilaminar embryonic disc (days 15 to 16). The arrows in the drawings indicate invagination and migration of mesenchymal cells between the ectoderm and endoderm. *A, C, E,* and *G,* Dorsal views of the embryonic disc early in the third week, exposed by removal of the amnion. *B, D, F,* and *H,* Transverse sections through the embryonic disc at the levels indicated. The prechordal plate, indicating the head region, is depicted by a broken outline because it is a thickening of endoderm that cannot be seen from the dorsal surface.

Primitive Streak

The first sign of gastrulation is the appearance of the primitive streak at the caudal end of the embryo (Fig. 5-2B). At the beginning of the third week, an opacity formed by a thickened linear band of epiblast, known as the primitive streak, appears caudally in the median plane of the dorsal aspect of the embryonic disc (Fig. 5-3; see also Fig. 5-2C). The primitive streak results from the proliferation and migration of cells of the epiblast to the median plane of the embryonic disc. As the primitive streak elongates by addition of cells to its caudal end, its cranial end proliferates to form a **primitive node** (Figs. 5-2B and C and 5-3). Concurrently, a narrow **primitive groove** develops in the primitive streak that is continuous with a small depression in the primitive node, the **primitive pit**. As soon as the primitive streak appears, it is possible to identify the embryo's craniocaudal axis, its cranial and caudal ends, its dorsal and ventral surfaces, and its right and left sides. The primitive groove and pit result from the invagination (an inward movement) of epiblastic cells, which is indicated by arrows in Figure 5-2E.

Shortly after the primitive streak appears (Fig. 5-4A), cells leave its deep surface and form a loose network of embryonic connective tissue called *mesenchyme,* or mesoblast (Fig. 5-4B). Mesenchyme forms the supporting tissues of the embryo, such as most of the connective tissues of the body and the stromal components or framework of glands. Some mesenchyme forms a layer known as **intraembryonic mesoderm** (Fig. 5-2D). Some cells of the epiblast of the primitive streak also displace the hypoblast forming the **intraembryonic (embryonic) endoderm** in the roof of the yolk sac. Cells remaining in the epiblast form the **intraembryonic (embryonic) ectoderm**. Under the influence of various *embryonic growth factors* (Slack, 1987; Tabin, 1991), mesenchymal cells migrate widely from the primitive streak. These cells have the potential to proliferate and differentiate into diverse types of cells, such as fibroblasts, chondroblasts, and osteoblasts. In summary, cells of the epiblast, through the process of gastrulation, give rise to all three germ layers in the embryo, which are the primordia of all its tissues and organs.

FATE OF PRIMITIVE STREAK

The primitive streak actively forms mesoderm until the early part of the fourth week (Fig. 5-5A to C); thereafter, production of mesoderm slows down. The primitive streak diminishes in relative size and becomes an insignificant structure in the sacrococcygeal region of the embryo (Fig. 5-5D). Normally the primitive streak undergoes degenerative changes and disappears by the end of the fourth week.

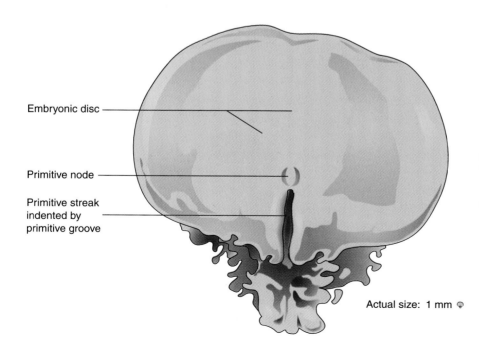

Embryonic disc

Primitive node

Primitive streak indented by primitive groove

Actual size: 1 mm

■ **Figure 5-3.** Photograph of a dorsal view of an embryo about 16 days old. (From Moore KL, Persaud TVN, Shiota K: *Color Atlas of Clinical Embryology.* Philadelphia, WB Saunders, 1994.)

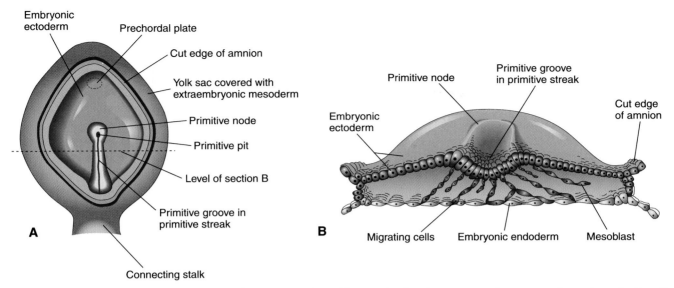

A

- Embryonic ectoderm
- Prechordal plate
- Cut edge of amnion
- Yolk sac covered with extraembryonic mesoderm
- Primitive node
- Primitive pit
- Level of section B
- Primitive groove in primitive streak
- Connecting stalk

B

- Primitive node
- Primitive groove in primitive streak
- Cut edge of amnion
- Embryonic ectoderm
- Migrating cells
- Embryonic endoderm
- Mesoblast

■ **Figure 5–4.** *A,* Drawing of a dorsal view of a 16-day embryo. The amnion has been removed to expose the embryonic disc. *B,* Drawing of the cranial half of the embryonic disc during the third week. The disc has been cut transversely to show the migration of mesenchymal cells from the primitive streak to form mesoblast or mesenchyme that soon organizes to form the intraembryonic mesoderm. This illustration also shows that most of the embryonic endoderm also arises from the epiblast. Most of the hypoblastic cells are displaced to extraembryonic regions such as the wall of the yolk sac.

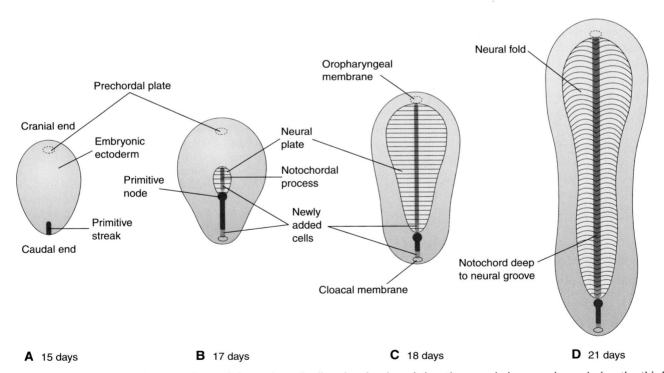

A 15 days   **B** 17 days   **C** 18 days   **D** 21 days

- Neural fold
- Oropharyngeal membrane
- Prechordal plate
- Cranial end
- Embryonic ectoderm
- Neural plate
- Notochordal process
- Primitive node
- Newly added cells
- Primitive streak
- Caudal end
- Cloacal membrane
- Notochord deep to neural groove

■ **Figure 5–5.** Sketches of dorsal views of the embryonic disc showing how it lengthens and changes shape during the third week. The primitive streak lengthens by addition of cells at its caudal end; the notochordal process lengthens by migration of cells from the primitive node. The notochordal process and adjacent mesoderm induce the overlying embryonic ectoderm to form the neural plate, the primordium of the central nervous system. Observe that as the notochordal process elongates, the primitive streak shortens. At the end of the third week the notochordal process is transformed into the notochord. Note that the embryonic disc is originally egg-shaped but soon becomes pear-shaped and then slipperlike as the notochord develops.

Sacrococcygeal Teratoma

Remnants of the primitive streak may persist and give rise to a large tumor known as a *sacrococcygeal teratoma* (Fig. 5-6). Because they are derived from pleuripotent primitive streak cells, these tumors contain various types of tissues containing elements of the three germ layers in incomplete stages of differentiation. Sacrococcygeal teratomas are the most common tumor in newborns and have an incidence of about 1 in 35,000 newborns (Holzgreve et al, 1991; Marina, 1996). The incidence of malignancy in sacrococcygeal teratomas increases from 10% at birth to 50 to 70% at 2 months

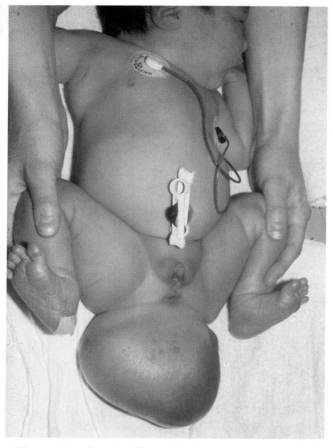

■ **Figure 5–6.** Female infant with a large sacrococcygeal teratoma that developed from remnants of the primitive streak. The tumor, a neoplasm made up of several different types of tissue, was surgically removed. About 76% of infants with these tumors are female; the reason for this preponderance is unknown. (Courtesy of Dr. A. E. Chudley, Section of Genetics and Metabolism, Department of Pediatrics and Child Health, Children's Hospital, University of Manitoba, Winnipeg, Manitoba, Canada.)

of age (Marina, 1996). These tumors are usually surgically excised promptly, and the prognosis is good.

NOTOCHORDAL PROCESS AND NOTOCHORD

Some mesenchymal cells migrate cranially from the primitive node and pit, forming a median cellular cord, the **notochordal process** (Fig. 5-7A to C). This process soon acquires a lumen, the **notochordal canal**. The notochordal process grows cranially between the ectoderm and endoderm until it reaches the **prechordal plate** (prochordal plate), a small circular area of columnar endodermal cells. The rodlike notochordal process can extend no farther because the prechordal plate is firmly attached to the overlying ectoderm. These fused layers form the **oropharyngeal membrane** located at the future site of the oral cavity (mouth).

Some mesenchymal cells from the primitive streak and notochordal process migrate laterally and cranially between the ectoderm and mesoderm, until they reach the margins of the embryonic disc. There, these cells are continuous with the extraembryonic mesoderm covering the amnion and yolk sac (Fig. 5-2C). This extraembryonic mesoderm is derived from the endoderm of the yolk sac; see Chapter 4). Some cells from the primitive streak migrate cranially on each side of the notochordal process and around the prechordal plate. Here they meet cranially to form the cardiogenic mesoderm in the **cardiogenic area**, where the primordium of the heart begins to develop at the end of the third week.

Caudal to the primitive streak there is a circular area — the **cloacal membrane** — which indicates the future site of the anus (Fig. 5-7E). The embryonic disc remains bilaminar here and at the **oropharyngeal membrane** because the embryonic ectoderm and endoderm are fused at these sites, thereby preventing migration of mesenchymal cells between them (Fig. 5-8A to C). By the middle of the third week, intraembryonic mesoderm separates the ectoderm and endoderm everywhere except

- At the oropharyngeal membrane cranially
- In the median plane cranial to the primitive node, where the notochordal process is located
- At the cloacal membrane caudally

The **notochord** is a cellular rod that develops by transformation of the notochordal process. The notochord

- Defines the primordial axis of the embryo and gives it some rigidity

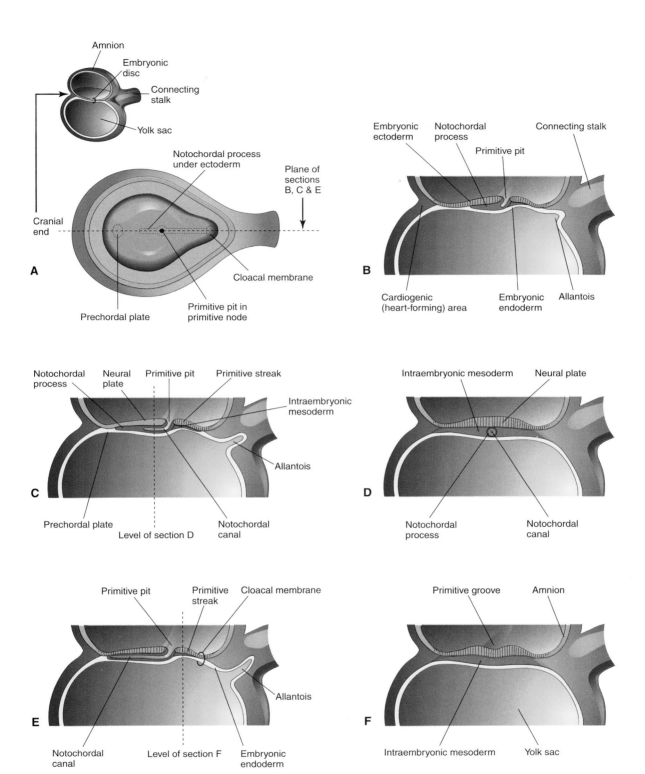

■ **Figure 5-7.** Drawings illustrating development of the notochordal process. The small sketch at the upper left is for orientation; the short arrow indicates the dorsal aspect of the embryonic disc. *A,* Dorsal view of the embryonic disc (about 16 days), exposed by removal of the amnion. The notochordal process is shown as if it were visible through the embryonic ectoderm. *B, C,* and *E,* Median sections at the plane shown in *A,* illustrating successive stages in the development of the notochordal process and canal. Stages shown in *C* and *E* occur at about 18 days. *D* and *F,* Transverse sections through the embryonic disc at the levels shown in *C* and *E.*

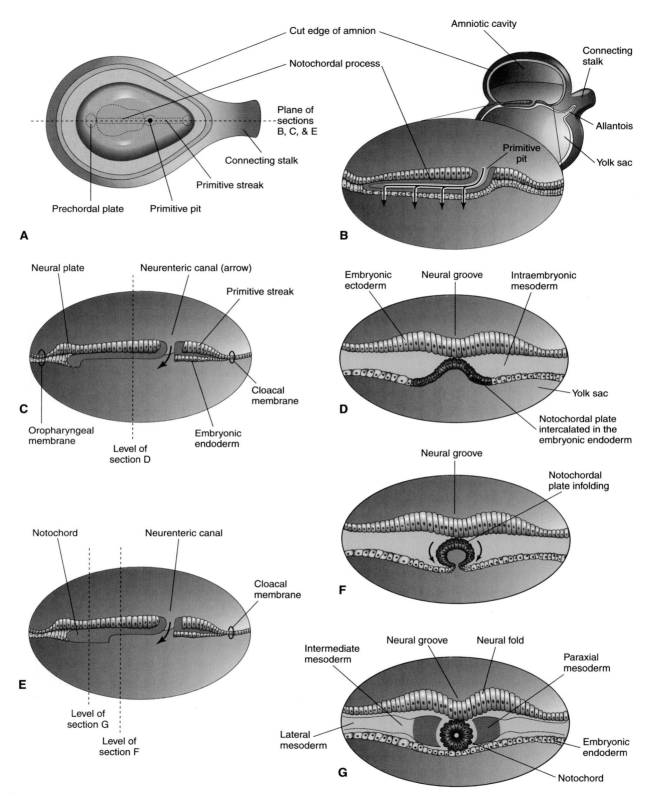

■ **Figure 5–8.** Drawings illustrating further development of the notochord by transformation of the notochordal process. *A,* Dorsal view of the embryonic disc (about 18 days), exposed by removing the amnion. *B,* Three-dimensional median section of the embryo. C and E, Similar sections of slightly older embryos. *D, F,* and *G,* Transverse sections of the trilaminar embryonic disc shown in *C* and *E.*

- Serves as the basis for the development of the axial skeleton (bones of head and vertebral column)
- Indicates the future site of the vertebral bodies

The notochord develops as follows:

- The notochordal process elongates by invagination of cells from the primitive pit (Fig. 5 – 5*B* and *C*).
- The primitive pit extends into the notochordal process, forming the *notochordal canal* (Fig. 5 – 7*B* to *E*).
- The notochordal process is now a cellular tube that extends cranially from the primitive node to the prechordal plate.
- The floor of the notochordal process fuses with the underlying intraembryonic endoderm of the yolk sac.
- The fused layers gradually undergo degeneration, resulting in the formation of openings in the floor of the notochordal process, which brings the notochordal canal into communication with the yolk sac (Fig. 5 – 8*B*).
- The openings rapidly become confluent, and the floor of the notochordal canal disappears (Fig. 5 – 8*C*); the remains of the notochordal process form a flattened, grooved *notochordal plate* (Fig. 5 – 8*D*).
- Beginning at the cranial end of the embryo, the notochordal cells proliferate and the notochordal plate infolds to form the rod-shaped notochord (Fig. 5 – 8*F* and *G*).
- The proximal part of the notochordal canal persists temporarily as the *neurenteric canal* (Fig. 5 – 8*C* and *E*), which forms a transitory communication between the amniotic and yolk sac cavities. When development of the notochord is complete, the neurenteric canal is normally obliterated.
- The notochord becomes detached from the endoderm of the yolk sac, which again becomes a continuous layer (Fig. 5 – 7*G*).

Three-dimensional reconstruction studies on serial sections of human embryos revealed that the cranial end of the notochord is complex with a forked termination; the caudal end also appear to branch, with separated fragments of chordal tissue (Salisbury et al, 1993). The notochord is an intricate structure around which the vertebral column forms (see Chapter 16). It extends from the oropharyngeal membrane to the primitive node. The notochord degenerates and disappears as the bodies of the vertebrae form, but it persists as the *nucleus pulposus* of each intervertebral disc. See Moore and Agur (1995) for a description and illustrations of the intervertebral discs.

The notochord functions as the primary inductor in the early embryo; "it is a prime mover in a series of signal-calling episodes that ultimately transform unspecialized embryonic cells into definitive adult tissues and organs" (Carlson, 1994). The developing notochord induces the overlying embryonic ectoderm to thicken and form the **neural plate** (Fig. 5 – 8*C*), the primordium of the central nervous system (CNS).

The Allantois

The **allantois** (Gr. *allas*, sausage) appears on about day 16 as a small, sausage-shaped diverticulum (outpouching) from the caudal wall of the yolk sac that extends into the connecting stalk (Fig. 5 – 7*B*, *C*, and *E*). The allantois is a large saclike structure in embryos of reptiles, birds, and some mammals that has a respiratory function and/or acts as a reservoir for urine during embryonic life. The allantois remains very small in human embryos because the placenta and amniotic sac take over its functions. The allantois is involved with early blood formation in the human embryo and is associated with development of the urinary bladder (see Chapter 14). As the bladder enlarges, the allantois becomes the urachus, which is represented in adults by the *median umbilical ligament*. The blood vessels of the allantois become the umbilical arteries and veins (see Fig. 5 – 12).

Persistence of Neurenteric Canal

Uncommonly the neurenteric canal persists, giving rise to a very rare congenital anomaly in which the central canal of the spinal cord is connected with the lumen of the intestine.

Remnants of Notochordal Tissue

Both benign and malignant tumors arising from remnants of notochordal tissue have been reported (Salisbury et al, 1993). These *chordomas* grow slowly and infiltrate bone (Rubin and Farber, 1988).

Allantoic Cysts

Allantoic cysts, remnants of the extraembryonic portion of the allantois, are usually found between the fetal umbilical vessels and can be detected by ultrasonography. They are most commonly detected in the proximal part of the umbilical cord, near its attachment to the ventral abdominal wall.

NEURULATION: FORMATION OF NEURAL TUBE

The processes involved in the formation of the neural plate and neural folds and closure of these folds to form the neural tube constitute neurulation. These processes are completed by the end of the fourth week, when closure of the caudal (posterior) neuropore occurs (see Chapter 6). During neurulation, the embryo is referred to as a *neurula*.

Neural Plate and Neural Tube

As the notochord develops, the embryonic ectoderm over it thickens to form an elongated, slipperlike plate of thickened neuroepithelial cells—the **neural plate**. *Neural plate formation is induced by the developing notochord.* The ectoderm of the neural plate (neuroectoderm) gives rise to the **CNS**—the brain and spinal cord. Neuroectoderm also gives rise to various other structures, such as the retina. At first the elongated neural plate corresponds precisely in length to the underlying notochord. It appears cranial to the primitive node and dorsal to the notochord and the mesoderm adjacent to it (Fig. 5-5*B*). As the notochord elongates, the neural plate broadens and eventually extends cranially as far as the oropharyngeal membrane (Figs. 5-5*C* and 5-8*C*). Eventually the neural plate extends beyond the notochord. On about day 18, the neural plate invaginates along its central axis to form a median longitudinal **neural groove,** which has neural folds on each side (Figs. 5-8*G*). The **neural folds** become particularly prominent at the cranial end of the embryo and are *the first signs of brain development.* By the end of the third week, the neural folds have begun to move together and fuse, converting the neural plate into a **neural tube** (Figs. 5-9 and 5-10).

Neural tube formation is a complex, multifactorial process involving extrinsic forces (Smith and Schoenwolf, 1991). The neural tube soon separates from the surface ectoderm. The free edges of the ectoderm fuse so that this layer becomes continuous over the neural tube and back of the embryo (Fig. 5-10*E*). Subsequently, the surface ectoderm differentiates into the epidermis of the skin. Neurulation is completed during the fourth week (see Chapter 6).

Neural Crest Formation

As the neural folds fuse to form the neural tube, some neuroectodermal cells lying along the crest of each neural fold lose their epithelial affinities and attachments to neighboring cells (Fig. 5-10). As the neural tube separates from the surface ectoderm, **neural crest cells** migrate dorsolaterally on each side of the neural tube. They soon form a flattened irregular mass, the **neural crest**, between the neural tube and the overlying surface ectoderm (Fig. 5-10*E* and *F*). The neural crest soon separates into right and left parts that migrate to the dorsolateral aspects of the neural tube. Many neural crest cells migrate in various directions and disperse within the mesenchyme. Although these cells are difficult to identify, special tracer techniques have revealed that neural crest cells disseminate widely.

Neural crest cells give rise to the spinal ganglia (dorsal root ganglia) and the ganglia of the autonomic nervous system. The ganglia of cranial nerves V, VII, IX, and X are also partly derived from neural crest cells. In addition to forming ganglion cells, neural crest cells form the sheaths of peripheral nerves (composed of Schwann cells). They also form the meningeal coverings of the brain and spinal cord (at least the pia mater and arachnoid). Neural crest cells also contribute to the formation of pigment cells, the suprarenal (adrenal) medulla, and several skeletal and muscular components in the head (see Chapter 11).

Congenital Anomalies Resulting from Abnormal Neurulation

Because the neural plate, primordium of the CNS, appears during the third week and gives rise to the neural folds and the beginning of the neural tube, disturbance of neurulation may result in severe abnormalities of the brain and spinal cord (see Chapter 19). **Neural tube defects** (NTDs) are among the most common congenital anomalies (Filly, 1991). The incidence of NTDs has been estimated to be as high as 16 per 10,000 births in the eastern United States (Greenberg et al, 1983). *Meroanencephaly* or anencephaly—partial absence of the brain—is the most severe defect and is also the most common anomaly affecting the CNS (see Chapter 19). Although the term anencephaly (Gr. *an*, without; *enkephalos*, brain) is commonly used, it is a misnomer because the brain is not completely absent. Available evidence suggests that the primary disturbance (e.g., a teratogenic drug; see Chapter 9) affects the neuroectoderm, resulting in failure of the neural folds to fuse and form the neural tube in the brain region. This results in meroanencephaly (absence of forebrain and midbrain and rudimentary development of hindbrain) and *spina bifida cystica* (see Chapter 19).

DEVELOPMENT OF SOMITES

As the notochord and the neural tube form, the intraembryonic mesoderm on each side of them prolifer-

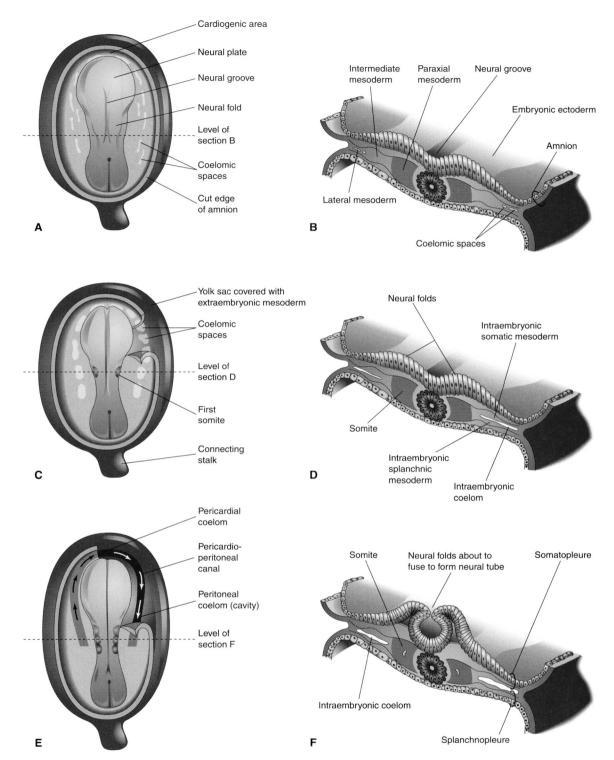

Figure 5–9. Drawings of embryos of 19 to 21 days, illustrating development of the somites and intraembryonic coelom. *A, C,* and *E,* Dorsal view of the embryo, exposed by removal of the amnion. *B, D,* and *F,* Transverse sections through the embryonic disc at the levels shown. *A,* Presomite embryo of about 18 days. *C,* An embryo of about 20 days, showing the first pair of somites. A portion of the somatopleure on the right has been removed to show the isolated coelomic spaces in the lateral mesoderm. *E,* A three-somite embryo (about 21 days), showing the horseshoe-shaped intraembryonic coelom, exposed on the right by removal of a portion of the somatopleure.

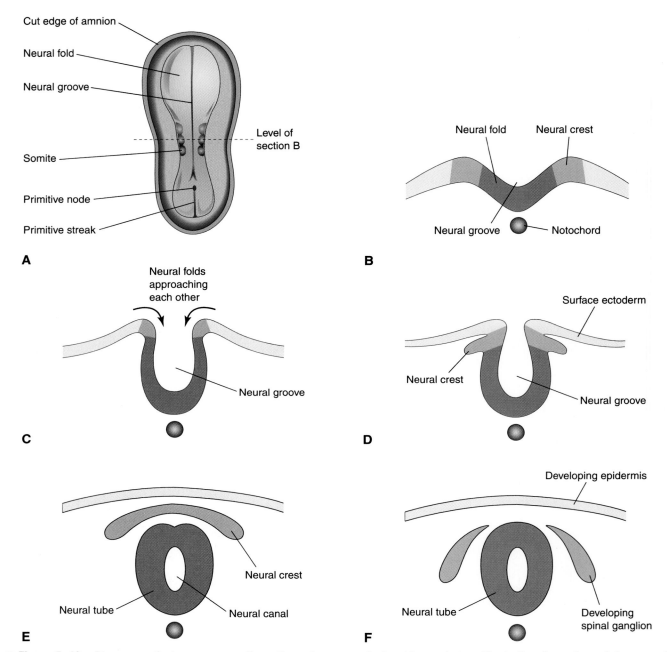

■ **Figure 5–10.** Diagrammatic transverse sections through progressively older embryos, illustrating formation of the neural groove, the neural tube, and the neural crest up to the end of the fourth week.

ates to form a thick, longitudinal column of **paraxial mesoderm** (Figs. 5-8*G* and 5-9*B*). Each column is continuous laterally with the **intermediate mesoderm**, which gradually thins into a layer of lateral mesoderm. The **lateral mesoderm** is continuous with the extraembryonic mesoderm covering the yolk sac and amnion.

Toward the end of the third week, the paraxial mesoderm differentiates and begins to divide into paired cuboidal bodies, the **somites** (Gr. *soma*, body). These blocks of mesoderm are located on each side of the developing neural tube (Fig. 5-9*C* to *E*). About 38 pairs of somites form during the *somite period of development* (days 20 to 30). By the end of the fifth week, 42 to 44 pairs of somites are present. The somites form distinct surface elevations on the embryo and are somewhat triangular in transverse section (Fig. 5–9C to F). An unimportant slitlike cavity, the myocoele, appears within each somite, but it soon disappears. Because the somites are so prominent during the fourth and fifth weeks, they are used as one of the criteria for determining an embryo's age (see Chapter 6, Table 6–1).

The somites first appear in the future occipital region of the embryo but soon extend craniocaudally and give rise to most of the *axial skeleton* (bones of the head and vertebral column) and associated musculature, as well as to the adjacent dermis of the skin (see Chapters 16 and 21). The first pair of somites appears at the end of the third week (Fig. 5–9C) near the cranial end of the notochord. Subsequent pairs form in a craniocaudal sequence.

DEVELOPMENT OF INTRAEMBRYONIC COELOM

The intraembryonic coelom (cavity) first appears as small, isolated *coelomic spaces* in the lateral mesoderm and cardiogenic (heart-forming) mesoderm (Fig. 5–9A to D). These spaces coalesce to form a single horseshoe-shaped cavity—the **intraembryonic coelom** (Fig. 5–9E)—which divides the lateral mesoderm into two layers (Fig. 5–9D):

- A somatic or *parietal layer* that is continuous with the extraembryonic mesoderm covering the amnion
- A splanchnic or *visceral layer* that is continuous with the extraembryonic mesoderm covering the yolk sac

The *somatic mesoderm* and overlying embryonic ectoderm form the embryonic body wall, or **somatopleure** (Fig. 5–9F), whereas the *splanchnic mesoderm* and underlying embryonic endoderm form the embryonic gut wall, or **splanchnopleure**. During the second month, the intraembryonic coelom is divided into three body cavities:

- *Pericardial cavity*
- *Pleural cavities*
- *Peritoneal cavity*

For a description of these divisions of the intraembryonic coelom, see Chapter 10.

EARLY DEVELOPMENT OF CARDIOVASCULAR SYSTEM

At the beginning of the third week, *angiogenesis* (Gr. *angeion*, vessel; *genesis*, production), or blood vessel formation, begins in the extraembryonic mesoderm of the yolk sac, connecting stalk, and chorion (Fig. 5–11). Embryonic blood vessels begin to develop about 2 days later. The early formation of the cardiovascular system is correlated with the absence of a significant amount of yolk in the ovum and yolk sac and the consequent urgent need for blood vessels to bring oxygen and nourishment to the embryo from the maternal circulation through the placenta. At the end of the second week, embryonic nutrition is obtained from the maternal blood by diffusion through the extraembryonic coelom and yolk sac. During the third week a primitive uteroplacental circulation develops (Fig. 5–12).

Angiogenesis and Hematogenesis

Blood vessel formation (angiogenesis) in the embryo and extraembryonic membranes during the third week may be summarized as follows (Fig. 5–11):

- Mesenchymal cells—**angioblasts** (vessel-forming cells)—aggregate to form isolated angiogenic cell clusters—**blood islands**.
- Small cavities appear within the blood islands by confluence of intercellular clefts.
- Angioblasts flatten to form endothelial cells that arrange themselves around the cavities in the blood islands to form the primitive endothelium.
- These endothelium-lined cavities soon fuse to form networks of endothelial channels.
- Vessels extend into adjacent areas by endothelial budding and fusion with other vessels.

Blood cells develop from the endothelial cells of vessels (*hemocytoblasts*) as they develop on the yolk sac and allantois at the end of the third week (Fig. 5–11E and F). Blood formation does not begin in the embryo until the fifth week. It occurs first in various parts of the embryonic mesenchyme, chiefly the liver, and later in the spleen, bone marrow, and lymph nodes. Fetal and adult erythrocytes are probably derived from different hematopoietic precursors (Nakano et al, 1996). The mesenchymal cells surrounding the primordial endothelial blood vessels differentiate into the muscular and connective tissue elements of the vessels.

Primitive Cardiovascular System

The heart and great vessels form from mesenchymal cells in the cardiogenic area (Fig. 5–11B). Paired, endothelium-lined channels—**endocardial heart tubes**—develop during the third week and fuse to form a primordial **heart tube**. The tubular heart joins with blood vessels in the embryo, connecting stalk, cho-

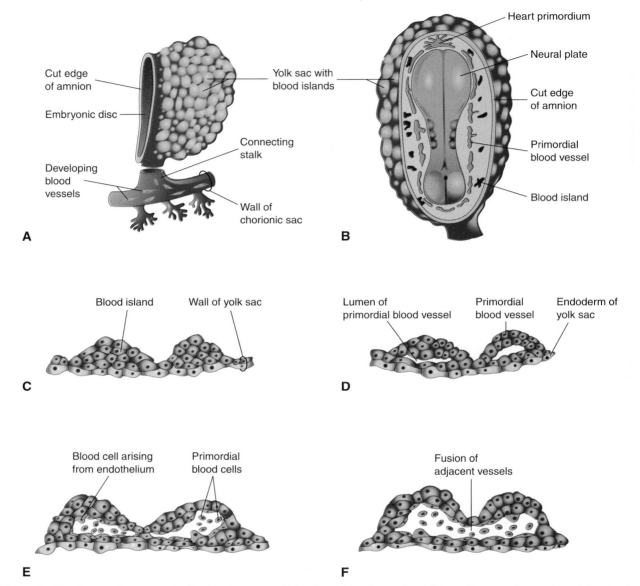

■ **Figure 5–11.** Successive stages in the development of blood and blood vessels. *A,* The yolk sac and a portion of the chorionic sac (about 18 days). *B,* Dorsal view of the embryo exposed by removing the amnion. *C* to *F,* Sections of blood islands showing progressive stages in the development of blood and blood vessels.

rion, and yolk sac to form a primordial cardiovascular system (Fig. 5-12). By the end of the third week, the blood is circulating and the heart begins to beat on the 21st or 22nd day (about 5 weeks after LNMP). The cardiovascular system is thus the first organ system to reach a functional state. The embryonic heart beat can be detected ultrasonographically using a Doppler probe during the fifth week, about 7 weeks after LNMP (Fig. 5-13).

DEVELOPMENT OF CHORIONIC VILLI

Shortly after the **primary chorionic villi** appear at the end of the second week, they begin to branch. Early in the third week, mesenchyme grows into the primary villi, forming a core of loose mesenchymal (connective) tissue. The villi at this stage — **secondary chorionic villi** — cover the entire surface of the chorionic sac (Fig. 5-14A and B). Some mesenchymal cells in the villi soon differentiate into capillaries and blood cells (Fig. 5–14*B* and *C*). When capillaries are visible in the villi, they are called **tertiary chorionic villi** (see Figs. 5–12 and 5–14*D*).

The capillaries in the chorionic villi fuse to form **arteriocapillary networks**, which soon become connected with the embryonic heart through vessels that differentiate in the mesenchyme of the chorion and connecting stalk (Fig. 5–12). By the end of the third

week, embryonic blood begins to flow slowly through the capillaries in the chorionic villi. Oxygen and nutrients in the maternal blood in the intervillous space diffuse through the walls of the villi (*placental membranes*) and enter the embryo's blood (Fig. 5–14*C* and *D*). Carbon dioxide and waste products diffuse from blood in the fetal capillaries through the wall of the villi into the maternal blood.

Concurrently, cytotrophoblast cells of the chorionic

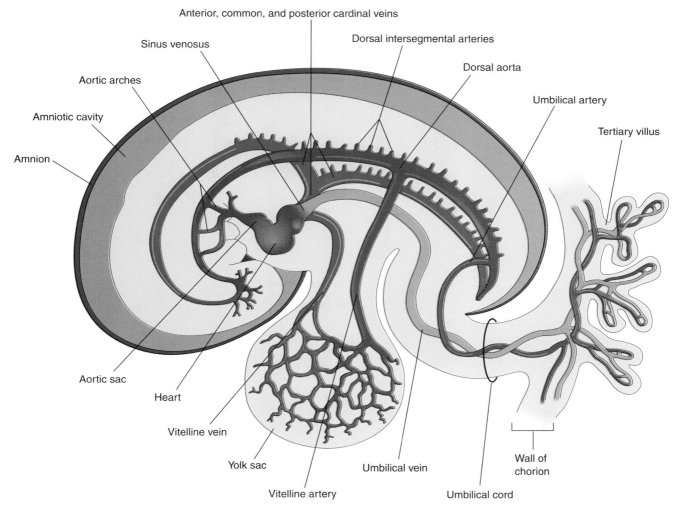

■ **Figure 5–12.** Diagram of the primitive cardiovascular system in an embryo of about 20 days, viewed from the left side. Observe the transitory stage of paired symmetric vessels. Each heart tube continues dorsally into a dorsal aorta that passes caudally. Branches of the aortae are (1) umbilical arteries, establishing connections with vessels in the chorion; (2) vitelline arteries to the yolk sac; and (3) dorsal intersegmental arteries to the body of the embryo. An umbilical vein returns blood from the chorion and divides into right and left umbilical veins within the embryo. Vessels on the yolk sac form a vascular plexus that is connected to the heart tubes by vitelline veins. The anterior cardinal veins return blood from the head region. The umbilical vein is shown in red to indicate that it carries oxygenated blood and nutrients from the chorion (embryonic part of the placenta to the embryo). The arteries are colored medium red to indicate that they are carrying poorly oxygenated blood and waste products to the chorionic villi for transfer to the maternal blood.

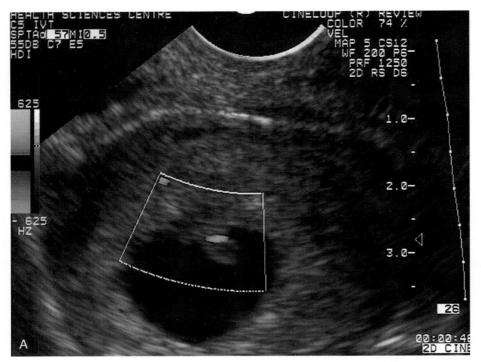

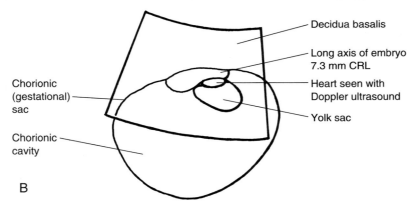

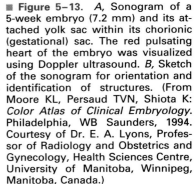

■ **Figure 5-13.** *A,* Sonogram of a 5-week embryo (7.2 mm) and its attached yolk sac within its chorionic (gestational) sac. The red pulsating heart of the embryo was visualized using Doppler ultrasound. *B,* Sketch of the sonogram for orientation and identification of structures. (From Moore KL, Persaud TVN, Shiota K: *Color Atlas of Clinical Embryology.* Philadelphia, WB Saunders, 1994. Courtesy of Dr. E. A. Lyons, Professor of Radiology and Obstetrics and Gynecology, Health Sciences Centre, University of Manitoba, Winnipeg, Manitoba, Canada.)

villi proliferate and extend through the syncytiotrophoblast to form a **cytotrophoblastic shell** (Fig. 5-14*C*), which gradually surrounds the chorionic sac and attaches it to the endometrium. Villi that attach to the maternal tissues through the cytotrophoblastic shell are **stem villi** (anchoring villi). The villi that grow from the sides of the stem villi are **branch villi** (terminal villi). It is through the walls of branch villi that the main exchange of material between the blood of the mother and the embryo takes place. The branch villi are bathed in continually changing maternal blood in the intervillous space.

Abnormal Growth of Trophoblast

Sometimes the embryo dies and the chorionic villi do not complete their development; that is, they do not become vascularized to form tertiary villi. These degenerating villi soon form cystic swellings—a *hydatidiform mole*, which resembles a bunch of grapes. The mole exhibits variable degrees of trophoblastic proliferation and produces excessive amounts of hCG.

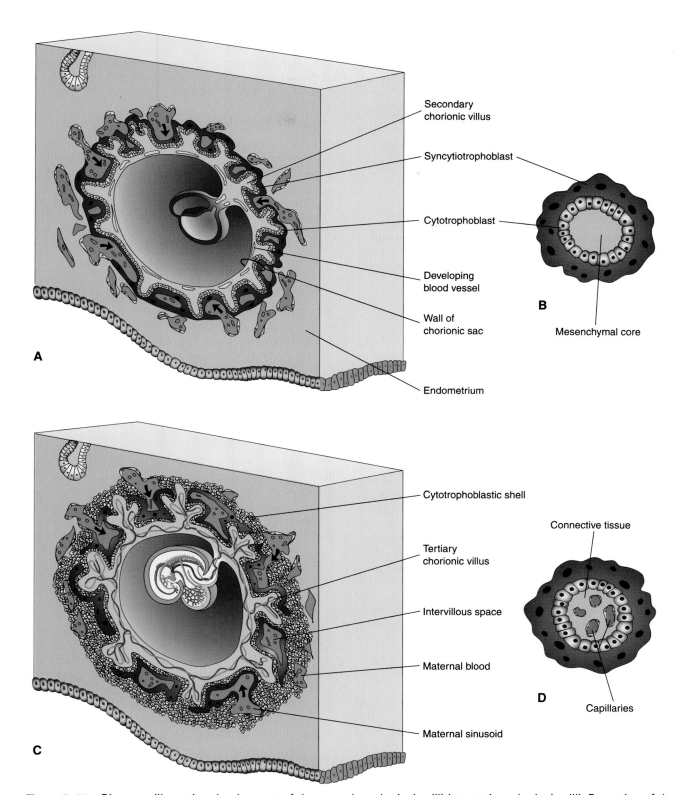

Labels in figure:

Secondary chorionic villus

Syncytiotrophoblast

Cytotrophoblast

Developing blood vessel

Wall of chorionic sac

Mesenchymal core

Endometrium

B

A

Cytotrophoblastic shell

Connective tissue

Tertiary chorionic villus

Intervillous space

Maternal blood

Capillaries

D

Maternal sinusoid

C

■ **Figure 5–14.** Diagrams illustrating development of the secondary chorionic villi into tertiary chorionic villi. Formation of the placenta is also shown. *A*, Sagittal section of an embryo (about 16 days). *B*, Section of a secondary chorionic villus. *C*, Section of an implanted embryo (about 21 days). *D*, Section of a tertiary chorionic villus. The fetal blood in the capillaries is separated from the maternal blood surrounding the villus by the placental membrane, composed of the endothelium of the capillary, mesenchyme, cytotrophoblast, and syncytiotrophoblast.

Three to 5% of moles develop into malignant trophoblastic lesions—**choriocarcinomas**. Some moles develop after spontaneous abortions, and others occur after normal deliveries. Choriocarcinomas invariably metastasize (spread) by way of the blood stream to various sites, such as the lungs, vagina, liver, bone, intestine, and brain (Berkowitz and Goldstein, 1996).

SUMMARY OF THE THIRD WEEK OF DEVELOPMENT

Major changes occur in the embryo as the bilaminar embryonic disc is converted into a trilaminar embryonic disc during **gastrulation.** These changes begin with the appearance of the primitive streak.

Primitive Streak

The primitive streak appears at the beginning of the third week as a localized thickening of the epiblast at the caudal end of the embryonic disc. The primitive streak results from migration of epiblastic cells to the median plane of the embryonic disc. Invagination of epiblastic cells from the primitive streak gives rise to mesenchymal cells that migrate ventrally, laterally, and cranially between the epiblast and the hypoblast. As soon as the primitive streak begins to produce mesenchymal cells, the epiblast layer becomes known as the embryonic ectoderm. Some cells of the epiblast displace the hypoblast and form the embryonic endoderm. Mesenchymal cells produced by the primitive streak soon organize into a third germ layer, the *intraembryonic mesoderm*. Cells from the primitive streak migrate to the edges of the embryonic disc, where they join the *extraembryonic mesoderm* covering the amnion and yolk sac. By the end of the third week, mesoderm exists between the ectoderm and the endoderm everywhere except at the oropharyngeal membrane, in the median plane occupied by the notochord, and at the cloacal membrane.

Notochord Formation

Early in the third week, mesenchymal cells arising from the primitive node of the primitive streak form the *notochordal process*, which extends cranially from the primitive node as a rod of cells between the embryonic ectoderm and endoderm. The primitive pit extends into the notochordal process and forms a *notochordal canal*. When fully developed, the notochordal process extends from the primitive node to the prechordal plate. Openings develop in the floor of the notochordal canal that soon coalesce, leaving a

notochordal plate. The notochordal plate soon infolds to form the notochord—the primitive axis of the embryo around which the axial skeleton forms.

Neural Tube Formation

The *neural plate* appears as a thickening of the embryonic ectoderm, cranial to the primitive node. The neural plate is induced to form by the developing notochord. A longitudinal *neural groove* develops in the neural plate which is flanked by *neural folds*. Fusion of the folds forms the neural tube, the primordium of the CNS. The process of neural plate formation and its infolding to form the neural tube is called *neurulation*.

Neural Crest Formation

As the neural folds fuse to form the neural tube, neuroectodermal cells migrate dorsolaterally to form a neural crest between the surface ectoderm and the neural tube. The neural crest soon divides into two cell masses that give rise to the sensory ganglia of the cranial and spinal nerves. Other neural crest cells migrate from the neural tube and give rise to various other structures, such as the retina.

Somite Formation

The mesoderm on each side of the notochord thickens to form longitudinal columns of paraxial mesoderm. Division of these paraxial columns into pairs of somites begins cranially by the end of the third week. The somites are compact aggregates of mesenchymal cells from which cells migrate to give rise to the vertebrae, ribs, and axial musculature. During the third week, the number of somites present is a reliable indicator of the age of the embryo.

Formation of Intraembryonic Coelom

The coelom (cavity) within the embryo arises as isolated spaces in the lateral mesoderm and cardiogenic mesoderm. The coelomic vesicles subsequently coalesce to form a single, horseshoe-shaped cavity that eventually gives rise to the body cavities, such as the peritoneal cavity.

Formation of Blood Vessels and Blood

Blood vessels first appear on the yolk sac and allantois and in the chorion. They develop within the embryo shortly thereafter. Spaces appear within aggregations of mesenchyme known as *blood islands*. The spaces soon become lined with endothelium derived from the mesenchymal cells. These primordial vessels unite with other vessels to form a primordial cardiovascular system. Toward the end of the third week, the heart is represented by paired endothelial heart tubes that are joined to blood vessels in the embryo and in the extraembryonic membranes (yolk sac, umbilical cord, and chorionic sac). By the end of the third week, the endothelial heart tubes have fused to form a tubular heart, which is joined to vessels in the embryo, yolk sac, chorion, and connecting stalk to form a *primordial cardiovascular system.* The primitive blood cells (hemocytoblasts) are derived mainly from the endothelial cells of blood vessels in the walls of the yolk sac and allantois.

Completion of Chorionic Villi Formation

Primary chorionic villi become secondary chorionic villi as they acquire mesenchymal cores. Before the end of the third week, capillaries develop in the *secondary chorionic villi,* transforming them into *tertiary chorionic villi.* Cytotrophoblastic extensions from these stem villi join to form a *cytotrophoblastic shell* that anchors the chorionic sac to the endometrium. The rapid development of chorionic villi during the third week greatly increases the surface area of the chorion for the exchange of nutrients and other substances between the maternal and embryonic circulations.

Clinically Oriented Questions

1. Do women who have been taking contraceptive pills for many years have more early spontaneous abortions than women who have used other contraceptive methods?

2. Is the third week of development part of the embryonic period? What are the main embryonic structures that form?

3. What is meant by the term *menstrual extraction?* Is this the same as an early induced abortion?

4. Can drugs and other agents cause congenital anomalies of the embryo if they are present in the mother's blood during the third week? If so, what organs would be most susceptible?

5. Are there increased risks for the embryo associated with women over 40 having children? If so, what are they?

The answers to these questions are given at the back of the book.

REFERENCES AND SUGGESTED READING

Berkowitz RS, Goldstein DP: Chorionic tumors. *N Engl J Med* 335:1740, 1996.

Bessis M: The blood cells and their formation. *In* Brachet J, Mirsky AE (eds): *The Cell,* vol. 5. New York, Academic Press, 1961.

Bianchi DW, Wilkins-Haug LE, Enders AC, Hay ED: Origin of extraembryonic mesoderm in experimental animals: Relevance to chorionic mosaicism in humans. *Am J Med Genet* 46:542, 1993.

Boué J, Boué A, Lazar P: Retrospective and prospective epidemiological studies of 1500 karyotyped spontaneous abortions. *Teratology* 12:11, 1975.

Callen PW: *Ultrasonography in Obstetrics and Gynecology,* 3rd ed. Philadelphia, WB Saunders, 1994.

Carlson BM: *Human Embryology and Developmental Biology.* St. Louis, CV Mosby, 1994.

Carr DH: Chromosomes and abortion. *Adv Hum Genet* 2:201, 1971.

Cooke J: The early embryo and the formation of body pattern. *Am Sci* 76:35, 1988.

Filly RA: The fetus with a CNS malformation: Ultrasound evaluation. *In* Harrison MR, Golbus MS, Filly RA (eds): *The Unborn Patient: Prenatal Diagnosis and Treatment,* 2nd ed. Philadelphia, WB Saunders, 1991.

Filly RA: Ectopic pregnancy. *In* Callen PW (ed): *Ultrasonography in Obstetrics and Gynecology,* 3rd ed. Philadelphia, WB Saunders, 1994.

Garcia-Martinez V, Darnell DK, Lopez-Sanchez C, et al: *Pathology.* Philadelphia, JB Lippincott, 1988.

Gilbert SF: *Developmental Biology,* 5th ed. Sunderland, Sinauer Associates, 1997.

Greenberg F, James LM, Oakley GP: Estimates of birth prevalence rates of spina bifida in the United States from computer generated maps. *Am J Obstet Gynecol* 145:570, 1983.

Holzgreve W, Flake AW, Langer JC: The fetus with sacrococcygeal teratoma. *In* Harrison MR, Golbus MS, Filly RA (eds): *The Unborn Patient: Prenatal Diagnosis and Treatment,* 2nd ed. Philadelphia, WB Saunders, 1991.

Marina N: Gonadal and germ cell neoplasms. *In* Behrman RE, Klugman RM, Arvin AM (eds): *Nelson Textbook of Pediatrics,* 15th ed. Philadelphia, WB Saunders, 1996.

Moore KL, Agur AMR: *Essential Clinical Anatomy.* Baltimore, Williams & Wilkins, 1995.

Moore KL, Persaud TVN: *The Developing Human: Clinically Oriented Embryology,* 6th ed. Philadelphia, WB Saunders, 1998.

Nakano T, Kodama H, Honjo T: In vitro development of primitive and definitive erythrocytes from different precursors. *Science* 272:772, 1996.

Rubin R, Farber JL: *Pathology.* Philadelphia, JB Lippincott, 1988.

Salisbury JR, Deverell MH, Cookson MJ, Whimster WF: Three-dimensional reconstruction of human embryonic notochords: Clue to pathogenesis of chordoma. *J Pathol* 17:59, 1993.

Sausedo RA, Schoenwolf GC: Quantitative analyses of cell behaviors underlying notochord formation and extension in mouse embryos. *Anat Rec* 239:103, 1994.

Slack JMW: We have a morphogen! *Nature* 327:553, 1987.

Smith JL, Schoenwolf GC: Further evidence of extrinsic forces in bending of the neural plate. *J Comp Neurol* 307:225, 1991.

Tabin CJ: Retinoids, homeoboxes, and growth factors: Toward molecular models for limb development. *Cell* 66:199, 1991.

Wolpert L: *The Triumph of the Embryo.* Oxford, Oxford University Press, 1991.

Organogenetic Period: The Fourth to Eighth Weeks of Human Development

6

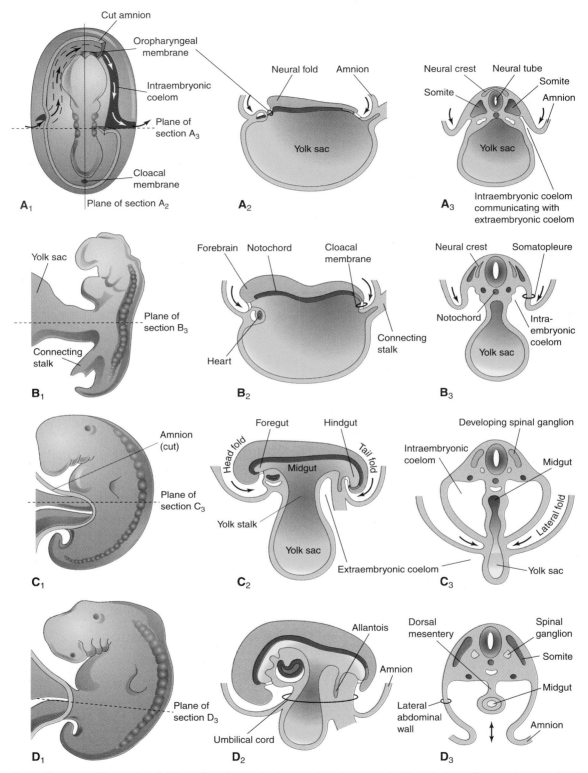

■ **Figure 6–1.** Drawings illustrating folding of embryos during the fourth week. A_1, Dorsal view of an embryo at the beginning of the fourth week. Three pairs of somites are visible. The continuity of the intraembryonic coelom and extraembryonic coelom is illustrated on the right side by removal of a part of the embryonic ectoderm and mesoderm. B_1, C_1, and D_1, Lateral views of embryos at 22, 26, and 28 days, respectively. A_2 to D_2, Sagittal sections at the plane shown in A_1 to D_3, Transverse sections at the levels indicated in A_1 to D_1.

■ The fourth to eighth weeks of development constitute most of the embryonic period; however, critical developmental events also occur during the first 3 weeks, such as *cleavage of the zygote, blastogenesis,* and early development of the nervous and cardiovascular systems. All major external and internal structures are established during the fourth to eighth weeks. By the end of this **organogenetic period**, all the main organ systems have begun to develop; however, the function of most of them is minimal, except for the cardiovascular system. As the tissues and organs form, the shape of the embryo changes so that by the eighth week it has a distinctly human appearance.

PHASES OF EMBRYONIC DEVELOPMENT

Human development may be divided into three phases, which to some extent are interrelated:

- The first phase of development is **growth** (increase in size), which involves cell division and the elaboration of cell products.
- The second phase of development is **morphogenesis** (development of form), which includes mass cell movements. The movement of cells allows them to interact with each other during the formation of tissues and organs.
- The third phase of development is **differentiation** (maturation of physiologic processes). Completion of differentiation results in the formation of tissues and organs that are capable of performing specialized functions.

Because the organ systems develop during the fourth to eighth weeks, exposure of embryos to teratogens during this period may cause major congenital anomalies. **Teratogens** are agents such as drugs and viruses that produce or raise the incidence of congenital anomalies (see Chapter 9). Teratogens act during the stage of active differentiation of a tissue or organ.

FOLDING OF THE EMBRYO

A significant event in the establishment of body form is folding of the flat trilaminar embryonic disc into a somewhat cylindrical embryo (Fig. 6-1). Folding occurs in both the median and horizontal planes and results from rapid growth of the embryo, particularly of its brain and spinal cord (central nervous system). The growth rate at the sides of the embryonic disc fails to keep pace with the rate of growth in the long axis as the embryo increases rapidly in length. As a result, folding of the embryo occurs. Folding at the cranial and caudal ends and sides of the embryo occurs simultaneously. Concurrently, a relative constric-

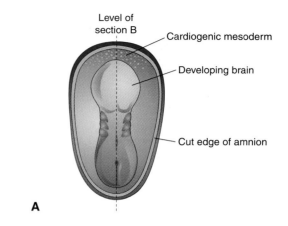

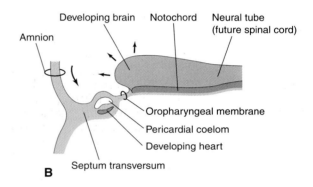

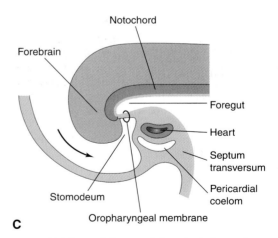

■ **Figure 6-2.** Folding of the cranial end of the embryo. *A,* Dorsal view of an embryo at 21 days. *B,* Sagittal section of the cranial part of the embryo at the plane shown in *A.* Observe the ventral movement of the heart. *C,* Sagittal section of an embryo at 26 days. Note that the septum transversum, heart, pericardial coelom, and oropharyngeal membrane have moved onto the ventral surface of the embryo. Observe also that part of the yolk sac is incorporated into the embryo as the foregut.

tion occurs at the junction of the embryo and yolk sac. Folding of the ends of the embryo ventrally produces head and tail folds that result in the cranial and caudal regions moving ventrally as the embryo elongates cranially and caudally (Fig. 6–1A_2 to D_2).

The Head Fold

By the beginning of the fourth week, the neural folds in the cranial region have thickened to form the primordium of the brain. Initially, the developing brain projects dorsally into the amniotic cavity. Later, the developing forebrain grows cranially beyond the oropharyngeal membrane and overhangs the developing heart. Concomitantly, the **septum transversum** (transverse mesodermal septum), primordial heart, pericardial coelom, and oropharyngeal membrane move onto the ventral surface of the embryo (Fig. 6–2). During longitudinal folding, part of the endoderm of the yolk sac is incorporated into the embryo as the **foregut** (primordium of pharynx, esophagus, and the like; see Chapter 13). The foregut lies between the brain and heart, and the oropharyngeal membrane separates the foregut from the **stomodeum** (see Fig. 6–2*C*). After folding, the septum transversum lies caudal to the heart, where it subsequently develops into the *central tendon of the diaphragm* (see Chapter 10). The head fold also affects the arrangement of the embryonic coelom (primordium of body cavities). Before folding, the coelom consists of a flattened, horseshoe-shaped cavity (Fig. 6–1A_1). After folding, the pericardial coelom lies ventral to the heart and cranial to the septum transversum (Fig. 6–2*C*). At this stage, the intraembryonic coelom communicates widely on each side with the extraembryonic coelom (Fig. 6–1A_3).

The Tail Fold

Folding of the caudal end of the embryo results primarily from growth of the distal part of the neural tube—the primordium of the spinal cord (Fig. 6–3). As the embryo grows, the tail region projects over the *cloacal membrane* (future site of the anus). During folding, part of the endodermal germ layer is incorporated into the embryo as the **hindgut** (primordium of the descending colon and similar organs; see Chapter 13). The terminal part of the hindgut soon dilates slightly to form the **cloaca** (primordium of the urinary bladder and rectum; see Chapters 13 and 14). Before folding, the primitive streak lies cranial to the cloacal membrane (Fig. 6–3*B*); after folding, it lies caudal to it (Fig. 6–3*C*). The connecting stalk (primordium of the umbilical cord) is now attached to the ventral surface of the embryo, and the *allantois*—an endodermal diverticulum of the yolk sac—is partially incorporated into the embryo.

A

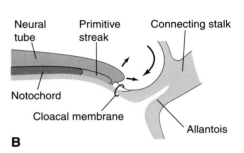

B

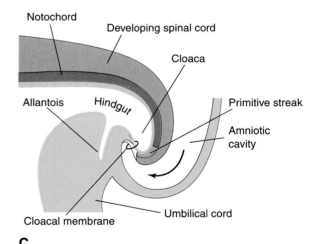

C

■ **Figure 6–3.** Folding of the caudal end of the embryo. *A,* Lateral view of a 4-week-old embryo. *B,* Sagittal section of the caudal part of the embryo at the beginning of the fourth week. *C,* Similar section at the end of the fourth week. Note that part of the yolk sac is incorporated into the embryo as the hindgut and that the terminal part of the hindgut has dilated to form the cloaca. Observe also the change in position of the primitive streak, allantois, cloacal membrane, and connecting stalk.

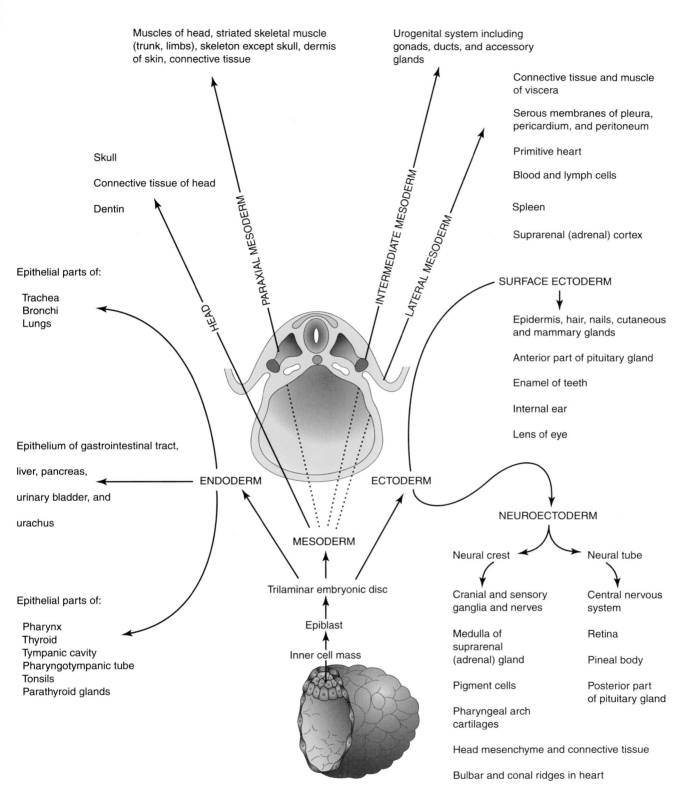

Muscles of head, striated skeletal muscle (trunk, limbs), skeleton except skull, dermis of skin, connective tissue

Urogenital system including gonads, ducts, and accessory glands

Connective tissue and muscle of viscera

Serous membranes of pleura, pericardium, and peritoneum

Primitive heart

Blood and lymph cells

Spleen

Suprarenal (adrenal) cortex

Skull

Connective tissue of head

Dentin

PARAXIAL MESODERM

INTERMEDIATE MESODERM

LATERAL MESODERM

HEAD

SURFACE ECTODERM

Epithelial parts of:

Trachea
Bronchi
Lungs

Epidermis, hair, nails, cutaneous and mammary glands

Anterior part of pituitary gland

Enamel of teeth

Internal ear

Lens of eye

Epithelium of gastrointestinal tract,

liver, pancreas,

urinary bladder, and

urachus

ENDODERM

ECTODERM

NEUROECTODERM

MESODERM

Neural crest

Neural tube

Trilaminar embryonic disc

Cranial and sensory ganglia and nerves

Central nervous system

Epiblast

Inner cell mass

Medulla of suprarenal (adrenal) gland

Retina

Pineal body

Epithelial parts of:

Pharynx
Thyroid
Tympanic cavity
Pharyngotympanic tube
Tonsils
Parathyroid glands

Pigment cells

Posterior part of pituitary gland

Pharyngeal arch cartilages

Head mesenchyme and connective tissue

Bulbar and conal ridges in heart

■ **Figure 6–4.** Schematic drawing illustrating the derivatives of the three germ layers: ectoderm, endoderm, and mesoderm. Cells from these layers make contributions to the formation of different tissues and organs; for example, the endoderm forms the epithelial lining of the gastrointestinal tract and the mesoderm gives rise to connective tissues and muscles.

The Lateral Folds

Folding of the sides of the embryo results from rapid growth of the spinal cord and somites, which produces right and left **lateral folds** (Fig. 6-1A_3 to D_3). The primordium of each lateral body wall folds toward the median plane, rolling the edges of the embryonic disc ventrally and forming a roughly cylindrical embryo. As the abdominal walls form, part of the endoderm germ layer is incorporated into the embryo as the **midgut** (primordium of the small intestine and similar organs; see Chapter 13). Initially, there is a wide connection between the midgut and yolk sac (Fig. 6-1A_2), but after lateral folding the connection is reduced to a *yolk stalk,* or vitelline duct (Fig. 6-1C_2). The region of attachment of the amnion to the ventral surface of the embryo is also reduced to a relatively narrow umbilical region (Figs. 6-1D_2 and D_3). As the **umbilical cord** forms from the connecting stalk, ventral fusion of the lateral folds reduces the region of communication between the intraembryonic and extraembryonic coelomic cavities to a narrow communication (Fig. 6-1C_2). As the amniotic cavity expands and obliterates most of the extraembryonic coelom, the amnion forms the epithelial covering of the umbilical cord (Fig. 6-1D_2). Body folding abnormalities are uncommon. Early diagnosis by antenatal ultrasonography is essential for the management of these cases (Hiett et al, 1992).

GERM LAYER DERIVATIVES

The three germ layers (ectoderm, mesoderm, and endoderm) formed during gastrulation (see Chapter 5) give rise to the primordia of all the tissues and organs. The specificity of the germ layers, however, is not rigidly fixed. The cells of each germ layer divide, migrate, aggregate, and differentiate in rather precise patterns as they form the various organ systems (*organogenesis*). The main germ layer derivatives are as follows (Fig. 6-4):

- **Ectoderm** gives rise to the central nervous system (brain and spinal cord); peripheral nervous system; sensory epithelia of eye, ear, and nose; epidermis and its appendages (hair and nails); mammary glands; pituitary gland; subcutaneous glands; and enamel of teeth.

    Neural crest cells, derived from neuroectoderm, give rise to the cells of the spinal, cranial (CNS V, VII, IX, and X), and autonomic ganglia; ensheathing cells of the peripheral nervous system; pigment cells of the dermis; muscle and connective tissues; bone of pharyngeal (branchial) arch origin (see Chapter 11); suprarenal (adrenal) medulla; and meninges (coverings) of the brain and spinal cord.
- **Mesoderm** gives rise to connective tissue, cartilage, bone, striated and smooth muscles, heart, blood and lymphatic vessels, kidneys, ovaries and testes, genital ducts, serous membranes lining the body cavities (pericardial, pleural, and peritoneal), spleen, and cortex of the suprarenal (adrenal) glands.
- **Endoderm** gives rise to the epithelial lining of the gastrointestinal and respiratory tracts; parenchyma of the tonsils, thyroid and parathyroid glands, thymus, liver, and pancreas; the epithelial lining of the urinary bladder and most of the urethra; and epithelial lining of the tympanic cavity, tympanic antrum, and pharyngotympanic or auditory tube.

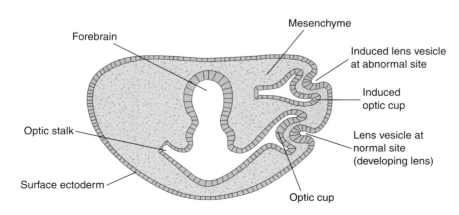

■ **Figure 6–5.** Schematic transverse section through the head of an embryo in the region of the developing eyes to illustrate inductive tissue interaction. At the normal site (*lower right*), observe that the optic vesicle, the precursor of the optic cup, has acted on the surface ectoderm of the head to induce formation of a lens vesicle, the primordium of the lens of the eye. On the opposite side, the optic stalk was cut and the optic vesicle removed. As a result, no lens placode (first indication of the lens) developed. At the abnormal site (*upper right*) the optic vesicle removed from the right side was inserted deep to the skin. Here, it acted on the surface ectoderm to induce the formation of a lens vesicle that has induced the formation of an optic cup (primordium of eyeball).

CONTROL OF EMBRYONIC DEVELOPMENT*

Development results from genetic plans in the chromosomes. Knowledge of the genes or hereditary units that control human development is increasing. Most information about developmental processes has come from studies in other organisms, especially *Drosophila* and mice, because of ethical problems associated with the use of human embryos for laboratory studies. For a discussion of the molecular genetics of mammalian development, see Thompson et al (1991). Most developmental processes depend upon a precisely coordinated interaction of genetic and environmental factors. Several control mechanisms guide differentiation and ensure synchronized development, such as tissue interactions, regulated migration of cells and cell colonies, controlled proliferation, and programmed cell death. Each system of the body has its own developmental pattern, but most processes of morphogenesis are similar and are relatively simple. Underlying all these changes are basic regulating mechanisms (Cooke, 1988).

Embryonic development is essentially a process of growth and increasing complexity of structure and function. Growth is achieved by mitosis (process of somatic reproduction of cells), together with the production of extracellular matrices, whereas complexity is achieved through morphogenesis and differentiation. The cells that make up the tissues of very early embryos are pluripotential—depending on circumstances, they are able to follow more than one pathway of development. This broad developmental potential becomes progressively restricted as tissues acquire the specialized features necessary for increasing their sophistication of structure and function. Such restriction presumes that choices must be made in order to achieve tissue diversification. At present, most evidence indicates that these choices are determined, not as a consequence of cell lineage, but rather in response to cues from the immediate surroundings, including the adjacent tissues. As a result, the architectural precision and coordination that are often required for the normal function of an organ appear to be achieved by the interaction of its constituent parts during development.

The interaction of tissues during development is a recurring theme in embryology (Guthrie, 1991). The interactions that lead to a change in the course of development of at least one of the interactants are termed **inductions**. Numerous examples of such inductive interactions can be found in the literature; for example, during development of the eye, the optic vesicle is believed to induce the development of the lens from the surface ectoderm of the head. When the optic vesicle is absent, the eye fails to develop. Moreover, if the optic vesicle is removed and placed in association with surface ectoderm that is not usually involved in eye development, lens formation can be induced (Fig. 6-5). Clearly then, development of a lens depends on the ectoderm acquiring an association with a second tissue. In the presence of the neuroectoderm of the optic vesicle, the surface ectoderm of

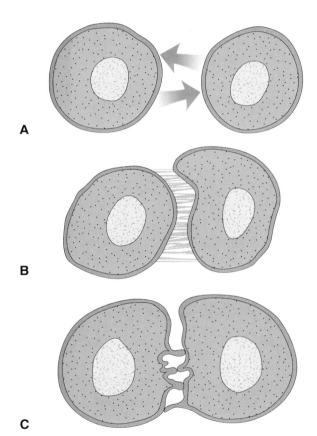

■ **Figure 6–6.** A series of sketches illustrating three possible methods of transmission of signal substances in inductive cell interactions. *A*, Diffusion of signal substances. The signal appears to take the form of a diffusible molecule that passes from the inductor to the reacting tissue. *B*, Matrix-mediated interaction. The signal is mediated through a nondiffusible extracellular matrix, secreted by the inductor, with which the reacting tissue comes in contact. *C*, Cell contact–mediated interaction. The signal requires physical contact between the inducing and responding tissues. (Modified from Grobstein C: Inductive tissue interactions in development. *Adv Cancer Res* 4:187, 1956; Saxen L: Interactive mechanisms in morphogenesis. *In* Tarin D (ed): *Tissue Interactions in Carcinogenesis.* London, Academic Press, 1972.)

* The authors are grateful to Dr. Michael Wiley, Associate Professor of Anatomy and Cell Biology, Faculty of Medicine, University of Toronto, for his assistance in preparing this section.

the head adopts a pathway of development that it would not otherwise have taken. In a similar fashion, many of the morphogenetic tissue movements that play such important roles in shaping the embryo also provide for the changing tissue associations that are fundamental to inductive tissue interactions.

The fact that one tissue can influence the developmental pathway adopted by another tissue presumes that a signal passes between the two interactants. The precise nature of the signal is not known; however, the mechanism of signal transfer appears to vary with the specific tissues involved. In some cases, the signal appears to take the form of a diffusible molecule, such as sonic hedgehog (Tanabe et al, 1995; Placzek and Furley, 1996), that passes from the inductor to the reacting tissue (Fig. 6–6A). In others, the message appears to be mediated through a nondiffusible extracellular matrix that is secreted by the inductor and

Table 6–1 ■ Criteria for Estimating Developmental Stages in Human Embryos

Age (Days)	Figure Reference	Carnegie Stage	No. of Somites	Length (mm)*	Main External Characteristics[†]
20–21	6–1A₁ 6–2A	9	1–3	1.5–3.0	*Flat embryonic disc. Deep neural groove and prominent neural folds. One to three pairs of somites present.* Head fold evident.
22–23	6–7A, B 6–8	10	4–12	2.0–3.5	*Embryo straight or slightly curved.* Neural tube forming or formed opposite somites, but widely open at rostral and caudal neuropores. First and second pairs of branchial arches visibe.
24–25	6–7C 6–9	11	13–20	2.5–4.5	*Embryo curved owing to head and tail folds.* Rostral neuropore closing. Otic placodes present. Optic vesicles formed.
26–27	6–7D 6–10	12	21–29	3.0–5.0	*Upper limb buds appear.* Rostral neuropore closed. Caudal neuropore closing. Three pairs of branchial arches visible. Heart prominence distinct. Otic pits present.
28–30	6–7E 6–11	13	30–35	4.0–6.0	*Embryo has C-shaped curve.* Caudal neuropore closed. Upper limb buds are flipperlike. Four pairs of branchial arches visible. Lower limb buds appear. *Otic vesicles present.* Lens placodes distinct. Attenuated *tail* present.
31–32	6–12	14	‡	5.0–7.0	*Upper limbs are paddle-shaped.* Lens pits and nasal pits visible. Optic cups present.
33–36		15		7.0–9.0	*Hand plates formed; digital rays present.* Lens vesicles present. Nasal pits prominent. *Lower limbs are paddle-shaped.* Cervical sinuses visible.
37–40		16		8.0–11.0	*Foot plates formed.* Pigment visible in retina. Auricular hillocks developing.
41–43	6–13	17		11.0–14.0	*Digital rays clearly visible in hand plates.* Auricular hillocks outline future auricle of external ear. Trunk beginning to straighten. Cerebral vesicles prominent.
44–46		18		13.0–17.0	*Digital rays clearly in foot plates.* Elbow region visible. Eyelids forming. Notches between the digital rays in the hands. Nipples visible.
47–48	6–14	19		16.0–18.0	*Limbs extend ventrally.* Trunk elongating and straightening. Midgut herniation prominent.
49–51		20		18.0–22.0	*Upper limbs longer and bent at elbows. Fingers distinct but webbed.* Notches between the digital rays in the feet. Scalp vascular plexus appears.
52–53	6–15	21		22.0–24.0	*Hands and feet approach each other. Fingers are free and longer. Toes distinct but webbed.* Stubby tail present.
54–55		22		23.0–28.0	*Toes free and longer.* Eyelids and auricles of external ears more developed.
56	6–16	23		27.0–31.0	*Head more rounded and shows human characteristics.* External genitalia still have sexless appearance. Distinct bulge still present in umbilical cord, caused by herniation of intestines. *Tail has disappeared.*

* The embryonic lengths indicate the usual range. In stages 9 and 10, the measurement is greatest length *(GL)*; in subsequent stages crown-rump *(CR)* measurements are given.

† Based mainly on O'Rahilly R, Müller F: Developmental Stages in Human Embryos. Washington, Carnegie Institute of Washington, 1987.

‡At this and subsequent stages, the number of somites is difficult to determine and so is not a useful criterion. Refer to Moore KL, et al (1994) for more color photographs of embryos.

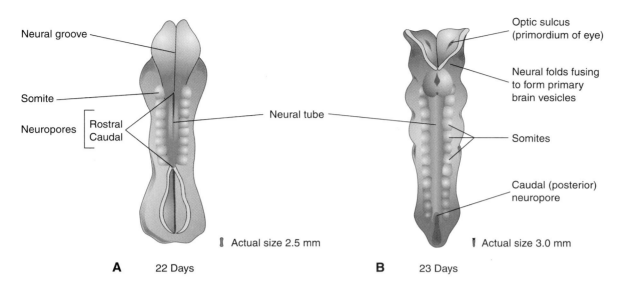

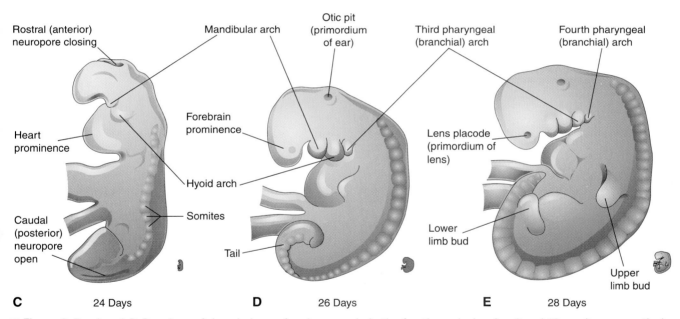

■ **Figure 6–7.** *A and B,* Drawings of dorsal views of embryos early in the fourth week showing 8 and 12 somites, respectively. *C, D,* and *E,* Lateral views of older embryos showing 16, 27, and 33 somites, respectively. The rostral neuropore is normally closed by 25 to 26 days, and the caudal neuropore is usually closed by the end of the fourth week.

with which the reacting tissue comes into contact (Fig. 6–6*B*). In still other cases, the signal appears to require that physical contacts occur between the inducing and responding tissues (Fig. 6–6*C*). Regardless of the mechanism of intercellular transfer involved, the signal is translated into an intracellular message that influences the genetic activity of the responding cells. For further discussion of induction, see Moore and Persaud, 1998.

HIGHLIGHTS OF THE FOURTH TO EIGHTH WEEKS

The following descriptions summarize the main developmental events and changes in external form of the embryo during the fourth to eighth weeks. Criteria for estimating developmental stages in human embryos are listed in Table 6–1.

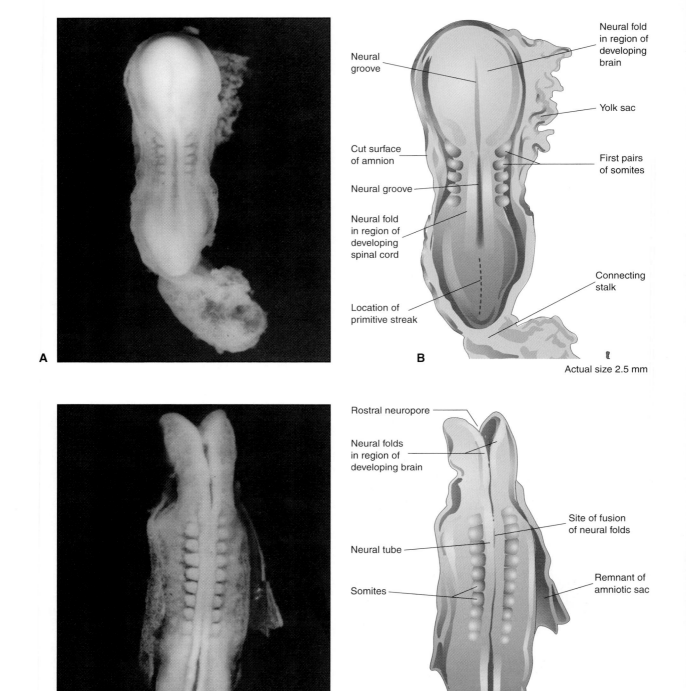

Neural groove

Neural fold in region of developing brain

Neural groove

Yolk sac

Cut surface of amnion

First pairs of somites

Neural fold in region of developing spinal cord

Location of primitive streak

Connecting stalk

A

B

Actual size 2.5 mm

Rostral neuropore

Neural folds in region of developing brain

Neural tube

Site of fusion of neural folds

Somites

Remnant of amniotic sac

Caudal neuropore

C

D

Actual size 3.0 mm

■ **Figure 6–8.** *A,* Dorsal view of a five-somite embryo at Carnegie stage 10, about 22 days. Observe the neural folds and deep neural groove. The neural folds in the cranial region have thickened to form the primordium of the brain. *B,* Drawing indicating the structures shown in *A.* Most of the amniotic and chorionic sacs have been cut away to expose the embryo. The neural folds have fused opposite the somites to form the neural tube (primordium of the spinal cord in this region). *C,* Dorsal view of a 10-somite embryo at Carnegie stage 10, about 23 days. The neural tube is in open communication with the amniotic cavity at the cranial and caudal ends through the rostral and caudal neuropores, respectively. *D,* Diagram indicating the structures shown in *C.*

Fourth Week

Major changes in body form occur during the fourth week. At the beginning, the embryo is almost straight and has 4 to 12 somites that produce conspicuous surface elevations (Fig. 6-7A). The neural tube is formed opposite the somites, but it is widely open at the rostral (anterior) and caudal (posterior) neuropores (Fig. 6-7B and 6-8). By 24 days the first pha-

ryngeal (branchial) arches have appeared. The first or mandibular arch and the second or hyoid arch are distinct (Figs. 6-7C and 6-9). The major part of the first pharyngeal arch gives rise to the mandible (lower jaw), and a rostral extension of the arch—the maxillary prominence—contributes to the maxilla (upper jaw). The embryo is now slightly curved because of the head and tail folds. The heart produces a large ventral prominence and pumps blood.

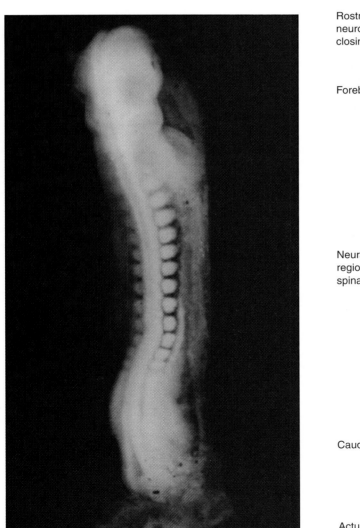

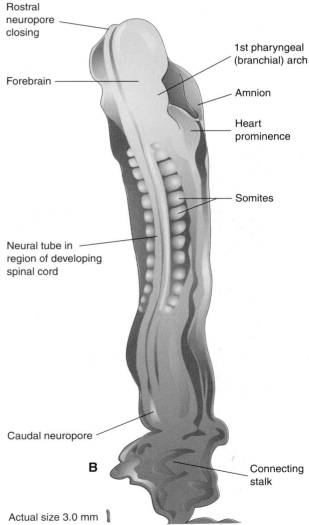

A

B

Actual size 3.0 mm

■ **Figure 6-9.** *A,* Dorsal view of a 13-somite embryo at Carnegie stage 11, about 24 days. The rostral neuropore is closing, but the caudal neuropore is wide open. *B,* Drawing indicating the structures shown in *A.* The embryo is curved because of folding at the cranial and caudal ends.

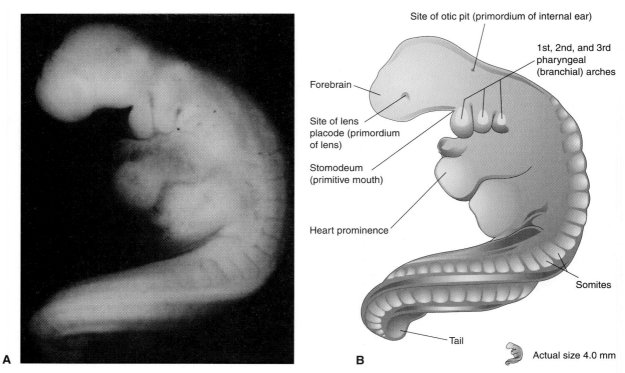

■ **Figure 6–10.** *A,* Lateral view of a 27-somite embryo at Carnegie stage 12, about 26 days. The embryo is very curved, especially its long tail. Observe the lens placode (primordium of the lens of the eye) and the otic pit indicating early development of the internal ear. *B,* Drawing indicating the structures shown in *A.* The rostral neuropore is closed, and three pairs of pharyngeal arches are present. (*A* from Nishimura H, et al: *Prenatal Development of the Human with Special Reference to Craniofacial Structures: An Atlas.* Washington, DC, National Institutes of Health, 1977.)

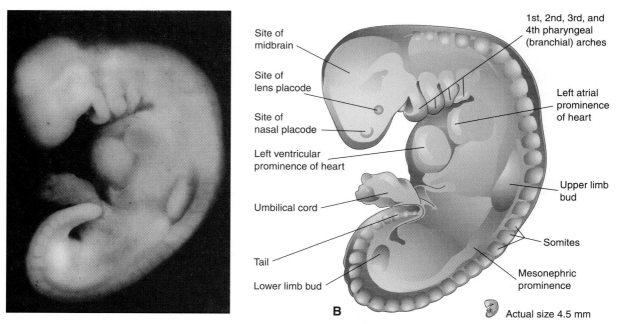

■ **Figure 6–11.** *A,* Lateral view of an embryo at Carnegie stage 13, about 28 days. The heart is large, and its division into a primordial atrium and ventricle is visible. The rostral and caudal neuropores are closed. *B,* Drawing indicating the structures shown in *A.* The embryo has a characteristic C-shaped curvature, four pharyngeal arches, and upper and lower limb buds. (*A* from Nishimura H, et al: *Prenatal Development of the Human with Special Reference to Craniofacial Structures: An Atlas.* Washington, DC, National Institutes of Health, 1977.)

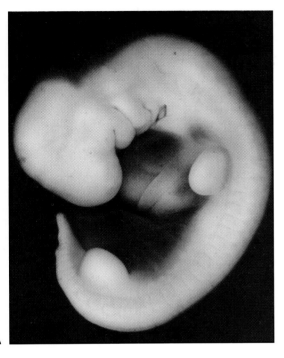

A

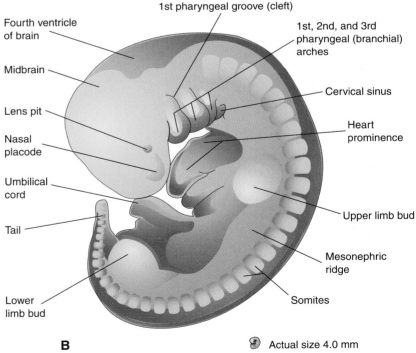

Fourth ventricle
of brain

Midbrain

Lens pit

Nasal
placode

Umbilical
cord

Tail

Lower
limb bud

1st pharyngeal groove (cleft)

1st, 2nd, and 3rd
pharyngeal (branchial)
arches

Cervical sinus

Heart
prominence

Upper limb bud

Mesonephric
ridge

Somites

B

Actual size 4.0 mm

▨ **Figure 6–12.** *A,* Lateral view of an embryo at Carnegie stage 14, about 32 days. The second pharyngeal arch has overgrown the third arch, forming a depression known as the cervical sinus. The mesonephric ridge indicates the site of the mesonephric kidney, an interim kidney (see Chapter 14). *B,* Drawing indicating the structures shown in *A.* The upper limb buds are paddle-shaped, and the lower limb buds are flipperlike. (*A* from Nishimura H, et al: *Prenatal Development of the Human with Special Reference to Craniofacial Structures: An Atlas.* Washington, DC, National Institutes of Health, 1977.)

Three pairs of **pharyngeal arches** are visible by 26 days (Fig. 6-10; see also Fig. 6-7*D*), and the rostral neuropore is closed. The **forebrain** produces a prominent elevation of the head, and folding of the embryo has given the embryo a characteristic C-shaped curvature. A long *curved tail* is present. **Upper limb buds** are recognizable by day 26 or 27 as small swellings on the ventrolateral body walls (Fig. 6-7*D* and *E*). The **otic pits**, the primordia of the internal ears, are also visible. Ectodermal thickenings called **lens placodes,** indicating the future lenses of the eyes, are visible on the sides of the head. The fourth pair of pharyngeal arches and the **lower limb buds** are visible by the end of the fourth week (Fig. 6-7*E*). Toward the end of the fourth week, the *attenuated tail* is a characteristic feature (Fig. 6-11; see also Fig. 6-10). Rudiments of many of the organ systems, especially the *cardiovascular system*, are established. By the end of the fourth week, the caudal neuropore is normally closed.

Fifth Week

Changes in body form are minor during the fifth week compared with those that occurred during the fourth week, but growth of the head exceeds that of other regions (Fig. 6-12). Enlargement of the head is caused mainly by the rapid development of the brain and facial prominences. The face soon contacts the heart prominence. The rapidly growing second lateral pharyngeal arch overgrows the third and fourth arches, forming a lateral ectodermal depression on each side — the **cervical sinus**. The upper limb buds are paddle-shaped, and the lower limb buds are flipperlike. The *mesonephric ridges* indicate the site of the mesonephric kidneys, which are interim kidneys in humans.

Sixth Week

The upper limbs begin to show regional differentiation as the elbows and large **hand plates** develop (Fig. 6-13). The primordia of the digits (fingers) — *digital rays* — begin to develop in the hand plates, which indicate the formation of digits. It has been reported that embryos in the sixth week show spontaneous movements, such as twitching of the trunk and limbs. Development of the lower limbs occurs somewhat later than that of the upper limbs. Several small swellings — **auricular hillocks** — develop around the pharyngeal (branchial) groove or cleft between the first two pharyngeal arches. This groove (cleft) becomes the **external acoustic meatus** (external auditory canal), and the hillocks fuse to form the *auricle*, the shell-shaped part of the external ear. Largely because

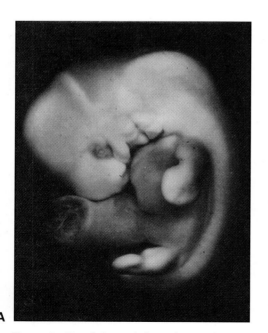

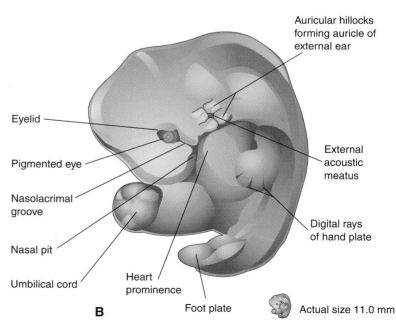

A

B

■ **Figure 6–13.** *A*, Lateral view of an embryo at Carnegie stage 17, about 42 days. Digital rays are visible in the large hand plate, indicating the future site of the digits. *B*, Drawing indicating the structures shown in *A*. The eye, auricular hillocks, and external acoustic meatus (auditory canal) are now obvious.

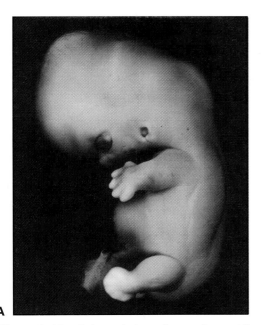

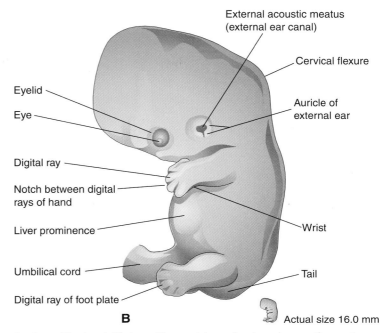

External acoustic meatus
(external ear canal)

Cervical flexure

Eyelid

Eye

Auricle of
external ear

Digital ray

Notch between digital
rays of hand

Liver prominence

Wrist

Umbilical cord

Tail

Digital ray of foot plate

A

B

Actual size 16.0 mm

■ **Figure 6–14.** *A*, Lateral view of an embryo at Carnegie stage 19, about 48 days. The auricle and external acoustic meatus are now clearly visible. Note the relatively low position of the ear at this stage. Digital rays are now visible in the large foot plate. The prominence of the abdomen is caused mainly by the large size of the liver. *B*, Drawing indicating the structures shown in *A*. Observe the large hand and the notches between the digital rays, which clearly indicate the developing digits.

retinal pigment has formed, the eye is now obvious. The head is now much larger relative to the trunk and is bent over the *large heart prominence*. This head position results from bending in the cervical (neck) region. The trunk and neck have begun to straighten. It has been reported that embryos during the sixth week show reflex responses to touch.

Seventh Week

The limbs undergo considerable change during the seventh week. Notches appear between the digital rays in the hand plates, partially separating the future digits (Figs. 6–14). Communication between the primitive gut and yolk sac is now reduced to a relatively slender duct, the *yolk stalk*. The intestines enter the extraembryonic coelom in the proximal part of the umbilical cord. This **umbilical herniation** is a normal event in the embryo, which occurs because the abdominal cavity is too small at this stage to accommodate the rapidly growing intestines.

Eighth Week

At the beginning of this final week of the embryonic period, the digits of the hand are separated but notice-

ably webbed (Fig. 6–15). Notches are now clearly visible between the digital rays of the fan-shaped feet. The tail is still present but is stubby. The **scalp vascular plexus** has appeared and forms a characteristic band around the head. By the end of the eighth week, all regions of the limbs are apparent, and the digits have lengthened and are completely separated (Fig. 6–16). *Purposeful limb movements first occur during this week.* Ossification begins in the lower limbs in the eighth week and is first recognizable in the femur. All evidence of the tail has disappeared by the end of the eighth week. The *scalp vascular plexus* now forms a slender band near the vertex (crown) of the head. The hands and feet approach each other ventrally. At the end of the eighth week, the embryo has distinct human characteristics; however, the head is still disproportionately large, constituting almost half of the embryo. The neck region is established, and the eyelids are more obvious. The eyelids are closing, and by the end of the eighth week they begin to unite by epithelial fusion. The intestines are still in the proximal portion of the umbilical cord. The auricles of the external ears begin to assume their final shape, but they are still low-set on the head. Although sex differences exist in the appearance of the external genitalia, they are not distinctive enough to permit accurate sexual identification (see Chapter 14).

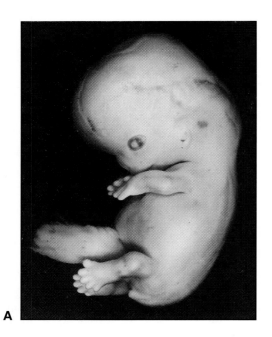

A

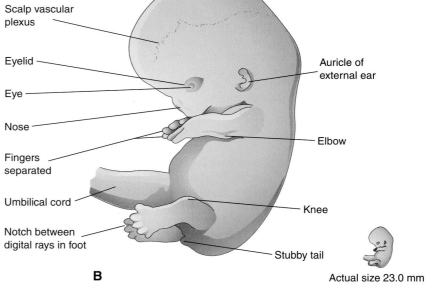

Scalp vascular plexus

Eyelid

Eye

Nose

Fingers separated

Umbilical cord

Notch between digital rays in foot

Auricle of external ear

Elbow

Knee

Stubby tail

B

Actual size 23.0 mm

■ **Figure 6–15.** *A,* Lateral view of an embryo at Carnegie stage 21, about 52 days. Note that the feet are fan-shaped and that the tail is very short. The scalp vascular plexus now forms a characteristic band across the head. The nose is stubby, and the eye is heavily pigmented. *B,* Drawing indicating the structures shown in *A.* The fingers are separated, and the toes are beginning to separate. (*A* from Nishimura H, et al: *Prenatal Development of the Human with Special Reference to Craniofacial Structures: An Atlas.* Washington, DC, National Institutes of Health, 1977.)

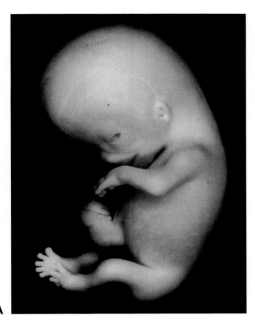
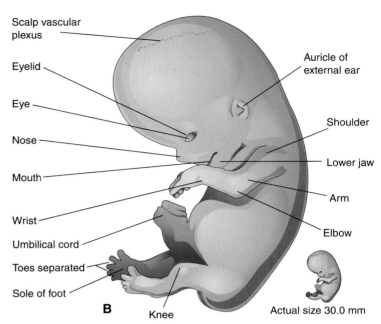

Scalp vascular plexus

Eyelid

Eye

Nose

Mouth

Wrist

Umbilical cord

Toes separated

Sole of foot

Auricle of external ear

Shoulder

Lower jaw

Arm

Elbow

Knee

Actual size 30.0 mm

A   B

■ **Figure 6–16.** *A,* Lateral view of an embryo at Carnegie stage 23, about 56 days. The embryo now has a distinct human appearance. *B,* Drawing indicating the structures shown in *A.* The scalp vascular plexus is reduced, and the tail has disappeared. (*A* from Nishimura H, et al: *Prenatal Development of the Human with Special Reference to Craniofacial Structures: An Atlas.* Washington, DC, National Institutes of Health, 1977.)

Estimation of Gestational Age

Determination of the starting date of a pregnancy may be difficult in some instances, partly because it depends on the mother's memory of an event that occurred several weeks before she realized she was pregnant. Two reference points are commonly used for estimating age:

- Onset of last normal menstrual period (LNMP)
- Probable time of fertilization (conception)

In some women, the estimation of gestational age from the menstrual history alone is unreliable. The probability of error in establishing LNMP is highest in women who become pregnant after cessation of oral contraception because the interval between the discontinuance of hormones and the onset of ovulation is highly variable. The LNMP is commonly used by clinicians to estimate the age of embryos and is a reliable criterion in most cases.

Ultrasound assessment of the size of the chorionic (gestational) sac and its contents (Fig. 6–17) enables clinicians to obtain an accurate estimate of the date of conception. The zygote does not form until about 2 weeks after LNMP; consequently 14 ± 2 days must be deducted from the gestational (menstrual) age to ob-

tain the fertilization (conceptional) age of an embryo. Because it may be important to know the fertilization age of an embryo for determining its sensitivity to teratogenic agents (see Chapter 9), all statements about age should indicate the reference point used (i.e., days after LNMP or after the estimated time of fertilization).

ESTIMATION OF EMBRYONIC AGE

Estimates of the age of recovered embryos (e.g., after spontaneous abortion) are determined from their external characteristics and measurements of their length (Table 6–1). Size alone may be an unreliable criterion because some embryos undergo a progressively slower rate of growth prior to death. The appearance of the developing limbs is a very helpful criterion for estimating embryonic age.

Because embryos of the third and early fourth weeks are straight (Fig. 6–18*A*), measurements of them indicate the *greatest length* (GL). The sitting height, or *crown-rump length* (CRL), is used for older embryos (Fig. 6–18*B*). In embryos with greatly flexed necks, the CRL is actually a head-rump measurement (Fig. 6–18*C*). Standing height, or crown-heel length

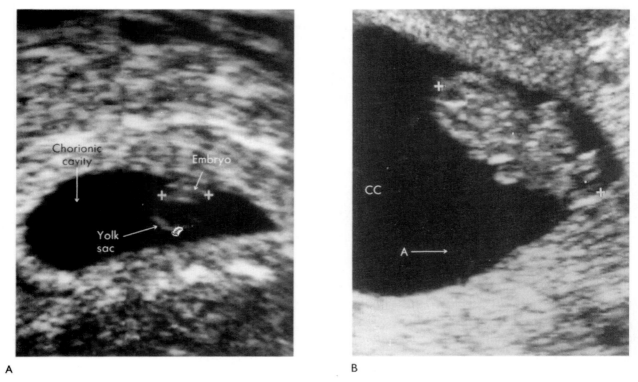

A   B

■ **Figure 6–17.** Ultrasound images of embryos. *A,* Crown-rump length (CRL), 4.8 mm. The 4.5-week-old embryo is indicated by the measurement cursors (+). Ventral to the embryo is the yolk sac. The chorionic cavity appears black. *B,* Coronal scan of 5-week-old embryo (CRL, 2.09 cm). The upper limbs are clearly shown. The embryo is surrounded by a thin amnion (A). The fluid in the chorionic sac (CC) is more particulate than the amniotic fluid. (Courtesy of Dr. E. A. Lyons, Professor of Radiology and Obstetrics and Gynecology, Health Sciences Centre, University of Manitoba, Winnipeg, Manitoba, Canada.)

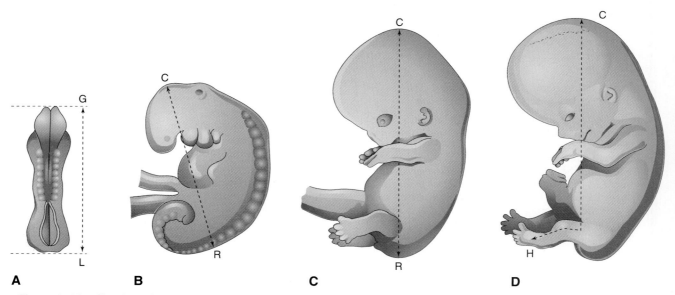

A   B   C   D

■ **Figure 6–18.** Sketches showing the methods used to measure the length of embryos. *A,* Greatest length. *B* and *C,* Crown-rump length. *D,* Crown-heel length.

(CHL), is sometimes measured for 8-week-old embryos. The CHL of formalin-fixed embryos may be difficult to determine because their limbs are not easy to straighten. Such embryos should be measured as shown in Figure 6–18D. Because the length of an embryo is only one criterion for establishing age, one should not refer to a 5-mm stage embryo. The *Carnegie Embryonic Staging System* is used internationally (Table 6–1); its usage enables comparisons to be made between the findings of one person and those of another.

Ultrasound Examination of Embryos

Most women seeking obstetric care have at least one ultrasound examination during their pregnancy (Callen, 1994) for one or more of the following reasons:

- Estimation of gestational and conceptional age for confirmation of clinical dating, which is usually calculated from the first day of the LNMP
- Evaluation of embryonic growth when intrauterine growth retardation is suspected
- Guidance during chorionic villus sampling (Chapter 7)
- Examination of a clinically detected pelvic mass
- Suspected ectopic pregnancy
- Possible uterine abnormality
- Detection of congenital anomalies

Current data indicate that no biologic effects of ultrasound on embryos or fetuses from the use of diagnostic ultrasound evaluation have been confirmed (Reece et al, 1990). The size of an embryo in a pregnant woman can be estimated using ultrasound measurements. *Transvaginal* or *endovaginal sonography* permits an earlier and more accurate measurement of CRL in early pregnancy. The embryonic CRL was determined as early as 25 days after follicle aspiration in pregnancies resulting from in vitro fertilization (Schats et al, 1991).

eral folds is a continuous sequence of events that results in a constriction between the embryo and the yolk sac. During folding, part of the endoderm-lined yolk sac is incorporated into the embryo and gives rise to the primordial gut. As the head region folds ventrally, part of the endodermal layer is incorporated into the developing embryonic head as the *foregut*. Folding of the head region also results in the oropharyngeal membrane and heart being carried ventrally, and the developing brain becomes the most cranial part of the embryo.

As the tail region folds ventrally, part of the endodermal layer is incorporated into the caudal end of the embryo as the *hindgut*. The terminal part of the hindgut expands to form the *cloaca*. Folding of the tail region also results in the cloacal membrane, allantois, and connecting stalk being carried to the ventral surface of the embryo. Folding of the embryo in the horizontal plane incorporates part of the endodermal germ layer into the embryo as the *midgut*. The yolk sac remains attached to the midgut by a narrow *yolk stalk*. During folding in the horizontal plane, the primordia of the lateral and ventral body walls are formed. As the amnion expands, it envelops the connecting stalk, yolk stalk, and allantois, thereby forming an epithelial covering for the *umbilical cord*. The three germ layers differentiate into various tissues and organs, so that by the end of the embryonic period the beginnings of all the main organ systems have been established.

The external appearance of the embryo is greatly affected by the formation of the brain, heart, liver, somites, limbs, ears, nose, and eyes. As these structures develop, the appearance of the embryo changes so that it has unquestionably human characteristics by the end of the eighth week. Because the beginnings of most essential external and internal structures are formed during the fourth to eighth weeks, this is the most critical period of development. Developmental disturbances during this period may give rise to major congenital anomalies of the embryo (see Chapter 9).

SUMMARY OF THE FOURTH TO EIGHTH WEEKS OF DEVELOPMENT

During these 5 weeks, representing the major part of the embryonic period, *all major organs and systems of the body form from the three germ layers* (Fig. 6–4). At the beginning of the fourth week, folding of the embryo in the median and horizontal planes converts the flat trilaminar embryonic disc into a C-shaped, cylindrical embryo. The formation of head, tail, and lat-

Clinically Oriented Questions

1. I have heard that the early human embryo could be confused with the offspring of several other species, such as a pig, mouse, or chick. Is this true? What is the distinctive feature of early human embryos?
2. I cannot see a difference between an 8-week em-

bryo and a 9-week fetus. Why do embryologists give them different names?

3. When does the embryo become a human being? What guidelines can be used?

4. Can the sex of embryos be determined by ultrasound study? What other methods can be used to diagnose sex?

5. What is the difference between the terms *primigravida* and *primipara*? I have also heard nurses refer to pregnant women as "primips." What does this mean?

The answers to these questions are given at the back of the book.

REFERENCES AND SUGGESTED READING

Barnea ER, Hustin J, Jauniaux E (eds): *The First Twelve Weeks of Gestation*. Berlin, Springer-Verlag, 1992.

Callen PW (ed): *Ultrasonography in Obstetrics and Gynecology*, 3rd ed. Philadelphia, WB Saunders, 1994.

Cooke J: The early embryo and the formation of body pattern. *Am Sci* 76:35, 1988.

Dickey RP, Gasser RF: Ultrasound evidence for variability in the size and development of normal human embryos before the tenth post-insemination week after assisted reproductive technologies. *Hum Reprod* 8:331, 1993.

Filly RA: Ultrasound evaluation during the first trimester. *In* Callen PW (ed): *Ultrasonography in Obstetrics and Gynecology*, 3rd ed. Philadelphia, WB Saunders, 1994.

Guthrie S: Horizontal and vertical pathways in neural induction. *Trends Neurosci* 14:123, 1991.

Hiett AK, Devoe LD, Falls DG, Martin SA: Ultrasound diagnosis of a twin gestation with concordant body stalk anomaly. *J Reprod Med* 37:944, 1992.

Kurtz AB, Needleman L: Ultrasound assessment of fetal age. *In* Callen PW (ed): *Ultrasonography in Obstetrics and Gynecology*, 3rd ed. Philadelphia, WB Saunders, 1994.

Moore KL, Persaud TVN: *The Developing Human: Clinically Oriented Embryology*, 6th ed. Philadelphia, WB Saunders, 1998.

Moore KL, Persaud TVN, Shiota K: *Color Atlas of Clinical Embryology*, Philadelphia, WB Saunders, 1994.

O'Rahilly R, Müller F: *Developmental Stages in Human Embryos*. Washington, Carnegie Institute of Washington, 1987.

Placzek M, Furley A: Neural development: Patterning cascades in the neural tube. *Curr Biol* 6:526, 1996.

Reece EA, Assimakopoulos E, Zheng X-Z, et al: The safety of obstetric ultrasonography: Concern for the fetus. *Obstet Gynecol* 6:139, 1990.

Schats R, Van Os HC, Jansen CAM, Wladimiroff JW: The crown-rump length in early human pregnancy: A reappraisal. *Br J Obstet Gynaecol* 98:460, 1991.

Tanabe Y, Roelink H, Jessell T: Induction of motor neurons by sonic hedgehog is independent of foreplate differentiation. *Curr Biol* 5:651, 1995.

Thompson MW, McInnes RR, Willard HF: *Thompson and Thompson Genetics in Medicine*, 5th ed. Philadelphia, WB Saunders, 1991.

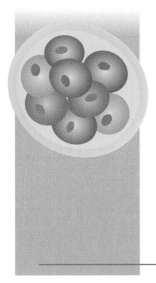

Fetal Period: Ninth Week to Birth

7

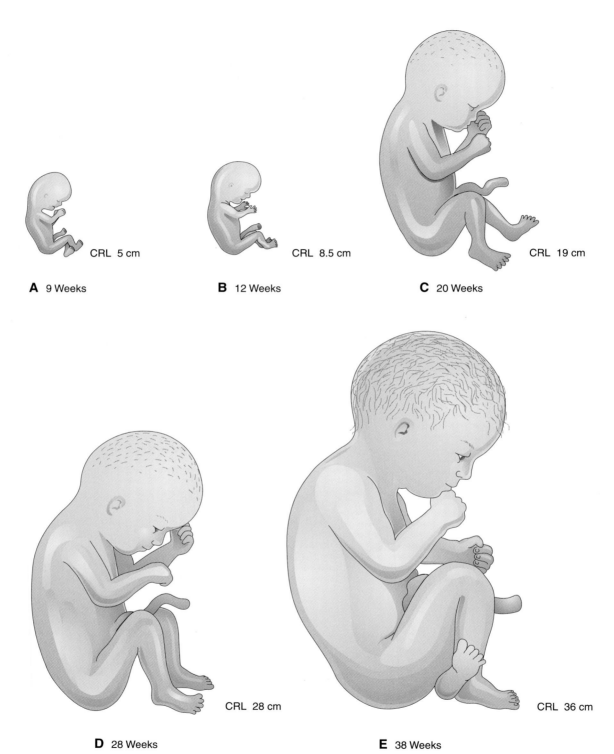

CRL 5 cm

A 9 Weeks

CRL 8.5 cm

B 12 Weeks

CRL 19 cm

C 20 Weeks

CRL 28 cm

D 28 Weeks

CRL 36 cm

E 38 Weeks

■ **Figure 7–1.** Drawings of fetuses at various stages of development. *A*, 9-week fetus. *B*, 12-week fetus. *C*, 20-week fetus. *D*, 28-week fetus. *E*, 38-week fetus. CRL, crown-rump length. Head hair begins to appear at about 20 weeks.

■ The transformation of an embryo to a fetus is gradual, but the name change is meaningful because it signifies that the embryo has developed into a recognizable human being and that all major systems have formed. Development during the fetal period is concerned primarily with rapid body growth and differentiation of tissues, organs, and systems. A notable change occurring during the fetal period is the relative slowdown in the growth of the head compared with the rest of the body (England, 1983; Barnea et al, 1992; Hadlock, 1994a). The rate of body growth during the fetal period is very rapid (Fig. 7–1; Table 7–1), and fetal weight gain is phenomenal during the terminal weeks. Periods of normal continuous growth alternate with prolonged intervals of absent growth (Bernstein et al, 1995).

Viability of Fetuses

Viability is defined as the ability of fetuses to survive in the extrauterine environment (i.e., after premature birth). Fetuses weighing less than 500 gm at birth usually do not survive. However, if given expert postnatal care, some fetuses weighing less than this may survive; they are referred to as *extremely low birth weight* (ELBW) or *immature infants*. Many full-term, *low birth weight babies* result from intrauterine growth retardation (IUGR). Most fetuses weighing between 1500 and 2500 gm survive but have difficulties; they are *premature infants*. Prematurity is one of the most common causes of morbidity and perinatal death (Behrman et al, 1996).

ESTIMATION OF FETAL AGE

If doubt arises about the age of a fetus in patients with an uncertain medical history, ultrasound measurements of the crown-rump length (CRL) can be taken to determine its size and probable age and to provide a reliable prediction of the *expected date of confinement* (EDC) for delivery of the fetus (Hadlock, 1994b). Fetal head measurements and femur length are also used to evaluate the age of the fetus.

Table 7–1 ■ Criteria for Estimating Fertilization Age During the Fetal Period

Age (weeks)	CR Length (mm)*	Foot Length (mm)*	Fetal Weight (gm)†	Main External Characteristics
Previable Fetuses				
9	50	7	8	*Eyes closing or closed.* Head more rounded. External genitalia still not distinguishable as male or female. Intestines in umbilical cord.
10	61	9	14	*Intestine in abdomen.* Early fingernail development.
12	87	14	45	*Sex distinguishable externally.* Well-defined neck.
14	120	20	110	*Head erect.* Lower limbs well developed. Early toenail development.
16	140	27	200	*Ears stand out from head.*
18	160	33	320	*Vernix caseosa covers skin.* Quickening (signs of life felt by mother).
20	190	39	460	*Head and body hair (lanugo) visible.*
Viable Fetuses‡				
22	210	45	630	*Skin wrinkled* and red.
24	230	50	820	*Fingernails present.* Lean body.
26	250	55	1000	*Eyes partially open.* Eyelashes present.
28	270	59	1300	*Eyes open.* Good head of hair. Skin slightly wrinkled.
30	280	63	1700	*Toenails present.* Body filling out. Testes descending.
32	300	68	2100	*Fingernails reach finger tips.* Skin pink and smooth.
36	340	79	2900	*Body usually plump.* Lanugo hairs almost absent. Toenails reach toe tips. Flexed limbs; firm grasp.
38	360	83	3400	*Prominent chest;* breasts protrude. Testes in scrotum or palpable in inguinal canals. Fingernails extend beyond finger tips.

* These measurements are averages and so may not apply to specific cases; dimensional variations increase with age.
† These weights refer to fetuses that have been fixed for about two weeks in 10% formalin. Fresh specimens usually weigh about 5% less.
‡ There is no sharp limit of development, age, or weight at which a fetus automatically becomes viable or beyond which survival is ensured, but experience has shown that it is uncommon for a baby to survive whose weight is less than 500 gm or whose fertilization age or developmental age is less than 22 weeks. Even fetuses born during the 26- to 28-week period have difficulty surviving, mainly because the respiratory and central nervous systems are not completely differentiated. The term *abortion* refers to all pregnancies that terminate before the period of viability.

Table 7–2 ■ Comparison of Gestational Time Units

Reference Point	Days	Weeks	Calendar Months	Lunar Months
Fertilization*	266	38	8¾	9½
LNMP	280	40	9¼	10

* The date of birth is calculated as 266 days after the estimated day of fertilization, or 280 days after the onset of the last normal menstrual period *(LNMP)*. From fertilization to the end of the embryonic period (8 weeks), age is best expressed in days; thereafter age is often given in weeks.

The intrauterine period may be divided into days, weeks, or months (Table 7–2), but confusion arises if it is not stated whether the age given is calculated from the onset of the last normal menstrual period (LNMP) — *gestational* or *menstrual age* — or from the estimated day of fertilization or conception — fertilization age. Most uncertainty arises when months are used, particularly when it is not stated whether calendar months (28 to 31 days) or lunar months (28 days) are meant. Unless otherwise stated, fetal age in this book is calculated from the estimated time of fertilization, and months refer to calendar months. It is best to express fetal age in weeks and to state whether the beginning or end of a week is meant, because statements such as "in the 10th week" are nonspecific.

Trimesters of Pregnancy

Clinically, the gestational period is divided into three *trimesters*, each lasting 3 months. At the end of the first trimester, all major systems are developed (Fig. 7–1*B*). By the end of the second trimester, the fetus may survive if born prematurely. The fetus reaches a major developmental landmark at 35 weeks of gestation. It weighs about 2500 gm, which is used to define the level of fetal maturity. At this stage the fetus usually survives if born prematurely.

External Characteristics of Fetuses

Various measurements and external characteristics are useful for estimating fetal age (Table 7–1). The CRL is the method of choice for estimating fetal age until the end of the first trimester because there is very little variability in fetal size during this period. In the second and third trimesters, several structures can be identified and measured ultrasonographically (Hadlock, 1994b), but the basic measurements are the following:

- *Biparietal diameter* (BPD) — the diameter of the head between the two parietal eminences
- Head circumference
- Abdominal circumference
- Femur length
- Foot length

Foot length correlates well with CRL and is particularly useful for estimating the age of incomplete or macerated fetuses. *Fetal weight* is often a useful criterion for estimating age, but a discrepancy may exist between the age and the weight of a fetus, particularly when the mother had metabolic disturbances during pregnancy such as diabetes mellitus. In these cases, fetal weight often exceeds values considered normal for CRL. Cheek-to-cheek (Abramowicz et al, 1991) and transverse cerebellar measurements (Lee et al, 1991) have also been used for assessment of fetal growth and gestational age, respectively. Determination of the size of a fetus, especially of its head, is of great value to the obstetrician for the management of patients, such as women with small pelves and/or fetuses with IUGR and/or congenital anomalies (Filly, 1991b).

HIGHLIGHTS OF THE FETAL PERIOD

There is no formal staging system for the fetal period; however, it is helpful to consider the changes that occur in periods of 4 to 5 weeks.

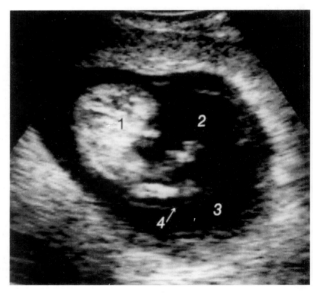

■ **Figure 7–2.** Transvaginal ultrasound scan of a fetus (1) early in the ninth week showing its relationship to the amniotic cavity (2), the extrafetal or chorionic cavity (3), and amnion (4). (From Wathen NC, Cass PL, Kitan MJ, Chard T: Human chorionic gonadotrophin and alpha-fetoprotein levels in matched samples of amniotic fluid, extra-embryonic coelomic fluid, and maternal serum in the first trimester of pregnancy. *Prenat Diagn* 11:145, 1991.)

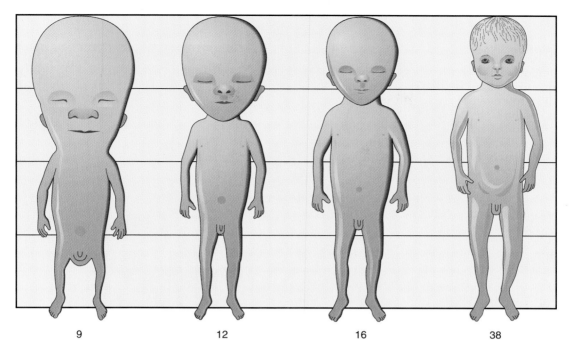

9   12   16   38

Fertilization (conception) age in weeks

■ **Figure 7-3.** Diagram illustrating the changing proportions of the body during the fetal period. At 9 weeks the head is about half the crown-rump length of the fetus. By 36 weeks, the circumferences of the head and the abdomen are approximately equal. After this, the circumference of the abdomen may be greater. All stages are drawn to the same total height.

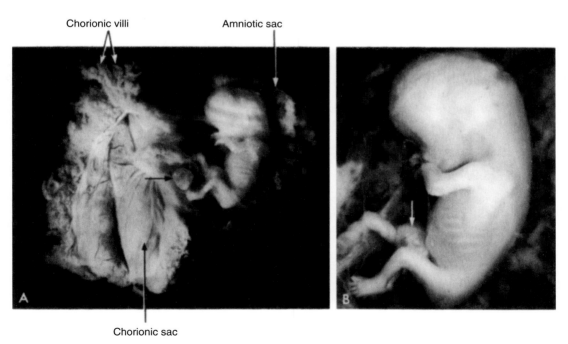

Chorionic villi   Amniotic sac

Chorionic sac

■ **Figure 7-4.** Photographs of a 9-week fetus in the amniotic sac exposed by removal from its chorionic sac. *A*, Actual size. The remnant of the yolk sac is indicated by an arrow. *B*, Enlarged photograph of the fetus (×2). Note the following features: large head, cartilaginous ribs, and intestines in the umbilical cord (*arrow*). (Courtesy of Professor Jean Hay [Retired], Department of Anatomy, University of Manitoba, Winnipeg, Manitoba, Canada.)

Nine to Twelve Weeks

At the beginning of the ninth week, the head constitutes half the CRL of the fetus (Figs. 7 – 2 and 7 – 3). Subsequently, growth in body length accelerates rapidly and by the end of 12 weeks, the CRL has more than doubled (see Table 7 – 1). Although growth of the head slows down considerably by the 12th week, it is still disproportionately large compared with the rest of the body. At 9 weeks the face is broad, the eyes are widely separated, the ears are low-set, and the eyelids are fused. By the end of 12 weeks, *primary ossification centers* appear in the skeleton, especially in the skull and long bones. The eyelids are fused throughout this period.

Early in the ninth week, the legs are short and the thighs are relatively small (Fig. 7 – 4*A*). By the end of 12 weeks, the upper limbs have almost reached their final relative lengths, but the lower limbs are still not so well developed and are slightly shorter than their final relative lengths. The external genitalia of males and females appear similar until the end of the ninth week. Their mature fetal form is not established until the 12th week. Intestinal coils are clearly visible in the proximal end of the umbilical cord until the middle of the 10th week (Fig. 7 – 4*B*). By the 11th week the intestines have returned to the abdomen (Fig. 7 – 5).

At the beginning of the fetal period, the liver is the major site of *erythropoiesis* (formation of red blood cells). By the end of the 12th week, this activity has decreased in the liver and has begun in the spleen. *Urine formation* begins between the 9th and 12th weeks, and urine is discharged into the amniotic fluid. The fetus reabsorbs some of this fluid after swallowing it. Fetal waste products are transferred to the maternal circulation by passing across the placental membrane (see Chapter 8).

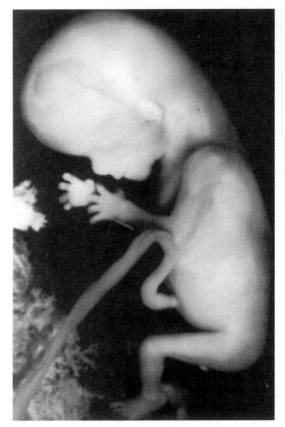

■ **Figure 7–5.** Photograph of an 11-week fetus exposed by removal from its chorionic and amniotic sacs (×1.5). Note that the head is relatively large and the intestines are no longer in the umbilical cord. (Courtesy of Professor Jean Hay [Retired], Department of Anatomy, University of Manitoba, Winnipeg, Manitoba, Canada.)

Thirteen to Sixteen Weeks

Growth is very rapid during this period (Figs. 7 – 6 and 7 – 7; Table 7 – 1). By 16 weeks the head is relatively small compared with that of the 12-week fetus, and the lower limbs have lengthened. Limb movements, which first occur at the end of the embryonic period (8 weeks), become coordinated by the 14th week, but are too slight to be felt by the mother. These movements are visible during ultrasound examinations.

Ossification of the fetal skeleton is active during this period, and the bones are clearly visible in ultrasound images of the mother's abdomen by the beginning of the 16th week. Birnholz (1981) revealed by ultrasonography that slow *eye movements occur at 14 weeks* (16 weeks after LNMP). Scalp hair patterning is also determined during this period. By 16 weeks the ovaries are differentiated and contain primordial follicles that have oogonia (see Chapter 14). The external genitalia can be recognized by 14 weeks, and by 16 weeks the appearance of the fetus is even more human because its eyes face anteriorly rather than anterolaterally. In addition, the external ears are close to their definitive position on the sides of the head.

Seventeen to Twenty Weeks

Growth slows down during this period, but the fetus still increases its CRL by about 50 mm (Figs. 7 – 6 and

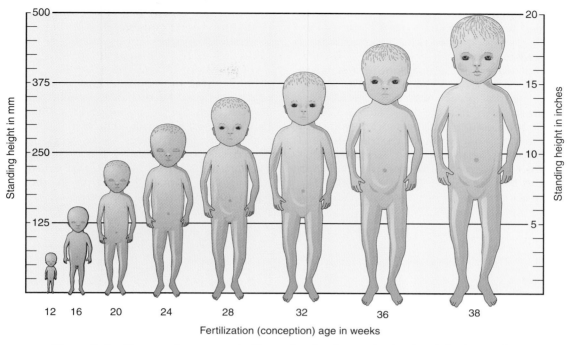

■ **Figure 7–6.** Diagram, drawn to scale, illustrating the changes in the size of the human fetus.

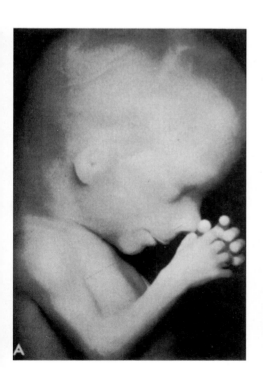

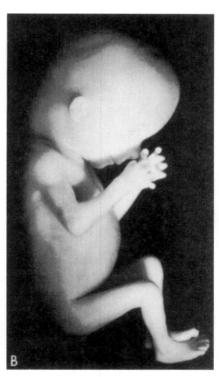

■ **Figure 7–7.** Photographs of a 13-week fetus. *A*, An enlarged photograph of the head and shoulders (×2). *B*, Actual size. (Courtesy of Professor Jean Hay [Retired], Department of Anatomy, University of Manitoba, Winnipeg, Manitoba, Canada.)

7-8; Table 7-1). The limbs reach their final relative proportions, and fetal movements — **quickening** — are commonly felt by the mother. The mean time that intervenes between a mother's first detection of fetal movements and delivery is 147 days, with a standard deviation of ±15 days (Page et al, 1981). The skin is now covered with a greasy material — **vernix caseosa**. It consists of a mixture of a fatty secretion from the fetal sebaceous glands and dead epidermal cells. The vernix caseosa protects the delicate fetal skin from abrasions, chapping, and hardening that could result from exposure to the amniotic fluid. Eyebrows and head hair are also visible at 20 weeks. The bodies of 20-week fetuses are usually completely covered with fine downy hair called *lanugo*, which helps to hold the vernix caseosa on the skin.

Brown fat forms during the 17th through 20th weeks and is the site of heat production, particularly in the newborn infant. This specialized adipose tissue produces heat by oxidizing fatty acids. Brown fat is found chiefly at the root of the neck, posterior to the sternum, and in the perirenal area (England, 1983). Brown fat has a high content of mitochondria, giving it a definite brown hue. By 18 weeks the uterus is formed, and canalization of the vagina has begun. By this time many *primordial ovarian follicles* containing oogonia have formed. By 20 weeks the *testes* have begun to descend, but they are still located on the

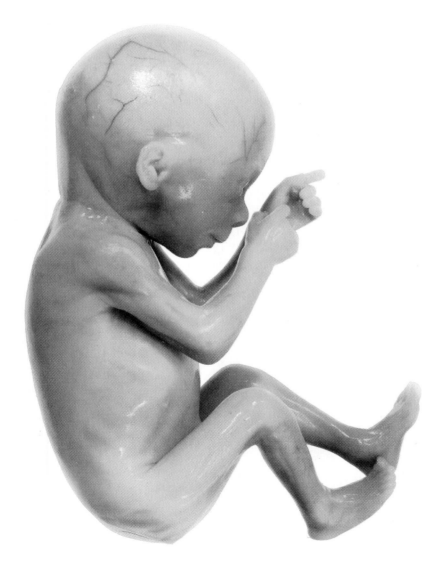

■ **Figure 7–8.** Photograph of a 17-week fetus. Actual size. Because no subcutaneous fat is present and the skin is thin, the blood vessels of the scalp are visible. Fetuses at this age are unable to survive if born prematurely, mainly because their respiratory system is immature. (From Moore KL, Persaud TVN, Shiota K: *Color Atlas of Clinical Embryology.* Philadelphia, WB Saunders, 1994.)

posterior abdominal wall, as are the *ovaries* in female fetuses.

Twenty-One to Twenty-Five Weeks

Substantial weight gain occurs during this period. Although still somewhat lean, the fetus is better proportioned (Fig. 7-9). The skin is usually wrinkled and more translucent, particularly during the early part of this period. The skin is pink to red in fresh specimens because blood is visible in the capillaries. At 21 weeks rapid eye movements begin, and *blink-startle responses* have been reported at 22 to 23 weeks following application of a vibroacoustic noise source to the mother's abdomen. By 24 weeks the secretory epithelial cells (type II pneumocytes) in the interalveolar walls of the lung have begun to secrete *surfactant*, a surface-active lipid that maintains the patency of the developing alveoli of the lungs (see Chapter 12). *Fingernails* are also present by 24 weeks. Although a 22- to 25-week fetus born prematurely may survive if given intensive care, it may die during early infancy because its respiratory system is still immature.

Twenty-Six to Twenty-Nine Weeks

At this age a fetus often survives if born prematurely and given intensive care because its *lungs are now capable of breathing air.* The lungs and pulmonary vasculature have developed sufficiently to provide adequate gas exchange. In addition, the central nervous system has matured to the stage at which it can direct rhythmic breathing movements and control body temperature. The greatest neonatal losses occur in infants of low (2500 gm or less) and very low (1500 gm or less) birth weight (Behrman et al, 1996).

The eyes are open at 26 weeks, and lanugo and head hair are well developed (Fig. 7-10). Toenails become visible, and considerable subcutaneous fat is now present under the skin, smoothing out many of the wrinkles. During this period the quantity of white fat increases to about 3.5% of body weight. *The fetal spleen is now an important site of hematopoiesis —* the process of formation and development of various types of blood cells and other formed elements. Erythropoiesis in the spleen ends by 28 weeks, by which time bone marrow has become the major site of this process (Boles, 1991).

Thirty to Thirty-Four Weeks

The pupillary light reflex of the eyes can be elicited by 30 weeks. Usually by the end of this period, the skin is pink and smooth and the upper and lower limbs have a chubby appearance. At this age, the quantity of white fat is about 8% of body weight. Fetuses 32 weeks and older usually survive if born prematurely. If a normal-weight fetus is born during this period, it is "premature by date" as opposed to being "premature by weight."

Thirty-Five to Thirty-Eight Weeks

Fetuses at 35 weeks have a firm grasp and exhibit a spontaneous orientation to light. As term approaches (37 to 38 weeks), the nervous system is sufficiently mature to carry out some integrative functions (Drife, 1985). Most fetuses during this "finishing period" are plump (Fig. 7-11). By 36 weeks the circumferences of the head and abdomen are approximately equal. After this, the circumference of the abdomen may be greater than that of the head. Growth slows as the time of birth approaches (Fig. 7-12).

Normal fetuses usually reach a CRL of 360 mm and weigh about 3400 gm. By full term the amount of white fat is about 16% of body weight. A fetus adds about 14 gm of fat a day during these last weeks of gestation. In general, male fetuses are longer and weigh more at birth than females. By full term (38 weeks after fertilization; 40 weeks after LNMP), the skin is normally bluish pink. The chest is prominent, and the breasts often protrude slightly in both sexes. The testes are usually in the scrotum in full-term male infants; premature male infants commonly have undescended testes. Although the head is smaller at full term in relation to the rest of the body than it was earlier in fetal life, it still is one of the largest regions of the fetus. This is an important consideration related to its passage through the birth canal (cervix and vagina; see Chapter 8).

EXPECTED DATE OF DELIVERY

The expected date of delivery (EDD) of a fetus is 266 days, or 38 weeks, after fertilization; that is, 280 days, or 40 weeks, after LNMP (Table 7-1). About 12% of babies, however, are born 1 to 2 weeks after the expected time of birth.

Determination of EDD

The common delivery date method (*Nägele's rule*) for determining the EDD or the expected date of confinement (EDC) is to count back 3 months from the first day of the LNMP and add 1 year and 7 days. For example:

continued on page 113

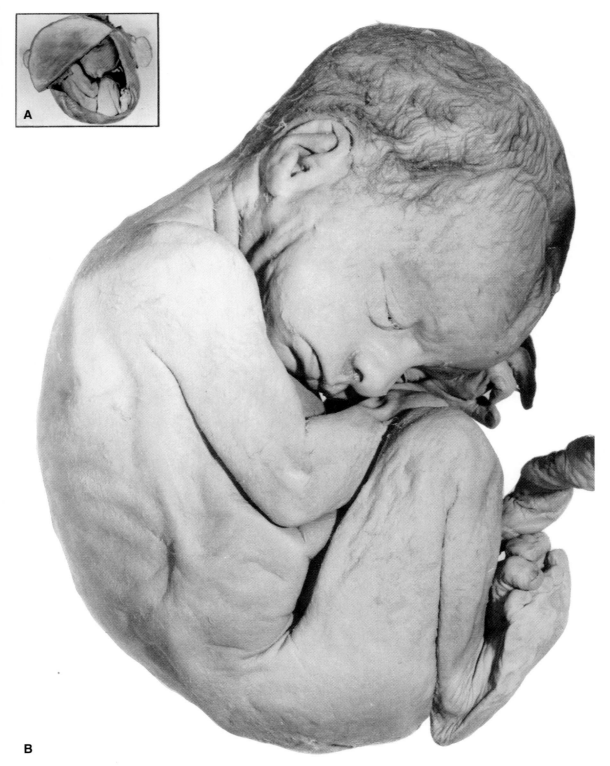

A

B

■ **Figure 7–9.** Photographs of a 25-week fetus. *A,* In the uterus. *B,* Actual size. Note the wrinkled skin and rather lean body caused by the scarcity of subcutaneous fat. Observe that the eyes are beginning to open. A fetus of this size might survive if born prematurely; hence it is considered a viable fetus. (From Moore KL, Persaud TVN, Shiota K: *Color Atlas of Clinical Embryology.* Philadelphia, WB Saunders, 1994.)

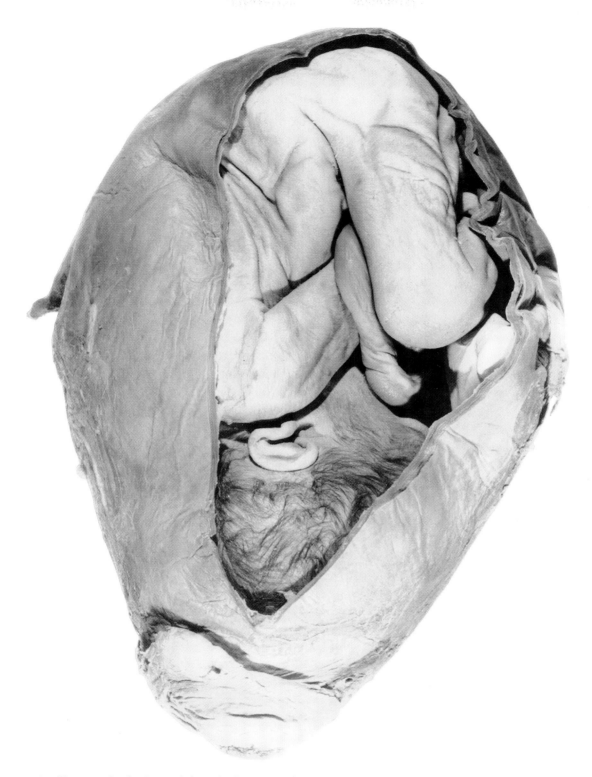

■ **Figure 7–10.** Photograph of a 29-week fetus in the uterus. Actual size. Note that the fetus is in a longitudinal lie and cephalic (head) presentation, which is normal at this period of gestation. Part of the wall of the uterus and parts of the chorion and amnion have been removed to show the fetus. This fetus and its mother died as the result of injuries sustained in an automobile accident. (From Moore KL, Persaud TVN, Shiota K: *Color Atlas of Clinical Embryology*. Philadelphia, WB Saunders, 1994.)

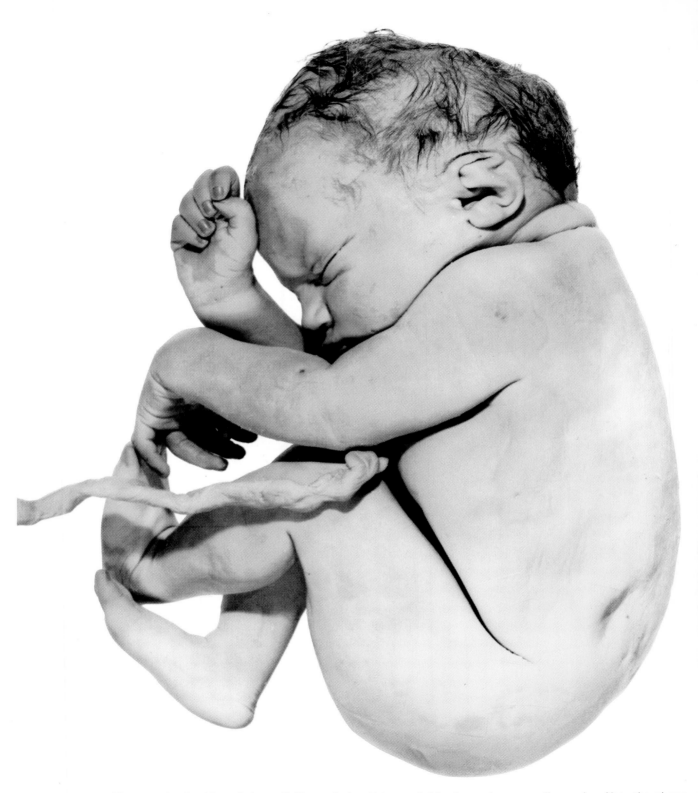

■ **Figure 7–11.** Photograph of a 36-week fetus. Half actual size. Fetuses at this size and age usually survive. Note the plump body resulting from the deposition of subcutaneous fat. This fetus's mother was killed in an automobile accident, and the fetus died before it could be delivered by cesarean section. (From Moore KL, Persaud TVN, Shiota K: *Color Atlas of Clinical Embryology.* Philadelphia, WB Saunders, 1994.)

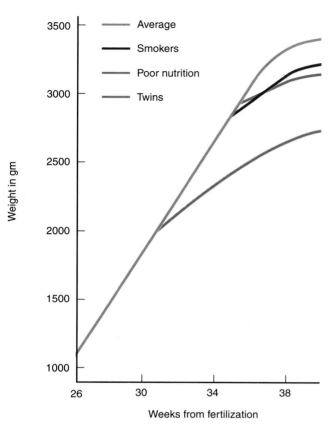

Figure 7–12. Graph showing the rate of fetal growth during the last trimester. Average refers to babies born in the United States. After 36 weeks the growth rate deviates from the straight line. The decline, particularly after full term (38 weeks) probably reflects inadequate fetal nutrition caused by placental changes. (Adapted from Gruenwald P: Growth of the human fetus. I. Normal growth and its variation. *Am J Obstet Gynecol* 94:1112, 1966.)

---

continued from page 109

- First day of LNMP—January 4, 1998
- Subtract 3 months = October 4, 1997
- Add a year and 7 days = October 11—the EDD

In women with regular menstrual cycles, this method gives a reasonably accurate EDD. However if the woman's cycles were irregular, miscalculations of 2 to 3 weeks may occur. In addition, *implantation bleeding* occurs in some pregnant women at the time of the first missed period (about 2 weeks after fertilization). Should the woman interpret this bleeding as a normal menstruation, the estimated time of birth could be miscalculated by 2 or more weeks. Ultrasound examinations of the fetus, in particular CRL measurements during the first trimester, are commonly used for a reliable prediction of the EDD.

FACTORS INFLUENCING FETAL GROWTH

The fetus requires substrates for growth and production of energy. Gases and nutrients pass freely to the fetus from the mother through the placental membrane (see Chapter 8). **Glucose** is a primary source of energy for fetal metabolism and growth; *amino acids* are also required. These substances pass from the mother's blood to the fetus through the placental membrane. **Insulin** required for the metabolism of glucose is secreted by the fetal pancreas; no significant quantities of maternal insulin reach the fetus because the placental membrane is relatively impermeable to this hormone. Insulin, human growth hormone, and some small polypeptides (such as somatomedin C) are believed to stimulate fetal growth. For a comprehensive account of human fetal growth, see Miller and Merritt (1979) and Hadlock (1994a).

Many factors may affect prenatal growth: maternal, fetal, and environmental. In general, factors operating throughout pregnancy, such as *cigarette smoking* and *consumption of alcohol*, tend to produce IUGR and small infants, whereas factors operating during the last trimester (e.g., maternal malnutrition) usually produce underweight infants with normal length and head size. Intrauterine growth retardation is usually defined as infant weight within the lowest 10th percentile for gestational age (Hadlock, 1994a; Behrman et al, 1996; Ghidini, 1996). Severe malnutrition resulting from a poor-quality diet is known to cause reduced fetal growth (Fig. 7–12). Poor nutrition and faulty food habits are common during pregnancy and are not restricted to mothers belonging to poverty groups (Illsley and Mitchell, 1984; Creasy and Resnik, 1989).

Cigarette Smoking

Smoking is a well-established cause of IUGR (Nash and Persaud, 1988). The growth rate for fetuses of mothers who smoke cigarettes is less than normal during the last 6 to 8 weeks of pregnancy (Fig. 7–12). On average, the birth weight of infants whose mothers smoke heavily during pregnancy is 200 gm less than normal, and *perinatal morbidity* is increased when adequate medical care is unavailable (Behrman et al, 1996). The effect of maternal smoking is greater on fetuses whose mothers also receive inadequate nutrition. Presumably, heavy smoking and poor-quality diet have an additive effect.

Multiple Pregnancy

Individuals of twin, triplet, and other multiple births usually weigh considerably less than infants resulting from a single pregnancy (Fig. 7–12). It is evident that the total requirements of two or more fetuses exceed the nutritional supply available from the placenta during the third trimester.

Social Drugs

Infants born to alcoholic mothers often exhibit IUGR as part of the *fetal alcohol syndrome* (see Chapter 9). Similarly, the use of *marijuana* and other illicit drugs (e.g., *cocaine*) can cause IUGR and other obstetrical complications (Persaud, 1988, 1990).

Impaired Uteroplacental Blood Flow

Maternal placental circulation may be reduced by conditions that decrease uterine blood flow (e.g., small chorionic or umbilical vessels, severe hypotension, and renal disease). Chronic reduction of uterine blood flow can cause *fetal starvation,* resulting in IUGR (Harding and Charlton, 1991; Ghidini, 1996). Placental dysfunction or defects (e.g., infarction; see Chapter 8) can also cause IUGR. The net effect of these placental abnormalities is a reduction of the total area for exchange of nutrients between the fetal and maternal blood streams. It is very difficult to separate the effect of these placental changes from the effect of reduced maternal blood flow to the placenta. In some instances of chronic maternal disease, the maternal vascular changes in the uterus are primary and the placental defects are secondary (Harding and Charlton, 1991).

Genetic Factors and Growth Retardation

It is well established that genetic factors can cause IUGR. Repeated cases of this condition in one family indicate that recessive genes may be the cause of the abnormal growth. In recent years, structural and numerical chromosomal aberrations have also been shown to be associated with cases of retarded fetal growth (Thompson et al, 1991). IUGR is pronounced in infants with Down syndrome and is very characteristic of fetuses with trisomy 18 syndrome (see Chapter 9).

PROCEDURES FOR ASSESSING FETAL STATUS

Perinatology is the branch of medicine that is concerned with the well-being of the fetus and newborn infant, generally covering the period from about 26 weeks after fertilization to 4 weeks after birth. The subspecialty of *perinatal medicine* combines aspects of obstetrics and pediatrics. A third-trimester fetus is commonly regarded as an *unborn patient* on whom diagnostic and therapeutic procedures may be performed (Harrison, 1991). Several techniques are now available for assessing the status of the fetus and providing prenatal treatment if required (Soothill, 1996). Fetal activity felt by the mother or palpated by the physician were the first clues to fetal well-being. Then the fetal heart beat was detected, first by auscultation and later by electronic monitors. These techniques indicated when fetal stress and distress were occurring. Later gonadotropic hormones were detected in maternal blood. Many new procedures for assessing the status of the fetus have been developed in the last two decades. It is now possible to treat many fetuses whose lives are in jeopardy (Harrison, 1991; Harman, 1995; Manning, 1995).

Diagnostic Amniocentesis

This is the most common invasive prenatal diagnostic procedure (Elias and Simpson, 1993). For prenatal diagnosis, amniotic fluid is sampled by inserting a hollow needle through the mother's anterior abdominal and uterine walls into the amniotic cavity by piercing the chorion and amnion (Fig. 7–13A). A syringe is attached, and amniotic fluid is withdrawn. Because relatively little amniotic fluid is present prior to the 14th week after LNMP, amniocentesis is difficult to perform prior to this time. The amniotic fluid volume is approximately 200 ml, and 20 to 30 ml can be safely withdrawn. The procedure is relatively devoid of risk, especially when the procedure is performed by an experienced physician who is guided by ultrasonography for outlining the position of the fetus and placenta.

Transabdominal Amniocentesis

Amniocentesis is a common technique for detecting genetic disorders (e.g., Down syndrome). Complications associated with amniocentesis are relatively uncommon. There is a small risk of inducing an abortion, estimated to be about 0.5% (Goldberg, 1994).

The common *indications for amniocentesis*:

- Advanced maternal age (38 years or older)
- Previous birth of a trisomic child (e.g., Down syndrome)
- Chromosome abnormality in either parent (e.g., a chromosome translocation; see Chapter 9)
- Women who are carriers of X-linked recessive disorders (e.g., *hemophilia*)
- History of neural tube defects (NTDs) in the family (e.g., spina bifida cystica; see Chapter 19)
- Carriers of inborn errors of metabolism (Elias and Simpson, 1993)

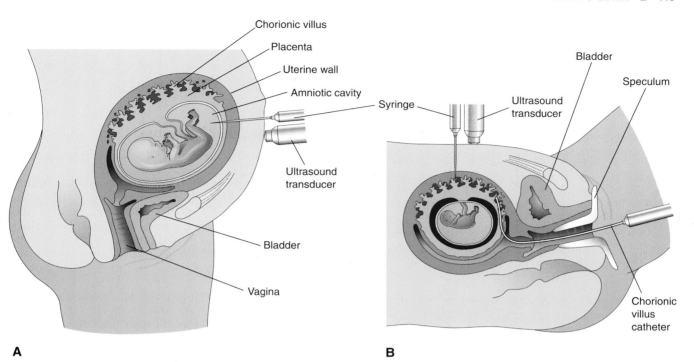

■ **Figure 7–13.** *A,* Drawing illustrating the technique of amniocentesis. A needle is inserted through the lower abdominal wall and uterine wall into the amniotic cavity. A syringe is attached, and amniotic fluid is withdrawn for diagnostic purposes. *B,* Drawing illustrating chorionic villus sampling (CVS). This technique is usually performed at about the ninth week after the last menstrual period. Two sampling approaches are illustrated: through the maternal anterior abdominal wall with a spinal needle, and through the vagina and cervical canal using a malleable cannula.

Alpha-Fetoprotein Assay

Alpha-fetoprotein (AFP) is a glycoprotein that is synthesized in the fetal liver and yolk sac and escapes from the circulation into the amniotic fluid from fetuses with open *NTDs,* such as spina bifida with myeloschisis, meroanencephaly, or anencephaly (see Chapter 19). Open NTDs refer to lesions that are not covered with skin. Alpha-fetoprotein also enters the amniotic fluid from open ventral wall defects (VWDs), such as gastroschisis and omphalocele (see Chapter 13).

Alpha-Fetoprotein and Fetal Anomalies

The concentration of AFP in the amniotic fluid surrounding fetuses with open NTDs and VWDs is remarkably high. Thus, it is possible to detect the presence of these severe anomalies of the central nervous system and ventral wall by measuring the concentration of AFP in amniotic fluid (Haddow, 1991; Filly et al, 1994). *Amniotic fluid AFP* concentration is measured by immunoassay; when it is used with ultrasonographic scanning, about 99% of fetuses with these severe defects can be diagnosed prenatally. When a fetus has an open NTD, the concentration of AFP is also likely to be higher than normal in the maternal serum. *Maternal serum AFP* concentration is low when the fetus has Down syndrome and other chromosome defects (Thompson et al, 1991).

Chorionic Villus Sampling

Biopsies of chorionic villi (mostly trophoblasts) may be obtained by inserting a needle, guided by ultrasonography, through the mother's abdominal and uterine walls into the uterine cavity (Fig. 7–13*B*). Chorionic villus sampling (CVS) is also performed transcervically using real-time ultrasound guidance (Hogge, 1991; Harman, 1995).

Diagnostic Value of Chorionic Villus Sampling

Biopsies of chorionic villi are used for detecting chromosomal abnormalities, inborn errors of metabolism, and X-linked disorders. Chorionic villus sampling can be performed as early as the ninth week of gestation (7 weeks after fertilization). The rate of fetal loss is about 1%, slightly more than the risk from amniocentesis (Thompson et al, 1991). The major advantage of CVS over amniocentesis is that it allows the results of chromosomal analysis to be available several weeks earlier than when performed by amniocentesis.

Sex Chromatin Patterns

Fetal sex can be diagnosed by noting the presence or absence of sex chromatin in the nuclei of cells recovered from amniotic fluid (Figs. 7-14*A* and *B*). By use of a special staining technique, the Y chromosome can also be identified in cells recovered from the amniotic fluid surrounding male fetuses (Fig. 7-14*C*). Knowledge of *fetal sex* can be useful in diagnosing the presence of severe sex-linked hereditary diseases, such as *hemophilia* and muscular dystrophy (Thompson et al, 1991; Simpson and Elias, 1993). Sex chromatin tests are not routine and are not performed to satisfy the parents' curiosity about the sex of a fetus.

Cell Cultures

Fetal sex and chromosomal aberrations can also be determined by studying the sex chromosomes in cultured fetal cells obtained during amniocentesis. These cultures are commonly done when an autosomal abnormality such as occurs in the Down syndrome is

suspected. *Inborn errors of metabolism* in fetuses can also be detected by studying cell cultures. Enzyme deficiencies can be determined by incubating cells recovered from amniotic fluid and then detecting the specific enzyme deficiency in the cells (Weaver, 1989).

Intrauterine Fetal Transfusion

Some fetuses with *hemolytic disease of the newborn* (HDN) can be saved by receiving intrauterine blood transfusions. The blood is injected through a needle inserted into the fetal peritoneal cavity (Bowman, 1989). Over a period of 5 to 6 days, most of the injected blood cells pass into the fetal circulation through the diaphragmatic lymphatics. With recent advances in *percutaneous umbilical cord puncture*, blood can be transfused directly into the fetal cardiovascular system.

In addition to red blood cell alloimmunization, or HDN, intrauterine fetal transfusion therapy with either red blood cells or platelets is now used for the management of other fetal cytopenias, including alloimmune thrombocytopenia and fetal parvovirus B19 infection (Skupsi et al, 1996; Soothill, 1996). The need for fetal blood transfusions is reduced now because of the treatment of Rh-negative mothers of Rh-positive fetuses with anti-Rh immunoglobulin. Consequently, *HDN is relatively uncommon now* because Rh immune globulin usually prevents development of this disease of the Rh system (Thompson et al, 1991).

Fetoscopy

Using fiberoptic lighting instruments, parts of the fetal body may be directly observed (Reece et al, 1993). It is possible to scan the entire fetus looking for congenital anomalies such as cleft lip and limb defects. The

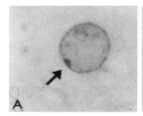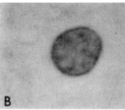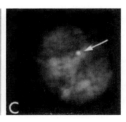

■ **Figure 7–14.** Nuclei of cells in amniotic fluid obtained by amniocentesis. *A*, Chromatin-positive nucleus indicating the presence of a female fetus; the sex chromatin is indicated by an arrow. *B*, Chromatin-negative nucleus indicating the presence of a male fetus. No sex chromatin is visible. Cresylecht violet stain (×1000). *C*, Y-chromatin–positive nucleus indicating presence of a male fetus. The arrow indicates the Y chromatin as an intensely fluorescent body obtained after staining the cell in quinacrine mustard. (*A* and *B* from Riis M, Fuchs F: Sex chromatin and antenatal sex diagnosis. *In* Moore KL (ed): *The Sex Chromatin.* Philadelphia, WB Saunders, 1966.)

fetoscope is usually introduced through the anterior abdominal and uterine walls into the amniotic cavity, similar to the way the needle is inserted during amniocentesis. Fetoscopy is usually carried out between 17 and 20 weeks of gestation, but with new approaches such as *transabdominal thin-gauge embryofetoscopy*, it is possible to detect certain anomalies in the embryo or fetus during the first trimester (Quintero et al, 1993). Because of the risk to the fetus compared with other prenatal diagnostic procedures, fetoscopy now has few indications for routine prenatal diagnosis or treatment of the fetus. For certain disorders, however, prenatal diagnosis depends on the availability of fetal tissues, such as skin, liver, and muscle samples (for more details, see Elias and Simpson, 1993).

Percutaneous Umbilical Cord Blood Sampling

Fetal blood samples may be obtained from the umbilical vessels for chromosome analysis by percutaneous umbilical cords blood sampling (PUBS). Ultrasonographic scanning facilitates the procedure by outlining the location of the vessels. PUBS is often used about 20 weeks after LNMP for chromosome analysis when ultrasonographic or other examinations have shown characteristics of fetal anomalies, such as trisomy 13 (see Chapter 9).

Ultrasonography

Ultrasonography is the primary imaging modality in the evaluation of the fetus because of its wide availability, low cost, and lack of known adverse effects (Feldstein and Popovitch, 1994). The chorionic (gestational) sac and its contents may be visualized by ultrasonography during the embryonic and fetal periods. Placental and fetal size, multiple births, abnormalities of placental shape, and abnormal presentations can also be determined (Townsend, 1994).

Ultrasound scans give accurate measurements of the BPD of the fetal skull, from which close estimates of fetal age and length can be made (Hadlock, 1994a,b). Figure 7–15 illustrates how details of the fetus can be observed in ultrasound scans. Ultrasound examinations are also helpful for diagnosing abnormal pregnancies at a very early stage (Filly, 1991b), such as the "blighted embryo."

Computed Tomography and Magnetic Resonance Imaging

When planning fetal treatment, such as surgery (Filly, 1991a,b), computed tomography (CT) and magnetic

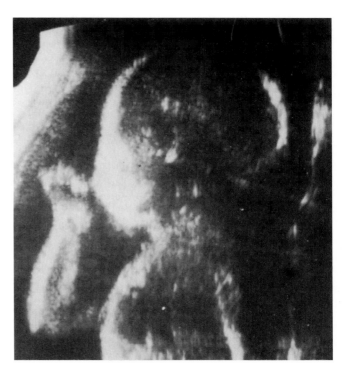

■ **Figure 7–15.** Ultrasound scan (sonogram) of a 30-week fetus that is sucking its thumb. Observe that its forearm bones are visible. The biparietal diameter of the head can be determined and compared with the abdominal diameter. Determination of these measurements facilitates estimation of the age and weight of the fetus. (From Thompson JS, Thompson MW: *Genetics in Medicine*, 3rd ed. Philadelphia, WB Saunders, 1980. Courtesy of Stuart Campbell.)

resonance imaging (MRI) may be used to provide more information about an abnormality that has been detected in ultrasonic images. The disadvantages of current MRI include high cost, fixed planes of section, and limited fetal resolution. Computed tomography is helpful for differentiating between monoamniotic and diamniotic twins, that is, in one or two amniotic sacs (see Chapter 8). This is important to know for management of the pregnancy because the perinatal mortality of monoamniotic twins is high — 30 to 50% risk of death (Finberg, 1994).

Fetal Monitoring

Continuous fetal heart rate monitoring in high-risk pregnancies is routine and provides information about the oxygenation of the fetus. *Fetal distress*, such as that indicated by an abnormal heart rate or rhythm, suggests that the fetus is in jeopardy.

Fetal Stress

Prenatal fetal distress has various causes, such as maternal diseases that reduce oxygen transport to the fetus (e.g., cyanotic heart disease). The external mode of monitoring uses transducers placed on the mother's abdomen. For example, an ultrasound transducer picks up high-frequency sound waves that reflect the mechanical action of the fetal heart. For more information on fetal distress and continuous fetal heart monitoring, see Harman (1995) and Manning (1995).

SUMMARY OF FETAL PERIOD

The fetal period begins 9 weeks after fertilization (11 weeks after LNMP) and ends at birth. It is characterized by rapid body growth and differentiation of tissues and organ systems. An obvious change in the fetal period is the relative slowing of head growth compared with that of the rest of the body. By the beginning of the 20th week, lanugo and head hair appear, and the skin is coated with vernix caseosa. The eyelids are closed during most of the fetal period but begin to reopen at about 26 weeks. At this time the fetus is usually capable of extrauterine existence, mainly because of the maturity of its respiratory system.

Until about 30 weeks, the fetus appears reddish and wizened because of the thinness of its skin and the relative absence of subcutaneous fat. Fat usually develops rapidly during the last 6 to 8 weeks, giving the fetus a smooth, plump appearance. This terminal ("finishing") period is devoted mainly to building up tissues and preparing systems involved in the transition from intrauterine to extrauterine environments, primarily the respiratory and cardiovascular systems. Changes occurring during the fetal period are not so dramatic as those appearing in the embryonic period, but they are very important. The fetus is less vulnerable to the teratogenic effects of drugs, viruses, and radiation, but these agents may interfere with growth and normal functional development, especially of the brain and eyes (see Chapter 9).

Various techniques are available for assessing the status of the fetus and for diagnosing certain diseases and developmental anomalies before birth. The physician can now determine whether or not a fetus has a particular disease or a congenital anomaly by using various diagnostic techniques, such as amniocentesis and ultrasonography. Prenatal diagnosis can be made early enough to allow early termination of the pregnancy if elected, such as when serious anomalies in-

compatible with postnatal life are diagnosed. In selected cases, various treatments can be given to the fetus (Soothill, 1996), for example, the administration of drugs to correct cardiac arrhythmia or thyroid disorders. Surgical correction of congenital anomalies in utero is also possible, such as ureterostomies on fetuses that have ureters that do not open into the bladder (Harrison, 1991).

Clinically Oriented Questions

1. I have heard that the mature embryo twitches and a first trimester fetus moves its limbs. Is this true? If so, can the mother feel her baby kicking at this time?

2. Some women have "morning sickness" during early pregnancy. What type of illness is this? How is it treated?

3. I have heard that the baby can cause cavities in the mother's teeth. Is this true?

4. I read in the paper that vitamin supplementation around the time of conception will prevent neural tube defects (NTDs) such as spina bifida. Is there scientific proof for this statement?

5. Can the fetus be injured by the needle during amniocentesis? Is there a risk of inducing a miscarriage or causing maternal or fetal infection?

The answers to these questions are given at the back of the book.

REFERENCES AND SUGGESTED READING

Abramowicz JS, Sherer DM, Bar-Tov E, Woods JR Jr: The cheek-to-cheek diameter in the ultrasonographic assessment of fetal growth. *Am J Obstet Gynecol* 165:846, 1991.

Barnea ER, Hustin J, Jauniaux E (eds): *The First Twelve Weeks of Gestation*. Berlin, Springer-Verlag, 1992.

Behrman RE, Kleigman RM, Arvin AM (eds): *Nelson Textbook of Pediatrics*, 15th ed. Philadelphia, WB Saunders, 1996.

Bernstein IM, Blake K, Wall B, Badger GJ: Evidence that normal fetal growth can be noncontinuous. *J Maternal-Fetal Med* 4:197, 1995.

Birnholz JC: The development of human fetal eye movement patterns. *Science* 213:679, 1981.

Boles ET Jr: The spleen. *In* Schiller M (ed): *Pediatric Surgery of the Liver, Pancreas and Spleen*. Philadelphia, WB Saunders, 1991.

Bowman JM: Hemolytic disease (erythroblastosis fetalis). *In* Creasy RK, Resnik R (eds): *Maternal-Fetal Medicine: Principles and Practice*, 2nd ed. Philadelphia, WB Saunders, 1989.

Creasy RK, Resnik R: Intrauterine growth retardation. *In* Creasy RK, Resnik R (eds): *Maternal-Fetal Medicine: Principles and Practice*, 2nd ed. Philadelphia, WB Saunders, 1989.

Drife JO: Can the fetus listen and learn? *Br J Obstet Gynaecol* 92:777, 1985.

Elias S, Simpson JL: Amniocentesis. *In* Simpson JL, Elias S (eds): *Essentials of Prenatal Diagnosis*. New York, Churchill Livingstone, 1993.

England MA: *Color Atlas of Life Before Birth*. Chicago, Year Book Medical Publishers, 1983.

Feldstein VA, Popovitch MJ: The role of computed tomography and magnetic resonance imaging in obstetrics. *In* Callen PW (ed): *Ultrasonography in Obstetrics and Gynecology,* 3rd ed. Philadelphia, WB Saunders, 1994.

Filly RA: Alternative imaging techniques: Computed tomography and magnetic resonance imaging. *In* Harrison MR, Golbus MS, Filly RA (eds): *The Unborn Patient: Prenatal Diagnosis and Treatment*, 2nd ed. Philadelphia, WB Saunders, 1991a.

Filly RA: Sonographic anatomy of the normal fetus. *In* Harrison MR, Golbus MS, Filly RA (eds): *The Unborn Patient: Prenatal Diagnosis and Treatment*, 2nd ed. Philadelphia, WB Saunders, 1991b.

Filly RA: Ultrasound evaluation during the first trimester. *In* Callen PW (ed): *Ultrasonography in Obstetrics and Gynecology*, 3rd ed. Philadelphia, WB Saunders, 1994.

Filly RA, Callen PW, Goldstein RB: α-Fetoprotein screening programs: What every obstetric sonologist should know. *In* Callen PW (ed): *Ultrasonography in Obstetrics and Gynecology*, 3rd ed. Philadelphia, WB Saunders, 1994.

Finberg HJ: Ultrasound evaluations in multiple gestation: *In* Callen PW (ed): *Ultrasonography in Obstetrics and Gynecology*, 3rd ed. Philadelphia, WB Saunders, 1994.

Ghidini A: Idiopathic fetal growth restriction: A pathophysiologic approach. *Obstet Gynecol Surv* 51:376, 1996.

Goldberg JD: The role of genetic screening in the obstetric patient. *In* Callen PW (ed): *Ultrasonography in Obstetrics and Gynecology*, 3rd ed. Philadelphia, WB Saunders, 1994.

Hadlock FP: Fetal growth. *In* Callen PW (ed): *Ultrasonography in Obstetrics and Gynecology*, 3rd ed. Philadelphia, WB Saunders, 1994a.

Hadlock FP: Ultrasound determination of menstrual age. *In* Callen PW (ed): *Ultrasonography in Obstetrics and Gynecology*, 3rd ed. Philadelphia, WB Saunders, 1994b.

Haddow JE: α-Fetoprotein. *In* Harrison MR, Golbus MS, Filly RA (eds): *The Unborn Patient: Prenatal Diagnosis and Treatment*, 2nd ed. Philadelphia, WB Saunders, 1991.

Harding JE, Charlton V: Experimental nutritional supplementation for intrauterine growth retardation. *In* Harrison MR, Golbus MS, Filly RA (eds): *The Unborn Patient: Prenatal Diagnosis and Treatment*, 2nd ed. Philadelphia, WB Saunders, 1991.

Harman CR (ed): *Invasive Fetal Testing and Treatment*. Boston, Blackwell Scientific Publication, 1995.

Harrison MR: Selection for treatment: Which defects are correctable? *In* Harrison MR, Golbus MS, Filly RA (eds): *The Unborn Patient: Prenatal Diagnosis and Treatment*, 2nd ed. Philadelphia, WB Saunders, 1991.

Hogge WA: Chorionic villus sampling. *In* Harrison MR, Golbus MS, Filly RA (eds): *The Unborn Patient: Prenatal Diagnosis and Treatment*, 2nd ed. Philadelphia, WB Saunders, 1991.

Illsley R, Mitchell RG: The developing concept of low birth weight and the present state of knowledge. *In* Illsley R, Mitchell RGF (eds): *Low Birth Weight: A Medical, Psychological and Social Study*. New York, John Wiley & Sons, 1984.

Lee W, Barton S, Comstock CH, et al: Transverse cerebellar diameter: A useful predictor of gestational age for fetuses with asymmetric growth retardation. *Am J Obstet Gynecol* 165:1044, 1991.

Manning FA: *Fetal Medicine: Principles and Practice*. Norwalk, Appleton & Lange, 1995.

Miller HC, Merritt TA: *Fetal Growth in Humans*. Chicago, Year Book Medical Publishers, 1979.

Nash JE, Persaud TVN: Embryopathic risks of cigarette smoking. *Exp Pathol* 33:65, 1988.

Page EW, Villee CA, Villee DB: *Human Reproduction: Essentials of Reproductive and Perinatal Medicine*, 3rd ed. Philadelphia, WB Saunders, 1981.

Persaud TVN: *Environmental Causes of Human Birth Defects*. Springfield, IL, Charles C Thomas, 1990.

Persaud TVN: Fetal alcohol syndrome. *CRC Critical Rev Anat Cell Biol* 1:277, 1988.

Quintero RA, Puder KS, Cotton DB: Embryoscopy and fetoscopy. *Obstet Gynecol Clin North Am* 20:563, 1993.

Reece EA, Whetham J, Rotmensch S, Wiznitzer, A: Gaining access to the embryonic-fetal circulation via first-trimester endoscopy: A step into the future. *Obstet Gynecol* 82:876, 1993.

Skupsi DW, Wolf CFW, Bussel JB: Fetal transfusion therapy. *Obstet Gynecol Surv* 51:181, 1996.

Soothill P: Fetal and perinatal medicine. *Br J Hosp Med* 56:141, 1996.

Thompson MW, McInnes RR, Willard HF (eds): *Thompson & Thompson Genetics in Medicine,* 5th ed. Philadelphia, WB Saunders, 1991.

Townsend RR: Ultrasound evaluation of the placenta and umbilical cord. *In* Callen PW (ed): *Ultrasonography in Obstetrics and Gynecology*, 3rd ed. Philadelphia, WB Saunders, 1994.

Weaver DD: Inborn errors of metabolism. *In* Weaver DD (ed): *Catalogue of Prenatally Diagnosed Conditions*. Baltimore, John Hopkins University Press, 1989.

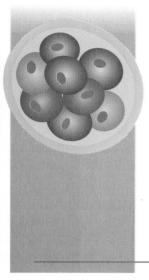

Placenta and Fetal Membranes

8

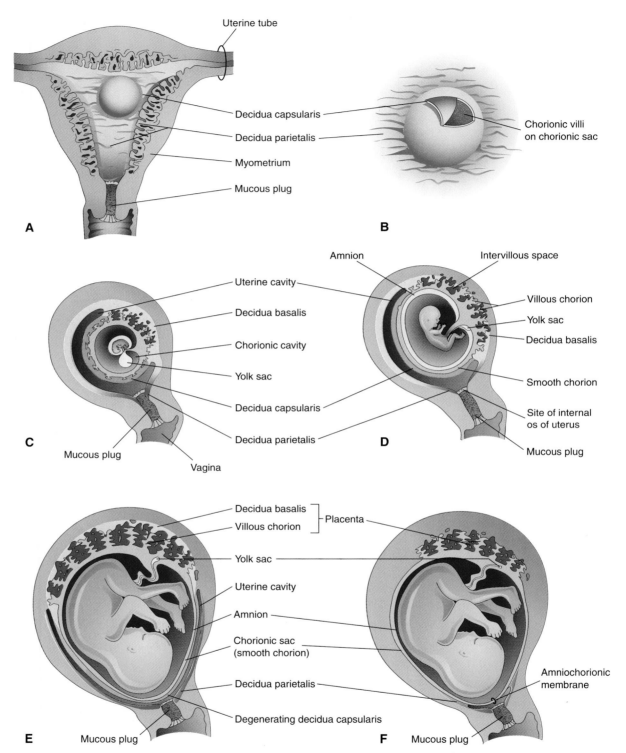

■ Figure 8–1. Drawings illustrating development of the placenta and fetal membranes. *A*, Coronal section of the uterus showing elevation of the decidua capsularis by the expanding chorionic sac of a 4-week embryo, implanted in the endometrium on the posterior wall. *B*, Enlarged drawing of the implantation site. The chorionic villi were exposed by cutting an opening in the decidua capsularis. *C* to *F*, Sagittal sections of the gravid uterus from the 5th to 22nd weeks, showing the changing relations of the fetal membranes to the decidua. In *F*, the amnion and chorion are fused with each other and the decidua parietalis, thereby obliterating the uterine cavity. Note in *D* to *F* that the chorionic villi persist only where the chorion is associated with the decidua basalis.

■ The fetal part of the placenta and the fetal membranes separate the fetus from the endometrium of the uterus. An interchange of substances (e.g., nutrients and oxygen) occurs between the maternal and fetal blood streams through the placenta. The vessels in the umbilical cord connect the placental circulation with the fetal circulation.

The chorion, amnion, yolk sac, and allantois constitute the fetal membranes. They develop from the zygote but do not participate in the formation of the embryo or fetus, except for parts of the yolk sac and allantois. Part of the yolk sac is incorporated into the embryo as the primordium of the gut. The allantois becomes a fibrous cord that is known as the urachus in the fetus and the median umbilical ligament in the adult. It extends from the apex of the urinary bladder to the umbilicus.

THE PLACENTA

The placenta is the primary site of nutrient and gas exchange between the mother and fetus. The placenta is a **fetomaternal organ** that has two components:

- A **fetal portion** that develops from part of the chorionic sac
- A **maternal portion** that is derived from the endometrium

The placenta and umbilical cord function as a *transport system* for substances passing between the mother and fetus. Nutrients and oxygen pass from the maternal blood through the placenta to the fetal blood, and waste materials and carbon dioxide pass from the fetal blood through the placenta to the maternal blood. The placenta and fetal membranes perform the following functions and activities:

- Protection
- Nutrition
- Respiration
- Excretion
- Hormone production

Shortly after the birth of a baby the placenta and fetal membranes are expelled from the uterus as the *afterbirth*.

Decidua

The decidua (L. *deciduus*, a falling off) refers to the *gravid endometrium* — the functional layer of the endometrium in a pregnant woman. The term *decidua* is appropriate because this part of the endometrium separates ("falls away") from the remainder of the uterus after *parturition* (childbirth).

Three regions of the decidua are named according to their relation to the implantation site (Fig. 8–1):

- The **decidua basalis** is the part of the decidua deep to the conceptus that forms the maternal component of the placenta.
- The **decidua capsularis** is the superficial part of the decidua overlying the conceptus.
- The **decidua parietalis** (decidua vera) is all the remaining parts of the decidua.

In response to increasing progesterone levels in the maternal blood, the stromal (connective tissue) cells of the decidua enlarge to form pale-staining **decidual cells**. These cells enlarge as glycogen and lipid accumulate in their cytoplasm. The decidual cellular and vascular changes resulting from pregnancy are referred to as the **decidual reaction**. Many decidual cells degenerate near the chorionic sac in the region of the *syncytiotrophoblast* and, together with maternal blood and uterine secretions, provide a rich source of nutrition for the embryo. Decidual regions clearly recognizable during *ultrasonography* are important in diagnosing early pregnancy (Filly, 1994; Townsend, 1994).

Development of Placenta

Previous descriptions of early placental development traced the rapid proliferation of the trophoblast and development of the chorionic sac and chorionic villi (see Chapters 4 and 5). By the end of the third week, the anatomic arrangements necessary for physiologic exchanges between the mother and embryo are established. A complex vascular network is established in the placenta by the end of the fourth week which facilitates maternal-embryonic exchanges of gases, nutrients, and metabolic waste products.

Chorionic villi cover the entire chorionic sac until the beginning of the eighth week (Figs. 8–1C, 8–2, and 8–3A). As this sac grows, the villi associated with the decidua capsularis are compressed, reducing the blood supply to them. These villi soon degenerate (Figs. 8–1D and 8–3B), producing a relatively avascular bare area, the **smooth chorion**. As the villi disappear, those associated with the decidua basalis rapidly increase in number, branch profusely, and enlarge (Fig. 8–4). This bushy portion of the chorionic sac is the **villous chorion**.

Ultrasonography of Chorionic Sac

The size of the chorionic sac is useful in determining *gestational age* of embryos in patients with uncertain menstrual histories (Filly, 1994). The early chorionic sac is filled with *chorionic fluid* because the amniotic

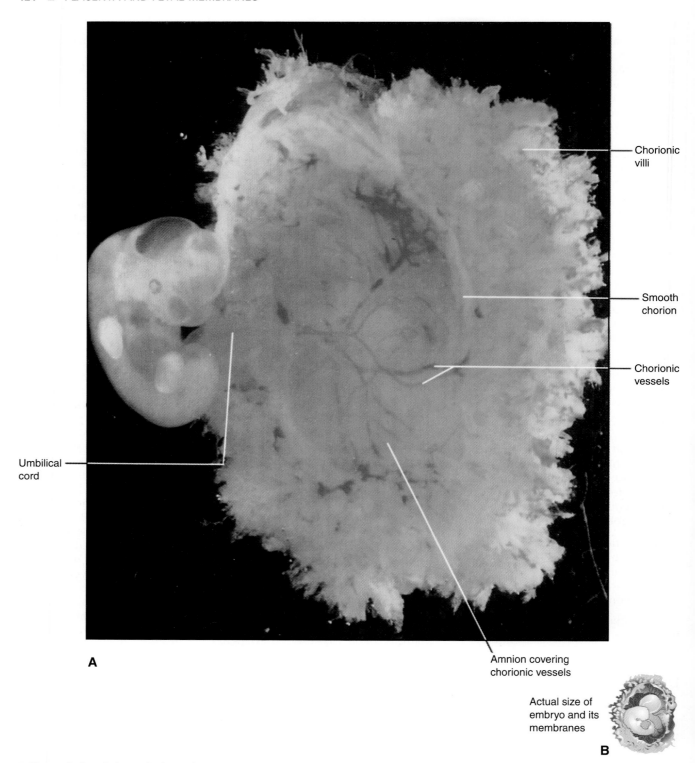

Chorionic
villi

Smooth
chorion

Chorionic
vessels

Umbilical
cord

Amnion covering
chorionic vessels

Actual size of
embryo and its
membranes

A

B

■ **Figure 8–2.** *A,* Lateral view of a spontaneously aborted embryo at Carnegie stage 14, about 32 days. The chorionic and amniotic sacs have been opened to show the embryo. Note the large size of the yolk sac at this stage. *B,* Actual size of the embryo and its membranes.

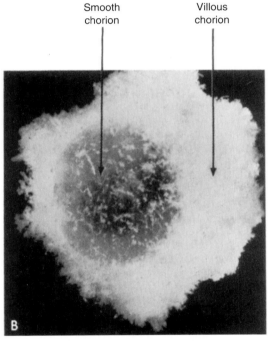

Smooth chorion   Villous chorion

■ **Figure 8-3.** Photographs of spontaneously aborted human chorionic sacs. *A,* At 21 days. The entire sac is covered with chorionic villi (×4). *B,* At 8 weeks. Actual size. As the decidua capsularis becomes stretched and thin, the chorionic villi on the corresponding part of the chorionic sac gradually degenerate and disappear, leaving a smooth chorion. The remaining villous chorion forms the fetal part of the placenta. (From Potter EL, Craig JM: *Pathology of the Fetus and the Infant,* 3rd ed. Chicago, Year Book Medical Publishers, 1975.)

sac containing the embryo and the yolk sac are relatively small (Fig. 8-1*C*). Growth of the chorionic sac is extremely rapid between the 5th and 10th weeks. Modern ultrasound equipment, especially instruments

equipped with intravaginal transducers, enables sonologists to detect the chorionic (gestational) sac when it has a *median sac diameter* of 2 to 3 mm (Fig. 8-5). Chorionic sacs with this diameter indicate that the gestational age is about 4 weeks and 3 to 4 days (Filly, 1994), that is, 18 days after fertilization.

The uterus, chorionic sac, and placenta enlarge as the embryo and fetus grow. Growth in the size and thickness of the placenta continues rapidly until the fetus is about 18 weeks old (20 weeks' gestation). The fully developed placenta covers 15 to 30% of the decidua and weighs about one-sixth that of the fetus. The placenta has two parts (Figs. 8-1*E* and 8-6):

• The **fetal component of the placenta** is formed by the *villous chorion*. The stem villi that arise from it project into the intervillous space containing maternal blood.
• **The maternal component of the placenta** is formed by the *decidua basalis*, the part of the decidua related to the fetal component of the placenta. By the end of the fourth month, the decidua basalis is almost entirely replaced by the fetal component of the placenta.

FETOMATERNAL JUNCTION

The fetal part of the placenta (villous chorion) is attached to the maternal part of the placenta (decidua basalis) by the **cytotrophoblastic shell** — the external layer of trophoblastic cells on the maternal surface of the placenta (Fig. 8-7). *Stem chorionic villi* (anchoring villi) are attached firmly to the decidua basalis through the cytotrophoblastic shell and anchor the *chorionic sac* to the decidua basalis. Endometrial arteries and veins pass freely through gaps in the cytotrophoblastic shell and open into the intervillous space.

The **shape of the placenta** is determined by the shape of the persistent area of chorionic villi (Fig. 8-1*F*). Usually this is a circular area, giving the placenta a discoid shape (see Fig. 8-7). As the chorionic villi invade the decidua basalis during placental formation, decidual tissue is eroded to enlarge the intervillous space. This erosion process produces several wedge-shaped areas of decidua, **placental septa**, that project toward the **chorionic plate** (Fig. 8-7). The placental septa divide the fetal part of the placenta into irregular convex areas called **cotyledons** (Fig. 8-4). Each cotyledon, visible on the maternal surface of the placenta, consists of two or more stem villi and their many branch villi. By the end of the fourth

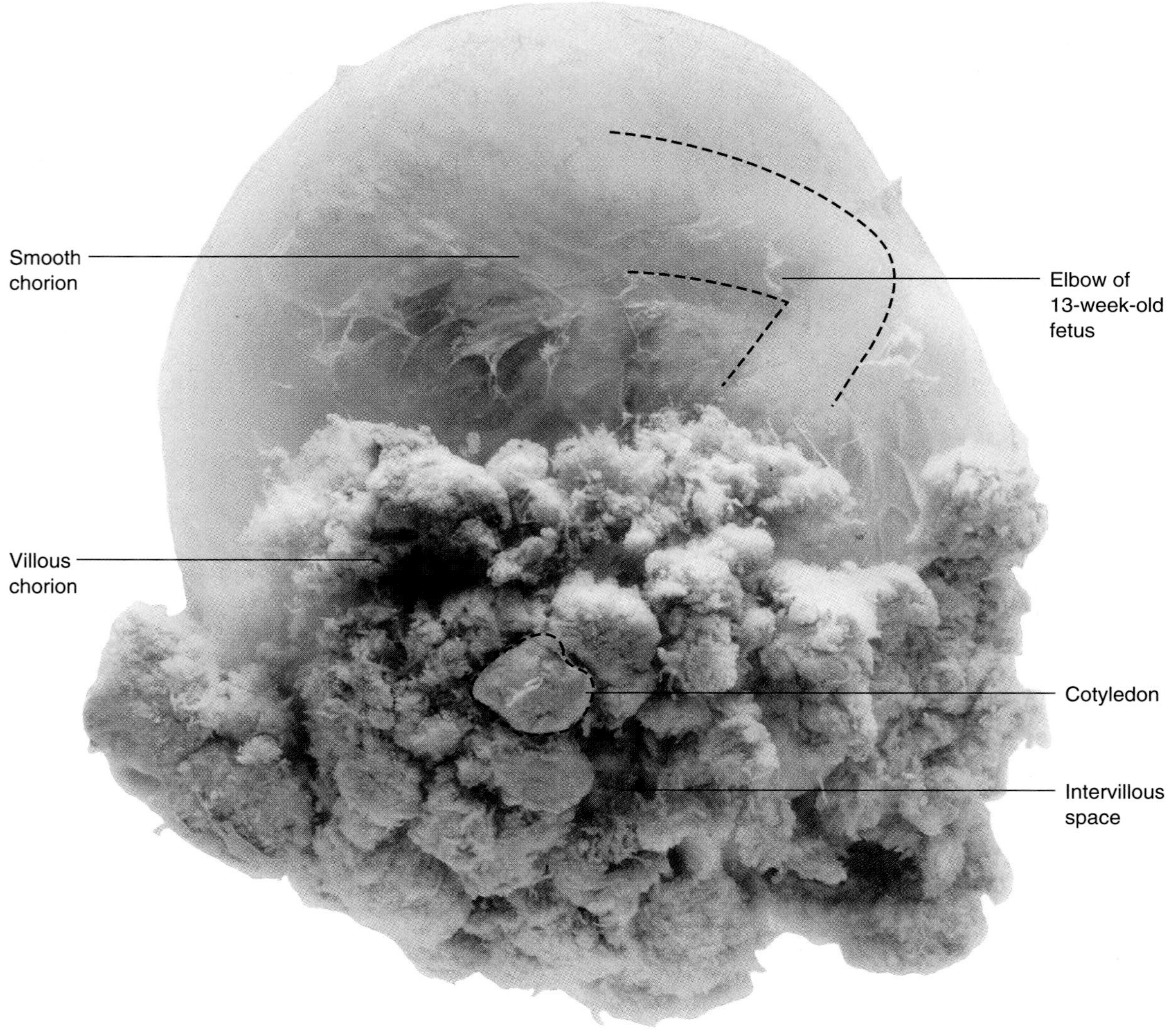

■ **Figure 8–4.** Photograph of a human chorionic sac containing a 13-week fetus. The smooth chorion formed when the chorionic villi degenerated and disappeared from this area of the chorionic sac. The villous chorion (chorion frondosum) is where chorionic villi persist and form the fetal part of the placenta. In situ the cotyledons were attached to the decidua basalis, and the intervillous space was filled with maternal blood.

month, the decidua basalis is almost entirely replaced by the cotyledons.

The **decidua capsularis**, the layer of decidua overlying the implanted chorionic sac, forms a capsule over the external surface of the sac (Fig. 8–1A to D). As the conceptus enlarges, the decidua capsularis bulges into the uterine cavity and becomes greatly attenuated. Eventually the decidua capsularis contacts and fuses with the decidua parietalis, thereby slowly obliterating the uterine cavity (Fig. 8–1E and F). By

22 to 24 weeks, reduced blood supply to the decidua capsularis causes it to degenerate and disappear. After disappearance of the decidua capsularis, the smooth part of the chorionic sac fuses with the decidua parietalis. This fusion can be separated and usually occurs when blood escapes from the intervillous space of the placenta (Fig. 8–6). The collection of blood (*hematoma*) pushes the chorionic membrane away from the decidua parietalis, thereby reestablishing the potential space of the uterine cavity.

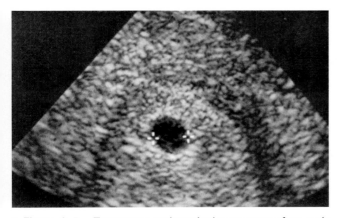

■ Figure 8–5. Transverse endovaginal sonogram of an early chorionic sac (before visualization of a yolk sac), showing how the mean sac diameter is measured. This image depicts the transverse diameter (between the cursors) measured from the chorionic tissue–fluid interfaces. (From Filly RA: Ultrasound evaluation during the first trimester. *In* Callen PW (ed): *Ultrasonography is Obstetrics and Gynecology*, 3rd ed. Philadelphia, WB Saunders, 1994.)

INTERVILLOUS SPACE

The intervillous space of the placenta contains maternal blood, which is derived from the lacunae that developed in the syncytiotrophoblast during the second week of development (Fig. 4–1*C*). This large blood-filled space results from the coalescence and enlargement of the lacunar networks. The intervillous space of the placenta is divided into compartments by the **placental septa**; however, free communication occurs between the compartments because the septa do not reach the *chorionic plate* (Fig. 8–7)—the part of the chorionic membrane associated with the placenta. Maternal blood enters the intervillous space from the *spiral endometrial arteries* in the decidua basalis. The spiral arteries pass through gaps in the cytotrophoblastic shell and discharge blood into the intervillous space. This large space is drained by endometrial veins that also penetrate the cytotrophoblastic shell. These veins are found over the entire surface of the decidua basalis. The numerous **branch villi**—arising from

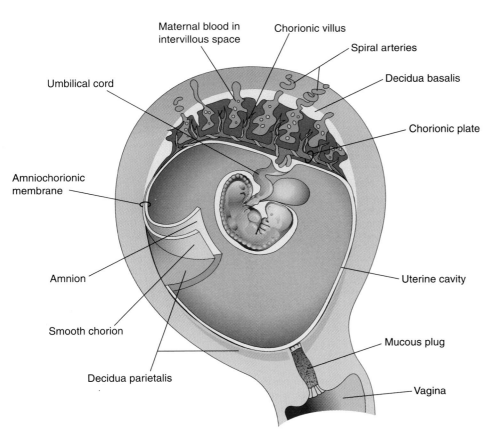

■ Figure 8–6. Drawing of a sagittal section of a gravid uterus at 4 weeks showing the relation of the fetal membranes to each other and to the decidua and embryo. The amnion and smooth chorion have been cut and reflected to show their relationship to each other and to the decidua parietalis.

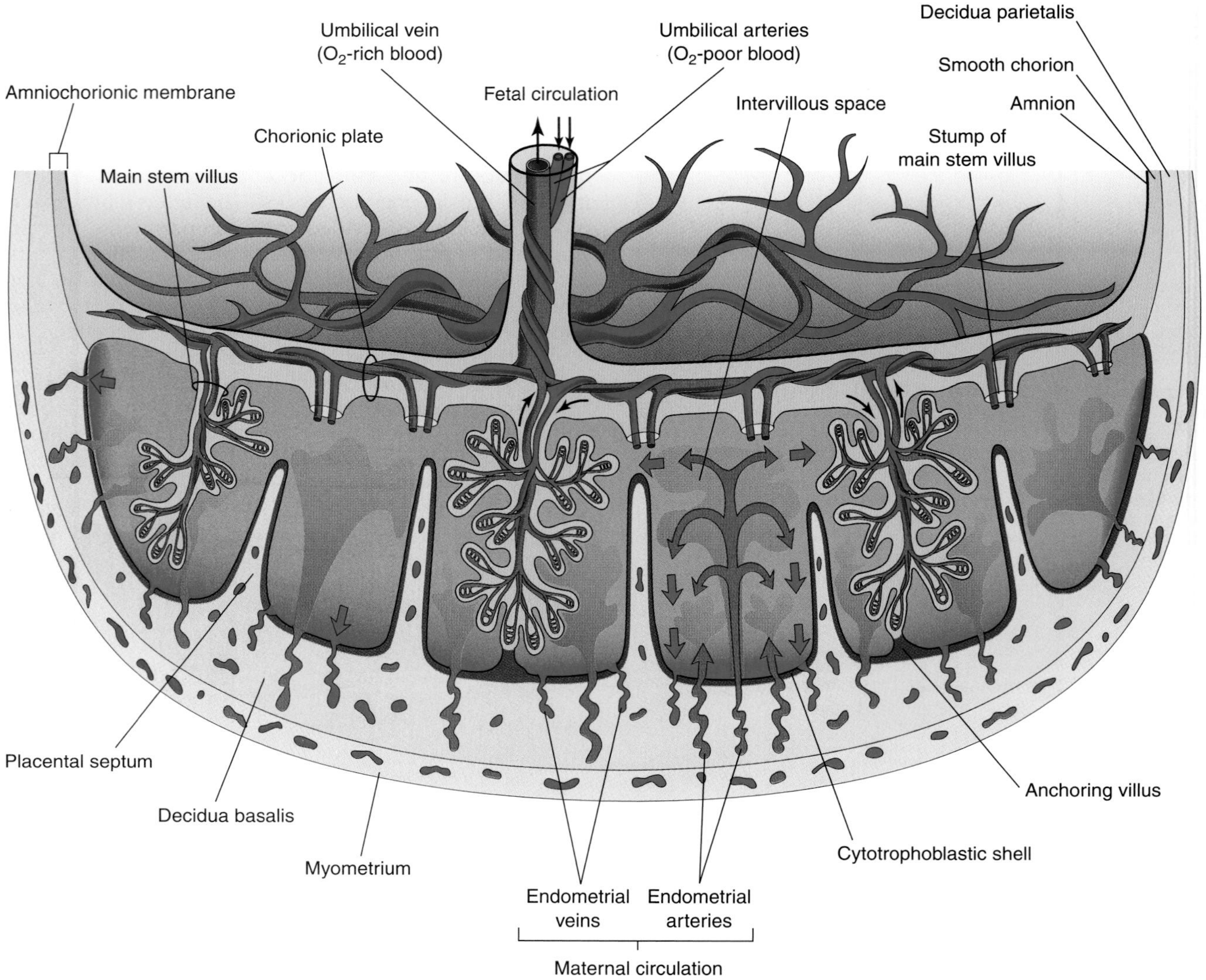

■ **Figure 8–7.**   Schematic drawing of a transverse section through a full-term placenta, showing (1) the relation of the villous chorion (fetal part of placenta) to the decidua basalis (maternal part of placenta); (2) the fetal placental circulation; and (3) the maternal placental circulation. Maternal blood flows into the intervillous spaces in funnel-shaped spurts from the spiral arteries, and exchanges occur with the fetal blood as the maternal blood flows around the branch villi. It is through the branch villi that the main exchange of material between the mother and embryo/fetus occurs. The inflowing arterial blood pushes venous blood out of the intervillous space into the endometrial veins, which are scattered over the entire surface of the decidua basalis. Note that the umbilical arteries carry poorly oxygenated fetal blood (shown in blue) to the placenta and that the umbilical vein carries oxygenated blood (shown in red) to the fetus. Note that the cotyledons are separated from each other by placental septa, projections of the decidua basalis. Each cotyledon consists of two or more main stem villi and their many branches. In this drawing, only one stem villus is shown in each cotyledon, but the stumps of those that have been removed are indicated.

stem chorionic villi — are continuously showered with maternal blood as it circulates through the intervillous space. The blood carries oxygen and nutritional materials that are necessary for fetal growth and development. The maternal blood also contains fetal waste products such as carbon dioxide, salts, and products of protein metabolism.

AMNIOCHORIONIC MEMBRANE

The amniotic sac enlarges faster than the chorionic sac. As a result, the amnion and smooth chorion soon fuse to form the amniochorionic membrane (Figs. 8–6 and 8–7). This composite membrane fuses with the decidua capsularis and, after disappearance of this capsular part of the decidua, adheres to the decidua parie-talis (Fig. 8–1*F*). It is the amniochorionic membrane that ruptures during labor. Preterm rupture of this membrane is the most common event leading to premature labor. When the amniochorionic membrane ruptures, the amniotic fluid escapes through the cervix and vagina to the exterior.

Placental Circulation

The many *branch chorionic villi* of the placenta provide a large surface area where materials may be exchanged across the very thin **placental membrane** (barrier) interposed between the fetal and maternal circulations (Figs. 8–7 and 8–8). It is through the numerous branch villi, which arise from the *stem villi*, that the main exchange of material between the mother and fetus takes place. The circulations of the fetus and the mother are separated by the placental membrane, consisting of extrafetal tissues (Figs. 8–8*B* and *C*).

FETAL PLACENTAL CIRCULATION

Poorly oxygenated blood leaves the fetus and passes through the **umbilical arteries** to the placenta. At the attachment of the cord to the placenta, these arteries divide into a number of radially disposed **chorionic arteries** that branch freely in the *chorionic plate* before entering the chorionic villi (Fig. 8–7). The blood vessels form an extensive **arterio-capillary-venous system** within the chorionic villi (Fig. 8–8*A*), which brings the fetal blood extremely close to the maternal blood. This system provides a very large area for the exchange of metabolic and gaseous products between the maternal and fetal blood streams.

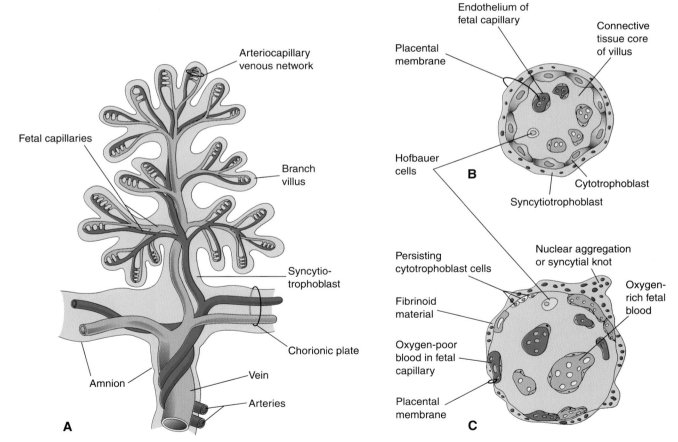

■ **Figure 8–8.** *A*, Drawing of a stem chorionic villus showing its arteriocapillary-venous system. The arteries carry poorly oxygenated fetal blood and waste products from the fetus, whereas the vein carries oxygenated blood and nutrients to the fetus. *B* and *C*, Drawings of sections through a branch villus at 10 weeks and full term, respectively. The placental membrane, composed of extrafetal tissues, separates the maternal blood in the intervillous space from the fetal blood in the capillaries in the villi. Note that the placental membrane becomes very thin at full term. Hofbauer cells are thought to be phagocytic cells.

Normally no intermingling of fetal and maternal blood occurs, but very small amounts of fetal blood may enter the maternal circulation through minute defects that sometimes develop in the placental membrane. The well-oxygenated fetal blood in the fetal capillaries passes into thin-walled veins that follow the chorionic arteries to the site of attachment of the umbilical cord, where they converge to form the **umbilical vein**. This large vessel carries oxygen-rich blood to the fetus (Fig. 8–7).

MATERNAL PLACENTAL CIRCULATION

The blood in the intervillous space is temporarily outside the maternal circulatory system. It enters the intervillous space through 80 to 100 **spiral endometrial arteries** in the decidua basalis. These vessels discharge into the intervillous space through gaps in the cytotrophoblastic shell. The blood flow from the spiral arteries is pulsatile and is propelled in jetlike fountains by the maternal blood pressure (Fig. 8–7). The entering blood is at a considerably higher pressure than that in the intervillous space and spurts toward the **chorionic plate**, forming the "roof" of the intervillous space. As the pressure dissipates, the blood flows slowly around the branch villi, allowing an exchange of metabolic and gaseous products with the fetal blood. The blood eventually returns through the endometrial veins to the maternal circulation.

The welfare of the embryo and fetus depends more on adequate bathing of the branch villi with maternal blood than on any other factor. Reductions of uteroplacental circulation result in fetal hypoxia and intrauterine growth retardation (IUGR) (Werler et al, 1986). Severe reductions of uteroplacental circulation may result in fetal death. The intervillous space of the mature placenta contains about 150 ml of blood that is replenished three or four times per minute.

THE PLACENTAL MEMBRANE

The placental membrane is a composite membrane that consists of the *extrafetal tissues separating the maternal and fetal blood*. Until about 20 weeks, the placental membrane consists of four layers (Figs. 8–8 and 8–9):

- Syncytiotrophoblast
- Cytotrophoblast
- Connective tissue of villus
- Endothelium of fetal capillaries

After the 20th week, histologic changes occur in the branch villi that result in the cytotrophoblast becoming attenuated in many of the villi. Eventually cytotrophoblast cells disappear over large areas of the villi, leaving only thin patches of syncytiotrophoblast. As a result, the placental membrane at full term consists of three layers only in most places (Fig. 8–8C). In some areas the placental membrane becomes markedly thinned and attenuated. At these sites the syncytiotrophoblast comes in direct contact with the endothelium of the fetal capillaries to form a *vasculosyncytial placental membrane*. The placental membrane was formerly called the *placental barrier*—an inappropriate term because only a few substances, endogenous or exogenous, are unable to pass through the placental membrane in detectable amounts (Kraemer and Noerr, 1997). The placental membrane acts as a true barrier only when the molecule has a certain size, configuration, and charge such as heparin and bacteria. Some metabolites, toxins, and hormones, although present in the maternal circulation, do not pass through the placental membrane in sufficient concentrations to affect the embryo/fetus.

Most drugs and other substances in the maternal plasma pass through the placental membrane and are found in the fetal plasma (Fig. 8–9). Electron micrographs of the syncytiotrophoblast show that its free surface has many *microvilli* that increase the surface area for exchange between the maternal and fetal circulations (Benirschke and Kaufman, 1990). As pregnancy advances, the placental membrane becomes progressively thinner so that blood in many fetal capillaries is extremely close to the maternal blood in the intervillous space (Fig. 8–8C).

During the third trimester, numerous nuclei in the syncytiotrophoblast of the villi aggregate to form multinucleated protrusions or nuclear aggregations—**syncytial knots**. These aggregations continually break off and are carried from the intervillous space into the maternal circulation. Some knots lodge in capillaries of the maternal lung, where they are rapidly destroyed by local enzyme action. Toward the end of pregnancy, **fibrinoid material** forms on the surfaces of villi. This material consists of fibrin and other unidentified substances that stain intensely with eosin. Fibrinoid material results mainly from aging and appears to reduce placental transfer.

Functions of the Placenta

The placenta has three main functions:

- Metabolism (e.g., synthesis of glycogen)
- Transport of gases and nutrients
- Endocrine secretion (e.g., human chorionic gonadotropin [hCG])

These comprehensive activities are essential for maintaining pregnancy and promoting normal fetal development. For a discussion of other placental transport mechanisms, see Moore and Persaud (1998).

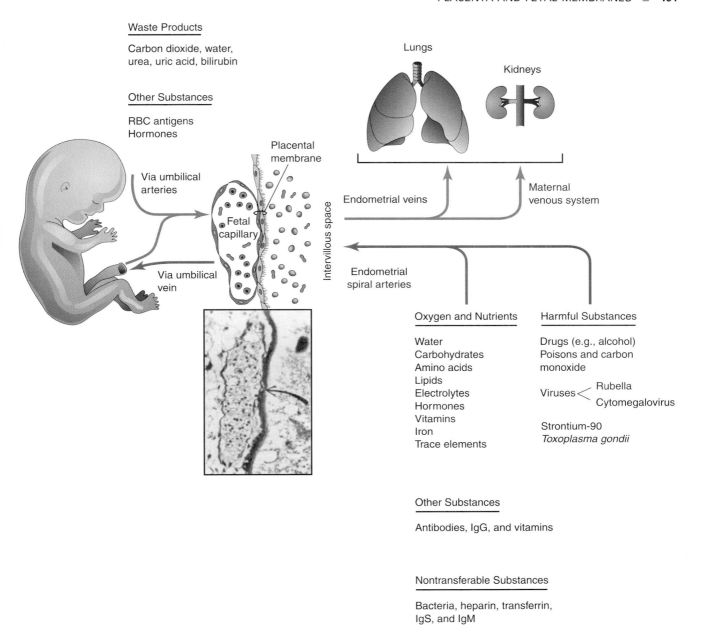

■ Figure 8–9. Diagrammatic illustration of transfer across the placental membrane (barrier). The extrafetal tissues, across which transport of substances between the mother and fetus occurs, collectively constitute the placental membrane. (Inset photo from Javert CT: *Spontaneous and Habitual Abortion.* 1957. Courtesy of The Blakiston Division, McGraw-Hill Book Co. Copyright 1957 by McGraw-Hill. Used by permission of McGraw-Hill Book Co.)

PLACENTAL METABOLISM

The placenta, particularly during early pregnancy, synthesizes glycogen, cholesterol, and fatty acids, which serve as sources of nutrients and energy for the embryo/fetus. Many of its metabolic activities are undoubtedly critical for its other two major placental activities (transport and endocrine secretion).

PLACENTAL TRANSPORT

The transport of substances in both directions between the placenta and maternal blood is facilitated by the great surface area of the placental membrane. Almost all materials are transported across the placental membrane by one of the following *four main transport mechanisms*:

- Simple diffusion
- Facilitated diffusion
- Active transport
- Pinocytosis

Passive transport by simple diffusion is usually characteristic of substances moving from areas of higher to lower concentration until equilibrium is established. In *facilitated diffusion,* transport occurs through electrical charges. *Active transport* against a concentration gradient requires energy. Such systems may involve enzymes that temporarily combine with the substances concerned. *Pinocytosis* is a form of endocytosis in which the material being engulfed is a small sample of extracellular fluid. This method of transport is usually reserved for large molecules. Some proteins are transferred very slowly through the placenta by pinocytosis.

Transfer of Gases. Oxygen, carbon dioxide, and carbon monoxide cross the placental membrane by simple diffusion. The exchange of oxygen and carbon dioxide is limited more by blood flow than by the efficiency of diffusion (Carlson, 1994). *Interruption of oxygen transport for several minutes endangers survival of the embryo or fetus.* The placental membrane approaches the efficiency of the lungs for gas exchange. The quantity of oxygen reaching the fetus is primarily flow-limited rather than diffusion-limited; hence, fetal hypoxia (decreased levels of oxygen) results primarily from factors that diminish either the uterine blood flow or fetal blood flow through the placenta. Inhaled anesthetics can also cross the placental membrane and affect breathing if used during parturition.

Nutritional Substances. Nutrients constitute the bulk of substances transferred from the mother to the fetus. **Water** is rapidly and freely exchanged by simple diffusion between the mother and fetus, and in increasing amounts as pregnancy advances. **Glucose** produced by the mother and placenta is quickly transferred to the embryo or fetus by diffusion. Little or no maternal cholesterol, triglycerides, or phospholipids are transferred. Although free fatty acids are transported, the amount transferred appears to be relatively small. **Vitamins** cross the placental membrane and are essential for normal development. Water-soluble vitamins cross the placental membrane more quickly than fat-soluble ones.

Hormones. *Protein hormones* do not reach the embryo or fetus in significant amounts, except for a slow transfer of thyroxine and triiodothyronine. Unconjugated *steroid hormones* cross the placental membrane rather freely. Testosterone and certain synthetic progestins cross the placental membrane and may cause masculinization of female fetuses (see Chapter 9).

Electrolytes. These compounds are freely exchanged across the placental membrane in significant quantities, each at its own rate. When a mother receives *intravenous fluids,* they also pass to the fetus and affect its water and electrolyte status.

Maternal Antibodies. The fetus produces only small amounts of antibodies because of its immature immune system. Some passive immunity is conferred upon the fetus by the placental transfer of maternal antibodies. The alpha and beta globulins reach the fetus in very small quantities, but many gamma globulins, such as the IgG (7S) class, are readily transported to the fetus by pinocytosis. *Maternal antibodies confer fetal immunity* to diseases such as diphtheria, smallpox, and measles; however, no immunity is acquired to pertussis (whooping cough) or chickenpox. A maternal protein, *transferrin,* crosses the placental membrane and carries iron to the embryo or fetus. The placental surface contains special receptors for this protein (Carlson, 1994).

Hemolytic Disease of the Newborn

Small amounts of fetal blood may pass to the maternal blood through microscopic breaks in the placental membrane. If the fetus is Rh-positive and the mother Rh-negative, the fetal cells may stimulate the formation of anti-Rh antibody by the immune system of the mother. This passes to the fetal blood and causes hemolysis of fetal Rh-positive blood cells and anemia in the fetus. Some fetuses with *hemolytic disease of the newborn* (HDN), or fetal erythroblastosis, fail to make a satisfactory intrauterine adjustment and may die unless delivered early or given intrauterine, intraperitoneal, or intravenous transfusions of packed Rh-negative blood cells in order to maintain the fetus until after birth. Hemolytic disease of the newborn is relatively uncommon now because Rh immunoglobulin given to the mother usually prevents development of this disease in the fetus (Behrman et al, 1996).

Waste Products. Urea and uric acid pass through the placental membrane by simple diffusion, and bilirubin is quickly cleared.

Drugs and Drug Metabolites. Most drugs and drug metabolites cross the placenta by simple diffusion, the exception being those with a structural similarity to amino acids such as methyldopa and antimetabolites. Some drugs cause major congenital anomalies (see Chapter 9). **Fetal drug addiction** may occur after maternal use of drugs such as heroin, and newborns may experience withdrawal symptoms (Behrman et al, 1996). Because psychic dependence on these drugs does not develop during the fetal period, no susceptibility to subsequent narcotic addiction exists in the infant after withdrawal is complete. Except for muscle relaxants such as succinylcholine and curare, most agents used for the management of labor readily cross the placental membrane. Depending on their dose and timing in relation to delivery, these drugs may cause respiratory depression of the newborn infant. All sedatives and analgesics affect the fetus to some degree. Drugs taken by the mother can affect the embryo/fetus directly or indirectly by interfering with maternal or placental metabolism. The amount of drug or metabolite reaching the placenta is controlled by the maternal blood level and blood flow through the placenta (Kraemer and Noerr, 1997).

Infectious Agents. Cytomegalovirus, rubella and Coxsackie viruses, and viruses associated with variola, varicella, measles, and poliomyelitis may pass through the placental membrane and cause *fetal infection*. In some cases, such as the **rubella virus**, severe congenital anomalies may be produced (see Chapter 9). Microorganisms, such as *Treponema pallidum* that causes syphilis and *Toxoplasma gondii* that produces destructive changes in the brain and eyes, also cross the placental membrane. These organisms enter the fetal blood, often causing congenital anomalies and/or death of the embryo or fetus.

PLACENTAL ENDOCRINE SYNTHESIS AND SECRETION

Using precursors derived from the fetus and/or the mother, the *syncytiotrophoblast* of the placenta synthesizes protein and steroid hormones. The **protein hormones** synthesized by the placenta are

- Human chorionic gonadotropin (hCG)
- Human chorionic somatomammotropin (hCS) or human *placental lactogen* (hPL)
- Human chorionic thyrotropin (hCT)
- Human chorionic corticotropin (hCACTH)

The glycoprotein hCG, similar to luteinizing hormone (LH), is first secreted by the syncytiotrophoblast during the second week. *Human chorionic gonadotropin maintains the corpus luteum*, preventing the onset of menstrual periods. The concentration of hCG in the maternal blood and urine rises to a maximum by the eighth week and then declines. The placenta also plays a major role in the production of **steroid hormones**—*progesterone* and *estrogens*. Progesterone is essential for the maintenance of pregnancy. The

ovaries of a pregnant woman can be removed after the first trimester without causing an abortion because the placenta takes over production of progesterone from the corpus luteum of the ovary. Estrogens are also produced in large quantities by the syncytiotrophoblast (Nathanielsz, 1996).

UTERINE GROWTH DURING PREGNANCY

The uterus of a nonpregnant woman lies in the pelvis minor, or true pelvis (Fig. 8–10A). It increases in size during pregnancy to accommodate the growing conceptus. While the uterus is enlarging, it also increases in weight and its walls become thinner (Fig. 8–10B and C). During the first trimester, the uterus moves out of the pelvic cavity by 20 weeks and usually reaches the level of the umbilicus. By 28 to 30 weeks, it reaches the epigastric region—the area between the xiphoid process of the sternum and the umbilicus. The increase in size of the uterus results largely from hypertrophy of preexisting smooth muscular fibers and partly from the development of new fibers.

PARTURITION (CHILDBIRTH)

Parturition is the birth process during which the fetus, placenta, and fetal membranes are expelled from the mother's reproductive tract (Fig. 8–11). **Labor** is the sequence of involuntary *uterine contractions* that result in dilation of the cervix and delivery of the fetus and placenta from the uterus. The factors that trigger labor are not completely understood, but several hormones are related to the initiation of contractions. The fetal hypothalamus secretes **corticotropin-releasing hormone**, which stimulates the anterior hypophysis or pituitary gland to produce **adrenocorticotropin hormone** (ACTH). ACTH causes the secretion of cortisol from the suprarenal (adrenal) cortex. **Cortisol** is involved in the synthesis of estrogens. These steroids stimulate uterine contraction (Nathanielsz, 1996).

Peristaltic contractions of uterine smooth muscle are elicited by **oxytocin**, which is released by the posterior cerebral hypophysis. This hormone is administered clinically when it is necessary to induce labor. Oxytocin also stimulates release of **prostaglandins** from the decidua that stimulate myometrial contractility by sensitizing the myometrial cells to oxytocin. **Estrogens** also increase myometrial contractile activity and stimulate the release of oxytocin and prostaglandins. From studies carried out in sheep and nonhuman primates, it seems that the duration of pregnancy and the process of birth are under the direct control of the fetus. Indeed, it is the fetal hypothalamus that initiates the birth process (Nathanielsz, 1996).

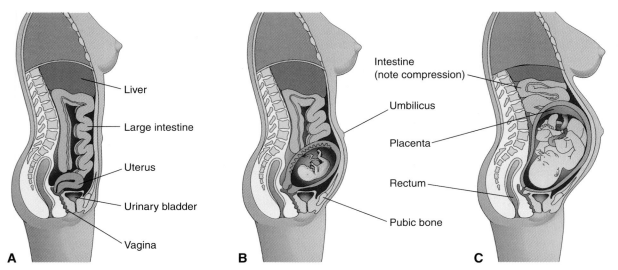

■ **Figure 8–10.** Drawings of median sections of a woman's body. *A*, Not pregnant. *B*, 20 weeks pregnant. *C*, 30 weeks pregnant. Note that as the conceptus enlarges, the uterus increases in size to accommodate the rapidly growing fetus. By 20 weeks the uterus and fetus reach the level of the umbilicus, and by 30 weeks they reach the epigastric region. The mother's abdominal viscera are displaced and compressed, and the skin and muscles of her anterior abdominal wall are greatly stretched.

The Stages of Labor

There are four stages of labor:

- **The first stage of labor** (dilation stage) begins with objective evidence of progressive dilation of the cervix (Fig. 8–11*A* and *B*). The dilation is mediated by changes in the circulating hormones and other regulatory factors, such as prostaglandins. *Labor begins with the onset of regular painful contractions of the uterus* (less than 10 minutes apart). The first stage ends with complete dilation of the cervix. The average duration of the first stage is about 12 hours for first pregnancies (nulliparous patients, or *primigravidas*) and about 7 hours for women who have had a child previously (multiparous patients, or *multigravidas*)
- **The second stage of labor** (expulsion stage) begins when the cervix is fully dilated and ends with delivery of the baby (Fig. 8–11*C* to *E*). *During this stage the fetus descends through the cervix and vagina.* As soon as the fetus is outside the mother, it is called a *newborn infant,* or neonate. The average duration of this stage is 50 minutes for primigravidas and 20 minutes for multigravidas. Uterine contractions begin again shortly after the baby is born.
- **The third stage of labor** (placental stage) begins as soon as the baby is born and ends when the placenta and membranes are expelled (Fig. 8–11*F*

to *H*). The duration of this stage is 15 minutes in about 90% of pregnancies. *Retraction of the uterus and manual compression of the abdomen reduce the area of placental attachment* (Fig. 8–11*G*). A **hematoma** soon forms deep to the placenta and separates it from the uterine wall. The placenta and fetal membranes separate from the uterine wall and are expelled through the vagina and pudendal cleft—the slit between the labia majora into which the vagina opens. After delivery of the baby, the uterus continues to contract.

- **The fourth stage of labor** (recovery stage) begins as soon as the placenta and fetal membranes are expelled. This stage lasts about 2 hours. The myometrial contractions constrict the spiral arteries that formerly supplied blood to the intervillous space. These contractions prevent excessive uterine bleeding.

Placenta and Fetal Membranes after Birth

The extruded placenta and fetal membranes are called the *afterbirth.* The placenta commonly has a discoid shape, with a diameter of 15 to 20 cm and a thickness of 2 to 3 cm (Fig. 8–12). The margins of the placenta are continuous with the ruptured amniotic and chorionic sacs.

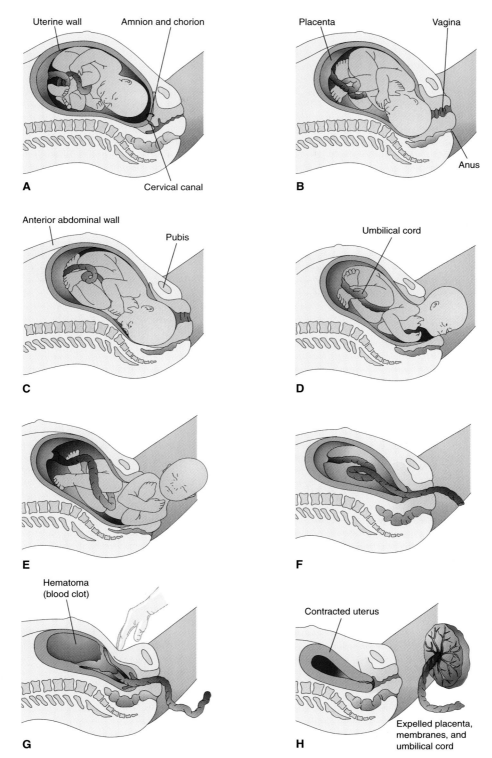

■ **Figure 8–11.** Drawings illustrating parturition. *A* and *B,* The cervix is dilating during the first stage of labor. *C* to *E,* The fetus is passing through the cervix and vagina during the second stage of labor. *F* and *G,* As the uterus contracts during the third stage of labor, the placenta folds and pulls away from the uterine wall. Separation of the placenta results in bleeding and the formation of a large hematoma (mass of blood). Pressure on the abdomen facilitates placental separation. *H,* The placenta is expelled, and the uterus contracts during the fourth stage of labor.

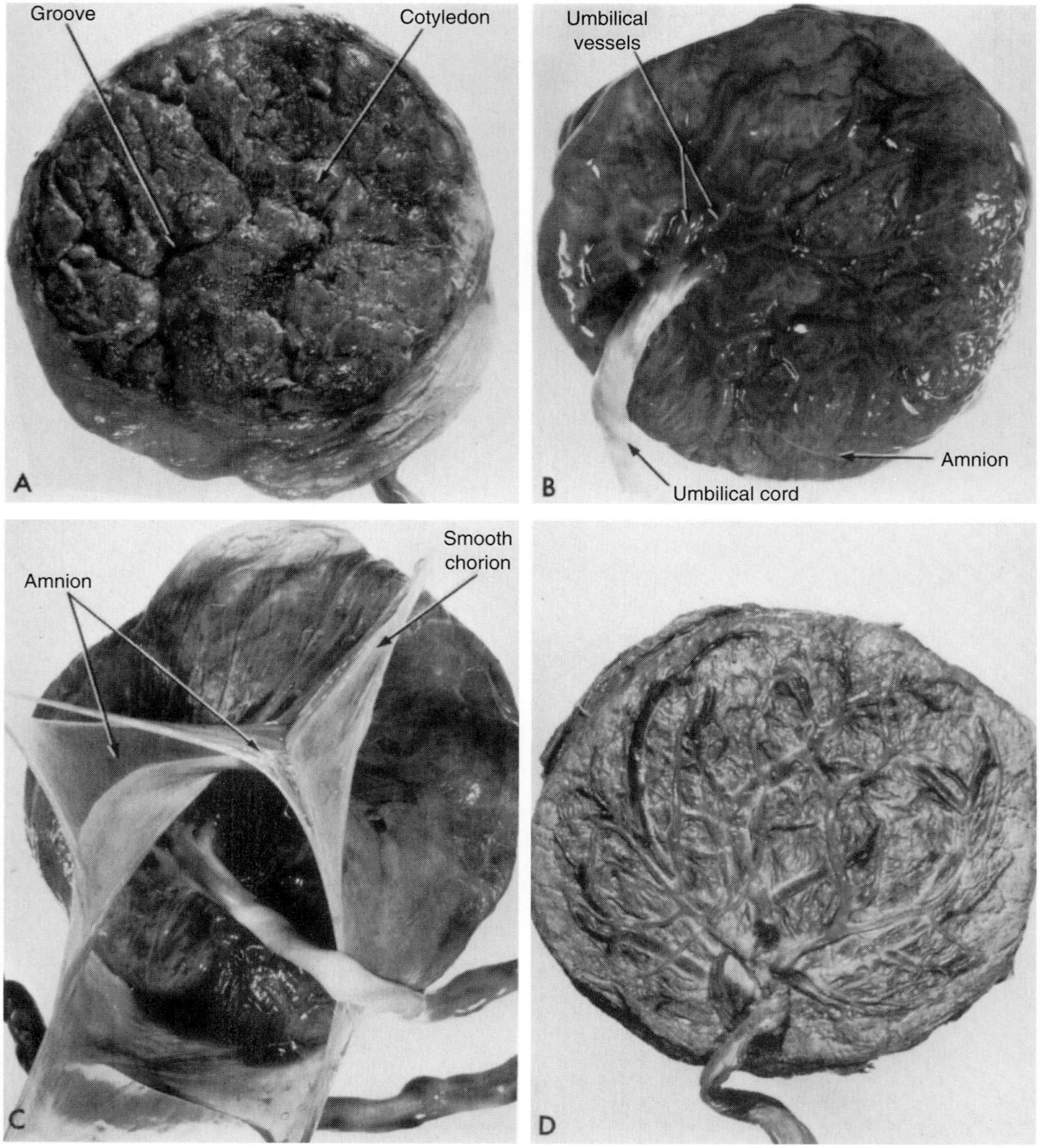

■ **Figure 8–12.** Photographs of placentas and fetal membranes after birth, about one-third actual size. *A,* Maternal surface, showing cotyledons and the grooves around them. Each convex cotyledon consists of a number of main stem villi with their many branch villi. The grooves were occupied by the placental septa when the maternal and fetal parts of the placenta were together (see Fig. 8–7). *B,* Fetal surface, showing blood vessels running in the chorionic plate deep to the amnion and converging to form the umbilical vessels at the attachment of the umbilical cord. *C,* The amnion and smooth chorion are arranged to show that they are fused and continuous with the margins of the placenta. *D,* Placenta with a marginal attachment of the cord, often called a battledore placenta because of its resemblance to the bat used in the medieval game of battledore and shuttlecock.

VARIATIONS IN PLACENTAL SHAPE

As the placenta develops, chorionic villi usually persist only where the villous chorion is in contact with the decidua basalis. This usually produces the typical discoid placenta (Fig. 8-12). When villi persist elsewhere, several variations in placental shape occur, such as *accessory placenta* (Fig. 8-13). Variations in the size and shape of the placenta are usually of little physiologic or clinical significance. For a discussion of other variations of placental shape, see Moore and Persaud (1998).

Examination of the placenta, prenatally by ultrasonography or postnatally by gross and microscopic study, may provide clinical information about the causes of:

- Placental dysfunction
- Intrauterine growth retardation (IUGR)
- Fetal distress and death
- Neonatal illness

Postnatal placental studies can also determine whether the placenta is complete. Retention of a cotyledon or an accessory placenta in the uterus causes *uterine hemorrhage*.

Gestational Choriocarcinoma

Abnormal proliferation of the trophoblast results in *gestational trophoblastic disease*, a spectrum of lesions including highly malignant tumors (Freedman et al, 1996). The cells invade the decidua basalis, penetrate its blood vessels and lymphatics, and metastasize to the maternal lungs, bone marrow, liver, and other organs. *Gestational choriocarcinomas* are highly sensitive to chemotherapy, and cures are usually achieved (Berkowitz and Goldstein, 1996).

MATERNAL SURFACE OF THE PLACENTA

The characteristic **cobblestone appearance** of this surface is produced by slightly bulging villous areas — the **cotyledons** — which are separated by grooves that were formerly occupied by **placental septa** (Figs. 8-7 and 8-12A). The surface of the cotyledons is covered by thin grayish shreds of decidua basalis that separated from the uterine wall with the placenta.

FETAL SURFACE OF THE PLACENTA

The **umbilical cord** usually attaches to the fetal surface, and its amniotic epithelium is continuous with the amnion adhering to the chorionic plate of the placenta (Figs. 8-6, 8-7, and 8-12B and C). The chorionic vessels radiating to and from the umbilical cord are clearly visible through the smooth, transparent amnion. The *umbilical vessels* branch on the fetal surface to form the *chorionic vessels,* which enter the chorionic villi.

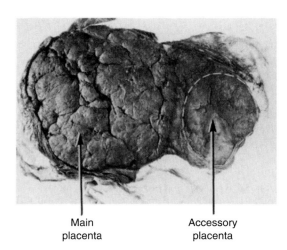

Main placenta   Accessory placenta

■ **Figure 8-13.** Photograph of the maternal surface of a full-term placenta and an accessory placenta, about one-quarter actual size. The accessory placental tissue developed from a patch of chorionic villi that persisted a short distance from the main placenta.

Placental Abnormalities

Abnormal adherence of chorionic villi of part or all of the uterine wall, with partial or complete absence of the decidua basalis, especially the spongy layer, is called **placenta accreta** (Fig. 8-14). When chorionic villi penetrate the myometrium all the way to the perimetrium (peritoneal covering), the abnormality is called **placenta percreta**. The villi are normal and show no evidence of trophoblastic proliferation. *Third trimester bleeding is the most common presenting sign of these placental abnormalities.* Most patients with placenta accreta have normal pregnancies and labors. After birth the placenta fails to separate from the uterine wall, and attempts to remove it may cause hemorrhage that is difficult to control. When the blastocyst implants close to or overlying the internal os of the uterus, the abnormality is called **placenta previa.** Late-pregnancy bleeding can result from this placental abnormality. The fetus has to be delivered by cesarean section because the placenta blocks the cervical canal.

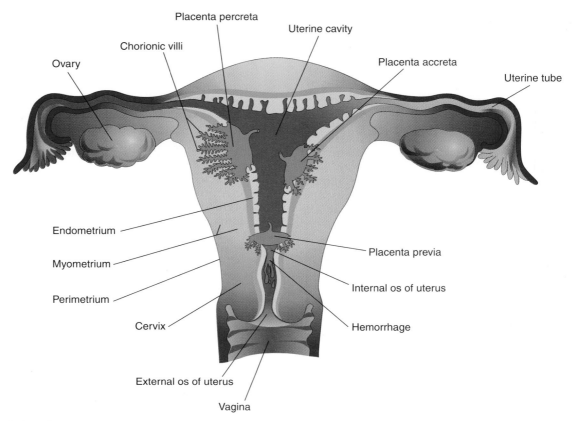

■ **Figure 8–14.** Placental abnormalities. In *placenta accreta* there is abnormal adherence of the placenta to the myometrium. In *placenta percreta* the placenta has penetrated the full thickness of the myometrium. In *placenta previa* the placenta overlies the internal os of the uterus and blocks the cervical canal.

Umbilical Cord

The attachment of the umbilical cord, connecting the embryo/fetus to the placenta, is usually near the center of the fetal surface of this fetomaternal organ (Fig. 8-12*B*), but it may be found at any point. For example, insertion of it at the placental margin produces a *battledore placenta* (Fig. 8-12*D*), and its attachment to the membranes is called a *velamentous insertion of the cord* (Fig. 8-15). *Color flow Doppler ultrasonography* may be used for the prenatal diagnosis of the position and structural abnormalities of the umbilical cord (Raga et al, 1995; Heinonen et al, 1996). The umbilical cord is usually 1 to 2 cm in diameter and 30 to 90 cm in length (average 55 cm). Excessively long or short cords are uncommon. Long cords have a tendency to prolapse and/or to coil around the fetus (Fig. 8-16). Prompt recognition of *prolapse of the cord* is important because the cord may be compressed between the presenting body part of the fetus and the mother's bony pelvis, causing

fetal hypoxia or anoxia. If the deficiency of oxygen persists for more than 5 minutes, the baby's brain may be damaged, producing mental retardation. A very short cord may cause premature separation of the placenta from the wall of the uterus during delivery.

The umbilical cord usually has two arteries and one vein that are surrounded by mucoid connective tissue (*Wharton jelly*). Because the umbilical vessels are longer than the cord, twisting and bending of the vessels is common. They frequently form loops, producing *false knots* that are of no significance; however, in about 1% of pregnancies, **true knots** form in the cord, which may tighten and cause fetal death, resulting from *fetal anoxia* (Fig. 8-17). In most cases the knots form during labor as a result of the fetus passing through a loop of the cord. Because these knots are usually loose, they have no clinical significance. Simple *looping of the cord around the fetus* occasionally occurs (Fig. 8-16*B*). In about one fifth of all deliveries, the cord is loosely looped around the neck without increased fetal risk.

Percutaneous Umbilical Cord Blood Sampling

Percutaneous umbilical cord blood sampling (PUBS) may be performed to assess fetal acid-base status for monitoring the fetus and newborn (Thorp et al, 1996).

Absence of an Umbilical Artery

In about 1 in 200 newborns, only *one umbilical artery* is present (Fig. 8–18), a condition that may be associated with chromosomal and fetal abnormalities, particularly of the cardiovascular system. *Absence of an umbilical artery is accompanied by a 15 to 20% incidence of cardiovascular anomalies in the fetus.* Absence of an artery results from either agenesis or degeneration of this vessel early in development. A single umbilical artery and the anatomic defects associated with it can be detected before birth by means of ultrasonography (Parilla et al, 1995).

Margin of placenta

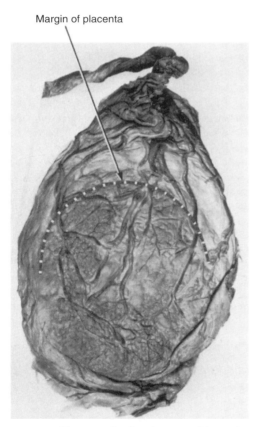

■ **Figure 8–15.** Photograph of a placenta with a velamentous insertion of the umbilical cord. The cord is attached to the membranes (amnion and chorion), not to the placenta. The umbilical vessels leave the cord and run between the amnion and chorion before spreading over the placenta. The vessels are easily torn in this location, especially when they cross over the inferior uterine segment; the latter condition is known as *vasa previa.* If the vessels rupture before birth, the fetus loses blood and could be near exsanguination when born.

AMNION AND AMNIOTIC FLUID

Amnion

The amnion forms a fluid-filled, membranous *amniotic sac* that surrounds the embryo and fetus (Fig. 8–19A). Because the amnion is attached to the margins of the embryonic disc, its junction with the embryo (future umbilicus) is located on the ventral surface after embryonic folding (Fig. 8–19B). As the amnion enlarges, it gradually obliterates the chorionic cavity and forms the epithelial covering of the umbilical cord (Fig. 8–19C and D).

Amniotic Fluid

Amniotic fluid plays a major role in fetal growth and development. Initially some fluid may be secreted by amniotic cells; however, most amniotic fluid is derived from *maternal tissue (interstitial) fluid* by diffusion across the amniochorionic membrane from the decidua parietalis (Figs. 8–1F and 8–7). Later there is diffusion of fluid through the chorionic plate from blood in the intervillous space of the placenta (Fig. 8–7). Before keratinization of the skin occurs, a major pathway for passage of water and solutes in tissue fluid from the fetus to the amniotic cavity is through the skin (Callen and Filly, 1990); thus, amniotic fluid is similar to fetal tissue fluid. Fluid is also secreted by the fetal respiratory tract and enters the amniotic cavity. Beginning in the 11th week, the fetus contributes to the amniotic fluid by expelling urine into the amniotic cavity. By late pregnancy, about 0.5 liter of urine is added daily. The volume of amniotic fluid normally increases slowly, reaching about 30 ml at 10 weeks, 350 ml at 20 weeks, and 700 to 1000 ml by 37 weeks.

CIRCULATION OF AMNIOTIC FLUID

The water content of amniotic fluid changes every 3 hours. Large amounts of water pass through the amniochorionic membrane into the maternal tissue fluid and enter the uterine capillaries. An exchange of fluid with fetal blood also occurs through the umbilical cord and where the amnion adheres to the chorionic plate on the fetal surface of the placenta (Figs. 8–7

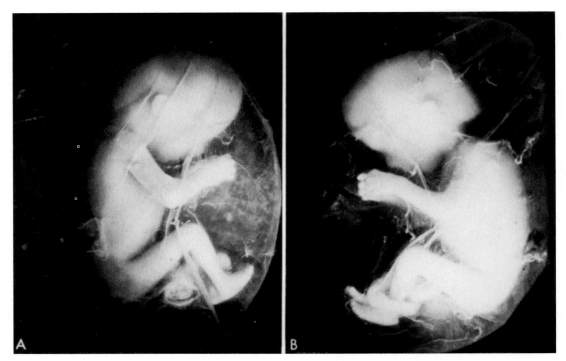

■ **Figure 8–16.** *A* and *B*, Photographs of a 12-week fetus within its amniotic sac. The fetus and its membranes aborted spontaneously. It was removed from its chorionic sac with its amniotic sac intact. Actual size. In *B*, note that the umbilical cord is looped around the left ankle of the fetus. Coiling of the cord around parts of the fetus affects their development when the coils are so tight that the circulation to the parts is affected.

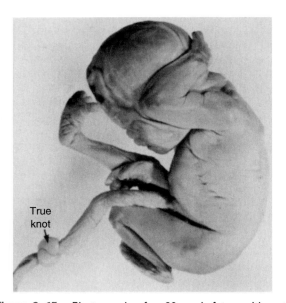

True knot

■ **Figure 8–17.** Photograph of a 20-week fetus with a true knot (*arrow*) in its umbilical cord. Half actual size. The diameter of the cord is greater in the part closest to the fetus, indicating that there was an obstruction of blood flow from the fetus in the umbilical arteries and compression of the umbilical vein. Undoubtedly, this knot caused severe anoxia (decreased oxygen in the fetal tissues and organs) and was a major cause of the fetus's death.

and 8–12*B*); thus, amniotic fluid is in balance with the fetal circulation. *Amniotic fluid is swallowed by the fetus* and absorbed by the fetus's respiratory and digestive tracts. It has been estimated that during the final stages of pregnancy, the fetus swallows up to 400 ml of amniotic fluid per day. The fluid passes into the fetal blood stream, and the waste products in it cross the placental membrane and enter the maternal blood in the intervillous space. Excess water in the fetal blood is excreted by the fetal kidneys and returned to the amniotic sac through the fetal urinary tract.

Disorders of Amniotic Fluid Volume

Low volumes of amniotic fluid for any particular gestational age—**oligohydramnios**—(e.g., 400 ml in the third trimester) result in most cases from placental insufficiency with diminished placental blood flow. Preterm rupture of the amniochorionic membrane occurs in approximately 10% of pregnancies and is the most common cause of oligohydramnios (Callen and Filly, 1990). When **renal agenesis** (failure of kidney formation) is present, the absence of fetal urine contri-

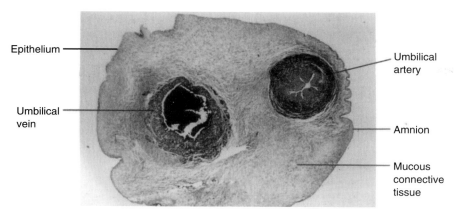

Epithelium

Umbilical vein

Umbilical artery

Amnion

Mucous connective tissue

■ **Figure 8–18.** A transverse section of an umbilical cord. Note that the cord is covered by a single-layered epithelium derived from the enveloping amnion and has a core of mucous connective tissue (Wharton jelly). Note also that the cord has one umbilical artery and one umbilical vein. Usually there are two arteries. Each artery has a thick muscular coat, or tunica media. The vein, which carries oxygenated blood from the placenta, is unusual in that its wall, unlike that of most veins, consists principally of a tunica media. (Courtesy of Professor V. Becker, Pathologisches Institut der Universität, Erlangen, Germany.)

bution to the amniotic fluid is the main cause of oligohydramnios. A similar decrease in amniotic fluid occurs with **obstructive uropathy** (urinary tract obstruction). Complications of oligohydramnios include fetal abnormalities (pulmonary hypoplasia, facial defects, and limb defects), which are caused by fetal compression by the uterine wall. Compression of the umbilical cord is also a potential complication of severe oligohydramnios (Doubilet and Benson, 1994).

High volumes of amniotic fluid — **polyhydramnios (hydramnios)** — in excess of 2000 ml, for example, results when the fetus does not swallow the usual amount of amniotic fluid. Most cases of polyhydramnios (60%) are idiopathic (unknown cause), 20% are caused by maternal factors, and 20% are fetal in origin. Polyhydramnios may be associated with severe anomalies of the central nervous system, such as meroanencephaly or anencephaly. When there are other anomalies such as **esophageal atresia**, the fetus is unable to swallow amniotic fluid (see Chapter 13), which accumulates because it is unable to pass to the fetal stomach and the intestines for absorption. *Ultrasonography* has become the technique of choice for diagnosing polyhydramnios (Callen and Filly, 1990; Doubilet and Benson, 1994).

EXCHANGE OF AMNIOTIC FLUID

Large volumes of amniotic fluid move in both directions between the fetal and maternal circulations, mainly via the placental membrane. Fetal swallowing of amniotic fluid is also a normal occurrence. Most fluid passes into the gastrointestinal tract, but some passes into the lungs. In either case, the fluid is absorbed and enters the fetal circulation. It then passes into the maternal circulation via the placental membrane. For more details of amniotic fluid dynamics, see Mann et al (1996).

COMPOSITION OF AMNIOTIC FLUID

About 99% of the fluid in the amniotic cavity is water. Amniotic fluid is a solution in which undissolved material is suspended, such as desquamated fetal epithelial cells and approximately equal portions of organic and inorganic salts. Half of the organic constituents are protein; the other half consists of carbohydrates, fats, enzymes, hormones, and pigments. As pregnancy advances, the composition of the amniotic fluid changes as fetal excreta (*meconium* [fetal feces] and urine) are added. Because fetal urine enters the amniotic fluid, studies of fetal enzyme systems, amino acids, hormones, and other substances can be conducted on fluid removed by **amniocentesis** (see Chapter 7). Studies of cells in the amniotic fluid permit diagnosis of the sex of the fetus and detection of fetuses with chromosomal abnormalities such as trisomy 21 in Down syndrome. High levels of *alpha-fetoprotein* (AFP) in the amniotic fluid usually indicate the presence of a severe neural tube defect (e.g., meroanencephaly). Low levels of AFP may indicate chromosomal aberrations, such as trisomy 21 that produces Down syndrome (see Chapter 9).

SIGNIFICANCE OF AMNIOTIC FLUID

The buoyant amniotic fluid:

- Permits symmetric external growth of the embryo
- Acts as a barrier to infection
- Permits normal fetal lung development
- Prevents adherence of the amnion to the embryo
- Cushions the embryo against injuries by distributing impacts the mother receives
- Helps control the embryo's body temperature by maintaining a relatively constant temperature
- Enables the fetus to move freely, thereby aiding muscular development (e.g., in the limbs)

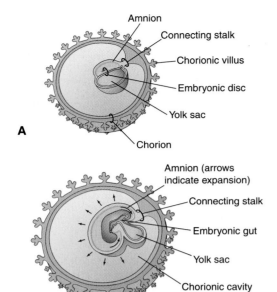

A

Amnion
Connecting stalk
Chorionic villus
Embryonic disc
Yolk sac
Chorion

B

Amnion (arrows indicate expansion)
Connecting stalk
Embryonic gut
Yolk sac
Chorionic cavity

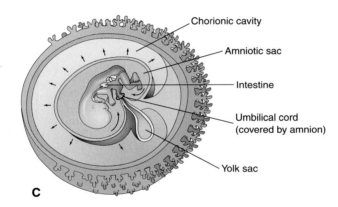

C

Chorionic cavity
Amniotic sac
Intestine
Umbilical cord (covered by amnion)
Yolk sac

■ **Figure 8–19.** Drawings illustrating how the amnion enlarges, fills the chorionic sac, and envelops the umbilical cord. Observe that part of the yolk sac is incorporated into the embryo as the primitive gut. Formation of the fetal part of the placenta and degeneration of chorionic villi are also shown. *A,* Three weeks. *B,* Four weeks. *C,* Ten weeks. *D,* Twenty weeks.

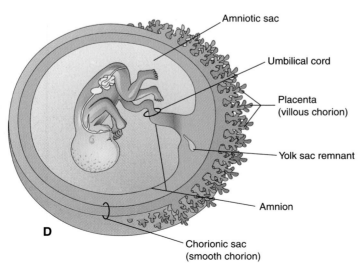

D

Amniotic sac
Umbilical cord
Placenta (villous chorion)
Yolk sac remnant
Amnion
Chorionic sac (smooth chorion)

- Is involved in maintaining homeostasis of fluid and electrolytes

Premature Rupture of Membranes

Premature rupture of the amniochorionic membrane is the most common event leading to premature labor and delivery and the most common complication resulting in oligohydramnios. The absence of amniotic fluid also removes the major protection the fetus has against infection. Rupture of the amnion may cause various fetal anomalies that constitute the *amniotic band syndrome* (ABS), or *amniotic band disruption complex* (ABDC). These anomalies vary from digital constriction to major scalp, craniofacial, and visceral defects (Callen and Filly, 1990). The cause of these anomalies is probably related to constriction by encircling amniotic bands (Fig. 8–20). The incidence of ABS is about 1 in every 1200 live births (Seed et al, 1982). Prenatal ultrasound diagnosis of ABS is now possible.

YOLK SAC

Early development of the yolk sac was described in Chapter 4. At 32 days the yolk sac is large (Fig. 8–2). By 10 weeks the yolk sac has shrunk to a pear-shaped remnant, about 5 mm in diameter (Fig. 8–19C), and is connected to the midgut by a narrow *yolk stalk*. By 20 weeks the yolk sac is very small (Fig. 8–19D); thereafter it is usually not visible. The yolk sac can be observed sonographically early in the fifth week. The

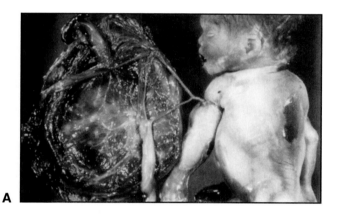

A

B

Chorion

Fibrous bands of disrupted amnion

Fibrous amniotic band constricting limb and causing edema distal to constriction

Fetal surface of placenta

Umbilical cord

■ **Figure 8–20.** *A*, Photograph of a fetus with the amniotic band syndrome (ABS), showing amniotic bands constricting the left arm. (Courtesy of Professor V. Becker, Pathologisches Institut der Universität, Erlangen, Germany.) *B*, Drawing indicating the structures shown in *A*.

presence of the amnion and yolk sac enables early recognition and measurement of the embryo. The yolk sac is recognizable in ultrasound examinations until the end of the first trimester (Filly, 1994).

Significance of the Yolk Sac

Although the yolk sac is nonfunctional as far as yolk storage is concerned, its presence is essential for several reasons:

- It has a role in the *transfer of nutrients* to the embryo during the second and third weeks when the uteroplacental circulation is being established.
- *Blood development* first occurs in the well-vascularized extraembryonic mesoderm covering the wall of the yolk sac beginning in the third week (see Chapter 5) and continues there until hemato-

poietic activity begins in the liver during the sixth week.
- During the fourth week the dorsal part of the yolk sac is incorporated into the embryo as the *primitive gut* (see Fig. 6–1). Its endoderm, derived from epiblast, gives rise to the epithelium of the trachea, bronchi, lungs, and digestive tract.
- *Primordial germ cells* appear in the endodermal lining of the wall of the yolk sac in the third week and subsequently migrate to the developing sex glands (see Chapter 14). They differentiate into the germ cells (spermatogonia in males and oogonia in females).

FATE OF THE YOLK SAC

At 10 weeks the small yolk sac lies in the chorionic cavity between the amnion and chorionic sac (Fig. 8–

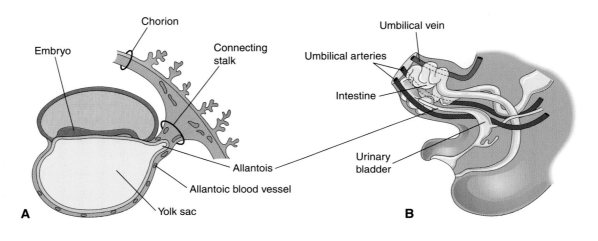

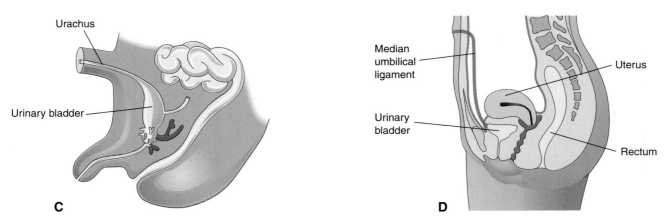

■ **Figure 8–21.** Drawings illustrating the development and usual fate of the allantois. *A*, Three-week embryo. *B*, Nine-week fetus. *C*, Three-month male fetus. *D*, Adult female. The nonfunctional allantois forms the urachus in the fetus and the median umbilical ligament in the adult.

21C). The *yolk stalk* usually detaches from the midgut loop by the end of the sixth week. In about 2% of adults, the proximal intra-abdominal part of the yolk stalk persists as an *ileal diverticulum* known clinically as *Meckel diverticulum* (see Chapter 13).

ALLANTOIS

Early development of the allantois was described in Chapter 5. During the second month the extraembryonic portion of the allantois degenerates (Fig. 8–21B). Although the allantois is not functional in human embryos, it is important for four reasons:

- Blood formation occurs in its wall during the third to fifth weeks.
- Its blood vessels become the umbilical vein and arteries (Fig. 8–21A and B).
- Fluid from the amniotic cavity diffuses into the umbilical vein and enters the fetal circulation for transfer to the maternal blood through the placental membrane.
- The intraembryonic portion of the allantois runs from the umbilicus to the urinary bladder, with which it is continuous (Fig. 8–21B). As the bladder enlarges, the allantois involutes to form a thick tube called the urachus (Fig. 8–21C). After birth, the *urachus* becomes a fibrous cord called the *median umbilical ligament* that extends from the apex of the urinary bladder to the umbilicus (Fig. 8–21D). For a discussion of urachal anomalies and their clinical significance, see Chapter 14.

MULTIPLE PREGNANCIES

Multiple gestations have higher risks of fetal morbidity and mortality than single gestations (Finberg, 1994). The risks are progressively greater as the number of fetuses increases. Multiple births are more common now owing to the stimulation of ovulation that occurs when exogenous gonadotropins are administered to women with ovulatory failure and to those being treated for infertility by in vitro fertilization and embryo transfer. In North America, **twins** normally occur about once in every 85 pregnancies; **triplets** about once in 90^2 pregnancies, **quadruplets** about once in 90^3, and **quintuplets** about once in 90^4. These estimates increase when ovulations have been primed with hormones, a technique that is in general use for women who are sterile because of tubal occlusion.

Twins and Fetal Membranes

Twins that originate from two zygotes are **dizygotic (DZ) twins,** or fraternal twins (Fig. 8–22), whereas twins that originate from one zygote are **monozygotic (MZ) twins,** or identical twins (Fig. 8–23). The fetal membranes and placenta(s) vary according to the origin of the twins and, in the case of MZ twins, the type of placenta and membranes formed depends on when the twinning process occurs. *About two-thirds of twins are DZ.* The frequency of DZ twinning shows marked racial differences, but *the incidence of MZ twinning is about the same in all populations* (Thompson et al, 1991). In addition, the rate of MZ twinning shows little variation with the mother's age, whereas *the rate of DZ twinning increases with maternal age.*

The study of twins is important in human genetics because it is useful for comparing the effects of genes and environment on development. If an abnormal condition does not show a simple genetic pattern, comparison of its incidence in MZ and DZ twins may reveal that heredity is involved. The tendency for DZ but not MZ twins to repeat in families is evidence of hereditary influence (Thompson et al, 1991). Studies in a Mormon population showed that the genotype of the mother affects the frequency of DZ twins, but the genotype of the father has no effect (Page et al, 1981). It has also been found that if the firstborn are twins, a repetition of twinning or some other form of multiple birth is about five times more likely to occur at the next pregnancy than in the general population.

Anastomosis of Placental Blood Vessels

Anastomoses between blood vessels of fused placentas of DZ twins may occur and result in **erythrocyte mosaicism.** The members of these DZ twins have red cells of two different types because red cells were exchanged between the two circulations. For more information about the results of anastomosis of placental vessels, see Moore and Persaud (1998).

Twin-Transfusion Syndrome

This syndrome occurs in 15 to 30% of monochorionic-diamniotic MZ twins. Arterial blood is shunted from one twin through arteriovenous anastomoses into the venous circulation of the other twin (Behrman et al, 1996). The donor twin is small, pale, and anemic (Fig. 8–24), whereas the recipient twin is large and polycythemic—an increase above the normal in the number

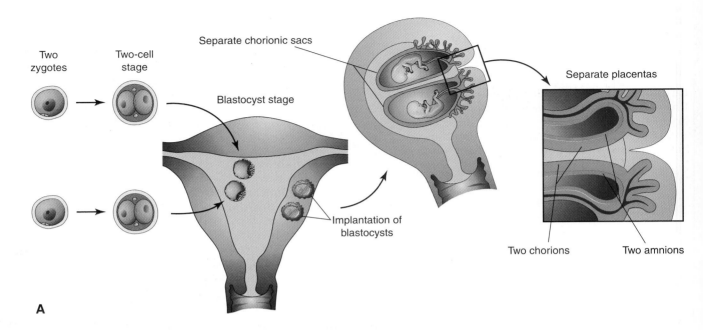

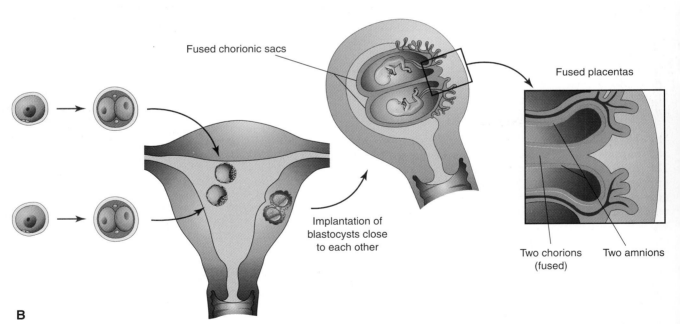

■ **Figure 8–22.** Diagrams illustrating how dizygotic (DZ) twins develop from two zygotes. The relations of the fetal membranes and placentas are shown for instances in which (A) the blastocysts implant separately and (B) the blastocysts implant close together. In both cases there are two amnions and two chorions. The placentas are usually fused when they implant close together.

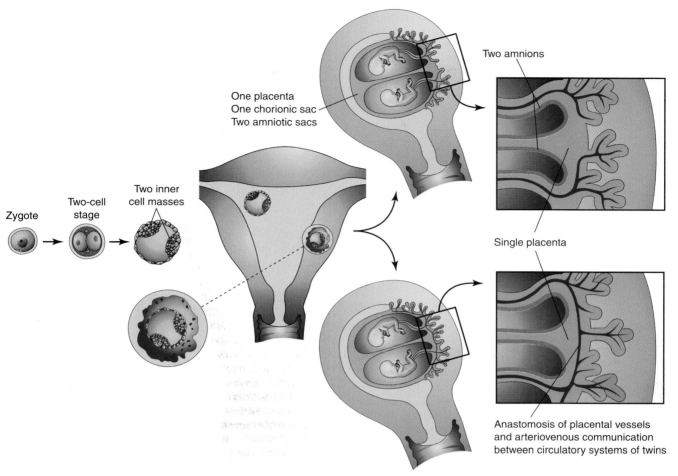

One placenta
One chorionic sac
Two amniotic sacs

Two amnions

Single placenta

Anastomosis of placental vessels
and arteriovenous communication
between circulatory systems of twins

Zygote

Two-cell stage

Two inner cell masses

■ **Figure 8–23.** Diagrams illustrating how about 65 per cent of monozygotic (MZ) twins develop from one zygote by division of the inner cell mass of the blastocyst. These twins always have separate amnions, a single chorionic sac, and a common placenta. If there is anastomosis of the placental vessels, one twin may receive most of the nutrition from the placenta (see Fig. 8–24).

of red blood cells. The placenta shows similar abnormalities; the part of the placenta supplying the anemic twin is pale, whereas the part supplying the polycythemic twin is dark red. In lethal cases, death results from anemia in the donor twin and congestive heart failure in the recipient twin.

DIZYGOTIC TWINS

Because they result from fertilization of two oocytes by two different sperms, DZ twins develop from two zygotes and may be of the same sex or different sexes (Fig. 8–22). For the same reason, they are no more alike genetically than brothers or sisters born at different times. The only thing they have in common is that

they were in their mother's uterus at the same time (i.e., "they were womb-mates"). *Dizygotic twins always have two amnions and two chorions,* but the chorions and placentas may be fused. *Dizygotic twinning shows a hereditary tendency.* The recurrence risk in families is about triple the general population risk. The incidence of DZ twinning shows considerable variation, being about 1 in 500 in Asians, 1 in 125 in Caucasians, and as high as 1 in 20 in some African populations (Thompson et al, 1991).

MONOZYGOTIC TWINS

Because they result from the fertilization of one oocyte and develop from one zygote (Fig. 8–23), *MZ twins are of the same sex, genetically identical, and very similar in physical appearance.* Physical differences

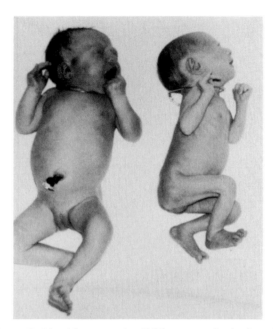

■ **Figure 8–24.** Monozygotic (MZ), monochorionic, diamniotic twins showing a wide discrepancy in size resulting from an uncompensated arteriovenous anastomosis of placental vessels. Blood was shunted from the smaller twin to the larger one, producing the fetal transfusion syndrome.

between MZ twins are environmentally induced, such as anastomosis of placental vessels resulting in differences in blood supply from the placenta (Fig. 8–24). Monozygotic twinning usually begins in the blastocyst stage, around the end of the first week, and results from division of the inner cell mass or embryoblast into two embryonic primordia. Subsequently two embryos, each in its own amniotic sac, develop within one chorionic sac and share a **common placenta**, a monochorionic-diamniotic twin placenta. Uncommonly early separation of embryonic blastomeres (e.g., during the two- to eight-cell stage) results in MZ twins with two amnions, two chorions, and two placentas that may or may not be fused (Fig. 8–25). In such cases it is impossible to determine, from the membranes alone, whether the twins are MZ or DZ. To determine the relationship of twins of the same sex with similar blood groups, one must wait until other characteristics such as eye color and fingerprints develop.

Establishing the Zygosity of Twins

Establishment of the zygosity of twins has become important, particularly since tissue and organ transplantation was introduced (e.g., bone marrow transplants).

The determination of twin zygosity is now done by *molecular diagnosis* because any two people who are not MZ twins are virtually certain to show differences in some of the large number of DNA markers that can be studied (Thompson et al, 1991).

Late division of early embryonic cells (i.e., division of the embryonic disc during the second week) results in MZ twins that are in one amniotic sac and one chorionic sac (Fig. 8–26A). A *monochorionic-monoamniotic twin placenta* is associated with a fetal mortality rate approaching 50%. Such twins are rarely delivered alive because the umbilical cords are frequently so entangled that circulation of the blood through their vessels ceases, and one or both fetuses die. Sonography plays an important role in the diagnosis and management of twin pregnancies. Ultrasound evaluation is necessary to identify various conditions that may complicate MZ twinning: intrauterine growth retardation, fetal distress, and premature labor (Finberg, 1994).

Early Death of a Twin

Because ultrasonographic studies are a common part of prenatal care, it is known that early death and resorption of one member of a twin pair are fairly common (Liu et al, 1992). This possibility must be considered when discrepancies occur between prenatal cytogenetic findings and the karyotype of an infant. Errors in prenatal diagnosis may arise if extraembryonic tissues (e.g., part of a chorionic villus) from the resorbed twin are examined.

Conjoined Twins

If the embryonic disc does not divide completely, various types of conjoined (MZ) twins may form (Fig. 8–26B and C). These twins are named according to the regions that are attached; for example, *thoracopagus* indicates anterior union of the thoracic regions. In some cases, the twins are connected to each other by skin only or by cutaneous and other tissues, such as fused livers. Some conjoined twins can be successfully separated by surgical procedures. For a discussion of the theoretical basis of conjoined twins, see Spencer (1992). The incidence of conjoined twins is 1 in 50,000 to 100,000 births (Finberg, 1994).

Other Types of Multiple Birth

Triplets may be derived from:

• One zygote and be identical

- Two zygotes and consist of identical twins and a singleton
- Three zygotes and be of the same sex or of different sexes. In the last case, the infants are no more similar than infants from three separate pregnancies. Similar combinations occur in quadruplets, quintuplets, sextuplets, and septuplets.

SUMMARY OF PLACENTA AND FETAL MEMBRANES

In addition to the embryo and fetus, the fetal membranes and the major part of the placenta originate from the zygote. The placenta consists of two parts:

- A larger fetal part derived from the villous chorion
- A smaller maternal part developed from the decidua basalis

The two parts are held together by stem chorionic villi that attach to the cytotrophoblastic shell surrounding the chorionic sac, which attaches the sac to the decidua basalis.

The principal *activities of the placenta* are:

- Metabolism such as synthesis of glycogen, cholesterol, and fatty acids
- Respiratory gas exchange (oxygen, carbon dioxide, and carbon monoxide)

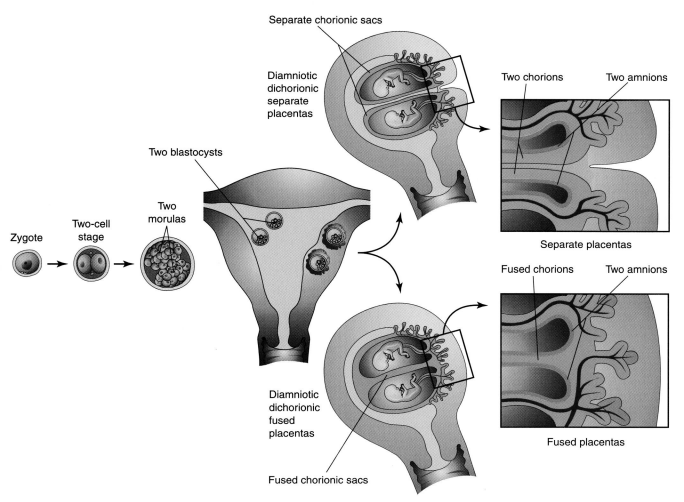

■ **Figure 8–25.** Diagrams illustrating how about 35% of monozygotic (MZ) twins develop from one zygote. Separation of the blastomeres may occur anywhere from the two-cell (blastomere) stage to the morula stage, producing two identical blastocysts. Each embryo subsequently develops its own amniotic and chorionic sacs. The placentas may be separate or fused. In 25% of cases there is a single placenta resulting from secondary fusion, and in 10% of cases there are two placentas. In the latter cases, examination of the placenta suggests that they are dizygotic (DZ) twins. This explains why some MZ twins are wrongly stated to be DZ twins at birth.

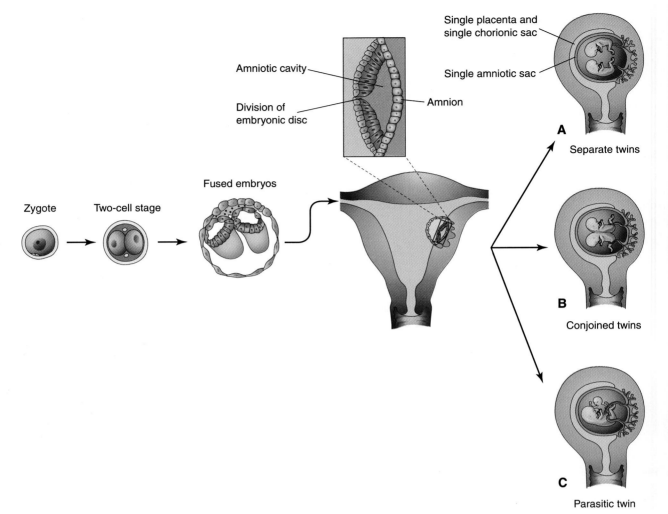

■ **Figure 8–26.** Diagrams illustrating how some monozygotic (MZ) twins develop. This method of development is very uncommon. Division of the embryonic disc results in two embryos within one amniotic sac. *A*, Complete division of the embryonic disc gives rise to twins. Such twins rarely survive because their umbilical cords are often so entangled that interruption of the blood supply to the fetuses occurs. *B* and *C*, Incomplete division of the disc results in various types of conjoined twins.

- Transfer of nutrients such as vitamins, hormones, and antibodies
- Elimination of waste products
- Endocrine secretion (e.g., hCG) for maintenance of pregnancy

All these activities are essential for maintaining pregnancy and promoting normal fetal development.

The fetal circulation is separated from the maternal circulation by a thin layer of extrafetal tissues — the **placental membrane**. It is a permeable membrane that allows water, oxygen, nutritive substances, hormones, and noxious agents to pass from the mother to the embryo or fetus. Excretory products pass through the placental membrane from the fetus to the mother.

The fetal membranes and placenta(s) in *multiple pregnancies* vary considerably, depending on the derivation of the embryos and the time when division of embryonic cells occurs. The common type of twins is *dizygotic twins (DZ)*, with two amnions, two chorions, and two placentas that may or may not be fused. *Monozygotic twins (MZ)*, the less common type, represent about a third of all twins; they are derived from one zygote. Monozygotic twins commonly have one chorion, two amnions, and one placenta. Twins with one amnion, one chorion, and one placenta are always monozygotic, and their umbilical cords are often entangled. Other types of multiple birth (triplets, etc.) may be derived from one or more zygotes.

The *yolk sac* and *allantois* are vestigial structures; however, their presence is essential to normal embryonic development. Both are early sites of blood formation and both are partly incorporated into the embryo. Primordial germ cells also originate in the wall of the yolk sac.

The *amnion* forms a sac for amniotic fluid and provides a covering for the umbilical cord. The amniotic fluid has three main functions:

- To provide a protective buffer for the embryo or fetus
- To allow room for fetal movements
- To assist in the regulation of fetal body temperature

Clinically Oriented Questions

1. What is meant by the term *stillbirth*? Do older women have more stillborn infants? I have heard that more males than females are born dead. Is this true?

2. My sister's baby was born dead because of a "cord accident." What does this mean? Do these accidents always kill the baby? If not, what defects may be present?

3. What is the scientific basis of the pregnancy tests that are sold in drug stores? Are they accurate?

4. What is the proper name for what lay people refer to as the "bag of waters"? What is meant by a "dry birth"? Does premature rupture of this "bag" induce the birth of the baby?

5. What does the term *fetal distress* mean? How is the condition recognized? What causes fetal stress and distress?

6. I have heard that twins are born more commonly to older mothers. Is this true? I have also heard that twinning is hereditary. Is this correct?

The answers to these questions are given at the back of the book.

REFERENCES AND SUGGESTED READING

Behrman RE, Kliegman RM, Arvin AM (eds): *Nelson Textbook of Pediatrics*, 15th ed. Philadelphia, WB Saunders, 1996.

Benirschke K: Obstetrically important lesions of the umbilical cord. *J Reprod Med* 39:226, 1994.

Benirschke K, Kaufman P: *The Pathology of the Human Placenta*. Berlin, Springer-Verlag, 1990.

Berkowitz RS, Goldstein DP: Chorionic twins. *N Engl J Med* 335: 1740, 1996.

Callen PW, Filly RA: Amniotic fluid evaluation. *In* Harrison MR, Golbus MS, Filly RA (eds): *The Unborn Patient: Prenatal Diagnosis and Treatment*, 2nd ed. Philadelphia, WB Saunders, 1990.

Carlson BM: *Human Embryology and Developmental Biology*. St. Louis, CV Mosby, 1994.

Doubilet PM, Benson CB: Ultrasound evaluation of amniotic fluid. *In* Callen PW: *Ultrasonography in Obstetrics and Gynecology*, 3rd ed. Philadelphia, WB Saunders, 1994.

Filly RA: Ultrasound evaluation during the first trimester. *In* Callen PW (ed): *Ultrasonography in Obstetrics and Gynecology*, 3rd ed. Philadelphia, WB Saunders, 1994.

Finberg HJ: Ultrasound evaluation in multiple pregnancy. *In* Callen PW (ed): *Ultrasonography in Obstetrics and Gynecology*, 3rd ed. Philadelphia, WB Saunders, 1994.

Freedman RS, Tortolero-Luna G, Pandey DK, et al: Gestational trophoblastic disease. *Obstet Gynecol Clin North Am* 23:545, 1996.

Gordon JF, Shifren JL, Foulk RA, et al: Angiogenesis in the human female reproductive tract. *Obstet Gynecol Surv* 50:688, 1995.

Heinonen S, Ryynänen M, Kirkinen P, Saarikoski S: Perinatal diagnostic evaluation of velamentous umbilical cord insertion: Clinical, Doppler, and ultrasonic findings. *Obstet Gynecol* 87:112, 1996.

Jones JM, Sbarra AJ, Cetrulo CL: Twin transfusion syndrome. *J Reprod Med* 41:11, 1996.

Kraemer K, Noerr B: Placental transfer of drugs. *J Obstet Gynecol Neonatal Nurs (Neonatal Network)* 16:65, 1997.

Liu S, Benirschke K, Scioscia AL, Mannino FL: Intrauterine death in multiple gestation. *Acta Genet Med Gemellol Roma* 41:5, 1992.

Love CDB: Pregnancies complicated by placenta praevia: What is appropriate management? *Br J Obstet Gynaecol* 103:864, 1996.

Mann SE, Nijland MJM, Ross MG: Mathematic modeling of human amniotic fluid dynamics. *Am J Obstet Gynecol* 175:937, 1996.

Moore KL, Persaud TVN: *The Developing Human: Clinically Oriented Embryology*, 6th ed. Philadelphia, WB Saunders, 1998.

Naeye RL: *Disorders of the Placenta, Fetus, and Neonate*. St. Louis, Mosby-Year Book, 1992.

Nash JE, Persaud TVN: Embryopathic risks of cigarette smoking. *Exp Pathol* 33:65, 1988.

Nathanielsz PW: *Life Before Birth: The Challenges of Fetal Development*. New York, WH Freeman and Company, 1996.

Page EW, Villee CA, Villee DB: *Human Reproduction: Essentials of Reproductive and Perinatal Medicine*, 3rd ed. Philadelphia, WB Saunders, 1981.

Parilla V, Tamura RK, MacGregor SN, et al: The clinical significance of a single umbilical artery as an isolated finding on prenatal ultrasound. *Obstet Gynecol* 85:570, 1995.

Raga R, Ballester MJ, Osborne NG, Barilla-Musoles F: Role of color flow Doppler ultrasonography in diagnosing velamentous insertion of the umbilical cord and vas previa. *J Reprod Med* 40:804, 1995.

Seed JW, Cefalo RC, Herbert WNP: Amniotic band syndrome. *Am J Obstet Gynecol* 144:243, 1982.

Spencer R: Conjoined twins: Theoretical embryologic basis. *Teratology* 45:591, 1992.

Terasaki PI, Gjertson D, Bernoco D, et al: Twins with two different fathers identified by HLA. *N Engl J Med* 299:590, 1978.

Thompson MW, McInnes RR, Willard HF: *Thompson and Thompson Genetics in Medicine*, 5th ed. Philadelphia, WB Saunders, 1991.

Thorp JA, Dildy GA, Yeomans ER, et al: Umbilical blood gas analysis at delivery. *Am J Obstet Gynecol* 175:517, 1996.

Townsend RR: Ultrasound evaluation of the placenta and umbilical cord. *In* Callen PW (ed): *Ultrasonography in Obstetrics and Gynecology*, 3rd ed. Philadelphia, WB Saunders, 1994.

Werler MM, Pober BR, Holmes LB: Smoking and pregnancy. *In* Sever JL, Brent RL (eds): *Teratogen Update: Environmentally Induced Birth Defect Risks*. New York, Alan R. Liss, 1986.

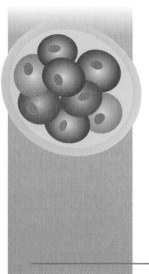

Human Birth Defects

9

■ *Congenital anomalies, birth defects,* and *congenital malformations* are terms currently used to describe developmental disorders present at birth (L. *congenitus,* born with). Birth defects are the leading cause of infant mortality and may be structural, functional, metabolic, behavioral, or hereditary (Persaud et al, 1985). The most widely used reference guide for classifying birth defects is the *International Classification of Diseases* (Medicode's Hospital and Payer ICD.9.Cm, 4th ed, 1995). This practical classification system for developmental defects, which takes into consideration the time of onset of the injury, possible cause, and pathogenesis, is now widely accepted among clinicians (Spranger et al, 1982; Jones, 1997).

A **congenital anomaly** is a structural abnormality of any type; however, *not all variations of development are anomalies.* Anatomic variations are common; for example, bones vary among themselves, not only in their basic shape but in lesser details of surface structure (Moore, 1992). *Congenital anomalies are of four clinically significant types*: malformation, disruption, deformation, and dysplasia. For a discussion of the meaning of these terms, see Moore and Persaud (1998).

TERATOLOGY: STUDY OF ABNORMAL DEVELOPMENT

Teratology is the branch of science that studies the causes, mechanisms, and patterns of abnormal development. A fundamental concept in teratology is that certain stages of embryonic development are more vulnerable to disruption than others. Until the 1940s it was generally believed that human embryos were protected from environmental agents such as drugs and viruses by their extraembryonic/fetal membranes (amnion and chorion) and their mothers' abdominal and uterine walls. Gregg (1941) presented the first well-documented evidence that an environmental agent (rubella virus) could produce severe developmental disruptions such as cataracts if it was present during the critical period of human development of the eyes, heart, and ears. However, the observations of Lenz (1961) and McBride (1961) focused attention on the role of drugs in the development of human birth defects. They described severe limb anomalies and developmental disruptions that were caused by **thalidomide** during early pregnancy (Brent and Holmes, 1988; Kliegman, 1996). It is estimated that 7 to 10% of human birth defects result from the disruptive actions of drugs, viruses, and other environmental factors (Persaud, 1990; Thompson et al, 1991). According to data from the U.S. Centers for Disease Control, the leading cause of death for white infants is birth defects.

More than 20% of infant deaths in North America are attributed to birth defects. Major structural anomalies, such as spina bifida cystica — a severe type of vertebral defect in which the neural tube fails to fuse, are observed in about 3% of newborn infants. Additional anomalies can be detected after birth; thus, the incidence reaches about 6% in 2-year-old children and 8% in 5-year-old children (Nelson and Holmes, 1989). For the contributions of epidemiology to the study of birth defects (registries, surveillance systems, prevention), see Khoury (1995).

The **causes of congenital anomalies** are divided into:

* *Genetic factors* such as chromosome abnormalities
* *Environmental factors* such as drugs and viruses

However, many common congenital anomalies are caused by genetic and environmental factors acting together — **multifactorial inheritance**.

For 50 to 60% of congenital anomalies, the causes are unknown (Fig. 9–1). Congenital anomalies may be single or multiple and of major or minor clinical significance. Single *minor anomalies* are present in about 14% of newborns (Jones, 1997). Anomalies of the external ear, for example, are of no serious medical significance, but they indicate to the clinician the possible presence of associated major anomalies; for example, the presence of a single umbilical artery alerts the clinician to the possible presence of cardiovascular and renal anomalies. Ninety percent of infants with three or more minor anomalies also have one or more major defects. Of the 3% born with clinically significant congenital anomalies, 0.7% have multiple major anomalies (Jones, 1997). Most of these infants die during infancy. Major developmental defects are much more common in early embryos (10 to 15%), but most of them abort spontaneously during the first 6 weeks. Chromosome abnormalities are present in 50 to 60% of spontaneously aborted conceptuses (Shiota et al, 1987; Shepard et al, 1989; Kaufman, 1991).

ANOMALIES CAUSED BY GENETIC FACTORS*

Numerically, genetic factors are the most important causes of congenital anomalies. It has been estimated that they cause about one third of all birth defects (Fig. 9–1) and nearly 85% of anomalies with known causes. Any mechanism as complex as mitosis or mejo-

---

*The authors are grateful to Dr. A. E. Chudley, MD, F.R.C.P.C., F.C.C.M.G., Professor of Pediatrics and Child Health, and Head, Section of Genetics and Metabolism, Children's Hospital, Health Sciences Centre, University of Manitoba, Winnipeg, Manitoba, Canada, for assistance with the preparation of this section.

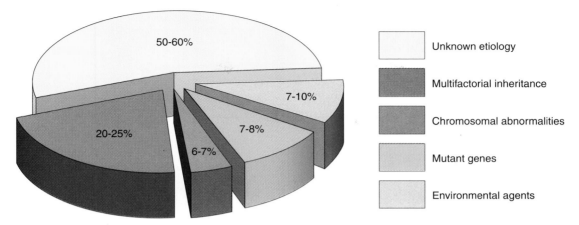

■ **Figure 9–1.** Graphic illustration of the causes of human congenital anomalies. Note that the causes of most anomalies are unknown and that 20 to 25% of them are caused by a combination of genetic and environmental factors (multifactorial inheritance).

sis may occasionally malfunction; thus, *chromosomal aberrations are common and are present in 6 to 7% of zygotes.* Many of these early embryos never undergo normal cleavage to become blastocysts. *In vitro studies* of cleaving zygotes less than 5 days old have revealed a high incidence of abnormalities. More than 60% of day two cleaving zygotes were found to be abnormal (Winston et al, 1991). Many defective zygotes, blastocysts, and 3-week-old embryos abort spontaneously, and the overall frequency of chromosome abnormalities in these embryos is at least 50% (Thompson et al, 1991).

Two kinds of change occur in chromosome complements: numerical and structural. The changes may affect the sex chromosomes and/or the autosomes — chromosomes other than sex chromosomes. In some instances, both kinds of chromosome are affected. Persons with chromosome abnormalities usually have characteristic phenotypes, such as the physical characteristics of infants with Down syndrome (Hall, 1996; Jones, 1997). They often look more like other persons with the same chromosome abnormality than their own siblings (brothers or sisters). This characteristic appearance results from genetic imbalance. Genetic factors initiate anomalies by biochemical or other means at the subcellular, cellular, or tissue level. The abnormal mechanisms initiated by the genetic factor may be identical or similar to the causal mechanisms initiated by a teratogen, a drug for example.

Numerical Chromosome Abnormalities

Numerical aberrations of chromosomes usually result from **nondisjunction**, an error in cell division in which a chromosome pair or two chromatids of a chromosome fail to disjoin during mitosis or meiosis. As a result, the chromosome pair or chromatids pass to one daughter cell, and the other daughter cell receives neither (Fig. 9–2). Nondisjunction may occur during maternal or paternal gametogenesis (see Chapter 2). The chromosomes in somatic (body) cells are normally paired; the homologous chromosomes making up a pair are *homologs.* Normal human females have 22 pairs of autosomes plus two X chromosomes, whereas normal males have 22 pairs of autosomes plus one X and one Y chromosome.

Inactivation of Genes

During embryogenesis, one of the two X chromosomes in female somatic cells is randomly inactivated and appears as a mass of **sex chromatin** (see Chapter 7). Inactivation of genes on one X chromosome in somatic cells of female embryos occurs during implantation (Thompson et al, 1991). *X-inactivation is important clinically* because it means that each cell from a carrier of an X-linked disease has the mutant gene causing the disease, either on the active X chromosome or on the inactivated X chromosome that is represented by sex chromatin. Uneven X-inactivation in monozygotic twins is one reason given for discordance in a variety of congenital anomalies. The genetic basis for discordance is that one twin preferentially expresses the paternal X, the other the maternal X.

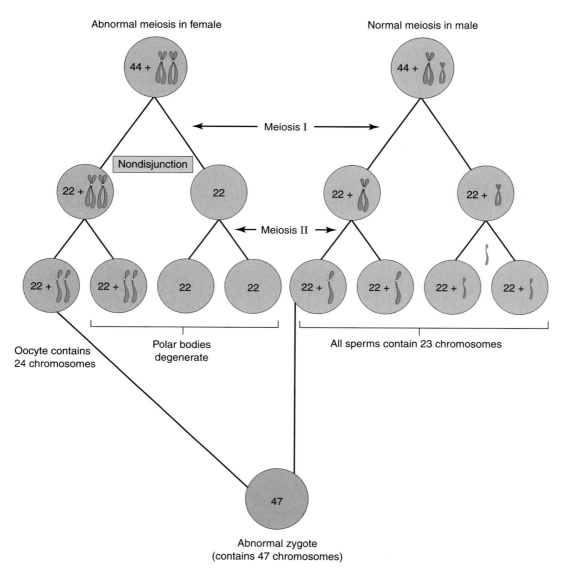

■ **Figure 9–2.** Diagram showing nondisjunction of chromosomes during the first meiotic division of a primary oocyte, resulting in an abnormal oocyte with 24 chromosomes. Subsequent fertilization by a normal sperm produces a zygote with 47 chromosomes — aneuploidy — a deviation from the human diploid number of 46.

Aneuploidy and Polyploidy

Changes in chromosome number represent either aneuploidy or polyploidy. **Aneuploidy** is any deviation from the human diploid number of 46 chromosomes. An *aneuploid* is an individual or a cell that has a chromosome number that is not an exact multiple of the haploid number of 23 (e.g., 45 or 47). The principal cause of aneuploidy is nondisjunction during cell division (Fig. 9-2), resulting in an unequal distribution of one pair of homologous chromosomes to the daughter cells. One cell has two chromosomes and the other has neither chromosome of the pair. As a result, the embryo's cells may be *hypodiploid* (45,X, as in *Turner syndrome* [Fig. 9-3]), or *hyperdiploid* (usually 47, as in trisomy 21, or *Down syndrome* [Fig. 9-4]). Embryos with **monosomy** — missing a chromosome — usually die. Monosomy of an autosome is extremely uncommon, and about 99% of embryos lacking a sex chromosome (45,X) abort spontaneously (Connor and Ferguson-Smith, 1987).

TURNER SYNDROME

About 1% of monosomy X female embryos survive. The incidence of 45,X or Turner syndrome in newborn females is approximately 1 in 8000 live births (Hall, 1996). Half the affected individuals have 45,X; the other half have a variety of abnormalities of a sex chromosome. *The phenotype of Turner syndrome is female* and is illustrated in Figure 9-3; secondary sexual characteristics do not develop in 90% of affected girls, and hormone replacement is required. **Phenotype** refers to the morphologic characteristics of an individual as determined by the genotype and the environment in which it is expressed (Thompson et al, 1991).

The *monosomy X chromosome abnormality is the most common cytogenetic abnormality observed in liveborn humans and fetuses that abort spontaneously,* and it accounts for about 18% of all abortions caused by chromosome abnormalities. The error in gametogenesis (nondisjunction) that causes monosomy X, when it can be traced, is in the paternal gamete in

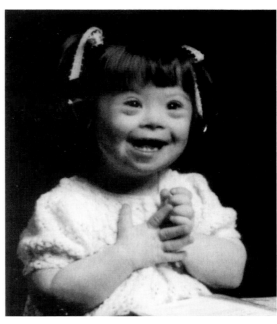

■ **Figure 9-4.** Photograph of a 2½-year-old girl with Down syndrome (trisomy 21). Observe her round face, upslanted palpebral fissures, short digits with incurving of the fifth digit (clinodactyly). (Courtesy of Dr. A. E. Chudley, Professor of Pediatrics and Child Health, Children's Hospital and University of Manitoba, Winnipeg, Manitoba, Canada.)

about 75% of cases; that is, it is the paternal X chromosome that is usually missing. The most frequent chromosome constitution in Turner syndrome is 45,X; however, nearly 50% of these people have other karyotypes (Hook and Warburton, 1983). For the clinical significance of these chromosome constitutions, such as a mosaic karyotype of 45,X/46,XX, see Thompson et al (1991).

TRISOMY OF THE AUTOSOMES

If three chromosomes are present instead of the usual pair, the abnormality is trisomy. Trisomies are the most common abnormalities of chromosome number (Hall, 1996). The usual cause of this numerical error is **meiotic nondisjunction of chromosomes** (Fig. 9-2), resulting in a gamete with 24 instead of 23 chromosomes and subsequently in a zygote with 47 chromosomes. Trisomy of the autosomes is associated with three main syndromes (Table 9-1):

- Trisomy 21, or Down syndrome (Fig. 9-4)
- Trisomy 18, or Edwards syndrome (Fig. 9-5)
- Trisomy 13, or Patau syndrome (Fig. 9-6)

Infants with trisomy 13 and trisomy 18 are severely malformed and mentally retarded and usually die early

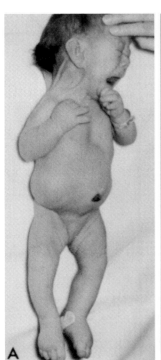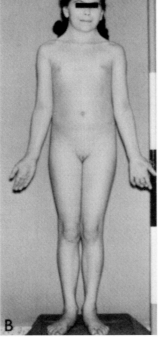

■ **Figure 9-3.** Female individuals with Turner syndrome. *A,* Newborn infant. Note the webbed neck and lymphedema of the hands and feet. *B,* A 13-year-old girl showing the classic features of the syndrome in older females: short stature, webbed neck, absence of sexual maturation, and broad, shieldlike chest with widely spaced nipples. (From Moore KL: *The Sex Chromosome.* Philadelphia, WB Saunders, 1966.)

Table 9–1 ■ Trisomy of the Autosomes

Chromosomal Aberration/Syndrome	Incidence	Usual Morphologic Characteristics	Figures
Trisomy 21 or Down syndrome*	1:800	Mental deficiency; brachycephaly, flat nasal bridge; upward slant to palpebral fissures; protruding tongue; simian crease; clinodactyly of 5th digit; congenital heart defects.	9–4
Trisomy 18 syndrome†	1:8000	Mental deficiency; growth retardation; prominent occiput; short sternum; ventricular septal defect; micrognathia; low-set malformed ears; flexed digits, hypoplastic nails; rocker-bottom feet.	9–5
Trisomy 13 syndrome†	1:25,000	Mental deficiency; severe central nervous system malformations; sloping forehead; malformed ears, scalp defects; microphthalmia; bilateral cleft lip and/or palate; polydactyly; posterior prominence of the heels.	9–6

*The importance of this disorder in the overall problem of mental retardation is indicated by the fact that persons with Down syndrome represent 10 to 15% of institutionalized mental defectives (Breg, 1975). *The incidence of trisomy 21 at fertilization is greater than at birth;* however, 75% of embryos are spontaneously aborted and at least 20% are stillborn.
† Infants with this syndrome rarely survive beyond 6 months.

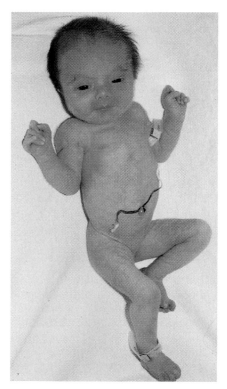

■ **Figure 9–5.** Female neonate with trisomy 18. Note the growth retardation, clenched fists with characteristic positioning of the fingers (second and fifth digits overlapping the third and fourth), short sternum, and narrow pelvis. (Courtesy of Dr. A. E. Chudley, Professor of Pediatrics and Child Health, Children's Hospital and University of Manitoba, Winnipeg, Manitoba, Canada.)

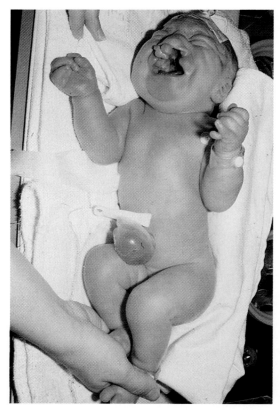

■ **Figure 9–6.** Female neonate with trisomy 13. Note particularly the bilateral cleft lip, low-set malformed ears, and polydactyly (extra digits). A small omphalocele (herniation of viscera into the umbilical cord) is also present. (Courtesy of Dr. A. E. Chudley, Professor of Pediatrics and Child Health, Children's Hospital and University of Manitoba, Winnipeg, Manitoba, Canada.)

Table 9-2 ■ Incidence of Down Syndrome in Newborn Infants

Maternal Age (Years)	Incidence
20-24	1:1400
25-29	1:1100
30-34	1:700
35	1:350
37	1:225
39	1:140
41	1:85
43	1:50
45+	1:25

in infancy. More than half of trisomic conceptions abort early in pregnancies. *Trisomy of the autosomes occurs with increasing frequency as maternal age increases*; for example, trisomy 21 syndrome occurs once in about 1400 births in mothers aged 20 to 24 years, but once in about 25 births in mothers 45 years and over (Table 9-2).

Mosaicism — two or more cell types containing different numbers of chromosomes (normal and abnormal) — leads to a less severe phenotype and the IQ may be nearly normal. For more information on trisomies, see Hall (1996).

TRISOMY OF THE SEX CHROMOSOMES

Trisomy of the sex chromosomes is a common condition (Table 9-3); however, because no characteristic physical findings are seen in infants or children, this disorder is not usually detected before puberty (Fig. 9-7). *Sex chromatin studies* were useful in the past

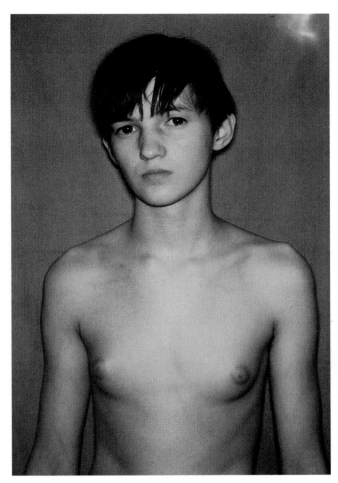

■ **Figure 9-7.** Young male with Klinefelter syndrome (XXY trisomy). Note the presence of breasts; about 40% of males with this syndrome have gynecomastia (excessive development of male mammary glands) and small testes.

Table 9-3 ■ Trisomy of the Sex Chromosomes

Chromosome Complement*	Sex	Incidence†	Usual Characteristics
47,XXX	Female	1:960	Normal in appearance; usually fertile; 15-25% are mildly mentally retarded.
47,XXY	Male	1:1080	Klinefelter syndrome; small testes, hyalinization of seminiferous tubules; aspermatogenesis; often tall with disproportionately long lower limbs. Intelligence is less than in normal siblings. About 40% of these males have gynecomastia.
47,XYY	Male	1:1080	Normal in appearance; usually tall; often exhibit aggressive behavior.

*The numbers designate the total number of chromosomes including the sex chromosomes shown after the comma.
†Data from Hook EB, Hamerton JL: The frequency of chromosome abnormalities detected in consecutive newborn studies—Differences between studies—Results by sex and by severity of phenotypic involvement. *In* Hook EB, Porter IH (eds): *Population Cytogenetics: Studies in Humans.* New York, Academic Press, 1977.

in detecting some types of trisomy of the sex chromosomes (Moore, 1966) because two masses of sex chromatin are present in nuclei of XXX females, and nuclei of XXY males contain a mass of sex chromatin (see Chapter 7). Today, diagnosis is best achieved by chromosome analysis.

Tetrasomy and Pentasomy

Tetrasomy and pentasomy of the sex chromosomes also occur. Persons with these abnormalities have four or five sex chromosomes; the following chromosome complexes have been reported in *females*: 48,XXXX and 49,XXXXX; and in *males*: 48,XXXY, 48,XXYY, 49,XXXYY, and 49,XXXXY. The extra sex chromosomes do not accentuate sexual characteristics; however, usually the greater the number of sex chromosomes present, the greater the severity of mental retardation and physical impairment (Thompson et al, 1991).

Mosaicism

A person who has at least two cell lines with *two or more different genotypes* (genetic constitutions) is a **mosaic**. Either the autosomes or sex chromosomes may be involved. Usually the anomalies are less serious than in persons with monosomy or trisomy. Mosaicism usually results from nondisjunction during early cleavage of the zygote (see Chapter 3). Mosaicism resulting from loss of a chromosome by *anaphase lagging* also occurs; the chromosomes separate normally, but one of them is delayed in its migration and is eventually lost.

Triploidy

The most common type of polyploidy is **triploidy** (69 chromosomes). Triploid fetuses have severe intrauterine growth retardation (IUGR) with a disproportionately small trunk. Several other anomalies are common. Triploidy could result from the second polar body failing to separate from the oocyte during the second meiotic division (see Chapter 2); more likely, triploidy results when an oocyte is fertilized by two sperms (dispermy) almost simultaneously. Triploidy occurs in about 2% of embryos, but most of them abort spontaneously. Triploid fetuses account for about 20% of chromosomally abnormal miscarriages (Crane, 1994). Although *triploid fetuses* have been born alive, this is exceptional. These infants all died within a few days because of multiple anomalies and low birth weight (Connor and Ferguson-Smith, 1987).

Tetraploidy

Doubling the diploid chromosome number to 92 (*tetraploidy*) probably occurs during the first cleavage division. Division of this abnormal zygote would subsequently result in an embryo with cells containing 92 chromosomes. *Tetraploid embryos* abort very early, and often all that is recovered is an empty chorionic sac, which is often referred to as a "blighted embryo" (Kaufman, 1991).

Structural Chromosome Abnormalities

Most abnormalities of chromosome structure result from chromosome breakage followed by reconstitution in an abnormal combination (Fig. 9–8). **Chromosome breaks** may be induced by various environmental factors, such as radiation, drugs, chemicals, and viruses (Hall, 1996). The resulting type of abnormality of chromosome structure depends upon what happens to the broken pieces. The only two aberrations of chromosome structure that are likely to be transmitted from parent to child are structural rearrangements, such as inversion and translocation (Thompson et al, 1991).

TRANSLOCATION

This is the transfer of a piece of one chromosome to a nonhomologous chromosome. If two nonhomologous chromosomes exchange pieces, it is a *reciprocal translocation* (Fig. 9–8A and G). Translocation does not necessarily cause abnormal development. Persons with a translocation between a number 21 chromosome and a number 14, for example (Fig. 9–8G), are phenotypically normal. Such persons are called *balanced translocation carriers*. They have a tendency, independent of age, to produce germ cells with an abnormal translocation chromosome. Three to 4% of persons with Down syndrome have translocation trisomies; that is, the extra 21 chromosome is attached to another chromosome.

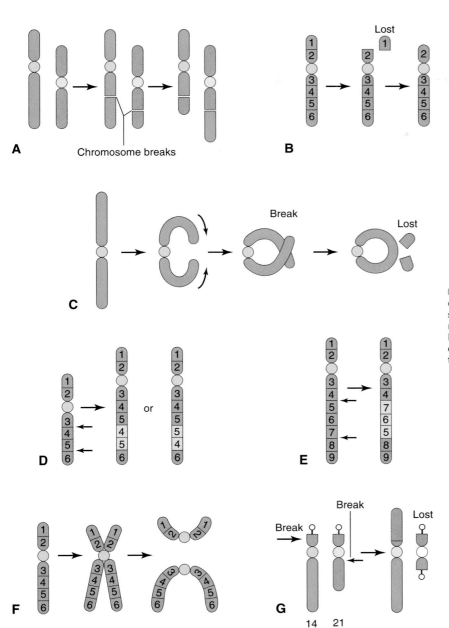

■ **Figure 9–8.** Diagrams illustrating various structural abnormalities of chromosomes. *A,* Reciprocal translocation. *B,* Terminal deletion. *C,* Ring chromosome. *D,* Duplication. *E,* Paracentric inversion. *F,* Isochromosome. *G,* Robertsonian translocation.

DELETION

When a chromosome breaks, a portion of the chromosome may be lost (Fig. 9–8*B*). A partial terminal deletion from the short arm of chromosome 5 causes the **cri du chat syndrome** (Fig. 9–9). Affected infants have a weak catlike cry, microcephaly (abnormally small head), severe mental retardation, and congenital heart disease. A **ring chromosome** is a type of deletion chromosome from which both ends have been lost, and the broken ends have rejoined to form a ring-shaped chromosome (Fig. 9–8*C*). Ring chromosomes are very rare, but they have been found for all chromosomes (Hall, 1996). These abnormal chromosomes have been described in persons with Turner syndrome, trisomy 18, and other abnormalities.

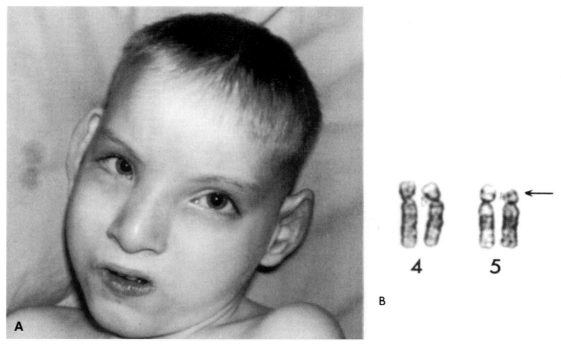

■ **Figure 9–9.** *A*, Male child with cri du chat syndrome. (From Gardner EJ: *Principles of Genetics*, 5th ed. New York, John Wiley & Sons, 1975). *B*, Partial karyotype of this child showing a terminal deletion of the short arm end of the chromosome number 5. The arrow indicates the site of deletion.

Microdeletions and Microduplications

High-resolution banding techniques have allowed detection of very small interstitial and terminal deletions in a number of disorders. Normal resolution chromosome banding reveals 350 bands per haploid set, whereas *high-resolution chromosome banding* reveals up to 1300 bands per haploid set. Because the deletions span several contiguous genes, these disorders, as well as those with microduplications, are referred to as **contiguous gene syndromes**. Two examples are:

* *Prader-Willi syndrome* (PWS), a sporadically occurring disorder associated with short stature, mild mental retardation, obesity, hyperphagia (overeating), and hypogonadism (inadequate gonadal function)
* *Angelman syndrome* (AS), characterized by severe mental retardation, microcephaly, brachycephaly (shortness of head), seizures, and ataxic (jerky) movements of the limbs and trunk

The clinical phenotype is determined by the parental origin of the deleted chromosome 15. If the deletion arises in the mother, AS occurs; if passed on by the father, the child exhibits the PWS phenotype. This suggests the phenomenon of **genetic imprinting**, whereby differential expression of genetic material depends on the sex of the transmitting parent (Kirkilionis et al, 1991).

Molecular Cytogenetics

Several new methods for merging classic cytogenetics with DNA technology have facilitated a more precise definition of chromosome abnormalities, location, or origins, including unbalanced translocations, accessory or marker chromosomes, and *gene mapping*. One new approach to chromosome identification is based on *fluorescent in situ hybridization* (FISH), whereby chromosome-specific DNA probes can adhere to complementary regions located on specific chromosomes (Pinkel et al, 1986). This allows improved identification of chromosome location and number in metaphase spreads or even in interphase cells. The FISH techniques using interphase cells may soon obviate the need to culture cells for specific chromosome analysis, such as in the case of prenatal diagnosis of fetal trisomies.

Duplications

Duplications may be represented as a duplicated part of a chromosome, within a chromosome (Fig. 9-8D), attached to a chromosome, or as a separate fragment. *Duplications are more common than deletions, and they are less harmful* because no loss of genetic material occurs. Duplication may involve part of a gene, whole genes, or a series of genes (Thompson et al, 1991).

Inversion

Inversion is a chromosomal aberration in which a segment of a chromosome is reversed. *Paracentric inversion* is confined to a single arm of the chromosome (Fig. 9-8E), whereas *pericentric inversion* involves both arms and includes the centromere. Carriers of pericentric inversions are at risk of having offspring with abnormalities because of unequal crossing-over and malsegregation at meiosis (Thompson et al, 1991).

Isochromosomes

The abnormality resulting in isochromosomes occurs when the centromere divides transversely instead of longitudinally (Fig. 9-8F). An isochromosome is a chromosome in which one arm is missing and the other is duplicated. It appears to be the *most common structural abnormality of the X chromosome*. Persons with this chromosomal abnormality are often short in stature and have other stigmata of Turner syndrome. These characteristics are related to the loss of an arm of an X chromosome (Thompson et al, 1991).

Anomalies Caused by Mutant Genes

Seven to 8% of congenital anomalies are caused by gene defects (Fig. 9-1). A mutation usually involves a loss or change in the function of a gene and is any permanent, heritable change in the sequence of genomic DNA (Thompson et al, 1991). Because a random change is unlikely to lead to an improvement in development, *most mutations are deleterious and some are lethal*. The mutation rate can be increased by a number of environmental agents, such as large doses of radiation and some chemicals, especially carcinogenic (cancer-inducing) ones. Anomalies resulting from gene mutations are inherited according to mendelian laws; consequently, predictions can be made about the probability of their occurrence in the affected person's children and other relatives.

An example of a *dominantly inherited congenital anomaly* is **achondroplasia** (Fig. 9-10), which is due to a G to A transition mutation at nucleotide 1138 of the cDNA in the *fibroblast growth factor receptor 3 (FGFR3) gene* on chromosome 4p. Other congenital anomalies are attributed to *autosomal recessive inheritance*. Autosomal recessive genes manifest themselves only when homozygous; as a consequence, many carriers of these genes (heterozygous persons) remain undetected.

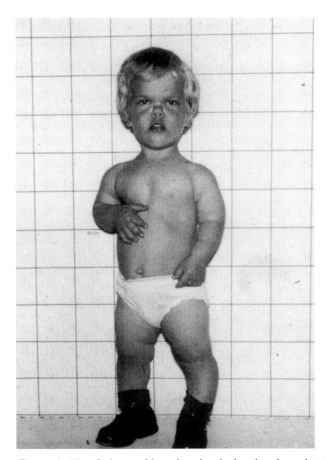

■ **Figure 9-10.** A boy with achondroplasia showing short stature, short limbs and fingers, normal length of the trunk, bowed legs, a relatively large head, prominent forehead, and depressed nasal bridge. (Courtesy of Dr. A. E. Chudley, Professor of Pediatrics and Child Health, Children's Hospital and University of Manitoba, Winnipeg, Manitoba, Canada.)

The **fragile-X syndrome** is the most common inherited cause of moderate mental retardation (Fig. 9-11) and is *second only to Down syndrome among all causes of moderate mental retardation in males* (Hall, 1996). The fragile-X syndrome has a frequency of 1 in 1500 male births and may account for much of the excess of males in the mentally retarded population (Thompson et al, 1991). The diagnosis can be confirmed by chromosome analysis demonstrating the fragile-X chromosome at x927.3 or by DNA studies, showing an expression of CGG nucleotides in a specific region of the fragile mental retardation I (FMRI) gene.

Several genetic disorders have been confirmed to be due to expansion of trinucleotides in specific genes. Other examples include myotonic dystrophy, Huntington chorea, spinobulbar atrophy (Kennedy disease), Friedreich ataxia, and others. X-linked recessive genes are usually manifest in affected (homozygous) males and occasionally in carrier (heterozygous) females; for example, fragile-X syndrome (Chudley and Hagerman, 1987; Heitz et al, 1991).

The **human genome** contains an estimated 50,000 to 100,000 structural genes per haploid set, or 3 billion base pairs. Many disease-causing genes are being identified because of international collaborations and the Human Genome Project. It is expected that most genetic diseases will be mapped and all genes sequenced by the early part of the 21st century. It is plausible that the majority of congenital anomalies of unknown cause will be determined to result from gene mutations. Molecular analysis has already confirmed this for many disorders.

Genomic imprinting is an epigenetic process whereby the female and male germlines confer a sex-specific mark on a chromosome subregion, so that only the paternal or maternal allele of a gene is active in the offspring. In other words, the sex of the transmitting parent influences expression or nonexpression of certain genes in the offspring. This is the reason for Prader-Willi syndrome and Angelman syndrome, in which the phenotype is determined by whether the microdeletion is transmitted by the father (PWS) or the mother (AS). For more information about these syndromes, see Moore and Persaud (1998).

Homeobox genes are a group of genes found in all vertebrates. They have highly conserved sequences and order. They are involved in early embryonic development and specify identity and spatial arrangements of body segments. Protein products of these genes bind to DNA and form transcriptional factors that regulate gene expression.

ANOMALIES CAUSED BY ENVIRONMENTAL FACTORS

Although the human embryo is well protected in the uterus, certain environmental agents — **teratogens** — may cause developmental disruptions following maternal exposure to them (Table 9-4). A teratogen is any

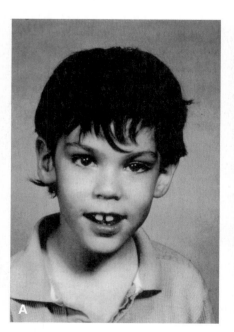
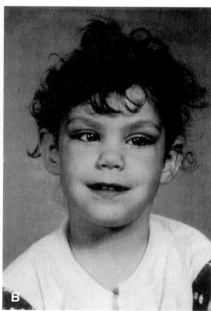

■ **Figure 9-11.** Fragile X syndrome. *A,* An 8-year-old, mentally retarded boy exhibiting a relatively normal appearance with a long face and prominent ears. *B,* His 6-year-old sister also has this syndrome. She has a mild learning disability and similar features of long face and prominent ears. Note the strabismus (crossed right eye). Although this is an X-linked disorder, sometimes female carriers have expression of the disease. (Courtesy of Dr. A. E. Chudley, Professor of Pediatrics and Child Health, Children's Hospital and University of Manitoba, Winnipeg, Manitoba, Canada.)

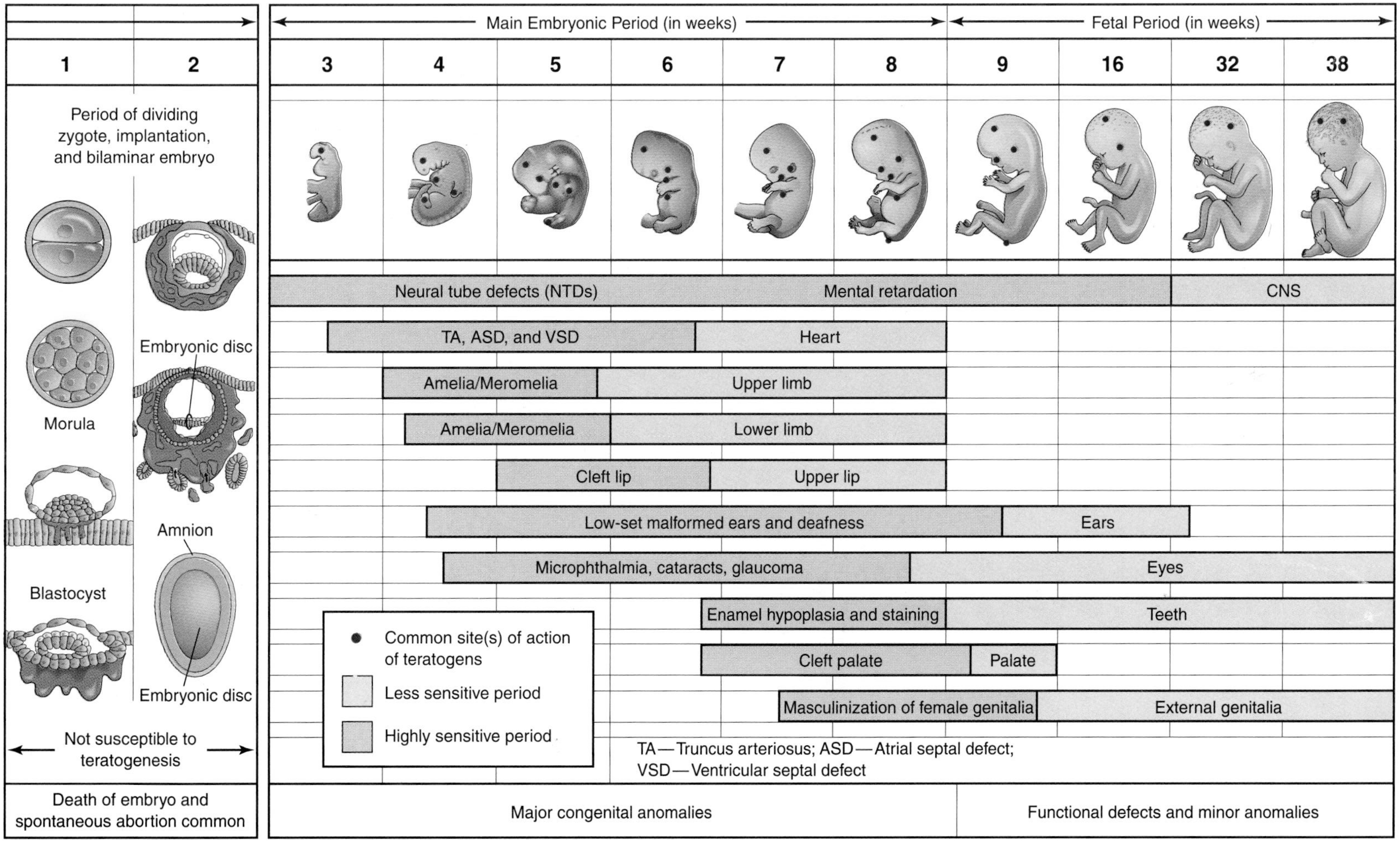

■ **Figure 9–12.** Schematic illustration of critical periods in human prenatal development. During the first 2 weeks of development, the embryo is usually not susceptible to teratogens; a teratogen either damages all or most of the cells, resulting in death of the embryo, or damages only a few cells, allowing the conceptus to recover and the embryo to develop without birth defects. Mauve denotes highly sensitive periods when major defects may be produced (e.g., amelia, absence of limbs). Green indicates stages that are less sensitive to teratogens when minor defects may be induced (e.g., hypoplastic thumbs).

66

Table 9–4 ■ Teratogens Known to Cause Human Birth Defects

Agents	Most Common Congenital Anomalies
DRUGS	
Alcohol	*Fetal alcohol syndrome (FAS):* intrauterine growth retardation (IUGR); mental retardation, microcephaly; ocular anomalies; joint abnormalities; short palpebral fissures.
Androgens and high doses of progestogens	Varying degrees of masculinization of female fetuses; ambiguous external genitalia resulting in labial fusion and clitoral hypertrophy.
Aminopterin	IUGR; skeletal defects; malformations of the central nervous system, notably meroanencephaly (most of the brain is absent).
Busulfan	Stunted growth; skeletal abnormalities; corneal opacities; cleft palate; hypoplasia of various organs.
Cocaine	IUGR; microcephaly; cerebral infarction; urogenital anomalies, neurobehavioral disturbances.
Diethylstilbestrol	Abnormalities of the uterus and vagina; cervical erosion and ridges.
Isotretinoin (13-cis-retinoic acid)	Craniofacial abnormalities; neural tube defects (NTDs), such as spina bifida cystica; cardiovascular defects.
Lithium carbonate	Various anomalies usually involving the heart and great vessels.
Methotrexate	Multiple anomalies, especially skeletal, involving the face, skull, limbs, and vertebral column.
Phenytoin (Dilantin)	*Fetal hydantoin syndrome (FHS):* IUGR; microcephaly; mental retardation; ridged metopic suture; inner epicanthal folds; eyelid ptosis; broad depressed nasal bridge; phalangeal hypoplasia.
Tetracycline	Stained teeth; hypoplasia of enamel.
Thalidomide	Abnormal development of the limbs; meromelia (partial absence) and amelia (complete absence); facial anomalies; systemic anomalies, e.g., cardiac and kidney defects.
Trimethadione	Developmental delay; V-shaped eyebrows; low-set ears; cleft lip and/or palate.
Valproic acid	Craniofacial anomalies; NTDs; often hydrocephalus; heart and skeletal defects.
Warfarin	Nasal hypoplasia; stippled epiphyses; hypoplastic phalanges; eye anomalies; mental retardation.
CHEMICALS	
Methylmercury	Cerebral atrophy; spasticity; seizures; mental retardation.
Polychlorinated biphenyls (PCBs)	IUGR; skin discolorization.
INFECTIONS	
Cytomegalovirus	Microcephaly; chorioretinitis; sensorineural loss; delayed psychomotor/mental development; hepatosplenomegaly; hydrocephaly; cerebral palsy; brain (periventricular) calcification.
Herpes simplex virus	Skin vesicles and scarring; chorioretinitis; hepatomegaly; thrombocytopenia; petechiae; hemolytic anemia; hydranencephaly.
Human immunodeficiency virus (HIV)	Growth failure; microcephaly; prominent boxlike forehead; flattened nasal bridge; hypertelorism; triangular philtrum and patulous lips.
Human parvovirus B19	Eye defects; degenerative changes in fetal tissues.
Rubella virus	IUGR; postnatal growth retardation; cardiac and great vessel abnormalities; microcephaly; sensorineural deafness; cataract; microphthalmos; glaucoma; pigmented retinopathy; mental retardation; newborn bleeding; hepatosplenomegaly; osteopathy.
Toxoplasma gondii	Microcephaly; mental retardation; microphthalmia; hydrocephaly; chorioretinitis; cerebral calcifications; hearing loss; neurologic disturbances.
Treponema pallidum	Hydrocephalus; congenital deafness; mental retardation; abnormal teeth and bones.
Venezuelan equine encephalitis virus	Microcephaly; microphthalmia; cerebral agenesis; CNS necrosis; hydrocephalus.
Varicella virus	Cutaneous scars (dermatome distribution); neurologic anomalies (e.g., limb paresis, hydrocephaly, seizures); cataracts; microphthalmia; Horner syndrome; optic atrophy; nystagmus; chorioretinitis; microcephaly; mental retardation; skeletal anomalies (e.g., hypoplasia of limbs, fingers, and toes); urogenital anomalies.
HIGH LEVELS OF IONIZING RADIATION	Microcephaly; mental retardation; skeletal anomalies; growth retardation; cataracts.

agent that can produce a congenital anomaly or raise the incidence of an anomaly in the population (Persaud, 1990; Kliegman, 1996). Environmental factors, such as infection and drugs, may simulate genetic conditions, such as when two or more children of normal parents are affected. The *important principle* is— "not everything that is familial is genetic." The organ and parts of an embryo are most sensitive to terate genic agents during periods of rapid differentiatio (Fig. 9–12).

Environmental factors cause 7 to 10% of congenital anomalies (Fig. 9–1). Because biochemical differentiation precedes morphologic differentiation, the period during which structures are sensitive to interference by teratogens often precedes the stage of their visible development by a few days. Teratogens do not appear to be effective in causing anomalies until cellular differentiation has begun; however, their early actions may cause the death of the embryo, for example, during the first 2 weeks of development. The exact *mechanisms* by which drugs, chemicals, and other environmental factors disrupt embryonic development and induce abnormalities still remain obscure. Even thalidomide's mechanisms of action on the embryo are a "mystery," and more than 20 hypotheses have been postulated to explain how it disrupts development of the embryo (Castella et al, 1996).

Many studies have shown that certain hereditary and environmental influences may adversely affect embryonic development by altering such fundamental processes as the intracellular compartment, surface of the cell, extracellular matrix, and fetal environment. No fundamental hypothesis explains the underlying mechanisms (Persaud et al, 1985). It has been suggested that the initial cellular response may take more than one form (genetic, molecular, biochemical, biophysical), resulting in different sequences of cellular changes (cell death, faulty cellular interaction-induction, reduced biosynthesis of substrates, impaired morphogenetic movements, and mechanical disruption). Eventually these different types of pathologic lesion could possibly lead to the final defect (intrauterine death, developmental anomalies, fetal growth retardation, or functional disturbances) through a common pathway (Beckman and Brent, 1984).

Rapid progress in molecular biology is providing more information on the genetic control of differentiation, as well as the cascade of events involved in the expression of homeobox genes and pattern formation. It is reasonable to speculate that disruption of gene activity at any critical stage could lead to a developmental defect. This view is supported by recent experimental studies that showed that exposure of mouse and amphibian embryos to the teratogen *retinoic acid* altered the domain of gene expression and disrupted normal morphogenesis. Researchers are now directing increasing attention to the molecular mechanisms of abnormal development in an attempt to better understand the pathogenesis of congenital anomalies (DeLuca, 1991).

Basic Principles in Teratogenesis

When considering the possible teratogenicity of an agent such as a drug or chemical, *three important principles* must be considered:

- Critical periods of development
- Dosage of the drug or chemical
- Genotype (genetic constitution) of the embryo

CRITICAL PERIODS OF HUMAN DEVELOPMENT

The stage of development of an embryo when an agent, such as a drug or virus, is present determines its susceptibility to a teratogen (Fig. 9–12). The most critical period in development is when cell division, cell differentiation, and morphogenesis are at their peak. Table 9–5 indicates the relative frequencies of anomalies for certain organs. *The most critical period for brain development is from 3 to 16 weeks,* but its development may be disrupted after this because the brain is differentiating and growing rapidly at birth and continues to do so throughout the first 2 years after birth. Teratogens (e.g., alcohol) may produce mental retardation during the embryonic and fetal periods. *Tooth development continues long after birth* (see Chapter 21); hence, development of permanent teeth may be disrupted by *tetracyclines* from 18 weeks (prenatal) to 16 years. *The skeletal system has a prolonged critical period of development* extending into childhood; hence, the growth of skeletal tissues provides a good gauge of general growth.

Environmental disturbances during the first 2 weeks after fertilization may interfere with cleavage of the zygote and implantation of the blastocyst and/or cause early death and spontaneous abortion of the embryo; however, they are not known to cause congenital anomalies in human embryos (Fig. 9–12). Either teratogens acting during the first 2 weeks kill the embryo or their disruptive effects are compensated for by powerful regulatory properties of the early embryo (Carlson, 1994). Most development during the first 2 weeks is concerned with the formation of extraem-

Table 9–5 ■ Incidence of Major Malformations in Human Organs at Birth

Organ	Incidence of Malformations
Brain	10 : 1000
Heart	8 : 1000
Kidneys	4 : 1000
Limbs	2 : 1000
All other	6 : 1000
Total	30 : 1000

Data from Connor JM, Ferguson-Smith MA: *Essential Medical Genetics,* 2nd ed. Oxford, Blackwell Scientific Publications, 1987.

bryonic structures such as the amnion, yolk sac, and chorionic sac (see Chapter 4); however, the early embryo also develops.

Development of the embryo is most easily disrupted when the tissues and organs are forming (Fig. 9-12). During this **organogenetic period,** teratogenic agents may induce major congenital anomalies. Physiologic defects — minor morphologic anomalies of the external ear, for example — and functional disturbances such as mental retardation are likely to result from disruption of development during the fetal period. *Each part, tissue, and organ of an embryo has a critical period during which its development may be disrupted* (Fig. 9-12). The type of congenital anomalies produced depends on which parts, tissues, and organs are most susceptible at the time the teratogen is active.

Embryologic timetables such as Figure 9-12 are helpful when considering the cause of human birth defects; however, it is wrong to assume that anomalies always result from a single event occurring during the critical period or that one can determine from these tables the day on which the anomaly was produced. All one can state is that the teratogen would have had to disrupt development before the end of the critical period of the tissue, part, or organ concerned. The *critical period for limb development, for example, is 24 to 36 days after fertilization.*

DOSAGE OF THE DRUG OR CHEMICAL

Animal research has shown a dose-response relationship for teratogens; however, *the dose used in animals to produce anomalies is often at levels much higher than human exposures. Consequently, animal studies are not readily applicable to human pregnancies.* For a drug to be considered a human teratogen, a dose-response relationship has to be observed; that is, the greater the exposure during pregnancy, the more severe the phenotypic effect.

GENOTYPE OF THE EMBRYO

Numerous examples in experimental animals and several suspected cases in humans show genetic differences in response to a teratogen. *Phenytoin*, for example, is a well-known human teratogen (Table 9-4). Five to 10% of embryos exposed to this anticonvulsant medication develop the *fetal Dilantin (phenytoin) syndrome.* About one third of exposed embryos, however, have only some congenital anomalies, and more than half of the embryos are unaffected. It appears, therefore, that the genotype of the embryo determines whether a teratogenic agent disrupts its development.

Known Human Teratogens

Awareness that certain agents can disrupt human prenatal development offers the opportunity to prevent some congenital anomalies; for example, if women are made aware of the harmful effects of drugs such as alcohol, environmental chemicals (e.g., polychlorinated biphenyls), and viruses, most women will not expose their embryos to these teratogenic agents. The general objective of teratogenicity testing of drugs, chemicals, food additives, and pesticides is to identify agents that may be teratogenic during human development and to alert physicians and pregnant women of their possible danger to the embryo/fetus.

Proof of Teratogenicity

To prove that an agent is a teratogen, one must show either that the frequency of anomalies is increased above the spontaneous rate in pregnancies in which the mother is exposed to the agent (*the prospective approach*) or that malformed infants have a history of maternal exposure to the agent more often than normal children (*the retrospective approach*). Both types of data are difficult to obtain in an unbiased form (Shepard, 1994). *Case reports are not convincing* unless both the agent and type of anomaly are so uncommon that their association in several cases can be judged not coincidental (e.g., thalidomide).

Drug Testing in Animals

Although testing of drugs in pregnant animals is important, the results are of limited value for predicting drug effects on human embryos. *Animal experiments can suggest only that similar effects may occur in humans.* If a drug or chemical produces teratogenic effects in two or more species, the probability of potential human hazard must be considered to be high; however, the dosage of the drug has to be considered.

DRUGS AS TERATOGENS

Drugs vary considerably in their teratogenicity. Some teratogens such as thalidomide cause severe disruption of development if administered during the organogenetic period of certain parts of the embryo (e.g., thalidomide and limb development). Other teratogens cause mental and growth retardation and other anomalies if used excessively throughout development (e.g., alcohol).

The use of prescription and nonprescription drugs during pregnancy is surprisingly high. From 40 to 90% of pregnant women consume at least one drug during pregnancy. Several studies have indicated that some pregnant women take an average of four drugs, excluding nutritional supplements, and about half of these women take them during the first trimester. Drug consumption also tends to be higher during the critical period of development among heavy smokers and drinkers (Persaud, 1990). Despite this, *less than 2% of congenital anomalies are caused by drugs and chemicals* (Brent, 1986). Only a few drugs have been positively implicated as human teratogenic agents (Table 9-4). Although only 7 to 10% of anomalies are caused by recognizable teratogens (Fig. 9-1), new agents continue to be identified (Behrman et al, 1996). It is best for women to avoid using all medication during the first trimester unless a strong medical reason exists for its use, and then only if it is recognized as reasonably safe for the human embryo.

Cigarette Smoking. Maternal smoking is a well-established cause of IUGR. Despite warnings that cigarette smoking is harmful to the fetus, more than 25% of women continue to smoke during their pregnancies. In heavy cigarette smokers (20 or more per day), premature delivery is twice as frequent as in mothers who do not smoke, and their infants weigh less than normal. *Low birth weight (below 2000 gm) is the chief predictor of infant death.* In a case-control study, a modest increase was found in the incidence of infants with conotruncal heart defects and limb deficiencies associated with both maternal and paternal smoking (Wasserman et al, 1996).

Nicotine constricts uterine blood vessels, causing a decrease in uterine blood flow, lowering the supply of oxygen and nutrients available to the embryo/fetus from the maternal blood in the intervillous space of the placenta. The resulting deficiency in the embryo impairs cell growth and may have an adverse effect on mental development. High levels of *carboxyhemoglobin*, resulting from cigarette smoking, appear in the maternal and fetal blood and may alter the capacity of the blood to transport oxygen. As a result, chronic *fetal hypoxia* (decrease below normal oxygen levels) may occur and affect fetal growth and development.

Caffeine. Caffeine is the most popular drug in North America because it is present in several widely consumed beverages (e.g., coffee, tea, and cola drinks), chocolate products, and some drugs. *Caffeine is not known to be a human teratogen*; however, there is no assurance that heavy maternal consumption of it is safe for the embryo.

Alcohol. Alcoholism is a drug abuse problem that affects 1 to 2% of women of childbearing age. Both moderate and high levels of alcohol intake during early pregnancy may result in alterations in growth and morphogenesis of the fetus (Behrman et al, 1996); the greater the intake, the more severe the signs. Infants born to chronic alcoholic mothers exhibit a specific pattern of defects (Persaud, 1988, 1990; Aase, 1994), including prenatal and postnatal growth deficiency, mental retardation, and other anomalies (Fig. 9-13; Table 9-4). Microcephaly, short palpebral fissures, epicanthal folds, maxillary hypoplasia, short nose, thin upper lip, abnormal palmar creases, joint anomalies, and congenital heart disease are also present in most infants. This pattern of anomalies — **the fetal alcohol syndrome (FAS)** — is detected in 1 to 2 infants per 1000 live births (Behrman et al, 1996). The incidence of FAS is related to the population studied. Clinical experience is often necessary in order to make an accurate diagnosis of FAS because the physical anomalies in affected children are nonspecific. Nonetheless, the overall pattern of clinical features present is unique but may vary from subtle to severe (Aase, 1994).

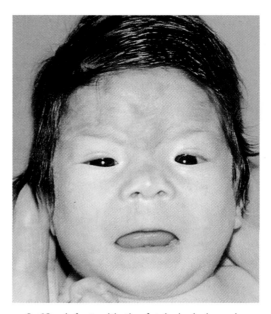

■ **Figure 9-13.** Infant with the fetal alcohol syndrome. Note the thin upper lip, short palpebral fissures, flat nasal bridge, short nose, and elongated and poorly formed philtrum (vertical groove in median part of upper lip). Maternal alcohol abuse is thought to be the most common environmental cause of mental retardation. (Courtesy of Dr. A. E. Chudley, Professor of Pediatrics and Child Health, Children's Hospital and University of Manitoba, Winnipeg, Manitoba, Canada.)

Maternal alcohol abuse is now thought to be the most common cause of mental retardation. Even moderate maternal alcohol consumption (e.g., 1 to 2 ounces per day) may produce **fetal alcohol effects (FAE)** — children with behavioral and learning difficulties, for example — especially if the drinking is associated with malnutrition. *Binge drinking* (heavy consumption of alcohol for 1 to 3 days during pregnancy) is very likely to produce FAE. The susceptible period of brain development spans the major part of gestation; therefore, the safest advice is total abstinence from alcohol during pregnancy.

Androgens and Progestogens. The terms *progestogens* and *progestins* are used for substances, natural or synthetic, that induce some or all of the biologic changes produced by progesterone, a hormone secreted by the corpus luteum that promotes and maintains a gravid endometrium (see Chapter 8). Some of these substances have androgenic, or masculinizing, properties that may affect the female fetus, producing masculinization of the external genitalia (Fig. 9–14). The incidence of anomalies varies with the drug and the dosage. The preparations that should be avoided are the progestins *ethisterone* and *norethisterone.* From a practical standpoint, the teratogenic risk of these hormones is low (Persaud, 1990; Jones, 1997). Progestin exposure during the critical period of development is also associated with an increased prevalence of cardiovascular abnormalities, and exposure of male fetuses during this period may double the incidence of *hypospadias* in the offspring (see Chapter 14). Obviously, the administration of *testosterone* also produces masculinizing effects in female fetuses.

Many women use contraceptive hormones (birth control pills). *Oral contraceptives* containing progestogens and estrogens, taken during the early stages of an unrecognized pregnancy, are suspected of being teratogenic agents, but the results of several recent epidemiologic studies are conflicting (Persaud, 1990). The infants of 13 of 19 mothers who had taken *progestogen-estrogen birth control pills* during the critical period of development exhibited the VACTERL syndrome (Nora and Nora, 1975). The acronym VACTERL stands for **v**ertebral, **a**nal, **c**ardiac, **t**racheal, **e**sophageal, **r**enal, and **l**imb anomalies. As a precaution, use of oral contraceptives should be stopped as soon as pregnancy is detected because of these possible teratogenic effects.

Diethylstilbestrol (DES, stilbestrol) is recognized as a human teratogen. Both gross and microscopic congenital abnormalities of the uterus and vagina have been detected in women who were exposed to DES in utero (Ulfelder, 1986). Three types of lesion were observed: vaginal adenosis, cervical erosions, and transverse vaginal ridges. A number of young women aged 16 to 22 years have developed *adenocarcinoma of the vagina* after a common history of exposure to the synthetic estrogen in utero. However, the probability of cancers developing at this early age in females exposed to DES in utero now appears to be low. Males who were exposed to DES in utero, following maternal treatment before the 11th week of gestation, had a higher incidence of genital tract anomalies, including epididymal cysts and hypoplastic testes. However, fertility in the men exposed to DES in utero seems to be unaffected (Wilcox et al, 1995).

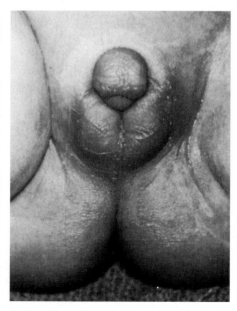

■ **Figure 9–14.** Masculinized external genitalia of a female infant. Observe the enlarged clitoris and fused labia majora. The virilization was caused by excessive androgens produced by the suprarenal (adrenal) glands during the fetal period (congenital adrenal hyperplasia).

Antibiotics. Tetracyclines cross the placental membrane and are deposited in the embryo's bones and teeth at sites of active calcification. As little as 1 gm per day of **tetracycline** during the third trimester of pregnancy can produce yellow staining of the primary and/or deciduous teeth (Cohlan, 1986). Tetracycline therapy during the 4th to 10th months of pregnancy may also cause tooth defects (e.g., enamel hypoplasia), yellow to brown discoloration of the teeth, and diminished growth of long bones. Calcification of the secondary (permanent) teeth begins at birth and, except for the third molars, is complete by 7 to 8 years of age; hence, long-term tetracycline therapy during childhood can affect the permanent teeth.

Deafness has been reported in infants of mothers who have been treated with high doses of streptomycin and dihydrostreptomycin as *antituberculosis agents*. More than 30 cases of hearing deficit and eighth cranial nerve damage have been reported in infants exposed to **streptomycin derivatives** in utero. *Penicillin* has been used extensively during pregnancy and appears to be harmless to the human embryo and fetus. *Acetohydroxamic acid* has been used for the treatment of chronic cervicitis resulting from a chronic infection with *Ureaplasma urealyticum*. Although no case of human teratogenicity involving hydroxamic acid has been reported, it is recommended that this antibiotic not be used during pregnancy because it is potentially a human teratogen (Holmes, 1996).

Anticoagulants. All anticoagulants except heparin cross the placental membrane and may cause hemorrhage in the embryo or fetus. Warfarin and other coumarin derivatives are antagonists of vitamin K. Warfarin is used for the treatment of thromboembolic disease and for patients with artificial heart valves. **Warfarin is definitely a teratogen.** There are reports of infants with hypoplasia of the nasal cartilage, stippled epiphyses, and various central nervous system (CNS) defects whose mothers took this anticoagulant during the critical period of their embryo's develop-

ment. The period of greatest sensitivity is between 6 and 12 weeks after fertilization — 8 to 14 weeks after last normal menstrual period (LNMP) (Behrman et al, 1996). Second- and third-trimester exposure may result in mental retardation, optic atrophy, and microcephaly. **Heparin is not a teratogen.** Furthermore, it does not cross the placental membrane and so is the drug of choice for pregnant women requiring anticoagulant therapy (Turrentine et al, 1995).

Anticonvulsants. Approximately 1 of 200 pregnant women is epileptic and requires treatment with an anticonvulsant. Of the anticonvulsant drugs available, there is strong evidence that **trimethadione** (Tridione) is a teratogen (Goldman et al, 1986). The main features of the *fetal trimethadione syndrome* are prenatal and postnatal growth retardation, developmental delay, V-shaped eyebrows, low-set ears, cleft lip and/or palate, and cardiac, genitourinary, and limb defects. Use of this drug is contraindicated during pregnancy.

Phenytoin (Dilantin, Novophenytoin) is definitely a teratogen (Fig. 9–15). The *fetal hydantoin syndrome* occurs in 5 to 10% of children born to mothers treated with phenytoins or hydantoin anticonvulsants. The pattern of anomalies consists of IUGR,

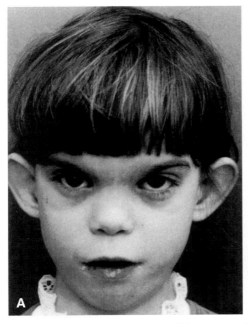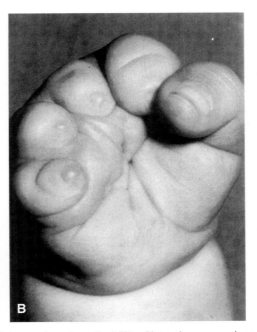

■ **Figure 9–15.** Fetal hydantoin syndrome. *A*, This young girl has a learning disability. Note the unusual ears, wide space between the eyes, epicanthal folds, short nose, and long philtrum. Her mother has epilepsy and took Dilantin throughout her pregnancy. (Courtesy of Dr. A. E. Chudley, Professor of Pediatrics and Child Health, Children's Hospital and University of Manitoba, Winnipeg, Manitoba, Canada.) *B*, Right hand of infant with severe digital hypoplasia (short fingers) born to a mother who took Dilantin throughout her pregnancy. (From Chodirker, BN, Chudley AE, Persaud TVN: Possible prenatal hydantoin effect in child born to a nonepileptic mother. *Am J Med Genet* 27:373, copyright © 1987. Reprinted by permission of Wiley-Liss, a division of John Wiley and Sons, Inc.)

microcephaly, mental retardation, ridged metopic (frontal) suture, inner epicanthal folds, eyelid ptosis, broad depressed nasal bridge, nail and/or distal phalangeal hypoplasia, and hernias (Behrman et al, 1996).

Valproic acid has been the drug of choice for the management of different types of epilepsy; however, its use by pregnant women has led to a *pattern of anomalies* consisting of craniofacial, heart, and limb defects. There is also an increased risk of neural tube defects (Kliegman, 1996). *Phenobarbital is considered to be a safe antiepileptic drug* for use during pregnancy (Persaud, 1990).

Antinauseants. There has been extensive debate in the lay press and in the courts as to whether *Bendectin* (Debendox, Lenotan, Diclectin) is a human teratogenic drug. Teratologists consider Bendectin to be nonteratogenic in humans because large-scale epidemiologic studies of infants have failed to show an increased risk of birth defects after its administration to pregnant woman (Fortin and Lalonde, 1995).

Antineoplastic Agents. About 20 cytotoxic agents are currently available for clinical use. With the exception of the folic acid antagonist **aminopterin**, few well-documented reports of teratogenic effects are available for assessment. Because the data available on the possible teratogenicity of antineoplastic drugs are inadequate, it is recommended that they be avoided, especially during the first trimester of pregnancy.

Tumor-inhibiting chemicals are highly teratogenic. This is not surprising because these agents inhibit mitosis in rapidly dividing cells. The use of aminopterin during the embryonic period often results in intrauterine death of the embryos, but the 20 to 30% of those that survive are severely malformed. *Busulfan* and *6-mercaptopurine* administered in alternating courses throughout pregnancy have produced multiple severe abnormalities, but neither drug alone appears to cause major anomalies (Table 9–4). For information on the long-term development of children exposed in utero to antineoplastic drugs, see Garber (1989).

Aminopterin is a potent teratogen that produces major congenital anomalies (Fig. 9–16), especially of the skeletal and central nervous systems (Kliegman, 1996). Aminopterin, an antimetabolite, is a *folic acid antagonist*. Multiple skeletal and other congenital anomalies were found in an infant born to a mother who attempted to terminate her pregnancy by taking

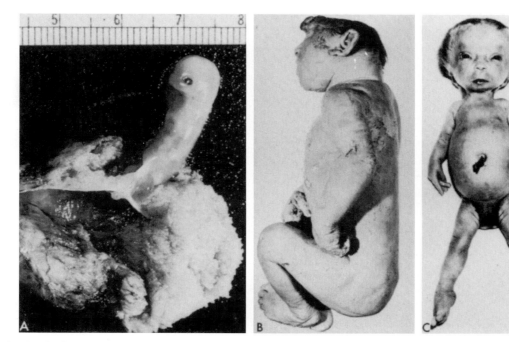

■ **Figure 9–16.** Aminopterin-induced congenital anomalies. *A*, Grossly malformed embryo and its membranes. (Courtesy of Dr. J. B. Thiersch, Seattle, Washington.) *B*, Newborn infant with meroanencephaly—partial absence of the brain. (From Thiersch JB: Aminopterin induced anomalies. *In* Wolstenholme GEW, O'Connor CM [eds]: *Ciba Foundation Symposium on Congenital Malformation.* London, J & A Churchill, 1960, pp 152–154). *C*, Newborn infant showing marked intrauterine growth retardation, a large head, a small mandible, deformed ears, clubhands, and clubfeet. (From Warkany J, Beaudry PH, Hornstein S: Attempted abortion with 4-aminopteroglutamic acid (Aminopterin): Malformations of the child. *Am J Dis Child* 97:274, 1960.)

methotrexate, a derivative of aminopterin that is also a folic acid antagonist.

Corticosteroids. Cortisone causes cleft palate and cardiac defects in susceptible strains of mice and rabbits. *Cortisone does not induce cleft palate or any other anomaly in human embryos.* The teratogenic risk of corticosteroids is minimal to nonexistent (Fraser and Sajoo, 1995).

Angiotensin-Converting Enzyme (ACE) Inhibitors. Exposure of the fetus to ACE inhibitors as antihypertensive agents causes oligohydramnios, fetal death, long-lasting hypoplasia of the bones of the calvaria, IUGR, and renal dysfunction. During early pregnancy, the risk to the embryo is apparently less, and there is no indication in such a case to terminate a wanted pregnancy. Because of the high incidence of serious perinatal complications, it is recommended that ACE inhibitors not be prescribed during pregnancy (Barr, 1994).

Insulin and Hypoglycemic Drugs. Insulin is not teratogenic in human embryos except possibly in maternal insulin coma therapy. Hypoglycemic drugs (e.g., tolbutamide) have been implicated, but evidence for their teratogenicity is very weak; consequently, despite their marked teratogenicity in rodents, no convincing evidence exists that oral hypoglycemic agents (particularly sulfonylureas) are teratogenic in human embryos. The incidence of congenital anomalies (e.g., **sacral agenesis**) is increased two to three times in the offspring of diabetic mothers, and about 40% of all perinatal deaths among diabetic infants are the result of congenital anomalies. The teratogenic mechanism of diabetic embryopathy is not known (Reece and Eriksson, 1996). Women with insulin-dependent diabetes mellitus may significantly decrease their risk of having infants with birth defects by achieving good control of their disease *before conception*.

Retinoic Acid (Vitamin A). Retinoic acid is a well-established teratogen in animals, and its teratogenicity in humans was recognized over a decade ago. **Isotretinoin (13-cis-retinoic acid)**, used for the oral treatment of severe cystic acne, **is teratogenic at very low doses in humans**. The critical period for exposure appears to be from the third week to the fifth week (5 to 7 weeks after LNMP). The risk of spontaneous abortion and birth defects after exposure to retinoic acid is high. The most common major anomalies observed are craniofacial dysmorphism (microtia, micrognathia), cleft palate and/or thymic aplasia defects, cardiovascular anomalies, and neural tube defects. Postnatal longitudinal follow-up of children exposed in

utero to isotretinoin revealed significant neuropsychological impairment (Persaud, 1990). Vitamin A is a valuable and necessary nutrient during pregnancy, but long-term exposure to large doses is unwise. Pregnant women should avoid high levels of vitamin A because an increased risk of birth defects among the offspring of women who took more than 10,000 IU of vitamin A daily was reported recently (Rothman et al, 1995).

Salicylates. Some evidence indicates that large doses of *acetylsalicylic acid* (ASA) or *aspirin*, the most commonly ingested drug during pregnancy, is potentially harmful to the embryo or fetus. Epidemiologic studies indicate that aspirin is not a teratogenic agent, but large doses of ASA should be avoided, especially during the first trimester.

Thyroid Drugs. *Potassium iodide* in cough mixtures and large doses of *radioactive iodine* may cause congenital goiter (Shepard, 1992). Iodides readily cross the placental membrane and interfere with thyroxin production. They may also cause thyroid enlargement and **cretinism** (arrested physical and mental development and dystrophy of bones and soft parts). *Maternal iodine deficiency* may cause congenital cretinism. Pregnant women have been advised to avoid douches or creams containing povidone-iodine because it is absorbed by the vagina, enters the maternal blood, and may be teratogenic. *Propylthiouracil* interferes with thyroxin formation in the fetus and may cause goiter. The administration of *antithyroid substances* for the treatment of maternal thyroid disorders may cause congenital goiter (Fig. 9 – 17) if the mother is given the substances in excess of requirements to control the disease.

Tranquilizers. *Thalidomide is a potent teratogen.* This hypnotic agent was once widely used in West Germany and Australia as a tranquilizer and sedative, but it is now used because of its immunosuppressive properties (Behrman et al, 1996). The **thalidomide epidemic** started in 1959. It has been estimated that nearly 12,000 infants were born with defects caused by this drug. Because thalidomide was not approved by the Food and Drug Administration (FDA) in the United States, relatively few anomalies occurred. The characteristic feature of the **thalidomide syndrome** is *meromelia* – phocomelia or "seal limbs," for example (Fig. 9 – 18), but the anomalies ranged from *amelia* (absence of limbs) through intermediate stages of development (rudimentary limbs) to *micromelia* (abnormal small and/or short limbs). *Thalidomide also caused anomalies of other organs;* such as absence of the external and internal ears, hemangioma on the forehead, heart defects, and anomalies of the urinary

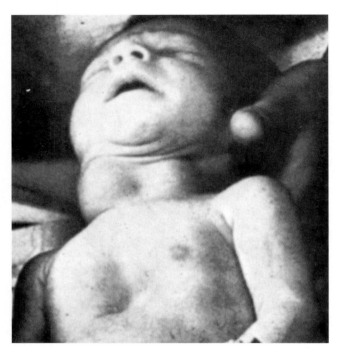

■ **Figure 9–17.** Newborn infant with congenital enlargement of the thyroid gland (goiter). The condition resulted from the administration of antithyroid drugs to the mother in excess of the amount needed to control the disease. (From Reid DF, Ryan KJ, Benirschke K: *Principles and Management of Human Reproduction.* Philadelphia, WB Saunders, 1972. Courtesy of Dr. Keith Russell.)

and alimentary systems (Persaud, 1990). It is well established clinically that the period when thalidomide caused congenital anomalies was from 24 to 36 days after fertilization (38 to 50 days after LNMP). This sensitive period coincides with the critical periods for the development of the affected parts and organs (Fig. 9–12). *Thalidomide is absolutely contraindicated in women of childbearing age* (Behrman et al, 1996).

Lithium is the drug of choice for the long-term maintenance of patients with manic-depressive psychosis; however, it has caused congenital anomalies, mainly of the heart and great vessels, in infants born to mothers given the drug early in pregnancy. Although **lithium carbonate is a human teratogen**, the FDA has stated that the agent may be used during pregnancy if "in the opinion of the physician the potential benefits outweigh the possible hazards." **Benzodiazepine derivatives** are psychoactive drugs frequently used by pregnant women. These include *diazepam* and *oxazepam*, which readily cross the placental membrane. The use of these drugs during the first trimester of pregnancy is associated with transient withdrawal symptoms and **craniofacial anomalies** in

the newborn. Patients are warned not to take these drugs during pregnancy because of their possible teratogenic effects (Laegreid et al, 1989).

Illicit Drugs. Several currently popular street drugs are used for their hallucinogenic properties. Jacobson and Berlin (1972) reported limb defects and noted a 9.6% incidence of nervous system defects in infants born to mothers who had used *lysergic acid diethylamide (LSD)* during pregnancy. No strong evidence indicates that LSD is teratogenic; however, in view of

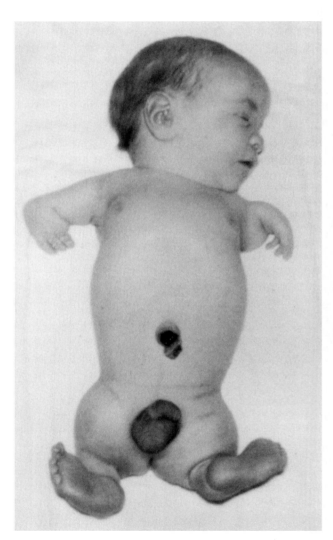

■ **Figure 9–18.** Newborn male infant showing typically malformed limbs (meromelia—limb reduction) caused by thalidomide ingested by his mother during the critical period of limb development. (From Moore KL: The vulnerable embryo. Causes of malformation in man. *Manitoba Med Rev* 43:306, 1963.)

the reported cases, it should be avoided during pregnancy (Persaud, 1990). There is little evidence that **marijuana** is a human teratogen, although there is some indication that marijuana use during the first 2 months of pregnancy affects fetal length and birth weight. In addition, sleep and electroencephalogram (EEG) patterns were altered in newborns exposed prenatally to marijuana.

Golden and colleagues (1980) reported a case of an infant with several birth defects and behavioral disturbances whose mother used *phencyclidine (PCP, angel dust)* throughout her pregnancy. This suggests, but does not prove, a causal association. **Cocaine** is one of the most commonly abused illicit drugs in North America, and its increasing use by women of childbearing age is of major concern. Many reports deal with the prenatal effects of cocaine. These include spontaneous abortion, prematurity, IUGR, microcephaly, cerebral infarction, urogenital anomalies, and neurobehavioral disturbances. The use of cocaine during pregnancy should be avoided because of its teratogenic effects (Behrman et al, 1996; Little et al, 1996).

Methadone, used for the treatment of heroin addiction, is considered to be a "behavioral teratogen," as is heroin (Persaud, 1990). Infants born to narcotic-dependent women maintained on methadone therapy were found to have CNS dysfunction and smaller birth weights and head circumferences than nonexposed infants. There is also concern about the long-term postnatal developmental effects of methadone. The problem, however, is difficult to resolve because other drugs are often used in combination with methadone, and heavy use of alcohol and cigarettes is prevalent among narcotic-dependent women (Kaltenbach and Finnegan, 1989).

ENVIRONMENTAL CHEMICALS AS TERATOGENS

In recent years there has been increasing concern about the possible teratogenicity of environmental, industrial, and agricultural chemicals, pollutants, and food additives.

Organic Mercury. Infants of mothers whose main diet during pregnancy consists of fish containing abnormally high levels of organic mercury acquire fetal **Minamata disease** and exhibit neurologic and behavioral disturbances resembling cerebral palsy. In some cases, *severe brain damage*, mental retardation, and blindness have been detected in infants whose mothers received *methylmercury* in their food. Similar observations have been made in infants whose mothers ate pork that became contaminated when the pigs ate corn grown from seeds sprayed with a mercury-con-

taining fungicide. **Methylmercury is a teratogen** that causes cerebral atrophy, spasticity, seizures, and *mental retardation* (Behrman et al, 1996).

Lead. Abundantly present in the workplace and environment, lead passes through the placental membrane and accumulates in fetal tissues. Prenatal exposure to lead is associated with increased abortions, fetal anomalies, IUGR, and functional deficits. Several reports have indicated that children born to mothers who were exposed to subclinical levels of lead revealed neurobehavioral and psychomotor disturbances (Persaud, 1990; Bellinger, 1994).

Polychlorinated Biphenyls (PCBs). These teratogenic chemicals produce IUGR and skin discoloration. The main dietary source of PCBs in North America is probably sport fish caught in contaminated waters. In Japan and Taiwan, the teratogenic chemical was detected in contaminated cooking oil.

Infectious Agents as Teratogens

Throughout prenatal life the embryo and fetus are endangered by a variety of microorganisms. In most cases the assault is resisted; in some cases, an abortion or stillbirth occurs, and in others the infants are born with IUGR, congenital anomalies, or neonatal diseases (Table 9–4). Many of these congenital defects can be detected in utero by sonography (Drose et al, 1991). The microorganisms cross the placental membrane and enter the fetal blood stream. The fetal blood-brain barrier also appears to offer little resistance to microorganisms because there is a propensity for the CNS to be affected.

Rubella (German or Three-day Measles). The rubella virus that causes rubella, a communicable disease, is the prime example of an *infective teratogen* (Korones, 1986). In cases of primary maternal infection during the first trimester of pregnancy, the overall risk of embryonic/fetal infection is about 20%. The **rubella virus** crosses the placental membrane and infects the embryo/fetus. The usual features of **congenital rubella syndrome** are *cataract, cardiac defects*, and *deafness*; however, the following abnormalities are occasionally observed: mental deficiency, chorioretinitis, glaucoma (Fig. 9–19), microphthalmia, and tooth defects. The earlier in pregnancy the maternal rubella infection occurs, the greater the danger that the embryo will be malformed (Behrman et al, 1996).

Cytomegalovirus. Infection with the cytomegalovirus (CMV) is the most common viral infection of the human fetus. Because the disease seems to be fatal when

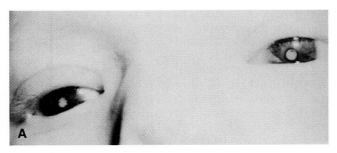

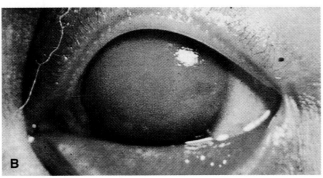

■ **Figure 9–19.** *A,* Typical bilateral congenital cataracts caused by the rubella virus. Cardiac defects and deafness are other common congenital defects. *B,* Severe congenital glaucoma caused by rubella virus. Observe the dense corneal haze, enlarged corneal diameter, and deep anterior chamber. (*A,* courtesy of Dr. Richard Bargy, Department of Ophthalmology, Cornell-New York Hospital. *B,* courtesy of Dr. Daniel I. Weiss, Department of Ophthalmology, New York University College of Medicine. From Cooper LA, et al: Neonatal thrombocytopenic purpura and other manifestations of rubella contracted in utero. *Am J Dis Child* 110:416, 1965. Copyright 1965, American Medical Association.)

it affects the embryo, it is believed that most pregnancies end in spontaneous abortion when the infection occurs during the first trimester. Newborn infants infected during the early fetal period usually show no clinical signs and are identified through screening programs. Later in pregnancy, *CMV infection may result in IUGR, microphthalmia, chorioretinitis, blindness, microcephaly, cerebral calcification, mental retardation, deafness, cerebral palsy, and hepatosplenomegaly* — enlargement of the liver and spleen (Persaud, 1990; Behrman et al, 1996). Of particular concern are cases of *asymptomatic CMV infection*, which are often associated with audiological, neurological, and neurobehavioral disturbances in infancy.

Herpes Simplex Virus. It has been reported that maternal infection with herpes simplex virus (HSV) in early pregnancy increases the abortion rate by threefold, and infection after the 20th week is associated with a higher rate of prematurity. Infection of the fetus with HSV usually occurs very late in pregnancy, probably most often during delivery. The congenital abnormalities that have been observed in newborns include typical cutaneous lesions and, in some cases, microcephaly, microphthalmia, spasticity, retinal dysplasia, and mental retardation (Persaud, 1990; Behrman et al, 1996).

Varicella (Chickenpox). Varicella and herpes zoster (shingles) are caused by the same virus, *varicella-zoster virus.* There is convincing evidence that maternal *varicella infection during the first 4 months of pregnancy causes congenital anomalies* (skin scarring, muscle atrophy, hypoplasia of the limb, rudimentary digits, eye and brain damage, and mental retardation (Koren, 1995). There is about a 20% chance of these or other anomalies when the infection occurs during the critical period of development (Fig. 9–12). After 20 weeks of gestation, there is no proven teratogenic risk.

Human Immunodeficiency Virus. Human immunodeficiency virus (HIV) is the retrovirus that causes acquired immunodeficiency syndrome (AIDS). Infection of pregnant women with HIV is now a prevalent and serious health problem. Information is conflicting on the fetal effects of in utero infection with HIV. Some of the congenital anomalies reported are growth failure, microcephaly, and specific craniofacial features (Parks, 1996). Preventing the transmission of the virus to women and their infants is of obvious importance because of potential embryopathic effects.

Toxoplasma gondii. This widespread protozoan, *an intracellular parasite,* was named after the gondi, a North African rodent in which the organism was first detected. This parasite may be found in the blood stream, tissues, or reticuloendothelial cells, leukocytes, and epithelial cells. *Maternal infection* (Lynfield and Eaton, 1995; Yokota, 1995) is usually acquired by:

- Eating raw or poorly cooked meat (usually pork or lamb containing *Toxoplasma* cysts)
- Close contact with infected domestic animals (usually *cats*) or soil. It is thought that the soil or garden vegetables may become contaminated with infected cat feces carrying oocysts, which can also be transported to food by flies and cockroaches.

The *Toxoplasma gondii organism crosses the placental membrane and infects the fetus*, causing destructive changes in the brain (intracranial calcifications) and eyes (chorioretinitis) that result in **mental deficiency**, microcephaly, microphthalmia, and hydrocephaly (Persaud, 1990; Yokota, 1995). Fetal death may follow infection, especially during the early stages of pregnancy. Mothers of congenitally defective infants are often unaware of having had **toxoplasmosis**, the disease caused by the parasitic organism. Because animals (cats, dogs, rabbits, and other domestic and wild animals) may be infected with this parasite, pregnant women should avoid them and the eating of raw or poorly cooked meat from them (e.g., rabbits). In addition, eggs off domestic fowl should be well cooked, and unpasteurized milk should be avoided. For more details, see Lynfield and Eaton (1995).

Congenital Syphilis. One in 10,000 liveborn infants in the United States is infected (Ricci et al, 1989). *Treponema pallidum*, the small, spiral microorganism that causes syphilis, rapidly crosses the placental membrane as early as 9 to 10 weeks of gestation. The fetus can become infected at any stage of the disease or at any stage of pregnancy (Azimi, 1996). *Primary maternal infections* (acquired during pregnancy and untreated) nearly always cause serious fetal infection and congenital anomalies; however, adequate treatment of the mother kills the organism, thereby preventing it from crossing the placental membrane and infecting the fetus. *Secondary maternal infections* (acquired before pregnancy) seldom result in fetal disease and anomalies. If the mother is untreated, stillbirths occur in about one fourth of cases. Only 20% of all untreated pregnant women deliver a normal infant at term. Early manifestations of untreated maternal syphilis are congenital deafness, abnormal teeth and bones, hydrocephalus, and mental retardation (Persaud, 1990). Late manifestations of untreated congenital syphilis are destructive lesions of the palate and nasal septum, dental abnormalities (centrally notched, widely spaced, peg-shaped upper central incisors — *Hutchinson teeth*), and abnormal facies (frontal bossing, saddle nose, and poorly developed maxilla). For more information, see Azimi (1996).

Radiation as a Teratogen

Exposure to **ionizing radiation** may injure embryonic cells, resulting in cell death, chromosome injury, and retardation of mental development and physical growth. The severity of the embryonic damage is related to the absorbed dose, the dose rate, and the stage of embryonic or fetal development when the exposure occurs. In the past, large amounts of ionizing radiation (hundreds to several thousand rads) were given inadvertently to embryos and fetuses of pregnant women who had cancer of the cervix. In all cases, their embryos were severely malformed or killed. Growth retardation, microcephaly, spina bifida cystica (see Chapter 19), pigment changes in the retina, cata-

racts, cleft palate, skeletal and visceral abnormalities, and mental retardation have been observed in infants who survived after receiving high levels of ionizing radiation. Development of the CNS was nearly always affected. Eight to 16 weeks after fertilization (10 to 18 weeks after LNMP) is the period of greatest sensitivity for radiation damage to the brain leading to *severe mental retardation*. Accidental exposure of pregnant women to radiation is a common cause for anxiety.

No conclusive proof exists that human congenital anomalies have been caused by diagnostic levels of radiation. Scattered radiation from an x-ray examination of a part of the body that is not near the uterus (e.g., the thorax, sinuses, teeth) produces a dose of only a few millirads, which is not teratogenic to the embryo. If the embryonic radiation exposure is 5 rads or less, the radiation risks to the embryo are minuscule (Bentur et al, 1991); however, it is prudent to be cautious during diagnostic examinations of the pelvic region in pregnant women (radiographic examinations and medical diagnostic tests using radioisotopes) because they result in exposure of the embryo to 0.3 to 2 rads. The recommended limit of maternal exposure of the whole body to radiation from all sources is 500 millirads for the entire gestational period.

Electromagnetic Fields. No evidence exists that the risk of IUGR or other developmental defects is increased by maternal exposure to low-frequency electromagnetic fields (e.g., electric blankets, video display terminals; see Robert, 1996).

Ultrasonic waves. Ultrasonography is widely used during pregnancy for fetal diagnosis and prenatal care. A review of the safety of obstetrical ultrasonography (Reece et al, 1990) concluded that "current data indicate that there are no confirmed biologic effects on patients and their fetuses from the use of diagnostic ultrasound evaluation, and the benefits to patients exposed to prudent use of this modality outweigh the risks, if any."

Maternal Factors as Teratogens

Maternal diseases can sometimes lead to a higher risk of abnormalities in the offspring. Poorly controlled *diabetes mellitus* in the mother with persisting hyperglycemia and ketosis, particularly during embryogenesis, is associated with a two- to three-fold higher incidence of birth defects (Reece and Eriksson, 1996). No specific diabetic embryopathic syndrome exists, but the infant of the diabetic mother is usually large (*macrosomia*), with prominent fat pads over the upper back and lower jaw. The common anomalies include *holoprosencephaly* (failure of the forebrain to divide into hemispheres), meroencephaly (partial absence of the brain), sacral agenesis, vertebral anomalies, congenital heart defects, and limb anomalies (Behrman et al, 1996; Tyrala, 1996). If untreated, women who are homozygous for phenylalanine hydroxylase deficiency — **phenylketonuria** (PKU) — and those with hyperphenylalaninemia are at a higher risk of having offspring with microcephaly, cardiac defects, mental retardation, and IUGR. The congenital anomalies can be prevented if the PKU mother is placed on a phenylalanine-restricted diet prior to and during the pregnancy (Levy and Ghavami, 1996).

Mechanical Factors as Teratogens

The amniotic fluid absorbs mechanical pressures, thereby protecting the embryo from most external trauma. It is generally accepted that congenital abnormalities caused by external injury to the mother are extremely rare but possible. *Congenital dislocation of the hip and clubfoot* may be caused by mechanical forces, particularly in a malformed uterus. Such deformations may be caused by any factor that restricts the mobility of the fetus, thereby causing prolonged compression in an abnormal posture. A significantly reduced quantity of amniotic fluid (*oligohydramnios*) may result in mechanically induced deformation of the limbs (see Chapter 8), such as hyperextension of the knee. Intrauterine amputations or other anomalies caused by local constriction during fetal growth may result from *amniotic bands* — rings formed as a result of rupture of the amnion during early pregnancy (Behrman et al, 1996).

ANOMALIES CAUSED BY MULTIFACTORIAL INHERITANCE

Many common congenital anomalies (e.g., cleft lip with or without cleft palate) have familial distributions consistent with multifactorial inheritance (MFI)(Fig. 9–1). For a list of the characteristics of MFI, see Thompson et al (1991). Multifactorial inheritance may be represented by a model in which "liability" to a disorder is a continuous variable determined by a combination of genetic and environmental factors, with a developmental threshold dividing individuals with the anomaly from those without it (Fig. 9–20). *Multifactorial traits are often single major anomalies*, such as cleft lip, isolated cleft palate, and neural tube defects. Some of these anomalies may also occur as part of the phenotype in syndromes determined by single-gene inheritance, chromosome abnormality, or an environmental teratogen. The *recurrence risks* used for genetic counseling of families having congenital anomalies determined by MFI are *empirical risks*

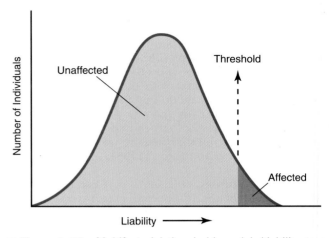

■ **Figure 9–20.** Multifactorial threshold model. Liability to a trait is distributed normally, with a threshold dividing the population into unaffected and affected classes. (From Thompson MW, McInnes RR, Willard FH: *Thompson and Thompson Genetics in Medicine*, 5th ed. Philadelphia, WB Saunders, 1991.)

based on the frequency of the anomaly in the general population and in different categories of relatives. In individual families, such estimates may be inaccurate because they are usually averages for the population rather than precise probabilities for the individual family. For further discussion of MFI and genetic counseling of families of patients with multifactorial traits, see Thompson et al (1991).

SUMMARY OF HUMAN BIRTH DEFECTS

A congenital anomaly is a structural abnormality of any type that is present at birth. It may be macroscopic or microscopic, on the surface or within the body. Four clinically significant types of anomalies occur: malformation, disruption, deformation, and dysplasia. Congenital anomalies may be induced by genetic factors or by environmental factors that cause derangements during prenatal development. Most common congenital anomalies, however, show the family patterns expected of *multifactorial inheritance* with a threshold and are determined by a combination of genetic and environmental factors.

About 3% of all liveborn infants have an obvious major anomaly. Additional anomalies are detected after birth; thus, the incidence is about 6% in 2-year-olds and 8% in 5-year-olds. Other anomalies (about 2%) are detected later in life (e.g., during surgery or autopsy). Congenital anomalies may be single or multiple and of minor or major clinical significance. *Single minor anomalies are present in about 14% of newborns.* These anomalies are of no serious medical consequence, but they alert the clinician to the possible presence of an associated major anomaly; 90% of infants with multiple minor anomalies have one or more associated major anomalies. Of the 3% of infants born with a major congenital anomaly, 0.7% have multiple major anomalies.

Major anomalies are more common in early embryos (up to 15%) than they are in newborn infants (up to 3%). Most severely malformed embryos are usually spontaneously aborted during the first 6 to 8 weeks. Some congenital anomalies are caused by *genetic factors* (chromosome abnormalities and mutant genes). A few congenital abnormalities are caused by *environmental factors* (infectious agents, environmental chemicals, and drugs); however, most common anomalies result from a complex *interaction between genetic and environmental factors.* The cause of most congenital anomalies is unknown.

During the first 2 weeks of development, teratogenic agents usually kill the embryo or have no effect rather than cause congenital anomalies. During the *organogenetic period*, teratogenic agents disrupt development and may cause *major congenital anomalies.* During the fetal period teratogens may produce morphologic and functional abnormalities, particularly of the brain and eyes. *Mental retardation* may result from high levels of radiation and infectious agents.

Clinically Oriented Questions

1. If a pregnant woman takes aspirin in normal doses, will it cause congenital anomalies?

2. If a woman is a drug addict, will her child show signs of drug addiction?

3. Are all drugs tested for teratogenicity (the ability to produce congenital anomalies) before they are marketed? If the answer is "yes," why are these teratogens still sold?

4. Is cigarette smoking during pregnancy harmful to the embryo or fetus? If the answer is "yes," would refraining from inhaling the smoke be safer?

5. Are any drugs safe to take during pregnancy? If so, what are they?

The answers to these questions are given at the back of the book.

REFERENCES AND SUGGESTED READING

Aase JM: Clinical recognition of FAS. Difficulties of detection and diagnosis. *Alcohol Health & Research World* 18:5, 1994.

Azimi P: Spirochetal infections. *In* Behrman RE, Kliegman RM, Arvin AM (eds): *Nelson Textbook of Pediatrics,* 15th ed. Philadelphia, WB Saunders, 1996.

Barr Jr M: Teratogen update: Angiotensin-converting enzyme inhibitors. *Teratology* 50:399, 1994.

Beckman DA, Brent RL: Mechanisms of teratogenesis. *Annu Rev Pharmacol Toxicol* 24:483, 1984.

Behrman RE, Kliegman RM, Arvin AM (eds): *Nelson Textbook of Pediatrics,* 15th ed. Philadelphia, WB Saunders, 1996.

Bellinger D: Teratogen update: Lead. *Teratology* 50:367, 1994.

Bentur Y, Horlatsch N, Koren G: Exposure to ionizing radiation during pregnancy: Perception of teratogenic risk and outcome. *Teratology* 43:109, 1991.

Breg WR: Autosomal abnormalities. *In* Gardner LI (ed): Endocrine and Genetic Diseases of Childhood and Adolescence, 2nd ed. Philadelphia, WB Saunders, 1975.

Brent RL: The complexities of solving the problem of human malformations. *In* Sever JL, Brent RL (eds): *Teratogen Update: Environmentally Induced Birth Defect Risks.* New York, Alan R. Liss, 1986.

Brent RL, Holmes LB: Clinical and basic science from the thalidomide tragedy; what have we learned about the causes of limb defects? *Teratology* 38:241,1988.

Carlson BM: *Human Embryology and Developmental Biology.* St. Louis, CV Mosby, 1994.

Castella EE, Ashton-Prolla P, Barreda-Mejia E, et al: Thalidomide, a current teratogen in South America. *Teratology* 54:273, 1996.

Chudley AE, Hagerman RJ: The fragile X syndrome. *J Pediatr* 110: 821, 1987.

Cohlan SQ: Tetracycline staining of teeth. *In* Sever JL, Brent RL (eds): *Teratogen Update: Environmentally Induced Birth Defect Risks.* New York, Alan R. Liss, 1986.

Connor JM, Ferguson-Smith MA: *Essential Medical Genetics,* 2nd ed. Oxford, Blackwell Scientific Publications, 1987.

Crane JP: Ultrasound evaluation of fetal chromosome disorders. *In* Callen PW (ed): *Ultrasonography in Obstetrics and Gynecology,* 3rd ed. Philadelphia, WB Saunders, 1994.

DeLuca LM: Retinoids and their receptors in differentiation, embryogenesis, and neoplasia. *FASEB J* 5:2924, 1991.

Drose JA, Dennis MA, Thickman D: Infection in utero: US findings in 19 cases. *Radiology* 178:369, 1991.

Fortin CF, Lalonde AB: The Bendectin affair (of legal and general interest). *J. SOGC* 17:61, 1995.

Fraser FC: Liability thresholds, malformations, and syndromes. *Am J Med Genet* 66:75, 1996.

Fraser FC, Sajoo A: Teratogenic potential of corticosteroids in humans. *Teratology* 51:45, 1995.

Garber JE: Long-term follow-up of children exposed *in utero* to antineoplastic agents. *Semin Oncol* 16:437, 1989.

Golden NL, Sokol RJ, Rubin I: Angel dust: Possible effects on the fetus. *Pediatrics* 65:18, 1980.

Goldman AS, Zackai EH, Yaffe SJ: Fetal trimethadione syndrome. *In* Sever JL, Brent RL (eds): *Teratogen Update: Environmentally Induced Birth Defect Risks.* New York, Alan R. Liss, 1986.

Gregg NM: Congenital cataract following German measles in the mother. *Trans Ophthalmol Soc Aust* 3:35, 1941.

Hall JG: Chromosomal clinical abnormalities. *In* Behrman RE, Kliegman RM, Arvin AM (eds): *Nelson Textbook of Pediatrics,* 15th ed. Philadelphia, WB Saunders, 1996.

Heitz D, Rousseau F, Devys D, et al: Isolation of sequences that span the fragile X and identification of a fragile X-related CpG island. *Science* 251:1236, 1991.

Holmes LB: Hydroxamic acid: A potential human teratogen that could be recommended to treat ureaplasma. *Teratology* 53:227, 1996.

Hook EB, Warburton D: The distribution of chromosomal genotypes associated with Turner syndrome: Livebirth prevalence rates and evidence for diminished fetal mortality and severity of genotypes associated with structural X abnormalities or mosaicism. *Hum Genet* 64:24, 1983.

Jacobson CB, Berlin CM: Possible reproductive detriment in LSD users. *JAMA* 222:1367, 1972.

Jones KL: *Smith's Recognizable Patterns of Human Malformation*, 5th ed. Philadelphia, WB Saunders, 1997.

Kaltenbach KA, Finnegan LP: Prenatal narcotic exposure: Perinatal and developmental effects. *Neurotoxicology* 10:597, 1989.

Kaufman RH: Consequence of in utero exposure to diethylstilbestrol. *In* Copelan LJ, Jarrell J, McGregor J (eds): *Textbook of Gynecology*. Philadelphia, WB Saunders, 1993.

Kaufman MH: New insights into triploidy and tetraploidy, from an analysis of model systems for these conditions. *Hum Reprod* 6:8, 1991.

Khoury MJ: Commentary: Contributions of epidemiology to the study of birth defects in humans. *Teratology* 52:186, 1995.

Kirkilionis AJ, Chudley AE, Gregory CA, Hamerton JL: Molecular and clinical overlap of Angelman and Prader-Willi syndrome phenotypes. *Am J Med Genet* 40:454, 1991.

Kliegman RM: Teratogens. *In* Behrman RE, Kliegman RM, Arvin AM (eds): *Nelson Textbook of Pediatrics*, 15th ed. Philadelphia, WB Saunders, 1996.

Koren G: Chickenpox during pregnancy. *Can Fam Physician* 41:1477, 1995.

Korones SB: Congenital rubella — an encapsulated review. *In* Sever JL, Brent RL (eds): *Teratogen Update: Environmentally Induced Birth Defect Risks*. New York, Alan R. Liss, 1986.

Laegreid L, Olegard R, Walstrom J, Conradi N: Teratogenic effects of benzodiazepine use during pregnancy. *J Pediatr* 114:126, 1989.

Lenz W: A short history of thalidomide embryopathy. *Teratology* 38:203, 1988.

Lenz W: Kindliche Missbildungen nach Medikament während der Gravidität? *Dtsch Med Wochenschr* 86:2555, 1961.

Levy HL, Ghavami M: Maternal phenylketonuria: A metabolic teratogen. *Teratology* 53:176, 1996.

Little BB, Wilson GN, Jackson G: Is there a cocaine syndrome? Dysmorphic and anthropometric assessment of infants exposed to cocaine. *Teratology* 54:145, 1996.

Lynfield R, Eaton RB: Teratogen update: Congenital toxoplasmosis. *Teratology* 52:176, 1995.

McBride WG: Thalidomide and congenital abnormalities. *Lancet* 2:1358, 1961.

Medicodes' Hospital and Payer: International Classification of Diseases, 9th Revision. *Clinical Modification,* 4th ed, vols 1–3, Salt Lake City, Medicode, Inc., 1995.

Milunsky A (ed): *Genetic Disorders and the Fetus,* 3rd ed. Baltimore, John Hopkins University Press, 1992.

Mittendorf R: Teratogen update: Carcinogenesis and teratogenesis associated with exposure to diethylstilbestrol (DES) in utero. *Teratology* 51:435, 1995.

Moore KL: *Clinically Oriented Anatomy,* 3rd ed. Baltimore, Williams & Wilkins, 1992.

Moore KL (ed): *The Sex Chromatin*. Philadelphia, WB Saunders, 1966.

Moore KL, Barr ML: Smears from the oral mucosa in the detection of chromosomal sex. *Lancet* 2:57, 1955.

Moore KL, Persaud TVN: *The Developing Human: Clinically Oriented Embryology*, 6th ed. Philadelphia, WB Saunders, 1998.

Nelson K, Holmes LB: Malformations due to presumed spontaneous mutations in newborn infants. *N Engl J Med* 320:19, 1989.

Nora AH, Nora JJ: A syndrome of multiple congenital anomalies associated with teratogenic exposure. *Arch Environ Health* 30:17, 1975.

Parks W: Human immunodeficiency virus. *In* Behrman RD, Kliegman RM, Arvin AM (eds): *Nelson Textbook of Pediatrics*, 15th ed. Philadelphia, WB Saunders, 1996.

Persaud TVN: *Environmental Causes of Human Birth Defects.* Springfield, IL, Charles C Thomas, 1990.

Persaud TVN: Fetal alcohol syndrome. *Crit Rev Anat Cell Biol* 1:277, 1988.

Persaud TVN: Pregnancy and the workplace. *Contemp Obstet Gynecol* 4:20, 1995.

Persaud TVN, Chudley AE, Skalko RG: *Basic Concepts in Teratology*. New York, Alan R. Liss, 1985.

Persaud TVN, Ellington AC: Teratogenic activity of cannabis resin. *Lancet* 2:406, 1968.

Pinkel D, Straume T, Gray JW: Cytogenic analysis using quantitative high sensitivity, fluorescence hybridization. *Proc Natl Acad Sci USA* 83:2934, 1986.

Reece EA, Assimakopoulos E, Zheng X-Z, et al: The safety of obstetric ultrasonography. Concern for the fetus. *Obstet Gynecol* 6:139, 1990.

Reece EA, Eriksson UJ: The pathogenesis of diabetes-associated congenital malformations. *Obstet Gynecol Clin North Am* 23:29, 1996.

Reece EA, Hobbins JC, Mahoney MJ, Petrie RH: *Handbook of Medicine of the Fetus and Mother*. Philadelphia, JB Lippincott, 1995.

Ricci JM, Fojaco RM, O'Sullivan MJ: Congenital syphilis: The University of Miami/Jackson Memorial Medical Centre experience, 1986–1988. *Obstet Gynecol* 74:687, 1989.

Robert E: Teratogen update: Electromagnetic fields. *Teratology* 54:305, 1996.

Rosenberg AA, Galan HL: Fetal drug therapy. *Pediatr Clin North Am* 44:113, 1997.

Rothman KJ, Moore LL, Singer MR, et al: Teratogenicity of high vitamin A intake. *N Engl J Med* 333:1369, 1995.

Shepard TH: *Catalog of Teratogenic Agents*, 7th ed. Baltimore, Johns Hopkins University Press, 1992.

Shepard TH: "Proof" of human teratogenicity. *Teratology* 50:97, 1994.

Shepard TH, Fantel AG, Fitzsimmons J: Congenital defect rates among spontaneous abortuses. Twenty years of monitoring. *Teratology* 39:325, 1989.

Shiota K, Uwabe C, Nishimura H: High prevalence of defective human embryos at the early postimplantation period. *Teratology* 35:309, 1987.

Spranger J, Benirschke K, Hall JG, et al: Errors of morphogenesis: Concepts and terms. *J Pediatr* 100:160, 1982.

Thompson MW, McInnes RR, Willard HF: *Thompson and Thompson Genetics in Medicine*, 5th ed. Philadelphia, WB Saunders, 1991.

Turrentine MA, Braems G, Ramirez MM: Use of thrombolytics for the treatment of thromboembolic disease during pregnancy. *Obstet Gynecol Surv* 50:534, 1995.

Tyrala EE: The infant of the diabetic mother. *Obstet Gynecol Clin North Am* 23:221, 1996.

Ulfelder H: DES—transplacental teratogen—and possible carcinogen. *In* Sever JL, Brent RL (eds): *Teratogen Update: Environmentally Induced Birth Defect Risks*. New York, Alan R. Liss, 1986.

Wasserman CR, Shaw GM, O'Malley CD, et al: Parental cigarette smoking and risk of congenital anomalies of the heart, neural tube, or limb. *Teratology* 53:261, 1996.

Wilcox AJ, Baird DD, Weinberg CR, et al: Fertility in men exposed prenatally to diethylstilbestrol. *N Engl J Med* 332:1441, 1995.

Winston NJ, Braude PR, Pickering SJ, et al: The instance of abnormal morphology and nucleocytoplasmic ratios in 2-, 3- and 5-day human pre-embryos. *Hum Reprod* 6:17, 1991.

Yokota K: Congenital anomalies induced by *Toxoplasma* infection. *Congenital Anomalies* 35:151, 1995.

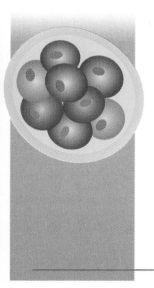

Body Cavities, Mesenteries, and Diaphragm

10

■ Early development of the intraembryonic coelom — primordium of the embryonic body cavities — is described in Chapter 5. Early in the fourth week, the **intraembryonic coelom** appears as a horseshoe-shaped cavity in the cardiogenic and lateral mesoderm (Fig. 10-1*A*). The curve or bend in this cavity at the cranial end of the embryo represents the future *pericardial cavity,* and its limbs (lateral extensions) indicate the future *pleural and peritoneal cavities.* The distal part of each limb of the intraembryonic coelom opens into the **extraembryonic coelom** at the lateral edges of the embryonic disc (Fig. 10-1*B*). This communication is important because most of the midgut normally herniates through this communication into the umbilical cord, where it develops into most of the small intestine and part of the large intestine (discussed in Chapter 13). In embryos of lower animal forms, the intraembryonic coelom provides short-term storage for excretory products. In human embryos, the coelom provides room for the organs to develop and move. During embryonic folding in the horizontal plane, the limbs of the intraembryonic coelom are brought together on the ventral aspect of the embryo (Fig. 10-2*A* to *F*). The ventral mesentery degenerates in the region of the future peritoneal cavity, resulting in a large embryonic peritoneal cavity extending from the heart to the pelvic region (Figs. 10-2*F* and 10-3*A* to *E*).

THE EMBRYONIC BODY CAVITY

The intraembryonic coelom, or embryonic body cavity, gives rise to three well-defined coelomic or body cavities during the fourth week (Figs. 10-2 and 10-4):

- A *pericardial cavity*
- Two *pericardioperitoneal canals* connecting the pericardial and peritoneal cavities
- A large *peritoneal cavity*

These body cavities have a parietal wall lined by mesothelium (major part of future parietal layer) derived from somatic mesoderm and a visceral wall covered by mesothelium (future visceral layer) derived from splanchnic mesoderm (Fig. 10-3*E*). The peritoneal cavity (major part of intraembryonic coelom) is connected with the extraembryonic coelom at the umbilicus (Fig. 10-4*C* and *D*). The **peritoneal cavity** loses its connection with the extraembryonic coelom during the 10th week as the intestines return to the abdomen from the umbilical cord (see Chapter 13). During formation of the *head fold,* the heart and **pericardial cavity** move ventrocaudally, anterior to the foregut (Fig. 10-2*B*). As a result, the pericardial cavity opens into the pericardioperitoneal canals, which pass dorsal to the foregut (Fig. 10-4*B* and *D*). After embryonic folding, the caudal part of the foregut, midgut,

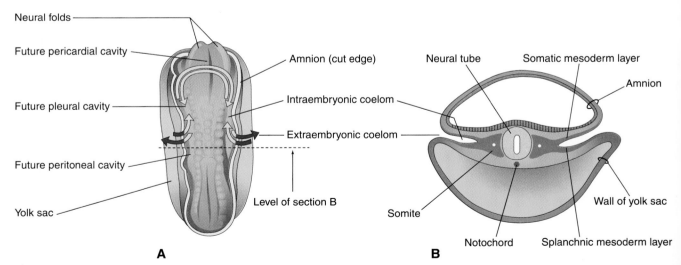

A   **B**

■ **Figure 10-1.** *A,* Drawing of a dorsal view of a 22-day embryo showing the outline of the horseshoe-shaped intraembryonic coelom. The amnion has been removed, and the coelom is shown as if the embryo were translucent. The continuity of the intraembryonic coelom, as well as the communication of its right and left limbs with the extraembryonic coelom, is indicated by arrows. *B,* Transverse section through the embryo at the level shown in *A.*

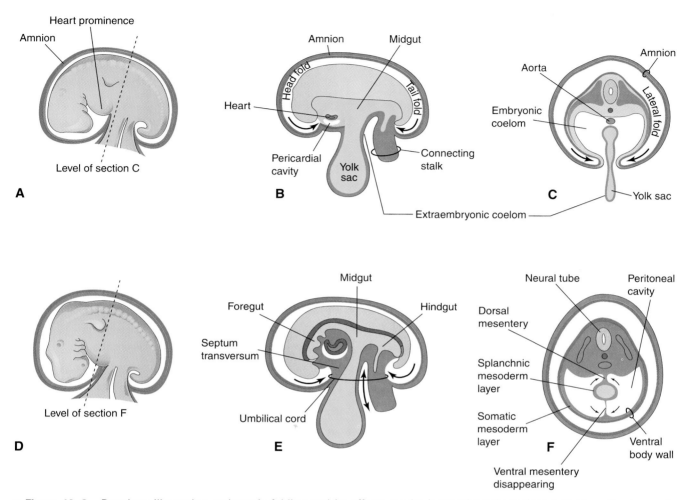

■ **Figure 10–2.** Drawings illustrating embryonic folding and its effects on the intraembryonic coelom and other structures. *A,* Lateral view of an embryo (about 26 days). *B,* Schematic sagittal section of this embryo showing the head and tail folds. *C,* Transverse section at the level shown in *A,* indicating how fusion of the lateral folds gives the embryo a cylindrical form. *D,* Lateral view of an embryo (about 28 days). *E,* Schematic sagittal section of this embryo showing the reduced communication between the intraembryonic and extraembryonic coeloms (*double-headed arrow*). *F,* Transverse section as indicated in *D,* illustrating formation of the ventral body wall and disappearance of the ventral mesentery. The arrows indicate the junction of the somatic and splanchnic layers of mesoderm. The somatic mesoderm will become the parietal peritoneum lining the abdominal wall, and the splanchnic mesoderm will become the visceral peritoneum covering the organs (e.g., the stomach).

and hindgut are suspended in the peritoneal cavity from the posterior abdominal wall by the *dorsal mesentery* (Figs. 10–2*F* and 10–3*C* to *E*).

Mesenteries

A mesentery is a double layer of peritoneum that begins as an extension of the visceral peritoneum covering an organ; it connects the organ to the body wall and conveys its vessels and nerves. Transiently, the dorsal and ventral mesenteries divide the peritoneal cavity into right and left halves (Fig. 10–3*C*); however, the ventral mesentery soon disappears (Fig. 10–3*E*), except where it is attached to the caudal part of the foregut (primordium of the stomach and proximal part of the duodenum). The peritoneal cavity then becomes a continuous space (Figs. 10–3 and 10–4). The arteries supplying the primitive gut — *celiac trunk* (foregut), *superior mesenteric artery* (midgut), and *inferior mesenteric artery* (hindgut) — pass between the layers of the dorsal mesentery (Fig. 10–3*C*).

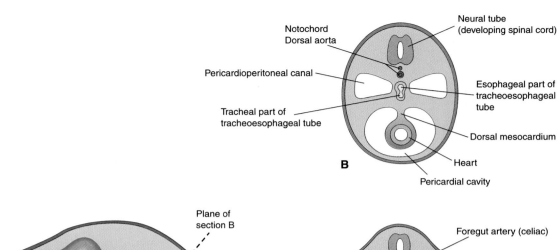

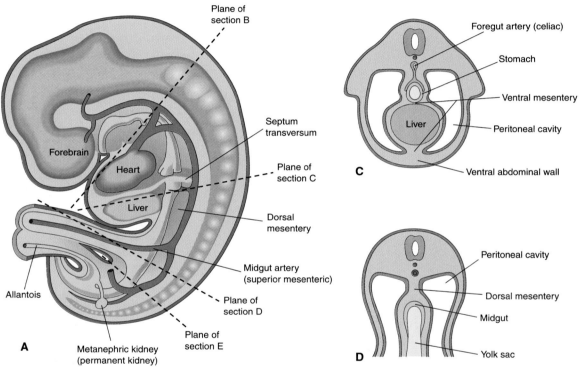

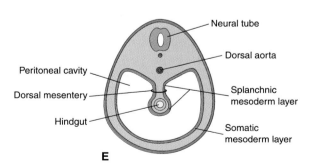

■ **Figure 10–3.** Diagrams illustrating the mesenteries at the beginning of the fifth week. *A,* Schematic sagittal section. Note that the dorsal mesentery serves as a pathway for the arteries supplying the developing gut. Nerves and lymphatics also pass between the layers of this mesentery. *B* to *E,* Transverse sections through the embryo at the levels indicated in *A.* The ventral mesentery disappears, except in the region of the terminal esophagus, stomach, and first part of the duodenum. Note that the right and left parts of the peritoneal cavity, separate in *C,* are continuous in *E.*

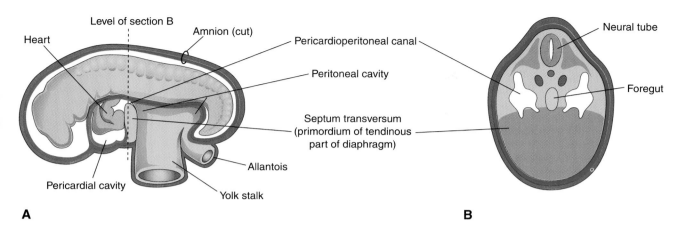

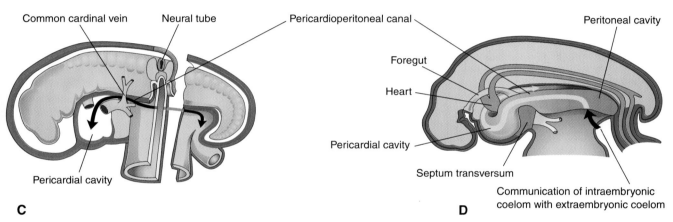

■ **Figure 10–4.** Schematic drawings of an embryo (about 24 days). *A,* The lateral wall of the pericardial cavity has been removed to show the primitive heart. *B,* Transverse section of the embryo illustrating the relationship of the pericardioperitoneal canals to the septum transversum (primordium of central tendon of diaphragm) and the foregut. *C,* Lateral view of the embryo with the heart removed. The embryo has also been sectioned transversely to show the continuity of the intraembryonic and extraembryonic coeloms. *D,* Sketch showing the pericardioperitoneal canals arising from the dorsal wall of the pericardial cavity and passing on each side of the foregut to join the peritoneal cavity. The arrows show the communication of the extraembryonic coelom with the intraembryonic coelom and the continuity of the intraembryonic coelom at this stage.

Division of Embryonic Body Cavity

Each pericardioperitoneal canal lies lateral to the foregut (future esophagus) and dorsal to the **septum transversum**—a thick plate of mesodermal tissue that occupies the space between the thoracic cavity and yolk stalk (Fig. 10–4*A* and *B*). The septum transversum is the primordium of the **central tendon of the diaphragm**. Partitions form concurrently in each pericardioperitoneal canal and separate the pericardial cavity from the pleural cavities and the pleural cavities from the peritoneal cavity. Because of the *growth of the bronchial buds* (primordia of bronchi and lungs) into the pericardioperitoneal canals (Fig. 10–5*A*), a

pair of membranous ridges is produced in the lateral wall of each canal.

- The cranial ridges—the *pleuropericardial folds*—are located superior to the developing lungs.
- The caudal ridges—the *pleuroperitoneal folds*—are located inferior to the lungs.

THE PLEUROPERICARDIAL MEMBRANES

As the pleuropericardial folds enlarge, they form partitions that separate the pericardial cavity from the pleural cavities. These partitions—*pleuropericardial membranes*—contain the **common cardinal veins** (Fig.

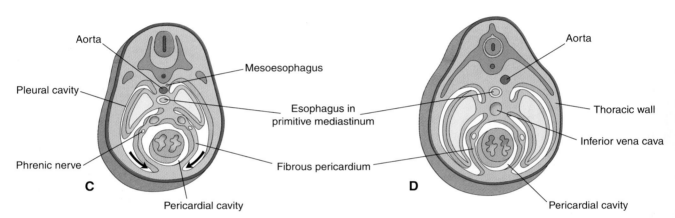

■ **Figure 10–5.** Schematic drawings of transverse sections through embryos cranial to the septum transversum, illustrating successive stages in the separation of the pleural cavities from the pericardial cavity. Growth and development of the lungs, expansion of the pleural cavities, and formation of the fibrous pericardium are also shown. *A,* Five weeks. The arrows indicate the communications between the pericardioperitoneal canals and the pericardial cavity. *B,* Six weeks. The arrows indicate development of the pleural cavities as they expand into the body wall. *C,* Seven weeks. Expansion of the pleural cavities ventrally around the heart is shown. The pleuropericardial membranes are now fused in the median plane with each other and with the mesoderm ventral to the esophagus. *D,* Eight weeks. Continued expansion of the lungs and pleural cavities and formation of the fibrous pericardium and thoracic wall are illustrated.

10–5*A* and *B*). These large veins drain the primordial venous system into the *sinus venosus* of the primordial heart (see Chapter 15). Initially the **bronchial buds** are small relative to the heart and pericardial cavity (Fig. 10–5*A*). They then grow laterally from the caudal end of the trachea into the pericardioperitoneal canals (future pleural canals). As the **primordial pleural cavities** expand ventrally around the heart, they extend into the body wall, splitting the mesenchyme into:

• An outer layer that becomes the thoracic wall
• An inner layer (the pleuropericardial membrane) that becomes the *fibrous pericardium*, the outer

layer of the pericardial sac enclosing the heart (Fig. 10–5*C* and *D*).

The pleuropericardial membranes project into the cranial ends of the *pericardioperitoneal canals* (Fig. 10–5*B*). With subsequent growth of the common cardinal veins, descent of the heart, and expansion of the pleural cavities, the pleuropericardial membranes become mesentery-like folds extending from the lateral thoracic wall. By the seventh week the pleuropericardial membranes fuse with the mesenchyme ventral to the esophagus, forming the *primordial mediastinum* and separating the pericardial cavity from the pleural cavities (Fig. 10–5*C*). The **mediastinum** consists of a mass of mesenchyme (embryonic connective tissue) that extends from the sternum to the vertebral column, separating the developing lungs (Fig. 10-5D). The right pleuropericardial opening closes slightly earlier than the left one, probably because the right common cardinal vein is larger than the left one and produces a larger pleuropericardial membrane.

Congenital Pericardial Defects

Defective formation or fusion of the pleuropericardial membranes, separating the pericardial and pleural cavities is an uncommon congenital anomaly. This abnormality results in a congenital defect of the pericardium, usually on the left side. Consequently, the pericardial cavity communicates with the pleural cavity. In very unusual cases, part of the left atrium herniates into the pleural cavity at each heart beat.

THE PLEUROPERITONEAL MEMBRANES

As the *pleuroperitoneal folds* enlarge, they project into the pericardioperitoneal canals. Gradually the folds become membranous, forming the *pleuroperitoneal membranes* (Figs. 10-6A to C and 10-7A and B). Eventually these membranes separate the pleural cavities from the peritoneal cavity. The pleuroperitoneal membranes are produced as the developing lungs and pleural cavities expand and invade the body wall. They are attached dorsolaterally to the abdominal wall, and initially their crescentic free edges project into the caudal ends of the pericardioperitoneal canals. They become relatively more prominent as the lungs enlarge cranially and the liver expands caudally. During the sixth week the pleuroperitoneal membranes extend ventromedially until their free edges fuse with the dorsal mesentery of the esophagus and septum transversum (Fig. 10-7C). This separates the pleural cavities from the peritoneal cavity.

Closure of the pleuroperitoneal openings is assisted by the migration of myoblasts (primitive muscle cells) into the pleuroperitoneal membranes (Fig. 10-7E). The pleuroperitoneal opening on the right side closes slightly before the left one. The reason for this is uncertain, but it may be related to the relatively large size of the right lobe of the liver at this stage of development.

DEVELOPMENT OF THE DIAPHRAGM

The diaphragm is a composite structure that develops from four embryonic components (Fig. 10-7):

- Septum transversum
- Pleuroperitoneal membranes
- Dorsal mesentery of esophagus
- Lateral body walls

The diaphragm is a dome-shaped, musculotendinous partition that separates the thoracic and abdominal cavities.

The Septum Transversum

The transverse septum, composed of mesodermal tissue, is the primordium of the **central tendon of the diaphragm** (Fig. 10-7D and E). The septum transversum grows dorsally from the ventrolateral body wall and forms a semicircular shelf, which separates the heart from the liver (Fig. 10-6). During its early development, a large part of the liver is embedded in the septum transversum. The septum transversum is located caudal to the pericardial cavity and partially separates it from the developing peritoneal cavity. The septum transversum is first identifiable at the end of the third week as a mass of mesodermal tissue cranial to the pericardial cavity (see Chapter 6). After the head folds ventrally during the fourth week, the septum transversum forms a thick incomplete partition between the pericardial and abdominal cavities (Fig. 10-4). The septum transversum does not separate the thoracic and abdominal cavities completely. A large opening, the **pericardioperitoneal canal**, is found on each side of the esophagus (Fig. 10-7B). The septum transversum expands and fuses with the mesenchyme ventral to the esophagus (primitive mediastinum) and the pleuroperitoneal membranes (Fig. 10-7C).

The Pleuroperitoneal Membranes

These membranes fuse with the dorsal mesentery of the esophagus and septum transversum (Fig. 10-7C). This completes the partition between the thoracic and abdominal cavities and forms the **primordial diaphragm**. Although the pleuroperitoneal membranes form large portions of the fetal diaphragm, they represent relatively small portions of the newborn infant's diaphragm (Fig. 10-7E).

The Dorsal Mesentery of the Esophagus

As previously described, the septum transversum and pleuroperitoneal membranes fuse with the dorsal mesentery of the esophagus. This mesentery constitutes the median portion of the diaphragm. The **crura of the diaphragm**—a leglike pair of diverging muscle bundles that cross in the median plane anterior to the

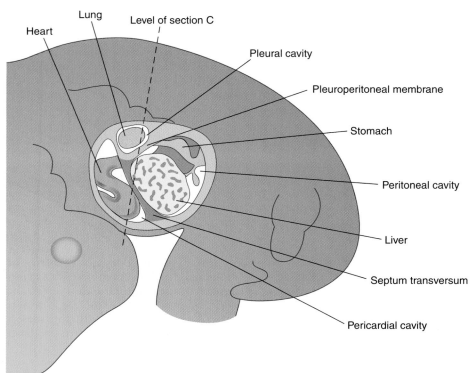

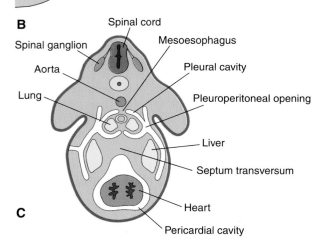

■ **Figure 10–6.** *A,* Sketch of a lateral view of an embryo (about 33 days). The rectangle indicates the area enlarged in *B. B,* The primordial cavities are viewed from the left side after removal of the lateral body wall. *C,* Transverse section through the embryo at the level shown in *B.*

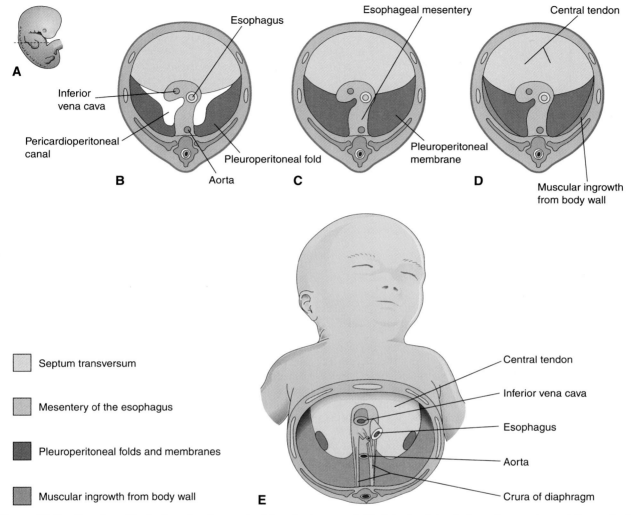

■ **Figure 10–7.** Drawings illustrating development of the diaphragm. *A*, Sketch of a lateral view of an embryo at the end of the fifth week (actual size), indicating the level of sections in *B* to *D*. *B* to *E* show the developing diaphragm as viewed inferiorly. *B*, Transverse section showing the unfused pleuroperitoneal membranes. *C*, Similar section at the end of the sixth week after fusion of the pleuroperitoneal membranes with the other two diaphragmatic components. *D*, Transverse section of a 12-week embryo after ingrowth of the fourth diaphragmatic component from the body wall. *E*, View of the diaphragm of a newborn infant, indicating the embryological origin of its components.

aorta (Fig. 10–7*E*)—develop from myoblasts that grow into the dorsal mesentery of the esophagus.

The Muscular Ingrowth from the Lateral Body Walls

During the 9th to 12th weeks, the lungs and pleural cavities enlarge, "burrowing" into the lateral body walls (Fig. 10–5). During this excavation process, the body-wall tissue is split into two layers:

• An external layer that becomes part of the definitive abdominal wall

• An internal layer that contributes muscle to peripheral portions of the diaphragm, external to the parts derived from the pleuroperitoneal membranes (Fig. 10–7*D* and *E*).

Further extension of the developing pleural cavities into the lateral body walls forms the right and left **costodiaphragmatic recesses** (Fig. 10–8), establishing the characteristic dome-shaped configuration of the diaphragm. After birth the costodiaphragmatic recesses become alternately smaller and larger as the lungs move in and out of them during inspiration and expiration.

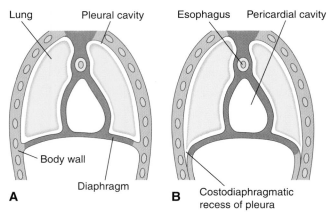

A

Lung — Pleural cavity — Body wall — Diaphragm

B

Esophagus — Pericardial cavity — Costodiaphragmatic recess of pleura

■ **Figure 10–8.** Diagrams illustrating extension of the pleural cavities into the body walls to form peripheral portions of the diaphragm, the costodiaphragmatic recesses, and the establishment of the characteristic dome-shaped configuration of the diaphragm. Note that body wall tissue is added peripherally to the diaphragm as the lungs and pleural cavities enlarge.

Positional Changes and Innervation of the Diaphragm

During the fourth week of development, the septum transversum, prior to its descent with the heart, lies opposite the third to fifth *cervical somites* (Fig. 10–9*A*). During the fifth week, myoblasts (primitive muscle cells) from these somites migrate into the developing diaphragm, bringing their nerve fibers with them. Consequently, the **phrenic nerves** that supply motor innervation to the diaphragm arise from the ventral rami of the third, fourth, and fifth cervical spinal nerves. The three twigs on each side join together to form a phrenic nerve. The phrenic nerves also supply sensory fibers to the superior and inferior surfaces of the right and left domes of the diaphragm.

Rapid growth of the dorsal part of the embryo's body results in the *apparent descent of the diaphragm*. By the sixth week, the developing diaphragm is at the level of the thoracic somites (Fig. 10–9*B*). The phrenic nerves now have a descending course. As the diaphragm "moves" relatively farther caudally in the body, the nerves are correspondingly lengthened. By the beginning of the eighth week, the dorsal part of the diaphragm lies at the level of the first lumbar vertebra (Fig. 10–9*C*). Because of the embryonic origin of the phrenic nerves, they are about 30 cm long in adults. The embryonic phrenic nerves enter the diaphragm by passing through the pleuropericardial membranes. This explains why the phrenic nerves subsequently lie on the fibrous pericardium, the adult derivative of the pleuropericardial membranes (Fig. 10–5*C* and *D*).

As the four parts of the diaphragm fuse (Fig. 10–7), mesenchyme in the septum transversum extends into the other three parts. It forms myoblasts that differentiate into the skeletal muscle of the diaphragm; hence the motor nerve supply to the diaphragm is from the phrenic nerves. The sensory innervation of the diaphragm is also from the phrenic nerves, but its costal rim receives sensory fibers from the lower intercostal nerves because of the origin of the peripheral part of the diaphragm from the lateral body walls (Fig. 10–7*D* and *E*).

CONGENITAL DIAPHRAGMATIC HERNIA

The development of the diaphragm is a complex process; as a consequence, congenital defects may occur. A posterolateral defect of the diaphragm through which hernias occur is the most common anomaly. A congenital diaphragmatic hernia (CDH) is characterized by the presence of abdominal viscera in the thoracic cavity.

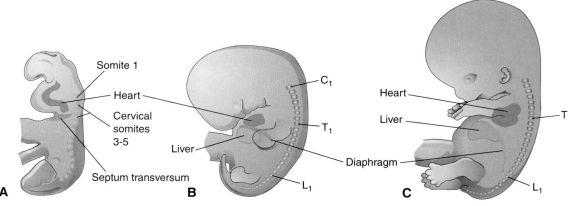

A — Somite 1, Heart, Cervical somites 3-5, Liver, Septum transversum

B — C_1, T_1, L_1

C — Heart, Liver, Diaphragm, T, L_1

■ **Figure 10–9.** Diagrams illustrating positional changes of the developing diaphragm. *A*, About 24 days. The septum transversum is at the level of the third, fourth, and fifth cervical segments. *B*, About 41 days. *C*, About 52 days.

Posterolateral Defect of the Diaphragm

Posterolateral defect of the diaphragm is the only relatively common congenital anomaly of the diaphragm (Figs. 10-10*A* and *B* and 10-11). This diaphragmatic defect occurs about once in 2200 newborn infants (Harrison, 1991) and is associated with **CDH**—herniation of abdominal contents into the thoracic cavity. Life-threatening breathing difficulties may be associated with CDH because of inhibition of development and inflation of lungs (Fig. 10-12). Moreover, fetal lung maturation may be delayed. *Congenital diaphragmatic hernia is the most common cause of pulmonary hy-*

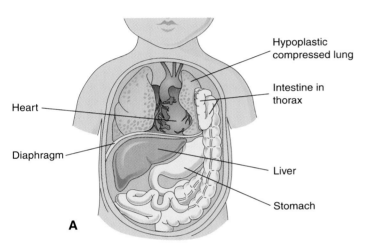

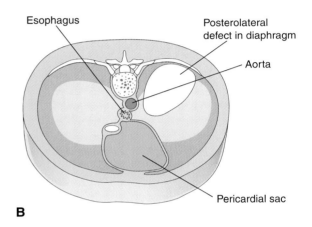

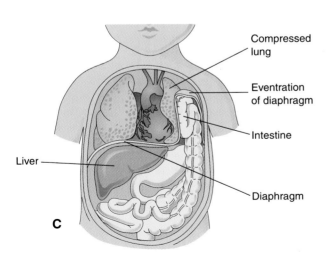

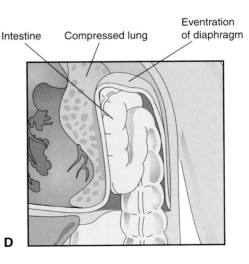

■ **Figure 10-10.** *A*, A "window" has been drawn on the thorax and abdomen to show the herniation of the intestine into the thorax through a posterolateral defect in the left side of the diaphragm. Note that the left lung is compressed and hypoplastic. *B*, Drawing of a diaphragm with a large posterolateral defect on the left side due to abnormal formation and/or fusion of the pleuroperitoneal membrane on the left side with the mesoesophagus and septum transversum. *C* and *D*, Eventration of the diaphragm resulting from defective muscular development of the diaphragm. The abdominal viscera are displaced into the thorax with a pouch of diaphragmatic tissue.

Aorta

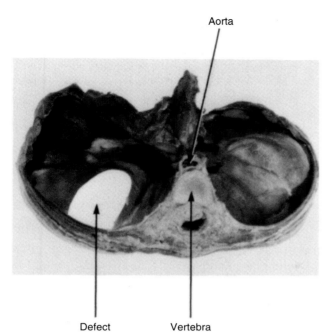

Defect   Vertebra

■ **Figure 10–11.** Photograph of a transverse section through the thoracic region of a stillborn infant, viewed from the thorax. Note the large left posterolateral defect of the diaphragm, which permitted the abdominal contents to pass into the thorax (congenital diaphragmatic hernia).

poplasia. **Polyhydramnios** (excess amniotic fluid) may also be present. Usually unilateral, CDH results from defective formation or fusion of the pleuroperitoneal membrane with the other three parts of the diaphragm (Fig. 10–7). This produces a large opening in the posterolateral region of the diaphragm. As a result, the peritoneal and pleural cavities are continuous with one another along the posterior body wall. The defect—sometimes referred to clinically as the foramen of Bochdalek—usually (85 to 90%) occurs on the left side. The preponderance of left-sided defects is likely related to the earlier closure of the right pleuroperitoneal opening. **Prenatal diagnosis of CDH** (Fig. 10–13) depends on the sonographic demonstration of abdominal organs in the thorax (Goldstein, 1994). The diagnosis can also be confirmed by amniography (see Chapter 7) because the fetus swallows amniotic fluid, which can be observed in the thoracic cavity.

The pleuroperitoneal membranes normally fuse with the other three diaphragmatic components by the end of the sixth week (Fig. 10–7C). If a pleuroperitoneal canal is still open when the intestines return to the abdomen from the umbilical cord in the 10th week (see Chapter 13), some intestine and other viscera may pass into the thorax. The presence of abdominal viscera in the thorax pushes the lungs and heart anteriorly, and compression of the lungs occurs. Often the stomach, spleen, and most of the intestines herniate

(Figs. 10–12 and 10–13). The abdominal viscera can usually move freely through the defect; consequently, they may be in the thoracic cavity when the infant is lying down and in the abdominal cavity when the infant is upright. Most babies born with CDH die not because there is a defect in the diaphragm or viscera in the chest, but because the lungs are hypoplastic because of compression of them during development (Harrison, 1991).

The severity of pulmonary developmental abnormalities depends on when and to what extent the abdominal viscera herniate into the thorax, that is, on the timing and degree of compression of the fetal lungs. The effect on the ipsilateral (same side) lung is greater, but the contralateral lung also shows morphologic changes. If the abdominal viscera are in the thoracic cavity at birth, the initiation of respiration is likely to be impaired. The intestines dilate with swallowed air and compromise the functioning of the heart and lungs. Because the abdominal organs are most often in the left side of the thorax, the heart and mediastinum are usually displaced to the right.

The lungs in infants with CDH are often hypoplastic and greatly reduced in size. The growth retardation of the lungs results from lack of room for them to develop normally. The lungs are often aerated and achieve their normal size after reduction (repositioning) of the herniated viscera and repair of the defect in the diaphragm (Harrison, 1991); however, the mortality rate is high (approximately 76%). If severe **lung hypoplasia** is present, some primitive alveoli may rupture, causing air to enter the pleural cavity—*pneumothorax.* If necessary, CDH can be diagnosed and repaired prenatally between 22 and 28 weeks of gestation (20 to 26 weeks after fertilization), but this intervention carries considerable risk to the fetus and mother.

Eventration of the Diaphragm

In this uncommon condition, half the diaphragm has defective musculature and balloons into the thoracic cavity as an aponeurotic (membranous) sheet, forming a diaphragmatic pouch (Fig. 10–10C and D). Consequently, the abdominal viscera are displaced superiorly into the pocketlike outpouching of the diaphragm. This congenital anomaly results mainly from failure of muscular tissue from the body wall to extend into the pleuroperitoneal membrane on the affected side. *An eventration of the diaphragm is not a true diaphragmatic herniation*; it is a superior displacement of viscera into a saclike part of the diaphragm; however, the clinical manifestations of diaphragmatic eventration may simulate CDH (Hartman, 1996). During surgical repair, a muscular flap (e.g., from a back muscle such as the latissimus dorsi) or a prosthetic patch is used to strengthen the diaphragm.

Gastroschisis and Congenital Epigastric Hernia

This uncommon hernia occurs in the median plane between the xiphoid process and umbilicus. These defects are similar to umbilical hernias (see Chapter 13) except for their location. Gastroschisis and epigastric hernias result from failure of the lateral body folds to fuse completely when forming the anterior abdominal wall during folding in the fourth week (Fig. 10-2C and F). The small intestine herniates into the amniotic fluid and can be detected prenatally by ultrasonography.

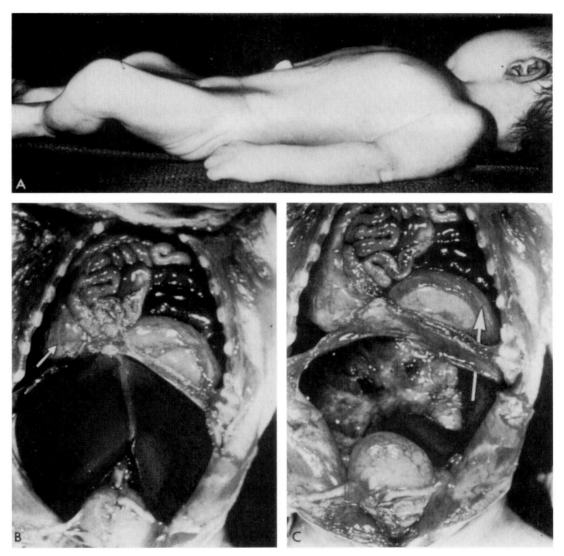

■ **Figure 10-12.** *A*, Photograph of an infant with congenital diaphragmatic hernia resulting from a large left posterolateral diaphragmatic defect similar to that shown in Figure 10-11. Note the relatively flat abdomen resulting from herniation of abdominal viscera into the thorax through the defect. *B*, The thoracic and abdominal cavities opened at autopsy to show the intestines and other viscera in the thoracic cavity. The arrow indicates the heart, which has been displaced to the right. *C*, The liver has been removed, showing that only attached parts of the intestine have remained in the abdominal cavity. The arrow passes through the diaphragmatic defect. (Courtesy of Dr. Jan Hoogstraten, Children's Hospital, Health Sciences Centre, Winnipeg, Manitoba, Canada.)

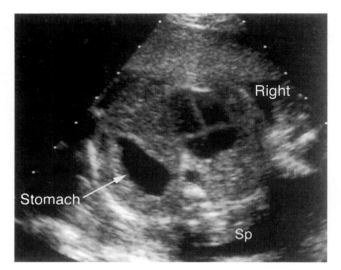

■ Figure 10–13. Ultrasound scan of the thorax showing the heart shifted to the right and the stomach on the left. The diaphragmatic hernia was detected at 23.4 weeks' gestation. The stomach has herniated through a posterolateral defect in the diaphragm (congenital diaphragmatic hernia). Sp, vertebral column or spine. (Courtesy of Dr. Wesley Lee, William Beaumont Hospital, Royal Oak, Michigan.)

Congenital Hiatal Hernia

There may be herniation of part of the fetal stomach through an excessively large esophageal hiatus—the opening in the diaphragm through which the esophagus and vagus nerves pass—however, this is an uncommon congenital defect. Although hiatal hernia is usually an acquired lesion occurring during adult life (Moore, 1992), a congenitally enlarged esophageal hiatus may be the predisposing factor in some cases.

Retrosternal (Parasternal) Hernia

Herniations may occur through the *sternocostal hiatus* (foramen of Morgagni), the opening for the superior epigastric vessels in the retrosternal area. This hiatus is located between the sternal and costal parts of the diaphragm (Moore, 1992). Herniation of intestine into the pericardial sac may occur (Behrman et al, 1996), or, conversely, part of the heart may descend into the peritoneal cavity in the epigastric region. Large defects are commonly associated with body wall defects in the umbilical region (e.g., omphalocele; see Chapter 13). Radiologists and pathologists often observe *fatty herni-*

ations through the sternocostal hiatus; however, they are usually of no clinical significance.

Accessory Diaphragm

More than 30 cases of this rare anomaly have been reported. It is often associated with lung hypoplasia and other respiratory complications. An accessory diaphragm can be diagnosed by magnetic resonance imaging and computed tomographic scanning and is treated by surgical excision (Becmeur et al, 1995).

SUMMARY OF DEVELOPMENT OF BODY CAVITIES

The intraembryonic coelom, the primordium of the body cavities, begins to develop near the end of the third week. By the fourth week, it appears as a horseshoe-shaped cavity in the cardiogenic and lateral mesoderm. The curve of the "horseshoe" represents the future pericardial cavity, and its lateral extensions represent the future pleural and peritoneal cavities.

During folding of the embryonic disc in the fourth week, lateral parts of the intraembryonic coelom move together on the ventral aspect of the embryo. When the caudal part of the ventral mesentery disappears, the right and left parts of the intraembryonic coelom merge to form the peritoneal cavity. As peritoneal parts of the intraembryonic coelom come together, the splanchnic layer of mesoderm encloses the primitive gut and suspends it from the dorsal body wall by a double-layered peritoneal membrane—the dorsal mesentery. The parietal layer of mesoderm lining the peritoneal, pleural, and pericardial cavities becomes the parietal peritoneum, parietal pleura, and serous pericardium, respectively.

Until the seventh week the embryonic pericardial cavity communicates with the peritoneal cavity through paired *pericardioperitoneal canals*. During the fifth and sixth weeks, folds (later membranes) form near the cranial and caudal ends of these canals. Fusion of the cranial *pleuropericardial membranes* with mesoderm ventral to the esophagus separates the pericardial cavity from the pleural cavities. Fusion of the caudal *pleuroperitoneal membranes* during formation of the diaphragm separates the pleural cavities from the peritoneal cavity.

The diaphragm develops from four structures:

- Septum transversum
- Pleuroperitoneal membranes
- Dorsal mesentery of esophagus
- Muscular ingrowth from lateral body walls

Clinically Oriented Questions

1. I heard about a baby who was born with its stomach and liver in its chest. Is this possible?

2. Can a baby with most of its abdominal viscera in its chest survive? I have heard that diaphragmatic defects can be operated on before birth. Is this true?

3. Do the lungs develop normally in babies who are born with CDH?

4. A friend of mine had routine chest radiography about a year ago and was told that a small part of his small intestine was in his chest. Is it possible for him to have a CDH without being aware of it? Would his lung on the affected side be normal?

The answers to these questions are given at the back of the book.

REFERENCES AND SUGGESTED READING

Becmeur F, Horta P, Donato L, et al: Accessory diaphragm—review of 31 cases in the literature. *Eur J Pediatr Surg* 5:43, 1995.

Behrman RE, Kliegman RM, Arvin AM (eds): *Nelson Textbook of Pediatrics,* 15th ed. Philadelphia, WB Saunders, 1996.

Gibbs DL, Rice HE, Farrell JA, et al: Familial diaphragmatic agenesis: An autosomal-recessive syndrome with a poor prognosis. *J Pediatr Surg* 32:366, 1997.

Goldstein RB: Ultrasound evaluation of the fetal thorax. *In* Callen PW (ed): *Ultrasonography in Obstetrics and Gynecology,* 3rd ed. Philadelphia, WB Saunders, 1994.

Harrison MR: The fetus with a diaphragmatic hernia: Pathophysiology, natural history, and surgical management. *In* Harrison MR, Golbus MS, Filly RA (eds): *The Unborn Patient: Prenatal Diagnosis and Treatment,* 2nd ed. Philadelphia, WB Saunders, 1991.

Hartman GE: Diaphragmatic hernia. *In* Behrman RE, Kliegman RM, Arvin AM (eds): *Nelson Textbook of Pediatrics,* 15th ed. Philadelphia, WB Saunders, 1996.

Moore KL: *Clinically Oriented Anatomy,* 3rd ed. Baltimore, Williams & Wilkins, 1992.

Moya FR, Thomas VL, Romaguera J, et al: Fetal lung maturation in congenital diaphragmatic hernia. *Am J Obstet Gynecol* 173:1401, 1995.

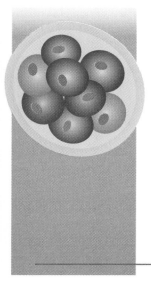

The Pharyngeal (Branchial) Apparatus

11

▪ The head and neck regions of a 4-week-old human embryo somewhat resemble those regions of a fish embryo of a comparable stage of development. This explains the former use of the adjective *branchial*, which is derived from the Greek word *branchia*, meaning gill. By the end of the embryonic period, these gill-like structures either have become rearranged and adapted to new functions or have disappeared.

The **pharyngeal (branchial) apparatus** (Fig. 11 – 1) consists of:

* Pharyngeal arches
* Pharyngeal pouches
* Pharyngeal grooves
* Pharyngeal membranes

These embryonic structures contribute greatly to the formation of the head and neck. Most congenital anomalies in these regions originate during transformation of the pharyngeal apparatus into its adult derivatives. **Branchial anomalies** result from persistence of parts of the pharyngeal apparatus that normally disappear. Study of the development and modification of the human pharyngeal apparatus during formation of the head and neck can be confusing if the function of the branchial apparatus in lower forms is not understood. In fish and larval amphibians, the branchial apparatus forms a system of gills for exchanging oxygen and carbon dioxide between the blood and water. The branchial arches support the gills. A primordial branchial or pharyngeal apparatus develops in human embryos; however, no gills form. Consequently, the term *pharyngeal arch* is now used instead of *branchial arch* when describing development of the head and neck regions of human embryos.

PHARYNGEAL ARCHES

The pharyngeal arches begin to develop early in the fourth week as **neural crest cells** migrate into the future head and neck regions (see Chapter 6). Laboratory studies in avian and mammalian embryos have contributed only partly to our understanding of the migration and distribution pattern of neural crest cells in relation to the pharyngeal arches (Noden, 1991; Kuratani and Aizawa, 1995; Sulik, 1996). The first pair of pharyngeal arches, the primordium of the jaws, appears as surface elevations lateral to the developing pharynx (Fig. 11 – 1*A* and *B*). Soon other arches appear as obliquely disposed, rounded ridges on each side of the future head and neck regions (Fig. 11 – 1*C* and *D*). By the end of the fourth week, four well-defined pairs of pharyngeal arches are visible externally (Fig. 11 – 2). The fifth and sixth arches are rudi-

mentary and are not visible on the surface of the embryo. The arches are separated from each other by prominent clefts — the **pharyngeal grooves**. Like the pharyngeal arches, the grooves are numbered in a craniocaudal sequence.

The **first pharyngeal arch**, or mandibular arch, develops two prominences (Figs. 11 – 1*E* and *F* and 11 – 2):

* The smaller **maxillary prominence** gives rise to the maxilla (upper jaw), zygomatic bone, and squamous part of the temporal bone.
* The larger **mandibular prominence** forms the mandible (lower jaw).

Consequently, the first pair of pharyngeal arches plays a major role in the development of the face.

The **second pharyngeal arch** (hyoid arch) makes a major contribution to the formation of the hyoid bone. The pharyngeal arches caudal to the second arch are referred to by number only. The pharyngeal arches support the lateral walls of the primordial pharynx, which is derived from the cranial part of the foregut. The primordial mouth or **stomodeum** initially appears as a slight depression of the surface ectoderm (Fig. 11 – 1*D* and *E*). It is separated from the cavity of the primordial pharynx by a bilaminar membrane — the **oropharyngeal membrane** — which forms during the third week (see Chapter 5). It is composed of ectoderm externally and endoderm internally. The oropharyngeal membrane ruptures at about 26 days, bringing the primordial pharynx and foregut into communication with the amniotic cavity (Fig. 11 – 1*F* and *G*).

Pharyngeal Arch Components

Initially, each pharyngeal arch consists of a core of mesenchyme (embryonic connective tissue) and is covered externally by ectoderm and internally by endoderm (Fig. 11 – 1*H* and *I*). The original mesenchyme is derived from mesoderm in the third week. During the fourth week, most of the mesenchyme is derived from **neural crest cells** that migrate into the pharyngeal arches. The migration of these neural crest cells into the arches and their differentiation into mesenchyme produce the maxillary and mandibular prominences of the first arch (Fig. 11 – 2). Neural crest cells are unique in that, despite their neuroectodermal origin, they make a major contribution to mesenchyme in the head as well as to structures in many other regions (see Chapter 6). Skeletal musculature and vascular endothelia, however, are derived from the original mesenchyme in the pharyngeal arches (Noden, 1991; Sulik, 1996).

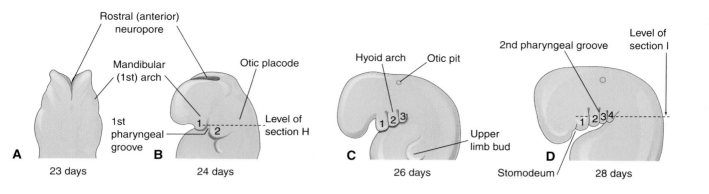

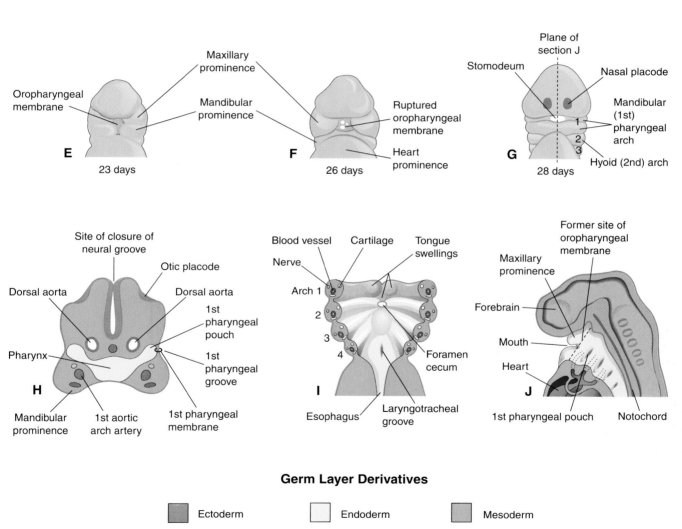

Germ Layer Derivatives

Ectoderm   Endoderm   Mesoderm

■ **Figure 11–1.** Drawings illustrating the human pharyngeal apparatus. *A,* Dorsal view of the cranial part of an early embryo. *B* to *D,* Lateral views showing later development of the pharyngeal arches. *E* to *G,* Ventral or facial views illustrating the relationship of the first pharyngeal arch to the stomodeum. *H,* Horizontal section through the cranial region of an embryo. *I,* Similar section illustrating the arch components and floor of the primordial pharynx. *J,* Sagittal section of the cranial region of an embryo, illustrating the openings of the pharyngeal pouches in the lateral wall of the primordial pharynx.

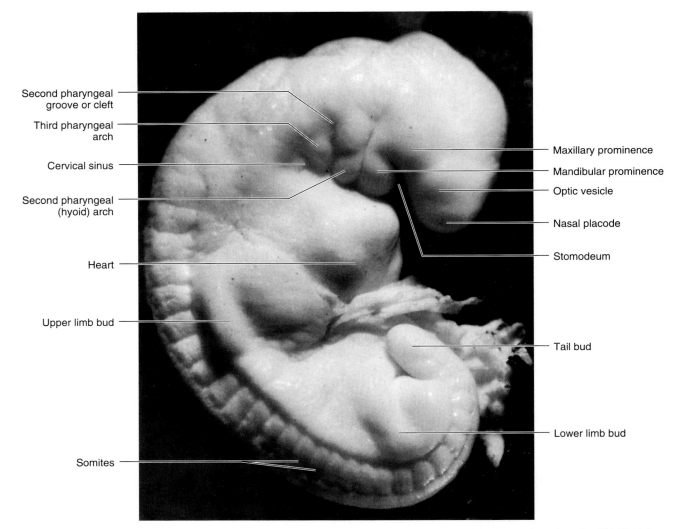

Second pharyngeal groove or cleft

Third pharyngeal arch

Cervical sinus

Second pharyngeal (hyoid) arch

Heart

Upper limb bud

Somites

Maxillary prominence

Mandibular prominence

Optic vesicle

Nasal placode

Stomodeum

Tail bud

Lower limb bud

■ **Figure 11-2.** Macrophotograph of a stage 13, 4½-week human embryo. (Courtesy of Professor Emeritus Dr. KV Hinrichsen, Medizinische Fakultät, Institut für Anatomie, Ruhr-Universität Bochum, Germany.)

Fate of the Pharyngeal Arches

The pharyngeal arches contribute extensively to the formation of the face, nasal cavities, mouth, larynx, pharynx, and neck (Figs. 11-3 and 11-4). During the fifth week, the second pharyngeal arch enlarges and overgrows the third and fourth arches, forming an ectodermal depression — the **cervical sinus** (Fig. 11-4*A* to *G*). By the end of the seventh week, the second to fourth pharyngeal grooves and the cervical sinus have disappeared, giving the neck a smooth contour.

A typical pharyngeal arch contains:

- An *aortic arch*, an artery that arises from the truncus arteriosus of the primordial heart (Fig. 11-3*B*) and runs around the primordial pharynx to enter the dorsal aorta
- A *cartilaginous rod* that forms the skeleton of the arch
- A *muscular component* that forms muscles in the head and neck
- A *nerve* that supplies the mucosa and muscles derived from the arch

The nerves that grow into the arches are derived from neuroectoderm of the primordial brain.

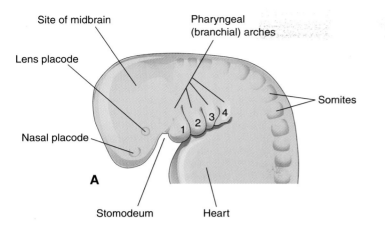

A

- Site of midbrain
- Lens placode
- Nasal placode
- Pharyngeal (branchial) arches
- Somites
- Stomodeum
- Heart
- 1 2 3 4

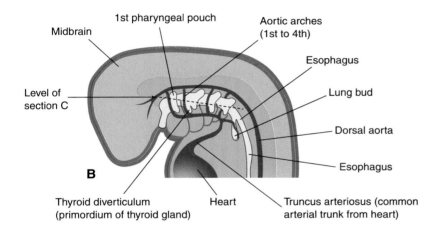

B

- Midbrain
- 1st pharyngeal pouch
- Aortic arches (1st to 4th)
- Esophagus
- Level of section C
- Lung bud
- Dorsal aorta
- Esophagus
- Thyroid diverticulum (primordium of thyroid gland)
- Heart
- Truncus arteriosus (common arterial trunk from heart)

■ **Figure 11–3.** *A,* Drawing of the head, neck, and thoracic regions of a human embryo (about 28 days), illustrating the pharyngeal apparatus. *B,* Schematic drawing showing the pharyngeal pouches and aortic arches. *C,* Horizontal section through the embryo showing the floor of the primordial pharynx and illustrating the germ layer of origin of the pharyngeal arch components.

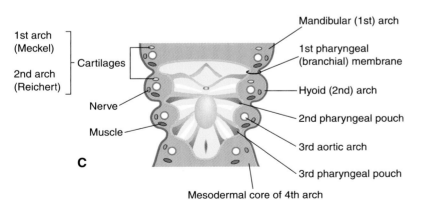

C

- 1st arch (Meckel)
- 2nd arch (Reichert)
- Cartilages
- Nerve
- Muscle
- Mandibular (1st) arch
- 1st pharyngeal (branchial) membrane
- Hyoid (2nd) arch
- 2nd pharyngeal pouch
- 3rd aortic arch
- 3rd pharyngeal pouch
- Mesodermal core of 4th arch

Germ Layer Derivatives

Ectoderm   Endoderm   Mesoderm

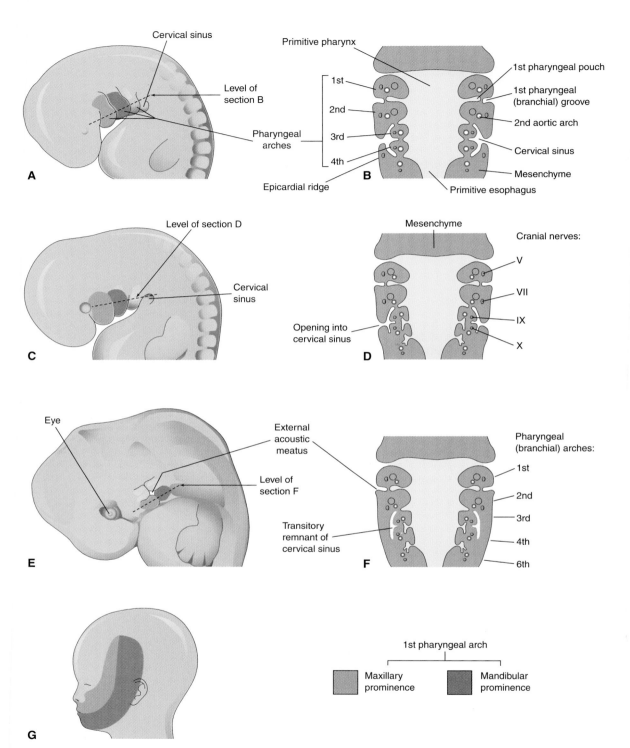

■ Figure 11–4. *A,* Lateral view of the head, neck, and thoracic regions of an embryo (about 32 days), showing the pharyngeal arches and cervical sinus. *B,* Diagrammatic section through the embryo at the level shown in *A,* illustrating growth of the second arch over the third and fourth arches. *C,* An embryo of about 33 days. *D,* Section of the embryo at the level shown in *C,* illustrating early closure of the cervical sinus. *E,* An embryo of about 41 days. *F,* Section of the embryo at the level shown in *E,* showing the transitory cystic remnant of the cervical sinus. *G,* Drawing of a 20-week fetus illustrating the area of the face derived from the first pair of pharyngeal arches.

DERIVATIVES OF THE AORTIC ARCHES (PHARYNGEAL ARCH ARTERIES)

The transformation of the aortic arches into the adult arterial pattern of the head and neck is described with the cardiovascular system in Chapter 15. In fish these arteries supply blood to the capillary network of the gills. In human embryos the blood in the aortic arches supplies the arches and then enters the dorsal aorta.

DERIVATIVES OF THE PHARYNGEAL ARCH CARTILAGES

The dorsal end of the **first arch cartilage** (Meckel cartilage) is closely related to the developing ear and becomes ossified to form two middle ear bones, the **malleus** and **incus** (Fig. 11-5A and B and Table 11-1). The middle part of the cartilage regresses, but its perichondrium forms the *anterior ligament of the malleus and the sphenomandibular ligament*. Ventral parts of the first arch cartilages form the horseshoe-shaped primordium of the mandible and, by keeping pace with its growth, guide its early morphogenesis. Each half of the mandible forms lateral to and in close association with its cartilage. The cartilage disappears as the mandible develops around it by intramembranous ossification (Fig. 11-5B).

The dorsal end of the **second arch cartilage** (Reichert cartilage), also closely related to the developing ear, ossifies to form the **stapes** of the middle ear and the **styloid process** of the temporal bone (Fig. 11-5B). The part of cartilage between the styloid process and hyoid bone regresses; its perichondrium forms the *stylohyoid ligament*. The ventral end of the second arch cartilage ossifies to form the lesser cornu (L. horn) and the superior part of the body of the *hyoid bone* (Fig. 11-5B).

The **third arch cartilage**, located in the ventral part of the arch, ossifies to form the greater cornu and the inferior part of the body of the hyoid bone. The **fourth and sixth arch cartilages** fuse to form the *laryngeal cartilages* (Fig. 11-5B and Table 11-1), except for the epiglottis. The cartilage of the epiglottis develops from mesenchyme in the *hypobranchial eminence* (see Fig. 11-24A), a prominence in the floor of the embryonic pharynx that is derived from the third and fourth pharyngeal arches.

DERIVATIVES OF THE PHARYNGEAL ARCH MUSCLES

The muscular components of the arches form various striated muscles in the head and neck; for example, the musculature of the first pharyngeal arch forms the

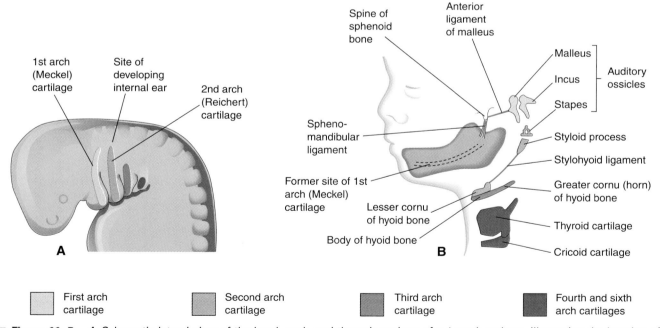

First arch cartilage · Second arch cartilage · Third arch cartilage · Fourth and sixth arch cartilages

■ **Figure 11-5.** *A,* Schematic lateral view of the head, neck, and thoracic regions of a 4-week embryo, illustrating the location of the cartilages in the pharyngeal arches. *B,* Similar view of a 24-week fetus illustrating the adult derivatives of the arch cartilages. Note that the mandible is formed by membranous ossification of mesenchymal tissue surrounding the first arch (Meckel) cartilage. This cartilage acts as a template for development of the mandible but does not contribute directly to the formation of it. Occasionally ossification of the second arch cartilage may extend from the styloid process along the stylohyoid ligament. When this occurs, it may cause pain in the region of the palatine tonsil.

Table 11–1 ■ **Structures Derived From Pharyngeal Arch Components***

Arch	Nerve	Muscles	Skeletal Structures	Ligaments
First (mandibular)	Trigeminal† (CN V)	Muscles of mastication‡ Mylohyoid and anterior belly of digastric Tensor tympanic Tensor veli palatini	Malleus Incus	Anterior ligament of malleus Sphenomandibular ligament
Second (hyoid)	Facial (CN VII)	Muscles of facial expression§ Stapedius Stylohyoid Posterior belly of digastric	Stapes Styloid process Lesser cornu of hyoid Upper part of body of hyoid bone	Stylohyoid ligament
Third	Glossopharyngeal (CN IX)	Stylopharyngeus	Greater cornu of hyoid Lower part of body of hyoid bone	
Fourth and Sixth ‖	Superior laryngeal branch of vagus (CN X) Recurrent laryngeal branch of vagus (CN X)	Cricothyroid Levator veli palatini Constrictors of pharynx Intrinsic muscles of larynx Striated muscles of esophagus	Thyroid cartilage Cricoid cartilage Arytenoid cartilage Corniculate cartilage Cuneiform cartilage	

* The derivatives of the aortic arch arteries are described in Chapter 15.
† The ophthalmic division does not supply any pharyngeal arch components.
‡ Temporalis, masseter, medial, and lateral pterygoids.
§ Buccinator, auricularis, frontalis, platysma, orbicularis oris and oculi.
‖ The fifth pharyngeal arch is often absent. When present, it is rudimentary and usually has no recognizable cartilage bar. The cartilaginous components of the fourth and sixth arches fuse to form the cartilages of the larynx.

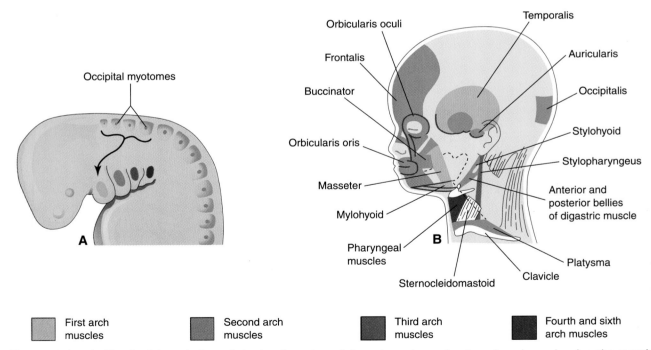

First arch muscles   **Second arch muscles**   **Third arch muscles**   **Fourth and sixth arch muscles**

■ **Figure 11–6.** *A,* Sketch of lateral view of the head, neck, and thoracic regions of a 4-week embryo showing the muscles derived from the pharyngeal arches. The arrow shows the pathway taken by myoblasts from the occipital myotomes to form the tongue musculature. *B,* Sketch of the head and neck regions of a 20-week fetus, dissected to show the muscles derived from the pharyngeal arches. Parts of the platysma and sternocleidomastoid muscles have been removed to show the deeper muscles. Note that myoblasts from the second arch migrate from the neck to the head, where they give rise to the muscles of facial expression. These muscles are supplied by the facial nerve (CN VII), the nerve of the second pharyngeal arch.

muscles of mastication and other muscles (Fig. 11–6*A* and *B*; Table 11–1).

DERIVATIVES OF THE PHARYNGEAL ARCH NERVES

Each arch is supplied by its own cranial nerve (CN). The *special visceral efferent (branchial) components* of the cranial nerves supply muscles derived from the pharyngeal arches (Fig. 11–7*A*; Table 11–1). Because mesenchyme from the pharyngeal arches contributes to the dermis and mucous membranes of the head and neck, these areas are supplied with *special visceral afferent nerves*.

The facial skin is supplied by the fifth cranial nerve — the **trigeminal nerve** (CN V); however, only its caudal two branches (*maxillary and mandibular*) supply derivatives of the first pharyngeal arch (Fig. 11–7*B*). Cranial nerve V is the principal sensory nerve of the head and neck and is the motor nerve for the muscles of mastication (Table 11–1). Its sensory branches innervate the face, teeth, and mucous membranes of the nasal cavities, palate, mouth, and tongue (Fig. 11–7*C*).

The seventh cranial nerve — the **facial nerve** (CN VII), the ninth cranial nerve — the **glossopharyngeal nerve** (CN IX), and the tenth cranial nerve — the **vagus nerve** (CN X) supply the second, third, and caudal (fourth to sixth) arches, respectively. The fourth arch is supplied by the superior laryngeal branch of the vagus nerve and the sixth arch by its recurrent laryngeal branch. The nerves of the second to sixth pharyngeal arches have little cutaneous distribution (Fig. 11–7*C*); however, they innervate the mucous membranes of the tongue, pharynx, and larynx.

PHARYNGEAL POUCHES

The *primordial pharynx*, derived from the foregut, widens cranially where it joins the primordial mouth or *stomodeum* and narrows caudally where it joins the esophagus (Figs. 11–3*A* and *B* and 11–4*B*). The endoderm of the pharynx lines the internal aspects of the pharyngeal arches and passes into balloonlike diverticula — the **pharyngeal pouches** (Figs. 11–1*H* to *J* and 11–3*B* and *C*). The pairs of pouches develop in a craniocaudal sequence between the arches. The first pair of pouches, for example, lies between the first and second pharyngeal arches. Four pairs of pharyngeal pouches are well-defined; the fifth pair is absent or rudimentary. The endoderm of the pouches contacts the ectoderm of the pharyngeal grooves, and together they form the thin double-layered **pharyngeal membranes** that separate the pharyngeal pouches from the pharyngeal grooves (Figs. 11–1*H* and 11–3*C*).

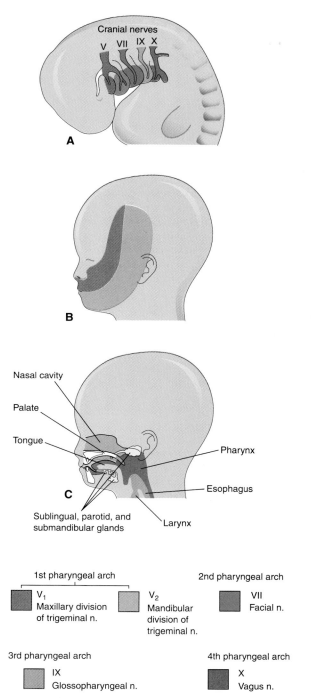

■ **Figure 11–7.** *A,* Lateral view of the head, neck, and thoracic regions of a 4-week embryo showing the cranial nerves supplying the pharyngeal arches. *B,* Sketch of the head and neck regions of a 20-week fetus showing the superficial distribution of the two caudal branches of the first arch nerve (CN V). *C,* Sagittal section of the fetal head and neck, showing the deep distribution of sensory fibers of the nerves to the teeth and mucosa of the tongue, pharynx, nasal cavity, palate, and larynx.

Derivatives of the Pharyngeal Pouches

The endodermal epithelial lining of the pharyngeal pouches (Fig. 11-8*A*) gives rise to important organs in the head and neck.

THE FIRST PHARYNGEAL POUCH

The first pharyngeal pouch expands into an elongate *tubotympanic recess* (Fig. 11-8*B*). The expanded distal part of this recess contacts the first pharyngeal groove, where it later contributes to the formation of the **tympanic membrane** (eardrum). The cavity of the tubotympanic recess gives rise to the **tympanic cavity** and **mastoid antrum**. The connection of the tubotympanic recess with the pharynx gradually elongates to form the **pharyngotympanic tube** (auditory tube, eustachian tube). More details about the developing ear are given in Chapter 20.

THE SECOND PHARYNGEAL POUCH

Although the second pharyngeal pouch is largely obliterated as the **palatine tonsil** develops, part of the cavity of this pouch remains as the **tonsillar sinus** or fossa (Figs. 11-8*C* and 11-9). The endoderm of the second pouch proliferates and grows into the underlying mesenchyme. The central parts of these buds break down, forming crypts (pitlike depressions). The pouch endoderm forms the surface epithelium and lining of the **tonsillar crypts.** At about 20 weeks the mesenchyme around the crypts differentiates into lymphoid tissue, which soon organizes into the *lymphatic nodules* of the palatine tonsil.

THE THIRD PHARYNGEAL POUCH

The third pharyngeal pouch expands and develops a solid, dorsal bulbar part and a hollow, elongate ventral part (Fig. 11-8*B*). Its connection with the pharynx is reduced to a narrow duct that soon degenerates. By the sixth week the epithelium of each dorsal bulbar part begins to differentiate into an **inferior parathyroid gland** (parathyroid III). The epithelium of the elongate ventral parts of the third pair of pouches proliferates, obliterating their cavities. These bilateral primordia of the thymus come together in the median plane to form the bilobed **thymus**, which descends into the superior mediastinum. The bilobed form of this lymphatic organ remains throughout life, discretely encapsulated; each lobe has its own blood supply, lymphatic drainage, and nerve supply. The primordia of the thymus and parathyroid glands lose their connections with the pharynx and migrate into the neck. Later the parathyroid glands separate from the thymus and come to lie on the dorsal surface of the thyroid gland (Figs. 11-8*C* and 11-9).

The thymic primordium is surrounded by a thin layer of mesenchyme that is essential for its development. This mesenchyme, as well as certain epithelial cells in the thymus, are derived from *neural crest cells.* Extirpation (removal) of these cells in animal experiments produces a wide range of developmental defects, including defects of the thymus (Bockman and Kirby, 1984). Growth and development of the thymus are not complete at birth. It is a relatively large organ during the perinatal period and may extend superiorly through the superior aperture of the thorax into the root of the neck. During late childhood, as puberty is reached, the thymus begins to diminish in relative size (i.e., undergoes involution). By adulthood it is often scarcely recognizable because of fat infiltrating the cortex of the gland (Steinman, 1986); however it is still functional and important for the maintenance of health. In addition to secreting thymic hormones, the adult thymus primes thymocytes before releasing them to the periphery (Kendall, 1991).

THE FOURTH PHARYNGEAL POUCH

The fourth pharyngeal pouch also expands into dorsal bulbar and elongate ventral parts (Figs. 11-8 and 11-9). Its connection with the pharynx is reduced to a narrow duct that soon degenerates. By the sixth week, each dorsal part develops into a **superior parathyroid gland** (parathyroid IV), which lies on the dorsal surface of the thyroid gland. As described, the parathyroid glands derived from the third pouches descend with the thymus and are carried to a more inferior position than the parathyroid glands derived from the fourth pouches. This explains why the parathyroid glands derived from the third pair of pouches are located inferior to those from the fourth pouches (Fig. 11-9).

The elongated ventral part of each fourth pouch develops into an **ultimobranchial body**, which received its name from the fact that it is the last of the series of structures derived from the pharyngeal pouches. The ultimobranchial body fuses with the thyroid gland and its cells disseminate within it, giving rise to the **parafollicular cells** of the thyroid gland; they are also called **C cells** to indicate that they produce *calcitonin*, a hormone that is involved in the regulation of the normal calcium level in body fluids (Gartner and Hiatt, 1997). *C cells differentiate from neural crest cells* that migrate from the pharyngeal arches into the fourth pair of pharyngeal pouches.

Germ Layer Derivatives

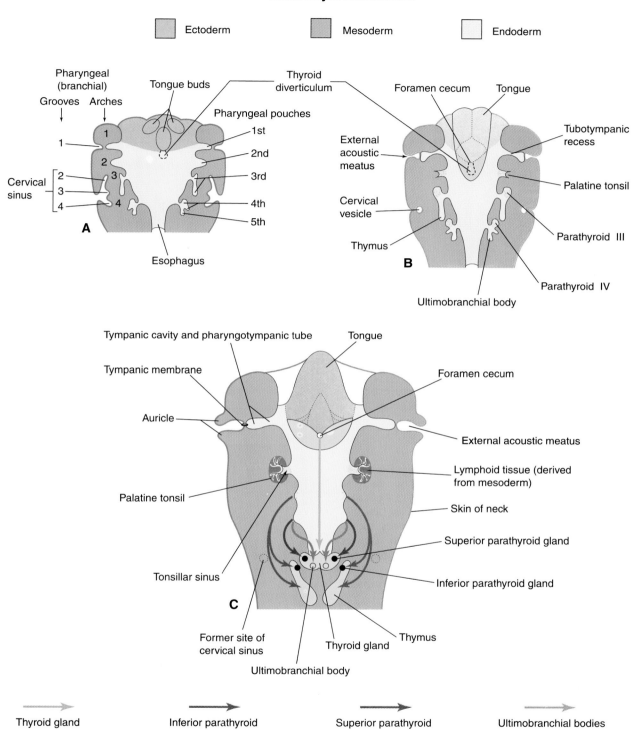

Ectoderm   Mesoderm   Endoderm

A

Pharyngeal (branchial)

Grooves   Arches

Tongue buds

Thyroid diverticulum

Pharyngeal pouches

1   1

2   2   3

Cervical sinus

2
3
4

3   4

1st
2nd
3rd
4th
5th

Esophagus

B

Foramen cecum   Tongue

External acoustic meatus

Cervical vesicle

Thymus

Ultimobranchial body

Tubotympanic recess

Palatine tonsil

Parathyroid III

Parathyroid IV

C

Tympanic cavity and pharyngotympanic tube   Tongue

Tympanic membrane

Auricle

Palatine tonsil

Tonsillar sinus

Former site of cervical sinus

Ultimobranchial body

Thyroid gland

Thymus

Foramen cecum

External acoustic meatus

Lymphoid tissue (derived from mesoderm)

Skin of neck

Superior parathyroid gland

Inferior parathyroid gland

Thyroid gland   Inferior parathyroid glands and thymus   Superior parathyroid glands   Ultimobranchial bodies

■ **Figure 11–8.** Schematic horizontal sections at the level shown in Figure 11–4A, illustrating the adult derivatives of the pharyngeal pouches. A, Five weeks. Note that the second pharyngeal arch grows over the third and fourth arches, burying the second to fourth pharyngeal grooves in the cervical sinus. B, Six weeks. C, Seven weeks. Note the migration of the developing thymus, parathyroid, and thyroid glands into the neck.

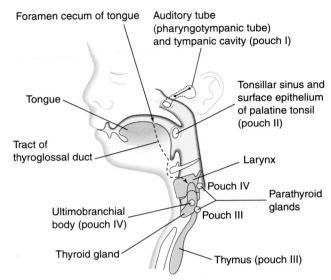

■ **Figure 11–9.** Schematic sagittal section of the head, neck, and upper thoracic regions of a 20-week fetus, showing the adult derivatives of the pharyngeal pouches and the descent of the thyroid gland into the neck.

THE FIFTH PHARYNGEAL POUCH

When it develops, this rudimentary structure becomes part of the fourth pharyngeal pouch and helps to form the ultimobranchial body.

PHARYNGEAL GROOVES

The head and neck regions of the human embryo exhibit four pharyngeal grooves (clefts) on each side during the fourth and fifth weeks (Fig. 11–1B to D). These grooves separate the pharyngeal arches externally. Only one pair of grooves contributes to adult structures; the first pair persists as the **external acoustic meatus** (Fig. 11–8C). The other grooves lie in a slitlike depression — the **cervical sinus** — and are normally obliterated with it as the neck develops (Fig. 11–4B, D, and F).

PHARYNGEAL MEMBRANES

The pharyngeal membranes appear in the floors of the pharyngeal grooves on each side of the head and neck regions of the human embryo during the fourth week (Figs. 11–1H and 11–3C). These membranes form where the epithelia of a groove and a pouch approach each other. The endoderm of the pouches and the ectoderm of the grooves are soon separated by mesenchyme. Only one pair of membranes contributes to the formation of adult structures; the *first pharyngeal membrane*, along with the intervening layer of mesenchyme, becomes the **tympanic membrane** (Fig. 11–8C).

Anomalies of the Head and Neck

Most congenital anomalies of the head and neck originate during transformation of the pharyngeal apparatus into adult structures. Most defects represent remnants of the pharyngeal apparatus that normally disappear as the adult structures develop (Stricker et al, 1990).

Congenital Auricular Sinuses and Cysts

Small auricular sinuses (pits) and cysts are usually found in a triangular area of skin anterior to the auricle of the external ear (Fig. 11–10F); however, they may occur in other sites around the auricle or in its lobule (earlobe). Although some sinuses and cysts are remnants of the first pharyngeal groove, others represent ectodermal folds sequestered during formation of the auricle from the auricular hillocks (swellings that form the auricle). These small sinuses and cysts are classified as minor anomalies that are of no serious medical consequence.

Branchial Sinuses

Branchial sinuses are uncommon, and almost all that open externally on the side of the neck result from failure of the second pharyngeal groove and cervical sinus to obliterate (Figs. 11–10D and 11–11A and B). The blind pit or sinus typically opens along the anterior border of the sternocleidomastoid muscle in the inferior third of the neck. Anomalies of the other pharyngeal grooves (first, third, or fourth) occur in about 5% of cases (Cote and Giandi, 1996).

External branchial sinuses are commonly detected during infancy because of the discharge of mucous material from their orifices in the neck (Fig. 11–11A). These *lateral cervical sinuses* are bilateral in about 10% of cases and are commonly associated with auricular sinuses.

Internal branchial sinuses open into the pharynx and are very rare. Because they usually open into the tonsillar sinus or near the palatopharyngeal arch (Fig. 11–10D and F), almost all these sinuses result from persistence of the proximal part of the second pharyngeal pouch. Normally this pouch disappears as the palatine tonsil develops; its normal remnant is the tonsillar sinus.

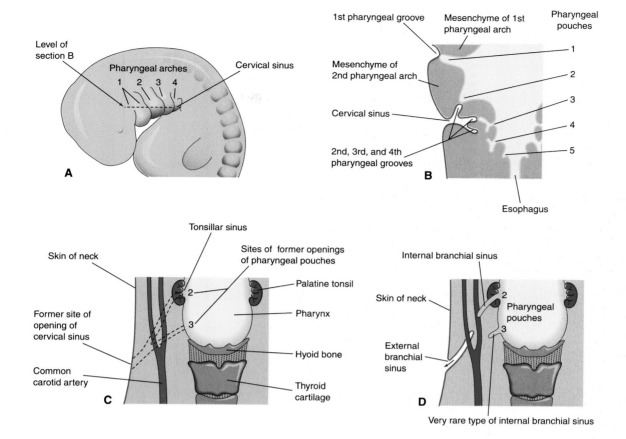

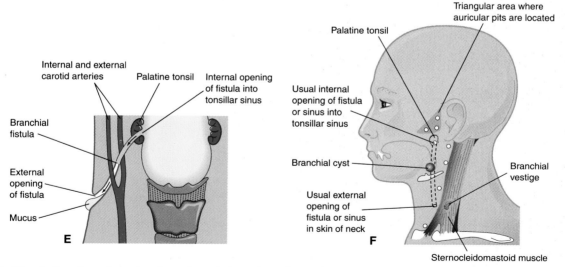

■ **Figure 11–10.** *A,* Drawing of the head, neck, and thoracic regions of a 5-week embryo, showing the cervical sinus that is normally present at this stage. *B,* Horizontal section of the embryo, at the level shown in *A,* illustrating the relationship of the cervical sinus to the pharyngeal arches and pouches. *C,* Diagrammatic sketch of the adult pharyngeal and neck regions, indicating the former sites of openings of the cervical sinus and pharyngeal pouches. The broken lines indicate possible courses of branchial fistulas. *D,* Similar sketch showing the embryological basis of various types of branchial sinus. *E,* Drawing of a branchial fistula resulting from persistence of parts of the second pharyngeal groove and second pharyngeal pouch. *F,* Sketch showing possible sites of branchial cysts and openings of branchial sinuses and fistulas. A branchial vestige is also illustrated (see also Fig. 11–14).

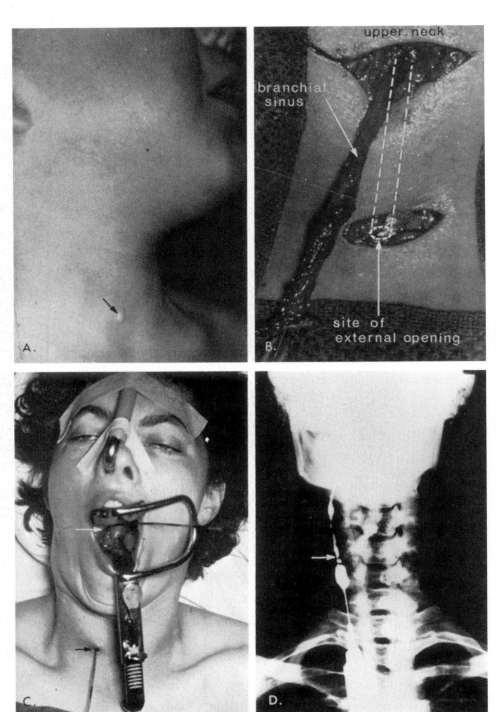

■ **Figure 11–11.** *A,* Photograph of a child's head and neck showing mucus oozing from the external opening of a branchial sinus (*arrow*), which is located just anterior to the sternocleidomastoid muscle. *B,* Photograph of a branchial sinus taken during its excision. Its external opening in the skin of the neck and the original course of the sinus in the subcutaneous tissue are indicated by broken lines. (From Swenson O: *Pediatric Surgery.* New York, Appleton-Century-Crofts, 1958.) *C,* Photograph illustrating a branchial fistula in an adult female. The catheter enters the internal opening in the tonsillar sinus (*white arrow*), passes through the fistula, and leaves through the opening in the neck (*black arrow*). *D,* Radiograph taken after injection of a contrast medium, showing the course of the fistula (*arrow*) through the neck. (Courtesy of Dr. DA Kernahan, The Children's Memorial Hospital, Chicago.)

Branchial Fistula

An abnormal canal that opens internally into the tonsillar sinus and externally on the side of the neck is a *branchial fistula*. This rare anomaly results from persistence of parts of the second pharyngeal groove and second pharyngeal pouch (Figs. 11-10*E* and *F* and 11-11*C* and *D*). The fistula ascends from its opening in the neck through the subcutaneous tissue and platysma muscle to reach the carotid sheath (Moore, 1992). The fistula then passes between the internal and external carotid arteries and opens into the tonsillar sinus. Older patients may have a disagreeable taste in the mouth because of the discharge of material into the oropharynx from the fistula.

Branchial Cysts

The third and fourth pharyngeal arches are buried in the *cervical sinus* (Fig. 11-10*B*). Remnants of parts of the cervical sinus and/or the second pharyngeal groove may persist and form a spherical or elongate cyst (Fig. 11-10*F*). Although they may be associated with branchial sinuses and drain through them, branchial cysts often lie free in the neck just inferior to the angle of the mandible. They may, however, develop anywhere along the anterior border of the sternoclei-

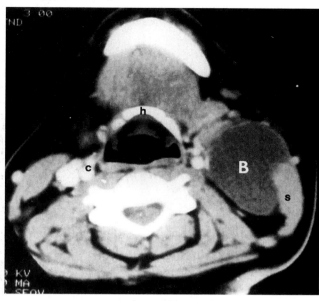

■ **Figure 11-13.** Branchial cleft cyst (B). This is a computed tomographic (CT) image of the neck region of a woman who presented with a "lump" in the neck, similar to that shown in Figure 11-12. The low-density cyst is anterior to the right sternocleidomastoid muscle (s) at the level of the hyoid bone (h). The normal appearance of the carotid sheath (c) is shown for comparison with the compressed sheath on the right side. (From McNab T, McLennan MK, Margolis M: Radiology rounds. *Can Fam Physician* 41:1673, 1995.)

domastoid muscle. Branchial cysts often do not become apparent until late childhood or early adulthood, when they produce a slowly enlarging, painless swelling in the neck (Fig. 11-12). The cysts enlarge because of the accumulation of fluid and cellular debris derived from desquamation of their epithelial linings (Fig. 11-13). Branchial cysts have been observed in the parathyroid glands and may arise from cystic degeneration and accumulation of secretions in embryological remnants that normally disappear (Chetty and Forder, 1991).

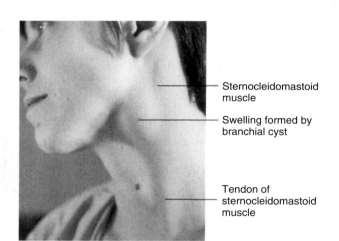

Sternocleidomastoid muscle

Swelling formed by branchial cyst

Tendon of sternocleidomastoid muscle

■ **Figure 11-12.** Photograph of the head, neck, and upper thoracic regions of a 27-year-old woman showing the swelling produced by a branchial cyst just anterior to her sternocleidomastoid muscle. The cyst was not visible at birth, but the swelling developed slowly during her mid-twenties. The cyst was successfully excised. (From Moore KL: *Clinically Oriented Anatomy*, 3rd ed. Baltimore, Williams & Wilkins, 1992.)

Branchial Vestiges

Normally the pharyngeal cartilages disappear, except for parts that form ligaments or bones; however, in unusual cases cartilaginous or bony remnants of pharyngeal arch cartilages appear under the skin in the side of the neck (Fig. 11-14). These are usually found anterior to the inferior third of the sternocleidomastoid muscle (Fig. 11-10*F*).

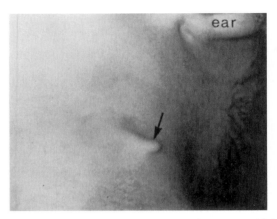

■ **Figure 11–14.** Photograph of a cartilaginous branchial vestige under the skin of a child's neck (*arrow*). (From Raffensperger JG: *Swenson's Pediatric Surgery*, 5th ed. New York, Appleton-Century-Crofts, 1990.)

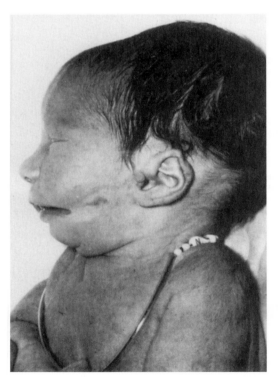

■ **Figure 11–15.** Photograph of an infant with the first arch syndrome, a pattern of anomalies resulting from insufficient migration of neural crest cells into the first pharyngeal arch. Note the following: deformed auricle of the external ear, preauricular appendage, defect in the cheek between the auricle and the mouth, hypoplasia of the mandible, and macrostomia (large mouth).

First Arch Syndrome

Abnormal development of the components of the first pharyngeal arch results in various congenital anomalies of the eyes, ears, mandible, and palate that together constitute the first arch syndrome (Fig. 11–15). This set of symptoms is believed to result from insufficient migration of neural crest cells into the first arch during the fourth week. *There are two main manifestations of the first arch syndrome* (Behrman et al, 1996; Sulik, 1996):

- The **Treacher Collins syndrome** (mandibulofacial dysostosis), caused by an autosomal dominant gene, causes malar hypoplasia (underdevelopment of the zygomatic bones of the face) with downslanting palpebral fissures, defects of the lower eyelids, deformed external ears, and sometimes abnormalities of the middle and internal ears.
- The **Pierre Robin syndrome** consists of hypoplasia of the mandible, cleft palate, and defects of the eye and ear. Many cases of this syndrome are sporadic; however, some appear to have a genetic basis. In the *Robin morphogenetic complex*, the initiating defect is a small mandible (micrognathia), which results in posterior displacement of the tongue and obstruction to full closure of the palatine processes, resulting in a bilateral cleft palate.

DiGeorge Syndrome: Congenital Thymic Aplasia and Absence of Parathyroid Glands

Infants with these anomalies are born without a thymus and parathyroid glands; in some cases, ectopic glandular tissue has been found. The disease is characterized by *congenital hypoparathyroidism*, increased susceptibility to infections, anomalies of the mouth (shortened philtrum of the lip [fish-mouth deformity]), low-set notched ears, nasal clefts, *thyroid hypoplasia*, and cardiac abnormalities (defects of the arch of the aorta and heart). The *DiGeorge syndrome* occurs because the third and fourth pharyngeal pouches fail to differentiate into the thymus and parathyroid glands. The facial abnormalities result primarily from abnormal development of the first arch components during formation of the face and ears. The DiGeorge syndrome usually results from a deletion (loss of a chromosome segment; Thompson et al, 1991). The syndrome may also result from a teratogen acting during the fourth to sixth weeks, when the pharyngeal arches are transforming into adult derivatives.

Ectopic Parathyroid Glands

The parathyroids are highly variable in number (two to six) and location. They may be found anywhere near or within the thyroid glands or thymus (Fig. 11–16). The superior glands are more constant in position than the inferior ones (Moore, 1992). Occasionally an inferior parathyroid gland fails to descend and remains near the bifurcation of the common carotid artery. In other cases it may accompany the thymus into the thorax.

Abnormal Number of Parathyroid Glands

Uncommonly there are more than four parathyroid glands. Supernumerary parathyroid glands probably result from division of the primordia of the original glands. Absence of a parathyroid gland results from failure of one of the primordia to differentiate or because of atrophy of a gland early in development.

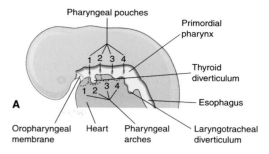

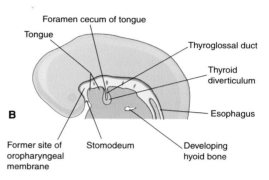

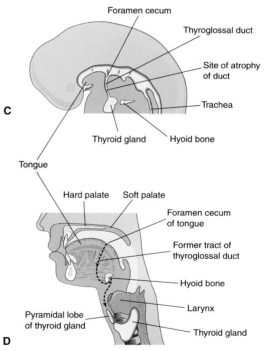

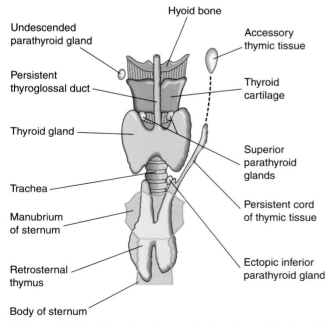

■ **Figure 11–16.** Drawing of an anterior view of the thyroid gland, thymus, and parathyroid glands illustrating various congenital anomalies that occur.

■ **Figure 11–17.** Development of the thyroid gland. *A, B,* and *C,* Schematic sagittal sections of the head and neck regions of embryos at 4, 5, and 6 weeks, illustrating successive stages in the development of the thyroid gland. *D,* Similar section of an adult head and neck, showing the path taken by the thyroid gland during its embryonic descent (indicated by the former tract of the thyroglossal duct).

DEVELOPMENT OF THE THYROID GLAND

The thyroid gland is the first endocrine gland to develop in the embryo. It begins to form about 24 days after fertilization from a median endodermal thickening in the floor of the primordial pharynx (Fig. 11–17A). This thickening soon forms a small outpouching—the **thyroid diverticulum**. As the embryo and tongue grow, the developing thyroid gland descends in the neck, passing ventral to the developing hyoid bone and laryngeal cartilages. For a short time the developing thyroid gland is connected to the tongue by a narrow tube, the **thyroglossal duct** (Fig. 11–17B and C).

At first the thyroid diverticulum is hollow, but it soon becomes solid and divides into right and left lobes that are connected by the *isthmus of the thyroid gland*, which lies anterior to the developing second and third tracheal rings. By 7 weeks the thyroid gland has assumed its definitive shape and has usually reached its final site in the neck (Fig. 11–17D). By this time the thyroglossal duct has normally degenerated and disappeared. The proximal opening of the thyroglossal duct persists as a small blind pit, the **foramen cecum of the tongue**. A pyramidal lobe extends superiorly from the isthmus in about 50% of people. The **pyramidal lobe** may be attached to the hyoid

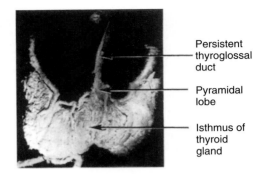

Figure 11–18. Photograph of the anterior surface of a dissected adult thyroid gland, showing persistence of the thyroglossal duct. Observe the pyramidal lobe ascending from the superior border of the isthmus. It represents a persistent portion of the inferior end of the thyroglossal duct.

bone by fibrous and/or some smooth muscle—the **levator glandulae thyroideae**. A pyramidal lobe and the associated smooth muscle represent a persistent part of the distal end of the thyroglossal duct (Fig. 11–18).

During the 11th week colloid begins to appear in the **thyroid follicles**; thereafter, iodine concentration and the synthesis of *thyroid hormones* can be demon-

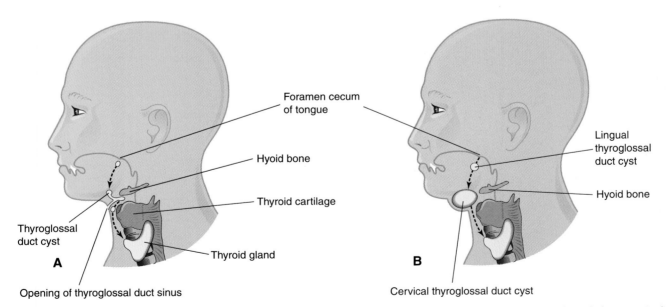

Figure 11–19. *A,* Diagrammatic sketch of the head and neck showing the possible locations of thyroglossal duct cysts. A thyroglossal duct sinus is also illustrated. The broken line indicates the course taken by the thyroglossal duct during descent of the developing thyroid gland from the foramen cecum to its final position in the anterior part of the neck. *B,* Similar sketch illustrating lingual and cervical thyroglossal duct cysts. Most thyroglossal duct cysts are located just inferior to the hyoid bone.

strated. Studies have shown that an insulin-like **epidermal growth factor**, as well as other related factors, are involved in the replication and growth of thyroid follicular cells (Fisher and Polk, 1989).

Thyroglossal Duct Cysts and Sinuses

Cysts may form anywhere along the course followed by the thyroglossal duct during descent of the thyroid gland from the tongue (Fig. 11-19A and B). Normally the thyroglossal duct atrophies and disappears, but a remnant of it may persist and form a cyst in the tongue (Urao et al, 1996) or in the anterior part of the neck, usually just inferior to the hyoid bone (Fig. 11-20). Most thyroglossal duct cysts are observed by the age of 5 years. Unless the lesions become infected, most of them are asymptomatic. The swelling produced by a *thyroglossal duct cyst* usually develops as a painless, progressively enlarging, movable mass (Fig. 11-21). The cyst may contain some thyroid tissue (Johnson et al, 1996). Following infection of a cyst, a perforation of the skin occurs in some cases, forming a **thyroglossal duct sinus** that usually opens in the median plane of the neck, anterior to the laryngeal cartilages (Fig. 11-19A).

Ectopic Thyroid Gland

An ectopic thyroid gland is an infrequent congenital anomaly and is usually located along the normal route of its descent from the tongue (Fig. 11-17C). **Lingual thyroid glandular tissue** is the most common type of ectopic thyroid tissues; intralingual thyroid masses are found in as many as 10% of autopsies, although they are clinically relevant in only 1 in 4000 patients with thyroid disease (Spinner et al, 1994). Incomplete descent of the thyroid gland results in a **sublingual thyroid gland** appearing high in the neck, at or just inferior to the hyoid bone (Figs. 11-22 and 11-23). As a rule, an ectopic sublingual thyroid gland in the neck is the only thyroid tissue present. It is clinically important to differentiate an ectopic thyroid gland from a thyroglossal duct cyst or an accessory thyroid gland in order to prevent *inadvertent surgical removal of the thyroid gland* (Leung et al, 1995) because this may be the only thyroid tissue present. Failure to recognize the thyroid gland may leave the person permanently dependent on thyroid medication.

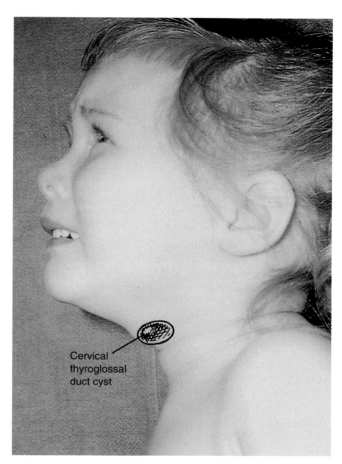

Cervical thyroglossal duct cyst

■ **Figure 11-20.** Typical thyroglossal duct cyst in a female child. The round, firm mass (indicated by the sketch) produced a swelling in the median plane of the neck just inferior to the hyoid bone.

DEVELOPMENT OF THE TONGUE

Near the end of the fourth week, a median triangular elevation appears in the floor of the primordial pharynx, just rostral to the foramen cecum (Fig. 11-24A). This swelling—the **median tongue bud** (tuberculum impar)—is the first indication of tongue development. Soon, two oval **distal tongue buds** (lateral lingual swellings) develop on each side of the median tongue bud. The three lingual buds result from the proliferation of mesenchyme in ventromedial parts of the first pair of pharyngeal arches. The distal tongue buds rapidly increase in size, merge with each other, and overgrow the median tongue bud. *The merged distal tongue buds form the anterior two thirds (oral part) of the tongue* (Fig. 11-24C). The plane of fusion of the distal tongue buds is indicated superficially by the

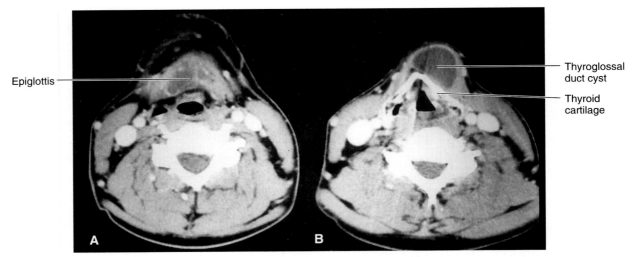

Epiglottis

Thyroglossal duct cyst

Thyroid cartilage

■ **Figure 11–21.** Computed tomographic (CT) images. *A,* Level of the thyrohyoid membrane and base of the epiglottis. *B,* Level of thyroid cartilage which is calcified. The thyroglossal duct cyst extends cranially to the margin of the hyoid bone. (Courtesy of Dr. Gerald S. Smyser, Altru Health System, Grand Forks, ND.)

median sulcus (groove) of the tongue and internally by the fibrous *lingual septum* (Moore, 1992). The median tongue bud forms no recognizable part of the adult tongue.

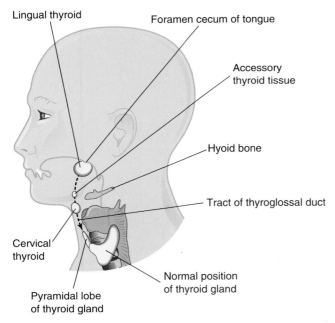

Lingual thyroid

Foramen cecum of tongue

Accessory thyroid tissue

Hyoid bone

Tract of thyroglossal duct

Cervical thyroid

Normal position of thyroid gland

Pyramidal lobe of thyroid gland

■ **Figure 11–22.** Diagrammatic sketch of the head and neck showing the usual sites of ectopic thyroid tissue. The broken line indicates the path followed by the thyroid gland during its descent and the former tract of the thyroglossal duct.

Formation of the posterior third (pharyngeal part) of the tongue is indicated by two elevations that develop caudal to the foramen cecum (Fig. 11–24A):

• The *copula* (L. bond, tie) forms by fusion of the ventromedial parts of the second pair of pharyngeal arches.
• The *hypobranchial eminence* develops caudal to the copula from mesenchyme in the ventromedial parts of the third and fourth pairs of arches.

As the tongue develops, the copula is gradually overgrown by the hypobranchial eminence and disappears (Fig. 11–24B and C). As a result, the pharyngeal part of the tongue develops from the rostral part of the hypobranchial eminence, a derivative of the third pair of pharyngeal arches.

The line of fusion of the anterior and posterior parts of the tongue is roughly indicated by a V-shaped groove — the **terminal sulcus** (Fig. 11–25; see also Fig. 11–24C). Pharyngeal arch mesenchyme forms the connective tissue and vasculature of the tongue. Most of the *tongue muscles* are derived from myoblasts that migrate from the occipital myotomes (Fig. 11–6A). The *hypoglossal nerve* (CN XII) accompanies the myoblasts during their migration and innervates the tongue muscles as they develop. The entire tongue is within the mouth at birth; its posterior third descends into the oropharynx by 4 years of age (Sperber, 1993).

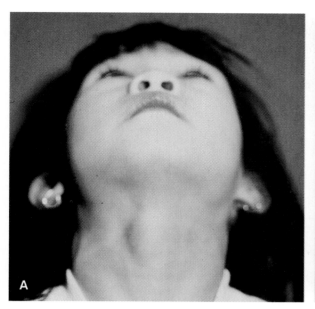
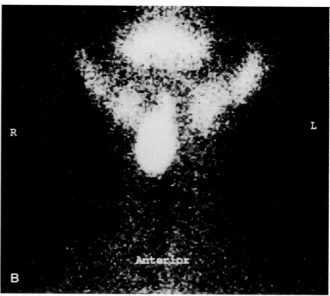

■ **Figure 11–23.** *A,* Photograph of a sublingual thyroid mass in a 5-year-old girl. *B,* Technetium-99m pertechnetate scan showing a sublingual thyroid without evidence of functioning thyroid tissue in lower neck. (From Leung AKC, Wong AL, Robson WLLM: Ectopic thyroid gland simulating a thyroglossal duct cyst: A case report. *Can J Surg* 38:87, 1995.)

Papillae and Taste Buds of the Tongue

The lingual papillae appear toward the end of the eighth week. The *vallate* and *foliate papillae* appear first, close to terminal branches of the glossopharyngeal nerve. The *fungiform papillae* appear later near terminations of the chorda tympani branch of the facial nerve. The most common lingual papillae, known as *filiform papillae* because of their threadlike shape (L. *filum,* thread), develop during the early fetal period (10 to 11 weeks). They contain afferent nerve endings that are *sensitive to touch.* For histologic and anatomic details of the lingual papillae and taste buds, see Cormack (1993) and Gartner and Hiatt (1997).

Taste buds develop during weeks 11 to 13 by inductive interaction between the epithelial cells of the tongue and invading gustatory nerve cells from the chorda tympani, glossopharyngeal, and vagus nerves (Sperber, 1993; Gartner and Hiatt, 1997). Most taste buds form on the dorsal surface of the tongue, and some develop on the palatoglossal arches, palate, posterior surface of the epiglottis, and posterior wall of the oropharynx. The injection of saccharin into the amniotic cavity results in increased swallowing by the fetus (Sperber, 1993). Fetal responses in the face can be induced by bitter-tasting substances at 26 to 28 weeks, indicating that reflex pathways between taste buds and facial muscles are established by this stage.

Nerve Supply of the Tongue

The development of the tongue explains its nerve supply. The sensory nerve supply to the mucosa of almost the entire *anterior two thirds of the tongue* (oral part) is from the lingual branch of the mandibular division of the *trigeminal nerve,* the nerve of the first pharyngeal arch, which forms the median and distal tongue buds (Fig. 11-24). Although the facial nerve is the nerve of the second pharyngeal arch, its chorda tympani branch supplies the taste buds in the anterior two thirds of the tongue, except for the vallate papillae. Because the second arch component, the copula, is overgrown by the third arch, the facial nerve does not supply any of the tongue mucosa, except for the taste buds in the oral part of the tongue. The *vallate papillae* in the oral part of the tongue (Fig. 11-25) are innervated by the *glossopharyngeal nerve* of the third pharyngeal arch (Fig. 11-24C). The reason usually given for this is that the mucosa of the posterior third of the tongue is pulled slightly anteriorly as the tongue develops. The *posterior third of the tongue* (pharyngeal part) is innervated mainly by the *glossopharyngeal nerve* of the third pharyngeal arch. The superior laryngeal branch of the vagus nerve of the fourth arch supplies a small area of the tongue anterior to the epiglottis (Fig. 11-24C). All **muscles of the tongue** are supplied by the *hypoglossal nerve*

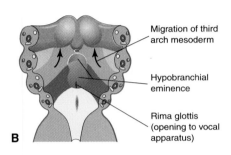

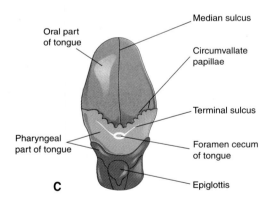

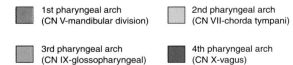

Arch Derivatives of Tongue

■ 1st pharyngeal arch (CN V-mandibular division)

■ 2nd pharyngeal arch (CN VII-chorda tympani)

■ 3rd pharyngeal arch (CN IX-glossopharyngeal)

■ 4th pharyngeal arch (CN X-vagus)

■ **Figure 11–24.** *A* and *B,* Schematic horizontal sections through the pharynx at the level shown in Figure 11–4*A,* showing successive stages in the development of the tongue during the fourth and fifth weeks. *C,* Drawing of the adult tongue showing the pharyngeal arch derivation of the nerve supply of its mucosa.

(CN XII), except for the palatoglossus, which is supplied from the pharyngeal plexus by fibers arising from the *vagus nerve.*

Congenital Anomalies of the Tongue

Abnormalities of the tongue are uncommon, except for fissuring of the tongue and hypertrophy of the lingual papillae, which are characteristics of infants with Down syndrome (see Chapter 9).

Congenital Lingual Cysts and Fistulas

Cysts in the tongue may be derived from remnants of the thyroglossal duct (Fig. 11–19). They may enlarge and produce symptoms of pharyngeal discomfort and/or *dysphagia* (difficulty in swallowing). Fistulas are also derived from persistence of lingual parts of the thyroglossal duct; they open through the *foramen cecum* into the oral cavity.

Ankyloglossia (Tongue-Tie)

The lingual frenulum normally connects the inferior surface of the tongue to the floor of the mouth (Moore, 1992). Sometimes the frenulum is short and extends to the tip of the tongue (Gr. glōssa). This interferes with its free protrusion and may make breast feeding difficult. Tongue-tie occurs in about 1 in 300 North American infants but is usually of no functional significance (Behrman et al, 1996). A short frenulum usually stretches with time, making surgical correction of the anomaly unnecessary.

DEVELOPMENT OF THE SALIVARY GLANDS

During the sixth and seventh weeks, the salivary glands begin as solid epithelial buds from the primordial oral cavity (Fig. 11–7*C*). The club-shaped ends of these epithelial buds grow into the underlying mesenchyme. The connective tissue in the glands is de-

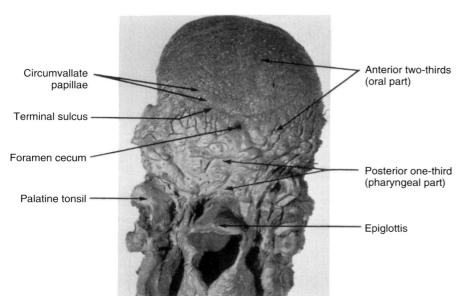

Circumvallate papillae

Terminal sulcus

Foramen cecum

Palatine tonsil

Anterior two-thirds (oral part)

Posterior one-third (pharyngeal part)

Epiglottis

■ **Figure 11–25.** Photograph of the dorsum of an adult tongue (cadaveric specimen). The foramen cecum indicates the site of origin of the thyroid diverticulum and thyroglossal duct in the embryo. The terminal sulcus demarcates the developmentally different pharyngeal and oral parts of the tongue.

rived from neural crest cells. All parenchymal (secretory) tissue arises by proliferation of the oral epithelium.

The **parotid glands** are the first to appear (early in the sixth week). They develop from buds that arise from the oral ectodermal lining near the angles of the stomodeum. The buds grow toward the ears and branch to form solid cords with rounded ends. Later the cords canalize — develop lumina — and become ducts by about 10 weeks. The rounded ends of the cords differentiate into acini. Secretions commence at 18 weeks (Sperber, 1993). The capsule and connective tissue develop from the surrounding mesenchyme.

The **submandibular glands** appear late in the sixth week. They develop from endodermal buds in the floor of the stomodeum. Solid cellular processes grow posteriorly, lateral to the developing tongue. Later they branch and differentiate. Acini begin to form at 12 weeks, and secretory activity begins at 16 weeks (Sperber, 1993). Growth of the submandibular glands continues after birth with the formation of mucous acini. Lateral to the tongue, a linear groove forms that soon closes over to form the *submandibular duct*.

The **sublingual glands** appear in the eighth week, about 2 weeks later than the other salivary glands. They develop from multiple endodermal epithelial buds in the paralingual sulcus (Fig. 11–7C). These buds branch and canalize to form 10 to 12 ducts that open independently into the floor of the mouth.

DEVELOPMENT OF THE FACE

The facial primordia begin to appear early in the fourth week around the large *stomodeum* (Fig. 11–26A and B). Facial development depends upon the inductive influence of the prosencephalic and rhombencephalic organizing centers (Sperber, 1993). The **prosencephalic organizing center**, derived from prechordal mesoderm that migrates from the primitive streak, is located rostral to the notochord and ventral to the prosencephalon or forebrain (see Chapter 19). The **rhombencephalic organizing center** is ventral to the rhombencephalon (hindbrain).

The **five facial primordia** appear as prominences around the stomodeum:

- The single frontonasal prominence
- The paired maxillary prominences
- The paired mandibular prominences

The paired prominences are derivatives of the first pair of pharyngeal arches. The prominences are produced by mesenchyme derived from **neural crest cells** that migrate into the arches during the fourth week of development. These cells are the major source of connective tissue components, including cartilage, bone, and ligaments in the facial and oral regions.

The **frontonasal prominence** (FNP) surrounds the ventrolateral part of the forebrain, which gives rise to the *optic vesicles* that form the eyes (Figs. 11–26A to C and 11–27). The frontal portion of the FNP forms

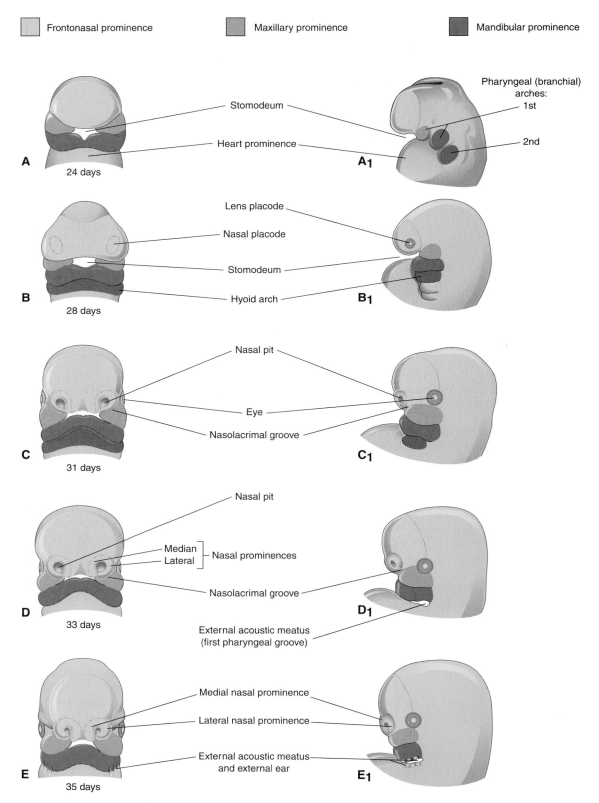

Figure 11-26. Diagrams illustrating progressive stages in the development of the human face.

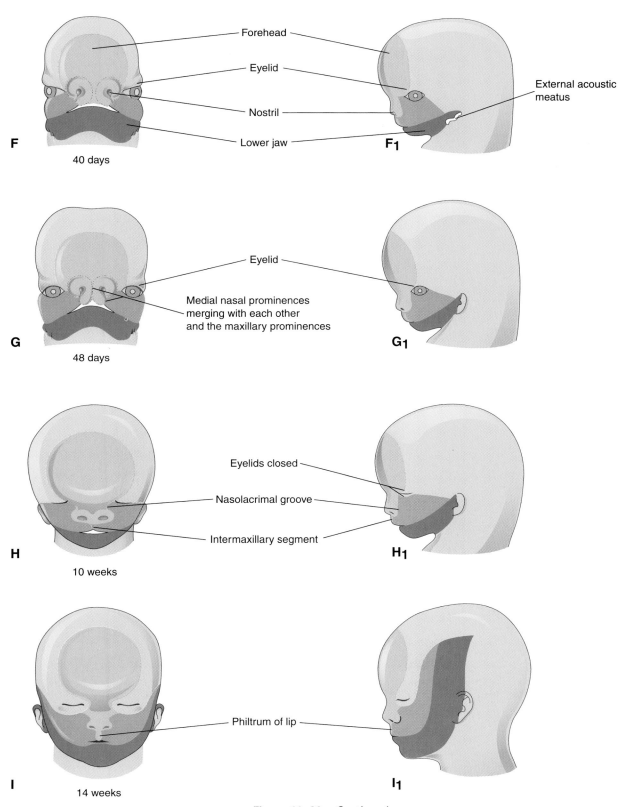

F   Forehead   F₁   External acoustic meatus

Eyelid

Nostril

Lower jaw

40 days

G   Eyelid   G₁

Medial nasal prominences merging with each other and the maxillary prominences

48 days

H   Eyelids closed   H₁

Nasolacrimal groove

Intermaxillary segment

10 weeks

I   Philtrum of lip   I₁

14 weeks

■ **Figure 11–26.** *Continued*

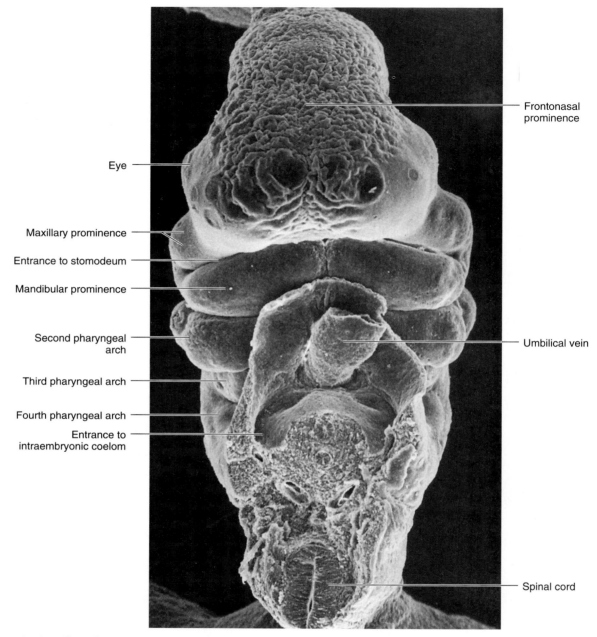

Frontonasal prominence

Eye

Maxillary prominence

Entrance to stomodeum

Mandibular prominence

Second pharyngeal arch

Third pharyngeal arch

Fourth pharyngeal arch

Entrance to intraembryonic coelom

Umbilical vein

Spinal cord

■ **Figure 11–27.** Scanning electron micrograph of a ventral view of a stage 14 embryo (30 to 32 days). (Courtesy of Professor Emeritus Dr. KV Hinrichsen, Medizinische Fakultät, Institut für Anatomie, Ruhr-Universität Bochum, Germany.)

the forehead; the nasal part of the FNP forms the rostral boundary of the stomodeum and nose. The **maxillary prominences** form the lateral boundaries of the stomodeum, and the **mandibular prominences** constitute the caudal boundary of the primitive mouth (Fig. 11–27). The five facial prominences are active **centers of growth** in the underlying mes- enchyme. This embryonic connective tissue is continu- ous from one prominence to the other. Facial develop- ment occurs mainly between the fourth and eighth weeks (Fig. 11–26A to G). By the end of the embry- onic period the face has an unquestionably human appearance. Facial proportions develop during the fe- tal period (Fig. 11–26H and I). The lower jaw and lower lip are the first parts of the face to form. They result from merging of the medial ends of the mandibular prominences in the median plane.

By the end of the fourth week, bilateral oval thickenings of the surface ectoderm — **nasal placodes** (primordia of the nose and nasal cavities) — have developed on the inferolateral parts of the frontonasal prominence (Figs. 11–28 and 11–29A and B). Initially these placodes are convex, but later they are stretched to produce a flat depression in each placode (Hinrichsen, 1985). Mesenchyme in the margins of the

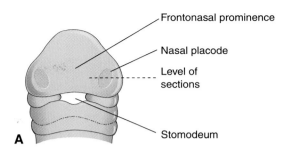

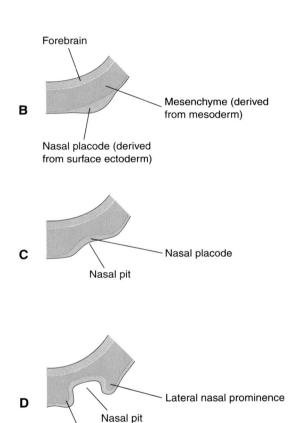

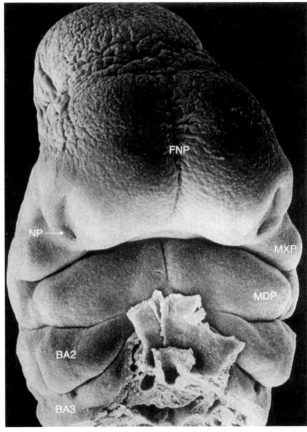

■ **Figure 11–28.** Scanning electron micrograph of a ventral view of a human embryo of about 33 days (Stage 15, CRL 8 mm). Observe the prominent frontonasal process (FNP) surrounding the telencephalon (forebrain). Also observe the nasal pits (NP) located in the ventrolateral regions of the frontonasal prominence. Medial and lateral nasal prominences surround these pits. The cuneiform, wedge-shaped maxillary prominences (MXP) form the lateral boundaries of the stomodeum. The fusing mandibular prominences (MDP) are located just caudal to the stomodeum. The second pharyngeal arch (BA2) is clearly visible and shows overhanging margins (opercula). The third pharyngeal arch (BA3) is also clearly visible. (From Hinrichsen K: The early development of morphology and patterns of the face in the human embryo. *Adv Anat Embryol Cell Biol* 98:1, 1985.)

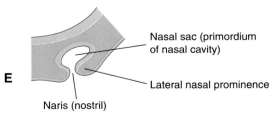

■ **Figure 11–29.** Progressive stages in the development of a human nasal sac (future nasal cavity). *A,* Ventral view of embryo of about 28 days. *B* to *E,* Transverse sections through the left side of the developing nasal sac.

placodes proliferates, producing horseshoe-shaped elevations — the **medial and lateral nasal prominences** (Fig. 11-29D and E). As a result, the nasal placodes now lie in depressions, called **nasal pits** (Fig. 11-29C and D). These pits are the primordia of the anterior nares (nostrils) and nasal cavities (Fig. 11-29E).

Proliferation of mesenchyme in the maxillary prominences causes them to enlarge and grow medially toward each other and the nasal prominences (Figs. 11-26D to G, 11-27, and 11-28). The medial migration of the maxillary prominences moves the medial nasal prominences toward the median plane and each other. Each lateral nasal prominence is separated from the maxillary prominence by a cleft called the **nasolacrimal groove** (Fig. 11-26C and D).

By the end of the fifth week, the *primordia of the auricles* of the external ears have begun to develop (Fig. 11-30; see also Fig. 11-26E). Six **auricular hillocks** (small mesenchymal swellings) form around the first pharyngeal groove (three on each side), the primordia of the auricle, and the external acoustic meatus (canal), respectively. Initially the external ears are located in the neck region (Fig. 11-31); however, as the mandible develops they ascend to the side of the head at the level of the eyes (Fig. 11-26H). By the end of the sixth week, each maxillary prominence has begun to merge with the lateral nasal prominence along the line of the **nasolacrimal groove** (Figs. 11-32 and 11-33A and B). This establishes continuity between the side of the nose, formed by the lateral nasal prominence, and the cheek region formed by the maxillary prominence.

The **nasolacrimal duct** develops from a rodlike thickening of ectoderm in the floor of the nasolacrimal groove. This thickening gives rise to a solid epithelial cord that separates from the ectoderm and sinks into the mesenchyme. Later, as a result of cell degeneration, this epithelial cord canalizes to form the nasolacrimal duct. The cranial end of this duct expands to form the **lacrimal sac**. By the late fetal period, the nasolacrimal duct drains into the inferior meatus in the lateral wall of the nasal cavity (Moore, 1992). The duct usually becomes completely patent only after birth. Part of the nasolacrimal duct occasionally fails to canalize, resulting in a congenital anomaly — *atresia of the nasolacrimal duct*.

During the seventh week the blood supply of the face shifts from the internal to the external carotid artery (Sperber, 1993). This change is related to transformation of the primordial aortic arch pattern into the postnatal arterial arrangement. Between the 7th and 10th weeks, the medial nasal prominences merge with each other and with the maxillary and lateral nasal prominences (Fig. 11-26G and H). Merging of these

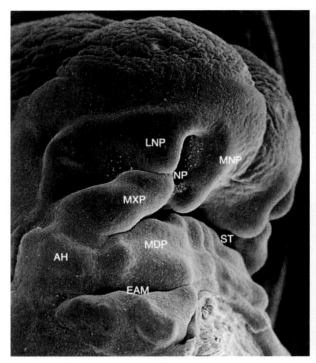

■ **Figure 11-30.** Scanning electron micrograph of the craniofacial region of a human embryo of about 41 days (Stage 16, CRL 10.8 mm) viewed obliquely. The maxillary prominence (MXP) appears puffed up laterally and is wedged between the lateral (LNP) and medial (MNP) nasal prominences surrounding the nasal pit (NP). Observe the mandibular prominence (MDP) and the stomodeum (ST) just above it. The auricular hillocks (AH) can be seen on both sides of the groove between the mandibular and hyoid arches, which will form the external acoustic meatus (EAM). (From Hinrichsen K: The early development of morphology and patterns of the face in the human embryo. *Adv Anat Embryol Cell Biol* 98:1, 1985.)

prominences requires disintegration of their contacting surface epithelia. This results in intermingling of the underlying mesenchymal cells. Merging of the medial nasal and maxillary prominences results in continuity of the upper jaw and lip and separation of the nasal pits from the stomodeum.

As the medial nasal prominences merge, they form an intermaxillary segment (Figs. 11-26H and 11-33C to F). The **intermaxillary segment** gives rise to:

- The middle part or philtrum of the upper lip
- The premaxillary part of the maxilla and its associated gingiva (gum)
- The primary palate

Lateral parts of the upper lip, most of the maxilla, and the secondary palate form from the maxillary prominences (Fig. 11-26H). These prominences merge laterally with the mandibular prominences. The primitive lips and cheeks are invaded by mesenchyme from the second pair of pharyngeal arches, which differentiates into the facial muscles (Fig. 11–6 and Table 11–1). These *muscles of facial expression* are supplied by the facial nerve, the nerve of the second arch. The mesenchyme in the first pair of arches differentiates into the *muscles of mastication* and a few others, all of which are innervated by the trigeminal nerves, which supply the first pair of arches.

Summary of Facial Development

- The frontonasal prominence forms the forehead and the dorsum and apex of the nose.
- The lateral nasal prominences form the sides of the nose.
- The medial nasal prominences form the nasal septum.
- The maxillary prominences form the upper cheek regions and most of the upper lip.
- The mandibular prominences give rise to the chin, lower lip, and lower cheek regions (Fig. 11–26).

In addition to these fleshy derivatives, various bones are derived from the mesenchyme in the facial prominences (Fig. 11–33). Until the end of the sixth week,

the primitive jaws are composed of masses of mesenchymal tissue. The lips and *gingivae* begin to develop when a linear thickening of the ectoderm, the *labiogingival lamina*, grows into the underlying mesenchyme (Fig. 11–36B). Gradually, most of the lamina degenerates, leaving a *labiogingival groove* between the lips and the gingivae (Fig. 11–36H). A small area of the labiogingival lamina persists in the median plane to form the *frenulum of the upper lip*, which attaches the lip to the gingiva.

Final development of the face occurs slowly during the fetal period and results mainly from changes in the proportion and relative positions of the facial components. During the early fetal period, the nose is flat and the mandible is underdeveloped (Fig. 11–26H); they obtain their characteristic form as facial development is completed (Fig. 11–26I). As the brain enlarges, a prominent forehead is created and the eyes move medially. As the mandible and head enlarge, the auricles of the external ears rise to the level of the eyes.

The smallness of the face prenatally results from:

- The rudimentary upper and lower jaws
- The unerupted primary teeth
- The small size of the nasal cavities and maxillary sinuses

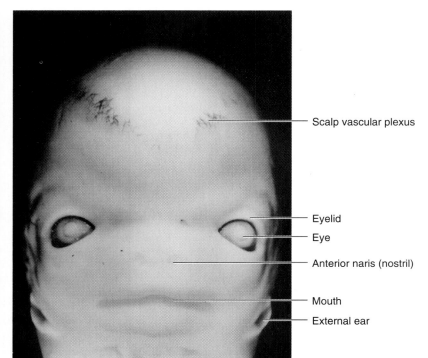

Scalp vascular plexus

Eyelid
Eye

Anterior naris (nostril)

Mouth
External ear

■ **Figure 11–31.** Ventral view of the face of an embryo at Carnegie stage 22, about 54 days. Observe that the eyes are widely separated and the ears low-set at this stage. (From Nishimura H, et al: *Prenatal Development of the Human with Special Reference to Craniofacial Structures: An Atlas.* Bethesda, MD, US Department of Health, Education, and Welfare, National Institutes of Health, 1977.)

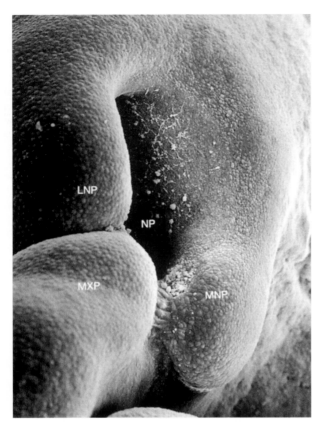

■ **Figure 11–32.** Scanning electron micrograph of the right nasal region of a human embryo of about 41 days (stage 17, CRL 10.8 mm) showing the maxillary prominence (MXP) fusing with the medial nasal prominence (MNP). Observe the large nasal pit (NP). Epithelial bridges can be seen between these prominences. Observe the furrow representing the nasolacrimal groove between the MXP and the lateral nasal prominence (LNP). (From Hinrichsen K: The early development of morphology and patterns of the face in the human embryo. *Adv Anat Embryol Cell Biol* 98:1, 1985.)

DEVELOPMENT OF THE NASAL CAVITIES

As the face develops, the *nasal placodes* become depressed, forming *nasal pits* (Figs. 11-28, 11-29, and 11-32). Proliferation of the surrounding mesenchyme forms the medial and lateral **nasal prominences** and results in deepening of the nasal pits and formation of primordial **nasal sacs.** Each nasal sac grows dorsally, ventral to the developing forebrain (Fig. 11-34A). At first the nasal sacs are separated from the oral cavity by the **oronasal membrane.** This membrane ruptures by the end of the sixth week, bringing the nasal and oral cavities into communication (Fig. 11-34B and *C*). A temporary epithelial plug is formed in the nasal cavity from proliferation of the cells lining it. Between 13 and 15 weeks the nasal plug disappears following its resorption (Nishimura, 1993). The regions of continuity between the nasal and oral cavities are the **primordial choanae,** which lie posterior to the primary palate. After the *secondary palate* develops, the choanae are located at the junction of the nasal cavity and pharynx (Fig. 11-34D).

While these changes are occurring, the *superior, middle, and inferior* **conchae** develop as elevations of the lateral walls of the nasal cavities (Fig. 11-34D). Concurrently the ectodermal epithelium in the roof of each nasal cavity becomes specialized to form the **olfactory epithelium.** Some epithelial cells differentiate into *olfactory receptor cells* (neurons). The axons of these cells constitute the **olfactory nerves,** which grow into the *olfactory bulbs* of the brain (Fig. 11-34C and *D*).

The Paranasal Sinuses

Some paranasal (air) sinuses begin to develop during late fetal life, especially the maxillary sinuses; the remainder of them develop after birth. They form from outgrowths or diverticula of the walls of the nasal cavities and become pneumatic (air-filled) extensions of the nasal cavities in the adjacent bones, such as the maxillary sinuses in the maxillae and the frontal sinuses in the frontal bones. The original openings of the diverticula persist as the orifices of the adult sinuses.

Paranasal Sinuses in the Newborn and Postnatal Development

Most of the paranasal sinuses are rudimentary or absent in newborn infants. The *maxillary sinuses* are small at birth (3 to 4 mm in diameter). They grow slowly until puberty and are not fully developed until all the permanent teeth have erupted in early adulthood. No frontal or sphenoidal sinuses are present at birth. The ethmoidal cells (sinuses) are small before the age of 2 years, and they do not begin to grow rapidly until 6 to 8 years of age. Around the age of 2 years, the two most anterior ethmoidal cells grow into the frontal bone, forming a frontal sinus on each side. Usually the *frontal sinuses* are visible in radiographs by the seventh year. The two most posterior ethmoidal cells grow into the sphenoid bone at about the age of 2 years, forming two *sphenoidal sinuses*. Growth of the paranasal sinuses is important in altering the size and shape of the face during infancy and childhood and in adding resonance to the voice during adolescence.

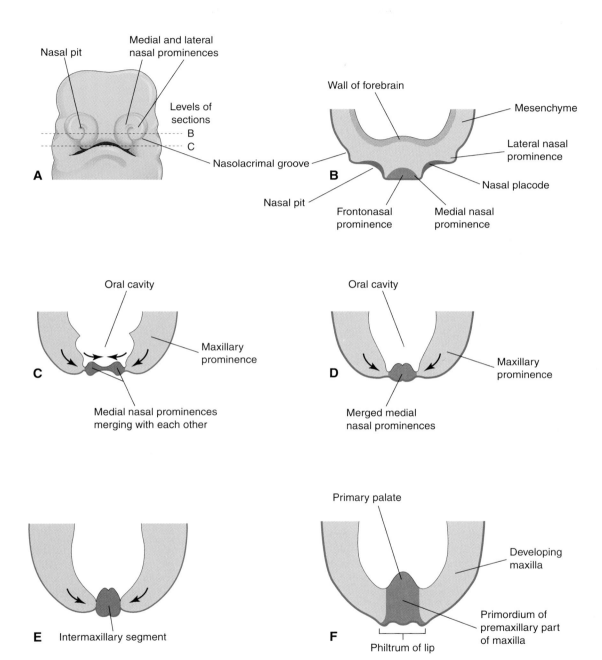

■ **Figure 11–33.** Diagrams illustrating early development of the maxilla, palate, and upper lip. *A,* Facial view of a 5-week embryo. *B* and *C,* Sketches of horizontal sections at the levels shown in *A.* The arrows in *C* indicate subsequent growth of the maxillary and medial nasal prominences toward the median plane and merging of the prominences with each other. *D* to *F,* Similar sections of older embryos illustrating merging of the medial nasal prominences with each other and the maxillary prominences to form the upper lip.

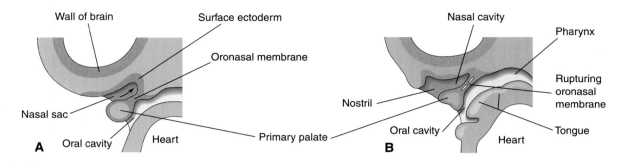

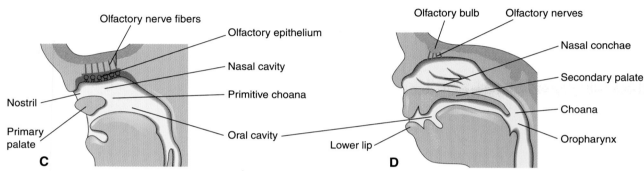

■ **Figure 11–34.** Drawings of sagittal sections of the head showing development of the nasal cavities. The nasal septum has been removed. *A,* Five weeks. *B,* Six weeks, showing breakdown of the oronasal membrane. *C,* Seven weeks, showing the nasal cavity communicating with the oral cavity and development of the olfactory epithelium. *D,* Twelve weeks, showing the palate and the lateral wall of the nasal cavity.

DEVELOPMENT OF THE PALATE

The palate develops from two primordia:

- The primary palate
- The secondary palate

Palatogenesis begins at the end of the fifth week; however, development of the palate is not completed until the 12th week. The *critical period of development of the palate* is from the end of the sixth week until the beginning of the ninth week.

The Primary Palate

Early in the sixth week the primary palate (median palatine process) begins to develop from the deep part of the *intermaxillary segment of the maxilla* (Figs. 11–33*F* and 11–34). Initially this segment, formed by merging of the medial nasal prominences, is a wedge-shaped mass of mesenchyme between the internal surfaces of the maxillary prominences of the developing maxillae. The primary palate forms the *premaxillary part of the maxilla* (Fig. 11–35*A* and *B*). It represents only a small part of the adult hard palate (i.e., the part anterior to the incisive fossa).

The Secondary Palate

The secondary palate is the primordium of the hard and soft parts of the palate that extend posteriorly from the **incisive fossa** (Fig. 11–35*A* and *B*). The secondary palate begins to develop early in the sixth week from two mesenchymal projections that extend from the internal aspects of the maxillary prominences. Initially these structures — the **lateral palatine processes,** or palatal shelves — project inferomedially on each side of the tongue (Figs. 11–36*A* to *C* and 11–37*A* and *B*). As the jaws develop, the tongue becomes relatively smaller and moves inferiorly. During the seventh and eighth weeks, the lateral palatine processes elongate and ascend to a horizontal position superior to the tongue (Sandham, 1985). Gradually the processes (shelves) approach each other and fuse in the median plane (Figs. 11-36E to H and 11-37C). They also fuse with the nasal septum and the posterior part of the primary palate. Elevation of the palatal processes or shelves to the horizontal position is believed to be caused by an intrinsic *shelf-elevating force* that is generated by the hydration of hyaluronic acid in the mesenchymal cells within the palatal processes (Ferguson, 1988).

The **nasal septum** develops as a downgrowth from internal parts of the merged medial nasal prominences (see Figs. 11-36 and 11-37). The fusion between the nasal septum and the palatine processes begins anteriorly during the 9th week and is completed posteriorly by the 12th week, superior to the primordium of the hard palate.

Bone gradually develops in the primary palate, forming the premaxillary part of the maxilla, which lodges the incisor teeth (see Fig. 11-35B). Concurrently, bone extends from the maxillae and palatine bones into the lateral palatine processes (palatal shelves) to form the **hard palate** (see Fig. 11-36E and G). The posterior parts of these processes do not become ossified. They extend posteriorly beyond the nasal septum and fuse to form the **soft palate**, including its soft conical projection — the **uvula** (Fig. 11-36D, F, and H). The *median palatine raphe* indicates the line of fusion of the lateral palatine processes.

A small **nasopalatine canal** persists in the median plane of the palate between the premaxillary part of the maxilla and the palatine processes of the maxillae. This canal is represented in the adult hard palate by the **incisive fossa** (Fig. 11-35B), which is the common opening for the right and left *incisive canals* (Moore, 1992). An irregular suture runs from the incisive fossa to the alveolar process of the maxilla, between the lateral incisor and canine teeth on each side. It is visible in the anterior region of the palates of young persons. This suture indicates where the embryonic primary and secondary palates fused.

Cleft Lip and Palate

Clefts of the upper lip and palate are common (Thompson et al, 1991; Behrman et al, 1996). The defects are usually classified according to developmental criteria, with the incisive fossa and papilla as reference landmarks (Figs. 11-35B and 11-39A). Cleft lip and palate are especially conspicuous because they result in an abnormal facial appearance and defective speech. There are *two major groups of cleft lip and palate* (Figs. 11-38 to 11-40):

- Clefts involving the upper lip and anterior part of the maxilla, with or without involvement of parts of the remaining hard and soft regions of the palate
- Clefts involving the hard and soft regions of the palate

Anterior cleft anomalies include cleft lip, with or without cleft of the alveolar part of the maxilla. A

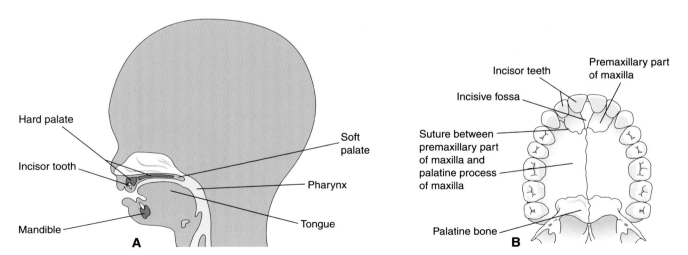

■ **Figure 11-35.** *A,* Drawing of a sagittal section of the head of a 20-week fetus illustrating the location of the palate. *B,* The bony palate and alveolar arch of a young adult. The suture between the premaxillary part of the maxilla and the fused palatine processes of the maxillae is usually visible in skulls of young persons. It is not visible in the hard palates of most dried skulls because they are usually from old adults.

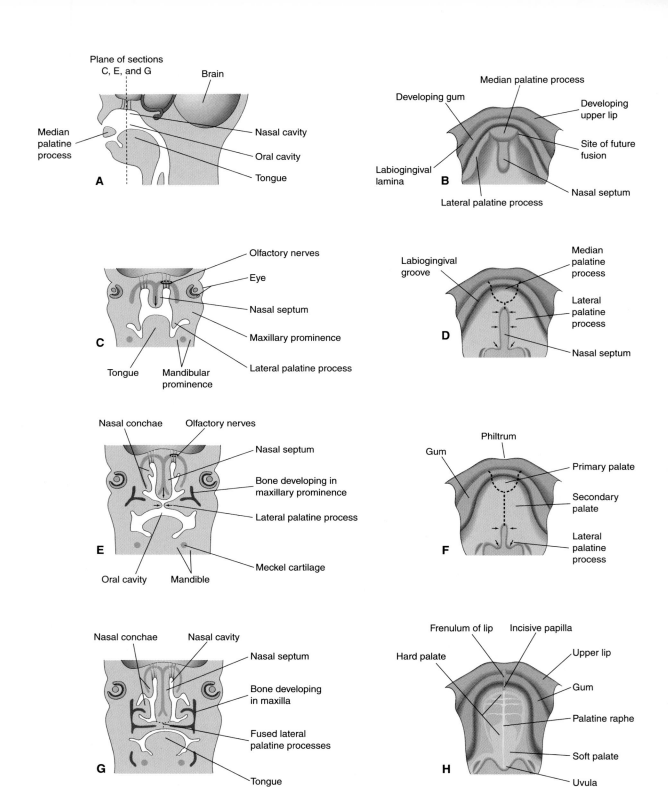

■ **Figure 11–36.** *A*, Sketch of a sagittal section of the embryonic head at the end of the sixth week showing the median palatine process or primary palate. *B, D, F,* and *H,* Drawings of the roof of the mouth from the sixth to twelfth weeks illustrating development of the palate. The broken lines in *D* and *F* indicate sites of fusion of the palatine processes. The arrows indicate medial and posterior growth of the lateral palatine processes. *C, E,* and *G,* Drawings of frontal sections of the head illustrating fusion of the lateral palatine processes with each other and the nasal septum, and separation of the nasal and oral cavities.

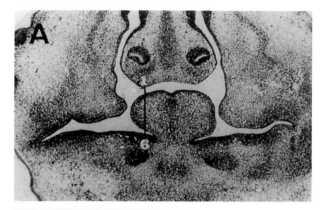

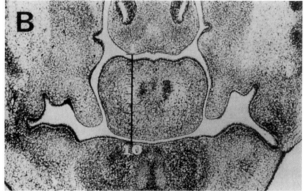

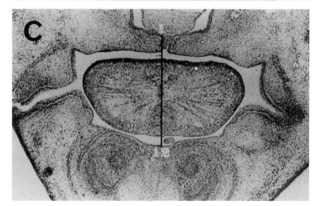

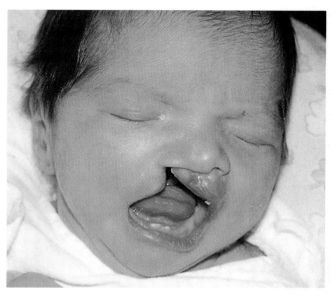

■ Figure 11–38. Infant with unilateral cleft lip and palate. Clefts of the lip, with or without cleft palate, occur about once in 1000 births; 60 to 80% of affected infants are males. (Courtesy of Dr. AE Chudley, Professor of Pediatrics and Child Health, Children's Hospital and University of Manitoba, Winnipeg, Manitoba, Canada.)

■ Figure 11–37. Coronal sections of human embryonic heads showing palatal process (shelf) development during the eighth week. A, Embryo with a crown-rump length (CRL) of 24 mm. This section shows early development of the palatine processes. The scale shows 6 units from the lowest point of the nasal septum to the floor of the oral cavity. B, Embryo with a CRL of 27 mm. This section shows the palate just prior to palatal process elevation. The scale shows 10 units from the lowest point of the nasal septum to the floor of the oral cavity. C, Embryo with a CRL of 29 mm (near the end of the eighth week). The palatine processes are elevated and fused. The scale shows 12 units from the lowest point of the nasal septum to the floor of the oral cavity. (From Sandham A: Embryonic facial vertical dimension and its relationship to palatal shelf elevation. *Early Hum Develop* 12:241, 1985.)

complete anterior cleft anomaly is one in which the cleft extends through the lip and the alveolar part of the maxilla to the incisive fossa, separating the anterior and posterior parts of the palate (Fig. 11–39E and F). Anterior cleft anomalies result from a deficiency of mesenchyme in the maxillary prominence(s) and the intermaxillary segment (Fig. 11–33E).

Posterior cleft anomalies include clefts of the secondary or posterior palate that extend through the soft and hard regions of the palate to the incisive fossa, separating the anterior and posterior parts of the palate (Fig. 11–39G and H). Posterior cleft anomalies are caused by defective development of the secondary palate and result from growth distortions of the lateral palatine processes which prevent their medial migration and fusion.

Clefts involving the upper lip, with or without cleft palate, occur about once in 1000 births; however, their frequency varies widely among ethnic groups (Thompson et al, 1991); 60 to 80% of affected infants are males. The clefts vary from small notches of the vermilion border of the lip (Fig. 11–40B) to larger ones that extend into the floor of the nostril and through the alveolar part of the maxilla (Figs. 11–39 and 11–40A, C, and D). Cleft lip can be unilateral or bilateral.

Unilateral cleft lip (Figs. 11–38 and 11–40A) results from failure of the maxillary prominence on the affected side to unite with the merged medial nasal prominences (Fig. 11–41*A* to *H*). This is the consequence of failure of the mesenchymal masses to merge and the mesenchyme to proliferate and smooth out the overlying epithelium. This results in a *persistent labial groove*. In addition, the epithelium in the labial groove becomes stretched, and the tissues in the floor of the persistent groove break down. As a result, the

lip is divided into medial and lateral parts. Sometimes a bridge of tissue, a **Simonart band**, joins the parts of the incomplete cleft lip (Fig. 11–40*B*).

Bilateral cleft lip (Figs. 11–40*C* and *D* and 11–42*B*) results from failure of the mesenchymal masses in the maxillary prominences to meet and unite with the merged medial nasal prominences. The epithelium in

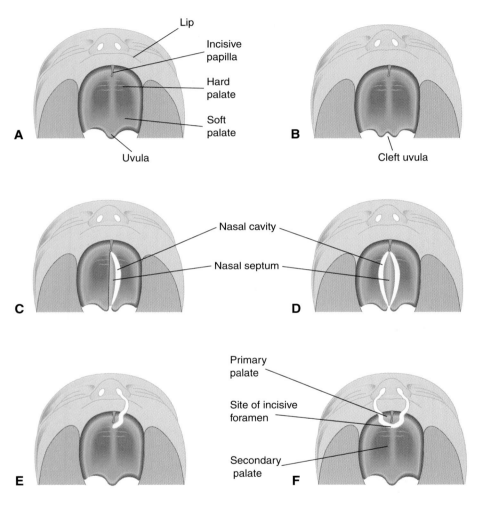

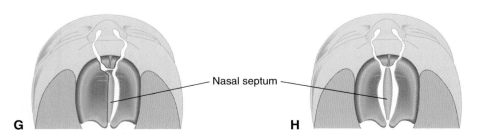

■ **Figure 11–39.** Drawings illustrating various types of cleft lip and palate. *A,* Normal lip and palate. *B,* Cleft uvula. *C,* Unilateral cleft of the posterior or secondary palate. *D,* Bilateral cleft of the posterior palate. *E,* Complete unilateral cleft of the lip and alveolar process of the maxilla with a unilateral cleft of the anterior or primary palate. *F,* Complete bilateral cleft of the lip and alveolar processes of the maxillae with bilateral cleft of the anterior palate. *G,* Complete bilateral cleft of the lip and alveolar processes of the maxillae with bilateral cleft of the anterior palate and unilateral cleft of the posterior palate. *H,* Complete bilateral cleft of the lip and alveolar processes of the maxillae with complete bilateral cleft of the anterior and posterior palate.

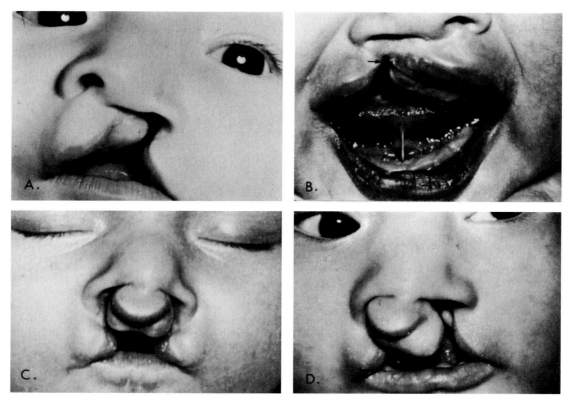

■ **Figure 11–40.** Photographs illustrating various types of cleft lip. *A* and *B*, Unilateral cleft lip. The cleft in *B* is incomplete; the arrow indicates a band of tissue (Simonart band) connecting the cleft parts of the lip. *C* and *D*, Bilateral cleft lip. (Courtesy of Dr. DA Kernahan, The Children's Memorial Hospital, Chicago.)

both labial grooves becomes stretched and breaks down. In bilateral cases the defects may be dissimilar, with varying degrees of defect on each side. When there is a complete bilateral cleft of the lip and alveolar part of the maxilla, the intermaxillary segment hangs free and projects anteriorly. These defects are especially deforming because of the loss of continuity of the *orbicularis oris muscle*, which closes the mouth and purses the lips as occurs when whistling (Moore, 1992).

Median cleft of the upper lip is an extremely rare defect (Fig. 11–43*A*). It results from a mesenchymal deficiency, which causes partial or complete failure of the medial nasal prominences to merge and form the intermaxillary segment. A median cleft of the lip is a characteristic feature of the *Mohr syndrome*, which is transmitted as an autosomal recessive trait (Gorlin et al, 1990). **Median cleft of the lower lip** (Fig. 11–43*B*) is also very rare and is caused by failure of the mesenchymal masses in the mandibular prominences to merge completely and smooth out the embryonic cleft between them.

A **complete cleft palate** indicates the maximal degree of clefting of any particular type; for example, a *complete cleft of the posterior palate* is an anomaly in which the cleft extends through the soft palate and anteriorly to the incisive fossa. The landmark for distinguishing anterior from posterior cleft anomalies is the *incisive fossa*. Anterior and posterior cleft anomalies are embryologically distinct.

Cleft palate, with or without cleft lip, occurs about once in 2500 births and is more common in females than in males. The cleft may involve only the uvula, giving it a fishtail appearance (Fig. 11–39*B*), or it may extend through the soft and hard regions of the palate (Figs. 11–39*C* and *D* and 11–42*C* and *D*). In severe cases associated with cleft lip, the cleft in the palate extends through the alveolar part of the maxilla and the lips on both sides (Figs. 11–39*G* and *H* and 11–42*A* and *B*).

The embryological basis of cleft palate is failure of the mesenchymal masses in the lateral palatine processes to meet and fuse with each other, with the nasal septum, and/or with the posterior margin of the median palatine process (Figs. 11–33*D* and 11–39). Unilateral and bilateral clefts in the palate are classified into three groups:

• *Clefts of the anterior (primary) palate* (i.e., clefts anterior to the incisive fossa) result from failure of mesenchymal masses in the lateral palatine proc-

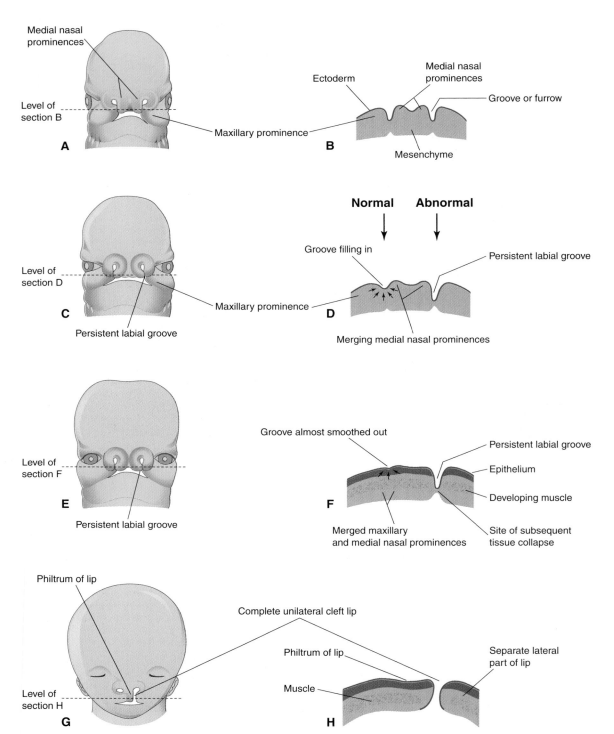

■ **Figure 11–41.** Drawings illustrating the embryological basis of complete unilateral cleft lip. *A,* Five-week embryo. *B,* Horizontal section through the head illustrating the grooves between the maxillary prominences and the merging medial nasal prominences. *C,* Six-week embryo showing a persistent labial groove on the left side. *D,* Horizontal section through the head showing the groove gradually filling in on the right side following proliferation of mesenchyme (*arrows*). *E,* Seven-week embryo. *F,* Horizontal section through the head showing that the epithelium on the right has almost been pushed out of the groove between the maxillary and medial nasal prominences. *G,* Ten-week fetus with a complete unilateral cleft lip. *H,* Horizontal section through the head after stretching of the epithelium and breakdown of the tissues in the floor of the persistent labial groove on the left side, forming a complete unilateral cleft lip.

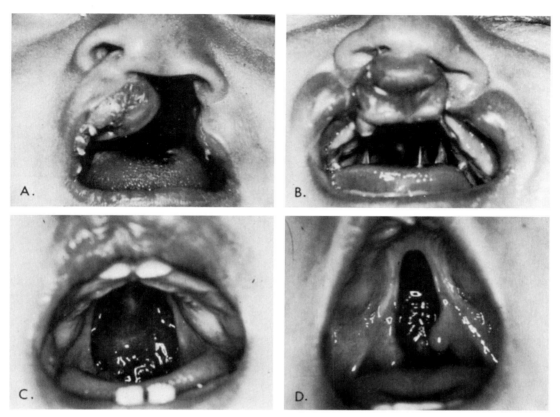

■ **Figure 11–42.** Photographs illustrating congenital anomalies of the lip and palate. *A,* Complete unilateral cleft of the lip and alveolar process. *B,* Complete bilateral cleft of the lip and alveolar process with bilateral cleft of the anterior palate. *C* and *D,* Bilateral cleft of the posterior or secondary palate; the lip is normal.

esses (palatine shelves) to meet and fuse with the mesenchyme in the primary palate (Fig. 11–39*E* and *F*).

- *Clefts of the posterior (secondary) palate* (i.e., clefts posterior to the incisive fossa) result from failure of mesenchymal masses in the lateral palatine processes to meet and fuse with each other and the nasal septum (Fig. 11–39*B* to *D*).
- *Clefts of the anterior and posterior parts of the palate* (i.e., clefts of the primary and secondary palates) result from failure of the mesenchymal masses in the lateral palatine processes to meet and fuse with mesenchyme in the primary palate, with each other, and with the nasal septum (Fig. 11–39*G* and *H*).

Most clefts of the lip and palate result from multiple factors (*multifactorial inheritance*; see Chapter 9): genetic and nongenetic, each causing a minor developmental disturbance (Thompson et al, 1991; Behrman et al, 1996). How teratogenic factors induce cleft lip and

palate is still unknown. Experimental studies have given us some insight into the cellular and molecular basis of these defects (Sulik, 1996).

Some clefts of the lip and/or palate appear as part of syndromes determined by single mutant genes (Thompson et al, 1991). Other clefts are parts of chromosomal syndromes, especially *trisomy 13* (see Chapter 9). A few cases of cleft lip and/or palate appear to have been caused by teratogenic agents (e.g., anticonvulsant drugs). Studies of twins indicate that genetic factors are of more importance in cleft lip, with or without cleft palate, than in cleft palate alone. A sibling of a child with a cleft palate has an elevated risk of having a cleft palate but no increased risk of having a cleft lip. A cleft of the lip and alveolar process of the maxilla that continues through the palate is usually transmitted through a male sex-linked gene. When neither parent is affected, the *recurrence risk* in subsequent siblings (brother or sister) is about 4%. For further discussion of recurrence risks, see Thompson et al (1991).

Facial Clefts

Various types of facial cleft may occur, but they are all extremely rare. Severe clefts are usually associated with gross anomalies of the head. *Oblique facial clefts* (orbitofacial fissures) are often bilateral and extend from the upper lip to the medial margin of the orbit (Fig. 11–43C). When this occurs, the nasolacrimal ducts are open grooves (persistent nasolacrimal grooves). Oblique facial clefts associated with cleft lip result from failure of the mesenchymal masses in the maxillary prominences to merge with the lateral and medial nasal prominences. Lateral or transverse facial clefts run from the mouth toward the ear. Bilateral clefts result in a very large mouth, a condition called *macrostomia* (Fig. 11–43D). In severe cases, the clefts in the cheeks extend almost to the ears.

Other Facial Anomalies

Congenital *microstomia* (small mouth) results from excessive merging of the mesenchymal masses in the maxillary and mandibular prominences of the first arch (Fig. 11–43E). In severe cases the abnormality may be associated with underdevelopment (hypoplasia) of the mandible. *Absence of the nose* occurs when no nasal placodes form. A *single nostril* results when only one nasal placode forms. *Bifid nose* results when the medial nasal prominences do not merge completely; the nostrils are widely separated and the nasal bridge is bifid (Fig. 11–43F). In mild forms of bifid nose, a groove is apparent in the tip of the nose.

By the beginning of the second trimester (see Fig. 11–26I), features of the fetal face can be identified sonographically. Using this imaging technique (Fig. 11–44), fetal facial anomalies are readily recognizable (Benacerraf, 1994).

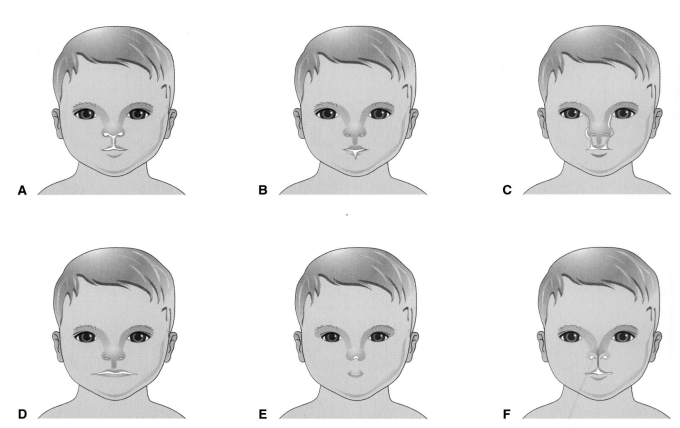

■ **Figure 11–43.** Drawings of unusual congenital anomalies of the face. *A,* Median cleft of the upper lip. *B,* Median cleft of the lower lip. *C,* Bilateral oblique facial clefts with complete bilateral cleft lip. *D,* Macrostomia. *E,* Single nostril and microstomia; these anomalies are not usually associated. *F,* Bifid nose and incomplete median cleft lip.

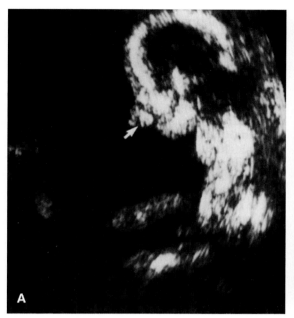
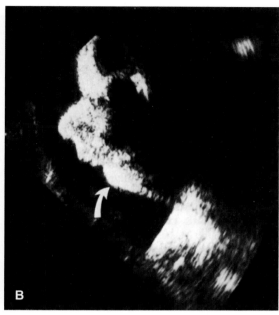

■ **Figure 11–44.** Ultrasound images of the head. *A,* Sagittal view of an early second-trimester fetus with complete bilateral cleft lip and palate showing anterior displacement of the intermaxillary part of the upper lip (*arrow*). (From Benacerraf BR: Ultrasound evaluation of the fetal face. *In* Callen PW (ed): *Ultrasonography in Obstetrics and Gynecology,* 3rd ed. Philadelphia, WB Saunders, 1994.) *B,* Sagittal view of the profile of a third-trimester fetus with trisomy 13, showing severe micrognathia (*arrow*). (From Benacerraf B, Miller W, Frigoletto F: Sonographic detection of fetuses with trisomy 13 and 18: Accuracy and limitations. *Am J Obstet Gynecol* 158:404, 1988.)

SUMMARY OF THE PHARYNGEAL APPARATUS

During the fourth and fifth weeks the primitive pharynx is bounded laterally by *pharyngeal arches*. Each arch consists of a core of mesenchyme covered externally by ectoderm and internally by endoderm. The original mesenchyme of each arch is derived from mesoderm; later *neural crest cells* migrate into the arches and are the major source of their connective tissue components, including cartilage, bone, and ligaments, in the oral and facial regions. Each pharyngeal arch contains an artery, a cartilage rod, a nerve, and a muscular component. Externally the pharyngeal arches are separated by *pharyngeal grooves* (clefts). Internally the arches are separated by evaginations of the pharynx—*pharyngeal pouches*. Where the ectoderm of a groove contacts the endoderm of a pouch, *pharyngeal membranes* are formed. The arches, pouches, grooves, and membranes make up the pharyngeal apparatus. Development of the tongue, face, lips, jaws, palate, pharynx, and neck largely involves transformation of the pharyngeal apparatus into adult structures. The adult derivatives of the various pharyngeal arch components are summarized in Table 11–1, and the derivatives of the pouches are illustrated in Figure 11–8.

The *pharyngeal grooves* disappear except for the first pair, which persists as the *external acoustic meatus*. The pharyngeal membranes also disappear, except for the first pair, which becomes the *tympanic membranes*. The first pharyngeal pouch gives rise to the *tympanic cavity*, mastoid antrum, and pharyngotympanic tube. The second pharyngeal pouch is associated with the development of the palatine tonsil. The *thymus* is derived from the third pair of pharyngeal pouches, and the *parathyroid glands* are formed from the third and fourth pairs of pharyngeal pouches.

The **thyroid gland** develops from a downgrowth from the floor of the primitive pharynx in the region where the tongue develops. The parafollicular (C) cells in the thyroid gland are derived from the *ultimobranchial bodies*, which are derived mainly from the fourth pair of pharyngeal pouches.

Most congenital anomalies of the head and the neck originate during transformation of the pharyngeal apparatus into adult structures. Branchial cysts, sinuses, and fistulas may develop from parts of the second pharyngeal groove, the cervical sinus, or the second pharyngeal pouch which fail to obliterate.

An *ectopic thyroid gland* results when the thyroid gland fails to descend completely from its site of origin in the tongue. The thyroglossal duct may persist, or remnants of it may give rise to *thyroglossal duct cysts* and *ectopic thyroid tissue masses*. Infected cysts may perforate the skin and form *thyroglossal duct sinuses* that open anteriorly in the median plane of the neck.

Because of the complicated development of the face and palate, congenital anomalies of the face and palate are common. Anomalies result from *maldevelopment of neural crest tissue* that gives rise to the skeletal and connective tissue primordia of the face. Neural crest cells may be deficient in number, may not complete their migration to the face, or may fail in their inductive capacity. Anomalies of the face and palate result from an arrest of development and/or a failure of fusion of the facial prominences and palatal processes involved.

Cleft lip is a common congenital anomaly. Although frequently associated with cleft palate, *cleft lip and palate are etiologically distinct anomalies* that involve different developmental processes occurring at different times. Cleft lip results from failure of mesenchymal masses in the medial nasal and maxillary prominences to merge, whereas **cleft palate** results from failure of mesenchymal masses in the palatine processes (palatal shelves) to meet and fuse. Most cases of cleft lip, with or without cleft palate, are caused by a combination of genetic and environmental factors (*multifactorial inheritance*). These factors interfere with the migration of *neural crest cells* into the maxillary prominences of the first pharyngeal arch. If the number of cells is insufficient, clefting of the lip and/or palate may occur. Other cellular and molecular mechanisms may be involved.

Clinically Oriented Questions

1. My mother said that my uncle had a "harelip." What kind of lip defect is this? What is the clinical name for this birth defect?

2. I was told that embryos have cleft lips and that this common facial anomaly represents a persistence of this embryonic condition. Are these statements accurate?

3. Neither my husband nor I have a cleft lip or palate, and no one in our families is known to have or to have had these anomalies. What are our chances of having a child with a cleft lip with or without a cleft palate?

4. I have a son with cleft lip and cleft palate. My brother has a similar defect of his lip and palate. Although I do not plan to have any more children, my husband says that I am entirely to blame for our son's birth defects. Was the defect likely inherited only from my side of the family?

5. My sister's son has minor anomalies of his external ears, but he does not have hearing problems or a facial malformation. Would the ear abnormalities be considered branchial defects?

The answers to these questions are given at the back of the book.

REFERENCES AND SUGGESTED READING

Arreola GA, Serna NP, Parra RH, Salinas MGA: Morphogenesis of the lateral nasal wall from 6 to 36 weeks. *Otolaryngol Head Neck Surg* 114:54, 1996.

Behrman RE, Kliegman RM, Arvin AM (eds): *Nelson Textbook of Pediatrics*, 15th ed. Philadelphia, WB Saunders, 1996.

Benacerraf BR: Ultrasound evaluation of the fetal face. *In* Callen PW (ed): *Ultrasonography in Obstetrics and Gynecology*, 3rd ed. Philadelphia, WB Saunders, 1994.

Bockman DE, Kirby ML: Dependence of thymus development on derivatives of the neural crest. *Science* 223:498, 1984.

Chetty R, Forder MD: Parathyroiditis associated with hyperthyroidism and branchial cysts. *Am J Clin Pathol* 96:348, 1997.

Cormack DH: *Essential Histology*. Philadelphia, JB Lippincott, 1993.

Cote DN, Giandi GJ: Fourth branchial cleft cysts. *Otolaryngol Head Neck Surg* 114:95, 1996.

Ferguson MWJ: Palate development. *Development* 103(Suppl):41, 1988.

Fisher DA, Polk DH: Development of the thyroid. *Bailliere's Clin Endocrinol Metab* 3:627, 1989.

Gartner LP, Hiatt JL: *Color Textbook of Histology*. Philadelphia, WB Saunders, 1997.

Gorlin RJ, Cohen MM Jr, Levin LS: *Syndromes of the Head and Neck*, 3rd ed. New York, Oxford University Press, 1990.

Hall BK: Evolutionary aspects of craniofacial structures and development. *Cleft Palate Craniofac J* 32:520, 1995.

Hall BK, Miyake T: Divide, accumulate, differentiate: Cell condensation in skeletal development revisited. *Int J Dev Biol* 39:881, 1995.

Hinrichsen K: The early development of morphology and patterns of the face in the human embryo. *Adv Anat Embryol Cell Biol* 98:1, 1985.

Johnson IJM, Smith I, Akintunde MO, et al: Assessment of pre-operative investigations of thyroglossal cysts. *JR Coll Surg Edinb* 41:48, 1996.

Källén B, Harris J, Robert E: The epidemiology of orofacial clefts. 2. Associated malformations. *J Craniofac Genet Dev Biol* 16:242, 1996.

Kendall MD: Functional anatomy of the thymic microenvironment. *J Anat* 177:1, 1991.

Kuratani S, Aizawa S: Patterning of the cranial nerves in the chick embryo is dependent on cranial mesoderm and rhombomeric metamerism. *Dev Growth Differ* 37:717, 1995.

Leung AKC, Wong AL, Robson WLLM: Ectopic thyroid gland simulating a thyroglossal duct cyst: A case report. *Can J Surg* 38:87, 1995.

Moore KL: *Clinically Oriented Anatomy*, 3rd ed. Baltimore, Williams & Wilkins, 1992.

Moore KL, Persaud TVN: *The Developing Human: Clinically Oriented Embryology*, 6th ed. Philadelphia, WB Saunders, 1998.

Nishimura Y: Embryological study of nasal cavity development in human embryos with reference to congenital nasal atresia. *Acta Anat* 147:140, 1993.

Noden DM: Cell movements and control of patterned tissue assembly during craniofacial development. *J Craniofac Genet Dev Biol* 11:192, 1991.

Robert E, Källén B, Harris J: The epidemiology of orofacial clefts. I. Some general epidemiological characteristics. *J Craniofac Genet Dev Biol* 16:234, 1996.

Sandham A: Embryonic facial vertical dimension and its relationship to palatal shelf elevation. *Early Hum Dev* 12:241, 1985.

Schubert J, Schmidt R, Raupach H-W: New findings explaining the mode of action in prevention of facial clefting and first clinical experience. *J Craniomaxillofac Surg* 18:343, 1990.

Severtson M, Petruzzelli GJ: Macroglossia. *Otolaryngol Head Neck Surg* 114:501, 1996.

Sperber GH: *Craniofacial Embryology,* 4th ed (rev. reprint). London, Butterworths, 1993.

Spinner RJ, Moore KL, Gottfried MR, et al: Thoracic intrathymic thyroid. *Ann Surg* 220:91, 1994.

Steinman GG: Changes of the human thymus during ageing. *In* Müller-Hermelink HK (ed): The human thymus: Histophysiology and pathology. *Curr Topics Pathol* 75:43, 1986.

Stricker M, Raphael B, Van der Meulen J, Mazzola R: Craniofacial growth and development. *In* Stricker M, Van der Meulen JC, Raphael B, Mazzola R (eds): *Craniofacial Malformations.* Edinburgh, Churchill Livingstone, 1990.

Sulik KK: Craniofacial development. *In* Turvey TA, Vig KWL, Fonseca RJ (eds): *Facial Clefts and Craniosynostosis: Principles and Management.* Philadelphia, WB Saunders, 1996.

Thompson MW, McInnes RR, Willard HF: *Thompson and Thompson Genetics in Medicine,* 5th ed. Philadelphia, WB Saunders, 1991.

Urao M, Teitelbaum DH, Miyano T: Lingual thyroglossal duct cyst: A unique surgical approach. *J Pediatr Surg* 31:1574, 1996.

The Respiratory System

12

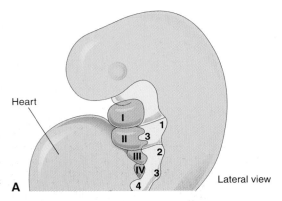

Heart

A

Roman numerals indicate pharyngeal arches
and numbers indicate pharyngeal pouches

Lateral view

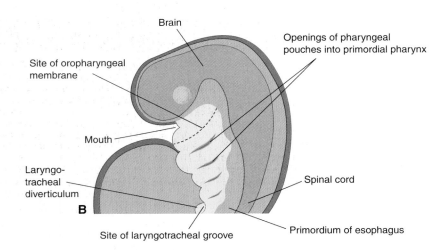

Brain

Openings of pharyngeal
pouches into primordial pharynx

Site of oropharyngeal
membrane

Mouth

Laryngo-
tracheal
diverticulum

B

Site of laryngotracheal groove

Spinal cord

Primordium of esophagus

■ **Figure 12–1.** *A,* Drawing of a lateral
view of a 4-week-old embryo, illustrating
the relationship of the pharyngeal apparatus to the developing respiratory system. *B,* Diagrammatic sagittal section of
the cranial half of the embryo. *C,* Horizontal section of the embryo, illustrating the
floor of the primordial pharynx and the
location of the laryngotracheal groove.

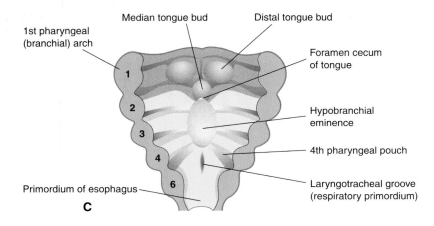

Median tongue bud

Distal tongue bud

1st pharyngeal
(branchial) arch

Foramen cecum
of tongue

Hypobranchial
eminence

4th pharyngeal pouch

Primordium of esophagus

Laryngotracheal groove
(respiratory primordium)

C

■ Development of the upper respiratory organs, the nasal cavities for example, is described in Chapter 11. The **lower respiratory organs** (larynx, trachea, bronchi, and lungs) begin to form during the fourth week of development. The **respiratory primordium** is indicated at 26 to 27 days by a median outgrowth from the caudal end of the ventral wall of the primordial pharynx — the **laryngotracheal groove** (Figs. 12–1A to C and 12–3A). This rudiment of the tracheobronchial tree develops caudal to the fourth pair of pharyngeal pouches. The endoderm lining the laryngotracheal groove gives rise to the epithelium and glands of the larynx, trachea, bronchi, and pulmonary epithelium. The connective tissue, cartilage, and smooth muscle in these structures develop from the splanchnic mesenchyme surrounding the foregut (see Fig. 12–4). By the end of the fourth week, the laryngotracheal groove has evaginated to form a pouchlike **laryngotracheal diverticulum** (respiratory diverticulum), which is located ventral to the caudal part of the foregut (Figs. 12–1B and 12–2A). As this diverticulum elongates, it is invested with splanchnic mesenchyme, and its distal end enlarges to form a globular **lung bud** (Fig. 12–2B).

The **laryngotracheal diverticulum** soon separates from the **primordial pharynx**; however, it maintains communication with it through the *primordial laryngeal inlet* (Fig. 12–2C). Longitudinal **tracheoesophageal folds** (ridges) develop in the laryngotracheal diverticulum, which approach each other and fuse to form a partition — the **tracheoesophageal septum** (Fig. 12–2D and E). This septum divides the cranial part of the foregut into a ventral portion, the **laryngotracheal tube** (primordium of the larynx, trachea, bronchi, and lungs), and a dorsal portion (primordium of the oropharynx and esophagus (Fig. 12–2F). The opening of the laryngotracheal tube into the pharynx becomes the **laryngeal inlet** (Figs. 12–2C and 12–3A to C).

DEVELOPMENT OF THE LARYNX

The epithelial lining of the larynx develops from the endoderm of the cranial end of the laryngotracheal tube. The cartilages of the larynx develop from the cartilages in the fourth and sixth pairs of pharyngeal arches (see Chapter 11). The laryngeal cartilages develop from mesenchyme that is derived from *neural*

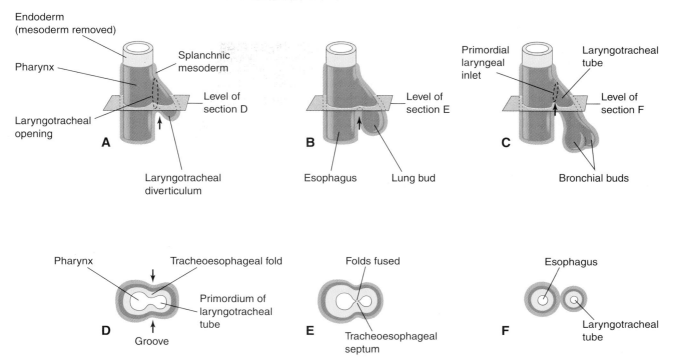

■ **Figure 12–2.** Drawings illustrating successive stages in the development of the tracheoesophageal septum during the fourth and fifth weeks. *A* to *C*, Lateral views of the caudal part of the primordial pharynx showing the laryngotracheal diverticulum and partitioning of the foregut into the esophagus and laryngotracheal tube. *D* to *F*, Transverse sections illustrating formation of the tracheoesophageal septum and showing how it separates the foregut into the laryngotracheal tube and esophagus.

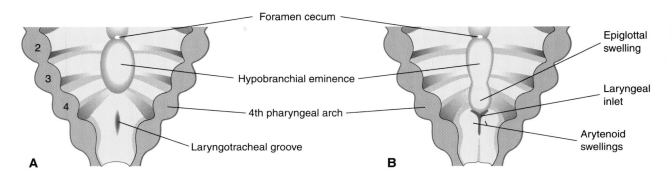

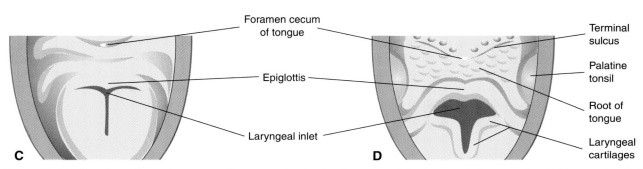

■ **Figure 12–3.** Drawings illustrating successive stages in the development of the larynx. *A,* Four weeks. *B,* Five weeks. *C,* Six weeks. *D,* Ten weeks. The epithelium lining the larynx is of endodermal origin. The cartilages and muscles of the larynx arise from mesenchyme in the fourth and sixth pairs of pharyngeal arches. Note that the laryngeal inlet or aditus changes in shape from a slitlike opening to a T-shaped inlet as the mesenchyme surrounding the developing larynx proliferates.

crest cells. The mesenchyme at the cranial end of the laryngotracheal tube proliferates rapidly, producing paired **arytenoid swellings** (Fig. 12–3*B*). These swellings grow toward the tongue, converting the slit-like aperture—the *primordial glottis*—into a T-shaped **laryngeal inlet** and reducing the developing laryngeal lumen to a narrow slit. The laryngeal epithelium proliferates rapidly, resulting in *temporary occlusion of the laryngeal lumen.* Recanalization of the larynx occurs by the 10th week. The *laryngeal ventricles* form during this recanalization process. These recesses are bounded by folds of mucous membrane that become the *vocal folds* (cords) and *vestibular folds* (Sañudo and Domenech-Mateu, 1990).

The **epiglottis** develops from the caudal part of the *hypobranchial eminence,* a prominence produced by proliferation of mesenchyme in the ventral ends of the third and fourth pharyngeal arches (Fig. 12–3*B* to *D*). The rostral part of this eminence forms the posterior third or pharyngeal part of the tongue (see Chapter 11). Because the *laryngeal muscles* develop from myoblasts in the fourth and sixth pairs of pharyngeal

arches, they are innervated by the laryngeal branches of the vagus nerves (CN X) that supply these arches (see Table 11–1). Growth of the larynx and epiglottis is rapid during the first 3 years after birth. By this time the epiglottis reaches its adult form (De Vries and De Vries, 1991).

Laryngeal Atresia

This rare anomaly results in obstruction of the upper fetal airway—**congenital high airway obstruction syndrome** (CHAOS). Distal to the atresia (blockage) or stenosis (narrowing), the airways become dilated, the lungs are enlarged and echogenic (capable of producing echoes), the diaphragm is either flattened or inverted, and fetal ascites and/or hydrops (accumulation of serous fluid) is present. Prenatal ultrasonography permits diagnosis of these anomalies (Hedrick et al, 1994).

DEVELOPMENT OF THE TRACHEA

The endodermal lining of the laryngotracheal tube distal to the larynx differentiates into the epithelium and glands of the trachea and the pulmonary epithelium. The cartilage, connective tissue, and muscles of the trachea are derived from the splanchnic mesenchyme surrounding the laryngotracheal tube (Fig. 12–4).

Tracheoesophageal Fistula

A **fistula** (abnormal communication) between the trachea and esophagus occurs about once in 3000 to 4500 live births (Fig. 12–5); most affected infants are males. In most cases, the fistula is associated with **esophageal atresia** (Behrman et al, 1996). Tracheoesophageal fistula results from incomplete division of the cranial part of the foregut into respiratory and esophageal parts during the fourth week. Incomplete fusion of the tracheoesophageal folds results in a **defective tracheoesophageal septum** and an abnormal communication between the trachea and esophagus.

Tracheoesophageal fistula is the most common anomaly of the lower respiratory tract. Four main varieties of tracheoesophageal fistula may develop (Fig. 12–5). The most common anomaly is a blind ending of the superior part of the esophagus (*esophageal atresia*) and a joining of the inferior part to the trachea near its bifurcation (Fig. 12–5A). Other varieties of this anomaly are illustrated in Figure 12–5B to D. Infants with the common type of tracheoesophageal fistula and esophageal atresia cough and choke when swallowing because of the accumulation of excessive amounts of saliva in the mouth and upper respiratory tract. When the infant attempts to swallow milk, it rapidly fills the esophageal pouch and is regurgitated. Gastric contents may also reflux from the stomach through the fistula into the trachea and lungs. This causes choking and may result in pneumonia or *pneumonitis* (inflammation of the lungs).

Polyhydramnios (see Chapter 8) is often associated with esophageal atresia and tracheoesophageal fistula. The excess amniotic fluid develops because fluid cannot pass to the stomach and intestines for absorption and subsequent transfer through the placenta to the mother's blood for disposal.

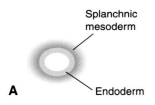

Splanchnic mesoderm

Endoderm

A

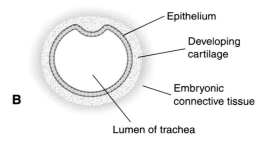

Epithelium

Developing cartilage

Embryonic connective tissue

Lumen of trachea

B

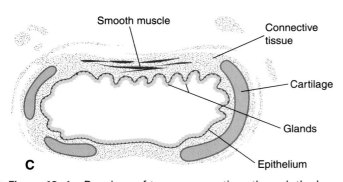

Smooth muscle

Connective tissue

Cartilage

Glands

Epithelium

C

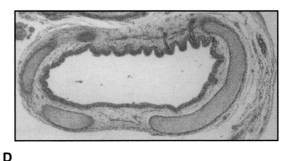

D

■ **Figure 12–4.** Drawings of transverse sections through the laryngotracheal tube illustrating progressive stages in the development of the trachea. *A,* Four weeks. *B,* Ten weeks. *C,* Eleven weeks. Note that endoderm of the tube gives rise to the epithelium and glands of the trachea and that mesenchyme surrounding the tube forms the connective tissue, muscle, and cartilage. *D,* Photomicrograph of a transverse section of the developing trachea at 14 weeks. (From Moore KL, Persaud TVN, Shiota K: *Color Atlas of Clinical Embryology.* Philadelphia, WB Saunders, 1994.)

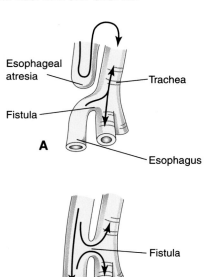

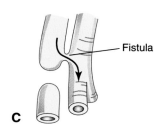

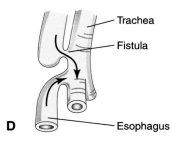

■ **Figure 12–5.** Sketches illustrating the four main varieties of tracheoesophageal fistula, shown in order of frequency. Possible directions of the flow of the contents are indicated by arrows. Esophageal atresia, as illustrated in *A,* is associated with tracheoesophageal fistula in more than 85% of cases. The abdomen rapidly becomes distended as the intestines fill with air. *B,* Fistula between the trachea and esophagus; this type of anomaly accounts for about 4% of cases. In *C,* air cannot enter the distal esophagus and stomach. *D,* Shows atresia of the proximal segment of the esophagus, with fistulas between the trachea and both proximal and distal segments of the esophagus. All infants born with tracheoesophageal fistula have esophageal dysmotility and most have reflux.

Tracheal Stenosis and Atresia

Narrowing (stenosis) and obstruction (atresia) of the trachea are uncommon anomalies that are usually associated with one of the varieties of tracheoesophageal fistula. Stenoses and atresias probably result from unequal partitioning of the foregut into the esophagus and trachea. Sometimes a web of tissue obstructs airflow (*incomplete tracheal atresia*). For a description of uncommon congenital anomalies of the trachea, see Moore and Persaud (1998).

DEVELOPMENT OF THE BRONCHI AND LUNGS

The lung bud that developed at the caudal end of the laryngotracheal tube during the fourth week (Fig. 12–2*B*) soon divides into two outpouchings—the **bronchial buds** (Fig. 12–6*A*). These endodermal buds grow laterally into the pericardioperitoneal canals, the primordia of the pleural cavities (Fig. 12–6*B*). Together with the surrounding splanchnic mesenchyme, the bronchial buds differentiate into the bronchi and their ramifications in the lungs. Early in the fifth week, the connection of each bronchial bud with the trachea enlarges to form the primordium of a **primary** or **main bronchus** (Fig. 12–7). The embryonic right main bronchus is slightly larger than the left one and is oriented more vertically. This embryonic relationship persists in the adult; consequently, a foreign body is more likely to enter the right main bronchus than the left one. The primary or main bronchi subdivide into **secondary** or **stem bronchi** (Fig. 12–6). On the right the superior secondary bronchus supplies the upper or superior lobe of the lung, whereas the inferior secondary bronchus subdivides into two bronchi, one to the middle lobe of the right lung and the other to the lower or inferior lobe. On the left the two secondary bronchi supply the upper and lower lobes of the lung. Each secondary bronchus undergoes progressive branching.

Tertiary or **segmental bronchi**, 10 in the right lung and 8 or 9 in the left lung, begin to form by the seventh week. As this occurs, the surrounding mesenchyme also divides. Each segmental bronchus with its surrounding mass of mesenchyme is the primordium of a **bronchopulmonary segment**. For a description of the adult anatomy of these clinically important segments, see Moore (1992). By 24 weeks, about 17 orders of branches have formed and **respiratory bronchioles** have developed (Fig. 12–8*B*). An additional seven orders of airways develop after birth.

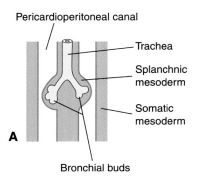

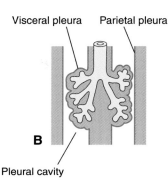

■ **Figure 12–6.** Diagrams illustrating growth of the developing lungs into the splanchnic mesenchyme adjacent to the medial walls of the pericardioperitoneal canals (primordial pleural cavities). Development of the layers of the pleura is also shown. *A,* Five weeks. *B,* Six weeks.

As the bronchi develop, cartilaginous plates develop from the surrounding splanchnic mesenchyme. The bronchial smooth musculature and connective tissue and the pulmonary connective tissue and capillaries are also derived from this mesenchyme. As the lungs develop, they acquire a layer of *visceral pleura* from the splanchnic mesenchyme. With expansion, the lungs and pleural cavities grow caudally into the mesenchyme of the body wall and soon lie close to the heart. The thoracic body wall becomes lined by a layer of *parietal pleura*, derived from the somatic mesoderm (Fig. 12–6B).

Maturation of the Lungs

Maturation of the lungs is divided into four periods:

- Pseudoglandular period
- Canalicular period

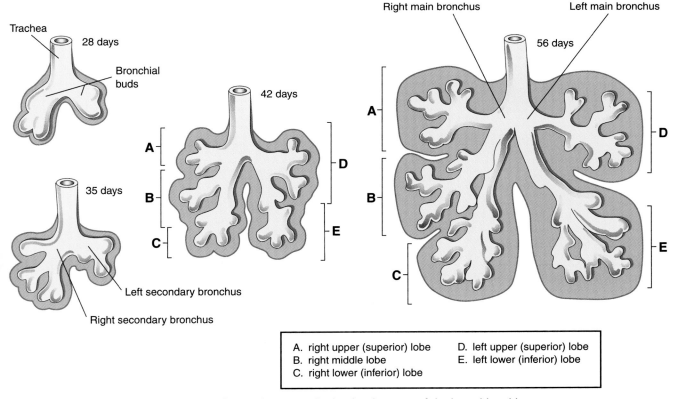

A. right upper (superior) lobe   D. left upper (superior) lobe
B. right middle lobe   E. left lower (inferior) lobe
C. right lower (inferior) lobe

■ **Figure 12–7.** Successive stages in the development of the bronchi and lungs.

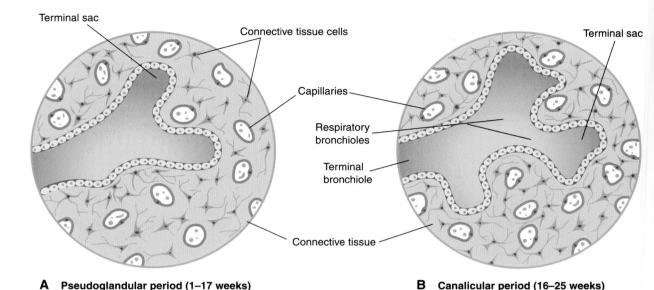

A Pseudoglandular period (1–17 weeks)

B Canalicular period (16–25 weeks)

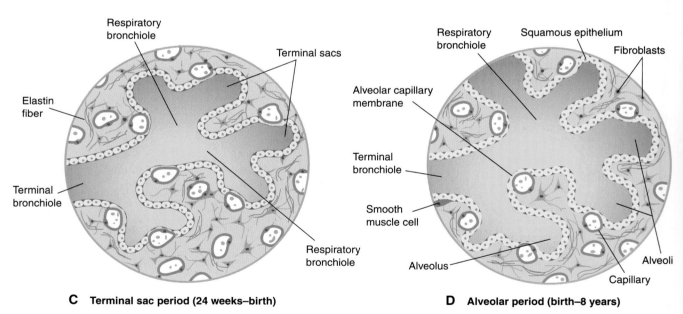

C Terminal sac period (24 weeks–birth)

D Alveolar period (birth–8 years)

■ Figure 12–8. Diagrammatic sketches of histologic sections, illustrating progressive stages of lung development. In *C* and *D*, note that the alveolocapillary membrane is thin and that some capillaries bulge into the terminal sacs (future alveoli).

- Terminal sac period
- Alveolar period

For information on the regulation of normal lung growth and the hormonal control of lung maturation, see Thurlbeck (1995) and Adamson (1997).

PSEUDOGLANDULAR PERIOD (5 TO 17 WEEKS)

The developing lung somewhat resembles an exocrine gland during this period (Figs. 12-8*A* and 12-9*A*). By 17 weeks all major elements of the lung have formed

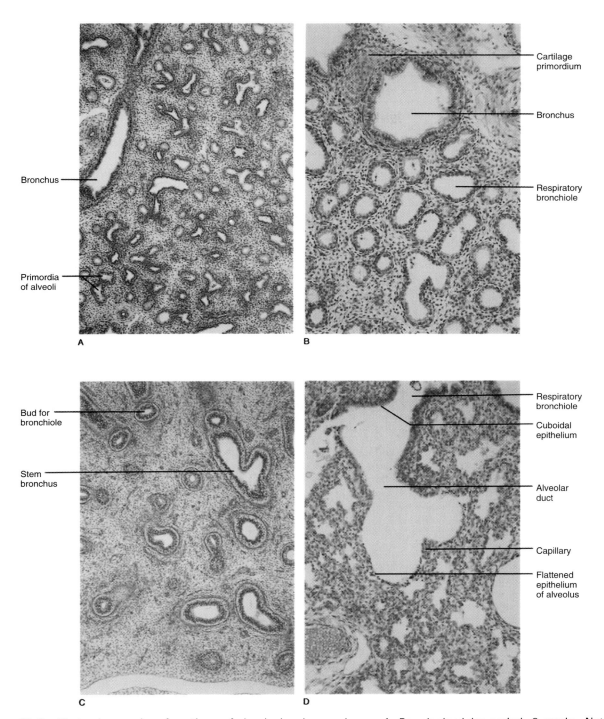

Bronchus

Primordia of alveoli

A

Cartilage primordium

Bronchus

Respiratory bronchiole

B

Bud for bronchiole

Stem bronchus

C

Respiratory bronchiole

Cuboidal epithelium

Alveolar duct

Capillary

Flattened epithelium of alveolus

D

■ **Figure 12–9.** Photomicrographs of sections of developing human lungs. *A,* Pseudoglandular period, 8 weeks. Note the "glandular" appearance of the lung at this stage. *B,* Canalicular period, 16 weeks. The lumina of the bronchi and terminal bronchioles are enlarging. *C,* Canalicular period, 18 weeks. Note that many blood vessels are developing in the mesenchyme surrounding the sections of bronchi and terminal bronchioles. *D,* Terminal sac period, 24 weeks. Observe the thin-walled terminal sacs (primordial alveoli) that have developed at the ends of the respiratory bronchioles. Also observe that the number of blood vessels has increased and that some of them are closely associated with the developing alveoli. (From Moore KL, Persaud TVN, Shiota K: *Color Atlas of Clinical Embryology.* Philadelphia, WB Saunders, 1994.)

except those involved with gas exchange. Respiration is not possible; hence, *fetuses born during this period are unable to survive.*

CANALICULAR PERIOD (16 TO 25 WEEKS)

This period overlaps the pseudoglandular period because cranial segments of the lungs mature faster than caudal ones. During the canalicular period the lumina of the bronchi and terminal bronchioles become larger, and the lung tissue becomes highly vascular (Figs. 12–8*B* and 12–9*B*). By 24 weeks, each terminal bronchiole has given rise to two or more **respiratory bronchioles**, each of which then divides into three to six tubular passages — the **alveolar ducts**. Respiration is possible toward the end of the canalicular period because some thin-walled *terminal sacs* (primordial alveoli) have developed at the ends of the respiratory bronchioles, and *the lung tissue is well vascularized.* Although a fetus born toward the end of this period may survive if given intensive care, it often dies because its respiratory and other systems are still relatively immature.

TERMINAL SAC PERIOD (24 WEEKS TO BIRTH)

During this period, many more terminal sacs develop (Figs. 12–8*C* and 12–9*C*), and *their epithelium becomes very thin.* Capillaries begin to bulge into these developing alveoli. The intimate contact between epithelial and endothelial cells establishes the **blood-air barrier**, which permits adequate gas exchange for survival of the fetus if it is born prematurely. By 24 weeks, the terminal sacs are lined mainly by squamous epithelial cells of endodermal origin — **Type I alveolar cells** or pneumocytes — across which gas exchange occurs. The capillary network proliferates rapidly in the mesenchyme around the developing alveoli and there is concurrent active development of lymphatic capillaries. Scattered among the squamous epithelial cells are rounded secretory epithelial cells — **Type II alveolar cells** or pneumocytes — *which secrete pulmonary surfactant,* a complex mixture of phospholipids. **Surfactant** forms as a monomolecular film over the internal walls of the terminal sacs, lowering surface tension at the air-alveolar interface (Whitsett, 1991). The maturation of alveolar type II cells and surfactant production vary widely in fetuses of different gestational ages (Chernick and Kryger, 1990). The production of surfactant increases during the terminal stages of pregnancy, particularly during the last 2 weeks before birth.

Surfactant counteracts surface tension forces and facilitates expansion of the terminal sacs (primitive alveoli). Consequently, fetuses born prematurely at 24 to 26 weeks after fertilization may survive if given intensive care; however, they may suffer from respiratory distress because of *surfactant deficiency*. Surfactant production begins by 20 weeks, but it is present in only small amounts in premature infants; it does not reach adequate levels until the late fetal period. By 26 to 28 weeks after fertilization, the fetus usually weighs about 1000 gm, and sufficient terminal sacs and surfactant are present to permit survival of a prematurely born infant. Before this, the lungs are usually incapable of providing adequate gas exchange, partly because the alveolar surface area is insufficient and the vascularity underdeveloped. It is not the presence of thin terminal sacs or a primordial alveolar epithelium so much as the development of an adequate pulmonary vasculature and sufficient surfactant that are critical to the survival of premature infants.

ALVEOLAR PERIOD (LATE FETAL PERIOD TO CHILDHOOD)

Exactly when the terminal sac period ends and the alveolar period begins depends on the definition of what is called an **alveolus** (Behrman et al, 1996). Structures analogous to alveoli are present at 32 weeks of gestation. The epithelial lining of the terminal sacs attenuates to an extremely thin squamous epithelial layer. The type I alveolar cells become so thin that the adjacent capillaries bulge into the terminal sacs (Figs. 12–8*D* and 12–9*D*). By the late fetal period, the lungs are capable of respiration because the **alveolocapillary membrane** (pulmonary diffusion barrier or respiratory membrane) is sufficiently thin to allow gas exchange. Although the lungs do not begin to perform this vital function until birth, they must be well developed so that they are capable of functioning as soon as the baby is born. At the beginning of the alveolar period, each respiratory bronchiole terminates in a cluster of thin-walled terminal sacs, separated from one another by loose connective tissue. These terminal sacs represent future alveolar ducts. The transition from dependence on the placenta for gas exchange to autonomous gas exchange requires the following adaptive changes in the lungs:

- Production of adequate surfactant in the alveoli
- Transformation of the lungs from secretory into gas-exchanging organs
- Establishment of parallel pulmonary and systemic circulations

For more information about adaptation of the newborn to air breathing, see Behrman et al (1996).

Characteristic mature alveoli do not form until after birth; about 95% of alveoli develop postnatally.

Before birth the immature alveoli appear as small bulges on the walls of respiratory bronchioles and terminal sacs (future alveolar ducts). After birth the primordial alveoli enlarge as the lungs expand; however, most of the increase in the size of the lungs results from an increase in the number of respiratory bronchioles and primordial alveoli rather than from an increase in the size of the alveoli. From the third to the eighth year or so, the number of immature alveoli continues to increase (Thurlbeck, 1995). Unlike mature alveoli, immature alveoli have the potential for forming additional alveoli. As the primordial alveoli increase in size, they become mature alveoli.

Lung development during the first few months after birth is characterized by an exponential increase in the surface of the air-blood barrier. This increase is accomplished by the multiplication of pulmonary alveoli and capillaries. About 50 million alveoli, one sixth of the adult number, are present in the lungs of a full-term newborn infant. On chest radiographs, therefore, the lungs of newborn infants are denser than adult lungs. By about the eighth year, the adult complement of 300 million alveoli is present. Molecular studies have led to the recognition of several regulatory substances that participate in mesenchymal-epithelial interactions and in lung development. For example, *keratinocyte growth factor*, a member of the family of fibroblast growth factors, was shown to be involved in lung morphogenesis by influencing branching, epithelial growth differentiation, and patterning of rat lung explants in culture (Shiratori et al, 1996).

Breathing movements occur before birth, exerting sufficient force to cause aspiration of some amniotic fluid into the lungs. These fetal breathing movements, which can be detected by real-time ultrasonography, are not continuous; however, they are essential for normal lung development. The pattern of fetal breathing movements is widely used in the diagnosis of labor and as a predictor of fetal outcome in preterm delivery. By birth the fetus has had the advantage of several months of breathing exercise (Behrman et al, 1996). *Fetal breathing movements*, which increase as the time of delivery approaches, probably condition the respiratory muscles. In addition, these movements stimulate lung development, possibly by creating a pressure gradient between the lungs and the amniotic fluid.

At birth the lungs are about half-filled with fluid derived from the amniotic cavity, lungs, and tracheal glands. Aeration of the lungs at birth is not so much the inflation of empty collapsed organs as the rapid replacement of intra-alveolar fluid by air. The fluid in the lungs is cleared at birth by three routes:

- Through the mouth and nose by pressure on the thorax during delivery

- Into the pulmonary capillaries
- Into the lymphatics and pulmonary arteries and veins

In the fetus near term, the pulmonary lymphatic vessels are relatively larger and more numerous than in the adult. Lymph flow is rapid during the first few hours after birth and then diminishes. *Three factors are important for normal lung development* (Goldstein, 1994):

- Adequate thoracic space for lung growth
- Fetal breathing movements
- Adequate amniotic fluid volume

Oligohydramnios and Lung Development

The fluid in the lungs is an important stimulus for lung development. When oligohydramnios (an insufficient amount of amniotic fluid) is severe and chronic because of amniotic fluid leakage, for example, lung development in retarded and severe pulmonary hypoplasia results (Goldstein, 1994).

Lungs of a Newborn

Fresh healthy lungs always contain some air; consequently, pulmonary tissue removed from them floats in water. A diseased lung partly filled with fluid may not float. Of medicolegal significance is the fact that the lungs of a stillborn infant are firm and sink when placed in water because they contain fluid, not air.

Respiratory Distress Syndrome

Respiratory distress syndrome (RDS) affects about 2% of live newborn infants, and those born prematurely are most susceptible. These infants develop rapid, labored breathing shortly after birth. Respiratory distress syndrome is also known as *hyaline membrane disease* (HMD). An estimated 30% of all neonatal disease results from HMD or its complications (Verma, 1995; Behrman et al, 1996).

Surfactant deficiency is a major cause of RDS or HMD. The lungs are underinflated, and the alveoli contain a fluid of high protein content that resembles a glassy or *hyaline membrane*. This membrane is believed to be derived from a combination of substances in the circulation and from the injured pulmonary epithelium. It has been suggested that prolonged *intra-uterine asphyxia* may produce irreversible changes in the type II alveolar cells, making them incapable of producing surfactant. There appear to be other causes for absence or deficiency of surfactant in premature and full-term infants (Toki et al, 1995). Not all the growth factors and hormones controlling surfactant production have been identified (Ballard, 1989), but *thyroxine* is a potent stimulator of surfactant production.

Glucocorticoid treatment during pregnancy accelerates fetal lung development and surfactant production. This finding has led to the routine clinical use of corticosteroids (betamethasone) for the *prevention of RDS*. In addition, clinical trials with exogenous surfactant (**surfactant replacement therapy**) are in progress in many centers.

Pleural Effusion

Pleural effusion (fluid in the pleural cavity) can be detected sonographically (Goldstein, 1994). **Chylothorax**—an accumulation of chyle (lymph and triglyceride fat) in the pleural cavity—is the most frequent cause of isolated pleural effusion resulting in respiratory distress. In severe cases, the pleural effusion causes the lungs to collapse (Fig. 12–10). Fluid can be

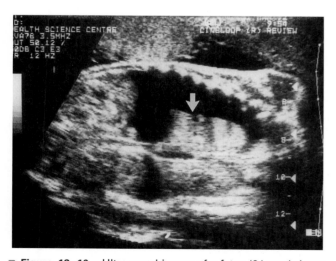

■ **Figure 12–10.** Ultrasound image of a fetus (24 weeks' gestation) with large bilateral pleural effusions. The collapsed left lung (*arrow*) is clearly outlined by the larger left pleural effusion. This fetus had severe upper body edema and required intrauterine treatment by insertion of a pleural-amniotic shunt to reach term in good condition. (Courtesy of Dr. CR Harman, Department of Obstetrics, Gynecology and Reproductive Sciences, Women's Hospital and University of Manitoba, Winnipeg, Manitoba, Canada.)

drained from the pleural cavity of the fetus through a catheter to permit better lung expansion and lung growth. The catheter drains the fluid in the pleural cavity into the amniotic sac.

Lung Hypoplasia

In infants with congenital diaphragmatic hernia (CDH; see Chapter 10), the lung is unable to develop normally because it is compressed by the abnormally positioned abdominal viscera. Lung hypoplasia is characterized by a markedly reduced lung volume (Lee et al, 1996). Most infants with CDH die of pulmonary insufficiency, despite optimal postnatal care, because their lungs are too hypoplastic to support extrauterine life (Harrison, 1991).

SUMMARY OF THE RESPIRATORY SYSTEM

The lower respiratory system begins to develop around the middle of the fourth week from a median *laryngotracheal groove* in the floor of the primordial pharynx. The groove deepens to produce a *laryngotracheal diverticulum*, which soon becomes separated from the foregut by tracheoesophageal folds that fuse to form a *tracheoesophageal septum*. This septum results in the formation of the esophagus and laryngotracheal tube. The endoderm of the *laryngotracheal tube* gives rise to the epithelium of the lower respiratory organs and the tracheobronchial glands. The splanchnic mesenchyme surrounding the laryngotracheal tube forms the connective tissue, cartilage, muscle, and blood and lymphatic vessels of these organs.

Pharyngeal arch mesenchyme contributes to formation of the epiglottis and connective tissue of the larynx. The *laryngeal muscles* are derived from mesenchyme in the caudal pharyngeal arches. The *laryngeal cartilages* are derived from the cartilaginous bars in the fourth and sixth pairs of pharyngeal arches, which are derived from *neural crest cells* (see Table 11–1).

During the fourth week the laryngotracheal tube develops a lung bud at its distal end, which divides into two bronchial buds during the early part of the fifth week. Each **bronchial bud** soon enlarges to form a *primary* or *main bronchus,* and then each primary bronchus gives rise to two new bronchial buds, which develop into *secondary bronchi*. The right inferior secondary bronchus soon divides into two bronchi. The secondary bronchi supply the lobes of the developing lungs. Each secondary bronchus undergoes progressive branching to form *segmental bronchi*. Each segmental bronchus with its surrounding mesenchyme is the primordium of a *bronchopulmonary segment*. Branching continues until about 17 orders of branches have formed. Additional airways are formed after birth, until about 24 orders of branches are present.

Lung development is divided into four periods. During the *pseudoglandular period* (5 to 17 weeks), the bronchi and terminal bronchioles form. During the *canalicular period* (16 to 25 weeks), the lumina of the bronchi and terminal bronchioles enlarge, the respiratory bronchioles and alveolar ducts develop, and the lung tissue becomes highly vascular. During the *terminal sac period* (24 weeks to birth), the alveolar ducts give rise to terminal sacs (primordial alveoli). The terminal sacs are initially lined with cuboidal epithelium that begins to attenuate to squamous epithelium at about 26 weeks. By this time, capillary networks have proliferated close to the alveolar epithelium and the lungs are usually sufficiently well developed to permit survival of the fetus if it is born prematurely. The *alveolar period*, the final stage of lung development, occurs from the late fetal period to about 8 years of age, as the lungs mature. The number of respiratory bronchioles and primitive alveoli increases.

The respiratory system develops so that it is capable of immediate function at birth. To be capable of respiration, the lungs must acquire an *alveolocapillary membrane* that is sufficiently thin, and an adequate amount of *surfactant* must be present. A deficiency of surfactant appears to be responsible for the failure of primordial alveoli to remain open, resulting in *respiratory distress syndrome*. Growth of the lungs after birth results mainly from an increase in the number of respiratory bronchioles and alveoli. New alveoli form for at least 8 years after birth.

Major congenital anomalies of the lower respiratory system are uncommon except for *tracheoesophageal fistula*, which is usually associated with *esophageal atresia*. These anomalies result from faulty partitioning of the foregut into the esophagus and trachea during the fourth and fifth weeks.

Clinically Oriented Questions

1. I recently read in the newspaper about *fetal breathing*. Does the fetus breathe before birth?

2. What stimulates the baby to start breathing when it is born? Is "slapping the buttocks" necessary?

3. My sister's baby died about 72 hours after birth from the effects of the *respiratory distress syndrome*. What is this condition? By what other name

is this condition called? Is its cause genetic or environmental?

4. Can an infant born 22 weeks after fertilization survive?

The answers to these questions are given at the back of the book.

REFERENCES AND SUGGESTED READING

Achiron R, Strauss S, Seidman DS, et al: Fetal lung hyperechogenicity: Prenatal ultrasonographic diagnosis, natural history and neonatal outcome. *Ultrasound Obstet Gynecol* 6:40, 1995.

Adamson IYR: Development of lung structure. *In* Crystal RG, West JB, Weibel ER (eds): *The Lung: Scientific Foundations,* 2nd ed. Philadelphia, Lippincott-Raven, 1997.

Ballard PL: Hormonal control of lung maturation. *Bailliere's Clin Endocrinol Metab* 3:723, 1989.

Behrman RE, Kliegman RM, Arvin AM (eds): *Nelson Textbook of Pediatrics,* 15th ed. Philadelphia, WB Saunders, 1996.

Chernick V, Kryger MH: Pediatric lung disease. *In* Kryger MH (ed): *Introduction to Respiratory Medicine,* 2nd ed. New York, Churchill Livingstone, 1990.

De Vries PA, De Vries CR: Embryology and development. *In* Othersen HB Jr (ed): *The Pediatric Airway.* Philadelphia, WB Saunders, 1991.

Goldstein RB: Ultrasound evaluation of the fetal thorax. *In* Callen PW (ed): *Ultrasonography in Obstetrics and Gynecology,* 3rd ed. Philadelphia, WB Saunders, 1994.

Harrison MR: The fetus with a diaphragmatic hernia: pathology, natural history, and surgical management. *In* Harrison MR, Golbus MS, Filly RA (eds): *The Unborn Patient. Prenatal Diagnosis and Treatment,* 2nd ed. Philadelphia, WB Saunders, 1991.

Hedrick MH, Ferro MM, Filly RA, et al: Congenital high airway obstruction syndrome (CHAOS): A potential for perinatal intervention. *J Pediatr Surg* 29:271, 1994.

Herbst JL: The esophagus. *In* Behrman RE (ed): *Nelson Textbook of Pediatrics,* 15th ed. Philadelphia, WB Saunders, 1996.

Hume R: Fetal lung development. *In* Hillier SG, Kitchener HC, Neilson JP (eds): *Scientific Essentials of Reproductive Medicine.* Philadelphia, WB Saunders, 1996.

Lauria MR, Gonik B, Romero R: Pulmonary hypoplasia: Pathogenesis, diagnosis and antenatal prediction. *Obstet Gynecol* 86:466, 1995.

Lee A, Kratochwil A, Stümpflen I, et al: Fetal lung volume determination by three-dimensional ultrasonography. *Am J Obstet Gynecol* 175:588, 1996.

Moore KL: *Clinically Oriented Anatomy,* 3rd ed. Baltimore, Williams & Wilkins, 1992.

Moore KL, Persaud TVN: *The Developing Human: Clinically Oriented Embryology,* 6th ed. Philadelphia, WB Saunders, 1998.

Sañudo JR, Domenech-Mateu JM: The laryngeal primordium and epithelial lamina. A new interpretation. *J Anat* 171:207, 1990.

Schwartz M, Ramachandran P: Congenital malformations of the lung and mediastinum—a quarter century of experience from a single institution. *J Pediatr Surg* 32:44, 1997.

Shiratori M, Oshika E, Ung LP, et al: Keratinocyte growth factor and embryonic rat lung morphogenesis. *Am J Respir Cell Mol Biol* 15:328, 1996.

Thrane EV, Becher R, Lag M, et al: Differential distribution and increased levels of RAS proteins during lung development. *Lung Res* 23:35, 1997.

Thurlbeck WM: Lung growth and development. *In* Thurlbeck WM, Churg AM (eds): *Pathology of the Lung,* 2nd ed. New York, Thieme Medical Publishers, 1995.

Toki N, Sueishi K, Minamitani M, et al: Immunohistochemical distribution of surfactant apoproteins in hypoplastic lungs of nonimmunologic hydrops fetalis. *Hum Pathol* 26:1252, 1995.

Verma RP: Respiratory distress syndrome of the newborn infant. *Obstet Gynecol Surv* 50:542, 1995.

Whitsett JA: Molecular aspects of the pulmonary surfactant system in the newborn. *In* Chernick V, Mellins RB (eds): *Basic Mechanisms of Pediatric Respiratory Disease: Cellular and Integrative.* Philadelphia, BC Decker, 1991.

Wiseman NE, Macpherson RI: Pulmonary sequestration. *In* Persaud TVN (ed): *Advances in the Study of Birth Defects: Cardiovascular, Respiratory, Gastrointestinal and Genitourinary Malformations,* Vol 6. New York, Alan R. Liss, 1982.

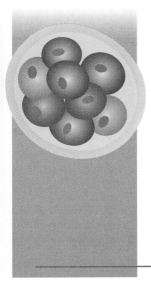

The Digestive System

13

■ The **primordial (primitive) gut** at the beginning of the fourth week is closed at its cranial end by the **oropharyngeal membrane** (see Fig. 11–1) and at its caudal end by the **cloacal membrane** (Fig. 13–1*B*). The primordial gut forms during the fourth week as the head, tail, and lateral folds incorporate the dorsal part of the yolk sac into the embryo (see Chapter 6). The endoderm of the primordial gut gives rise to most of the epithelium and glands of the digestive tract. The epithelium at the cranial and caudal extremities of the tract is derived from ectoderm of the **stomodeum** (primordial mouth) and **proctodeum** (anal pit), respectively (Fig. 13–1*A* and *B*). The muscular tissue, connective tissue, and other layers of the wall of the digestive tract are derived from the splanchnic mesenchyme surrounding the primordial gut. For descriptive purposes the primordial gut is divided into three parts: foregut, midgut, and hindgut.

THE FOREGUT

The derivatives of the foregut are:

- The *primordial pharynx* and its derivatives (oral cavity, pharynx, tongue, tonsils, salivary glands, and upper respiratory system), which are discussed in Chapter 11
- The *lower respiratory system* (described in Chapter 12)

- The *esophagus and stomach*
- The *duodenum*, proximal to the opening of the bile duct
- The *liver, biliary apparatus* (hepatic ducts, gallbladder, and bile duct), and *pancreas*

All these foregut derivatives *except* the pharynx, respiratory tract, and most of the esophagus are supplied by the *celiac artery*, the artery of the foregut (Fig. 13–1*B*).

Development of the Esophagus

The esophagus develops from the foregut immediately caudal to the primordial pharynx (Fig. 13–1*B*). The partitioning of the trachea from the esophagus by the **tracheoesophageal septum** is described in Chapter 12. Initially, the esophagus is short but it elongates rapidly, mainly because of the growth and descent of the heart and lungs. The esophagus reaches its final relative length by the seventh week. Its epithelium and glands are derived from endoderm. The epithelium proliferates and partly or completely obliterates the lumen; however, recanalization of the esophagus normally occurs by the end of the embryonic period. The striated muscle constituting the muscularis externa of the superior third of the esophagus is derived from mesenchyme in the caudal pharyngeal arches. The smooth muscle, mainly in the inferior third of the esophagus, develops from the surrounding splanchnic

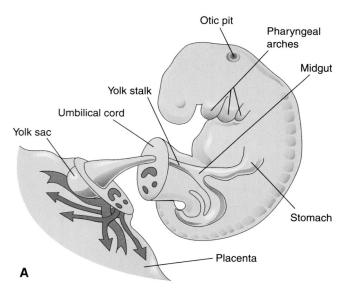

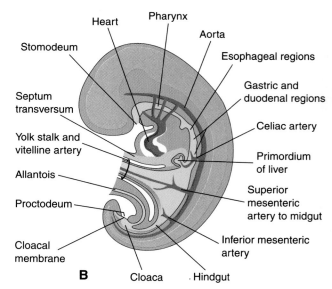

■ **Figure 13–1.** *A,* Lateral view of a 4-week embryo showing the relationship of the primordial gut to the yolk sac. *B,* Drawing of a median section of the embryo showing the early digestive system and its blood supply. The primordial gut is a long tube extending the length of the embryo. Its blood vessels are derived from the vessels that supplied the yolk sac.

mesenchyme. Both types of muscle are innervated by branches of the vagus nerves (CN X), which supply the caudal pharyngeal arches (see Table 11-1).

Esophageal Atresia

Blockage of the esophagus occurs with an incidence of 1 in 3000 to 4500 live births (Herbst, 1996). About one third of affected infants are born prematurely. Esophageal atresia is associated with **tracheoesophageal fistula** in more than 85% of cases (see Fig. 11-5). It may occur as a separate anomaly, but this is less common. Esophageal atresia results from deviation of the *tracheoesophageal septum* in a posterior direction (see Fig. 12-2); as a result, separation of the esophagus from the laryngotracheal tube is incomplete. Isolated esophageal atresia may be associated with other congenital anomalies, such as *anorectal atresia* and anomalies of the urogenital system. In these cases, the atresia results from *failure of recanalization of the esophagus* during the eighth week of development. The cause of this arrest of development is thought to be defective growth of endodermal cells (Herbst, 1996).

A fetus with esophageal atresia is unable to swallow amniotic fluid; consequently, this fluid cannot pass to the intestine for absorption and transfer through the placenta to the maternal blood for disposal. This results in **polyhydramnios**, the accumulation of an excessive amount of amniotic fluid. Newborn infants with esophageal atresia usually appear healthy, and their first swallows are normal. Suddenly, fluid returns through the nose and mouth and *respiratory distress* occurs. Inability to pass a catheter through the esophagus into the stomach strongly suggests esophageal atresia. A radiographic examination demonstrates the anomaly by imaging the nasogastric tube arrested in the proximal esophageal pouch. Surgical repair of esophageal atresia now results in survival rates of more than 85%.

Esophageal Stenosis

Narrowing of the lumen of the esophagus can exist anywhere, but it usually occurs in its distal third, either as a web or as a long segment of esophagus with a threadlike lumen. Esophageal stenosis usually results from incomplete recanalization of the esophagus during the eighth week of development, but it may result from a failure of esophageal blood vessels to develop in the affected area. As a result, atrophy of a segment of the esophageal wall occurs.

Development of the Stomach

The distal part of the foregut is initially a simple tubular structure (Fig. 13-1B). Around the middle of the fourth week, a slight dilation indicates the site of the future stomach. It first appears as a fusiform enlargement of the caudal part of the foregut and is initially oriented in the median plane (Figs. 13-1 and 13-2B). This primordium soon enlarges and broadens ventrodorsally. During the next 2 weeks the dorsal border of the primordial stomach grows faster than its ventral border; this demarcates the **greater curvature of the stomach** (Fig. 13-2D, F, and G).

ROTATION OF THE STOMACH

As the stomach enlarges and acquires its adult shape, it slowly rotates 90 degrees in a clockwise direction around its longitudinal axis. The effects of rotation on the stomach are the following (Figs. 13-2 and 13-3A to J):

- The ventral border (lesser curvature) moves to the right, and the dorsal border (greater curvature) moves to the left.
- The original left side becomes the ventral surface, and the original right side becomes the dorsal surface.
- Before rotation, the cranial and caudal ends of the stomach are in the median plane (Fig. 13-2B). During rotation and growth of the stomach, its cranial region moves to the left and slightly inferiorly, and its caudal region moves to the right and superiorly.
- After rotation, the stomach assumes its final position, with its long axis almost transverse to the long axis of the body (Fig. 13-2E). The rotation and growth of the stomach explain why the left vagus nerve supplies the anterior wall of the adult stomach and the right vagus nerve innervates its posterior wall.

MESENTERIES OF THE STOMACH

The stomach is suspended from the dorsal wall of the abdominal cavity by a dorsal mesentery—the **dorsal mesogastrium** (Fig. 13-3A). This mesentery is originally in the median plane, but it is carried to the left during rotation of the stomach and formation of the *omental bursa* or lesser sac of peritoneum (Fig. 13-3A to C). A ventral mesentery or **ventral mesogastrium** attaches the stomach and duodenum to the liver and the ventral abdominal wall (Fig. 13-2C).

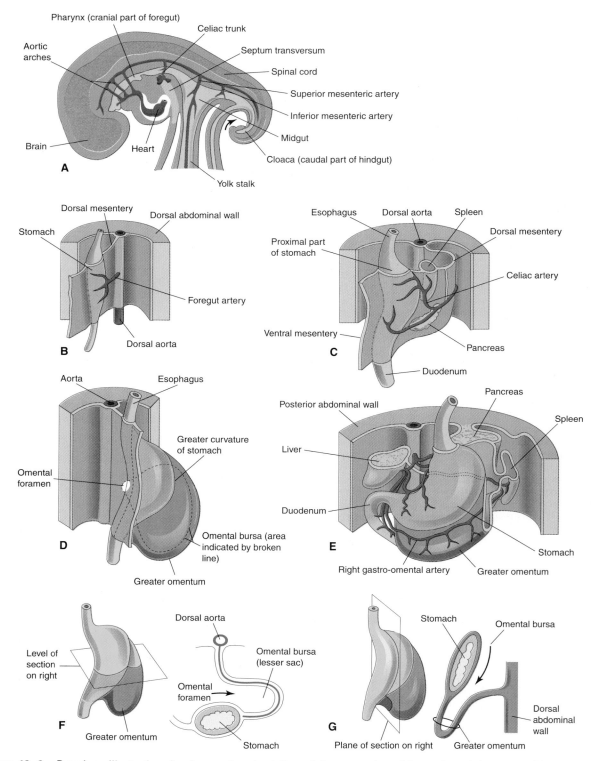

■ **Figure 13-2.** Drawings illustrating development and rotation of the stomach and formation of the omental bursa (lesser sac) and greater omentum. *A,* Drawing of a median section of a 28-day embryo. *B,* Anterolateral view of a 28-day embryo. *C,* Embryo about 35 days. *D,* Embryo about 40 days. *E,* Embryo about 48 days. *F,* Lateral view of the stomach and greater omentum of an embryo at about 52 days. The transverse section shows the omental foramen and omental bursa. *G,* Sagittal section showing the omental bursa and greater omentum.

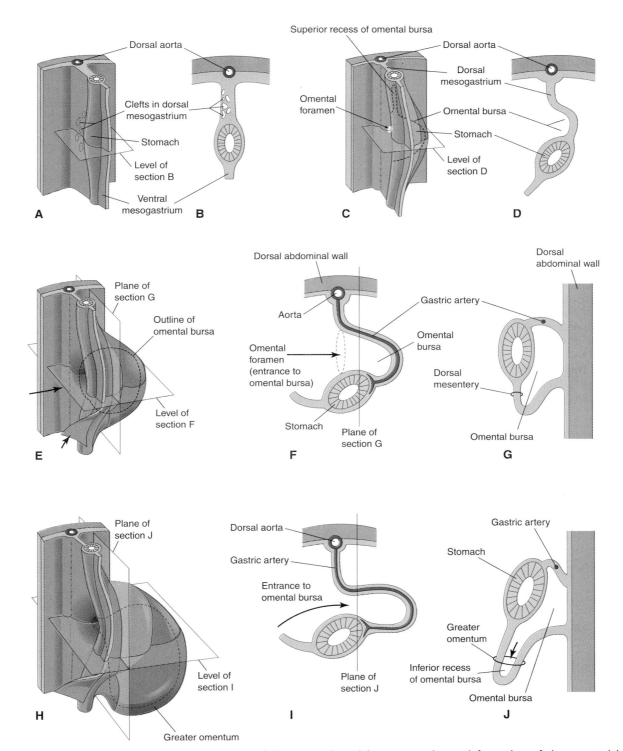

■ **Figure 13–3.** Drawings illustrating development of the stomach and its mesenteries and formation of the omental bursa (lesser sac). *A*, Five weeks. *B*, Transverse section showing clefts in the dorsal mesogastrium. *C*, Later stage after coalescence of the clefts to form the omental bursa. *D*, Transverse section showing the initial appearance of the omental bursa. *E*, The dorsal mesentery has elongated and the omental bursa has enlarged. *F* and *G*, Transverse and sagittal sections, respectively, showing elongation of the dorsal mesogastrium and expansion of the omental bursa. *H*, Six weeks, showing the greater omentum and expansion of the omental bursa. *I* and *J*, Transverse and sagittal sections, respectively, showing the inferior recess of the omental bursa and the omental foramen.

The Omental Bursa (Lesser Peritoneal Sac)

Isolated clefts (cavities) develop in the mesenchyme, forming the thick dorsal mesogastrium (Fig. 13-3A and B). The clefts soon coalesce to form a single cavity—the **omental bursa** or lesser peritoneal sac (Figs. 13-2F and G and 13-3C and D). Rotation of the stomach is thought to pull the dorsal mesogastrium to the left, thereby enlarging the bursa, a large recess of the peritoneal cavity. The omental bursa expands transversely and cranially and soon lies between the stomach and the posterior abdominal wall. This pouchlike bursa (L. purse) facilitates movements of the stomach.

The superior part of the omental bursa is cut off as the diaphragm develops, forming a closed space—the *infracardiac bursa*. If it persists, it usually lies medial to the base of the right lung. The inferior portion of the superior part of the omental bursa persists as the **superior recess of the omental bursa** (Moore, 1992). As the stomach enlarges, the omental bursa expands and acquires an **inferior recess of the omental bursa** between the layers of the elongated dorsal mesogastrium—the **greater omentum** (L. "fat skin"). This four-layered membrane overhangs the de-

veloping intestines (Fig. 13-3G to J). The inferior recess disappears as the layers of the greater omentum fuse (see Fig. 13-15F). The omental bursa communicates with the main part of the peritoneal cavity through a small opening—the **omental foramen** (Figs. 13-2D and F and 13-3E and F). In the adult, this foramen is located posterior to the free edge of the lesser omentum (Moore, 1992).

Congenital Hypertrophic Pyloric Stenosis

Anomalies of the stomach are uncommon except for hypertrophic pyloric stenosis (Wyllie, 1996). This anomaly affects 1 in every 150 males and 1 in every 750 females. Infants with this abnormality have a marked **thickening of the pylorus**, the distal sphincteric region of the stomach (Fig. 13-4). The circular and, to a lesser degree, the longitudinal muscles in the pyloric region are hypertrophied. This results in severe *stenosis (narrowing) of the pyloric canal* and obstruction to the passage of food. As a result, the stomach becomes markedly distended and the infant expels the

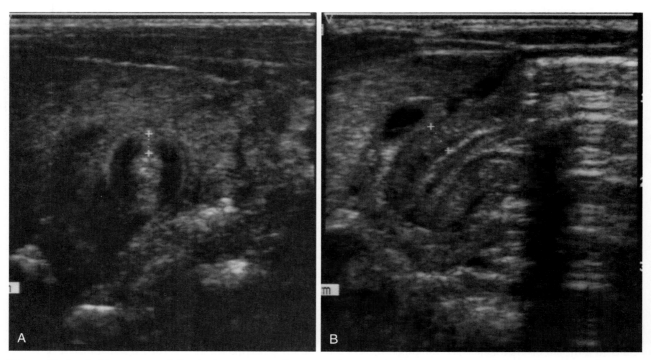

■ **Figure 13-4.** *A,* Transverse abdominal sonogram demonstrating a pyloric muscle wall thickness of greater than 4 mm (distance between crosses). *B,* Horizontal image demonstrating a pyloric channel length greater than 14 mm (wall thickness outlined between crosses) in an infant with hypertrophic pyloric stenosis. (From Wyllie R: Pyloric stenosis and other congenital anomalies of the stomach. *In* Berhman RE, Kliegman RM, Arvin AM (eds): *Nelson Textbook of Pediatrics,* 15th ed. Philadelphia, WB Saunders, 1996.)

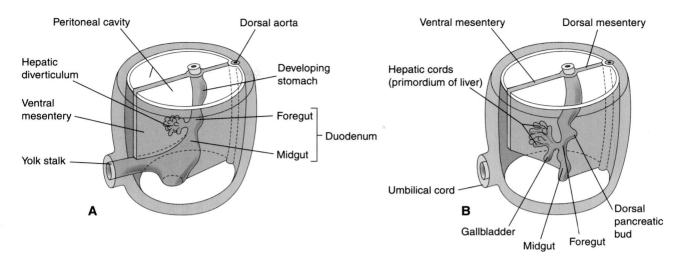

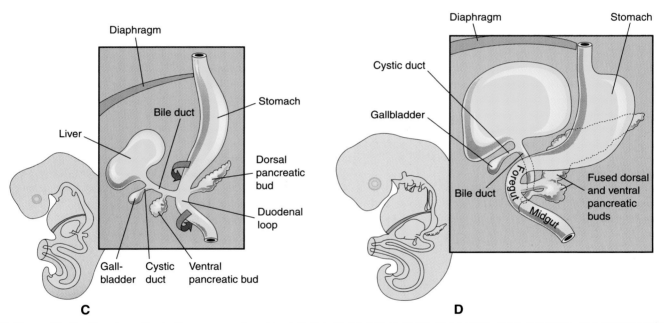

■ **Figure 13–5.** Drawings illustrating progressive stages in the development of the duodenum, liver, pancreas, and extrahepatic biliary apparatus. *A,* Four weeks. *B* and *C,* Five weeks. *D,* Six weeks. The pancreas develops from dorsal and ventral buds that fuse to form the pancreas. Note that the entrance of the bile duct into the duodenum gradually shifts from its initial position to a posterior one. This explains why the bile duct in the adult passes posterior to the duodenum and the head of the pancreas.

stomach's contents with considerable force (**projectile vomiting**). Surgical relief of the pyloric obstruction is the usual treatment. The cause of congenital pyloric stenosis is unknown, but the high incidence of the condition in both infants of monozygotic twins suggests the involvement of genetic factors. Multifactorial inheritance of this disorder is likely (Wyllie, 1996). For a discussion of the inheritance of congenital pyloric stenosis, see Thompson et al (1991).

Development of the Duodenum

Early in the fourth week the duodenum begins to develop from the caudal part of the foregut, the cranial part of the midgut, and the splanchnic mesenchyme associated with these endodermal parts of the primordial gut (Fig. 13–5*A*). The junction of the two parts of the duodenum is just distal to the origin of the bile duct (common bile duct). The developing duodenum

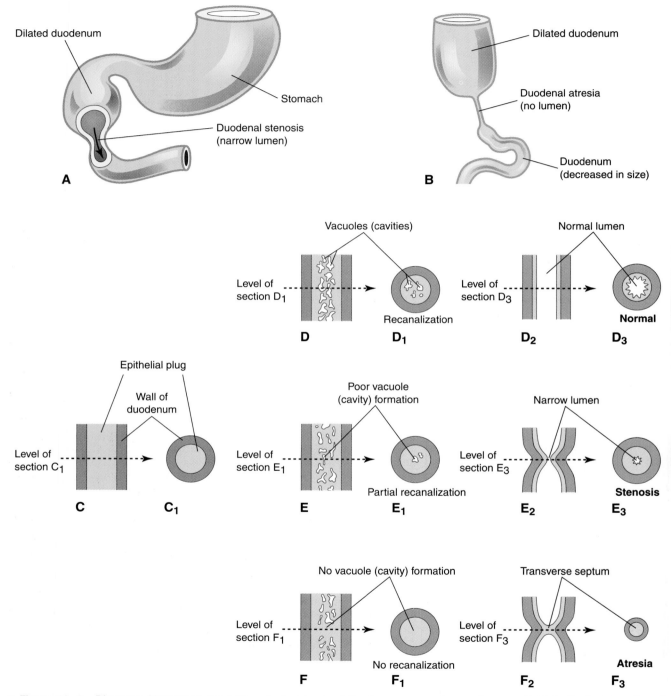

■ **Figure 13–6.** Diagrams illustrating the embryological basis of the two common types of congenital intestinal obstruction. *A,* Duodenal stenosis. *B,* Duodenal atresia. *C* to *F,* Diagrammatic longitudinal and transverse sections of the duodenum showing (1) normal recanalization (*D* to *D_3*), (2) stenosis (*E* to *E_3*), and atresia (*F* to *F_3*). Most duodenal atresias occur in the descending (second) and horizontal (third) parts of the duodenum.

grows rapidly, forming a C-shaped loop that projects ventrally (Fig. 13–5B to D). As the stomach rotates, the duodenal loop rotates to the right and comes to lie retroperitoneally (external to the peritoneum). Because of its derivation from the foregut and midgut, the duodenum is supplied by branches of the celiac and superior mesenteric arteries that supply these parts of the primitive gut (Fig. 13–1). During the fifth and sixth weeks, the lumen of the duodenum becomes progressively smaller and is temporarily obliterated because of the proliferation of its epithelial cells. Normally vacuolation occurs because of regeneration of the epithelial cells; as a result, the duodenum normally becomes recanalized by the end of the embryonic period (Fig. 13–6C and D). By this time most of the ventral mesentery of the duodenum has disappeared.

Duodenal Stenosis

Partial occlusion of the duodenal lumen—duodenal stenosis (Fig. 13–6A)—is usually caused by incomplete recanalization of the duodenum resulting from defective vacuolization (Fig. 13–6E₃). Most stenoses involve the horizontal (third) and/or ascending (fourth) parts of the duodenum. Because of the occlusion, the stomach's contents (usually containing bile) are often expelled.

Duodenal Atresia

Complete occlusion of the lumen of the duodenum—duodenal atresia (Fig. 13–6B)—is not common. Twenty to 30% of affected infants have Down syndrome, and an additional 20% are premature (Wyllie, 1996). In about 20% of cases, the bile duct enters the duodenum just distal to the opening of the hepatopancreatic ampulla (Moore, 1992). During duodenal development, the lumen is completely occluded by epithelial cells. If reformation of the lumen fails to occur (Fig. 13–6D), a short segment of the duodenum is occluded (Fig. 13–6F₂). Investigation of families with *familial duodenal atresia* suggests an autosomal recessive inheritance. Most atresias involve the descending (second) and horizontal (third) parts of the duodenum and are located distal to the opening of the bile duct.

In infants with duodenal atresia, vomiting begins within a few hours of birth. The vomitus almost always contains bile; often, *distention of the epigastrium*—the upper central area of the abdomen—results from an overfilled stomach and superior part of the duodenum. Duodenal atresia may occur as an iso-

lated anomaly, but other severe congenital anomalies are often associated with it, such as Down syndrome, anular pancreas, cardiovascular abnormalities, and anorectal anomalies. **Polyhydramnios** also occurs because duodenal atresia prevents normal absorption of amniotic fluid by the intestines. The diagnosis of duodenal atresia is suggested by the presence of a "double-bubble sign" on plain radiographs or ultrasound scans (Fig. 13–7). The double-bubble appearance is caused by a distended, gas-filled stomach and proximal duodenum.

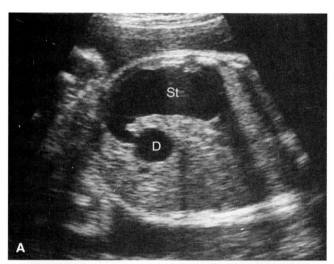

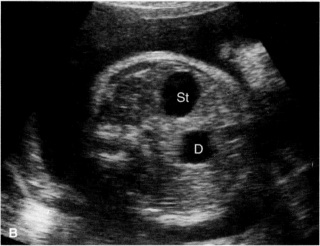

■ **Figure 13–7.** Ultrasound scans of a fetus at 33 weeks of gestation (31 weeks after fertilization) showing duodenal atresia. *A,* An oblique scan showing the dilated, fluid-filled stomach **(St)** entering the proximal duodenum **(D),** which is also enlarged because of the atresia (blockage) distal to it. *B,* Transverse scan illustrating the characteristic "double bubble" appearance of the stomach and duodenum when there is duodenal atresia. (Courtesy of Dr. Lyndon M. Hill, Magee-Women's Hospital, Pittsburgh, Pennsylvania.)

Development of the Liver and Biliary Apparatus

The liver, gallbladder, and biliary duct system arise as a ventral outgrowth from the caudal part of the foregut early in the fourth week (Figs. 13-5A and 13-8A). The **hepatic diverticulum** (liver bud) extends into the septum transversum (Fig. 13-8B), a mass of splanchnic mesoderm between the developing heart and midgut. The septum transversum forms the central tendon of the diaphragm (see Chapter 10) and the ventral mesentery in this region. The hepatic diverticulum enlarges rapidly and divides into two parts as it grows between the layers of the *ventral mesentery* (Fig. 13-5A). The larger cranial part of the hepatic diverticulum is the **primordium of the liver**. The proliferating endodermal cells give rise to interlacing cords of hepatic cells and to the epithelial lining of the intrahepatic portion of the biliary apparatus. The *hepatic cords* anastomose around endothelium-lined

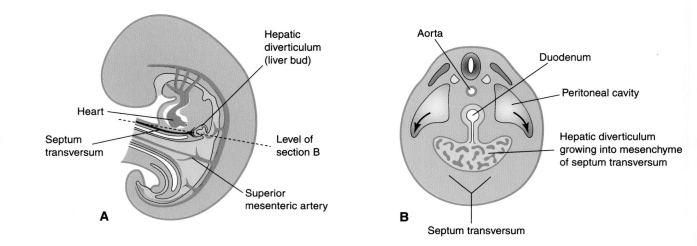

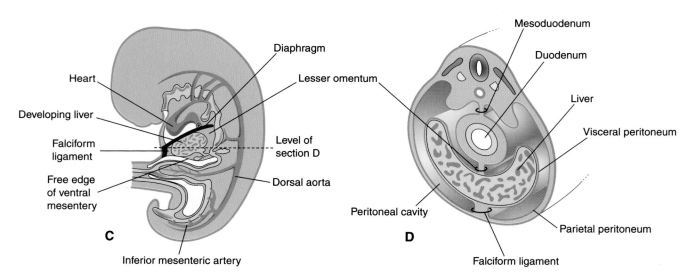

■ **Figure 13-8.** Drawings illustrating how the caudal part of the septum transversum becomes stretched and membranous as it forms the ventral mesentery. *A,* Median section of a 4-week embryo. *B,* Transverse section of the embryo showing expansion of the peritoneal cavity (*arrows*). *C,* Sagittal section of a 5-week embryo. *D,* Transverse section of the embryo after formation of the dorsal and ventral mesenteries. Note that the liver is joined to the ventral abdominal wall and to the stomach and the duodenum by the falciform ligament and lesser omentum, respectively.

spaces the primordia of the *hepatic sinusoids.* The fibrous and *hematopoietic tissue* and *Kupffer cells* of the liver are derived from mesenchyme in the septum transversum.

The liver grows rapidly and, from the 5th to 10th weeks, fills a large part of the abdominal cavity (Fig. 13–8*C* and *D*). The quantity of oxygenated blood flowing from the umbilical vein into the liver determines the development and functional segmentation of the liver. Initially, the right and left lobes are about the same size, but the right lobe soon becomes larger. *Hematopoiesis begins during the sixth week,* giving the liver a bright reddish appearance. This hematopoietic activity (formation of various types of blood cells and other formed elements) is mainly responsible for the relatively large size of the liver between the seventh and ninth weeks of development. By the ninth week, the liver accounts for about 10% of the total weight of the fetus. *Bile formation* by the hepatic cells begins during the 12th week.

The small caudal part of the hepatic diverticulum becomes the **gallbladder,** and the stalk of the diverticulum forms the **cystic duct** (Fig. 13–5*C*). Initially, the extrahepatic biliary apparatus is occluded with epithelial cells, but it is later canalized because of vacuolation resulting from degeneration of these cells. The stalk connecting the hepatic and cystic ducts to the duodenum becomes the **bile duct** (common bile duct). Initially, this duct attaches to the ventral aspect of the duodenal loop; however, as the duodenum grows and rotates, the entrance of the bile duct is carried to the dorsal aspect of the duodenum (Fig. 13–5*C* and *D*). The bile entering the duodenum through the bile duct after the 13th week gives the **meconium** (intestinal contents) a dark green color.

THE VENTRAL MESENTERY

This thin, double-layered membrane gives rise to two structures:

- The *lesser omentum,* passing from the liver to the lesser curvature of the stomach (*hepatogastric ligament*) and from the liver to the duodenum (*hepatoduodenal ligament*)
- The *falciform ligament,* extending from the liver to the ventral abdominal wall

The *umbilical vein* passes in the free border of the falciform ligament on its way from the umbilical cord to the liver. The ventral mesentery also forms the *visceral peritoneum of the liver.* The liver is covered by peritoneum except for the *bare area* that is in direct contact with the diaphragm.

Anomalies of the Liver

Minor variations of liver lobulation are common, but congenital anomalies of the liver are rare. Variations of the hepatic ducts, bile duct, and cystic duct are common and clinically significant (Moore, 1992). *Accessory hepatic ducts* may be present, and awareness of their possible presence is of surgical importance. These accessory ducts are narrow channels running from the right lobe of the liver into the anterior surface of the body of the gallbladder. In some cases, the cystic duct opens into an accessory hepatic duct rather than into the common hepatic duct.

Extrahepatic Biliary Atresia

This is the most serious anomaly of the extrahepatic biliary system and occurs in 1 in 10,000 to 15,000 live births (Balistreri, 1996). The most common form of extrahepatic biliary atresia (present in 85% of cases) is obstruction of the ducts at or superior to the *porta hepatis*—a deep transverse fissure on the visceral surface of the liver, about 5 cm long in adults (Moore, 1992). Failure of the bile ducts to canalize often results from persistence of the solid stage of duct development. Biliary atresia could also result from liver infection during late fetal development. *Jaundice* occurs soon after birth. When biliary atresia cannot be corrected surgically, the child may die if a liver transplant is not performed (Karrer and Raffensperger, 1990).

Development of the Pancreas

The pancreas develops between the layers of the mesentery from dorsal and ventral **pancreatic buds of endodermal cells,** which arise from the caudal part of the foregut that develops into the proximal part of the duodenum (Fig. 13–9). Most of the pancreas is derived from the dorsal pancreatic bud. The larger **dorsal pancreatic bud** appears first and develops a slight distance cranial to the ventral bud. It grows rapidly between the layers of the dorsal mesentery. The **ventral pancreatic bud** develops near the entry of the bile duct into the duodenum and grows between the layers of the ventral mesentery (Fig. 13–10*A* and *B*). As the duodenum rotates to the right and becomes C-shaped, the ventral pancreatic bud is carried dorsally with the bile duct (Fig. 13–10*C* to *F*). It soon lies posterior to the dorsal pancreatic bud and later fuses with it.

The ventral pancreatic bud forms the *uncinate pro-*

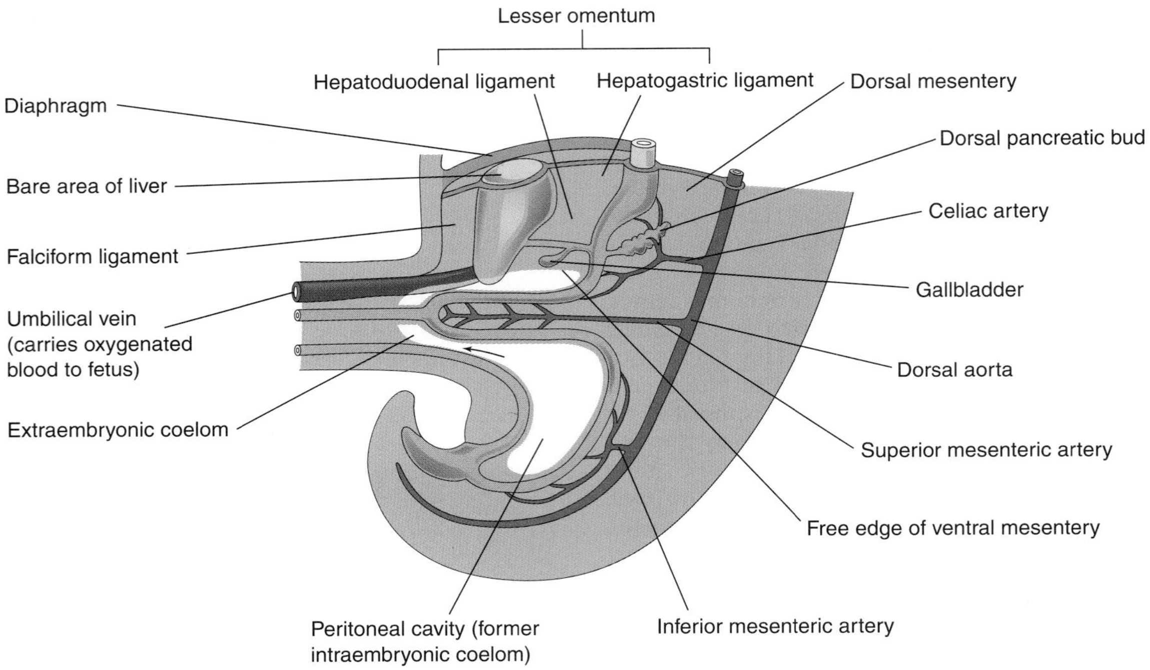

■ **Figure 13–9.** Diagrammatic sketch of a median section of the caudal half of an embryo at the end of the fifth week showing the liver and its associated ligaments. The arrow indicates the communication of the peritoneal cavity with the extraembryonic coelom. Because of the rapid growth of the liver and the midgut loop, the abdominal cavity temporarily becomes too small to contain the developing intestines; consequently, they enter the extraembryonic coelom in the proximal part of the umbilical cord.

cess and part of the head of the pancreas. As the stomach, duodenum, and ventral mesentery rotate, the pancreas comes to lie along the dorsal abdominal wall. As the pancreatic buds fuse, their ducts anastomose. The **main pancreatic duct** forms from the duct of the ventral bud and the distal part of the duct of the dorsal bud (Fig. 13–10*G*). The proximal part of the duct of the dorsal bud often persists as an *accessory pancreatic duct* that opens into the *minor duodenal papilla*, located about 2 cm cranial to the main duct. The two ducts often communicate with each other. In about 9% of people, the pancreatic duct systems fail to fuse and the original two ducts persist (Moore, 1992).

Insulin secretion begins during the early fetal period (10 weeks [von Dorsche, 1990]). The *glucagon-* and *somatostatin*-containing cells develop before differentiation of the insulin-secreting cells. Glucagon has been detected in fetal plasma at 15 weeks. With increasing fetal age, the total pancreatic insulin and glucagon content also increases. The connective tissue sheath and interlobular septa of the pancreas develop from the surrounding splanchnic mesenchyme. When *maternal diabetes mellitus* is present, the insulin-secreting beta cells in the fetal pancreas are chronically exposed to high levels of glucose. As a result, these cells undergo hypertrophy in order to increase the rate of insulin secretion.

Accessory Pancreatic Tissue

Accessory pancreatic tissue is most often located in the wall of the stomach or duodenum or in an ileal (Meckel) diverticulum.

Anular Pancreas

Anular (annular) pancreas is a rare anomaly, but it warrants description because it may cause duodenal obstruction (Fig. 13–11*C*). The ringlike or anular part of the pancreas consists of a thin, flat band of pancreatic tissue surrounding the descending or second part of the duodenum. An anular pancreas may cause obstruction of the duodenum shortly after birth or much

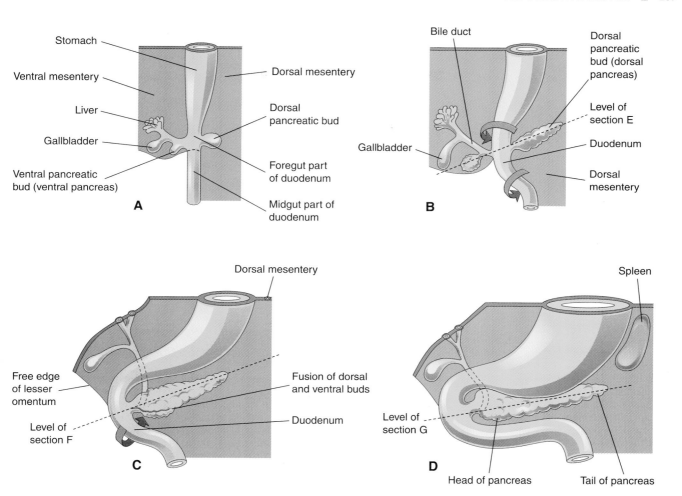

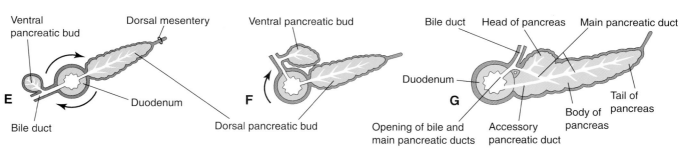

■ **Figure 13–10.** *A* to *D*, Schematic drawings showing successive stages in the development of the pancreas from the fifth to the eighth weeks. *E* to *G*, Diagrammatic transverse sections through the duodenum and developing pancreas. Growth and rotation (*arrows*) of the duodenum bring the ventral pancreatic bud toward the dorsal bud; they subsequently fuse. Note that the bile duct initially attaches to the ventral aspect of the duodenum and is carried around to the dorsal aspect as the duodenum rotates. The main pancreatic duct is formed by the union of the distal part of the dorsal pancreatic duct and the entire ventral pancreatic duct. The proximal part of the dorsal pancreatic duct usually obliterates, but it may persist as an accessory pancreatic duct.

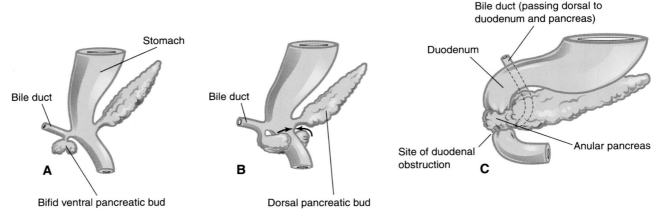

■ **Figure 13–11.** *A* and *B,* Drawings illustrating the probable embryological basis of an anular (annular) pancreas. *C,* An anular pancreas encircling the duodenum. This anomaly sometimes produces complete obstruction (atresia) or partial obstruction (stenosis) of the duodenum. In most cases the anular pancreas encircles the second part of the duodenum, distal to the hepatopancreatic ampulla; see Moore (1992) for a discussion of the clinical anatomy of this ampulla.

later. Blockage of the duodenum develops if inflammation or malignant disease develops in an anular pancreas. An increased incidence of pancreatitis and peptic ulcer have been detected in patients with this abnormal pancreas. Males are affected much more frequently than females. Anular pancreas probably results from the growth of a bifid ventral pancreatic bud around the duodenum (Fig. 13-11*A* to *C*). The parts of the bifid ventral bud then fuse with the dorsal bud, forming a pancreatic ring (L. anulus).

Accessory Spleen

One or more small splenic masses may develop in one of the peritoneal folds, commonly near the hilum of the spleen or adjacent to the tail of the pancreas. An accessory spleen occurs in about 10% of people and is usually about 1 cm in diameter. An accessory spleen may be embedded partly or wholly in the tail of the pancreas or within the gastrosplenic ligament.

DEVELOPMENT OF THE SPLEEN

Development of the spleen is described with the digestive system because this organ is derived from a mass of mesenchymal cells located between the layers of the dorsal mesogastrium (Fig. 13-12*A* and *B*). The spleen, a large vascular lymphatic organ, begins to develop during the fifth week but does not acquire its characteristic shape until early in the fetal period. The spleen is lobulated in the fetus, but the lobules normally disappear before birth. The notches in the superior border of the adult spleen are remnants of the grooves that separated the fetal lobules (Moore, 1992). As the stomach rotates, the left surface of the mesogastrium fuses with the peritoneum over the left kidney. This fusion explains the dorsal attachment of the *splenorenal ligament* (lienorenal ligament) and why the adult splenic artery, the largest branch of the celiac trunk, follows a tortuous course posterior to the omental bursa and anterior to the left kidney (Fig. 13-12*C* to *E*).

THE MIDGUT

The derivatives of the midgut are:

- The small intestine, including most of the duodenum
- The cecum, vermiform appendix, ascending colon, and right half to two thirds of the transverse colon

All these midgut derivatives are supplied by the **superior mesenteric artery**, the artery of the midgut (Fig. 13-1). The midgut loop is suspended from the dorsal abdominal wall by an elongated mesentery (Fig. 13-13*A*). As the midgut elongates, it forms a ventral, U-shaped loop of gut—the **midgut loop**—which projects into the remains of the extraembryonic coelom in the proximal part of the umbilical cord. At this stage, the intraembryonic coelom communicates with extraembryonic coelom at the umbilicus (Fig. 13-9). This movement of the intestine is a **physiologic umbilical herniation**. It occurs at the beginning of the

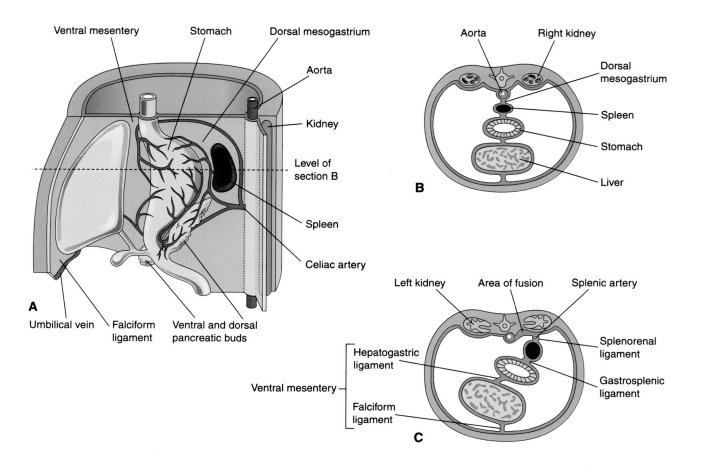

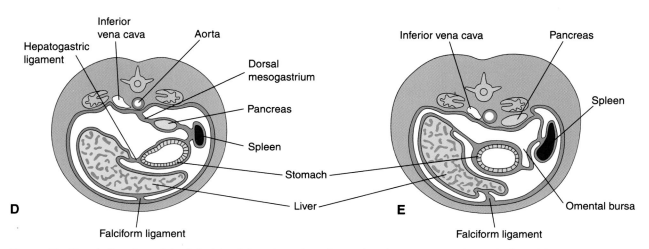

■ Figure 13–12. *A,* Drawing of the left side of the stomach and associated structures at the end of the fifth week. Note that the pancreas, spleen, and celiac artery are between the layers of the dorsal mesogastrium. *B,* Transverse section of the liver, stomach, and spleen at the level shown in *A,* illustrating their relationship to the dorsal and ventral mesenteries. *C,* Transverse section of a fetus showing fusion of the dorsal mesogastrium with the peritoneum on the posterior abdominal wall. *D* and *E,* Similar sections showing movement of the liver to the right and rotation of the stomach. Observe the fusion of the dorsal mesogastrium to the dorsal abdominal wall. As a result, the pancreas becomes retroperitoneal.

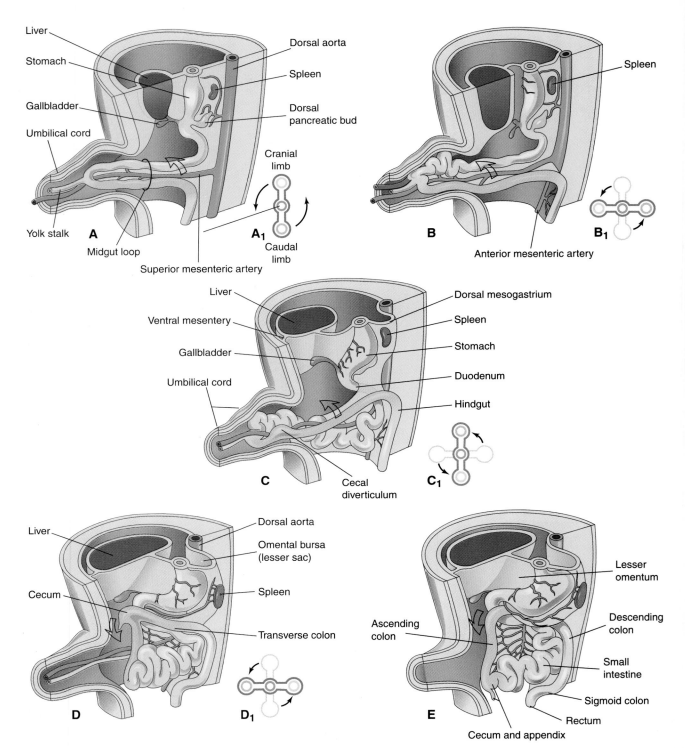

■ **Figure 13–13.** Schematic drawings illustrating the rotation of the midgut, as seen from the left. *A,* Around the beginning of the sixth week, showing the midgut loop in the proximal part of the umbilical cord. *A₁,* Transverse section through the midgut loop, illustrating the initial relationship of the limbs of the midgut loop to the artery. *B,* Later stage showing the beginning of midgut rotation. *B₁,* Illustrates the 90-degree counterclockwise rotation that carries the cranial limb of the midgut to the right. *C,* About 10 weeks, showing the intestines returning to the abdomen. *C₁,* Illustrates a further rotation of 90 degrees. *D,* About 11 weeks, after return of intestines to the abdomen. *D₁,* Shows a further 90-degree rotation of the gut, for a total of 270 degrees. *E,* Later fetal period, showing the cecum rotating to its normal position in the lower right quadrant of the abdomen.

sixth week and is the normal migration of the midgut into the umbilical cord (Figs. 13 – 13 and 13 – 14). The midgut loop communicates with the yolk sac through the narrow *yolk stalk* until the 10th week. Umbilical herniation occurs because there is not enough room in the abdomen for the rapidly growing midgut. The shortage of space is caused mainly by the relatively massive liver and the two sets of kidneys that exist during this period of development.

The midgut loop has a cranial limb and a caudal limb. The *yolk stalk* is attached to the apex of the midgut loop where the two limbs join (Fig. 13 – 13A). The cranial limb grows rapidly and forms small intestinal loops, but the caudal limb undergoes very little change except for development of the **cecal diverticulum**, the primordium of the cecum and appendix (Fig. 13 – 13C).

Rotation of the Midgut Loop

While it is in the umbilical cord, the midgut loop rotates 90 degrees counterclockwise around the axis of the *superior mesenteric artery* (Fig. 13 – 13B). This brings the cranial limb of the midgut loop to the right and the caudal limb to the left. During rotation, the midgut elongates and forms loops of small bowel (jejunum and ileum).

RETURN OF THE MIDGUT TO THE ABDOMEN

During the 10th week, the intestines return to the abdomen (Fig. 13 – 13C and D). It is not known what causes the intestine to return, but the decrease in the size of the liver and kidneys and the enlargement of the abdominal cavity are important factors. This process has been called *reduction of the physiologic midgut hernia*. The small intestine (formed from the cranial limb) returns first, passing posterior to the superior mesenteric artery and occupying the central part of the abdomen. As the large intestine returns, it undergoes a further 180-degree counterclockwise rotation (Fig. 13 – 13C, and D,). Later it comes to occupy the right side of the abdomen. The ascending colon becomes recognizable as the posterior abdominal wall progressively elongates (Figs. 13 – 13E and 13 – 15A).

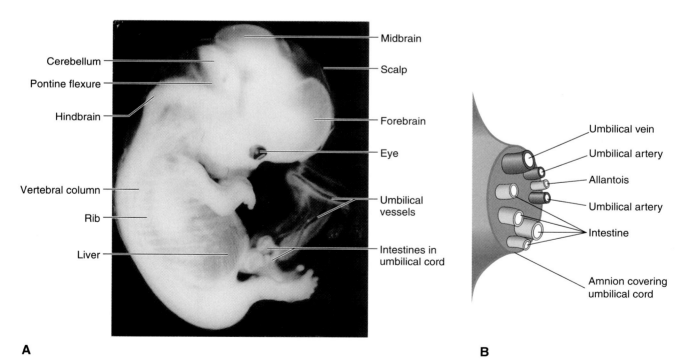

A

B

■ Figure 13–14. *A*, Photograph of a 28-mm human embryo (about 56 days). Note the herniated intestine derived from the midgut loop in the proximal part of the umbilical cord. Also note the umbilical blood vessels. Observe also the cartilaginous ribs, the prominent eye, the large liver, and the relatively well-developed brain. (Courtesy of Dr. Bruce Fraser, former Associate Professor of Anatomy, Faculty of Medicine, Memorial University, St. John's, Newfoundland, Canada.) *B*, Schematic drawing showing the structures in the proximal part of the umbilical cord.

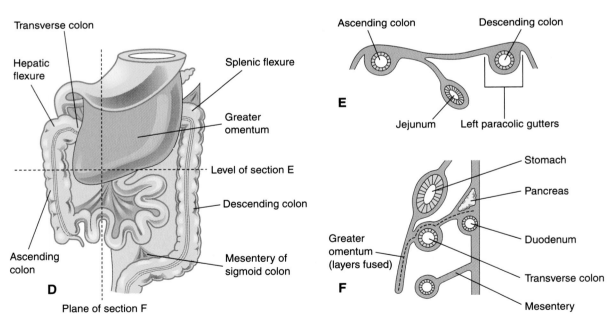

■ **Figure 13–15.** Fixation of the intestines. *A,* Ventral view of the intestines prior to their fixation. *B,* Transverse section at the level shown in *A*. The arrows indicate areas of subsequent fusion. *C,* Sagittal section at the plane shown in *A,* illustrating the greater omentum overhanging the transverse colon. The *arrows* indicate areas of subsequent fusion. *D,* Ventral view of the intestines after their fixation. *E,* Transverse section at the level shown in *D* after disappearance of the mesentery of the ascending and descending colon. *F,* Sagittal section at the plane shown in *D,* illustrating fusion of the greater omentum with the mesentery of the transverse colon and fusion of the layers of the greater omentum.

FIXATION OF THE INTESTINES

Rotation of the stomach and duodenum causes the duodenum and pancreas to fall to the right, where they are pressed against the posterior abdominal wall by the colon. The adjacent layers of peritoneum fuse and subsequently disappear (Fig. 13–15C and F); consequently, most of the duodenum and the head of the pancreas become retroperitoneal (posterior to the peritoneum). The attachment of the dorsal mesentery to the posterior abdominal wall is greatly modified after the intestines return to the abdominal cavity. At first the dorsal mesentery is in the median plane. As the intestines enlarge, lengthen, and assume their final positions, their mesenteries are pressed against the posterior abdominal wall. The mesentery of the ascending colon fuses with the parietal peritoneum on this wall and disappears; consequently, the ascending colon also becomes retroperitoneal (Fig. 13–15B and E).

The enlarged colon presses the duodenum against the posterior abdominal wall; as a result, most of the duodenal mesentery is absorbed (Fig. 13–15C, D, and F). Consequently, the duodenum, except for about the first 2.5 cm (derived from the foregut), has no mesentery and lies retroperitoneally. Other derivatives of the midgut loop (e.g., the jejunum and ileum) retain their mesenteries. The mesentery is at first attached to the median plane of the posterior abdominal wall (Fig. 13–13B and C). After the mesentery of the ascending colon disappears, the fan-shaped mesentery of the small intestines acquires a new line of attachment that passes from the duodenojejunal junction inferolaterally to the ileocecal junction (Fig. 13–15D).

The Cecum and Vermiform Appendix

The primordium of the cecum and wormlike (L. vermiform) appendix—the **cecal diverticulum**—appears in the sixth week as a swelling on the antimesenteric border of the caudal limb of the midgut loop (Figs. 13–13C and D and 13–16A). The apex of the cecal

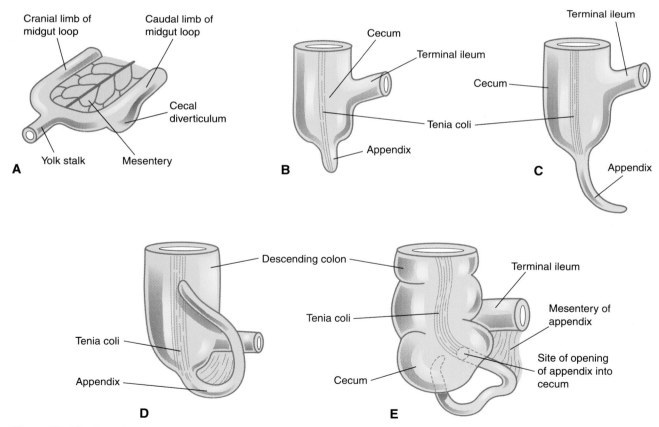

■ **Figure 13–16.** Drawings showing successive stages in the development of the cecum and vermiform appendix. *A,* Six weeks. *B,* Eight weeks. *C,* Twelve weeks. *D,* At birth. Note that the appendix is relatively long and is continuous with the apex of the cecum. *E,* Adult. Note that the appendix is now relatively short and lies on the medial side of the cecum. In about 64% of people, the appendix is located posterior to the cecum (retrocecal). In about 32% of people, it appears as illustrated in *E.* The tenia coli is a thickened band of longitudinal muscle in the wall of the colon, which ends at the base of the appendix.

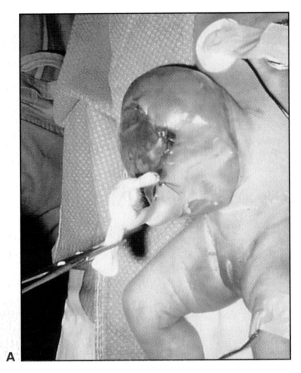

A

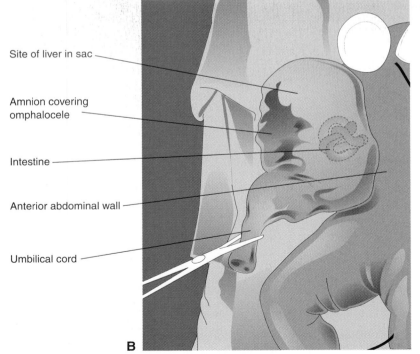

Site of liver in sac

Amnion covering
omphalocele

Intestine

Anterior abdominal wall

Umbilical cord

B

■ **Figure 13–17.** *A,* Photograph of an infant with an omphalocele. (Courtesy of Dr. NE Wiseman, Pediatric Surgeon, Children's Hospital, Winnipeg, Manitoba, Canada.) *B,* Drawing of the same infant with a large omphalocele resulting from a median defect of the abdominal muscles, fascia, and skin at the umbilicus. The defect resulted in the herniation of intra-abdominal structures (liver and intestine) into the proximal end of the umbilical cord. It is covered by a membrane composed of peritoneum and amnion. In some cases, an omphalocele may be a persistence of the normal embryonic stage of umbilical herniation.

diverticulum does not grow as rapidly as the rest of it; thus, the appendix is initially a small diverticulum of the cecum. The appendix increases rapidly in length so that at birth it is a relatively long, worm-shaped tube arising from the distal end of the cecum (Fig. 13-16D). After birth the wall of the cecum grows unequally, with the result that the appendix comes to enter its medial side (Fig. 13-16E). The appendix is subject to considerable variation in position. As the ascending colon elongates, the appendix may pass posterior to the cecum (*retrocecal appendix*) or colon (*retrocolic appendix*). It may also descend over the brim of the pelvis (*pelvic appendix*). *In about 64% of people, the appendix is located retrocecally* (Moore, 1992).

Anomalies of the Midgut

Congenital abnormalities of the intestine are common; most of them are anomalies of gut rotation — **malrotation of the gut** — that result from incomplete rotation and/or fixation of the intestines.

Congenital Omphalocele

Congenital omphalocele is a persistence of the herniation of abdominal contents into the proximal part of the umbilical cord (Figs. 13-17 and 13-18). Herniation of intestines into the cord occurs in about 1 in 5000 births and herniation of liver and intestines in 1 in about 10,000 births (Kliegman, 1996). The size of the hernia depends on its contents. The abdominal cavity is proportionately small when an omphalocele is present because the impetus for it to grow is absent. Immediate surgical repair is required (Behrman et al, 1996). Omphalocele results from failure of the intestines to return to the abdominal cavity during the 10th week. The covering of the hernial sac is the epithelium of the umbilical cord, a derivative of the amnion.

Umbilical Hernia

When the intestines return to the abdominal cavity during the 10th week and then herniate through an imperfectly closed umbilicus, an umbilical hernia forms. This common type of hernia is different from an omphalocele. In umbilical hernia, the protruding mass (usually the greater omentum and some of the small intestine) is covered by subcutaneous tissue and skin. The hernia usually does not reach its maximum size until the end of the first month after birth. It usually ranges from 1 to 5 cm. The defect through which the hernia occurs is in the linea alba (Moore, 1992). The hernia protrudes during crying, straining, or coughing and can be easily reduced through the fibrous ring at the umbilicus. Surgery is not usually

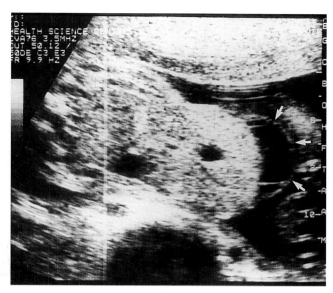

■ **Figure 13-18.** Sonogram of the abdomen of a fetus (28 weeks' gestation) showing a large omphalocele, with much of the liver protruding from the abdomen. The mass also contained a small membrane-covered sac (*small arrows*). The umbilical cord was integrally involved in the anomaly. (Courtesy of Dr. CR Harman, Department of Obstetrics, Gynecology and Reproductive Sciences, Women's Hospital and University of Manitoba, Winnipeg, Manitoba, Canada.)

performed unless the hernia persists to the age of 3 to 5 years (Kliegman, 1996).

Gastroschisis

This anomaly is among the more common of the congenital abdominal wall defects (Fig. 13-19). Gastroschisis results from a defect near the median plane of the ventral abdominal wall. The linear defect permits extrusion of the abdominal viscera without involving the umbilical cord. The viscera protrude into the amniotic cavity and are bathed by amniotic fluid. The term *gastroschisis*, which literally means a "split or open stomach," is a misnomer because the anterior abdominal wall, not the stomach, is split. The defect usually occurs on the right side near the median plane and is more common in males than females. The anomaly results from incomplete closure of the lateral folds during the fourth week (see Chapter 6). Exposure to environmental drugs and chemicals might be involved in the development of gastroschisis.

Nonrotation of the Midgut

This relatively common condition, sometimes called *left-sided colon*, is generally asymptomatic, but twisting of the intestines (*volvulus*) may occur (Fig. 13-20A). Nonrotation occurs when the midgut loop does

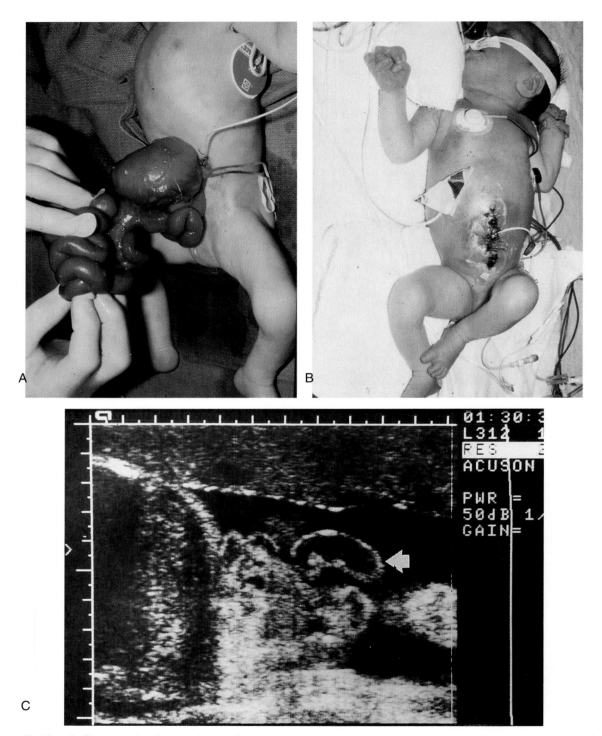

■ **Figure 13–19.** *A,* Photograph of a newborn infant with an anterior abdominal wall defect—gastroschisis. The defect was relatively small (2 to 4 cm) and involved all layers of the abdominal wall. It was located to the right of the umbilicus. *B,* Photograph of the infant after the viscera were returned to the abdomen and the defect was surgically closed. *C,* Sonogram of fetus (20 weeks' gestation) with gastroschisis. Loops of small bowel can be seen floating freely in the amniotic fluid (arrow) anterior to the fetal abdomen (left). *A* and *B,* courtesy of Dr. AE Chudley, Section of Genetics and Metabolism, Department of Pediatrics and Child Health, Children's Hospital, Winnipeg, Manitoba, Canada. *C,* courtesy of Dr. CR Harman, Department of Obstetrics, Gynecology and Reproductive Services, Women's Hospital and University of Manitoba, Winnipeg, Manitoba, Canada.)

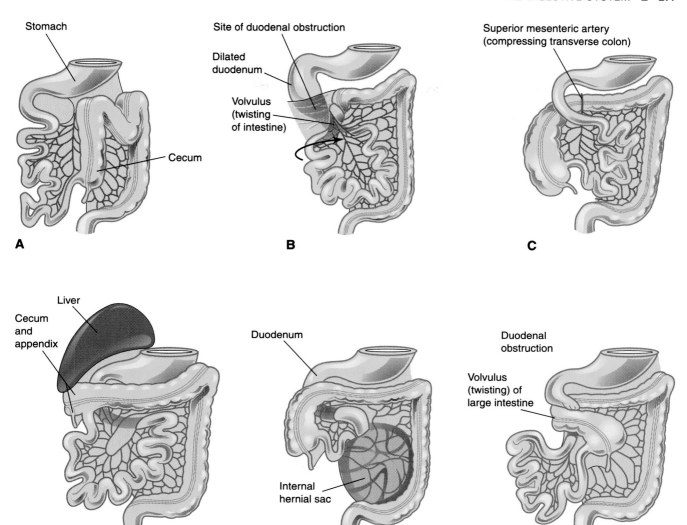

■ Figure 13–20. Drawings illustrating various abnormalities of midgut rotation. *A,* Nonrotation. *B,* Mixed rotation and volvulus. *C,* Reversed rotation. *D,* Subhepatic cecum and appendix. *E,* Internal hernia. *F,* Midgut volvulus.

not rotate as it reenters the abdomen. As a result, the caudal limb of the loop returns to the abdomen first, and the small intestine lies on the right side of the abdomen and the entire large intestine on the left. When volvulus occurs, the superior mesenteric artery may be obstructed, resulting in infarction and gangrene of the bowel supplied by it.

Mixed Rotation and Volvulus

In this condition, the cecum lies just inferior to the pylorus of the stomach and is fixed to the posterior abdominal wall by peritoneal bands that pass over the duodenum (Fig. 13–20B). These bands and the volvulus of the intestines usually cause **duodenal obstruction**. This type of malrotation results from failure of the midgut loop to complete the final 90 degrees of rotation (Fig. 13–13D); consequently, the terminal part of the ileum returns to the abdomen first.

Reversed Rotation

In very unusual cases, the midgut loop rotates in a clockwise rather than a counterclockwise direction (Fig. 13–20C). As a result, the duodenum lies anterior to the superior mesenteric artery (SMA) rather than posterior to it, and the transverse colon lies posterior to the SMA instead of anterior to it. In these infants, the transverse colon may be obstructed by pressure from the SMA. In very rare cases, the small intestine lies on the left side of the abdomen and the large intestine lies on the right side, with the cecum in the center. This unusual situation results from malrotation of the midgut followed by failure of fixation of the intestines.

Subhepatic Cecum and Appendix

If the cecum adheres to the inferior surface of the liver when it returns to the abdomen (Fig. 13-13D), it is drawn superiorly as the liver diminishes in size; as a result, the cecum remains in its fetal position (Fig. 13-20D). Subhepatic cecum and appendix are more common in males and occur in about 6% of fetuses. Subhepatic cecum is not common in adults; however, when it occurs, it may create a problem in the diagnosis of appendicitis and during the surgical removal of the appendix (*appendectomy*).

Mobile Cecum

In about 10% of people, the cecum has an unusual amount of freedom. *In very unusual cases* it may herniate into the right inguinal canal. A mobile cecum results from incomplete fixation of the ascending colon. This condition is clinically significant because of the possible variations in position of the appendix (Moore, 1992) and because twisting or volvulus of the cecum may occur.

Internal Hernia

In this anomaly, the small intestine passes into the mesentery of the midgut loop during the return of the intestines to the abdomen (Fig. 13-20E). As a result, a hernialike sac forms. This very uncommon condition usually does not produce symptoms and is often detected at autopsy or during an anatomic dissection.

Midgut Volvulus

In this anomaly the small intestine fails to enter the abdominal cavity normally, and the mesenteries fail to undergo normal fixation; as a result, twisting of the intestines occurs (Fig. 13-20F). Only two parts of the intestine are attached to the posterior abdominal wall, the duodenum and the proximal colon. The small intestine hangs by a narrow stalk that contains the superior mesenteric artery and vein. These vessels are usually twisted in this stalk and become obstructed at or near the duodenojejunal junction. The circulation to the twisted segment is often restricted; if the vessels are completely obstructed, gangrene develops.

Stenosis and Atresia of the Intestine

Partial occlusion (stenosis) and complete occlusion (atresia) of the intestinal lumen (Fig. 13-6) account for about one third of cases of intestinal obstruction

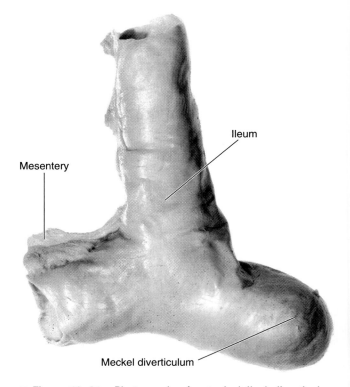

■ **Figure 13-21.** Photograph of a typical ileal diverticulum, commonly referred to clinically as a Meckel diverticulum. This is a cadaveric specimen. Only a small percentage of these diverticula produce symptoms. Ileal diverticula are one of the most common anomalies of the digestive tract. They occur in 2 to 4% of people and are three to four times more prevalent in males than females. (From Moore KL, Persaud TVN, Shiota K: Color Atlas of Clinical Embryology. Philadelphia, WB Saunders, 1994.)

(Wyllie, 1996). The obstructive lesion occurs most often in the duodenum (25%) and ileum (50%). The length of the area affected varies. These anomalies result from failure of an adequate number of vacuoles to form during recanalization of the intestine (Fig. 13-6). In some cases a transverse diaphragm forms, producing **diaphragmatic atresia** (Fig. 13-6F₂). Another possible cause of stenoses and atresias is interruption of the blood supply to a loop of fetal intestine resulting from a **fetal vascular accident**; for example, an excessively mobile loop of intestine may become twisted, thereby interrupting its blood supply and leading to necrosis of the section of bowel involved. This necrotic segment later becomes a fibrous cord connecting the proximal and distal ends of normal intestine. Most atresias of the ileum are probably caused by infarction of the fetal bowel as the result of impairment of its blood supply resulting from volvulus. This impairment most likely occurs during the 10th week as the intestines return to the abdomen. Malfixation of the gut predisposes it to volvulus, strangulation, and impairment of its blood supply.

Ileal Diverticulum and Other Yolk Stalk Remnants

This outpouching is one of the most common anomalies of the digestive tract (Fig. 13–21). A congenital ileal diverticulum (Meckel diverticulum) occurs in 2 to 4% of people (Moore, 1992) and is three to five times more prevalent in males than females. *An ileal diverticulum is of clinical significance* because it sometimes becomes inflamed and causes symptoms that mimic appendicitis. The wall of the diverticulum contains all layers of the ileum and may contain small patches of gastric and pancreatic tissues. The gastric mucosa often secretes acid, producing ulceration and bleeding (Fig. 13–22A). An ileal diverticulum is the remnant of the proximal portion of the yolk stalk. It typically appears as a fingerlike pouch about 3 to 6 cm long that *arises from the antimesenteric border of the ileum* (Fig. 13–18) 40 to 50 cm from the ileocecal junction. An ileal diverticulum may be connected to the umbilicus by a fibrous cord or an **umbilicoileal fistula** (Fig. 13–22B and C and 13–23A and B); other possible remnants of the yolk stalk are illustrated in Figure 13–22D to F.

Duplication of the Intestine

Most intestinal duplications are cystic duplications or tubular duplications. *Cystic duplications* are more common (Fig. 13–24A and B). Tubular duplications usually communicate with the intestinal lumen (Fig. 13–24C and D). Almost all duplications are caused by failure of normal recanalization; as a result, two lumina form (Fig. 13–24E to I). The duplicated segment of the bowel lies on the mesenteric side of the intestine.

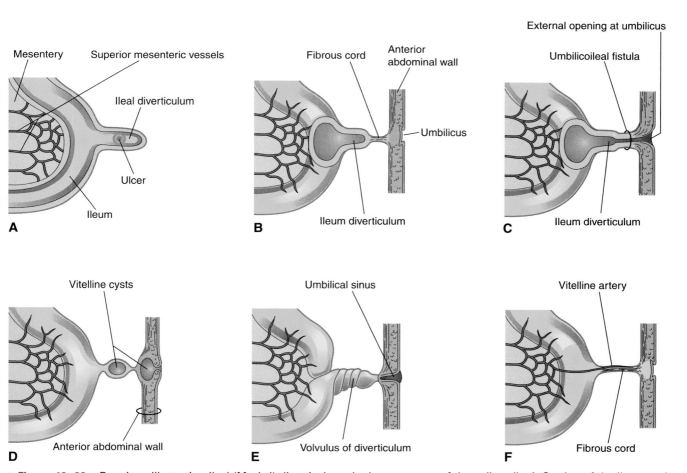

■ **Figure 13–22.** Drawings illustrating ileal (Meckel) diverticula and other remnants of the yolk stalk. *A,* Section of the ileum and a diverticulum with an ulcer. *B,* A diverticulum connected to the umbilicus by a fibrous cord. *C,* Umbilicoileal fistula resulting from persistence of the entire intra-abdominal portion of the yolk stalk. *D,* Vitelline cysts at the umbilicus and in a fibrous remnant of the yolk stalk. *E,* Umbilical sinus resulting from the persistence of the yolk stalk near the umbilicus. *F,* The yolk stalk has persisted as a fibrous cord connecting the ileum with the umbilicus. A persistent vitelline artery extends along the fibrous cord to the umbilicus.

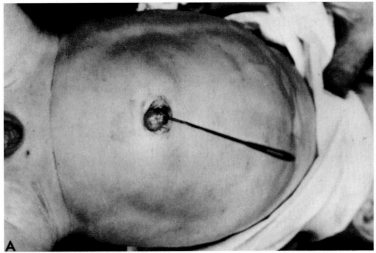

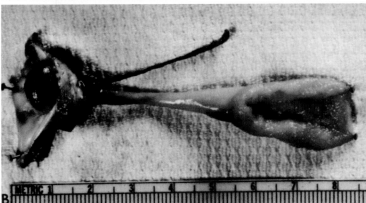

■ **Figure 13–23.** *A,* Photograph of the abdomen of an infant with an umbilicoileal fistula. A probe has been inserted into the fistula. It extends from the umbilicus to the ileum (a distance of about 5 cm). *B,* The excised fistula with a granulomatous-looking bulge at the ileal end. (From Avery ME and Taeusch HW: *Schaffers Diseases of the Newborn,* 5th ed. Philadelphia, WB Saunders, 1984, p. 383.)

THE HINDGUT

The derivatives of the hindgut are the following:

- The left one third to one half of the transverse colon; the descending colon and sigmoid colon; the rectum and the superior part of the anal canal
- The epithelium of the urinary bladder and most of the urethra (see Chapter 14)

All these hindgut derivatives are supplied by the *inferior mesenteric artery,* the artery of the hindgut. The junction between the segment of transverse colon derived from the midgut and that originating from the hindgut is indicated by the change in blood supply from a branch of the superior mesenteric artery (midgut artery) to a branch of the inferior mesenteric artery (hindgut artery). The descending colon becomes retroperitoneal as its mesentery fuses with the peritoneum on the left posterior abdominal wall and then disappears (Fig. 13–15). The mesentery of the sigmoid colon is retained, but it is shorter than in the embryo.

The Cloaca

This terminal portion of the hindgut is an endoderm-lined cavity that is in contact with the surface ectoderm at the **cloacal membrane** (Fig. 13–25A and *B*). This membrane is composed of endoderm of the cloaca and ectoderm of the **proctodeum** or anal pit (Fig. 13–25D). The cloaca, the expanded terminal part of the hindgut, receives the *allantois* ventrally (Fig. 13–25A); the allantois is a fingerlike diverticulum of the yolk sac. For a description of this rudimentary structure, see Chapter 5.

PARTITIONING OF THE CLOACA

The cloaca is divided into dorsal and ventral parts by a wedge of mesenchyme—the **urorectal septum**—

which develops in the angle between the allantois and hindgut. As the septum grows toward the cloacal membrane, it develops forklike extensions that produce infoldings of the lateral walls of the cloaca (Fig. 13-25B_1). These folds grow toward each other and fuse, forming a partition that divides the cloaca into two parts (Fig. 13-25D_1 and F_1):

- The *rectum* and cranial part of the *anal canal* dorsally
- The *urogenital sinus* ventrally

By the seventh week, the urorectal septum has fused with the cloacal membrane, dividing it into a dorsal **anal membrane** and a larger ventral **urogenital membrane** (Fig. 13-25E and F). The area of fusion of the urorectal septum with the cloacal membrane is represented in the adult by the **perineal body**, the tendinous center of the perineum (Moore, 1992). This fibromuscular node is the *landmark of the perineum* where several muscles converge and attach. The urorectal septum also divides the **cloacal sphincter** into anterior and posterior parts. The posterior part becomes the *external anal sphincter*, and the anterior part develops into the superficial transverse perineal, bulbospongiosus, and ischiocavernosus muscles (Moore, 1992). This developmental fact explains

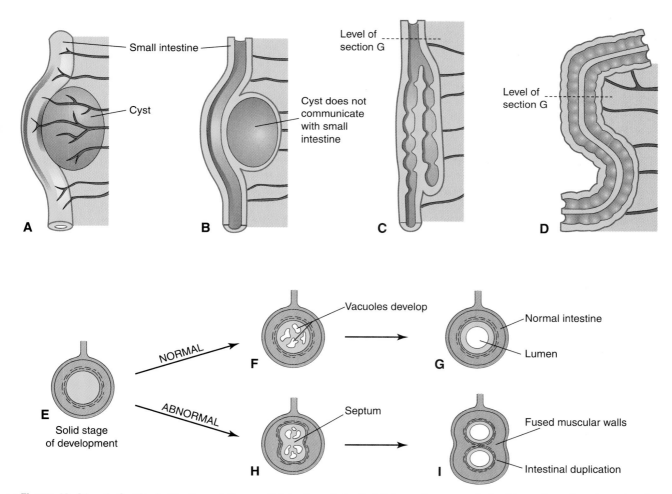

■ **Figure 13–24.** *A,* Cystic duplication of the small intestine. Note that it is on the mesenteric side and receives branches from the arteries supplying the intestine. *B,* Longitudinal section of the duplication shown in *A.* It does not communicate with the intestine, but its musculature is continuous with the gut wall. *C,* A short tubular duplication of the small intestine. *D,* A long duplication of the small intestine showing a partition consisting of the fused muscular wall. *E,* Transverse section of the intestine during the solid stage. *F,* Normal vacuole formation. *G,* Coalescence of the vacuoles and reformation of the lumen. *H,* Two groups of vacuoles have formed. *I,* Coalescence of the vacuoles illustrated in *H* results in intestinal duplication.

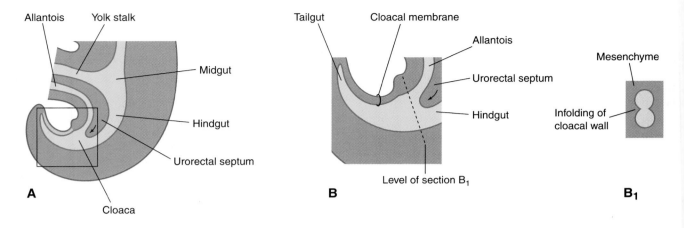

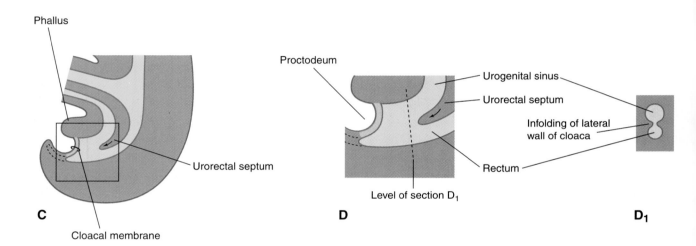

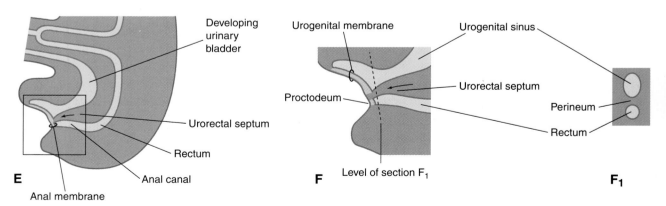

■ **Figure 13–25.** Drawings illustrating successive stages in the partitioning of the cloaca into the rectum and urogenital sinus by the urorectal septum. *A, C,* and *E,* Views from the left side at 4, 6, and 7 weeks respectively. *B, D,* and *F,* Enlargements of the cloacal region. *B₁, D₁* and *F₁,* Transverse sections of the cloaca at the levels shown in *B, D,* and *F,* respectively. Note that the tailgut (shown in *B*) degenerates and disappears as the rectum forms from the dorsal part of the cloaca (shown in *C*).

why one nerve, the **pudendal nerve**, supplies all these muscles. Mesenchymal proliferations produce elevations of the surface ectoderm around the **anal membrane**. As a result, this membrane is soon located at the bottom of an ectodermal depression — the **proctodeum** or anal pit (Fig. 13 – 25E). The anal membrane usually ruptures at the end of the eighth week, bringing the distal part of the digestive tract (anal canal) into communication with the amniotic cavity.

THE ANAL CANAL

The superior two thirds (about 25 mm) of the adult anal canal are derived from the *hindgut*; the inferior one third (about 13 mm) develops from the **proctodeum** (Fig. 13 – 26). The junction of the epithelium derived from the ectoderm of the proctodeum and the endoderm of the hindgut is roughly indicated by the irregular **pectinate line**, located at the inferior limit of the anal valves (Moore, 1992). This line indicates the approximate former site of the anal membrane. About 2 cm superior to the anus is an **anocutaneous line** ("white line"). This is approximately where the composition of the anal epithelium changes from columnar to stratified squamous cells. At the anus, the epithelium is keratinized and continuous with the skin around the anus. The other layers of the wall of the anal canal are derived from splanchnic mesenchyme. Scanty information is available on the morphologic differentiation of the anal sphincter muscles (Bourdelat et al, 1990).

Because of its hindgut origin, the superior two thirds of the anal canal are supplied mainly by the *superior rectal artery*, the continuation of the inferior mesenteric artery (hindgut artery). The venous drainage of this superior part is mainly via the *superior rectal vein*, a tributary of the inferior mesenteric vein. The lymphatic drainage of the superior part is eventually to the *inferior mesenteric lymph nodes*. Its nerves are from the autonomic nervous system. Because of its origin from the proctodeum, the inferior one third of the anal canal is supplied mainly by the *inferior rectal arteries*, branches of the internal pudendal artery. The venous drainage is through the *inferior rectal vein*, a tributary of the internal pudendal vein that drains into the internal iliac vein. The lymphatic drainage of the inferior part of the anal canal is to the *superficial inguinal lymph nodes*. Its nerve supply is from the *inferior rectal nerve*; hence, it is sensitive to pain, temperature, touch, and pressure.

The differences in blood supply, nerve supply, and venous and lymphatic drainage of the anal canal are important clinically (Moore, 1992), such as when considering the metastasis (spread) of tumor cells. The characteristics of carcinomas in the two parts also differ. Tumors in the superior part are painless and arise from columnar epithelium, whereas those in the inferior part are painful and arise from squamous epithelium.

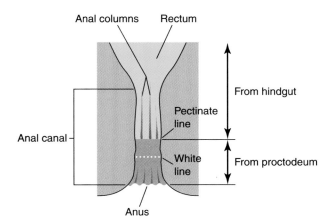

■ **Figure 13–26.** Sketch of the rectum and anal canal showing their developmental origins. Note that the superior two thirds of the anal canal are derived from the hindgut and are endodermal in origin, whereas the inferior one third of the anal canal is derived from the proctodeum and is ectodermal in origin. Because of their different embryological origins, the superior and inferior parts of the anal canal are supplied by different arteries and nerves and have different venous and lymphatic drainages.

Anomalies of the Hindgut

Most anomalies of the hindgut are located in the anorectal region and result from abnormal development of the urorectal septum. Clinically, they are divided into high and low anomalies, depending on whether the rectum terminates superior or inferior to the *puborectal sling* formed by the puborectalis, a part of the levator ani muscle (Moore, 1992).

Congenital Megacolon

In infants with congenital megacolon, or **Hirschsprung disease** (Fig. 13 – 27), a part of the colon is dilated because of the *absence of autonomic ganglion cells* in the myenteric plexus distal to the dilated segment of colon. The enlarged colon — **megacolon** (Gr. *megas*, big) — has the normal number of ganglion cells. The dilation results from failure of peristalsis in the aganglionic segment, which prevents movement of the intestinal contents. In most cases only the rectum and sigmoid colon are involved, but occasionally ganglia are also absent from more proximal parts of the colon. Congenital megacolon is the most common cause of neonatal obstruction of the colon and accounts for 33% of all neonatal obstructions; males are affected more often than females (4:1). Congenital

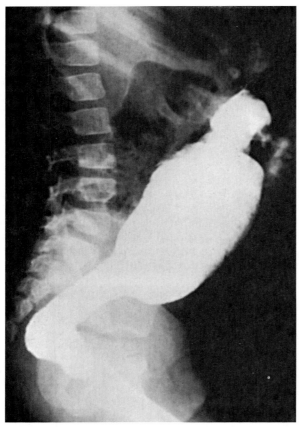

■ **Figure 13–27.** Lateral radiographic view of the colon after a barium enema in a 3-year-old girl with Hirschsprung disease. The aganglionic distal segment is narrow, with distended normal ganglionic bowel above it. (From Behrman RE, Kliegman RM, Arvin AM (eds): *Nelson Textbook of Pediatrics*, 15th ed. Philadelphia, WB Saunders, 1996.)

megacolon results from failure of neural crest cells to migrate into the wall of the colon during the fifth to seventh weeks. This results in failure of parasympathetic ganglion cells to develop in the *Auerbach and Meissner plexuses.* The cause of failure of some neural crest cells to complete their migration is unknown.

Imperforate Anus and Anorectal Anomalies

Imperforate anus occurs about once in every 5000 newborn infants and is more common in males (Figs. 13–28 and 13–29*C*). *Most anorectal anomalies result from abnormal development of the urorectal septum,* resulting in incomplete separation of the cloaca into urogenital and anorectal portions (Fig. 13–29*A*). Normally a temporary communication exists between the rectum and anal canal dorsally from the bladder and urethra ventrally (Fig. 13–25*C*), but it closes when the urorectal septum fuses with the cloacal membrane (Fig. 13–25*E*). Lesions are classified as "low" or

"high," depending on whether the rectum ends superior or inferior to the puborectalis muscle (Moore, 1992). The following are low anomalies of the anorectal region.

Anal Agenesis, With or Without a Fistula

The anal canal may end blindly or there may be an ectopic opening (**ectopic anus**) or an **anoperineal fistula** that commonly opens into the perineum (Fig. 13–29*D* and *E*). The abnormal canal may, however, open into the vagina in females or the urethra in males (Fig. 13–29*F* and *G*). More than 90% of low anorectal anomalies are associated with an external fistula. **Anal agenesis with a fistula** results from incomplete separation of the cloaca by the urorectal septum.

Anal Stenosis

The anus is in the normal position, but the anus and anal canal are narrow (Fig. 13–29*B*). This anomaly is probably caused by a slight dorsal deviation of the urorectal septum as it grows caudally to fuse with the cloacal membrane. As a result, the anal canal and anal membrane are small. Sometimes only a small probe can be inserted into the anal canal.

Membranous Atresia of the Anus

The anus is in the normal position, but a thin layer of tissue separates the anal canal from the exterior (Figs. 13–28 and 13–29*C*). The membrane is thin enough to

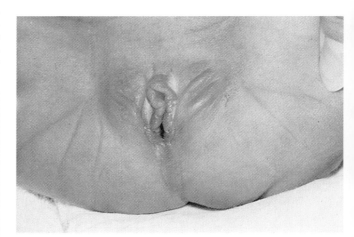

■ **Figure 13–28.** Female neonate with membranous anal atresia (imperforate anus). A tracheoesophageal fistula was also present. In most cases of anal atresia, a thin layer of tissue separates the anal canal from the exterior. This anomaly results from failure of the anal membrane to perforate at the end of the eighth week. Some form of imperforate anus occurs about once in every 5000 neonates; it is more common in males. (Courtesy of Dr. AE Chudley, Section of Genetics and Metabolism, Department of Pediatrics and Child Health, Children's Hospital, Winnipeg, Manitoba, Canada.)

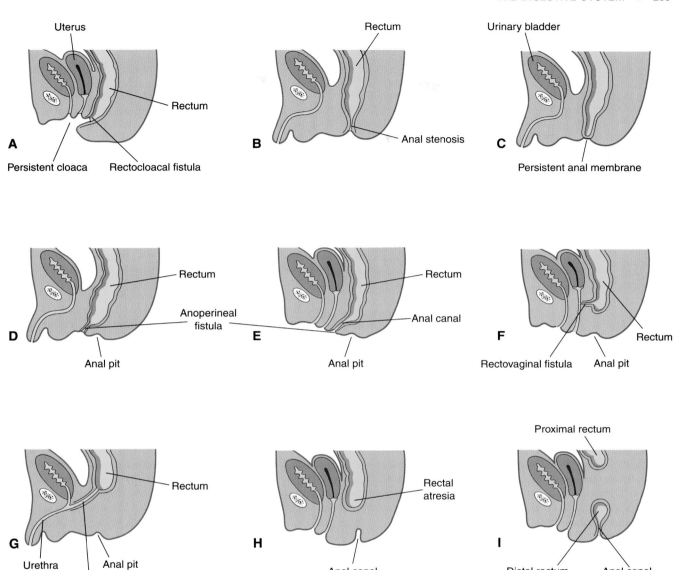

A, Persistent cloaca — Uterus, Rectum, Persistent cloaca, Rectocloacal fistula

B, Rectum, Anal stenosis

C, Urinary bladder, Persistent anal membrane

D, Rectum, Anoperineal fistula, Anal pit

E, Rectum, Anal canal, Anal pit

F, Rectum, Rectovaginal fistula, Anal pit

G, Rectum, Urethra, Anal pit, Rectourethral fistula

H, Rectal atresia, Anal canal

I, Proximal rectum, Distal rectum, Anal canal

■ **Figure 13–29.** Drawings illustrating various types of anorectal anomaly. *A,* Persistent cloaca. Note the common outlet for the intestinal, urinary, and reproductive tracts. *B,* Anal stenosis. *C,* Membranous anal atresia (covered anus). *D* and *E,* Anal agenesis with a perineal fistula. *F,* Anorectal agenesis with a rectovaginal fistula. *G,* Anorectal agenesis with a rectourethral fistula. *H* and *I,* Rectal atresia.

bulge on straining and appears blue from the presence of meconium superior to it. This anomaly results from failure of the anal membrane to perforate at the end of the eighth week.

Anorectal Agenesis, With or Without a Fistula

This anomaly and those that follow are classified as high anomalies of the anorectal region. The rectum ends superior to the puborectalis muscle when anorectal agenesis is present. This is the most common type of anorectal anomaly, which accounts for about two thirds of anorectal defects. Although the rectum ends blindly, there is usually a fistula to the bladder (*rectovesical fistula*) or urethra (*rectourethral fistula*) in males or to the vagina (*rectovaginal fistula*) or the vestibule of the vagina (*rectovestibular fistula*) in females (Fig. 13–29*F* and *G*). Passage of meconium or flatus (gas) in the urine is diagnostic of a rectourinary fistula. *Anorectal agenesis with a fistula* is the result of incomplete separation of the cloaca by the urorectal septum. In newborn males with this condition, *meconium* (feces) may be observed in the urine, whereas fistulas in females result in the presence of meconium in the vestibule of the vagina.

Rectal Atresia

The anal canal and rectum are present, but they are separated (Fig. 13–29*H* and *I*). Sometimes the two segments of bowel are connected by a fibrous cord, the remnant of the atretic portion of the rectum. The cause of rectal atresia may be abnormal recanalization of the colon or more likely defective blood supply, as discussed with atresia of the small intestine. For more information on atresia and stenosis at different levels of the gastrointestinal tract, see Harris et al (1995).

SUMMARY OF THE DIGESTIVE SYSTEM

The *primordial gut* forms during the fourth week from the part of the yolk sac that is incorporated into the embryo. The endoderm of the primordial gut gives rise to the epithelial lining of most of the digestive tract and biliary passages, together with the parenchyma of its glands, including the liver and pancreas. The epithelium at the cranial and caudal extremities of the digestive tract is derived from the ectoderm of the stomodeum and proctodeum, respectively. The muscular and connective tissue components of the digestive tract are derived from the splanchnic mesenchyme surrounding the primordial gut.

The *foregut* gives rise to the pharynx, lower respiratory system, esophagus, stomach, duodenum (proximal to the opening of the bile duct), liver, pancreas, and biliary apparatus. Because the trachea and esophagus have a common origin from the foregut (see Chapter 12), incomplete partitioning by the tracheoesophageal septum results in stenoses or atresias, with or without fistulas between them.

The *hepatic diverticulum*, the primordium of the liver, gallbladder, and biliary duct system, is an outgrowth of the endodermal epithelial lining of the foregut. The epithelial liver cords and primordia of the *biliary system*, which develop from the hepatic diverticulum, grow into the septum transversum. Between the layers of the *ventral mesentery* derived from the septum transversum, these primordial cells differentiate into the *parenchyma of the liver* and the lining of the ducts of the biliary system.

Congenital duodenal atresia results from failure of the vacuolization and recanalization process to occur following the normal solid stage of the duodenum. Usually these epithelial cells degenerate and the lumen of the duodenum is restored. Obstruction of the duodenum can also be caused by an *anular pancreas*.

The *pancreas* develops from dorsal and ventral *pancreatic buds* that originate from the endodermal lining of the foregut. When the duodenum rotates to the right, the ventral pancreatic bud moves dorsally and fuses with the dorsal pancreatic bud. The *ventral pancreatic bud* forms most of the head of the pancreas, including the uncinate process. The *dorsal pancreatic bud* forms the remainder of the pancreas. In some fetuses the duct systems of the two buds fail to fuse, and an *accessory pancreatic duct* forms.

The *midgut* gives rise to the duodenum (distal to the bile duct), jejunum, ileum, cecum, vermiform appendix, ascending colon, and right half to two thirds of the transverse colon. The midgut forms a U-shaped intestinal loop that herniates into the umbilical cord during the sixth week because there is no room for it in the abdomen. While in the umbilical cord, the *midgut loop* rotates counterclockwise through 90 degrees. During the 10th week, the intestines rapidly return to the abdomen, rotating a further 180 degrees during this process.

Omphaloceles, malrotations, and abnormal fixation of the gut result from failure of return or abnormal rotation of the intestine in the abdomen. Because the gut is normally occluded during the fifth and sixth weeks due to rapid mitotic activity of its epithelium, *stenosis* (partial obstruction), *atresia* (complete obstruction), and *duplications* result if recanalization fails to occur or occurs abnormally. Various remnants of the yolk stalk may persist. *Ileal (Meckel) diverticula* are common; however, only a few of them become inflamed and produce pain.

The *hindgut* gives rise to the left one third to one half of the transverse colon, the descending and sigmoid colon, the rectum, and the superior part of the anal canal. The inferior part of the anal canal develops from the proctodeum. The caudal part of the hindgut, known as the *cloaca*, is divided by the *urorectal septum* into the urogenital sinus and rectum. The urogenital sinus gives rise mainly to the urinary bladder and urethra (see Chapter 14). At first the rectum and the superior part of the anal canal are separated from the exterior by the *anal membrane*, but this membrane normally breaks down by the end of the eighth week.

Most *anorectal anomalies* result from abnormal partitioning of the cloaca by the urorectal septum into the rectum and anal canal posteriorly and the urinary bladder and urethra anteriorly. Arrested growth and/or deviation of the urorectal septum in a dorsal direction cause most anorectal abnormalities, such as rectal atresia and abnormal connections (fistulas) between the rectum and the urethra, urinary ladder, or vagina.

Clinically Oriented Questions

1. About 2 weeks after birth, my sister's baby began to vomit shortly after feeding. The unusual thing was that the vomitus was propelled about 2 feet. The physician told her that the baby had a stomach tumor resulting in a narrow outlet from its stomach. Is there an embryological basis for this anomaly? Is the tumor malignant?

2. I have heard that infants with *Down syndrome* have an increased incidence of *duodenal atresia*. Is this true? Can the condition be corrected?

3. My friend said that his appendix is on his left side. Is this possible and, if so, how could this happen?

4. A nurse told me about a friend of his who supposedly had two appendices and had had separate operations to remove them. Do people ever have two appendices?

5. What is *Hirschsprung disease*? I have heard that it is a congenital condition resulting from large bowel obstruction. Is this correct? If so, what is its embryological basis?

6. A nurse friend of mine told me that feces can sometimes be expelled from a baby's umbilicus. She said she has even seen urine dripping from the umbilicus. Was she "pulling my leg"?

The answers to these questions are given at the back of the book.

REFERENCES AND SUGGESTED READING

Ackerman P: Congenital defects of the abdominal wall. *In* Huffstadt AJC (ed): *Congenital Malformations*. Amsterdam, Excerpta Medica, 1980.
Balistreri WF: Liver and biliary atresia. *In* Behrman RE, Kliegman RM, Arvin AM (eds): *Nelson Textbook of Pediatrics,* 15th ed. Philadelphia, WB Saunders, 1996.
Behrman RE, Kliegman RM, Arvin AM (eds): *Nelson Textbook of Pediatrics,* 15th ed. Philadelphia, WB Saunders, 1996.
Bourdelat D, Barbet JP, Hidden G: The morphological differentiation of the internal sphincter muscle of the anus in the human embryo and fetus. *Surg Radiol Anat* 12:151, 1990.
Cockburn F, Carachi R, Goel KN, Young DG: *Children's Medicine and Surgery*. London, Arnold, 1996.
Harris J, Källén B, Robert E: Descriptive epidemiology of alimentary tract anomalies. *Teratology* 52:15, 1995.
Herbst JJ: The esophagus. *In* Behrman RE, Kliegman RM, Arvin AM (eds): *Nelson Textbook of Pediatrics*, 15th ed. Philadelphia, WB Saunders, 1996.
Karrer FM, Raffensperger JG: Biliary atresia. *In* Raffensperger JG (ed): *Swenson's Pediatric Surgery*, 5th ed. Norwalk, CT, Appleton & Lange, 1990.
Kliegman RM: The umbilicus. *In* Behrman RE, Kliegman RM, Arvin AM (eds): *Nelson Textbook of Pediatrics,* 15th ed. Philadelphia, WB Saunders, 1996.
Meizner I, Levy A, Barnhard Y: Cloacal exstrophy sequence: An exceptional ultrasound diagnosis. *Obstet Gynecol* 86:446, 1995.
Moore KL: *Clinically Oriented Anatomy,* 3rd ed. Baltimore, Williams & Wilkins, 1992.
Moore KL, Persaud, TVN: *The Developing Human: Clinically Oriented Embryology*, 6th ed. Philadelphia, WB Saunders, 1998.
Pena A: Total urogenital mobilization—an easier way to repair cloacas. *J Pediatr Surg* 32:263, 1997.
Ulshen M: Stomach and intestines. *In* Behrman RE, Kliegman RM, Arvin AM (eds): *Nelson Textbook of Pediatrics*, 15th ed. Philadelphia, WB Saunders, 1996.
von Dorsche HH: Inselorgan. *In* Hinrichsen KV (ed): *Humanembryologie*. Berlin, Springer-Verlag, 1990.
Wyllie R: Pyloric stenosis and other congenital anomalies of the stomach; intestinal atresia, stenosis, and malformations; intestinal duplications, Meckel diverticulum, and other remnants of the omphalomesenteric duct. *In* Behrman RE, Kliegman RM, Arvin AM (eds): *Nelson Textbook of Pediatrics*, 15th ed. Philadelphia, WB Saunders, 1996.
Yoon PW, Bresee JS, Olney RS, et al: Epidemiology of biliary atresia: A population-based study. *Pediatrics* 99:376, 1997.

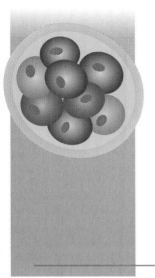

The Urogenital System

14

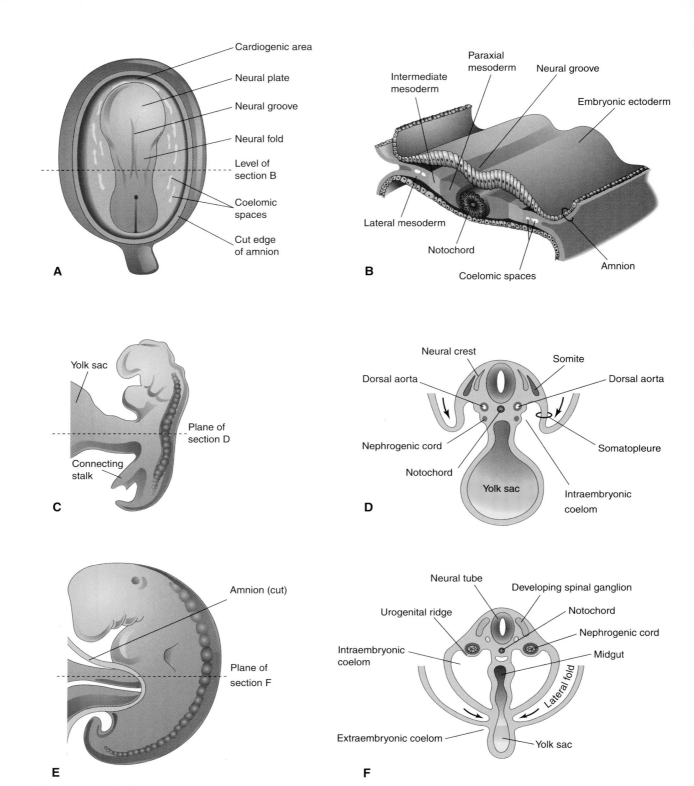

Figure 14–1. *A,* Dorsal view of an embryo during the third week (about 18 days). *B,* Transverse section of the embryo showing the position of the intermediate mesoderm before lateral folding of the embryo. *C,* Lateral view of an embryo during the fourth week (about 24 days). *D,* Transverse section of the embryo after the commencement of folding, showing the nephrogenic cords of mesoderm. *E,* Lateral view of an embryo later in the fourth week (about 26 days). *F,* Transverse section of the embryo showing the lateral folds meeting each other ventrally. Observe the position of the urogenital ridges and nephrogenic cords.

■ The urogenital system can be divided functionally into the *urinary (excretory) system* and the *genital (reproductive) system*. Embryologically these systems are closely associated. They are also closely associated anatomically especially in adult males; for example, the urethra conveys both urine and semen. Although these systems are separate in normal adult females, the urethra and vagina open into a common space or cavity — the vestibule of the vagina — between the labia minora (Moore, 1992).

Development of the *suprarenal (adrenal) glands* is described in this chapter for two reasons:

* They are closely related to the superior poles of the kidneys.
* *Congenital adrenal hyperplasia* (CAH) causes virilization (masculinization) of female external genitalia, such as enlargement of the clitoris.

The urogenital system develops from the intermediate mesoderm, which extends along the dorsal body wall of the embryo (Fig. 14–1A and B). During folding of the embryo in the horizontal plane (see Chapter 6), this mesoderm is carried ventrally and loses its connection with the somites (Fig. 14–1C). A longitudinal elevation of mesoderm — the **urogenital ridge** — forms on each side of the dorsal aorta (Fig. 14–1D to F). It gives rise to parts of the urinary and genital systems. The part of the urogenital ridge giving rise to the urinary system is the **nephrogenic cord** or ridge (Fig. 14–1C to F); the part giving rise to the genital system is the **genital** or **gonadal ridge**.

DEVELOPMENT OF THE URINARY SYSTEM

The urinary system begins to develop before the genital system. The urinary system consists of the following:

* The *kidneys*, which excrete urine
* The *ureters*, which convey urine from the kidneys to the bladder
* The *urinary bladder*, which stores urine temporarily
* The *urethra*, which carries urine from the bladder to the exterior

Development of the Kidneys and Ureters

Three sets of excretory organs or kidneys develop in human embryos:

* The *pronephros*
* The *mesonephros*
* The *metanephros*

The first set of kidneys — the *pronephroi* (pleural of *pronephros*) — are rudimentary and nonfunctional. They are analogous to the kidneys in primitive fishes. The second set of kidneys — the *mesonephroi* — are well developed and function briefly; they are analogous to the kidneys of amphibians. The third set of kidneys — the *metanephroi* — become the permanent kidneys.

Pronephroi. These transitory, nonfunctional structures appear in human embryos early in the fourth week.

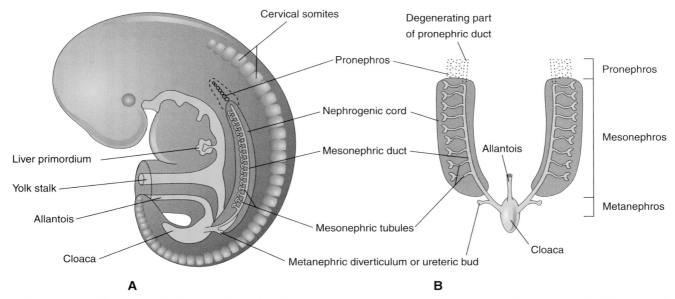

■ **Figure 14–2.** Diagrammatic sketches illustrating the three sets of excretory systems in an embryo during the fifth week. *A,* Lateral view. *B,* Ventral view. The mesonephric tubules have been pulled laterally; their normal position is shown in *A.*

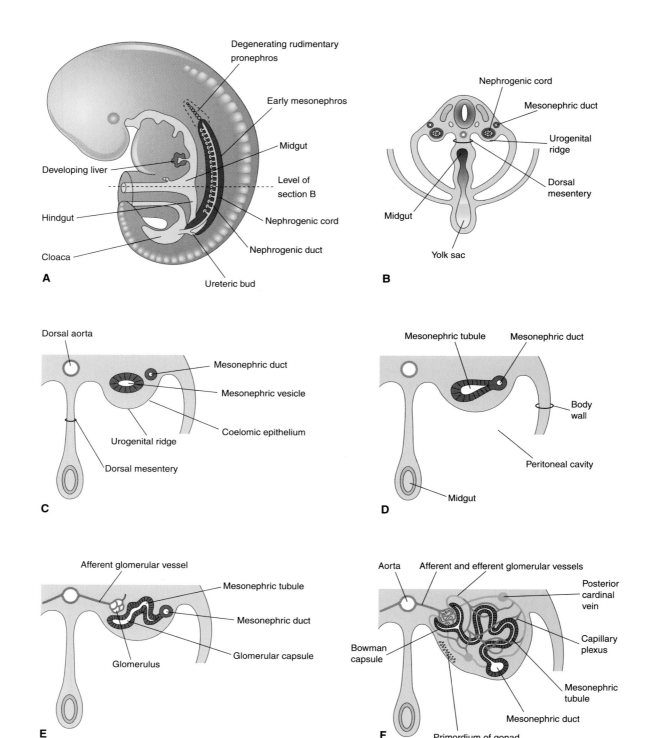

■ **Figure 14–3.** *A*, Sketch of a lateral view of a 5-week embryo showing the extent of the mesonephros and the primordium of the metanephros or permanent kidney. *B*, Transverse section of the embryo showing the nephrogenic cords from which the mesonephric tubules develop. *C* to *F*, Sketches of transverse sections showing successive stages in the development of a mesonephric tubule between the 5th and 11th weeks. Note that the mesenchymal cell cluster in the nephrogenic cord develops a lumen, thereby forming a mesonephric vesicle. The vesicle soon becomes an S-shaped mesonephric tubule and extends laterally to join the pronephric duct, now renamed the mesonephric duct. The expanded medial end of the mesonephric tubule is invaginated by blood vessels to form a glomerular capsule (Bowman capsule). The cluster of capillaries projecting into this capsule is the glomerulus.

They are represented by a few cell clusters and tortuous tubular structures in the neck region (Fig. 14-2A). The pronephric ducts run caudally and open into the cloaca (Fig. 14-2B). The rudimentary pronephroi soon degenerate; however, most of the pronephric ducts persist and are utilized by the next set of kidneys.

Mesonephroi. These large elongated organs appear late in the fourth week, caudal to the rudimentary pronephroi (Fig. 14-2). They are well developed and function as *interim kidneys* until the permanent kidneys develop (Fig. 14-3). The mesonephric kidneys consist of glomeruli and mesonephric tubules. The tubules open into the **mesonephric duct**, which was originally the pronephric duct. The mesonephric duct opens into the cloaca. The mesonephroi degenerate toward the end of the first trimester; however, their tubules become the efferent ductules of the testes, and the mesonephric ducts have several adult derivatives in the male.

Metanephroi. The metanephroi or **permanent kidneys** begin to develop early in the fifth week and start to function about 4 weeks later (Behrman et al, 1996). *Urine formation* continues throughout fetal life. Urine is excreted into the amniotic cavity and mixes with the amniotic fluid. A mature fetus swallows several hundred milliliters of amniotic fluid each day, which is absorbed by the intestine. The waste products are transferred through the placental membrane into the maternal blood for elimination. The permanent kidneys develop from two sources:

- The *metanephric diverticulum* or ureteric bud
- The *metanephric mass of intermediate mesoderm* (metanephrogenic blastema)

The metanephric diverticulum is an outgrowth from the mesonephric duct near its entrance into the cloaca, and the metanephric mesoderm is derived from the caudal part of the nephrogenic cord (Fig. 14-4). Both primordia of the metanephros are of mesodermal

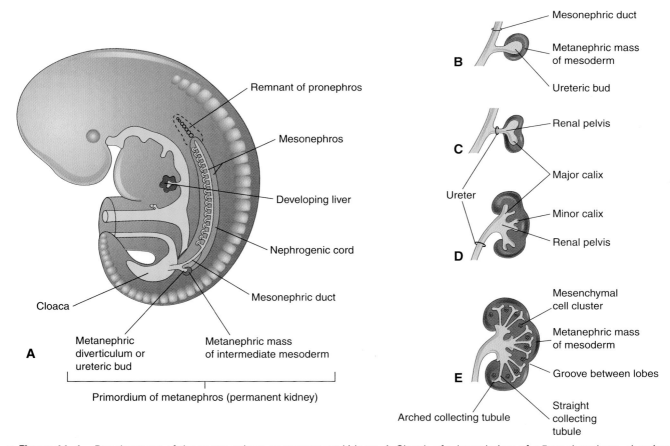

■ **Figure 14-4.** Development of the metanephros or permanent kidney. *A*, Sketch of a lateral view of a 5-week embryo, showing the primordium of the metanephros. *B* to *E*, Sketches showing successive stages in the development of the metanephric diverticulum or ureteric bud (fifth to eighth weeks). Observe the development of the ureter, renal pelvis, calices, and collecting tubules.

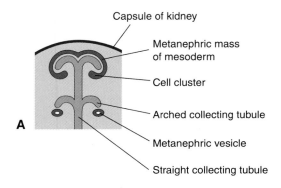

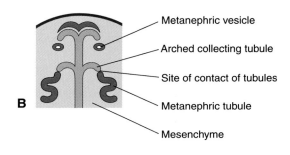

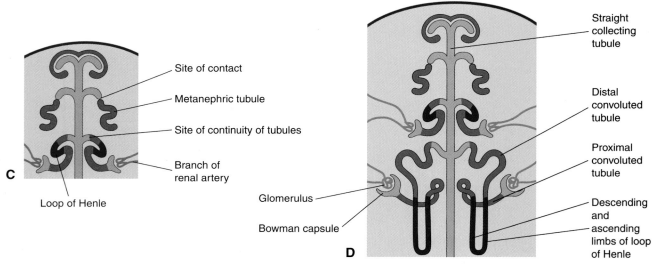

■ **Figure 14–5.** *A* to *D*, Diagrammatic sketches illustrating stages in nephrogenesis—the development of nephrons. *A*, Nephrogenesis commences around the beginning of the eighth week. *B* and *C*, Note that the metanephric tubules, the primordia of the nephrons, become continuous with the collecting tubules to form uriniferous tubules. *D*, The number of nephrons more than doubles from 20 weeks to 38 weeks. Observe that nephrons are derived from the metanephric mass of mesoderm and that the collecting tubules are derived from the metanephric diverticulum.

origin. See Bard (1996) for information regarding molecular mechanisms in kidney morphogenesis. The expression pattern of more than 200 genes associated with the kidneys has been reported, but their function is largely unknown. The **metanephric diverticulum,** or **ureteric bud,** is the primordium of the *ureter, renal pelvis, calices,* and *collecting tubules* (Fig. 14–4C to *E*). As it elongates, the diverticulum penetrates the metanephric mesoderm, inducing the formation of a **metanephric mass of intermediate mesoderm**

over its expanded end (Fig. 14–4*B*). Cell surface *N*-linked oligosaccharides appear to be important for this inductive interaction between the ureteric bud and the metanephric mesoderm (Fleming, 1990). The stalk of the metanephric diverticulum becomes the **ureter,** and its cranial end forms the *renal pelvis.*

The straight **collecting tubules** undergo repeated branching, forming successive generations of collecting tubules. The first four generations of tubules enlarge and become confluent to form the **major cali-**

ces (Fig. 14-4C to E), and the second four generations coalesce to form the **minor calices**. The remaining generations of tubules form the collecting tubules. The end of each arched collecting tubule induces clusters of mesenchymal cells in the metanephric mass of mesoderm to form small **metanephric vesicles** (Fig. 14-5A). These vesicles elongate and become **metanephric tubules** (Fig. 14-5B and C). As these renal tubules develop, their proximal ends are invaginated by glomeruli. The **renal corpuscle** (glomerulus and Bowman capsule) and its proximal convoluted tubule, loop of Henle, and distal convoluted tubule constitute a **nephron** (Fig. 14-5D). Each distal convoluted tubule contacts an arched collecting tubule and the tubules become confluent. Between the 10th and 18th weeks of gestation, the number of glomeruli increases gradually; then it increases rapidly until the 32nd week, when an upper limit is reached (Gasser et al, 1993).

A **uriniferous tubule** consists of two embryologically different parts (Figs. 14-4 and 14-5):

* A *nephron* derived from the metanephric mass of mesoderm
* A *collecting tubule* derived from the metanephric diverticulum

Tissue culture studies have shown that branching of the metanephric diverticulum depends upon induction by the metanephric mesoderm and that differentiation of the nephrons depends upon induction by the collecting tubules (Moore and Persaud, 1998).

The **fetal kidneys** are subdivided into lobes that are visible externally (Fig. 14-6). This lobulation diminishes toward the end of the fetal period, but the lobes are still indicated in the kidneys of a newborn infant. The lobulation usually disappears during infancy as the nephrons increase and grow. The lobulated character of the kidneys is obscured in adults; however, in very rare cases the lobes are recognizable externally, as they are in certain animals (e.g., cattle). At term, each kidney contains 800,000 to 1,000,000 nephrons. The increase in kidney size after birth results mainly from the elongation of the proximal convoluted tubules of Henle, but from an increase of interstitial tissue as well. It is now believed that nephron formation is complete at birth (Behrman et al, 1996) except in premature infants. Functional maturation of the kidneys occurs after birth. Glomerular filtration begins around the ninth fetal week and the rate of filtration increases after birth.

POSITIONAL CHANGES OF THE KIDNEYS

Initially the permanent or metanephric kidneys lie close to each other in the pelvis, ventral to the sacrum (Fig. 14-7A). As the abdomen and pelvis grow, the kidneys gradually come to lie in the abdomen and move farther apart (Fig. 14-7B and C). They attain their adult position by the ninth week (Fig. 14-7D). This "migration" (relative ascent) results mainly from the growth of the embryo's body caudal to the kidneys. In effect, the caudal part of the embryo grows away from the kidneys so that they progressively occupy more cranial levels. Eventually they are retroperitoneal (external or posterior to the peritoneum) on the posterior abdominal wall. Initially the hilum of the kidney, where vessels and nerves enter and leave, faces ventrally; however, as the kidney "ascends," it rotates medially almost 90 degrees. By the ninth week the hilum is directed anteromedially (Fig. 14-7C and D).

CHANGES IN THE BLOOD SUPPLY OF THE KIDNEYS

As the kidneys "ascend" from the pelvis, they receive their blood supply from vessels that are close to them. Initially the renal arteries are branches of the common iliac arteries (Fig. 14-7A and B). As they "ascend" further, the kidneys receive their blood supply from the distal end of the aorta. When they reach a higher level, they receive new branches from the aorta (Fig. 14-7C and D). Normally the caudal branches undergo involution and disappear. When the kidneys come into

Suprarenal or adrenal glands

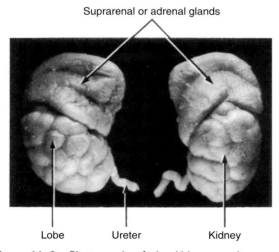

Lobe   Ureter   Kidney

■ **Figure 14-6.** Photograph of the kidneys and suprarenal glands of a 28-week fetus (×2). The external evidence of the lobes usually disappears by the end of the first postnatal year. Note the large size of the suprarenal glands at this age. During the first 2 weeks after birth, these glands reduce to about half this size.

contact with the *suprarenal glands* in the ninth week, their "ascent" stops. The kidneys receive their most cranial arterial branches from the abdominal aorta; these branches become the permanent **renal arteries**.

Accessory Renal Arteries

The relatively common variations in the blood supply to the kidneys reflect the manner in which the blood supply continually changes during embryonic and early fetal life (Fig. 14-7). A single renal artery to each kidney is present in about 70% of people. About 25% of adult kidneys have two to four renal arteries (Moore, 1992). Accessory (supernumerary) renal arteries usually arise from the aorta superior or inferior to the main renal artery and follow it to the hilum (Fig. 14-8*A* and *B*). Accessory renal arteries may enter the kidneys directly, usually into the superior or inferior poles. An accessory artery to the inferior pole may cross anterior to the ureter and obstruct it, causing **hydronephrosis** — distention of the pelvis and calices with urine (Fig. 14-8*B*). If the artery enters the inferior pole of the right kidney, it usually crosses anterior to the inferior vena cava and ureter. It is important to be aware that accessory renal arteries are end arteries; consequently, if an accessory artery is damaged or ligated, the part of the kidney supplied by it is likely to become ischemic. Accessory arteries are about twice as common as accessory veins (Fig. 14-8*C* and *D*).

Congenital Anomalies of the Kidneys and Ureters

Some abnormality of the kidneys and ureters occurs in 3 to 4% of newborn infants. Anomalies in shape and position are most common. Many fetal urinary tract abnormalities can be detected before birth by ultrasonography (Mahony, 1994).

Renal Agenesis

Unilateral renal agenesis is relatively common, occurring about once in every 1000 newborn infants (Fig. 14-9*A*). Males are affected more often than females, and the left kidney is usually the one that is absent. Unilateral absence of a kidney often causes no symptoms and is usually not discovered during infancy because the other kidney usually undergoes compensatory hypertrophy and performs the function of the missing kidney. Unilateral renal agenesis should be suspected in infants with a *single umbilical artery* (see Chapter 8). If discovered during infancy, agenesis is usually detected during the course of evaluation for other congenital anomalies or because of urinary tract symptoms (Mahony, 1994).

Bilateral renal agenesis *is associated with oligohydramnios* (see Chapter 8) because little or no urine is excreted into the amniotic cavity (Peipert and Donnenfeld, 1991). Decreased amniotic fluid volume in the absence of other causative factors, such as rupture of the fetal membranes, alerts the sonographer to search

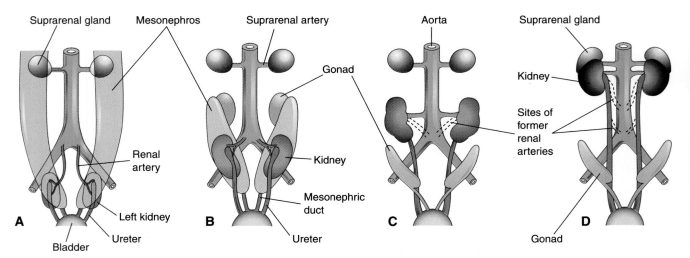

■ **Figure 14-7.** *A* to *D*, Diagrammatic ventral views of the abdominopelvic region of embryos and fetuses (sixth to ninth weeks) showing medial rotation and "ascent" of the kidneys from the pelvis to the abdomen. *A* and *B*, Observe also the size regression of the mesonephroi. *C* and *D*, Note that as the kidneys "ascend," they are supplied by arteries at successively higher levels and that the hilum of the kidney (where the vessels and nerves enter) is eventually directed anteromedially.

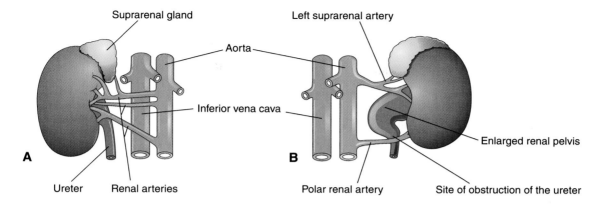

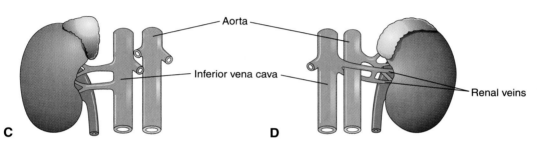

■ **Figure 14-8.** Drawings illustrating common variations of renal vessels. *A* and *B*, Multiple renal arteries. Note the accessory vessels entering the poles of the kidney. The polar renal artery illustrated in *B* has obstructed the ureter and produced an enlarged renal pelvis. *C* and *D*, Multiple renal veins are less common than supernumerary arteries.

for urinary tract anomalies (Mahony, 1994). Bilateral absence of the kidneys occurs about once in 3000 births and is incompatible with postnatal life. These infants have a characteristic facial appearance: the eyes are widely separated and have epicanthic folds; the ears are low set; the nose is broad and flat; the chin is receding; and limb defects are present. Most infants with bilateral renal agenesis die shortly after birth or during the first months of life.

Absence of kidneys results when the metanephric diverticula fail to develop or the ureteric primordia degenerate. Failure of the metanephric diverticulum to penetrate the metanephric mesoderm results in absence of kidney development because no nephrons are induced by the collecting tubules to develop from the metanephric mass of mesoderm. Renal agenesis probably has a multifactorial cause.

Malrotation of the Kidneys

If a kidney fails to rotate, the hilum faces anteriorly; that is, the fetal kidney retains its embryonic position (Figs. 14-7A and 14-9C). If the hilum faces posteriorly, rotation of the kidney proceeded too far; if it faces laterally, lateral instead of medial rotation oc-

curred. Abnormal rotation of the kidneys is often associated with ectopic kidneys.

Ectopic Kidneys

A kidney may fail to develop (Fig. 14-9A) or one or both kidneys may be in an abnormal position (Fig. 14-9B, E, and F). Usually they are more inferior than usual and have not rotated; consequently, the hilum faces anteriorly. Most ectopic kidneys are located in the pelvis, but some lie in the inferior part of the abdomen. **Pelvic kidneys** and other forms of ectopia result from failure of the kidneys to "ascend." Pelvic kidneys are close to each other and may fuse to form a discoid or *pancake kidney* (Fig. 14-9E). Ectopic kidneys receive their blood supply from blood vessels near them (internal or external iliac arteries and/or aorta). They are often supplied by multiple vessels. Sometimes a kidney crosses to the other side, resulting in **crossed renal ectopia** with or without fusion. An unusual type of abnormal kidney is *unilateral fused kidney* (Fig. 14-9D). The developing kidneys fuse while they are in the pelvis, and one kidney "ascends" to its normal position, carrying the other one with it.

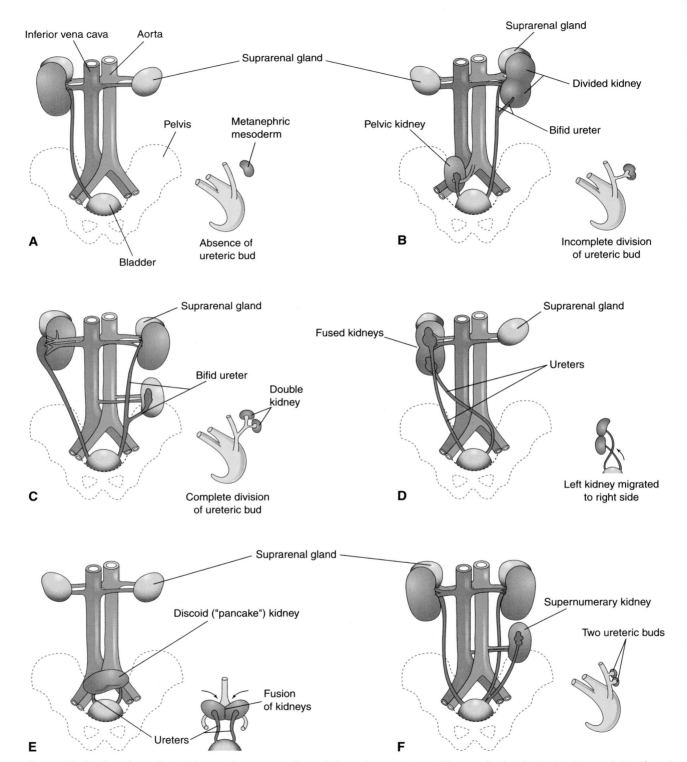

■ **Figure 14–9.** Drawings illustrating various anomalies of the urinary system. The small sketch to the lower right of each drawing illustrates the probable embryological basis of the anomaly. *A,* Unilateral renal agenesis. *B,* Right side, pelvic kidney; left side, divided kidney with a bifid ureter. *C,* Right side, malrotation of the kidney; left side, bifid ureter and supernumerary kidney. *D,* Crossed renal ectopia. The left kidney crossed to the right side and fused with the right kidney. *E,* Discoid kidney resulting from fusion of the kidneys while they were in the pelvis. *F,* Supernumerary left kidney resulting from the development of two ureteric buds.

Horseshoe Kidney

In 1 in about 500 persons, the poles of the kidneys are fused; usually it is the inferior poles that fuse. About 7% of persons with Turner syndrome have horseshoe kidneys (Behrman et al, 1996). The large U-shaped kidney usually lies in the hypogastrium, anterior to the inferior lumbar vertebrae (Fig. 14–10). Normal ascent of the fused kidneys is prevented because they are caught by the root of the inferior mesenteric artery. *A horseshoe kidney usually produces no symptoms* because its collecting system develops normally and the ureters enter the bladder. If urinary flow is impeded, signs and symptoms of obstruction and/or infection may appear.

Duplications of the Urinary Tract

Duplications of the abdominal part of the ureter and the renal pelvis are common, but a **supernumerary kidney** is rare (Fig. 14–9C and F). These anomalies result from division of the metanephric diverticulum (ureteric bud). The extent of the duplication depends on how complete the division of the diverticulum was. Incomplete division of the ureteric primordium results in a divided kidney with a bifid ureter (Fig. 14–9B). Complete division results in a double kidney with a bifid ureter or separate ureters (Fig. 14–11). A supernumerary kidney with its own ureter prob-

ably results from the formation of two ureteric diverticula.

Ectopic Ureter

An ectopic ureter opens anywhere except into the urinary bladder. In males an ectopic ureter usually opens into the neck of the bladder or into the prostatic part of the urethra (Moore, 1992), but it may enter the ductus deferens, prostatic utricle, or seminal vesicle. In females, an ectopic ureteric orifice may be in the bladder neck, urethra, vagina, or vestibule of the vagina (Behrman et al, 1996). *Incontinence* is the common complaint resulting from an ectopic ureteric orifice because the urine flowing from the orifice does not enter the bladder; instead, it continually dribbles from the urethra in males and the urethra and/or vagina in females.

Ureteric ectopia results when the ureter is not incorporated into the posterior part of the urinary bladder; instead it is carried caudally with the mesonephric duct and is incorporated into the caudal portion of the vesical part of the urogenital sinus. Because this part of the sinus becomes the prostatic urethra in males and the urethra in females, the common location of ectopic ureteric orifices is understandable. When two ureters form on one side (Fig. 14–11), they usually open into the urinary bladder. In some males the extra

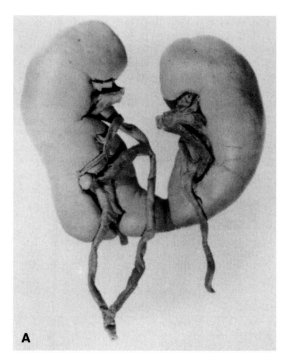
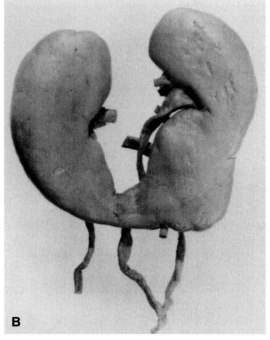

A **B**

■ **Figure 14–10.** Photographs of a horseshoe kidney resulting from fusion of the inferior poles of the kidneys while they were in the pelvis. *A,* Anterior view. *B,* Posterior view. The larger right kidney has a bifid ureter.

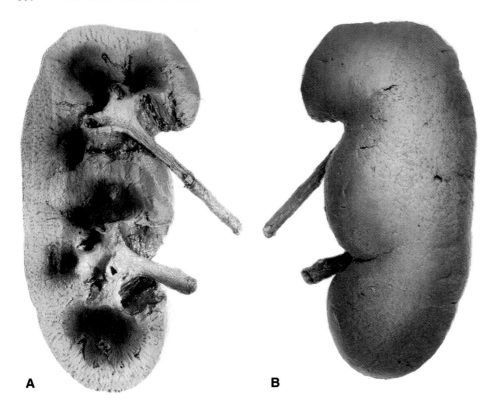

A   **B**

■ **Figure 14–11.** Photographs of a duplex kidney with two ureters and renal pelves. This congenital anomaly results from incomplete division of the metanephric diverticulum or ureteric bud. *A,* Longitudinal section through the kidney showing two renal pelves and calices. *B,* Anterior surface of the kidney.

ureter is carried caudally and drains into the neck of the bladder or into the prostatic part of the urethra.

Multicystic Dysplastic Kidney

The congenital form of multicystic dysplastic kidney is relatively common. Death usually occurs shortly after birth; however, an increasing number of these infants are surviving because of hemodialysis and kidney transplants. The kidneys contain multiple small to large cysts, which cause severe renal insufficiency. About 90% of dysplastic kidneys result from urinary tract obstruction during kidney formation (Mahony, 1994).

Development of the Urinary Bladder

Division of the cloaca by the **urorectal septum** (Fig. 14-12*A*) into a dorsal rectum and a ventral urogenital sinus is described in Chapter 13. For descriptive purposes, the **urogenital sinus** is divided into three parts (Fig. 14-12*A* and *C*):

- A cranial *vesical part* that is continuous with the allantois
- A middle *pelvic part* that becomes the urethra in the bladder neck and the prostatic part of the urethra in males and the entire urethra in females
- A caudal *phallic part* that grows toward the genital tubercle

The bladder develops mainly from the vesical part of the urogenital sinus (Fig. 14-12*D*), but its trigone region is derived from the caudal ends of the mesonephric ducts. The epithelium of the bladder is derived from the endoderm of the vesical part of the urogenital sinus. The other layers of its wall develop from adjacent splanchnic mesenchyme. Initially the bladder is continuous with the **allantois**, a vestigial structure (Fig. 14-12*C*). The allantois soon constricts and becomes a thick fibrous cord, the **urachus**. It extends from the apex of the bladder to the umbilicus (Fig. 14-13; see also Fig. 14-12*G*). In the adult the urachus is represented by the *median umbilical ligament* (Moore, 1992).

As the bladder enlarges, distal portions of the mesonephric ducts are incorporated into its dorsal wall (Fig. 14-12*B* to *H*). These ducts contribute to the formation of the connective tissue in the *trigone of the bladder*, but the epithelium of the entire bladder is derived from the endoderm of the urogenital sinus. As the mesonephric ducts are absorbed, the ureters come to open separately into the urinary bladder (Fig. 14-12*C* to *H*). Partly because of traction exerted by the kidneys during their "ascent," the orifices of the ureters move superolaterally and the ureters enter obliquely through the base of the bladder. The orifices of the mesonephric ducts move close together and

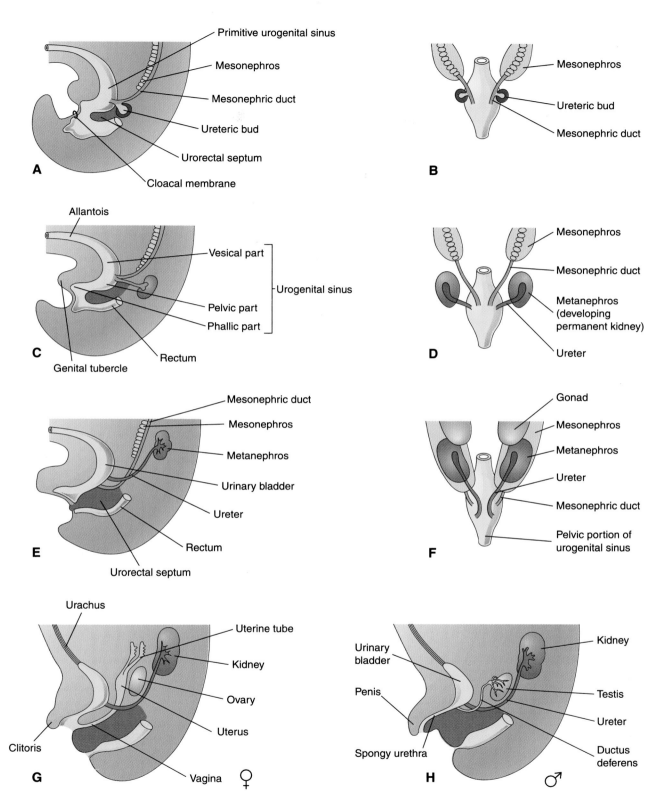

Figure 14–12. Diagrams showing division of the cloaca into the urogenital sinus and rectum; absorption of the mesonephric ducts; development of the urinary bladder, urethra, and urachus; and changes in the location of the ureters. *A*, Lateral view of the caudal half of a 5-week embryo. *B, D,* and *F,* Dorsal views. *C, E, G,* and *H,* Lateral views. The stages shown in *G* and *H* are reached by the 12th week.

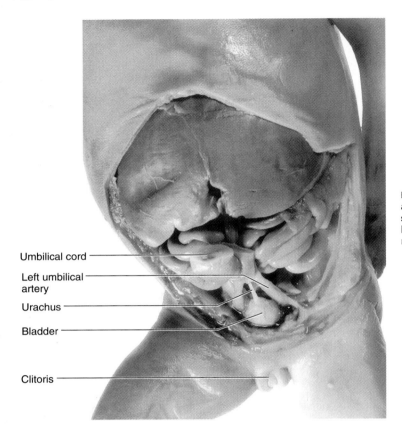

Umbilical cord

Left umbilical
artery

Urachus

Bladder

Clitoris

■ **Figure 14–13.** Photograph of a dissection of the abdomen and pelvis of an 18-week-old female fetus, showing the relation of the urachus to the urinary bladder and umbilical arteries. Note that the clitoris is relatively large at this stage.

enter the prostatic part of the urethra as the caudal ends of these ducts become the *ejaculatory ducts*. The distal ends of the mesonephric ducts in females degenerate.

In infants and children the urinary bladder, even when empty, is in the abdomen. It begins to enter the pelvis major at about 6 years of age, but it does not enter the pelvis minor and become a pelvic organ until after puberty (Moore, 1992). The apex of the urinary bladder in adults is continuous with the **median umbilical ligament**, which extends posteriorly along the posterior surface of the anterior abdominal wall; this ligament is the fibrous remnant of the urachus. The *median umbilical ligament* lies between the *medial umbilical ligaments*, which are the fibrous remnants of the umbilical arteries (see Chapter 15).

Urachal Anomalies

A remnant of the lumen usually persists in the inferior part of the urachus in infants, and in about 50% of

cases the lumen is continuous with the cavity of the bladder. Remnants of the epithelial lining of the urachus may give rise to **urachal cysts** (Fig. 14–14*A*). Small cysts can be observed in about one third of cadavers, but urachal cysts are not usually detected in living persons unless they become infected and enlarge. The patent inferior end of the urachus may dilate to form a **urachal sinus** that opens into the bladder. The lumen in the superior part of the urachus may also remain patent and form a urachal sinus that opens at the umbilicus (Fig. 14–14*B*). Very rarely the entire urachus remains patent and forms a **urachal fistula** that allows urine to escape from its umbilical orifice (Fig. 14–14*C*).

Exstrophy of the Bladder

This severe anomaly occurs about once in every 10,000 to 40,000 births (Behrman et al, 1996). Exstrophy of the bladder (Fig. 14–15*A* and *B*) occurs chiefly in males. Exposure and *protrusion of the posterior* *wall of the bladder* characterize this congenital anomaly. The trigone of the bladder and the ureteric orifices are exposed, and urine dribbles intermittently from the everted bladder. **Epispadias** and wide separation of the pubic bones are associated with complete exstrophy of the bladder (Fig. 14–15*A*). In some cases the penis is divided into two parts, and the halves of the scrotum are widely separated.

Exstrophy of the bladder is caused by incomplete median closure of the inferior part of the anterior abdominal wall (Fig. 14–16*A* to *F*). The defect involves the anterior abdominal wall and the anterior wall of the urinary bladder. The anomaly is the result of failure of mesenchymal cells to migrate between the ectoderm of the abdomen and cloaca during the fourth week (Fig. 14–16*B* and *C*). As a result, the inferior parts of the rectus muscles are absent, and the external and internal oblique and transversus abdominis muscles are deficient. No muscle and connective tissue form in the anterior abdominal wall over the urinary bladder. Later, the thin epidermis and anterior wall of the bladder rupture, causing wide communication between the exterior and the mucous membrane of the bladder.

Development of the Urethra

The epithelium of most of the male urethra and the entire female urethra is derived from endoderm of the urogenital sinus (Fig. 14–17; see also Fig. 14–12). The distal part of the urethra in the male is derived from the **glandular plate**. This ectodermal plate grows from the tip of the glans penis to meet the part of the spongy urethra derived from the phallic part of the urogenital sinus (Fig. 14–17*A* to *C*). The glandular plate becomes canalized and joins the rest of the spongy urethra; consequently, the epithelium of the terminal part of the urethra is derived from surface ectoderm. The connective tissue and smooth muscle of the urethra in both sexes are derived from the adjacent splanchnic mesenchyme.

DEVELOPMENT OF THE SUPRARENAL GLANDS

The cortex and medulla of the suprarenal (adrenal) glands have different origins (Fig. 14–18*A* to *H*). The **cortex** develops from mesoderm, and the **medulla** differentiates from **neural crest cells**. The cortex is first indicated during the sixth week by an aggregation of mesenchymal cells on each side, between the root of the dorsal mesentery and the developing gonad (Fig. 14–20*C*). The cells that form the *fetal cortex* are derived from the mesothelium lining the posterior abdominal wall. The cells that form the medulla are derived from an adjacent *sympathetic ganglion*, which is derived from the neural crest. Initially the neural crest cells form a mass on the medial side of the fetal cortex (Fig. 14–18*B*). As they are surrounded by the fetal cortex, these cells differentiate into the *secretory cells* of the suprarenal medulla.

Later more mesenchymal cells arise from the mesothelium and enclose the fetal cortex. These cells give rise to the permanent cortex (Fig. 14–18*C*). Differentiation of the characteristic suprarenal cortical zones begins during the late fetal period. The zona glomerulosa and zona fasciculata are present at birth, but the

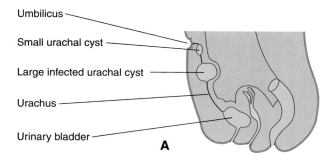

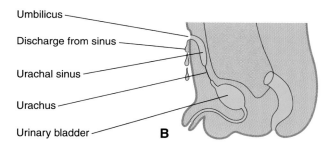

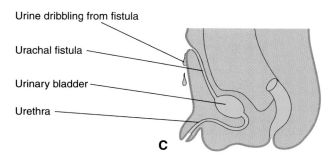

■ **Figure 14–14.** Diagrams illustrating urachal anomalies. *A,* Urachal cysts. The most common site is in the superior end of the urachus just inferior to the umbilicus. *B,* Two types of urachal sinus are illustrated: One opens into the bladder; the other opens at the umbilicus. *C,* Patent urachus or urachal fistula connecting the bladder and umbilicus.

Labels for A:
Umbilicus
Small urachal cyst
Large infected urachal cyst
Urachus
Urinary bladder

Labels for B:
Umbilicus
Discharge from sinus
Urachal sinus
Urachus
Urinary bladder

Labels for C:
Urine dribbling from fistula
Urachal fistula
Urinary bladder
Urethra

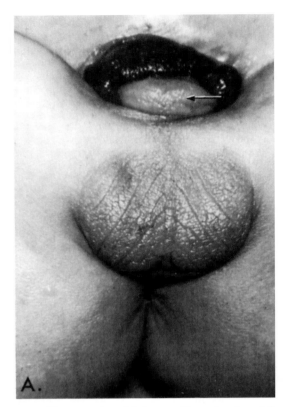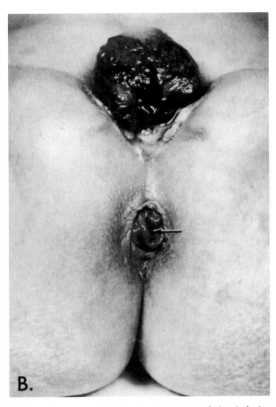

■ **Figure 14–15.** Photographs of infants with exstrophy of the bladder. Because of defective closure of the inferior part of the anterior abdominal wall and the anterior wall of the bladder, the urinary bladder appears as an everted bulging mass inferior to the umbilicus. *A*, Male. Epispadias is also present, and the penis (*arrow*) is small and flattened. (Courtesy of Dr. CC Ferguson, Children's Hospital, Winnipeg, Manitoba, Canada.) *B*, Female with bladder exstrophy and a slight prolapse (*arrow*) of the rectum. (Courtesy of Mr. Innes Williams, Genitourinary Surgeon, The Hospital for Sick Children, London, England.)

zona reticularis is not recognizable until the end of the third year (Fig. 14–18*H*). The suprarenal glands of the human fetus are 10 to 20 times larger than the adult glands relative to body weight and are large compared with the kidneys (Fig. 14–6). These large glands result from the extensive size of the fetal cortex. The suprarenal medulla remains relatively small until after birth (Fig. 14–18*F*). The suprarenal glands rapidly become smaller as the fetal cortex regresses during the first year. The glands lose about one third of their weight during the first 2 to 3 weeks after birth and do not regain their original weight until the end of the second year (Fig. 14–18*G*).

Congenital Adrenal Hyperplasia

An abnormal increase in the cells of the suprarenal cortex results in excessive androgen production during the fetal period. In females this usually causes masculinization of the external genitalia and enlargement of the clitoris, for example (Fig. 14–19). Affected male infants have normal external genitalia and may go undetected in early infancy. Later in childhood in both sexes, androgen excess leads to rapid growth and accelerated skeletal maturation (Thompson et al, 1991). The **adrenogenital syndrome** associated with CAH manifests itself in various clinical forms that can be correlated with enzymatic deficiencies of cortisol biosynthesis. Congenital adrenal hyperplasia is a group of *autosomal recessive disorders* that result in virilization of female fetuses. It is caused by a genetically determined mutation in the cytochrome P450c21-steroid 21-hydroxylase gene, which causes a deficiency of adrenal cortical enzymes that are necessary for the biosynthesis of various steroid hormones. The reduced hormone output results in an increased release of adrenocorticotropic hormone, which causes adrenal hyperplasia and overproduction of androgens by the hyperplastic suprarenal glands.

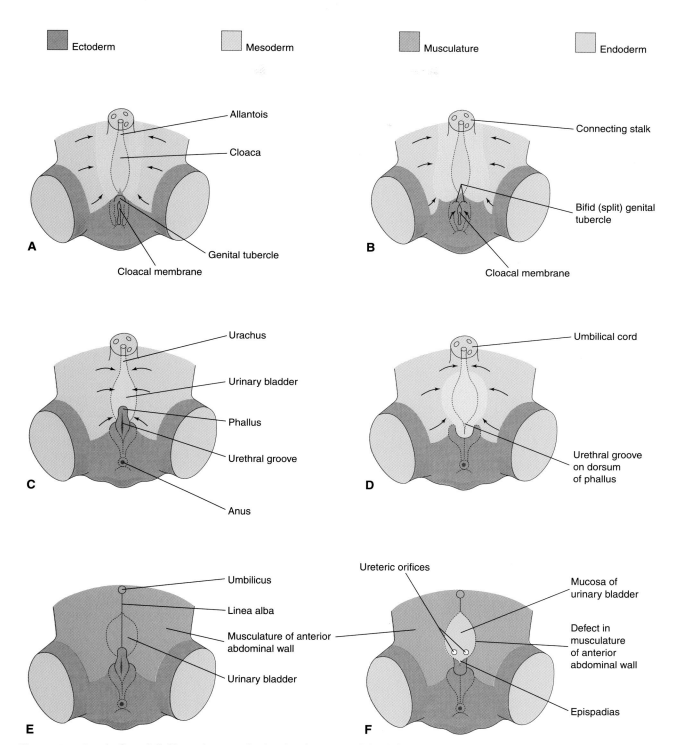

■ **Figure 14–16.** *A, C,* and *E,* Normal stages in the development of the infraumbilical abdominal wall and the penis during the fourth to eighth weeks. Note that mesoderm and later muscle reinforce the ectoderm of the developing anterior abdominal wall. *B, D,* and *F,* Probable stages in the development of exstrophy of the bladder and epispadias. In *B* and *D,* note that the mesenchyme (embryonic connective tissue) fails to extend into the anterior abdominal wall anterior to the urinary bladder. Also note that the genital tubercle is located in a more caudal position than usual and that the urethral groove has formed on the dorsal surface of the penis. In *F,* the surface ectoderm and anterior wall of the bladder have ruptured, resulting in exposure of the posterior wall of the bladder. Note that the musculature of the anterior abdominal wall is present on each side of the defect. (Based on Patten BM, Barry A: The genesis of exstrophy of the bladder and epispadias. *Am J Anat* 90:35, 1952.)

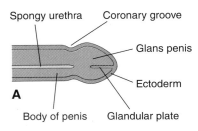

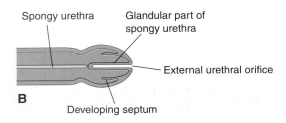

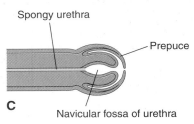

■ **Figure 14–17.** Schematic longitudinal sections of the distal part of the developing penis, illustrating development of the prepuce (foreskin) and the glandular part of the spongy urethra. *A,* Eleven weeks. *B,* Twelve weeks. *C,* Fourteen weeks. The epithelium of the spongy urethra has a dual origin; most of it is derived from endoderm of the phallic part of the urogenital sinus. The distal part of the urethra lining the navicular fossa is derived from surface ectoderm.

DEVELOPMENT OF THE GENITAL SYSTEM

Although the chromosomal and genetic sex of an embryo is determined at fertilization by the kind of sperm that fertilizes the ovum (see Chapter 3), male and female morphologic characteristics do not begin to develop until the seventh week. The early genital systems in the two sexes are similar; therefore, the initial period of genital development is referred to as the *indifferent stage of sexual development.*

Development of the Gonads

The gonads (testes and ovaries) are derived from three sources (Fig. 14–20*A* to *C*):

- The *mesothelium* (mesodermal epithelium) lining the posterior abdominal wall
- The underlying *mesenchyme* (embryonic connective tissue)
- The *primordial germ cells*

THE INDIFFERENT GONADS

The initial stages of gonadal development occur during the fifth week, when a thickened area of mesothelium develops on the medial side of the mesonephros (Fig. 14–20*A* to *C*). Proliferation of this epithelium and the underlying mesenchyme produces a bulge on the medial side of the mesonephros — the **gonadal (genital) ridge** (Fig. 14–20*B* and *C*). Fingerlike epithelial cords — **primary sex cords** — soon grow into the underlying mesenchyme (Fig. 14–20*D*). The indifferent gonad now consists of an external *cortex* and an internal *medulla*. In embryos with an XX sex chromosome complex, the cortex of the **indifferent gonad** differentiates into an ovary and the medulla regresses. In embryos with an XY sex chromosome complex, the medulla differentiates into a testis and the cortex regresses, except for vestigial remnants (see Table 14–1).

PRIMORDIAL GERM CELLS

These large, spherical primitive sex cells are visible early in the fourth week among the endodermal cells of the yolk sac near the origin of the allantois. During folding of the embryo (see Chapter 6), the dorsal part of the yolk sac is incorporated into the embryo. As this occurs, the primordial germ cells migrate along the dorsal mesentery of the hindgut to the gonadal ridges (Fig. 14–20*A*). During the sixth week the primordial germ cells enter the underlying mesenchyme and are incorporated in the *primary sex cords* (Fig. 14–20*E*).

SEX DETERMINATION

Chromosomal and genetic sex is established at fertilization and depends upon whether an X-bearing sperm or a Y-bearing sperm fertilizes the X-bearing ovum. The type of gonads that develop is determined by the sex chromosome complex (XX or XY). Before the seventh week the gonads of the two sexes are identical in appearance and are called **indifferent gonads**

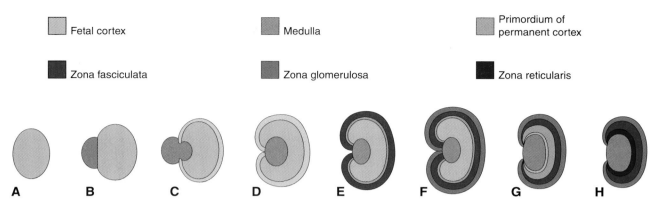

■ **Figure 14–18.** Schematic drawings illustrating development of the suprarenal (adrenal) glands. *A,* Six weeks, showing the mesodermal primordium of the fetal cortex. *B,* Seven weeks, showing the addition of neural crest cells. *C,* Eight weeks, showing the fetal cortex and the early permanent cortex beginning to encapsulate the medulla. *D* and *E,* Later stages of encapsulation of the medulla by the cortex. *F,* Newborn, showing the fetal cortex and two zones of the permanent cortex. *G,* One year; the fetal cortex has almost disappeared. *H,* Four years, showing the adult pattern of cortical zones. Note that the fetal cortex has disappeared and that the gland is smaller than it was at birth (*F*).

(Fig. 14–21). Development of the male phenotype requires a Y chromosome, but only the short arm of this chromosome is critical for sex determination. The SRY gene for a *testis-determining factor* (TDF) has been localized in the "sex-determining region of the Y chromosome" (Berta et al, 1990; Thompson et al, 1991).

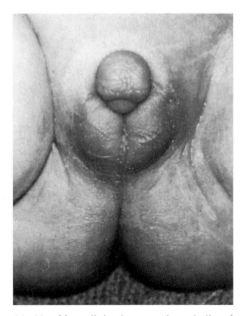

■ **Figure 14–19.** Masculinized external genitalia of a female infant with congenital adrenal hyperplasia. The virilization was caused by excessive androgens produced by the suprarenal (adrenal) glands during the fetal period.

Two X chromosomes are required for the development of the female phenotype. A number of genes and regions of the X chromosome have special roles in sex determination.

The Y chromosome has a testis-determining effect on the medulla of the indifferent gonad. It is the TDF regulated by the Y chromosome that determines testicular differentiation. Under the influence of this organizing factor, the primary sex cords differentiate into seminiferous tubules (Fig. 14–21). The absence of a Y chromosome (i.e., an XX sex chromosome complement) results in the formation of an ovary. Consequently, the type of sex chromosome complex established at fertilization determines the type of gonad that differentiates from the indifferent gonad (Mittwoch, 1992). The type of gonads present then determines the type of sexual differentiation that occurs in the genital ducts and external genitalia. It is the androgen **testosterone**, produced by the fetal testes, that determines maleness. Primary female sexual differentiation in the fetus does not depend on hormones; it occurs even if the ovaries are absent and apparently is not under hormonal influence.

Abnormal Sex Chromosome Complexes

In embryos with abnormal sex chromosome complexes, such as XXX or XXY, the number of X chromosomes appears to be unimportant in sex determina-

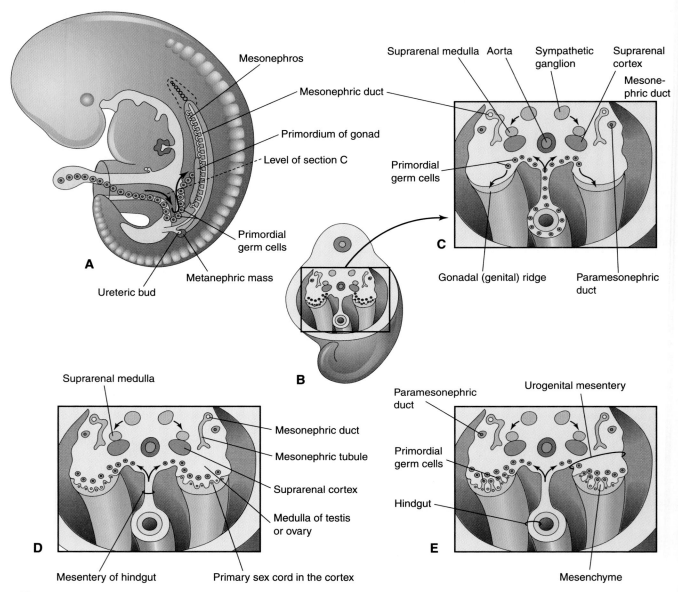

■ **Figure 14–20.** *A,* Sketch of a 5-week embryo illustrating the migration of primordial germ cells from the yolk sac into the embryo. *B,* Three-dimensional sketch of the caudal region of a 5-week embryo, showing the location and extent of the gonadal ridges. *C,* Transverse section showing the primordium of the suprarenal (adrenal) glands, the gonadal (genital) ridges, and the migration of primordial germ cells into the developing gonads. *D,* Transverse section of a 6-week embryo showing the primary sex cords. *E,* Similar section at a later stage showing the indifferent gonads and paramesonephric ducts.

tion. If a *normal* Y chromosome is present, the embryo develops as a male. If no Y chromosome is present or the testis-determining region of the Y chromosome has been lost, female development occurs. The loss of an X chromosome does not appear to interfere with the migration of primordial germ cells to the gonadal ridges because some germ cells have been observed in the fetal gonads of 45,X females with Turner syndrome. Two X chromosomes are needed, however, to bring about complete ovarian development.

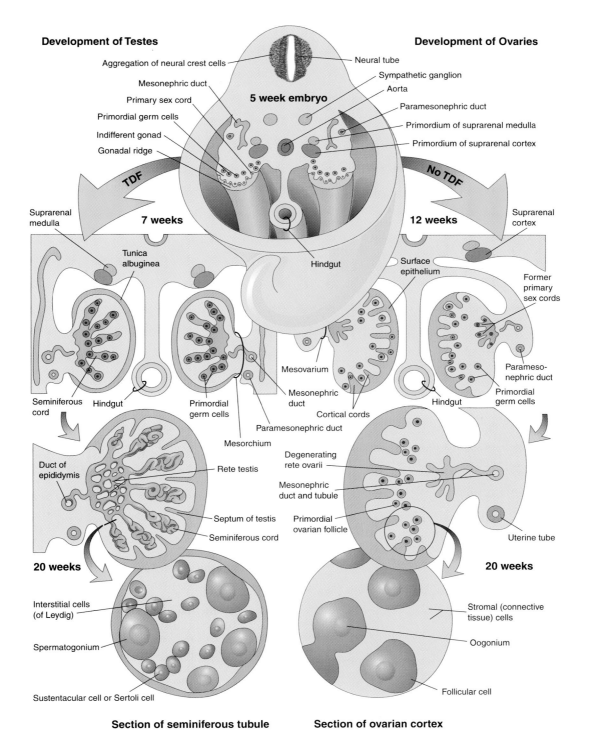

Development of Testes

Aggregation of neural crest cells

Mesonephric duct

Primary sex cord

Primordial germ cells

Indifferent gonad

Gonadal ridge

5 week embryo

TDF

Neural tube

Sympathetic ganglion

Aorta

Paramesonephric duct

Primordium of suprarenal medulla

Primordium of suprarenal cortex

Development of Ovaries

No TDF

Suprarenal medulla

7 weeks

Tunica albuginea

Suprarenal cortex

12 weeks

Surface epithelium

Former primary sex cords

Hindgut

Seminiferous cord

Hindgut

Primordial germ cells

Mesovarium

Mesonephric duct

Cortical cords

Paramesonephric duct

Mesorchium

Hindgut

Paramesonephric duct

Primordial germ cells

Duct of epididymis

Rete testis

Degenerating rete ovarii

Mesonephric duct and tubule

Primordial ovarian follicle

Uterine tube

Septum of testis

Seminiferous cord

20 weeks

20 weeks

Interstitial cells (of Leydig)

Stromal (connective tissue) cells

Oogonium

Spermatogonium

Sustentacular cell or Sertoli cell

Follicular cell

Section of seminiferous tubule   **Section of ovarian cortex**

■ **Figure 14–21.** Schematic illustrations showing differentiation of the indifferent gonads of a 5-week embryo (top) into ovaries or testes. Left side shows the development of testes resulting from the effects of the testis-determining factor (TDF) located on the Y chromosome. Note that the primary sex cords become seminiferous cords, the primordia of the semniniferous tubules. The parts of the primary sex cords that enter the medulla of the testis form the rete testis. In the section of the testis at the bottom left, observe that there are two kinds of cells—spermatogonia, derived from the primordial germ cells, and sustentacular or Sertoli cells derived from mesenchyme. Right side shows the development of ovaries in the absence of TDF. Cortical cords have extended from the surface epithelium of the gonad, and primordial germ cells have entered them. They are the primordia of the oogonia. Follicular cells are derived from the mesenchyme (primitive connective tissue) separating the oogonia.

309

DEVELOPMENT OF TESTES

Embryos with a Y chromosome in their sex chromosome complement usually develop testes. A coordinated sequence of genes induces the development of testes (Thompson et al, 1991). The SRY gene for TDF on the short arm of the Y chromosome acts as the switch that directs development of the indifferent gonad into a testis (Berta et al, 1990; DiGeorge, 1996). Testis-determining factor induces the primary sex cords to condense and extend into the medulla of the indifferent gonad, where they branch and anastomose to form the **rete testis**. The connection of the prominent sex cords—**seminiferous (testicular) cords**—with the surface epithelium is lost when a thick fibrous capsule, the tunica albuginea, develops (Fig. 14-21). The development of the dense **tunica albuginea** is the characteristic and diagnostic feature of testicular development in the fetus. Gradually the enlarging testis separates from the degenerating mesonephros and becomes suspended by its own mesentery, the **mesorchium**. The seminiferous cords develop into the seminiferous tubules, tubuli recti, and rete testis.

The **seminiferous tubules** become separated by mesenchyme that gives rise to the **interstitial cells** (of Leydig). By about the eighth week, these cells begin to secrete androgenic hormones—*testosterone* and *androstenedione*, which induce masculine differentiation of the mesonephric ducts and the external genitalia. Testosterone production is stimulated by human chorionic gonadotropin (hCG), which reaches peak amounts during the 8- to 12-week period (DiGeorge, 1996). In addition to testosterone, the fetal testes produces a glycoprotein known as **anti-müllerian hormone** (AMH) or *müllerian-inhibiting substance* (MIS). Anti-müllerian hormone is produced by the sustentacular cells (of Sertoli), which continue to puberty, after which the levels of AMH decrease. Anti-müllerian hormone suppresses development of the paramesonephric (müllerian) ducts.

The seminiferous tubules remain solid (i.e., no lumina) until puberty, at which time lumina begin to develop. The walls of the seminiferous tubules are composed of two kinds of cell (Fig. 14-21):

- *Sertoli cells*, supporting cells derived from the surface epithelium of the testis
- Spermatogonia, primordial sperm cells derived from the primordial germ cells

Sertoli cells constitute most of the seminiferous epithelium in the fetal testis (Fig. 14-21). During later development, the surface epithelium of the testis flattens to form the mesothelium on the external surface of the adult testis. The rete testis becomes continuous with 15 to 20 mesonephric tubules that become **effer-**ent ductules (ductuli efferentes). These ductules are connected with the mesonephric duct, which becomes the **ductus epididymis** (Figs. 14-21 and 14-22*A*).

DEVELOPMENT OF OVARIES

Gonadal development occurs slowly in female embryos. The X chromosomes bear genes for ovarian development, and an autosomal gene also appears to play a role in ovarian organogenesis (DiGeorge, 1996). The ovary is not identifiable histologically until about the 10th week. **Primary sex cords** do not become prominent, but they extend into the medulla and form a rudimentary *rete ovarii*. This structure and the primary sex cords normally degenerate and disappear (Fig. 14-21). **Secondary sex cords** (cortical cords) extend from the surface epithelium of the developing ovary into the underlying mesenchyme during the early fetal period. This epithelium is derived from the mesothelium. As the cortical cords increase in size, **primordial germ cells** are incorporated into them. At about 16 weeks these cords begin to break up into isolated cell clusters—**primordial follicles**—each of which consists of an **oogonium**, derived from a primordial germ cell, surrounded by a single layer of flattened follicular cells derived from the sex cord (Fig. 14-21). Active mitosis of oogonia occurs during fetal life, producing thousands of these primordial follicles.

No oogonia form postnatally. Although many oogonia degenerate before birth, the 2 million or so that remain enlarge to become primary oocytes before birth. After birth the surface epithelium of the ovary flattens to a single layer of cells continuous with the mesothelium of the peritoneum at the hilum of the ovary. The surface epithelium was formerly called the "germinal epithelium," which is inappropriate because it is now well established that the germ cells differentiate from the primordial germ cells (Fig. 14-21). The surface epithelium becomes separated from the follicles in the cortex by a thin fibrous capsule, the **tunica albuginea**. As the ovary separates from the regressing mesonephros, it is suspended by the **mesovarium**, which is its mesentery.

Development of Genital Ducts

Both male and female embryos have two pairs of genital ducts. The mesonephric (wolffian) ducts play an important part in the development of the male reproductive system, and the paramesonephric (müllerian) ducts have a leading role in the development of the female reproductive system. During the fifth and sixth weeks, the genital system is in an **indifferent stage,** when male and female genital ducts are present.

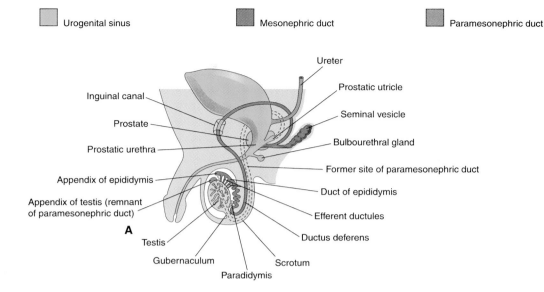

Urogenital sinus   Mesonephric duct   Paramesonephric duct

Ureter
Prostatic utricle
Inguinal canal
Seminal vesicle
Prostate
Bulbourethral gland
Prostatic urethra
Former site of paramesonephric duct
Appendix of epididymis
Duct of epididymis
Appendix of testis (remnant of paramesonephric duct)
Efferent ductules
Ductus deferens
A
Testis
Gubernaculum
Scrotum
Paradidymis

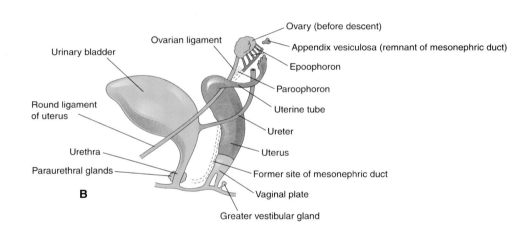

Ovary (before descent)
Ovarian ligament
Appendix vesiculosa (remnant of mesonephric duct)
Urinary bladder
Epoophoron
Paroophoron
Round ligament of uterus
Uterine tube
Ureter
Urethra
Uterus
Paraurethral glands
Former site of mesonephric duct
B
Vaginal plate
Greater vestibular gland

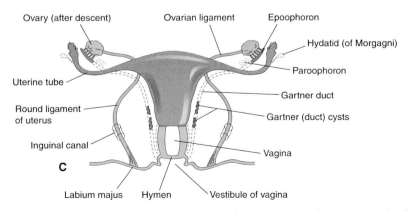

Ovary (after descent)
Ovarian ligament
Epoophoron
Hydatid (of Morgagni)
Paroophoron
Uterine tube
Gartner duct
Round ligament of uterus
Gartner (duct) cysts
Inguinal canal
Vagina
C
Labium majus   Hymen   Vestibule of vagina

■ **Figure 14–22.** Schematic drawings illustrating development of the male and female reproductive systems from the genital ducts and urogenital sinus. Vestigial structures are also shown. *A,* Reproductive system in a newborn male. *B,* Female reproductive system in a 12-week fetus. *C,* Reproductive system in a newborn female.

The **mesonephric ducts**, which drain urine from the mesonephric kidneys, play an essential role in the development of the **male reproductive system** (Fig. 14-22A). Under the influence of testosterone produced by the fetal testes in the eighth week, the proximal part of each mesonephric duct becomes highly convoluted to form the **epididymis**. The remainder of this duct forms the **ductus deferens** and **ejaculatory duct**. In female fetuses the mesonephric ducts almost completely disappear; only a few nonfunctional remnants persist (Fig. 14-22B and C; see Table 14-1).

The **paramesonephric ducts** develop lateral to the gonads and mesonephric ducts (Fig. 14-21) and play an essential role in the development of the **female reproductive system**. The paramesonephric ducts form on each side from longitudinal invaginations of the mesothelium on the lateral aspects of the mesonephroi. The funnel-shaped cranial ends of these ducts open into the peritoneal cavity (Fig. 14-22A, B, and C). The paramesonephric ducts pass caudally, parallel to the mesonephric ducts, until they reach the future pelvic region of the embryo. Here they cross ventral to the mesonephric ducts, approach each other in the median plane, and fuse to form a Y-shaped **uterovaginal primordium** (Fig. 14-23A). This tubular structure projects into the dorsal wall of the urogenital sinus and produces an elevation — the **sinus (müllerian) tubercle** (Fig. 14-23B).

DEVELOPMENT OF MALE GENITAL DUCTS AND GLANDS

The Sertoli cells of the fetal testes produce *masculinizing hormone* (e.g., testosterone) and MIS, the latter beginning at 6 to 7 weeks. The interstitial cells begin producing testosterone in the eighth week (DiGeorge, 1996). **Testosterone**, the production of which is stimulated by hCG, stimulates the mesonephric ducts to form male genital ducts, whereas MIS causes the paramesonephric ducts to disappear by epithelial-mesenchymal transformation (Hay, 1990). As the mesonephros degenerates, some mesonephric tubules persist and are transformed into **efferent ductules** (Fig. 14-22A). These ductules open into the mesonephric duct, which has transformed into the duct of the epididymis — the **ductus epididymis** — in this region. Distal to the epididymis, the mesonephric duct acquires a thick investment of smooth muscle and becomes the **ductus deferens**. A lateral outgrowth from the caudal end of each mesonephric duct gives rise to the **seminal vesicle**. This pair of glands produces a secretion that nourishes the sperms. The part of the mesonephric duct between the duct of this gland and the urethra becomes the **ejaculatory duct**.

Prostate. Multiple endodermal outgrowths arise from the prostatic part of the urethra and grow into the

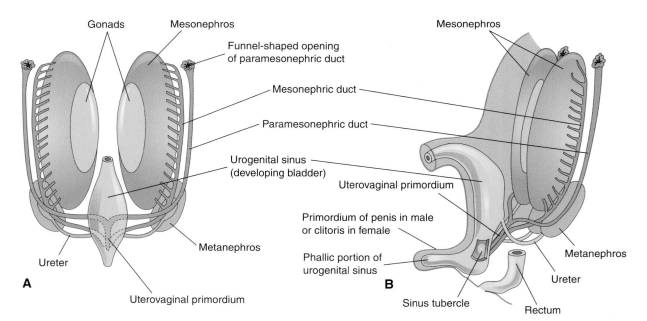

■ **Figure 14-23.** *A,* Sketch of a ventral view of the posterior abdominal wall of a 7-week embryo showing the two pairs of genital ducts present during the indifferent stage of sexual development. *B,* Lateral view of a 9-week fetus showing the sinus tubercle (müllerian tubercle) on the posterior wall of the urogenital sinus. It becomes the hymen in females and the seminal colliculus in males. The colliculus is an elevated part of the urethral crest on the posterior wall of the prostatic urethra.

surrounding mesenchyme (Fig. 14–24). The glandular epithelium of the prostate differentiates from these endodermal cells, and the associated mesenchyme differentiates into the dense stroma and smooth muscle of the prostate.

Bulbourethral Glands. These pea-sized structures develop from paired outgrowths from the spongy part of the urethra (Fig. 14–22A). The smooth muscle fibers and the stroma differentiate from the adjacent mesen-

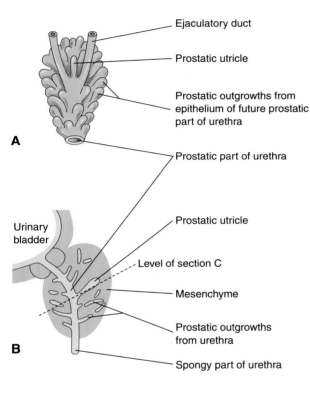

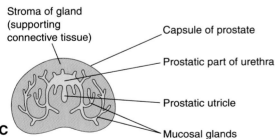

■ **Figure 14–24.** *A,* Dorsal view of the developing prostate in an 11-week fetus. *B,* Sketch of a median section of the developing urethra and prostate, showing numerous endodermal outgrowths from the prostatic urethra. The vestigial prostatic utricle is also shown. *C,* Section of the prostate (16 weeks) at the level shown in *B.*

chyme. The secretions of these glands contribute to the semen.

DEVELOPMENT OF FEMALE GENITAL DUCTS AND GLANDS

In embryos with ovaries, the mesonephric ducts regress because of lack of testosterone, and the paramesonephric ducts develop because of the absence of MIS. Although testosterone is essential for the stimulation of male sexual development, female sexual development does not depend on the presence of ovaries or hormones. The paramesonephric ducts form most of the female genital tract. The **uterine tubes** develop from the unfused cranial parts of the paramesonephric ducts (Fig. 14–22B and C). The caudal fused portions of these ducts form the **uterovaginal primordium**. As the name of this structure indicates, it gives rise to the uterus and vagina (superior part). The endometrial stroma and myometrium are derived from the adjacent splanchnic mesenchyme.

Fusion of the paramesonephric ducts also brings together two peritoneal folds that form the right and left **broad ligaments** and two peritoneal compartments — the **rectouterine pouch** and **vesicouterine pouch** (Fig. 14–25B to D). Along the sides of the uterus, between the layers of the broad ligament, the mesenchyme proliferates and differentiates into cellular tissue — the **parametrium** — which is composed of loose connective tissue and smooth muscle.

DEVELOPMENT OF THE VAGINA

The vaginal epithelium is derived from the endoderm of the urogenital sinus, and the fibromuscular wall of the vagina develops from the surrounding mesenchyme. Contact of the uterovaginal primordium with the urogenital sinus, forming the **sinus tubercle** (Fig. 14–23B), induces the formation of paired endodermal outgrowths called **sinovaginal bulbs** (Fig. 14–25A). They extend from the urogenital sinus to the caudal end of the uterovaginal primordium. The sinovaginal bulbs fuse to form a **vaginal plate** (Fig. 14–22B). Later the central cells of this plate break down, forming the lumen of the vagina. Its peripheral cells form the vaginal epithelium (Fig. 14–22C). The lining of the entire vagina is derived from the vaginal plate (Persaud, 1993).

Until late fetal life, the lumen of the vagina is separated from the cavity of the urogenital sinus by a membrane — the **hymen** (Fig. 14–26H; see also Fig. 14–22C). The hymen is formed by invagination of the posterior wall of the urogenital sinus, resulting from expansion of the caudal end of the vagina. The hymen

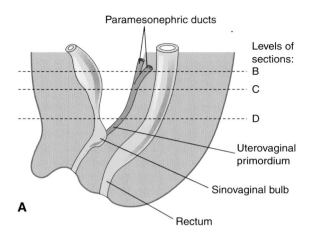

A

Paramesonephric ducts

Levels of
sections:
B
C
D

Uterovaginal
primordium

Sinovaginal bulb

Rectum

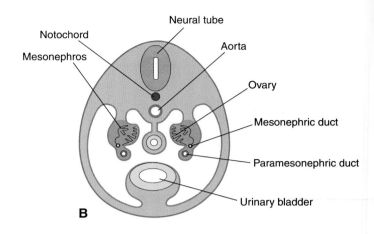

B

Neural tube
Notochord
Mesonephros
Aorta
Ovary
Mesonephric duct
Paramesonephric duct
Urinary bladder

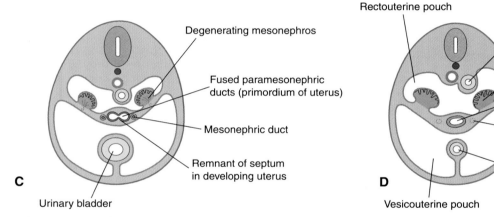

C

Degenerating mesonephros

Fused paramesonephric
ducts (primordium of uterus)

Mesonephric duct

Remnant of septum
in developing uterus

Urinary bladder

D

Rectouterine pouch
Rectum
Ovary
Uterovaginal
primordium
Regressing
mesonephric duct
Urinary bladder
Vesicouterine pouch

■ **Figure 14–25.** Early development of the ovaries and uterus. *A,* Schematic drawing of a sagittal section of the caudal region of an 8-week female embryo. *B,* Transverse section showing the paramesonephric ducts approaching each other. *C,* Similar section at a more caudal level illustrating fusion of the paramesonephric ducts. A remnant of the septum that initially separates them is shown. *D,* Similar section showing the uterovaginal primordium, broad ligament, and pouches in the pelvic cavity. Note that the mesonephric ducts have regressed.

usually ruptures during the perinatal period and remains as a thin fold of mucous membrane just within the vaginal orifice (entrance to the vagina).

AUXILIARY GENITAL GLANDS IN THE FEMALE

Buds grow from the urethra into the surrounding mesenchyme and form **urethral glands** and **paraurethral glands** (of Skene). These glands correspond to the prostate gland in the male. Outgrowths from the urogenital sinus form the **greater vestibular glands** (of Bartholin), which are homologous to the bulbourethral glands in the male (Table 14–1).

VESTIGIAL STRUCTURES DERIVED FROM EMBRYONIC GENITAL DUCTS

During conversion of the mesonephric and paramesonephric ducts into adult structures, parts of them remain as vestigial structures. These vestiges are rarely seen unless pathologic changes develop in them.

Mesonephric Remnants in Males

The cranial end of the mesonephric duct may persist as an *appendix of the epididymis,* which is usually at-

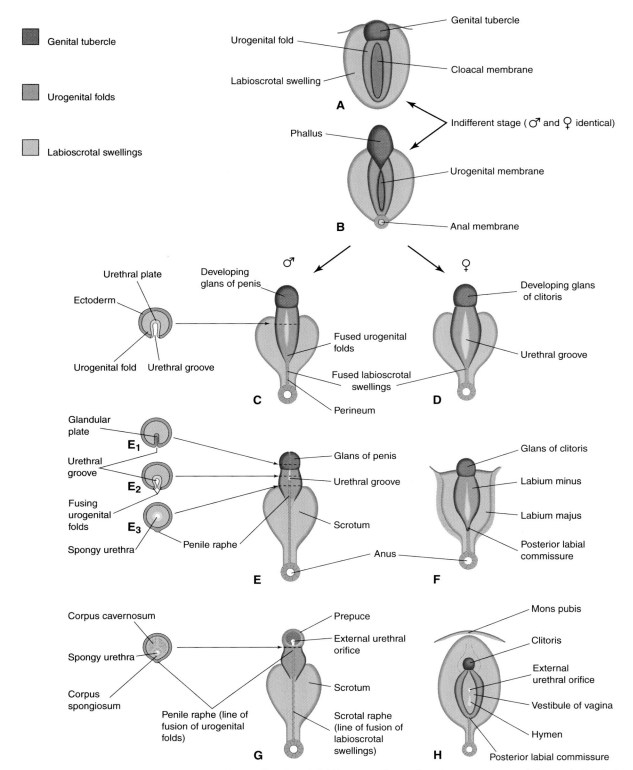

■ **Figure 14–26.** Development of the external genitalia. *A* and *B,* Diagrams illustrating the appearance of the genitalia during the indifferent stage (fourth to seventh weeks). *C, E,* and *G,* Stages in the development of male external genitalia at 9, 11, and 12 weeks, respectively. To the left are schematic transverse sections of the developing penis, illustrating formation of the spongy urethra. *D, F,* and *H,* Stages in the development of female external genitalia at 9, 11, and 12 weeks, respectively.

Table 14–1 ■ Adult Derivatives and Vestigial Remains of Embryonic Urogenital Structures*

Male	Embryonic Structure	Female
Testis	*Indifferent Gonad*	*Ovary*
Seminiferous tubules	*Cortex*	*Ovarian follicles*
Rete testis	*Medulla*	Rete ovarii
Gubernaculum testis	*Gubernaculum*	*Ovarian ligament*
		Round ligament of uterus
Ductuli efferentes	*Mesonephric Tubules*	Epoophoron
Paradidymis		Paroophoron
Appendix of epididymis	*Mesonephric Duct*	Appendix vesiculosa
Duct of epididymis		Duct of epoophoron
Ductus deferens		Duct of Gartner
Ureter, pelvis, calices and collecting tubules		*Ureter, pelvis, calices and collecting tubules*
Ejaculatory duct and seminal vesicle		
Appendix of testis	*Paramesonephric Duct*	Hydatid (of Morgagni)
		Uterine tube
		Uterus
Urinary bladder	*Urogenital Sinus*	*Urinary bladder*
Urethra (except *navicular fossa*)		*Urethra*
Prostatic utricle		*Vagina*
Prostate gland		*Urethral and paraurethral glands*
Bulbourethral glands		*Greater vestibular glands*
Seminal colliculus	*Sinus Tubercle*	Hymen
Penis	*Phallus*	*Clitoris*
Glans penis		*Glans clitoridis*
Corpora cavernosa penis		*Corpora cavenosa clitoridis*
Corpus spongiosum penis		*Bulb of the vestibule*
Ventral aspect of penis	*Urogenital Folds*	Labia minora
Scrotum	*Labioscrotal Swellings*	Labia majora

*Functional derivatives are in *italics*.

tached to the head of the epididymis (Fig. 14–22*A*). Caudal to the efferent ductules, some mesonephric tubules may persist as a small body, the *paradidymis*.

Mesonephric Remnants in Females

The cranial end of the mesonephric duct may persist as an *appendix vesiculosa* (Fig. 14–22*B*). A few blind tubules and a duct, the *epoophoron*, correspond to the efferent ductules and duct of the epididymis in the male. The epoophoron may persist in the mesovarium between the ovary and uterine tube (Fig. 14–22*B* and *C*). Closer to the uterus some rudimentary tubules may persist as the *paroophoron*. Parts of the mesonephric duct, corresponding to the ductus deferens and ejaculatory duct, may persist as the *duct of Gartner* between the layers of the broad ligament along the lateral wall of the uterus or in the wall of the vagina. These mesonephric duct remnants may give rise to *Gartner's duct cysts* (Fig. 14–22*C*).

Paramesonephric Remnants in Males

The cranial end of the paramesonephric duct may persist as a vesicular *appendix of the testis*, which is attached to the superior pole of the testis (Fig. 14–22*A*). The *prostatic utricle*, a small saclike structure that opens into the prostatic urethra, is homologous to the vagina. The lining of the prostatic utricle is derived from the epithelium of the urogenital sinus. The *seminal colliculus*, a small elevation in the posterior wall of the prostatic urethra (Moore, 1992), is the adult derivative of the sinus tubercle (Fig. 14–23*B*). It is homologous to the hymen in the female (Table 14–1).

Paramesonephric Remnants in Females

Part of the cranial end of the paramesonephric duct that does not contribute to the infundibulum of the uterine tube may persist as a vesicular appendage (Fig. 14-22C), a *hydatid (of Morgagni)*.

Development of External Genitalia

Up to the seventh week of development the external genitalia are similar in both sexes. Distinguishing sexual characteristics begin to appear during the ninth week, but the external genitalia are not fully differentiated until the 12th week. From the fourth to the early part of the seventh week, the external genitalia are sexually undifferentiated (Fig. 14-26A and B). Early in the fourth week, proliferating mesenchyme produces a **genital tubercle** in both sexes at the cranial end of the cloacal membrane. **Labioscrotal swellings** (genital swellings) and **urogenital folds** (urethral folds) soon develop on each side of the cloacal membrane. The genital tubercle soon elongates to form a **phallus**. When the urorectal septum fuses with the cloacal membrane at the end of the sixth week, it divides the cloacal membrane into a dorsal anal membrane and a ventral urogenital membrane (Fig. 14-12B). The **urogenital membrane** lies in the floor of a median cleft, the **urogenital groove**, which is bounded by the urogenital folds. The anal and urogenital membranes rupture a week or so later, forming the **anus** and **urogenital orifice**, respectively. In the female fetus, the urethra and vagina open into a common cavity, the **vestibule of the vagina**.

DEVELOPMENT OF MALE EXTERNAL GENITALIA

Masculinization of the indifferent external genitalia is induced by **testosterone** produced by the fetal testes (Fig. 14-26C, E, and G). As the phallus enlarges and elongates to become the penis, the urogenital folds form the lateral walls of the **urethral groove** on the ventral surface of the penis. This groove is lined by a proliferation of endodermal cells, the **urethral plate** (Fig. 14-26), which extends from the phallic portion of the urogenital sinus. The **urogenital folds** fuse with each other along the ventral surface of the penis to form the *spongy urethra* (Fig. 14-26E₁ to E₃). The surface ectoderm fuses in the median plane of the penis, forming the **penile raphe** and enclosing the spongy urethra within the penis. At the tip of the glans penis an ectodermal ingrowth forms a cellular cord, the **glandular plate**, which grows toward the root of the penis to meet the spongy urethra (Fig. 14-17A). This plate canalizes and joins the previously formed spongy urethra. This completes the terminal part of the urethra and moves the external urethral orifice to the tip of the glans penis (Fig. 14-17C).

During the 12th week a circular ingrowth of ectoderm occurs at the periphery of the glans penis (Fig. 14-17B). When this ingrowth breaks down, it forms the **prepuce** (foreskin)—a covering fold of skin (Fig. 14-17C). For some time the prepuce is adherent to the glans and is usually not retractable at birth. Breakdown of the adherent surfaces normally occurs during infancy. The *corpora cavernosa penis* and *corpus spongiosum penis* develop from mesenchyme in the phallus. The **labioscrotal swellings** grow toward each other and fuse to form the scrotum (Fig. 14-26E and G). The line of fusion of these folds is clearly visible as the **scrotal raphe** (Fig. 14-26G).

DEVELOPMENT OF FEMALE EXTERNAL GENITALIA

Feminization of the indifferent external genitalia is not clearly understood, but estrogens produced by the placenta and fetal ovaries appear to be involved (Fig. 14-26D, F, and H). Growth of the phallus gradually ceases, and it becomes the **clitoris**, a very sensitive sexual organ. The clitoris, still relatively large at 18 weeks (Fig. 14-13), develops like the penis, but the urogenital folds do not fuse, except posteriorly, where they join to form the *frenulum of the labia minora* (Moore, 1992). The unfused parts of the urogenital folds form the **labia minora**. The labioscrotal folds fuse posteriorly to form the *posterior labial commissure* and anteriorly to form the *anterior labial commissure* and *mons pubis* (Fig. 14-26H). Most parts of the **labioscrotal folds** remain unfused and form two large folds of skin, the **labia majora**, which are homologous to the scrotum.

Determination of Fetal Sex

Visualization of the external genitalia during ultrasonography is clinically important for several reasons, such as detection of fetuses at risk for severe X-linked disorders (Thompson et al, 1991; Mahony, 1994). Careful examination of the perineum may detect **ambiguous genitalia**. Only documentation of testes in the scrotum provides 100% gender determination, which is not possible in utero until 28 to 38 menstrual weeks (Mahony, 1994). Because early embryos have the potential to develop as either males or females, errors in sex determination and differentiation result in intermediate sex—**intersexuality** or **hermaphroditism**. Hermaphroditism implies a discrepancy between the morphology of the gonads (testes/ovaries) and the appearance of the external genitalia. A person with ambiguous external genitalia is an **intersex** or **hermaph-**

rodite. Intersexual conditions are classified according to the histologic appearance of the gonads:

- *True hermaphrodites* have ovarian and testicular tissue either in the same or in opposite gonads.
- *Female pseudohermaphrodites* have ovaries.
- *Male pseudohermaphrodites* have testes.

True Hermaphroditism

Persons with this extremely rare intersexual condition usually have a 46,XX sex chromosome constitution. *True hermaphroditism results from an error in sex determination.* The phenotype may be male or female, but the external genitalia are always ambiguous.

Female Pseudohermaphroditism

Persons with this intersexual condition have *chromatin-positive nuclei* and a 46,XX chromosome constitution. This anomaly results from exposure of the female fetus to excessive androgens, and the effects are principally virilization of the external genitalia (clitoral enlargement and labial fusion [Fig. 14–27; see also Fig.

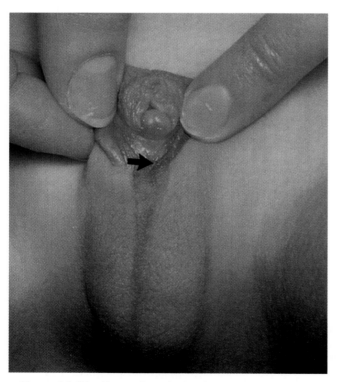

■ **Figure 14–27.** External genitalia of a 6-year-old girl showing an enlarged clitoris and fused labia majora that have formed a scrotumlike structure. The arrow indicates the opening into the urogenital sinus. This extreme masculinization is the result of congenital adrenal hyperplasia.

14–19]). The common cause of female pseudohermaphroditism is CAH. There is no ovarian abnormality, but the excessive production of androgens by the fetal suprarenal glands causes masculinization of the external genitalia, varying from enlargement of the clitoris to almost masculine genitalia. Commonly there is **clitoral hypertrophy**, partial fusion of the labia majora, and a persistent urogenital sinus. In very unusual cases, the masculinization may be so intense that a complete *clitoral urethra* results (DiGeorge, 1996). For more information, see Moore and Persaud (1998).

Male Pseudohermaphroditism

Persons with this intersexual condition have *chromatin-negative nuclei* (they do not contain sex chromatin) and a 46,XY chromosome constitution. The external and internal genitalia are variable, owing to varying degrees of development of the external genitalia and paramesonephric ducts. These anomalies are caused by inadequate production of testosterone and müllerian-inhibiting factor by the fetal testes. Testicular development in these males ranges from rudimentary to normal (Meacham et al, 1991). Five genetic defects have been described in the enzymatic synthesis of testosterone by the fetal testes, and a defect in Leydig cell differentiation has been described (DiGeorge, 1996). These defects produce male pseudohermaphroditism through inadequate virilization of the male fetus.

Androgen-Insensitivity Syndrome

Persons with this unusual condition—also called **testicular feminization syndrome**—(1 in 20,000 live births) are normal-appearing females, despite the presence of testes and a 46,XY chromosome constitution (Fig. 14–28). The external genitalia are female, but the vagina usually ends blindly in a pouch and the uterus and uterine tubes are absent or rudimentary. At puberty there is normal development of breasts and female characteristics, but menstruation does not occur and pubic hair is scanty or absent. The psychosexual orientation of women with androgen-insensitivity syndrome is entirely female, and medically, legally, and socially they are females. The testes are usually in the abdomen or the inguinal canals, but they may descend into the labia majora. The failure of masculinization to occur in these individuals results from a resistance to the action of testosterone at the cellular level in the genital tubercle and labioscrotal and urogenital folds. For more information about this syndrome, see Moore and Persaud (1998).

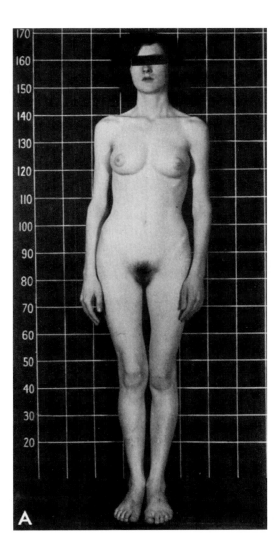

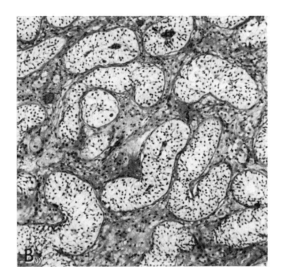

■ **Figure 14–28.** *A,* Photograph of a 17-year-old woman with androgen insensitivity syndrome (testicular feminization syndrome). The external genitalia are female, but the patient has a 46,XY karyotype and testes. *B,* Photomicrograph of a section through a testis removed from the inguinal region of this woman, showing seminiferous tubules lined by Sertoli cells. There are no germ cells, and the interstitial cells are hypoplastic. Medically, legally, and socially, these individuals are females. (From Jones HW, Scott WW: *Hermaphroditism, Genital Anomalies and Related Endocrine Disorders.* Baltimore, Williams & Wilkins, 1958.)

Hypospadias

Hypospadias is the most common anomaly of the penis. In 1 of every 300 male infants, the external urethral orifice is on the ventral surface of the glans penis (**glandular hypospadias**) or on the ventral surface of the body of the penis (**penile hypospadias**). Usually the penis is underdeveloped and curved ventrally—**chordee**. There are four types of hypospadias (Fig. 14-29*A* to *C*):

• Glandular hypospadias
• Penile hypospadias
• Penoscrotal hypospadias
• Perineal hypospadias

The glandular and penile types of hypospadias constitute about 80% of cases (Fig. 14-29*A* and *B*). In **penoscrotal hypospadias** the urethral orifice is at the junction of the penis and scrotum (Fig. 14-29*C*). In **perineal hypospadias,** the labioscrotal folds fail to fuse and the external urethral orifice is located between the unfused halves of the scrotum. Because the external genitalia in this severe type of hypospadias are ambiguous, persons with perineal hypospadias and cryptorchidism (undescended testes) are sometimes diagnosed as male pseudohermaphrodites. Hypospadias results from inadequate production of androgens by the fetal testes and/or inadequate receptor sites for the hormones.

Epispadias

In 1 of every 30,000 male infants, the urethra opens on the dorsal surface of the penis (Fig. 14–29D). Although epispadias may occur as a separate entity, it is *often associated with exstrophy of the bladder* (Fig. 14–15A). Epispadias may result from inadequate ectodermal-mesenchymal interactions during development of the genital tubercle. As a consequence, the genital tubercle develops more dorsally than in normal embryos. Consequently, when the urogenital membrane ruptures, the urogenital sinus opens on the dorsal sur-

face of the penis. Urine is expelled at the root of the malformed penis.

Anomalies of the Female Genital Tract

Various types of uterine duplication and vaginal anomalies result from arrests of development of the uterovaginal primordium during the eighth week (Fig. 14–30B to G):

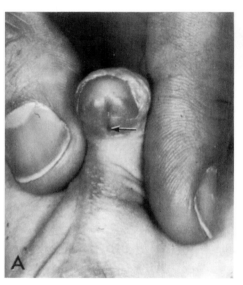
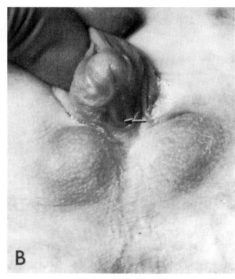
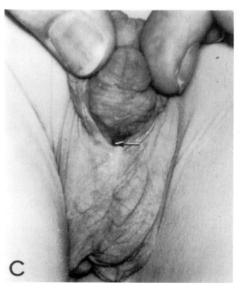
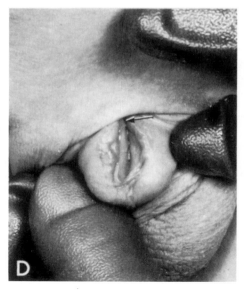

■ **Figure 14–29.** Photographs of penile anomalies. *A,* Glandular hypospadias. This is the most common form of hypospadias. The external urethral orifice (meatus) is on the ventral aspect of the glans (*arrow*). There is a shallow pit in the glans penis at the usual site of the urethral orifice. Note the moderate degree of chordee, causing the penis to curve ventrally. (From Jolly H: *Diseases of Children,* 2nd ed. London, Blackwell Scientific Publications, 1968.) *B,* Penile hypospadias. The penis is short and curved (chordee). The external urethral orifice (*arrow*) is near the penoscrotal junction. *C,* Penoscrotal hypospadias. The external urethral orifice (*arrow*) is located at the penoscrotal junction. *D,* Epispadias. The external urethral orifice (*arrow*) is on the dorsal surface of the penis. (Courtesy of Mr. Innes Williams, Genitourinary Surgeon, The Hospital for Sick Children, London, England.)

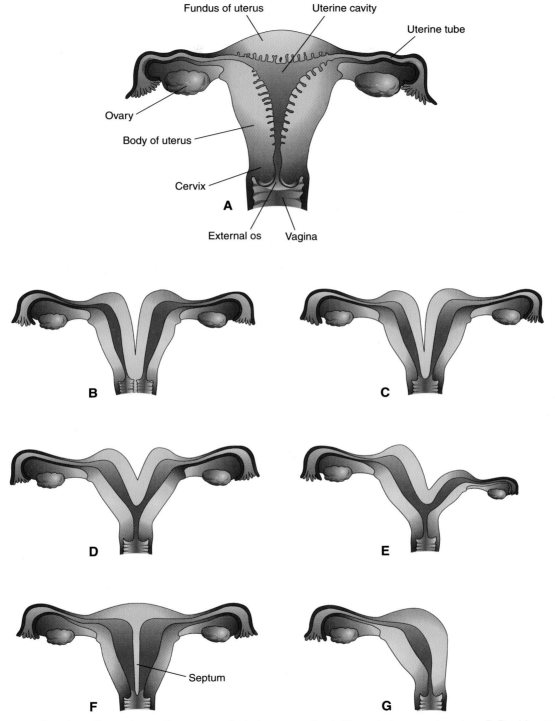

■ **Figure 14–30.** Drawings illustrating various types of uterine anomaly. *A*, Normal uterus and vagina. *B*, Double uterus (uterus didelphys) and double vagina. *C*, Double uterus with single vagina. *D*, Bicornuate uterus. *E*, Bicornuate uterus with a rudimentary left horn. *F*, Septate uterus. *G*, Unicornuate uterus.

- Incomplete fusion of the paramesonephric ducts
- Incomplete development of a paramesonephric duct
- Failure of parts of one or both paramesonephric ducts to develop
- Incomplete canalization of the vaginal plate to form the vagina

Double uterus (uterus didelphys) results from failure of fusion of the inferior parts of the paramesonephric ducts. It may be associated with a double or a single vagina (Fig. 14-30A to C). In some cases the uterus appears normal externally but is divided internally by a thin septum (Fig. 14-30F). If the duplication involves only the superior part of the body of the uterus, the condition is called **bicornuate uterus** (Fig. 14-30D and E). If one paramesonephric duct is retarded in its growth and does not fuse with the other one, a **bicornuate uterus with a rudimentary horn** (cornu) develops (Fig. 14-30E). The rudimentary horn may not communicate with the cavity of the uterus. A **unicornuate uterus** develops when one paramesonephric duct fails to develop; this results in a uterus with one uterine tube (Fig. 14-30G).

Once in about every 4000 to 5000 female births, **absence of the vagina** occurs. This results from failure of the sinovaginal bulbs to develop and form the vaginal plate (Fig. 14-22B). When the vagina is absent, the uterus is usually absent also, because the developing uterus (uterovaginal primordium) induces the formation of sinovaginal bulbs, which fuse to form the vaginal plate. Failure of canalization of the vaginal plate results in blockage of the vagina. A transverse vaginal septum occurs in approximately 1 in 80,000 women (Reid, 1993). Usually the septum is located at the junction of the middle and superior thirds of the vagina. Failure of the inferior end of the vaginal plate to perforate results in an **imperforate hymen**. Variations in the appearance of the hymen are common. The vaginal orifice varies in diameter from very small to large, and more than one orifice may be present (Moore and Persaud, 1998).

DEVELOPMENT OF THE INGUINAL CANALS

The inguinal canals form pathways for the testes to descend from their intra-abdominal position through the anterior abdominal wall into the scrotum. *Inguinal canals develop in both sexes* because of the morphologically indifferent stage of sexual development. As the mesonephros degenerates, a ligament — the **gubernaculum** — descends on each side of the abdomen from the inferior pole of the gonad (Fig. 14-31A). The gubernaculum passes obliquely through the developing anterior abdominal wall at the site of the future inguinal canal. The gubernaculum attaches caudally to the internal surface of the *labioscrotal swellings* (future halves of the scrotum or labium majora).

The **processus vaginalis,** or vaginal process, an evagination of peritoneum, develops ventral to the gubernaculum and herniates through the abdominal wall along the path formed by the gubernaculum (Fig. 14-31B to E). The vaginal process carries extensions of the layers of the abdominal wall before it, which form the walls of the inguinal canal. In males these layers also form the coverings of the spermatic cord and testis (Fig. 14-31E and F). The opening in the transversalis fascia produced by the vaginal process becomes the **deep inguinal ring**, and the opening created in the external oblique aponeurosis forms the **superficial inguinal ring** (Moore, 1992).

Descent of the Testes

Testicular descent is associated with:

- Enlargement of the testes and atrophy of the mesonephroi (mesonephric kidneys), which allow movement of the testes caudally along the posterior abdominal wall
- Atrophy of the paramesonephric ducts induced by the MIS, which enables the testes to move transabdominally to the deep inguinal rings
- Enlargement of the processus vaginalis, which guides the testis through the inguinal canal into the scrotum

By 26 weeks the testes have descended retroperitoneally (external to the peritoneum) from the posterior abdominal wall to the deep inguinal rings (Fig. 14-31B and C). This change in position occurs as the fetal pelvis enlarges and the trunk of the embryo elongates. Transabdominal movement of the testes is largely a relative movement that results from growth of the cranial part of the abdomen away from the caudal part (future pelvic region).

Little is known about the cause of testicular descent through the inguinal canals into the scrotum, but the process is controlled by androgens (e.g., testosterone) produced by the fetal testes. The role of the gubernaculum in testicular descent is uncertain; however, it appears to guide its descent into the scrotum. Descent of the testes through the inguinal canals into the scrotum usually begins during the 26th week and takes 2 or 3 days. The testes pass external to the peritoneum and processus vaginalis. After the testes enter the scrotum, the inguinal canal contracts around the spermatic cord. More than 97% of full-term newborn boys have both testes in the scrotum. During the first 3 months after birth, most undescended testes descend into the scrotum.

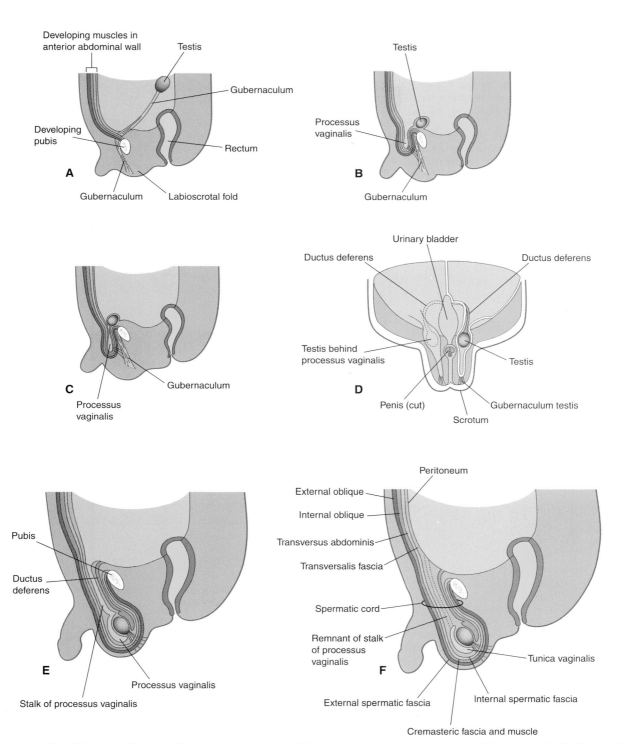

■ **Figure 14–31.** Schematic diagrams illustrating formation of the inguinal canals and descent of the testes. *A,* Sagittal section of a 7-week embryo showing the testis before its descent from the dorsal abdominal wall. *B* and *C,* Similar sections at about 28 weeks showing the processus vaginalis and the testis beginning to pass through the inguinal canal. Note that the processus vaginalis carries fascial layers of the abdominal wall before it. *D,* Frontal section of a fetus about 3 days later illustrating descent of the testis posterior to the processus vaginalis. The processus vaginalis has been cut away on the left side to show the testis and ductus deferens. *E,* Sagittal section of a newborn infant showing the processus vaginalis communicating with the peritoneal cavity by a narrow stalk. *F,* Similar section of a 1-month-old infant after obliteration of the stalk of the processus vaginalis. Note that the extended fascial layers of the abdominal wall now form the coverings of the spermatic cord.

When the testis descends, it carries its ductus deferens and vessels with it. As the testis and ductus deferens descend, they are ensheathed by the fascial extensions of the abdominal wall (Fig. 14–31*F*):

- The extension of the transversalis fascia becomes the **internal spermatic fascia**.
- The extensions of the internal oblique muscle and fascia become the **cremasteric muscle** and **fascia**.
- The extension of the external oblique aponeurosis becomes the **external spermatic fascia.**

Within the scrotum the testis projects into the distal end of the processus vaginalis. During the perinatal period, the connecting stalk of the process is normally obliterated, isolating the **tunica vaginalis** as a peritoneal sac related to the testis (Fig. 14–31*F*).

Descent of the Ovaries

The ovaries also descend from the posterior abdominal wall to the pelvis, just inferior to the pelvic brim. The gubernaculum is attached to the uterus near the attachment of the uterine tube. The cranial part of the gubernaculum becomes the **ovarian ligament,** and the caudal part forms the round ligament of the uterus (Fig. 14–22*C*). The **round ligaments** pass through the inguinal canals and terminate in the labium majora. The relatively small processus vaginalis in the female is usually obliterated and disappears long before birth.

Cryptorchidism or Undescended Testes

Cryptorchidism (Gr. *kryptos*, hidden) occurs in up to 30% of premature males and in about 3 to 4% of full-term males. Cryptorchidism may be unilateral or bilateral. In most cases the testes descend into the scrotum by the end of the first year. If both testes remain within or just outside the abdominal cavity, they fail to mature and sterility is common. Undescended testes are often histologically normal at birth, but failure of development and atrophy are detectable by the end of the first year (Behrman et al, 1996). **Cryptorchid testes** may be in the abdominal cavity or anywhere along the usual path of descent of the testis, but they are usually in the inguinal canal (Fig. 14–32*A*). The cause of most cases of cryptorchidism is unknown, but a deficiency of androgen production by the fetal testes is an important factor. Men with a history of cryptorchidism have a 20 to 44% increase in risk of developing testicular cancer (Behrman et al, 1996).

Ectopic Testes

After traversing the inguinal canal, the testis may deviate from its usual path of descent and lodge in various abnormal locations (Fig. 14–32*B*):

- Interstitial (external to aponeurosis of external oblique muscle)
- In the proximal part of the medial thigh
- Dorsal to the penis
- On the opposite side (crossed ectopia)

All types of ectopic testis are rare, but **interstitial ectopia** occurs most frequently. Ectopic testis occurs when a part of the gubernaculum passes to an abnormal location and the testis follows it.

Congenital Inguinal Hernia

If the communication between the tunica vaginalis and the peritoneal cavity fails to close, a **persistent processus vaginalis** exists. A loop of intestine may herniate through it into the scrotum or labium majus (Fig. 14–33*A* and *B*). Embryonic remnants resembling the ductus deferens or epididymis are often found in inguinal hernial sacs. Congenital inguinal hernia is much more common in males and is often associated with cryptorchidism and in females with the androgen insensitivity syndrome (Behrman et al, 1996).

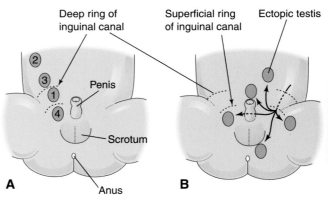

■ **Figure 14–32.** Diagrams showing the possible sites of cryptorchid and ectopic testes. *A*, Positions of cryptorchid testes, numbered in order of frequency. *B*, Usual locations of ectopic testes.

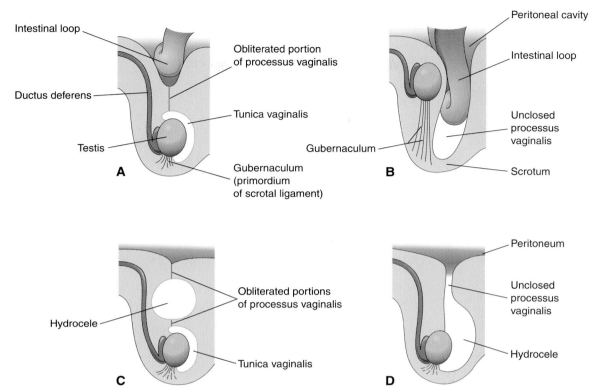

■ **Figure 14–33.** Diagrams of sagittal sections illustrating conditions resulting from failure of closure of the processus vaginalis. *A*, Incomplete congenital inguinal hernia resulting from persistence of the proximal part of the processus vaginalis. *B*, Complete congenital inguinal hernia into the scrotum resulting from persistence of the processus vaginalis. Cryptorchidism, a commonly associated anomaly, is also illustrated. *C*, Large cyst or hydrocele that arose from an unobliterated portion of the processus vaginalis. *D*, Hydrocele of the testis and spermatic cord resulting from peritoneal fluid passing into an unclosed processus vaginalis.

Hydrocele

Occasionally the abdominal end of the processus vaginalis remains open but is too small to permit herniation of intestine (Fig. 14-33*D*). Peritoneal fluid passes into the patent processus vaginalis and forms a **hydrocele of the testis.** If the middle part of the processus vaginalis canal remains open, fluid may accumulate and give rise to a **hydrocele of the spermatic cord** (Fig. 14-33*C*).

SUMMARY OF THE UROGENITAL SYSTEM

The urogenital system develops from the:

* Intermediate mesoderm
* Mesothelium lining the abdominal cavity
* Endoderm of the urogenital sinus

The urinary system begins to develop about 3 weeks before the genital system is evident. Three successive kidney systems develop:

* The *pronephroi,* which are nonfunctional
* The *mesonephroi,* which serve as temporary excretory organs
* The *metanephroi,* which become the permanent kidneys

The *metanephroi* or *permanent kidneys* develop from two sources:

* The *metanephric diverticulum,* or ureteric bud, which gives rise to the ureter, renal pelvis, calices, and collecting tubules
* The *metanephric mass of mesoderm,* which gives rise to the nephrons

At first the kidneys are located in the pelvis, but they gradually "ascend" to the abdomen. This apparent migration results from disproportionate growth of the fetal lumbar and sacral regions. Developmental abnormalities of the kidneys and ureters are common. Incomplete division of the metanephric diverticulum results in a double ureter and supernumerary kidney. Failure of the kidney to "ascend" from its embryonic position in the pelvis results in an ectopic kidney that is abnormally rotated.

The *urinary bladder* develops from the urogenital sinus and the surrounding splanchnic mesenchyme. The female urethra and almost all of the male urethra have a similar origin. *Exstrophy of the bladder* results from a rare ventral body wall defect through which the posterior wall of the urinary bladder protrudes onto the abdominal wall. In males, *epispadias* is a common associated anomaly.

The *genital* or *reproductive system* develops in close association with the urinary or excretory system. Genetic sex is established at fertilization, but the gonads do not begin to attain sexual characteristics until the seventh week. *Primordial germ cells* form in the wall of the yolk sac during the fourth week and migrate into the developing gonads, where they differentiate into germ cells (oogonia/spermatogonia). The external genitalia do not acquire distinct masculine or feminine characteristics until the 12th week. The reproductive organs develop from primordia that are identical in both sexes. During this *indifferent stage* an embryo has the potential to develop into either a male or a female.

Gonadal sex is determined by the testis-determining factor on the Y chromosome. Testis-determining factor is located on the sex-determining region of the short arm of the Y chromosome and directs testicular differentiation. The Leydig cells produce testosterone that stimulates development of the mesonephric ducts into male genital ducts. These androgens also stimulate development of the indifferent external genitalia into the penis and scrotum. A *müllerian-inhibiting substance* produced by the Sertoli cells of the testes inhibits development of the paramesonephric ducts.

In the absence of a Y chromosome and the presence of two X chromosomes, ovaries develop, the mesonephric ducts regress, the paramesonephric ducts develop into the uterus and uterine tubes, the vagina develops from the vaginal plate derived from the urogenital sinus, and the indifferent external genitalia develop into the clitoris and labia (majora and minora).

Persons with *true hermaphroditism*, an extremely rare intersexual condition, have both ovarian and testicular tissue and variable internal and external genitalia. *Male pseudohermaphroditism* results from failure of the fetal testes to produce adequate amounts of masculinizing hormones or from the tissue insensitivity of the sexual structures. *Female pseudohermaphroditism* usually results from congenital adrenal hyperplasia, a disorder of the fetal suprarenal (adrenal) glands that causes excessive production of androgens and masculinization of the external genitalia.

Most anomalies of the female genital tract, such as *double uterus*, result from incomplete fusion of the paramesonephric ducts. *Cryptorchidism* and *ectopic testes* result from abnormalities of testicular descent. *Congenital inguinal hernia* and hydrocele result from persistence of the processus vaginalis. Failure of the urogenital folds to fuse in males results in various types of *hypospadias.*

Clinically Oriented Questions

1. Does a horseshoe kidney usually function normally? What sort of problems may occur with this anomaly, and how can they be corrected?

2. My uncle has been told that he has two kidneys on one side and none on the other. How did this abnormality probably happen? Are there likely to be any problems associated with this condition?

3. Do true hermaphrodites ever marry? Are they ever fertile?

4. When a baby is born with ambiguous external genitalia, how long does it take to assign the appropriate sex? What does the physician tell the parents? How is the appropriate sex determined?

5. What is the most common type of disorder producing ambiguity of the external genitalia? Will masculinizing or androgenic hormones given during the fetal period of development cause ambiguity of external genitalia in female fetuses?

The answers to these questions are given at the back of the book.

REFERENCES AND SUGGESTED READING

Bard J: A new role for the stromal cells in kidney development. *Bioessays* 18:705, 1996.

Behrman RE, Kliegman RM, Arvin AM (eds): *Nelson Textbook of Pediatrics,* 15th ed. Philadelphia, WB Saunders, 1996.

Belman AB: Hypospadias update. *Urology* 49:166, 1997.

Berta P, Hawkins JR, Sinclair AH, et al: Genetic evidence equating SRY and the testis-determining factor. *Nature* 348:448, 1990.

DeKretser DM, Burger HG: The Y chromosome and spermatogenesis. *N Engl J Med* 336:576, 1997.

DiGeorge AM: Hermaphroditism. *In* Behrman RE, Kliegman RM, Arvin AM (eds): *Nelson Textbook of Pediatrics,* 15th ed. Philadelphia, WB Saunders, 1996.

Fleming S: *N*-linked oligosaccharides during human renal organogenesis. *J Anat* 170:151, 1990.

Gasser B, Mauss Y, Ghnassia JP, et al: A quantitative study of normal nephrogenesis in the human fetus: Its implication in the natural history of kidney changes due to low obstructive uropathies. *Fetal Diagn Ther* 8:371, 1993.

Hay ED: Epithelial-mesenchymal transitions. *Sem Dev Biol* 1:347, 1990.

Mahony BS: Ultrasound evaluation of the genitourinary system. *In* Callen PW (ed): *Ultrasonography in Obstetrics and Gynecology,* 3rd ed. Philadelphia, WB Saunders, 1994.

Meacham LR, Winn KJ, Culler FL, Parks JS: Double vagina, cardiac, pulmonary, and other genital malformations with 46,XY karyotype. *Am J Med Genet* 41:478, 1991.

Mittwoch U: Sex determination and sex reversal: Genotype, phenotype, dogma and semantics. *Hum Genet* 89:467, 1992.

Moore KL: *Clinically Oriented Anatomy,* 3rd ed. Baltimore, Williams & Wilkins, 1992.

Moore KL: The development of clinical sex chromatin tests. *In* Moore KL (ed): *The Sex Chromatin*. Philadelphia, WB Saunders, 1966.

Moore KL, Persaud TVN: *The Developing Human: Clinically Oriented Embryology*, 6th ed. Philadelphia, WB Saunders, 1998.

Peipert JF, Donnenfeld AE: Oligohydramnios: A review. *Obstet Gynecol Surv* 46:325, 1991.

Persaud TVN: Embryology of the female genital tract and gonads. *In* Copeland LJ, Jarrell J, McGregor J (eds): *Textbook of Gynecology*. Philadelphia, WB Saunders, 1993.

Reid RL: Amenorrhea. *In* Copeland LJ, Jarrell J, McGregor J (eds): *Textbook of Gynecology*. Philadelphia, WB Saunders, 1993.

Sivan E, Koch S, Recce EA: Sonographic prenatal diagnosis of ambiguous genitalia. *Fetal Diagn Ther* 10:311, 1995.

Thompson MW, McInnes RR, Willard HF: *Thompson and Thompson Genetics in Medicine*, 5th ed. Philadelphia, WB Saunders, 1991.

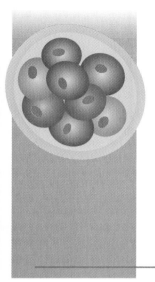

The Cardiovascular System

15

◼ *The cardiovascular system is the first major system to function in the embryo.* The primordial heart and vascular system appear in the middle of the third week of embryonic development. *The heart starts to function at the beginning of the fourth week.* This precocious cardiac development is necessary because the rapidly growing embryo can no longer satisfy its nutritional and oxygen requirements by diffusion alone. Consequently, it needs an efficient method of acquiring oxygen and nutrients from the maternal blood and disposing of carbon dioxide and waste products. The cardiovascular system is derived mainly from the following:

- *Splanchnic mesoderm,* which forms the primordium of the heart (Fig. 15-1*A* and *B*)
- *Paraxial and lateral mesoderm* near the otic placodes (thickened ectodermal areas located midway along the hindbrain), from which the internal (inner) ears develop
- Neural crest cells originating from the region between the otic vesicles (primordia of membranous labyrinths of internal ears) and the caudal limits of the third pair of somites

Blood vessel development—**angiogenesis**—is de-scribed in Chapter 5. Primordial blood vessels cannot be distinguished structurally as arteries or veins but are named according to their future fates and relationship to the heart.

EARLY DEVELOPMENT OF THE HEART AND VESSELS

The earliest sign of the heart is the appearance of paired endothelial strands—**angioblastic cords**—during the third week (Fig. 15-1*B* and *C*). These cords canalize to form **endocardial heart tubes** that fuse to form the tubular heart late in the third week (see Fig. 15-7). The heart begins to beat at 22 to 23 days (Fig. 15-2). An inductive influence from the embryonic endoderm appears to stimulate early formation of the heart (Carlson, 1994). Blood flow begins during the fourth week and can be visualized by Doppler ultrasonography (Fig. 15-3).

Development of Veins Associated with the Heart

Three paired veins drain into the tubular heart of a 4-week-old embryo (Fig. 15-2):

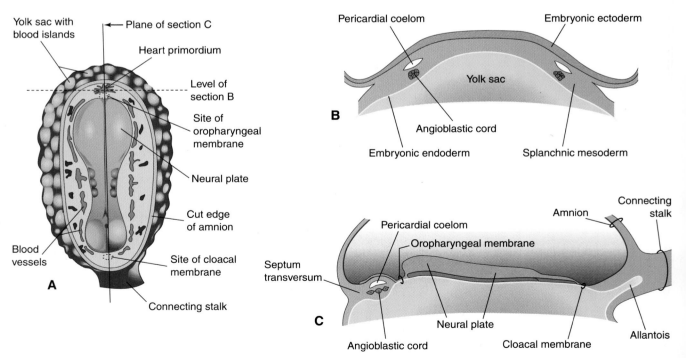

◼ **Figure 15-1.** *A,* Drawing of a dorsal view of an embryo (about 18 days). *B,* Transverse section of the embryo demonstrating the angioblastic cords and their relationship to the pericardial coelom. *C,* Longitudinal section through the embryo illustrating the relationship of the angioblastic cords to the oropharyngeal membrane, pericardial coelom, and septum transversum.

into the liver. The right umbilical vein disappears at the end of the embryonic period, leaving the left umbilical vein as the only vessel carrying well-oxygenated blood from the placenta to the embryo. Transformation of the umbilical veins may be summarized as follows (Fig. 15–5):

- The right umbilical vein and the caudal part of the left umbilical vein between the liver and the sinus venosus degenerate.
- The persistent caudal part of the left umbilical vein becomes the **umbilical vein**, which carries all the blood from the placenta to the embryo.
- A large venous shunt—the **ductus venosus**—develops within the liver (Fig. 15–5B) and connects the umbilical vein with the inferior vena cava (IVC). The ductus venosus forms a bypass through the liver, enabling most of the blood from the placenta to pass directly to the heart without passing through the capillary networks of the liver.

The **cardinal veins** (Figs. 15–2 and 15–4A) constitute the main venous drainage system of the embryo. The anterior and posterior cardinal veins drain cranial and caudal parts of the embryo, respectively (Fig. 15–4B). The anterior and posterior cardinal veins join the **common cardinal veins**, which enter the *sinus venosus* (Fig. 15–2). During the eighth week of embryonic development, the **anterior cardinal veins** become connected by an oblique anastomosis (Fig. 15–5B), which shunts blood from the left to the right anterior cardinal vein. This anastomotic shunt becomes the **left brachiocephalic vein** when the caudal part of the left anterior cardinal vein degenerates (Figs. 15–4D and 15–5C). The **superior vena cava** (SVC) forms from the right anterior cardinal vein and the right common cardinal vein.

The **posterior cardinal veins** develop primarily as the vessels of the mesonephroi and largely disappear with these transitory kidneys (see Chapter 14). The only adult derivatives of the posterior cardinal veins are the *root of the azygos vein* and the *common iliac veins*. The subcardinal and supracardinal veins gradually replace and supplement the posterior cardinal veins. The **subcardinal veins** appear first (Fig. 15–4A). They are connected with each other through the subcardinal anastomosis and with the posterior cardinal veins through the mesonephric sinusoids. The sub-

cardinal veins form the stem of the left renal vein, the suprarenal (adrenal) veins, the gonadal veins (testicular and ovarian), and a segment of the IVC (Fig. 15–4D). The **supracardinal veins** are the last pair of vessels to develop. They become disrupted in the region of the kidneys (Fig. 15–4C). Cranial to this they become united by an anastomosis that is represented in the adult by the **azygos** and **hemiazygos veins** (Figs. 15–4D and 15–5C). Caudal to the kidneys, the left supracardinal vein degenerates, but the right supracardinal vein becomes the inferior part of the IVC (Fig. 15–4D).

DEVELOPMENT OF THE INFERIOR VENA CAVA

The IVC forms during a series of changes in the primordial veins of the trunk that occur as blood returning from the caudal part of the embryo is shifted from the left to the right side of the body. The IVC is composed of four main segments (Fig. 15–4C):

- A *hepatic segment* derived from the hepatic vein (proximal part of right vitelline vein) and hepatic sinusoids
- A *prerenal segment* derived from the right subcardinal vein
- A *renal segment* derived from the subcardinal-supracardinal anastomosis
- A *postrenal segment* derived from the right supracardinal vein

Anomalies of the Venae Cavae

Because of the many transformations that occur during the formation of the SVC and IVC, variations in their adult form occur, but they are not common. The most common anomaly is a persistent left SVC, which drains into the right atrium through the enlarged orifice of the *coronary sinus* (Fig. 15–6), a short trunk receiving most of the cardiac veins. The most common anomaly of the IVC is interruption of its abdominal course; as a result, blood drains from the lower limbs, abdomen, and pelvis to the heart through the azygos system of veins. For a discussion of less common vena caval anomalies, see Moore and Persaud (1998).

■ **Figure 15–5.** Dorsal views of the developing heart. *A,* During the fourth week (about 24 days) showing the primordial atrium and sinus venosus and veins draining into them. *B,* Seven weeks, showing the enlarged right horn of the sinus venosus and venous circulation through the liver. The organs are not drawn to scale. *C,* Eight weeks, indicating the adult derivatives of the cardinal veins.

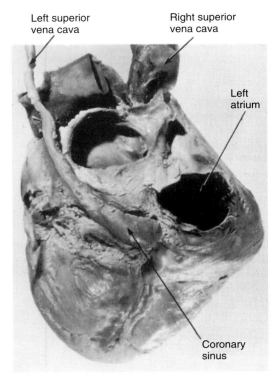

Left superior vena cava

Right superior vena cava

Left atrium

Coronary sinus

■ **Figure 15–6**. Photograph of the posterior aspect of an adult heart with double superior venae cavae. Parts of the walls of the atria have been removed. The small anomalous left superior vena cava opens into the coronary sinus.

Aortic Arches and Other Branches of the Dorsal Aorta

As the *pharyngeal arches* form during the fourth and fifth weeks, they are supplied by arteries — the **aortic arches** — that arise from the **aortic sac** and terminate in the dorsal aortae (Fig. 15–2). Initially, the paired dorsal aortae run through the entire length of the embryo, but they soon fuse to form a single **dorsal aorta**, just caudal to the pharyngeal arches.

INTERSEGMENTAL ARTERIES

Thirty or so branches of the dorsal aorta, the *intersegmental arteries*, pass between and carry blood to the somites and their derivatives (Fig. 15–2). The dorsal intersegmental arteries in the neck join to form a longitudinal artery on each side, the **vertebral artery**. Most of the original connections of the intersegmental arteries to the dorsal aorta disappear. In the thorax, the dorsal intersegmental arteries persist as **intercostal arteries**. Most of the dorsal intersegmental arteries in the abdomen become **lumbar arteries**, but the

fifth pair of lumbar intersegmental arteries remains as the **common iliac arteries** (Fig. 15–4D). In the sacral region, the intersegmental arteries form the **lateral sacral arteries**. The caudal end of the dorsal aorta becomes the median sacral artery (Moore, 1992).

FATE OF VITELLINE AND UMBILICAL ARTERIES

The unpaired ventral branches of the dorsal aorta supply the yolk sac, allantois, and chorion (Fig. 15–2). The **vitelline arteries** pass to the yolk sac and later the primordial gut, which forms from the incorporated part of the yolk sac. Three vitelline arteries remain as the

- *Celiac artery* to the foregut
- *Superior mesenteric artery* to the midgut
- *Inferior mesenteric artery* to the hindgut

The paired **umbilical arteries** pass through the connecting stalk (later the *umbilical cord*) and become continuous with vessels in the chorion, the embryonic part of the placenta (see Chapter 8). The umbilical arteries carry poorly oxygenated blood to the placenta (Fig. 15–2). Proximal parts of the umbilical arteries become the *internal iliac arteries* and *superior vesical arteries*, whereas distal parts obliterate after birth and become the *medial umbilical ligaments*. The major changes leading to the definitive arterial system, especially the *transformation of the aortic arches*, are described later.

FINAL PRENATAL DEVELOPMENT OF THE HEART

The primordium of the heart is first evident at 18 days (Fig. 15–1) and begins to beat at 22 to 23 days (Fig. 15–3). In the **cardiogenic area**, splanchnic mesenchymal cells ventral to the pericardial coelom aggregate and arrange themselves side by side to form two longitudinal, cellular cardiac primordia — **angioblastic cords**. These cords become canalized to form two thin-walled **endocardial heart tubes** (Figs. 15–7A and B and 15–8A and B). As lateral embryonic folding occurs, the endocardial tubes approach each other and fuse to form a single endocardial tube (Figs. 15–7B and C and 15–8D). Fusion of the endocardial tubes begins at the cranial end of the developing heart and extends caudally.

As the heart tubes fuse, an external layer of the embryonic heart — the **primordial myocardium** — is formed from splanchnic mesoderm surrounding the pericardial coelom (Fig. 15–8B and C). At this stage the developing heart is composed of a thin endothelial

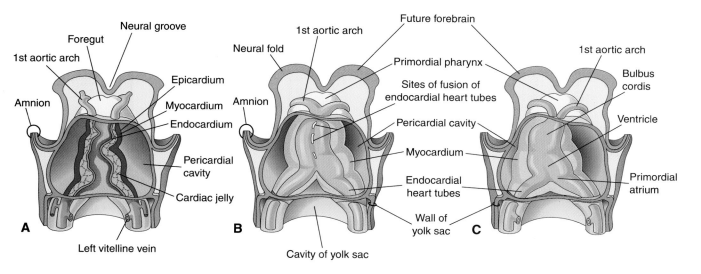

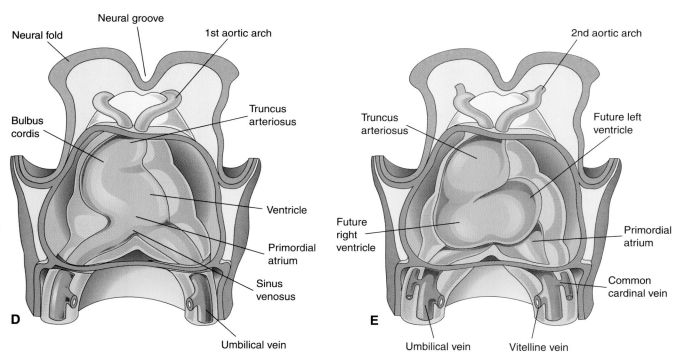

■ **Figure 15–7.** *A* to *C*, Sketches of ventral views of the developing heart and pericardial region (22 to 35 days). The ventral pericardial wall has been removed to show the developing myocardium and fusion of the endothelial tubes to form a single endocardial tube. The fusion begins at the cranial ends of the tubes and extends caudally until a single tubular heart is formed. The endothelium of the heart tube forms the endocardium of the heart. As the heart elongates, it bends upon itself, forming an S-shaped heart (*D* and *E*).

tube, separated from a thick muscular tube, the primordial myocardium, by gelatinous connective tissue —**cardiac jelly** (Fig. 15–8*D*). The endothelial tube becomes the internal endothelial lining of the heart or

endocardium, and the primordial myocardium becomes the muscular wall of the heart or **myocardium**. The visceral pericardium or **epicardium** is derived from mesothelial cells that arise from the

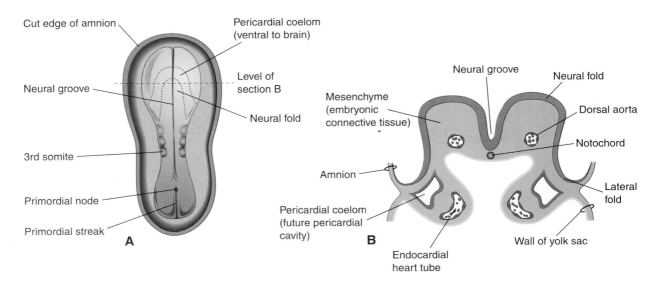

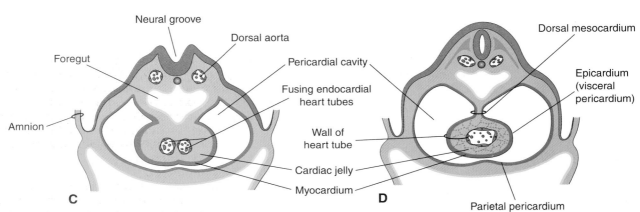

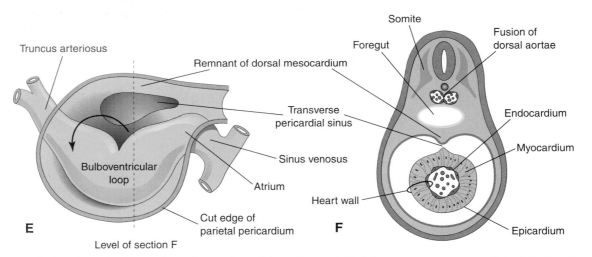

■ **Figure 15–8.** *A*, Drawing of a dorsal view of an embryo (about 20 days). *B*, Schematic transverse section of the heart region of the embryo illustrated in *A*, showing the two endocardial heart tubes and the lateral folds of the body. *C*, Transverse section of a slightly older embryo, showing the formation of the pericardial cavity and the fusing heart tubes. *D*, Similar section (about 22 days) showing the single heart tube suspended by the dorsal mesocardium. *E*, Schematic drawing of the heart (about 28 days) showing degeneration of the central part of the dorsal mesocardium and formation of the transverse sinus of the pericardium. *F*, Transverse section of the embryo at the level shown in *E*, showing the layers of the heart wall.

external surface of the sinus venosus and spread over the myocardium (Fig. 15–8F).

As folding of the head region occurs, the heart and pericardial cavity come to lie ventral to the foregut and caudal to the oropharyngeal membrane (Fig. 15–9A to C). Concurrently, the tubular heart elongates and develops alternate dilations and constrictions (Fig. 15–7C to E):

- Truncus arteriosus
- Bulbus cordis
- Ventricle

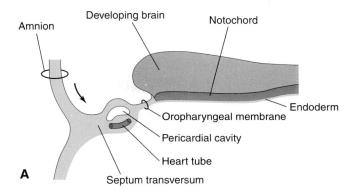

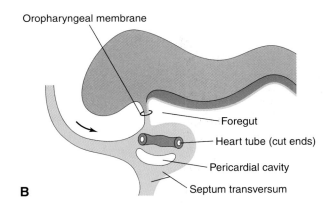

■ **Figure 15–9.** Schematic drawings of longitudinal sections through the cranial half of human embryos during the fourth week, showing the effect of the head fold *(arrow)* on the position of the heart and other structures. *A* and *B*, As the head fold develops, the heart tube and pericardial cavity come to lie ventral to the foregut and caudal to the oropharyngeal membrane. *C*, Note that the positions of the pericardial cavity and septum transversum have reversed with respect to each other. The septum transversum now lies posterior to the pericardial cavity, where it will form the central tendon of the diaphragm.

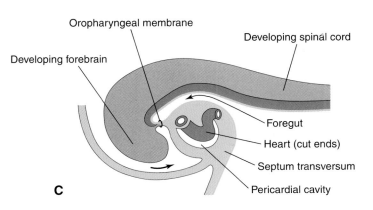

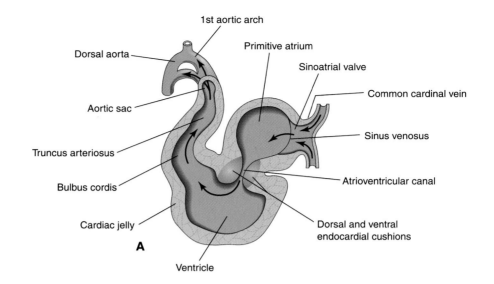

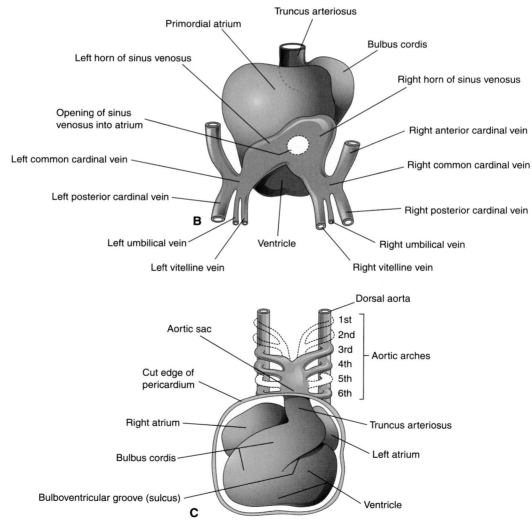

■ **Figure 15–10.** *See legend on opposite page*

- Atrium
- Sinus venosus

The tubular **truncus arteriosus** is continuous cranially with the **aortic sac** (Fig. 15 - 10A), from which the *aortic arches* arise. The **sinus venosus** receives the umbilical, vitelline, and common cardinal veins from the chorion, yolk sac, and embryo, respectively (Fig. 15 - 10B).

The arterial and venous ends of the heart are fixed by the pharyngeal arches and septum transversum, respectively. Because the bulbus cordis and ventricle grow faster than other regions, the heart bends upon itself, forming a U-shaped *bulboventricular loop* (Fig. 15 - 8E). As the primordial heart bends, the atrium and sinus venosus come to lie dorsal to the truncus arteriosus, bulbus cordis, and ventricle (Fig. 15 - 10A and B). By this stage the sinus venosus has developed lateral expansions, the right and left **horns of the sinus venosus**.

As the heart elongates and bends, it gradually invaginates into the **pericardial cavity** (Figs. 15 - 8C and D and 15 - 9C). The heart is initially suspended from the dorsal wall by a mesentery, the **dorsal mesocardium**, but the central part of this mesentery soon degenerates, forming a communication, the **transverse pericardial sinus**, between the right and left sides of the pericardial cavity (Fig. 15 - 8E and F). The heart is now attached only at its cranial and caudal ends.

Circulation Through the Primordial Heart

The initial contractions of the heart originate in muscle; that is, they are of myogenic origin. The muscle layers of the atrium and ventricle are continuous, and contractions occur in peristalsis-like waves that begin in the sinus venosus. At first, circulation through the primordial heart is of an ebb-and-flow type; however, by the end of the fourth week, coordinated contractions of the heart result in unidirectional flow. Blood enters the sinus venosus from the following (Fig. 15 - 10A and B):

- The embryo through the common cardinal veins
- The developing placenta through the umbilical veins
- The yolk sac through the vitelline veins

Blood from the sinus venosus enters the primordial atrium; flow from it is controlled by **sinoatrial valves** (Figs. 15 - 10A and 15 - 11A). The blood then passes through the **atrioventricular canal** into the primordial ventricle. When the ventricle contracts, blood is pumped through the **bulbus cordis** and **truncus arteriosus** into the aortic sac, from which it is distributed to the **aortic arches** in the pharyngeal arches (Fig. 15 - 10C). The blood then passes into the dorsal aortae for distribution to the embryo, yolk sac, and placenta.

Partitioning of the Primordial Heart

Partitioning of the atrioventricular canal, primordial atrium, and ventricle begins around the middle of the fourth week and is essentially completed by the end of the fifth week. Although described separately, these processes occur concurrently.

PARTITIONING OF ATRIOVENTRICULAR CANAL

Toward the end of the fourth week, **endocardial cushions** form on the dorsal and ventral walls of the atrioventricular (AV) canal. As these masses of tissue are invaded by mesenchymal cells during the fifth week (Fig. 15 - 11B), the AV endocardial cushions approach each other and fuse, dividing the AV canal into right and left AV canals (Fig. 15 - 11C). These canals partially separate the primordial atrium from the ventricle, and the endocardial cushions function as AV valves.

PARTITIONING OF PRIMORDIAL ATRIUM

Beginning at the end of the fourth week, the primordial atrium is divided into right and left atria by the formation and subsequent modification and fusion of two septa, the septum primum and septum secundum (Figs. 15 - 12A to E and 15 - 13).

The **septum primum,** a thin crescent-shaped membrane, grows toward the fusing endocardial cushions from the roof of the primordial atrium, partially dividing the common atrium into right and left halves. As this curtain-like septum grows, a large opening — the **foramen primum** (ostium primum) — forms between its crescentic free edge and the endocardial cushions

Text continued on page 346

■ **Figure 15-10.** *A,* Schematic sagittal section of the primordial heart (about 24 days), showing blood flow through it *(arrows).* *B,* Dorsal view of the heart (about 26 days), illustrating the horns of the sinus venosus and the dorsal location of the primordial atrium. *C,* Ventral view of the heart and aortic arches (about 35 days). The ventral wall of the pericardial sac has been removed to show the heart in the pericardial cavity.

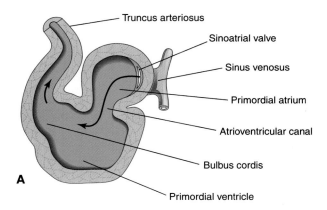

A

Truncus arteriosus

Sinoatrial valve

Sinus venosus

Primordial atrium

Atrioventricular canal

Bulbus cordis

Primordial ventricle

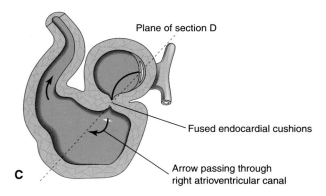

B

Atrium

Ventral ⎤ Endocardial
Dorsal ⎦ cushions

Future right ventricle

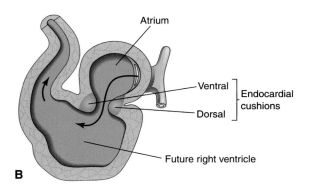

C

Plane of section D

Fused endocardial cushions

Arrow passing through
right atrioventricular canal

■ **Figure 15–11.** *A* to *C*, Schematic sketches of sagittal sections of the heart during the fourth and fifth weeks, illustrating blood flow through the heart and division of the atrioventricular canal. *D*, Coronal section of the heart at the plane shown in *C*. Note that the interatrial and interventricular septa have also started to develop.

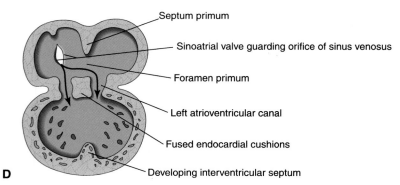

D

Septum primum

Sinoatrial valve guarding orifice of sinus venosus

Foramen primum

Left atrioventricular canal

Fused endocardial cushions

Developing interventricular septum

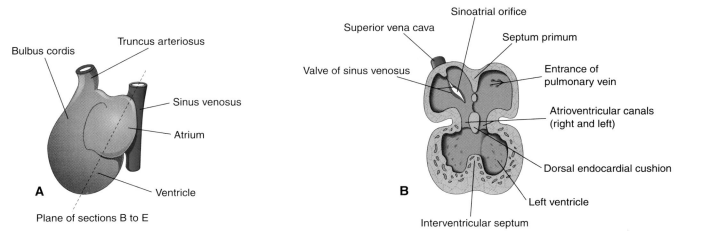

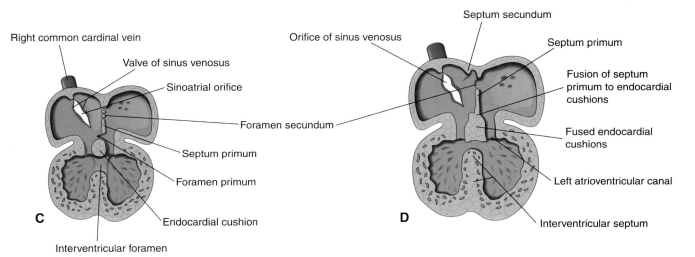

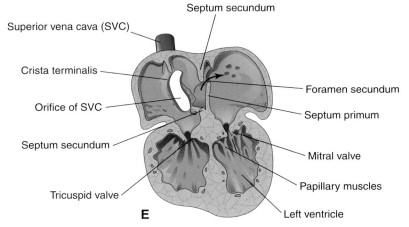

■ **Figure 15-12.** Schematic drawings of the developing heart showing partitioning of the atrioventricular canal, primordial atrium, and ventricle. *A*, Sketch showing the plane of the sections. *B*, During the fourth week (about 28 days), showing the early appearance of the septum primum, interventricular septum, and dorsal endocardial cushion. *C*, Section of the heart (about 32 days) showing perforations in the dorsal part of the septum primum. *D*, Section of the heart (about 35 days), showing the foramen secundum. *E*, About 8 weeks, showing the heart after it is partitioned into four chambers. The arrow indicates the flow of well-oxygenated blood from the right to the left atrium.

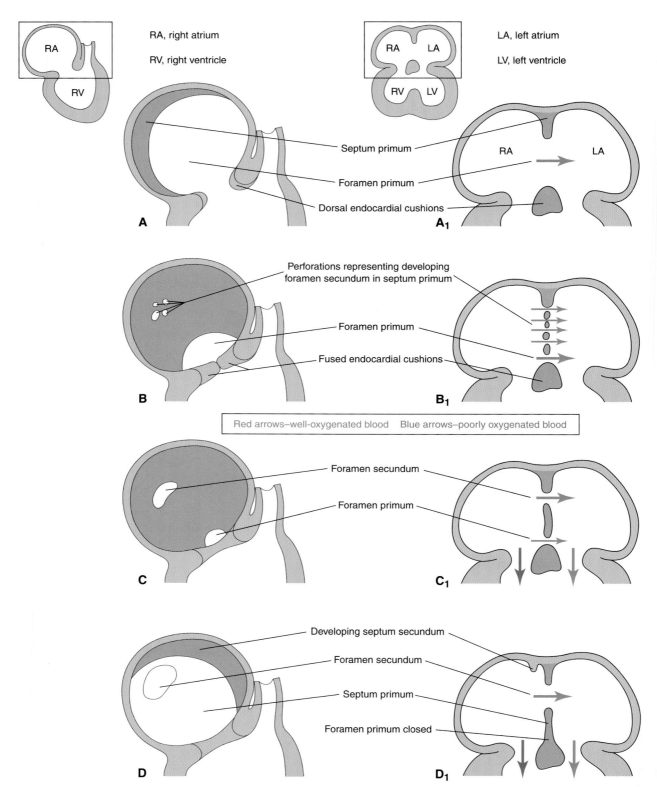

RA, right atrium

RV, right ventricle

LA, left atrium

LV, left ventricle

Septum primum

Foramen primum

Dorsal endocardial cushions

RA

LA

Perforations representing developing
foramen secundum in septum primum

Foramen primum

Fused endocardial cushions

Red arrows—well-oxygenated blood   Blue arrows—poorly oxygenated blood

Foramen secundum

Foramen primum

Developing septum secundum

Foramen secundum

Septum primum

Foramen primum closed

■ **Figure 15–13.** Diagrammatic sketches illustrating progressive stages in partitioning of the primitive atrium. *A* to *H* are views of the developing interatrial septum as viewed from the right side. *A₁* to *H₁* are coronal sections of the developing interatrial septum. As the septum secundum grows, note that it overlaps the opening in the septum primum (foramen secundum).

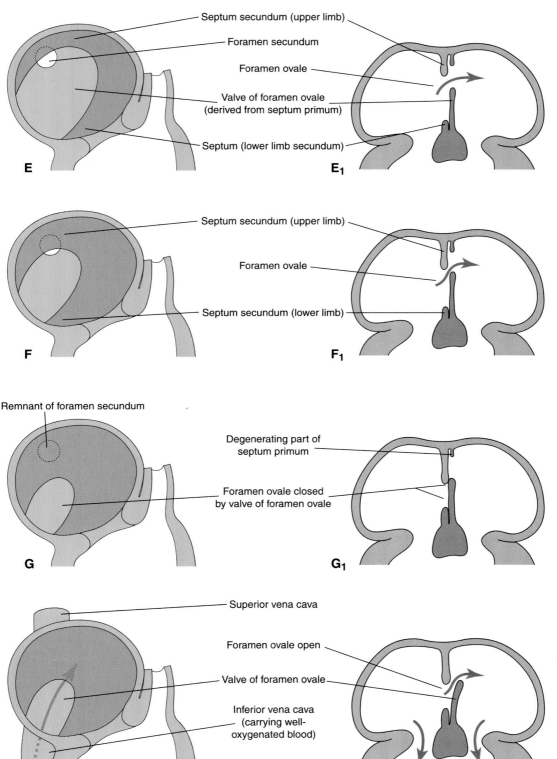

Septum secundum (upper limb)

Foramen secundum

Foramen ovale

Valve of foramen ovale (derived from septum primum)

Septum (lower limb secundum)

E   **E₁**

Septum secundum (upper limb)

Foramen ovale

Septum secundum (lower limb)

F   **F₁**

Remnant of foramen secundum

Degenerating part of septum primum

Foramen ovale closed by valve of foramen ovale

G   **G₁**

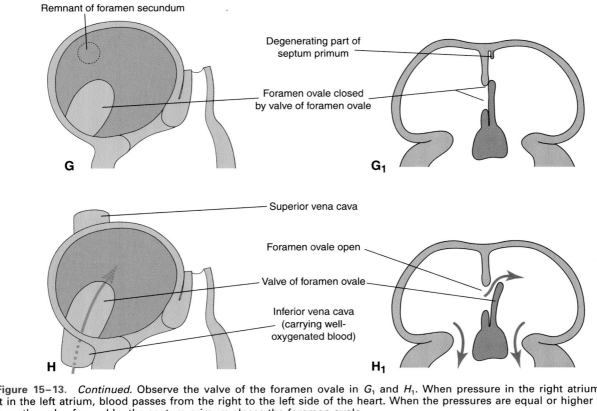

Superior vena cava

Foramen ovale open

Valve of foramen ovale

Inferior vena cava (carrying well-oxygenated blood)

H   **H₁**

■ **Figure 15–13.** *Continued.* Observe the valve of the foramen ovale in *G₁* and *H₁*. When pressure in the right atrium exceeds that in the left atrium, blood passes from the right to the left side of the heart. When the pressures are equal or higher in the left atrium, the valve formed by the septum primum closes the foramen ovale.

(Figs. 15-12*C* and 15-13*A* to *C*). The foramen primum serves as a shunt, enabling oxygenated blood to pass from the right to the left atrium. The foramen primum becomes progressively smaller and disappears as the septum primum fuses with the fused endocardial cushions to form a **primordial AV septum** (Fig. 15-13*D* and *D₁*). Before the foramen primum disappears, perforations—produced by programmed cell death—appear in the central part of the septum primum. As the septum fuses with the fused endocardial cushions, the perforations coalesce to form another opening, the **foramen secundum** (ostium secundum). Concurrently, the free edge of the septum primum fuses with the left side of the fused endocardial cushions, obliterating the foramen primum (Figs. 15-12*D* and 15-13*D*). The foramen secundum ensures a continuous flow of oxygenated blood from the right to the left atrium.

The **septum secundum,** a crescentic muscular membrane, grows from the ventrocranial wall of the atrium, immediately to the right of the septum primum (Fig. 15-13*D₁*). As this thick septum grows during the fifth and sixth weeks, it gradually overlaps the foramen secundum in the septum primum (Fig. 15-13*E* and *F*). The septum secundum forms an incomplete partition between the atria; consequently, an oval foramen—the **foramen ovale**—forms. The cranial part of the septum primum, initially attached to the roof of the left atrium, gradually disappears (Fig. 15-13*G₁* and *H₁*). The remaining part of the septum primum, attached to the endocardial cushions, forms the flaplike **valve of the foramen ovale**.

Before birth the foramen ovale allows most of the oxygenated blood entering the right atrium from the IVC to pass into the left atrium (Fig. 15-14*A*) and prevents the passage of blood in the opposite direction because the septum primum closes against the relatively rigid septum secundum (Fig. 15-14*B*). **After birth** the foramen ovale normally closes, and the valve of the foramen ovale fuses with the septum primum. As a result, the interatrial septum becomes a complete partition between the atria.

Changes in the Sinus Venosus

Initially the sinus venosus opens into the center of the dorsal wall of the primitive atrium, and its right and left horns are about the same size (Figs. 15-5*A* and

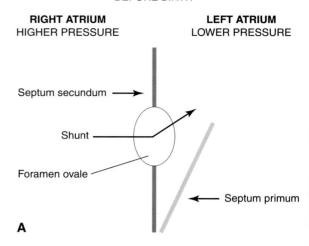

BEFORE BIRTH

RIGHT ATRIUM
HIGHER PRESSURE

LEFT ATRIUM
LOWER PRESSURE

Septum secundum →

Shunt

Foramen ovale

← Septum primum

A

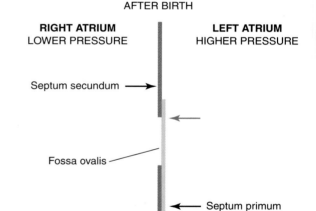

AFTER BIRTH

RIGHT ATRIUM
LOWER PRESSURE

LEFT ATRIUM
HIGHER PRESSURE

Septum secundum →

Fossa ovalis

← Septum primum

B

■ **Figure 15–14.** Diagrams illustrating the relationship of the septum primum to the foramen ovale and septum secundum. *A,* Before birth, well-oxygenated blood is shunted from the right atrium through the foramen ovale into the left atrium when the pressure rises. When the pressure falls in the right atrium, the flaplike valve of the foramen ovale is pressed against the relatively rigid septum secundum. This closes the foramen ovale. *B,* After birth the pressure in the left atrium rises as the blood returns from the lungs, which are now functioning. Eventually the septum primum is pressed against the septum secundum and adheres to it, permanently closing the foramen ovale and forming the fossa ovalis.

■ **Figure 15–15.** Diagrams illustrating the fate of the sinus venosus. *A,* Dorsal view of the heart (about 26 days) showing the primitive atrium and sinus venosus. *B,* Dorsal view at 8 weeks after incorporation of the right horn of the sinus venosus into the right atrium. The left horn of the sinus venosus has become the coronary sinus. *C,* Internal view of the fetal right atrium showing the smooth part of the wall of the right atrium (sinus venarum) derived from the right horn of the sinus venosus, and the crista terminalis and the valves of the inferior vena cava and coronary sinus derived from the right sinoatrial valve. The primitive right atrium becomes the right auricle, a conical muscular pouch.

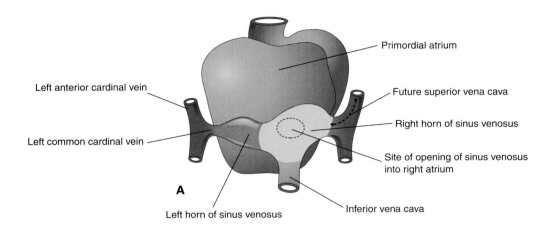

Left horn of sinus venosus   Right horn of sinus venosus

Primordial atrium

Left anterior cardinal vein

Future superior vena cava

Right horn of sinus venosus

Left common cardinal vein

Site of opening of sinus venosus into right atrium

A

Inferior vena cava

Left horn of sinus venosus

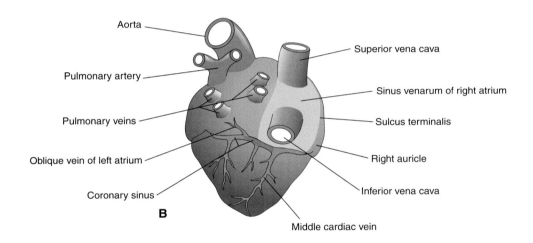

Aorta

Superior vena cava

Pulmonary artery

Sinus venarum of right atrium

Pulmonary veins

Sulcus terminalis

Oblique vein of left atrium

Right auricle

Coronary sinus

Inferior vena cava

B

Middle cardiac vein

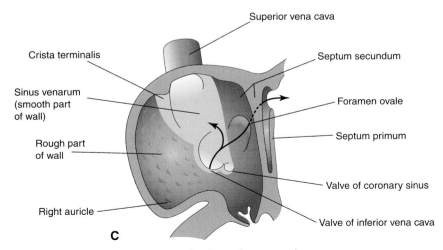

Superior vena cava

Crista terminalis

Septum secundum

Sinus venarum (smooth part of wall)

Foramen ovale

Septum primum

Rough part of wall

Valve of coronary sinus

Right auricle

Valve of inferior vena cava

C

■ **Figure 15–15.** *See legend on opposite page*

15–15A). Progressive enlargement of the right horn of the sinus venosus results from *two left-to-right shunts of blood*:

- The first shunt of blood results from transformation of the vitelline and umbilical veins, discussed previously.
- The second shunt of blood occurs when the anterior cardinal veins become connected by an oblique anastomosis (see Fig. 15–5*B* and *C*). This communication shunts blood from the left to the right anterior cardinal vein. The shunt eventually becomes the left *brachiocephalic vein*. The right anterior cardinal vein and the right common cardinal vein become the SVC.

By the end of the fourth week, the right horn is noticeably larger than the left (Fig. 15–15*A* and *B*). As this occurs, the sinoatrial orifice moves to the right and opens in the part of the primitive atrium that will become the adult right atrium (Figs. 15–11*D* and 15–15*C*). The results of the two left-to-right venous shunts are (Fig. 15–15):

- The left horn of the sinus venosus decreases in size and importance.
- The right horn enlarges and receives all the blood from the head and neck through the SVC, and from the placenta and caudal regions of the body through the IVC.

Initially the sinus venosus is a separate chamber of the heart and opens into the dorsal wall of the right atrium (Fig. 15–10*A* and *B*). As heart development proceeds, the left horn of the sinus venosus becomes the **coronary sinus**, and the right horn becomes incorporated into the wall of the right atrium (Fig. 15–15*B* and *C*).

Because it is derived from the sinus venosus, the smooth part of the wall of the right atrium is called the **sinus venarum** (Fig. 15–15*B* and *C*). The remainder of the internal surface of the wall of the right atrium and the conical muscular pouch, the **auricle** (auricular appendage), have a rough trabeculated appearance. These two parts are derived from the primordial atrium. The smooth part (sinus venarum) and the rough part (primordial atrium) are demarcated internally in the right atrium by a vertical ridge, the **crista terminalis** (Fig. 15–15*C*), and externally by a shallow inconspicuous groove, the **sulcus terminalis** (Fig. 15–15*B*). The crista terminalis represents the cranial part of the right sinoatrial valve (Fig. 15–15*C*); the caudal part of this valve forms the valves of the IVC and coronary sinus. The left sinoatrial valve fuses with the septum secundum and is incorporated with it into the interatrial septum.

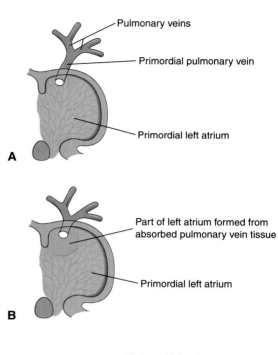

A

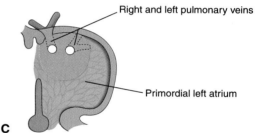

B

C

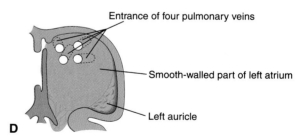

D

■ **Figure 15–16.** Diagrammatic sketches illustrating absorption of the pulmonary vein into the left atrium: *A,* Five weeks, showing the common pulmonary vein opening into the primordial left atrium. *B,* Later stage, showing partial absorption of the common pulmonary vein. *C,* Six weeks, showing the openings of two pulmonary veins into the left atrium resulting from absorption of the common pulmonary vein. *D,* Eight weeks, showing four pulmonary veins with separate atrial orifices. The primordial left atrium becomes the left auricle, a tubular appendage of the atrium. Most of the left atrium is formed by absorption of the primordial pulmonary vein and its branches.

PRIMORDIAL PULMONARY VEIN AND FORMATION OF THE LEFT ATRIUM

Most of the wall of the left atrium is smooth because it is formed by incorporation of the primordial pulmonary vein (Fig. 15–16A). This vein develops as an outgrowth of the dorsal atrial wall, just to the left of the septum primum. As the atrium expands, the primordial pulmonary vein and its main branches are gradually incorporated into the wall of the left atrium (Fig. 15–16B); as a result, four pulmonary veins are formed (Fig. 15–16C and D). The small left auricle (auricular appendage) is derived from the primordial atrium; its internal surface has a rough trabeculated appearance.

Anomalous Pulmonary Venous Connections

In total anomalous pulmonary venous connections, none of the pulmonary veins connects with the left atrium. They open into the right atrium, into one of the systemic veins, or into both. In partial anomalous pulmonary venous connections, one or more pulmonary veins have similar anomalous connections; the others have normal connections.

PARTITIONING OF THE PRIMORDIAL VENTRICLE

Division of the primordial ventricle into two ventricles is first indicated by a median muscular ridge — the **primordial IV septum** — in the floor of the ventricle near its apex (Fig. 15–12B). This thick crescentic fold has a concave free edge (Fig. 15–17A). Initially, most of its increase in height results from dilation of the ventricles on each side of the IV septum (Fig. 15–17B). The medial walls of the enlarging ventricles approach each other and fuse to form the primordium of the **muscular part of the IV septum**. Later, active proliferation of myoblasts in the septum increases its size. Until the seventh week there is a crescent-shaped **IV foramen** between the free edge of the IV septum and the fused endocardial cushions (Fig. 15–19A and B). The IV foramen permits communication between the right and left ventricles (Fig. 15–18B; see also Fig. 15–17). The IV foramen usually closes by the end of the seventh week as the bulbar ridges fuse with the endocardial cushion (Fig. 15–18C to E).

Closure of the IV foramen and formation of the membranous part of the IV septum result from fusion of tissues from three sources:

• The right bulbar ridge
• The left bulbar ridge
• The endocardial cushion

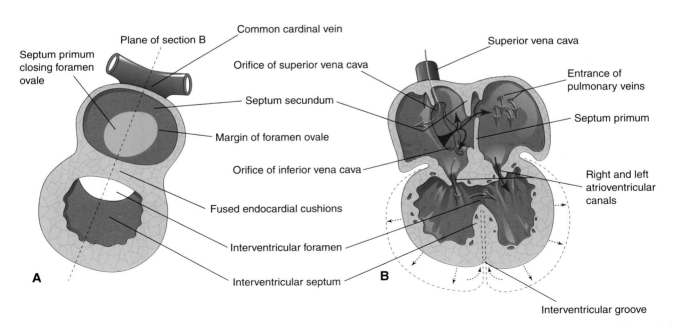

■ **Figure 15–17.** Schematic diagrams illustrating partitioning of the primordial heart. *A*, Sagittal section late in the fifth week, showing the cardiac septa and foramina. *B*, Coronal section at a slightly later stage illustrating the directions of blood flow through the heart and expansion of the ventricles.

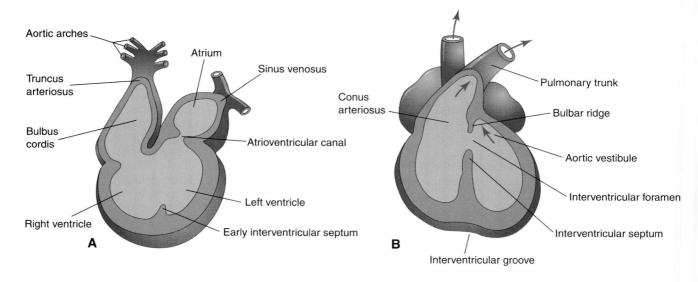

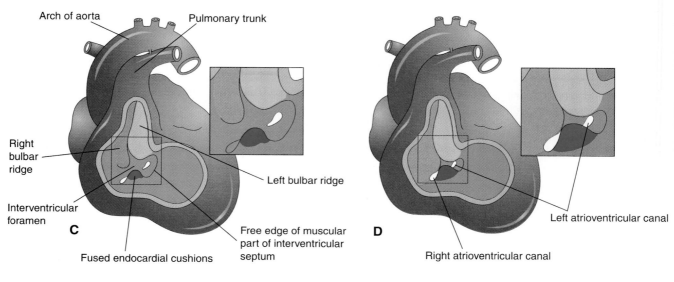

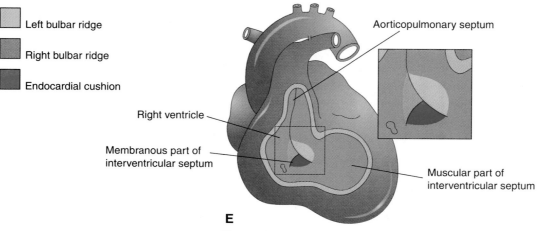

■ **Figure 15–18.** *See legend on opposite page*

The **membranous part of the IV septum** is derived from an extension of tissue from the right side of the endocardial cushion to the muscular part of the IV septum. This tissue merges with the aorticopulmonary septum and the thick muscular part of the IV septum (Fig. 15-19C). After closure of the IV foramen and formation of the membranous part of the IV septum, the pulmonary trunk is in communication with the right ventricle, and the aorta communicates with the left ventricle (Fig. 15-18E).

Cavitation of the ventricular walls forms a spongework of muscular bundles. Some of these bundles remain as the **trabeculae carneae** (muscular bundles on the lining of the ventricular walls) and others become the **papillary muscles** and tendinous cords (*chordae tendineae*). The tendinous cords run from the papillary muscles to the atrioventricular valves (Fig. 15-19C and D).

Fetal Cardiac Ultrasonography

Technologic advances in ultrasonography have made it possible for sonographers to recognize normal and abnormal fetal anatomy. In the presence of a very slow heart beat (less than 80 beats per minute), the fetus is at risk of associated heart disease (Silverman and Schmidt, 1994). Most studies are performed between 18 and 22 weeks of gestation because the heart is large enough to examine easily; however, fetal cardiac anatomy can be studied as early as 18 weeks if necessary. For details concerning the ultrasound evaluation of the heart, including color flow studies, see Silverman and Schmidt (1994) and Lee et al (1995).

PARTITIONING OF BULBUS CORDIS AND TRUNCUS ARTERIOSUS

During the fifth week of development, active proliferation of mesenchymal cells in the walls of the bulbus cordis results in the formation of **bulbar ridges** (Fig. 15-20B and C; see also Fig. 15-18C and D). Similar ridges form in the truncus arteriosus that are continuous with the bulbar ridges. The bulbar and **truncal ridges** are derived largely from neural crest mesenchyme (Clark, 1986). **Neural crest cells** migrate through the primordial pharynx and pharyngeal arches to reach the ridges. As this occurs, the bulbar and truncal ridges undergo 180-degree spiraling. The spiral orientation of the bulbar and truncal ridges, possibly caused by the streaming of blood from the ventricles, results in the formation of a spiral **aorticopulmonary septum** when the ridges fuse (Fig. 15-20D to G). This septum divides the bulbus cordis and truncus arteriosus into two arterial channels, the **aorta** and **pulmonary trunk**. Because of the spiraling of the aorticopulmonary septum, the pulmonary trunk twists around the ascending aorta (Fig. 15-20H).

The **bulbus cordis** is incorporated into the walls of the definitive ventricles (Fig. 15-18A and B):

- In the right ventricle, the bulbus cordis is represented by the **conus arteriosus** (infundibulum), which gives origin to the pulmonary trunk.
- In the left ventricle, the bulbus cordis forms the walls of the **aortic vestibule**, the part of the ventricular cavity just inferior to the aortic valve.

DEVELOPMENT OF CARDIAC VALVES

When partitioning of the truncus arteriosus is nearly completed (Fig. 15-20A to C), the **semilunar valves** begin to develop from three swellings of subendocardial tissue around the orifices of the aorta and pulmonary trunk. These swellings are hollowed out and reshaped to form three thin-walled cusps (Fig. 15-21; see also Fig. 15-19C and D). The **atrioventricular (AV) valves** (tricuspid and mitral valves) develop similarly from localized proliferations of tissue around the AV canals.

Conducting System of the Heart

Initially the muscle layers of the atrium and ventricle are continuous. The primordial atrium acts as the in-

■ **Figure 15-18.** Sketches illustrating incorporation of the bulbus cordis into the ventricles and partitioning of the bulbus cordis and truncus arteriosus into the aorta and pulmonary trunk. *A*, Sagittal section at 5 weeks showing the bulbus cordis as one of the chambers of the primordial heart. *B*, Schematic coronal section at 6 weeks after the bulbus cordis has been incorporated into the ventricles to become the conus arteriosus (infundibulum) of the right ventricle and the aortic vestibule of the left ventricle. *C to E*, Schematic drawings illustrating closure of the interventricular foramen and formation of the membranous part of the interventricular septum. The walls of the truncus arteriosus, bulbus cordis, and right ventricle have been removed. *C*, Five weeks, showing the bulbar ridges and fused endocardial cushions. *D*, Six weeks, showing how proliferation of subendocardial tissue diminishes the interventricular foramen. *E*, Seven weeks, showing the fused bulbar ridges, the membranous part of the interventricular septum formed by extensions of tissue from the right side of the endocardial cushions, and closure of the interventricular foramen.

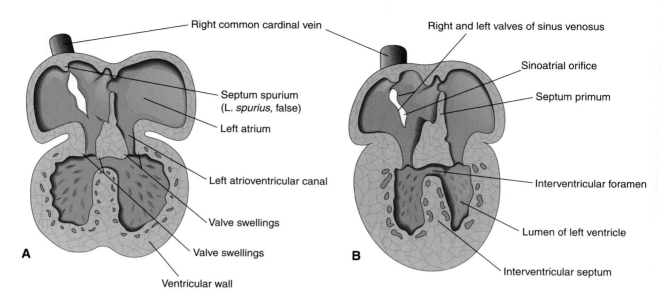

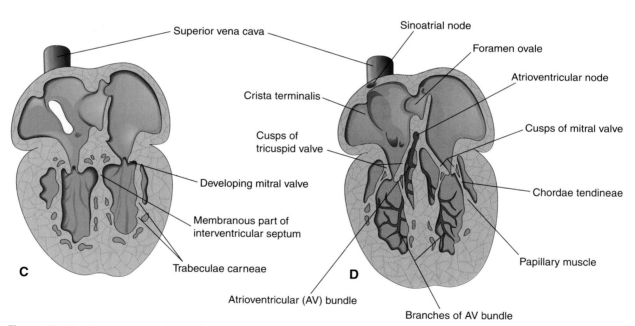

■ **Figure 15–19.** Schematic sections of the heart illustrating successive stages in the development of the atrioventricular valves, chordae tendineae, and papillary muscles. *A,* Five weeks. *B,* Six weeks. *C,* Seven weeks. *D,* Twenty weeks, showing the conducting system of the heart.

■ **Figure 15–20.** Schematic drawings illustrating partitioning of the bulbus cordis and truncus arteriosus. *A,* Ventral aspect of heart at 5 weeks. *B,* Transverse sections of the truncus arteriosus and bulbus cordis, illustrating the truncal and bulbar ridges. *C,* The ventral wall of the heart and truncus arteriosus has been removed to demonstrate these ridges. *D,* Ventral aspect of heart after partitioning of the truncus arteriosus. *E,* Sections through the newly formed aorta (A) and pulmonary trunk (PT), showing the aorticopulmonary septum. *F,* Six weeks. The ventral wall of the heart and pulmonary trunk has been removed to show the aorticopulmonary septum. *G,* Diagram illustrating the spiral form of the aorticopulmonary septum. *H,* Drawing showing the great arteries twisting around each other as they leave the heart.

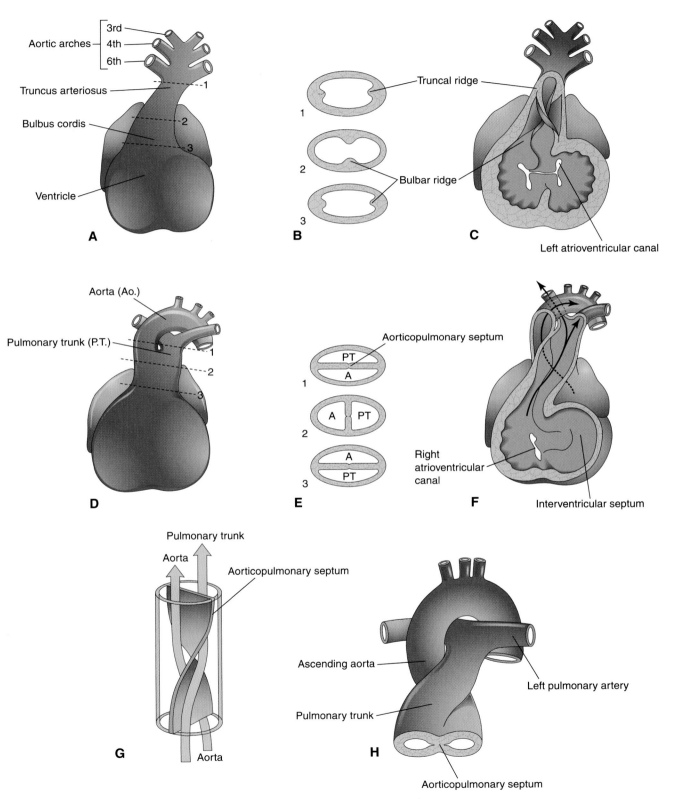

Figure 15–20. *See legend on opposite page*

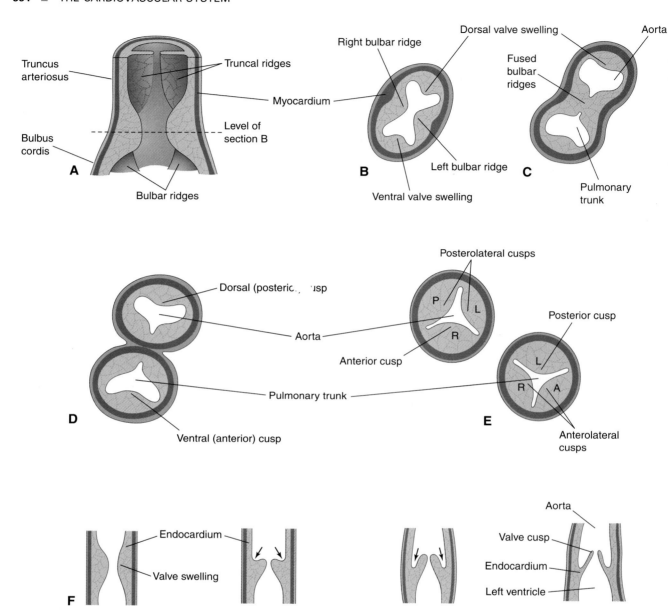

■ Figure 15–21. Schematic drawings illustrating development of the semilunar valves of the aorta and pulmonary trunk. *A,* Sketch of a section of the truncus arteriosus and bulbus cordis, showing the valve swellings. *B,* Transverse section of the bulbus cordis. *C,* Similar section after fusion of the bulbar ridges. *D,* Formation of the walls and valves of the aorta and pulmonary trunk. *E,* Rotation of the vessels has established the adult relations of the valves. *F,* Longitudinal sections of the aorticoventricular junction, illustrating successive stages in the hollowing *(arrows)* and thinning of the valve swellings to form the valve cusps.

terim pacemaker of the heart, but the sinus venosus soon takes over this function. The **sinuatrial node** (sinoatrial [SA] node) develops during the fifth week. It is originally in the right wall of the sinus venosus, but it is incorporated into the wall of the right atrium with the sinus venosus (Fig. 15–19*D*). The SA node is located high in the right atrium, near the entrance of the SVC. After incorporation of the sinus venosus,

cells from its left wall are found in the base of the interatrial septum just anterior to the opening of the coronary sinus. Together with cells from the AV region, they form the **AV node** and **bundle**, which are located just superior to the endocardial cushions. The fibers arising from the **AV bundle** pass from the atrium into the ventricle and split into right and left **bundle branches**, which are distributed throughout the ventricular myocardium (Fig. 15-19D). The SA node, AV node, and AV bundle are richly supplied by nerves; however, the conducting system is well developed before these nerves enter the heart. This specialized tissue is normally the only pathway from the atria to the ventricles because, as the four chambers of the heart develop, a band of connective tissue grows in from the epicardium. This tissue subsequently separates the muscle of the atria from that of the ventricles and forms part of the **cardiac skeleton**.

Abnormalities of the Conducting System

Abnormalities of the conducting tissue may cause unexpected death during infancy. Anderson and Ashley (1974) observed conducting tissue abnormalities in the hearts of several infants who died unexpectedly from a disorder classified as "crib death," or **sudden infant death syndrome (SIDS)**. There remains a lack of consensus that a single mechanism is responsible for the sudden and unexpected deaths of apparently healthy infants. Some findings in infants who later died of SIDS suggest that they have an abnormality in the autonomic nervous system. Sudden infant death syndrome is the most common cause of postnatal death in developed countries, generally accounting for 40 to 50% of infant deaths during the first year. A **brain stem developmental abnormality** or maturational delay related to neuroregulation of cardiorespiratory control appears to be the most compelling hypothesis (Hunt, 1996).

ANOMALIES OF THE HEART AND GREAT VESSELS

Congenital heart defects (CHDs) are common, with a frequency of 6 to 8 cases per 1000 births (Bernstein, 1996). Some cases of CHD are caused by single-gene or chromosomal mechanisms (Thompson et al, 1991), and others result from exposure to teratogens such as the *rubella virus* (see Chapter 9); however, in most cases the cause is unknown. Most CHDs are thought to be caused by multiple factors (Clark, 1996), genetic and environmental, each of which has a minor effect (i.e., **multifactorial inheritance**). Recent technology, such as real-time two-dimensional echocardiography, permits detection of fetal CHDs as early as the 17th or 18th week of gestation (Silverman and Schmidt, 1994; Lee et al, 1995).

Most CHDs are well tolerated during fetal life; however, at birth, when the fetus loses its contact with the maternal circulation, the impact of CHDs becomes apparent. Some types of CHD cause very little disability; others are incompatible with extrauterine life. Be-

cause of recent advances in cardiovascular surgery, many types of CHD can be corrected surgically, and fetal cardiac surgery may soon be possible for complex CHDs. Not all CHDs are described in this book. Emphasis is on those that are compatible with life or are currently amenable to surgery. The subsequent discussion of cardiac anomalies is understandably brief. Readers interested in more comprehensive discussions should consult Bernstein (1996).

Dextrocardia

If the heart tube bends to the left instead of to the right (Fig. 15-22), the heart is displaced to the right and there is transposition in which the heart and its vessels are reversed left to right as in a mirror image. **Dextrocardia** is the most frequent positional abnormality of the heart. In **dextrocardia with situs inversus** (transposition of viscera such as the liver), the incidence of accompanying cardiac defects is low. If there are no other associated vascular abnormalities, these hearts function normally. In **isolated dextrocardia**, the abnormal position of the heart is not accompanied by displacement of other viscera. This anomaly is usually complicated by severe cardiac anomalies (e.g., single ventricle and arterial transposition). For a

NORMAL

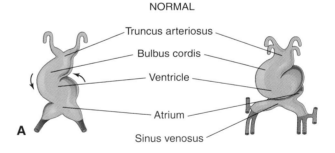

DEXTROCARDIA

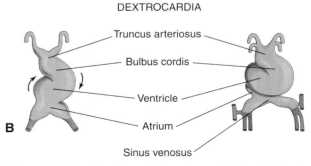

■ **Figure 15–22.** Sketches of the primordial heart tube during the fourth week. *A,* Normal bending to the right. *B,* Abnormal bending to the left.

discussion of the prognosis and treatment of dextrocardia, see Bernstein (1996).

Ectopia Cordis

In ectopia cordis, an extremely rare condition, the heart is in an abnormal location (Fig. 15–23). In the thoracic form of ectopia cordis, the heart is partly or completely exposed on the surface of the thorax. It is usually associated with widely separated halves of the sternum and an open pericardial sac. Death occurs in most cases during the first few days after birth, usually from infection, cardiac failure, or hypoxemia. If no severe cardiac defects are present, surgical therapy usually consists of covering the heart with skin. The clinical outcome for patients with ectopia cordis has improved, and many have survived to adulthood (Hornberger et al, 1996). The most common thoracic form of ectopia cordis results from faulty development of the sternum and pericardium because of failure of complete fusion of the lateral folds in the formation of the thoracic wall during the fourth week.

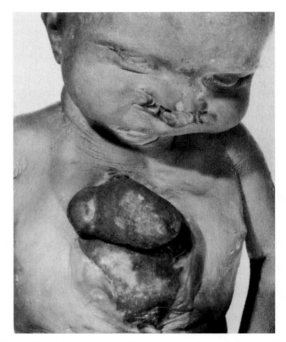

■ **Figure 15–23.** Photograph of a newborn infant with ectopia cordis, cleft sternum, and bilateral cleft lip. Death occurred in the first days of life from infection, cardiac failure, and hypoxemia.

Atrial Septal Defects

Atrial septal defects (ASDs) are common congenital heart anomalies, occurring more frequently in females than in males. The most common form of ASD is **patent foramen ovale** (Figs. 15–24A and 15–25A to D). A small isolated patent foramen ovale is of no hemodynamic significance; however, if other defects

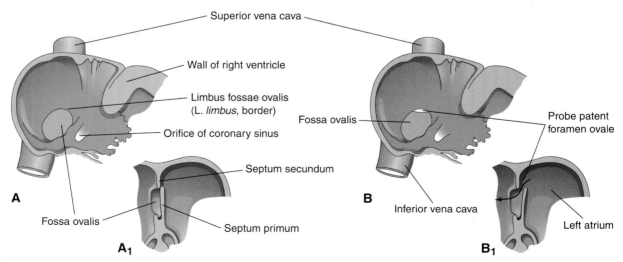

■ **Figure 15–24.** *A,* Drawing illustrating the normal postnatal appearance of the right side of the interatrial septum after adhesion of the septum primum to the septum secundum. *A₁,* Sketch of a section of the interatrial septum illustrating formation of the fossa ovalis in the right atrium. Note that the floor of this fossa is formed by the septum primum. *B* and *B₁,* Similar views of a probe patent foramen ovale resulting from incomplete adhesion of the septum primum to the septum secundum.

are present (e.g., pulmonary stenosis or atresia), blood is shunted through the foramen ovale into the left atrium, producing **cyanosis**, a dark bluish or purplish coloration of the skin and mucous membranes resulting from deficient oxygenation of the blood.

A **probe patent foramen ovale** is present in up to 25% of people (Fig. 15-24A and B). A probe can be passed from one atrium to the other through the superior part of the floor of the fossa ovalis. This defect, usually small, is not clinically significant, but a probe patent foramen ovale may be forced open because of other cardiac defects and contribute to the functional pathology of the heart. Probe patent foramen ovale results from incomplete adhesion between the original flap of the valve of the foramen ovale and the septum secundum after birth.

There are four clinically significant types of ASD (Fig. 15-25):

- Ostium secundum defect
- Endocardial cushion defect with ostium primum defect
- Sinus venosus defect
- Common atrium

The first two types of ASD are relatively common.

Ostium secundum ASDs (Fig. 15-25A to D) are in the area of the fossa ovalis and include defects of both the septum primum and the septum secundum. The defects may be multiple and, in symptomatic older children, defects of 2 cm or more in diameter are not unusual (Bernstein, 1996). Females with these defects outnumber males 3 to 1. Ostium secundum ASDs are one of the most common types of CHD. The patent foramen ovale usually results from abnormal resorption of the septum primum during the formation of the foramen secundum. If resorption occurs in abnormal locations, the septum primum is fenestrated or netlike (Fig. 15-25A). If excessive resorption of the septum primum occurs, the resulting short septum primum does not close the foramen ovale (Fig. 15-25B). If an abnormally large foramen ovale occurs because of defective development of the septum secundum, a normal septum primum does not close the abnormal foramen ovale at birth (Fig. 15-25C). Large ostium secundum ASDs may occur because of a combination of excessive resorption of the septum primum and a large foramen ovale (Fig. 15-25D). Ostium secundum ASDs are well tolerated during childhood; symptoms such as pulmonary hypertension usually appear in the thirties or later. Closure of the ASD is carried out at open heart surgery, and the mortality rate is less than 1% (Bernstein, 1996).

Endocardial cushion and AV septal defects with ostium primum ASDs (Fig. 15-25E) are less common forms of ASD. Several cardiac abnormalities are grouped together under this heading because they result from the same developmental defect, a deficiency of the endocardial cushions and the AV septum. The septum primum does not fuse with the endocardial cushions, resulting in a **patent foramen primum**.

Usually there is also a cleft in the anterior cusp of the mitral valve.

All **sinus venosus defects** are located in the superior part of the interatrial septum close to the entry of the SVC (Fig. 15-25F). A sinus venosus defect is one of the rarest types of ASD. It results from incomplete absorption of the sinus venosus into the right atrium and/or abnormal development of the septum secundum. This type of ASD is commonly associated with partial anomalous pulmonary venous connections.

Ventricular Septal Defects

Ventricular septal defects (VSDs) are the most common type of CHD, accounting for about 25% of defects. Ventricular septal defects occur more frequently in males than in females. Most VSDs occur in the membranous part of the IV septum (Fig. 15-26A and B); however, they may occur in any part of the IV septum. Many small VSDs close spontaneously (30 to 50%), most frequently during the first year. Isolated VSDs are detected at a rate of 10 to 12 per 10,000 between birth and 5 years. Most patients with a large VSD have a massive left-to-right shunt of blood. **Muscular VSD** is a less common type of defect and may appear anywhere in the muscular part of the interventricular septum. **Transposition of the great arteries** (Fig. 15-27) and a rudimentary outlet chamber are present in most infants with this severe CHD. Some patients die during infancy of congestive heart failure, but others survive until early adult life.

Truncus Arteriosus

Truncus arteriosus (TA) or **persistent TA** results from failure of the truncal ridges and aorticopulmonary septum to develop normally and divide the truncus arteriosus into the aorta and pulmonary trunk (Fig. 15-26). In this anomaly a single arterial trunk, the TA, arises from the heart and supplies the systemic, pulmonary, and coronary circulations (Bernstein, 1996). A VSD is always present with the TA anomaly, and the TA overrides the VSD (Fig. 15-26B). The cause of this condition is largely unknown (Yu and Hutchins, 1996). The most common type of TA is a single arterial vessel that branches to form the pulmonary trunk and ascending aorta (Fig. 15-26A and B). In the next most common type, the right and left pulmonary arteries arise close together from the dorsal wall of the TA (Fig. 15-26C). Less common types are illustrated in Figure 15-26D and E.

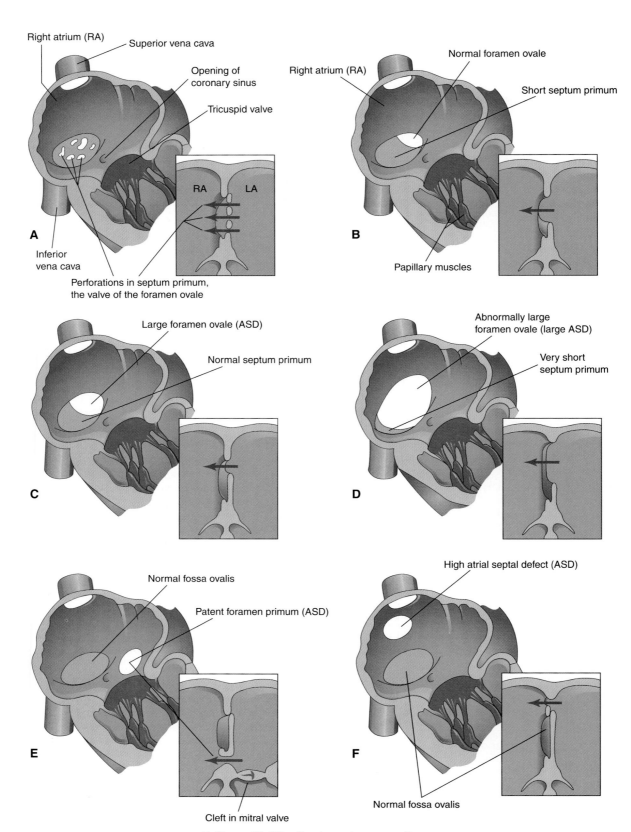

Right atrium (RA) — Superior vena cava

Opening of coronary sinus

Tricuspid valve

RA   LA

A

Inferior vena cava

Perforations in septum primum, the valve of the foramen ovale

Normal foramen ovale

Right atrium (RA)

Short septum primum

B

Papillary muscles

Large foramen ovale (ASD)

Normal septum primum

C

Abnormally large foramen ovale (large ASD)

Very short septum primum

D

Normal fossa ovalis

Patent foramen primum (ASD)

E

Cleft in mitral valve

High atrial septal defect (ASD)

F

Normal fossa ovalis

■ **Figure 15–25.** *See legend on opposite page*

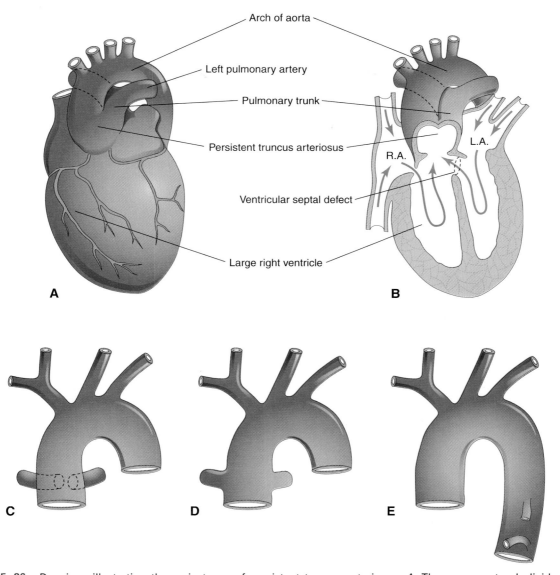

Arch of aorta

Left pulmonary artery

Pulmonary trunk

Persistent truncus arteriosus

Ventricular septal defect

Large right ventricle

R.A.

L.A.

A

B

C

D

E

■ **Figure 15–26.** Drawings illustrating the main types of persistent truncus arteriosus. *A,* The common trunk divides into the aorta and a short pulmonary trunk. *B,* Coronal section of the heart shown in *A.* Observe the circulation in this heart *(arrows)* and the ventricular septal defect. *C,* The right and left pulmonary arteries arise close together from the truncus arteriosus. *D,* The pulmonary arteries arise independently from the sides of the truncus arteriosus. *E,* No pulmonary arteries are present; the lungs are supplied by the bronchial arteries.

■ **Figure 15–25.** Drawings of the right aspect of the interatrial septum. The adjacent sketches of sections of the septa illustrate various types of atrial septal defect (ASD). *A,* Patent foramen ovale resulting from resorption of the septum primum in abnormal locations. *B,* Patent foramen ovale caused by excessive resorption of the septum primum ("short flap defect"). *C,* Patent foramen ovale resulting from an abnormally large foramen ovale. *D,* Patent foramen ovale resulting from an abnormally large foramen ovale and excessive resorption of the septum primum. *E,* Endocardial cushion defect with primum-type ASD. The adjacent section shows the cleft in the anterior cusp of the mitral valve. *F,* Sinus venosus ASD. The high septal defect resulted from abnormal absorption of the sinus venosus into the right atrium. In *E* and *F,* note that the fossa ovalis has formed normally.

ASD

Right atrium

Aorta

Patent ductus arteriosus

Pulmonary
trunk

VSD

Left ventricle

■ **Figure 15–27.** Diagram of a malformed heart illustrating transposition of the great arteries. The ventricular (VSD) and atrial septal defects (ASD) allow mixing of the arterial and venous blood. Transposition of the great arteries is the most common single cause of cyanotic heart disease in newborn infants. As here, it is often associated with other cardiac anomalies (VSD and ASD).

Transposition of the Great Arteries

Transposition of the great arteries (TGA) is the most common cause of **cyanotic heart disease** in newborn infants (Fig. 15-27). Transposition of the great arteries is often associated with other cardiac anomalies. In typical cases the aorta lies anterior and to the right of the pulmonary trunk and arises anteriorly from the morphologic right ventricle, and the pulmonary trunk arises from the morphologic left ventricle. There is also an *ASD* with or without an associated *patent duc-*

tus arteriosus (PDA) and VSD. These associated defects permit some interchange between the pulmonary and systemic circulations. Because of these anatomic abnormalities, deoxygenated systemic venous blood returning to the right atrium enters the right ventricle and then passes to the body through the aorta. Oxygenated pulmonary venous blood passes through the left ventricle back into the pulmonary circulation. Because of the patent foramen ovale, some mixing of the blood occurs; without surgical correction of the transposition, these infants usually die within a few months. This defect is thought to result from failure of the conus arteriosus to develop normally during incorporation of the bulbus cordis into the ventricles.

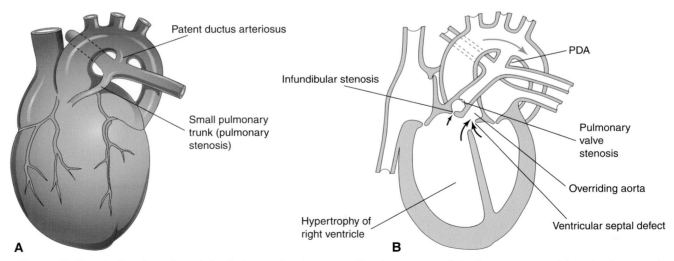

Patent ductus arteriosus

Small pulmonary
trunk (pulmonary
stenosis)

Infundibular stenosis

PDA

Pulmonary
valve
stenosis

Overriding aorta

Hypertrophy of
right ventricle

Ventricular septal defect

A

B

■ **Figure 15–28.** *A,* Drawing of an infant's heart showing a small pulmonary trunk (pulmonary stenosis) and a large aorta resulting from unequal partitioning of the truncus arteriosus. There is also hypertrophy of the right ventricle and a patent ductus arteriosus (PDA). *B,* Frontal section of a heart illustrating tetralogy of Fallot. Observe the four cardiac deformities: pulmonary valve stenosis, ventricular septal defect, overriding aorta, and hypertrophy of the right ventricle. In this case, infundibular stenosis is also shown.

Unequal Division of Truncus Arteriosus

Unequal division of the TA (Figs. 15–28A and B and 15–29A to C) results when partitioning of the TA superior to the valves is unequal; one great artery is large and the other small. As a result, the aorticopul-monary septum is not aligned with the IV septum, and a VSD results. The larger vessel (aorta or pulmonary trunk) usually straddles (overrides) the VSD (Fig. 15–28A and B). In **pulmonary valve stenosis**, the cusps of the pulmonary valve are fused together to form a dome with a narrow central opening (Fig. 15–29D). In **infundibular stenosis**, the conus arteriosus (infundibulum) of the right ventricle is underdeveloped. The two types of pulmonary stenosis may occur together.

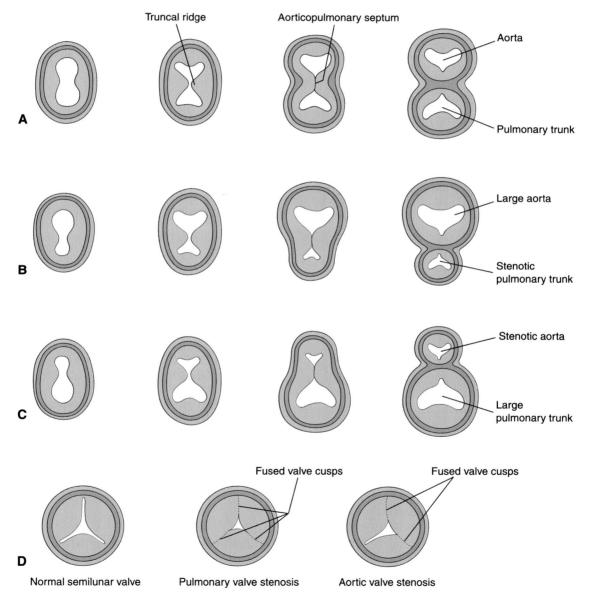

■ **Figure 15–29.** Abnormal division of the truncus arteriosus (TA). A to C, Sketches of transverse sections of the TA illustrating normal and abnormal partitioning of the TA. A, Normal. B, Unequal partitioning of the TA resulting in a small pulmonary trunk. C, Unequal partitioning resulting in a small aorta. D, Sketches illustrating a normal semilunar valve and stenotic pulmonary and aortic valves.

Depending upon the degree of obstruction to blood flow, there is a variable degree of hypertrophy of the right ventricle (Fig. 15-28*B*).

Tetralogy of Fallot

This classic group of four cardiac defects consists of the following (Fig. 15-28*A* and *B*):

- Pulmonary stenosis (obstruction to right ventricular outflow)
- Ventricular septal defect
- Dextroposition of aorta (overriding aorta)
- Right ventricular hypertrophy

The pulmonary trunk is usually small, and there may be various degrees of pulmonary artery stenoses as well (Bernstein, 1996). **Cyanosis** is one of the obvious signs of tetralogy of Fallot, but it is not often present at birth.

Aortic Stenosis and Atresia

In **aortic valve stenosis**, the edges of the valve are usually fused to form a dome with a narrow opening (Fig. 15-29*D*). This anomaly may be present at birth (congenital), or it may develop after birth (acquired). The valvular stenosis causes extra work for the heart and results in hypertrophy of the left ventricle and abnormal heart sounds (**heart murmurs**). In *subaortic stenosis*, there is often a band of fibrous tissue just inferior to the aortic valve. The narrowing of the aorta results from persistence of tissue that normally degenerates as the valve forms. Aortic atresia is present when obstruction of the aorta or its valve is complete.

AORTIC ARCH DERIVATIVES

As the pharyngeal arches develop during the fourth week (Fig. 15-30*A*), they are supplied by arteries— the **aortic arches**—from the *aortic sac*, the homologue of the ventral aorta in other mammals (Fig. 15-30*B*). The aortic arches terminate in the dorsal aorta of the ipsilateral side. Although six pairs of aortic arches usually develop, they are not all present at the same time. By the time the sixth pair of aortic arches has formed, the first two pairs have disappeared (Fig. 15-30*C*). During the sixth to eighth weeks, the aortic arch pattern is transformed into the adult arterial arrangement.

Derivatives of the First Pair of Aortic Arches

These arteries largely disappear, but the remaining parts form the **maxillary arteries**, which supply the ears, teeth, and muscles of the eye and face. These aortic arches may also contribute to the formation of the **external carotid arteries**.

Derivatives of the Second Pair of Aortic Arches

Dorsal parts of these vessels persist and form the stems of the **stapedial arteries**, which are small vessels that run through the ring of the stapes, a small ear bone, in the embryo.

Derivatives of the Third Pair of Aortic Arches

Proximal parts of these arteries form the **common carotid arteries**, which supply structures in the head. Distal parts of the third pair of aortic arches join with the dorsal aortae to form the **internal carotid arteries**, which supply the ears, orbits, and brain and its meninges (protective membranes for the brain).

Derivatives of the Fourth Pair of Aortic Arches

The **left fourth aortic arch** forms part of the arch of the aorta (Fig. 15-31*C* and *D*). The proximal part of the arch develops from the aortic sac, and the distal part is derived from the left dorsal aorta.

The **right fourth aortic arch** becomes the proximal part of the **right subclavian artery**. The distal part of the subclavian artery forms from the right dorsal aorta and right seventh intersegmental artery. The left subclavian artery is not derived from an aortic arch; it forms from the left seventh intersegmental artery (Fig. 15-31*A*). As development proceeds, differential growth shifts the origin of the left subclavian artery cranially; consequently, it comes to lie close to the origin of the left common carotid artery (Fig. 15-31*D*).

Derivatives of the Fifth Pair of Aortic Arches

In about 50% of embryos, the fifth pair of aortic arches are rudimentary vessels that soon degenerate, leaving no vascular derivatives. In other embryos, these arteries do not develop.

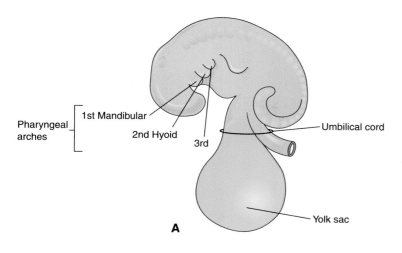

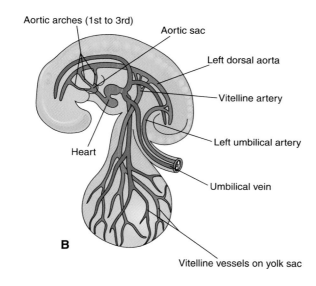

■ **Figure 15–30.** Drawings illustrating the pharyngeal arches and aortic arches. *A*, Left side of an embryo (about 26 days). *B*, Schematic drawing of this embryo showing the left aortic arches arising from the aortic sac, running through the pharyngeal arches, and terminating in the left dorsal aorta. *C*, An embryo (about 37 days) showing the single dorsal aorta and showing that most of the first two pairs of aortic arches have degenerated.

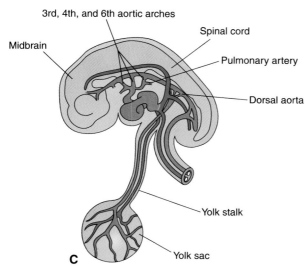

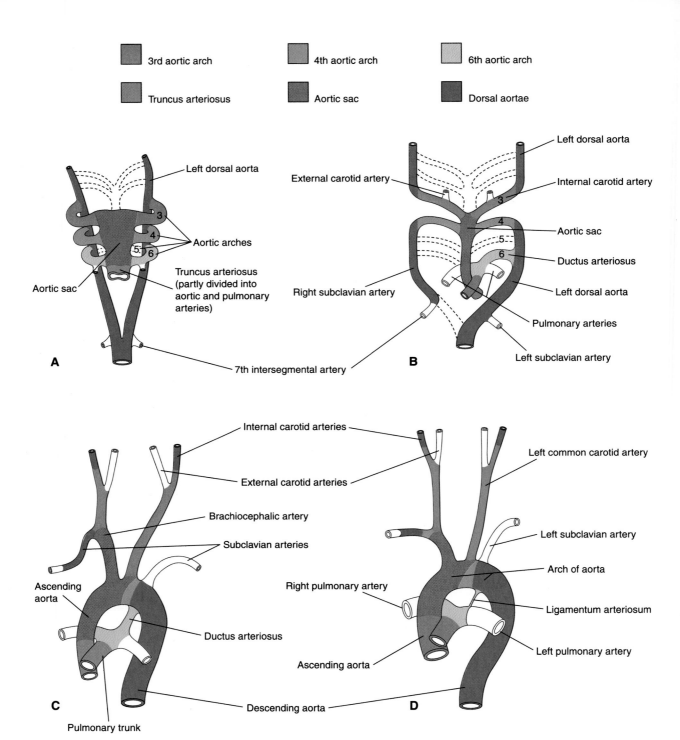

■ **Figure 15–31.** Schematic drawings illustrating the arterial changes that result during transformation of the truncus arteriosus, aortic sac, aortic arches, and dorsal aortae into the adult arterial pattern. The vessels that are not colored are not derived from these structures. *A*, Aortic arches at 6 weeks; by this stage the first two pairs of aortic arches have largely disappeared. *B*, Aortic arches at 7 weeks; the parts of the dorsal aortae and aortic arches that normally disappear are indicated with broken lines. *C*, Arterial arrangement at 8 weeks. *D*, Sketch of the arterial vessels of a 6-month-old infant. Note that the ascending aorta and pulmonary arteries are considerably smaller in *C* than in *D*. This represents the relative flow through these vessels at the different stages of development. Observe the large size of the ductus arteriosus (DA) in *C*; it is essentially a direct continuation of the pulmonary trunk. The DA normally becomes functionally closed within the first few days after birth. Eventually the DA becomes the ligamentum arteriosum, as shown in *D*.

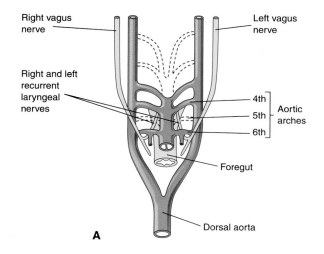

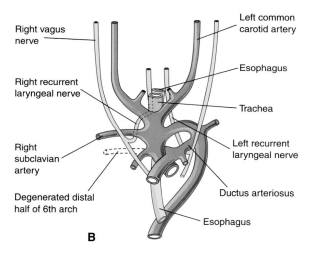

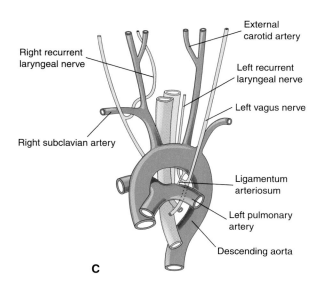

Derivatives of the Sixth Pair of Aortic Arches

The **left sixth aortic arch** develops as follows (Fig. 15-31B and C):

* The proximal part of the arch persists as the proximal part of the **left pulmonary artery**.
* The distal part of the arch passes from the left pulmonary artery to the dorsal aorta to form a prenatal shunt, the ductus arteriosus (DA).

The **right sixth aortic arch** develops as follows:

* The proximal part of the arch persists as the proximal part of the **right pulmonary artery.**
* The distal part of the arch degenerates.

The transformation of the sixth pair of aortic arches explains why the course of the **recurrent laryngeal nerves** differs on the two sides. These nerves supply the sixth pair of pharyngeal arches and hook around the sixth pair of aortic arches on their way to the developing larynx (Fig. 15-32A). **On the right**, because the distal part of the right sixth aortic arch degenerates, the right recurrent laryngeal nerve moves superiorly and hooks around the proximal part of the right subclavian artery, the derivative of the fourth aortic arch (Fig. 15-32B). **On the left**, the left recurrent laryngeal nerve hooks around the DA formed by the distal part of the sixth aortic arch. When this vessel involutes after birth, the nerve hooks around the *ligamentum arteriosum* (remnant of DA) and the arch of the aorta (Fig. 15-32C).

AORTIC ARCH ANOMALIES

Because of the many changes involved in transformation of the embryonic pharyngeal arch system of arteries into the adult arterial pattern, it is understandable why anomalies may occur. Most irregularities result from the persistence of parts of aortic arches that usually disappear or from disappearance of parts that normally persist.

■ **Figure 15-32.** Diagrams showing the relation of the recurrent laryngeal nerves to the aortic arches. *A*, Six weeks, showing the recurrent laryngeal nerves hooked around the sixth pair of aortic arches. *B*, Eight weeks, showing the right recurrent laryngeal nerve hooked around the right subclavian artery and the left recurrent laryngeal nerve hooked around the ductus arteriosus and arch of the aorta. *C*, Child, showing the left recurrent laryngeal nerve hooked around the ligamentum arteriosum and arch of the aorta.

Coarctation of the Aorta

Aortic coarctation (constriction) occurs in about 10% of children and adults with congenital heart diseases (Tikkanen and Heinonen, 1993). Coarctation is characterized by a constriction of varying length of the aorta (Fig. 15-33). Most constrictions of the aorta occur distal to the origin of the left subclavian artery at the entrance of the DA (**juxtaductal coarctation**). The classification into preductal and postductal coarctations is commonly used; however, in 90% of instances, the coarctation is directly opposite the DA (Bernstein, 1996). Coarctation of the aorta occurs twice as often in males as in females and is associated with a bicuspid aortic valve in 70% of cases.

In an infant with severe aortic coarctation, closure of the DA results in hypoperfusion and rapid deterioration. These patients are usually infused with prostaglandin E_2 in an attempt to reopen the DA and establish an adequate blood flow to the lower limbs (Bernstein, 1996). The causes of coarctation of the aorta are not clearly understood, but genetic and/or environmental factors appear to cause coarctation. For a full discussion, see Moore and Persaud (1998).

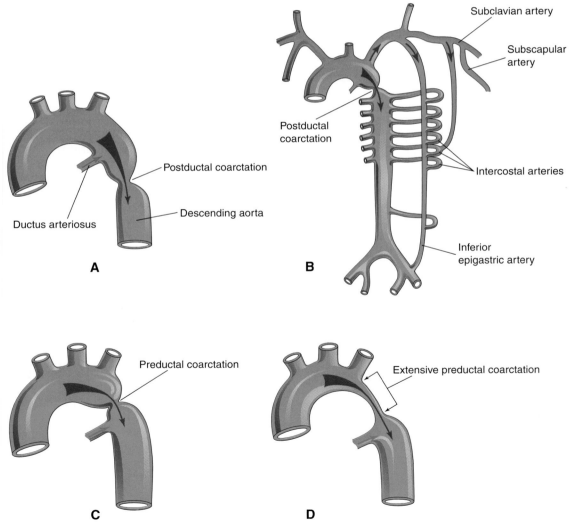

A

B

C

D

■ **Figure 15-33.** *A*, Postductal coarctation of the aorta. *B*, Diagrammatic representation of the common routes of collateral circulation that develop in association with postductal coarctation of the aorta. *C* and *D*, Preductal coarctation.

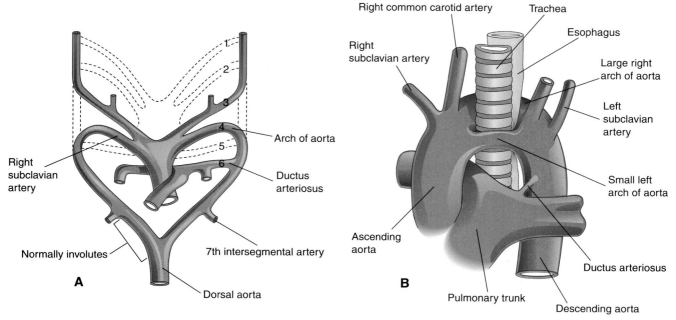

■ **Figure 15–34.** *A*, Drawing of the embryonic aortic arches illustrating the embryologic basis of double aortic arch. The distal portion of the right dorsal aorta persists and forms a right aortic arch. *B*, A large right aortic arch and a small left aortic arch arise from the ascending aorta and form a vascular ring around the trachea and esophagus. Note the compression of the esophagus and trachea. The right common carotid and subclavian arteries arise separately from the large right arch of the aorta.

Double Aortic Arch

Double aortic arch is a rare anomaly characterized by a **vascular ring** around the trachea and esophagus (Fig. 15–34). Varying degrees of compression of these structures may occur. If the compression is significant, it causes wheezing respirations that are aggravated by crying, feeding, and flexion of the neck (Bernstein, 1996). The vascular ring results from failure of the distal part of the right dorsal aorta to disappear (Fig. 15–34*A*); as a result, right and left arches form. Usually the right arch of the aorta is larger and passes posterior to the trachea and esophagus (Fig. 15–34*B*).

Right Arch of Aorta

When the entire right dorsal aorta persists (Fig. 15–35*A*) and the distal part of the left dorsal aorta involutes, a right aortic arch results. There are two main types:

* *Right arch of the aorta without a retroesophageal component* (Fig. 15–35*B*). The DA (or liga-

mentum arteriosum) passes from the right pulmonary artery to the right arch of the aorta. Because no vascular ring is formed, this condition is usually asymptomatic.
* *Right arch of the aorta with a retroesophageal component* (Fig. 15–35*C*). Originally there was probably a small left arch of the aorta that involuted, leaving the right arch of the aorta posterior to the esophagus. The DA (or ligamentum arteriosum) attaches to the distal part of the arch of the aorta and forms a ring, which may constrict the esophagus and trachea.

Anomalous Right Subclavian Artery

The right subclavian artery arises from the distal part of the arch of the aorta and passes posterior to the trachea and esophagus to supply the right upper limb (Fig. 15–36). A **retroesophageal right subclavian artery** occurs when the right fourth aortic arch and the right dorsal aorta disappear cranial to the seventh intersegmental artery. As a result, the right subclavian artery forms from the right seventh intersegmental ar-

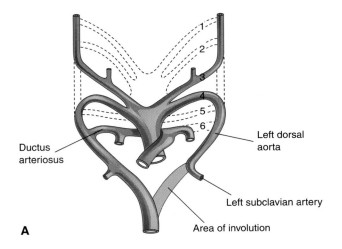

Ductus arteriosus

Left dorsal aorta

Left subclavian artery

Area of involution

A

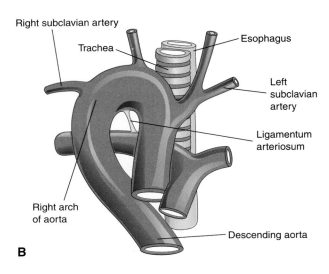

Right subclavian artery

Trachea

Esophagus

Left subclavian artery

Ligamentum arteriosum

Right arch of aorta

Descending aorta

B

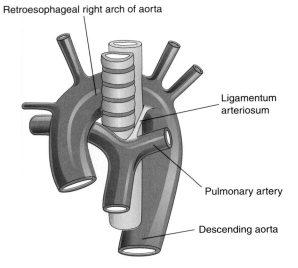

Retroesophageal right arch of aorta

Ligamentum arteriosum

Pulmonary artery

Descending aorta

C

tery and the distal part of the right dorsal aorta. As development proceeds, differential growth shifts the origin of the right subclavian artery cranially until it comes to lie close to the origin of the left subclavian artery. Although an anomalous right subclavian artery is fairly common and always forms a vascular ring, it is rarely significant clinically because the ring is usually not tight enough to constrict the esophagus and trachea.

FETAL AND NEONATAL CIRCULATIONS

The fetal cardiovascular system (Fig. 15–37) is designed to serve prenatal needs and permit modifications at birth that establish the neonatal circulatory pattern (Fig. 15–38). Good respiration in the newborn infant depends upon normal circulatory changes occurring at birth, which result in oxygenation of the blood in the lungs when fetal blood flow through the placenta ceases (Sansoucie and Cavaliere, 1997). Prenatally the lungs do not provide gas exchange and the pulmonary vessels are vasoconstricted. Three vascular structures are most important in the transitional circulation:

* Ductus venosus
* Foramen ovale
* Ductus arteriosus

Fetal Circulation

Highly oxygenated, nutrient rich blood returns from the placenta in the **umbilical vein** (Fig. 15–37). On approaching the liver, about half of the blood under high pressure passes directly into the **ductus venosus**, a fetal vessel connecting this umbilical vein to the IVC; consequently, the blood bypasses the liver. The other half of the blood in the umbilical vein flows into the *sinusoids of the liver* and enters the IVC through the **hepatic veins**. Blood flow through the ductus venosus is regulated by a *sphincter mechanism* close to the umbilical vein. When the sphincter relaxes, more blood passes through the ductus venosus. When the sphincter contracts, more blood is diverted to the portal vein and hepatic sinusoids.

■ **Figure 15–35.** *A,* Sketch of the aortic arches showing abnormal involution of the distal portion of the left dorsal aorta. There is also persistence of the entire right dorsal aorta and the distal part of the right sixth aortic arch artery. *B,* Right aortic arch without a retroesophageal component. *C,* Right aortic arch with a retroesophageal component. The abnormal right aortic arch and the ligamentum arteriosum (postnatal remnant of the ductus arteriosus) form a vascular ring that compresses the esophagus and trachea.

After a short course in the IVC, the blood enters the right atrium of the heart. Because the IVC contains poorly oxygenated blood from the lower limbs, abdomen, and pelvis, the blood entering the right atrium is not as well oxygenated as that in the umbilical vein, but it still has a high oxygen content (Fig. 15–37). Most blood from the IVC is directed by the inferior border of the septum secundum, the **crista dividens**, through the **foramen ovale** into the left atrium. There it mixes with the relatively small amount of poorly oxygenated blood returning from the lungs through the pulmonary veins. The fetal lungs extract oxygen from the blood instead of providing it. From the left atrium, the blood passes to the left ventricle and leaves through the ascending aorta.

The arteries to the heart, head, neck, and upper limbs receive well-oxygenated blood. The liver also receives well-oxygenated blood from the umbilical vein. The small amount of well-oxygenated blood from the IVC that remains in the right atrium mixes with poorly oxygenated blood from the SVC and coronary sinus and passes into the right ventricle. This blood, with a medium oxygen content, leaves through the pulmonary trunk. About 10% of the blood goes to the lungs, but most of it passes through the DA into the aorta to perfuse the caudal part of the fetal body and return to the placenta through the umbilical arteries (Fig. 15–37). The DA protects the lungs from circulatory overloading and allows the right ventricle to strengthen in preparation for functioning at full capacity at birth (Carlson, 1994). Because of the high pulmonary vascular resistance in fetal life, pulmonary blood flow is low. Only a small volume of blood from the ascending aorta (about 10% of the cardiac output) enters the descending aorta. About 65% of the blood in the descending aorta passes into the umbilical arteries and is returned to the placenta for reoxygenation. The remaining 35% of the blood supplies the viscera and the inferior half of the body (Bernstein, 1996).

Transitional Neonatal Circulation

Important circulatory adjustments occur at birth when the circulation of fetal blood through the placenta

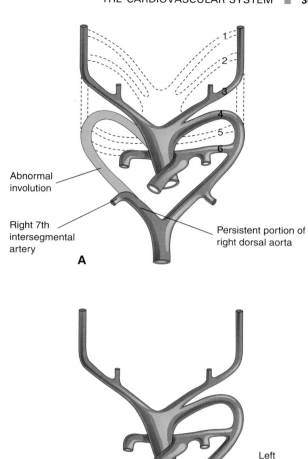

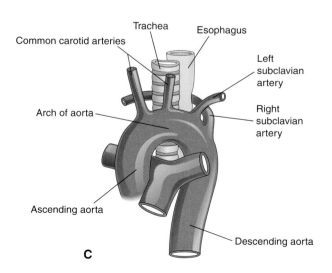

■ **Figure 15–36.** Sketches illustrating the possible embryologic basis of abnormal origin of the right subclavian artery. *A,* The right fourth aortic arch and cranial part of the right dorsal aorta have involuted. As a result, the right subclavian artery forms from the right seventh intersegmental artery and the distal segment of the right dorsal aorta. *B,* As the arch of the aorta forms, the right subclavian artery is carried cranially *(arrows)* with the left subclavian artery. *C,* The abnormal right subclavian artery arises from the aorta and passes posterior to the trachea and esophagus.

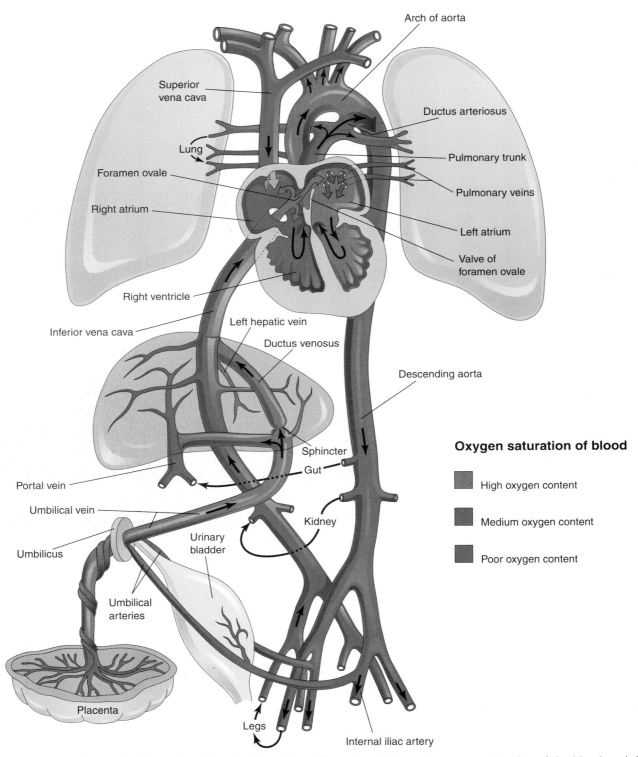

■ **Figure 15–37.** Schematic illustration of the fetal circulation. The colors indicate the oxygen saturation of the blood, and the arrows show the course of the blood from the placenta to the heart. The organs are not drawn to scale. Observe that three shunts permit most of the blood to bypass the liver and lungs: (1) ductus venosus, (2) foramen ovale, and (3) ductus arteriosus. The poorly oxygenated blood returns to the placenta for oxygen and nutrients through the umbilical arteries.

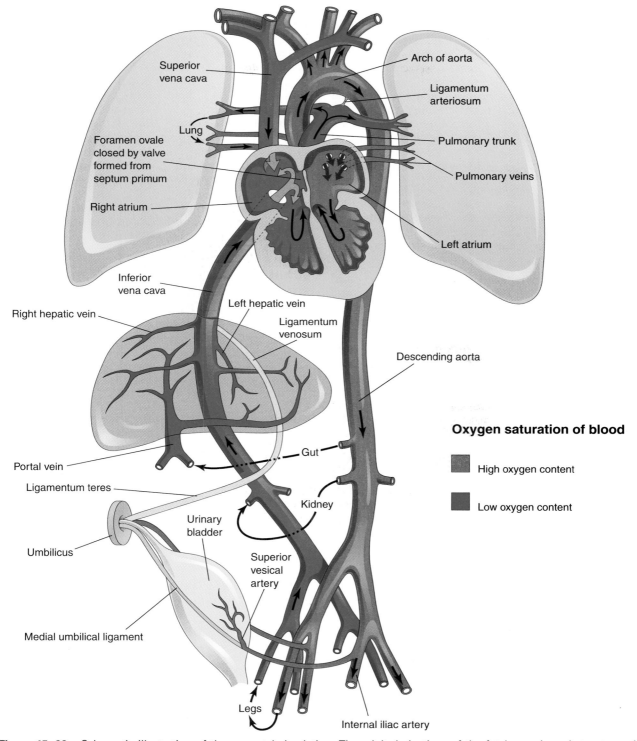

■ **Figure 15–38.** Schematic illustration of the neonatal circulation. The adult derivatives of the fetal vessels and structures that become nonfunctional at birth are also shown. The arrows indicate the course of the blood in the infant. The organs are not drawn to scale. After birth the three shunts that short-circuited the blood during fetal life cease to function, and the pulmonary and systemic circulations become separated.

ceases and the infant's lungs expand and begin to function (Fig. 15-38). The three shunts that permitted much of the blood to bypass the liver and lungs close and become obliterated. *As soon as the baby is born, the foramen ovale, ductus arteriosus, ductus venosus, and umbilical vessels are no longer needed.* The sphincter in the ductus venosus constricts, so that all blood entering the liver passes through the hepatic sinusoids. Occlusion of the placental circulation causes an immediate fall of blood pressure in the IVC and right atrium.

Aeration of the lungs at birth is associated with:

- A dramatic fall in pulmonary vascular resistance
- A marked increase in pulmonary blood flow
- A progressive thinning of the walls of the pulmonary arteries. This thinning results mainly from stretching as the lungs increase in size with the first few breaths.

The foramen closes at birth. Because of increased pulmonary blood flow, the pressure in the left atrium is higher than in the right atrium. The increased left atrial pressure closes the foramen ovale by pressing the valve of the foramen ovale against the septum secundum (Fig. 15-38). The output from the right ventricle then flows entirely into the pulmonary circulation. Because pulmonary vascular resistance is lower than systemic vascular resistance, blood flow in the DA reverses, passing from the aorta to the pulmonary trunk.

The right ventricular wall is thicker than the left ventricular wall in fetuses and newborn infants because the right ventricle has been working harder. By the end of the first month, the left ventricular wall is thicker than the right ventricular wall because the left ventricle is now working harder than the right one. The right ventricular wall becomes thinner because of the atrophy associated with its lighter workload.

The DA constricts at birth, but there is often a small shunt of blood from the aorta to the left pulmonary artery for a few days in a healthy, full-term infant (Sansoucie and Cavaliere, 1997). In premature infants and in those with persistent hypoxia, the DA may remain open much longer. Oxygen is the most important factor in controlling closure of the DA in full-term infants. Closure of the DA appears to be mediated by **bradykinin**, a substance released from the lungs during their initial inflation. Bradykinin has potent contractile effects on smooth muscle. The action of this substance appears to depend on the high oxygen content of the aortic blood resulting from aeration of the lungs at birth. When the PO_2 of the blood passing through the DA reaches about 50 mm Hg, the wall of the ductus constricts. The mechanisms by which oxygen causes ductal restrictions is not well understood.

The effects of oxygen on the ductal smooth muscle may be direct or may be mediated by its effects on prostaglandin E_2 and prostacyclin secretion.

The umbilical arteries constrict at birth, preventing loss of the infant's blood. The umbilical cord is not tied for a minute or so; consequently, blood flow through the umbilical vein continues, transferring fetal blood from the placenta to the infant.

The change from the fetal to the adult pattern of blood circulation is not a sudden occurrence. Some changes occur with the first breath; others are effected over hours and days (Bernstein, 1996). During the transitional stage, a right-to-left flow may occur through the foramen ovale. The closure of fetal vessels and the foramen ovale is initially a functional change. Later anatomic closure results from proliferation of endothelial and fibrous tissues.

Adult Derivatives of Fetal Vascular Structures

Because of the changes in the cardiovascular system at birth, certain vessels and structures are no longer required. Over a period of months, these fetal vessels form nonfunctional ligaments, and fetal structures such as the foramen ovale persist as anatomic vestiges of the prenatal circulatory system.

UMBILICAL VEIN AND LIGAMENTUM TERES

The intra-abdominal part of the *umbilical vein* eventually becomes the *ligamentum teres* (Fig. 15-38), which passes from the umbilicus to the porta hepatis (Moore, 1992); there it is attached to the left branch of the portal vein (Fig. 15-39). The umbilical vein remains patent for a considerable period and may be used for *exchange transfusions of blood* during early infancy. These transfusions are done to prevent brain damage and death of anemic erythroblastotic infants. Most of the infant's blood is replaced with donor blood. The lumen of the umbilical vein usually does not disappear completely; hence, the ligamentum teres can sometimes be cannulated even in adults, if necessary, for the injection of contrast media or chemotherapeutic drugs.

DUCTUS VENOSUS AND LIGAMENTUM VENOSUM

The *ductus venosus* becomes the *ligamentum venosum*; however, its closure is more prolonged than that of the DA (Carlson, 1994). The ligamentum venosum passes through the liver from the left branch of the

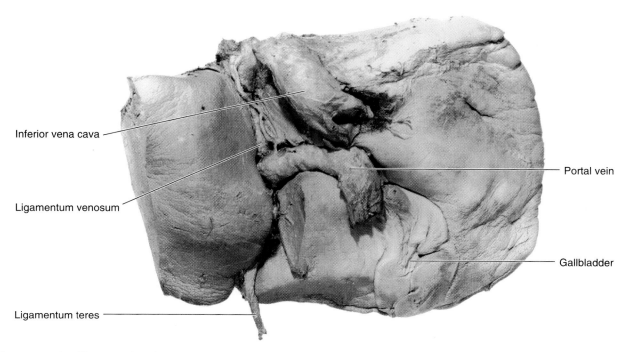

Inferior vena cava

Ligamentum venosum

Ligamentum teres

Portal vein

Gallbladder

■ **Figure 15–39.** Photographs of a dissection of the visceral surface of an adult liver. Note that in the adult the umbilical vein is represented by the ligamentum teres and the ductus venosus by the ligamentum venosum.

portal vein to the IVC, to which it is attached (Fig. 15-39).

UMBILICAL ARTERIES AND ABDOMINAL LIGAMENTS

Most of the intra-abdominal parts of the umbilical arteries become the *medial umbilical ligaments* (Fig. 15-38); the proximal parts of these vessels persist as the *superior vesical arteries*, which supply the urinary bladder (Moore, 1992).

FORAMEN OVALE AND FOSSA OVALIS

The foramen ovale normally closes functionally at birth. Anatomic closure occurs by the third month and results from tissue proliferation and adhesion of the septum primum (valve of foramen ovale) to the left margin of the septum secundum. The septum primum forms the floor of the fossa ovalis (Fig. 15-40). The inferior edge of the septum secundum forms a rounded fold, the *limbus fossae ovalis* (anulus ovalis), which marks the former boundary of the foramen ovale. There is often a lunate impression on the left side of the interatrial septum, which indicates the former site of the foramen ovale.

DUCTUS ARTERIOSUS AND LIGAMENTUM ARTERIOSUM

Functional closure of the DA is usually completed by 10 to 15 hours after birth (Fig. 15-41A). It passes from the left pulmonary artery to the arch of the aorta. Anatomic closure of the ductus and formation of the ligamentum arteriosum normally occurs by the 12th week (Fig. 15-41C).

Patent Ductus Arteriosus

Patent ductus arteriosus is a common anomaly that is two to three times more frequent in females than in males (Fig. 15-41B). The reason for this preponderance is not known. A dominant form of PDA has been reported in the medical literature. Functional closure of the DA usually occurs soon after birth; however, if it remains patent, aortic blood is shunted into the pulmonary artery. Patent ductus arteriosus is the most common congenital anomaly associated with maternal rubella infection during early pregnancy (see Chapter 9), but the mode of action of the rubella virus is unclear. *Premature infants usually have a PDA;* the patency is the result of hypoxia and immaturity. Virtu-

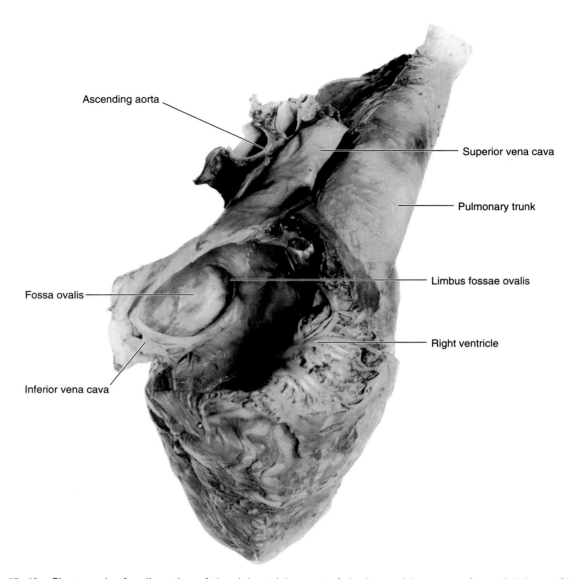

Ascending aorta

Superior vena cava

Pulmonary trunk

Limbus fossae ovalis

Fossa ovalis

Right ventricle

Inferior vena cava

■ **Figure 15–40.** Photograph of a dissection of the right atrial aspect of the interatrial septum of an adult heart. Observe the fossa ovalis and the limbus fossae ovalis. The floor of this oval fossa is formed by the septum primum, whereas the limbus fossae ovalis is formed by the free edge of the septum secundum. Aeration of lungs at birth is associated with a dramatic fall in pulmonary vascular resistance and a marked increase in pulmonary flow. Because of the increased pulmonary blood flow, the pressure in the left atrium is raised above that in the right atrium. This increased left atrial pressure closes the foramen ovale by pressing the valve of the foramen ovale against the septum secundum. This forms the fossa ovalis, a landmark of the interatrial septum.

ally all infants whose birth weight is less than 1750 g have a PDA in the first 24 hours of postnatal life. A PDA that persists in a full-term infant is a pathologic entity. Surgical closure of a PDA is achieved by ligation and division of the DA.

The embryological basis of PDA is failure of the DA to involute after birth and form the ligamentum arter-

iosum. Failure of contraction of the muscular wall of the DA after birth is the primary cause of patency. Some evidence suggests that the low oxygen content of the blood in newborn infants with the *respiratory distress syndrome* can adversely affect closure of the DA; for example, PDA commonly occurs in small premature infants with respiratory difficulties associated with a deficiency of surfactant. Isolated PDA is more common in infants born at high altitude. Patent ductus arteriosus may occur as an isolated anomaly or in association with cardiac defects. Large differences between aortic and pulmonary blood pressures can cause a heavy flow of blood through the DA, thereby preventing normal constriction. Such pressure differences may be caused by coarctation of the aorta, transposition of the great arteries, or pulmonary stenosis and atresia.

DEVELOPMENT OF THE LYMPHATIC SYSTEM

The lymphatic system begins to develop at the end of the sixth week, about 2 weeks after the primordia of the cardiovascular system are recognizable. Lymphatic vessels develop in a manner similar to that previously described for blood vessels (see Chapter 5) and make connections with the venous system. The early lymphatic capillaries join each other to form a network of lymphatics (Fig. 15–42).

Development of Lymph Sacs and Lymphatic Ducts

There are **six primary lymph sacs** at the end of the embryonic period (Fig. 15–42A):

- Two *jugular lymph sacs* near the junction of the subclavian veins with the anterior cardinal veins (the future internal jugular veins)
- Two *iliac lymph sacs* near the junction of the iliac veins with the posterior cardinal veins
- One *retroperitoneal lymph sac* in the root of the mesentery on the posterior abdominal wall

- One *cisterna chyli* located dorsal to the retroperitoneal lymph sac

Lymphatic vessels soon join the lymph sacs and pass along main veins to the head, neck, and upper limbs from the jugular lymph sacs; to the lower trunk and lower limbs from the iliac lymph sacs; and to the primitive gut from the retroperitoneal lymph sac and the cisterna chyli. Two large channels (right and left thoracic ducts) connect the jugular lymph sacs with the cisterna chyli. Soon a large anastomosis forms between these channels (Fig. 15–42B).

THE THORACIC DUCT

The thoracic duct develops from

- The caudal part of the right thoracic duct
- The anastomosis between the thoracic ducts and the cranial part of the left thoracic duct

Because there are initially right and left thoracic ducts, there are many variations in the origin, course, and termination of the adult thoracic duct.

The *right lymphatic duct* is derived from the cranial part of the right thoracic duct (Fig. 15–42C). The thoracic duct and right lymphatic duct connect with the venous system at the angle between the internal jugular and subclavian veins. The superior part of the embryonic **cisterna chyli** persists. In the adult, the cisterna chyli is about 5 cm long and 6 mm wide.

DEVELOPMENT OF LYMPH NODES

Except for the superior part of the cisterna chyli, the lymph sacs are transformed into groups of lymph nodes during the early fetal period. Mesenchymal cells

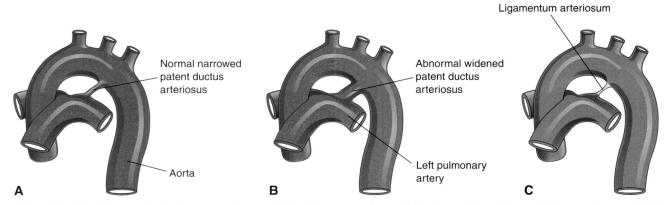

■ **Figure 15–41.** Closure of the ductus arteriosus. *A*, The ductus arteriosus (DA) of a newborn infant. *B*, Abnormal patent DA in a 6-month-old infant. The large ductus is nearly the same size as the left pulmonary artery. *C*, The ligamentum arteriosum in a 6-month-old infant.

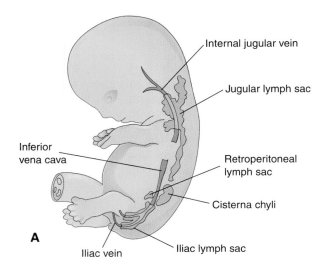

A

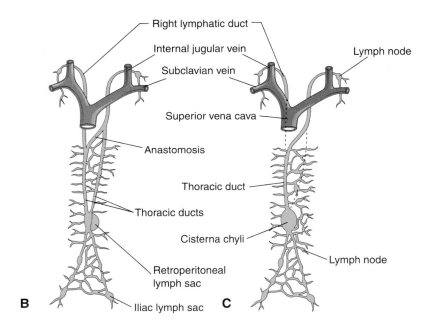

B   **C**

■ **Figure 15–42.** Drawings illustrating development of the lymphatic system. *A*, Left side of an 8-week embryo showing the primary lymph sacs. *B*, Ventral view of the lymphatic system at 9 weeks, showing the paired thoracic ducts. *C*, Later in the fetal period, illustrating formation of the definitive thoracic duct and right lymphatic duct.

invade each lymph sac and break up its cavity into a network of lymphatic channels — the primordia of the *lymph sinuses*. Other mesenchymal cells give rise to the capsule and connective tissue framework of the lymph node.

DEVELOPMENT OF LYMPHOCYTES

The lymphocytes are derived originally from primitive stem cells in the yolk sac mesenchyme and later from the liver and spleen. The lymphocytes eventually enter the bone marrow, where they divide to form *lymphoblasts*. The lymphocytes that appear in lymph nodes before birth are derived from the *thymus gland*, a derivative of the third pair of pharyngeal pouches (see Chapter 11). Small lymphocytes leave the thymus and circulate to other lymphoid organs. Later some mesenchymal cells in the lymph nodes differentiate into lymphocytes. Lymph nodules do not appear in the lymph nodes until just before or after birth.

DEVELOPMENT OF THE SPLEEN AND TONSILS

The spleen develops from an aggregation of mesenchymal cells in the dorsal mesentery of the stomach (see Chapter 13). The **palatine tonsils** develop from the second pair of pharyngeal pouches. The **tubal tonsils** develop from aggregations of lymph nodules around the pharyngeal openings of the pharyngotympanic (auditory) tubes. The **pharyngeal tonsils** (adenoids) develop from an aggregation of lymph nodules in the wall of the nasopharynx. The **lingual tonsil** develops from an aggregation of lymph nodules in the root of the tongue. Lymph nodules also develop in the mucosa of the respiratory and digestive systems.

Anomalies of the Lymphatic System

Congenital anomalies of the lymphatic system are uncommon. There may be diffuse swelling of a part of the body—**congenital lymphedema**. This condition may result from dilation of primitive lymphatic channels or from congenital hypoplasia of lymphatic vessels. More rarely, diffuse cystic dilatation of lymphatic channels involves widespread portions of the body. **Cystic hygromas** are large swellings that usually appear in the inferolateral part of the neck and consist of large single or multilocular, fluid-filled cavities. Hygromas may be present at birth, but they often enlarge and become evident during infancy. Most hygromas appear to be derived from abnormal transformation of the jugular lymph sacs. Hygromas are believed to arise from parts of a jugular lymph sac that are pinched off or from lymphatic spaces that fail to establish connections with the main lymphatic channels.

SUMMARY OF THE CARDIOVASCULAR SYSTEM

The cardiovascular system begins to develop toward the end of the third week, and the heart starts to beat at the beginning of the fourth week. Mesenchymal cells derived from the splanchnic mesoderm proliferate and form isolated cell clusters, which soon develop into endothelial tubes that join to form the primitive vascular system. The heart develops from splanchnic mesenchyme in the *cardiogenic area*. Paired endothelial tubes form and fuse into a single endocardial heart tube. Splanchnic mesoderm surrounding the heart tube forms the *primordial myocardium*.

The primordium of the heart consists of four chambers:

- Bulbus cordis
- Ventricle
- Atrium
- Sinus venosus

The *truncus arteriosus* (primordium of ascending aorta and pulmonary trunk) is continuous caudally with the *bulbus cordis*, which becomes part of the ventricles. As the heart grows, it bends to the right and soon acquires the general external appearance of the adult heart. The heart becomes partitioned into four chambers between the fourth and seventh weeks. Three systems of paired veins drain into the primordial heart:

- The *vitelline system*, which becomes the *portal system*
- The *cardinal veins*, which form the *caval system*
- The *umbilical system*, which involutes after birth

As the pharyngeal arches form during the fourth and fifth weeks, they are penetrated by arteries—the *aortic arches*—that arise from the *aortic sac*. During the sixth to eighth weeks, the aortic arches are transformed into the adult arterial arrangement of the carotid, subclavian, and pulmonary arteries.

The critical period of heart development is from day 20 to day 50 after fertilization. Numerous critical events occur during cardiac development, and deviation from the normal pattern at any time may produce one or more congenital heart defects. Because partitioning of the primordial heart results from complex processes, defects of the cardiac septa are relatively common, particularly VSDs. Some congenital anomalies result from abnormal transformation of the aortic arches into the adult arterial pattern (e.g., right aortic arch).

Because the lungs are nonfunctional during prenatal life, the *fetal cardiovascular system* is structurally designed so that the blood is oxygenated in the placenta and largely bypasses the lungs. The modifications that establish the postnatal circulatory pattern at birth are not abrupt but extend into infancy. Failure of these changes in the circulatory system to occur at birth results in two of the most common congenital anomalies of the heart and great vessels:

- Patent foramen ovale
- Patent ductus arteriosus

The *lymphatic system* begins to develop late in the sixth week in close association with the venous system. Six primary *lymph sacs* develop, which later become interconnected by lymphatic vessels. Lymph nodes develop along the network of lymphatic vessels; lymph nodules do not appear until just before or after birth. Sometimes a part of a jugular lymph sac becomes pinched off and may give rise to a mass of dilated lymphatic spaces, a *cystic hygroma* (Moore and Persaud, 1998).

Clinically Oriented Questions

1. The pediatrician said that our newborn baby had a heart murmur. What does this mean? What causes this condition and what does it indicate?

2. Are congenital anomalies of the heart common? What is the most common congenital heart defect in children?

3. What are the causes of congenital anomalies of the cardiovascular system? Can drugs taken by the mother during pregnancy cause congenital cardiac defects? A friend of mine who drank heavily during her pregnancy had a child with a heart defect. Could her drinking have caused her infant's heart defect?

4. Can viral infections cause congenital heart disease? I have heard that if a mother has measles during pregnancy her baby will have an abnormality of the cardiovascular system. Is this true? I have also heard that women can be given a vaccine that will protect their babies against certain viruses. Is this true?

5. My sister's baby had its aorta arising from the right ventricle and its pulmonary artery arising from the left ventricle. The baby died during the first week. What is this anomaly called and how common is this disorder? Can the condition be corrected surgically? If so, how is this done?

6. I know a set of healthy identical twin sisters in their forties. It was found during a routine examination that one of them had a *reversed heart*. Is this a serious heart anomaly? How common is this among identical twins and what causes this condition to develop?

The answers to these questions are given at the back of the book.

REFERENCES AND SUGGESTED READING

Anderson RH, Ashley GT: Growth and development of the cardiovascular system. *In* Davis JA, Dobbing J (eds): *Scientific Foundation of Paediatrics*. Philadelphia, WB Saunders, 1974.

Behrman RE, Kliegman RM, Arvin AM (eds): *Nelson Textbook of Pediatrics,* 15th ed. Philadelphia, WB Saunders, 1996.

Bernstein E: The cardiovascular system. *In* Behrman RE, Kliegman RM, Arvin AM (eds): *Nelson Textbook of Pediatrics*, 15th ed. Philadelphia, WB Saunders, 1996.

Carlson BM: *Human Embryology and Developmental Biology*. St. Louis, CV Mosby, 1994.

Clark EB: Cardiac embryology: Its relevance to congenital heart disease. *Am J Dis Child* 140:41, 1986.

Clark EB: Pathogenetic mechanisms of congenital cardiovascular malformations revisited. *Semin Perinatol* 20:465, 1996.

Gilbert-Barness E (ed): *Potter's Pathology of the Fetus and Infant*. St. Louis, CV Mosby, 1997.

Goldstein RB: Ultrasound evaluation of the fetal abdomen. *In* Callen PW (ed): *Ultrasonography in Obstetrics and Gynecology*, 3rd ed. Philadelphia, WB Saunders, 1996.

Hornberger LK, Colan SD, Lock JE, et al: Outcome of patients with ectopia cordis and significant intracardiac defects. *Circulation* 94(Suppl II):32, 1996.

Hunt CE: Sudden infant death syndrome. *In* Behrman RE, Kliegman RM, Arvin AM (eds): *Nelson Textbook of Pediatrics*, 15th ed. Philadelphia, WB Saunders, 1996.

Hutchins GM: Letter to the editor. *Teratology* 43:393, 1993.

Lee W, Smith RS, Comstock CH, et al: Tetralogy of Fallot: Prenatal diagnosis and postnatal survival. *Obstet Gynecol* 86:583, 1995.

Moore KL: *Clinically Oriented Anatomy*, 3rd ed. Baltimore, Williams & Wilkins, 1992.

Moore KL, Persaud TVN: *The Developing Human: Clinically Oriented Embryology*, 6th ed. Philadelphia, WB Saunders, 1998.

O'Malley CD, Shaw GM, Wasserman CR, Lammer EJ: Epidemiological characteristics of conotruncal heart defects in California, 1987–1988. *Teratology* 53:374, 1996.

Sansoucie DA, Cavaliere TA: Transition from fetal to extrauterine circulation. *Neonatal Network* 16:5, 1997.

Silverman NH, Schmidt KG: Ultrasound evaluation of the fetal heart. *In* Callen PW (ed): *Ultrasonography in Obstetrics and Gynecology*, 3rd ed. Philadelphia, WB Saunders, 1994.

Thompson MW, McInnes RR, Willard HF: *Thompson and Thompson Genetics in Medicine*, 5th ed. Philadelphia, WB Saunders, 1991.

Tikkanen J, Heinonen OP: Risk factors for coarctation of the aorta. *Teratology* 47:565, 1993.

Yu IT, Hutchins GM; Truncus arteriosus malformation: A developmental arrest at Carnegie stage 14. *Teratology* 53:31, 1996.

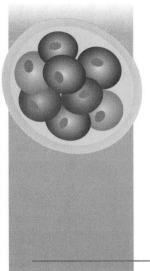

The Skeletal System

16

■ The skeletal system develops from mesodermal and neural crest cells. As the notochord and neural tube form, the *intraembryonic mesoderm* lateral to these structures thickens to form two longitudinal columns of *paraxial mesoderm* (Fig. 16–1*A* to *C*). Toward the end of the third week, these columns become segmented into blocks of mesodermal tissue, the **somites** (see Chapter 5). Externally the somites appear as bead-like elevations along the dorsolateral surface of the embryo (see Chapter 6). Each somite differentiates into two parts (Fig. 16–1*D* and *E*):

- The ventromedial part is the **sclerotome**; its cells form the vertebrae and ribs.
- The dorsolateral part is the **dermomyotome**; cells from its *myotome* region form myoblasts (primordial muscle cells) and those from its *dermatome* region form the dermis of the skin.

Mesodermal cells give rise to a *mesenchyme* — loosely organized embryonic connective tissue. Considerable mesenchyme in the head region is also derived from the neural crest. **Neural crest cells** migrate into the pharyngeal arches and form the bones and connective tissue of craniofacial structures. Regardless of their origin, mesenchymal cells have the ability to differentiate in many different ways (e.g., into fibroblasts, chondroblasts, or osteoblasts).

DEVELOPMENT OF BONE AND CARTILAGE

Bones first appear as condensations of mesenchymal cells that form models of the bones. Condensation marks the beginning of selective gene activity, which precedes cell differentiation (Hall and Miyake, 1995). Most flat bones develop in mesenchyme within pre-existing membranous sheaths (Gartner and Hiatt, 1997); this type of osteogenesis is **intramembranous bone formation**. Mesenchymal models of most limb bones are transformed into cartilage bone models, which later become ossified by **endochondral bone formation**. Significant differences exist in the kinetics of the mineralization process in endochondral and intramembranous bone formation (Dziedzic-Goclawska et al, 1988).

Histogenesis of Cartilage

Cartilage develops from mesenchyme and first appears in embryos during the fifth week. In areas where cartilage is to develop, the mesenchyme condenses to form **chondrification centers**. The mesenchymal cells proliferate and become rounded. Cartilage-forming cells — **chondroblasts** — secrete collagenous fibrils and the ground substance of the matrix. Subsequently collagenous and/or elastic fibers are deposited in the intercellular substance or matrix. *Three types of cartilage* are distinguished according to the type of matrix that is formed:

- Hyaline cartilage, the most widely distributed type (e.g., in joints)
- Fibrocartilage (e.g., in the intervertebral discs)
- Elastic cartilage (e.g., in the auricle of the ear)

For more details about the histogenesis and growth of cartilage, see Gartner and Hiatt (1997).

Histogenesis of Bone

Bone develops in two types of connective tissue, mesenchyme and cartilage. Like cartilage, bone consists of cells and an organic intercellular substance — the **bone matrix** — which comprises collagen fibrils embedded in an amorphous component. For an account of bone cells with respect to the regulation of development, structure, matrix formation, and mineralization, see Marks and Popoff (1988), Dziedzic-Goclawska et al (1988), and Gartner and Hiatt (1997).

INTRAMEMBRANOUS OSSIFICATION

This type of bone formation occurs in mesenchyme that has formed a membranous sheath (Fig. 16–2), hence the name *intramembranous ossification*. The mesenchyme condenses and becomes highly vascular; some cells differentiate into **osteoblasts** (bone-forming cells) and begin to deposit matrix or intercellular substances — **osteoid tissue** — or prebone. The osteoblasts are almost completely separated from one another, contact being maintained by a few tiny processes. Calcium phosphate is then deposited in the osteoid tissue as it is organized into bone. Bone osteoblasts are trapped in the matrix and become **osteocytes**. At first new bone has no organized pattern. Spicules of bone soon become organized and coalesce into lamellae, or layers. Concentric lamellae develop around blood vessels, forming **haversian systems**. Some osteoblasts remain at the periphery of the developing bone and continue to lay down layers, forming plates of compact bone on the surfaces. Between the surface plates, the intervening bone remains spiculated or spongy. This spongy environment is somewhat accentuated by the action of cells with a different origin — **osteoclasts**, which absorb bone. In the interstices of spongy bone, the mesenchyme differentiates into **bone marrow**.

During fetal and postnatal life, continuous remodeling of bone occurs by the simultaneous action of osteoclasts and osteoblasts. Studies on the cellular and

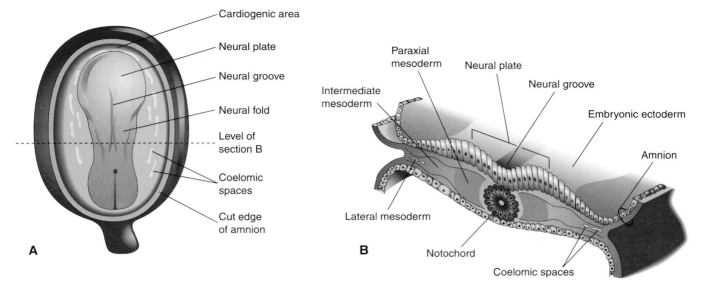

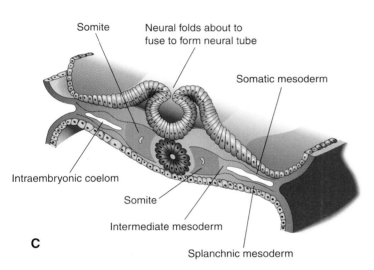

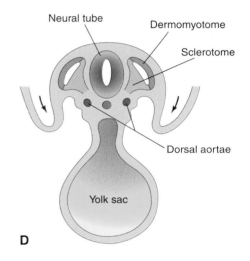

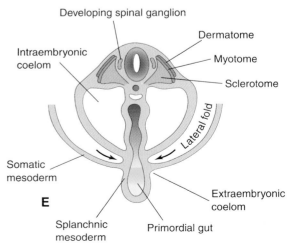

■ **Figure 16-1.** Drawings illustrating formation and early differentiation of somites. *A,* Dorsal view of a presomite embryo (about 18 days). *B,* Transverse section of the embryo shown in *A,* illustrating the paraxial mesoderm from which the somites are derived. *C,* Transverse section of an embryo of about 22 days, showing the appearance of the early somites. Note that the neural folds are about to fuse to form the neural tube. *D,* Transverse section of an embryo of about 24 days, showing folding of the embryo in the horizontal plane *(arrows).* The dermomyotome region of the somite gives rise to the dermatome and myotome. *E,* Transverse section of an embryo of about 26 days, showing the dermatome, myotome, and sclerotome regions of the somite.

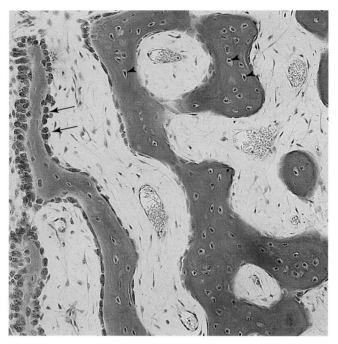

■ **Figure 16–2.** Light micrograph of intramembranous ossification (×132). Trabeculae of bone are being formed by osteoblasts lining their surface *(arrows).* Observe that osteocytes are trapped in lacunae *(arrowheads)* and that primitive osteons are beginning to form. The primitive osteons (canals) contain blood capillaries.

molecular events during embryonic bone formation suggest that osteogenesis and chondrogenesis are programmed early in development and are independent events under the influence of vascular factors.

INTRACARTILAGINOUS OSSIFICATION

This type of bone formation occurs in preexisting cartilaginous models (Fig. 16–3A to E). In a long bone, for example, the **primary center of ossification** appears in the *diaphysis* — the part of a long bone between its ends — which forms the **body** or **shaft** of the bone. Here the cartilage cells increase in size (hypertrophy), the matrix becomes calcified, and the cells die. Concurrently, a thin layer of bone is deposited under the **perichondrium** surrounding the diaphysis; thus, the perichondrium becomes the **periosteum.** Invasion of vascular connective tissue from the periosteum breaks up the cartilage. Some invading cells differentiate into **hemopoietic cells** — responsible for the formation of blood cells — of the bone marrow. Other invading cells differentiate into osteoblasts that

deposit bone matrix on the spicules of calcified cartilage. This process continues toward the **epiphyses** or ends of the bone. The spicules of bone are remodeled by the action of osteoclasts and osteoblasts.

Lengthening of long bones occurs at the diaphyseal-epiphyseal junction. The lengthening of bone depends on the **epiphyseal cartilage plates** (growth plates), whose chondrocytes proliferate and participate in endochondral bone formation (Fig. 16–3D and E). Cartilage cells in the diaphyseal-epiphyseal region proliferate by mitosis. Toward the diaphysis, the cartilage cells hypertrophy and the matrix becomes calcified and broken up into spicules by vascular tissue from the marrow or medullary cavity. Bone is deposited on these spicules; absorption of this bone keeps the spongy bone masses relatively constant in length and enlarges the marrow cavity.

Ossification of limb bones begins at the end of the embryonic period and thereafter makes demands on the maternal supply of calcium and phosphorus. Pregnant women are therefore advised to maintain an adequate intake of these elements in order to preserve healthy bones and teeth. The region of bone formation at the center of the body or shaft of a long bone is the **primary ossification center** (Fig. 16–3B and F). At birth the bodies or diaphyses are largely ossified, but most of the ends or *epiphyses* are still cartilaginous. Most **secondary ossification centers** appear in the epiphyses during the first few years after birth. The epiphyseal cartilage cells hypertrophy, and there is invasion by vascular connective tissue. Ossification spreads in all directions and only the articular cartilage and a transverse plate of cartilage, the **epiphyseal cartilage plate,** remain cartilaginous. Upon completion of growth, this plate is replaced by spongy bone; the epiphyses and diaphysis are united, and further elongation of the bone does not occur.

In most bones, the epiphyses have fused with the diaphysis by about the age of 20 years. Growth in the diameter of a bone results from deposition of bone at the periosteum and from absorption on the medullary surface. The rate of deposition and absorption is balanced to regulate the thickness of the compact bone and the size of the medullary (marrow) cavity. The internal reorganization of bone continues throughout life. The development of irregular bones is similar to that of the epiphyses of long bones. Ossification begins centrally and spreads in all directions. In addition to membranous and endochondral ossification, **chondroid tissue,** which also differentiates from mesenchyme, is now recognized as an important factor for skeletal growth (Dhem et al, 1989). For a comprehensive description of bone formation, see Gartner and Hiatt (1997).

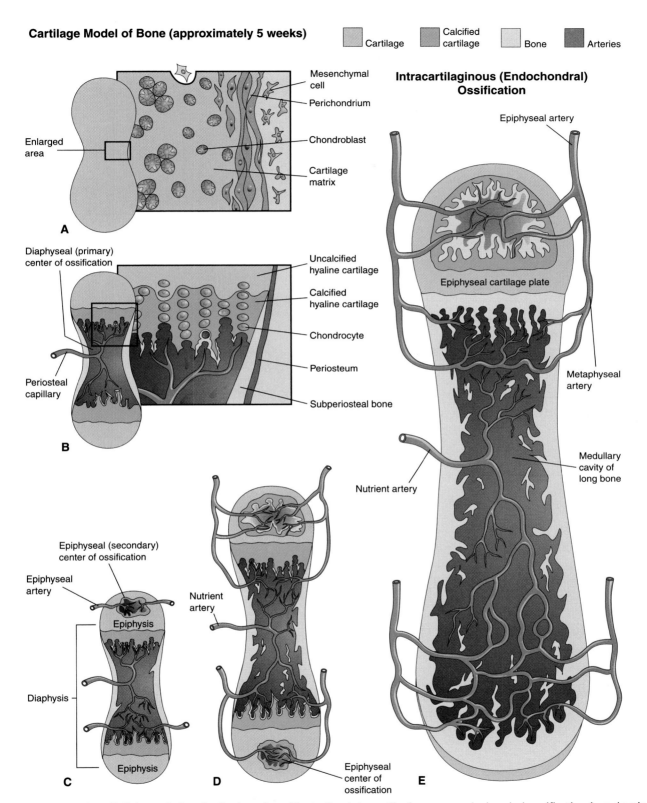

Cartilage Model of Bone (approximately 5 weeks)

Cartilage Calcified cartilage Bone Arteries

Mesenchymal cell
Perichondrium
Chondroblast
Cartilage matrix

Enlarged area

A

Intracartilaginous (Endochondral) Ossification

Epiphyseal artery

Epiphyseal cartilage plate

Diaphyseal (primary) center of ossification

Uncalcified hyaline cartilage
Calcified hyaline cartilage
Chondrocyte
Periosteum
Subperiosteal bone

Periosteal capillary

B

Metaphyseal artery

Nutrient artery

Medullary cavity of long bone

Epiphyseal (secondary) center of ossification

Epiphyseal artery

Epiphysis

Nutrient artery

Diaphysis

Epiphysis

C

D

E

Epiphyseal center of ossification

■ **Figure 16–3.** *A* to *E*, Schematic longitudinal sections illustrating intracartilaginous or endochondral ossification in a developing long bone.

Rickets

Rickets is a disease that occurs in children who have a vitamin D deficiency. Calcium absorption by the intestine is impaired, which causes disturbances of ossification of the epiphyseal cartilage plates (e.g., they are not adequately mineralized) and disorientation of cells at the metaphysis (Gartner and Hiatt, 1997). The limbs are shortened and deformed, with severe bowing of the limb bones (Moore, 1992). For more information about clinical, radiologic, and pathologic findings in rickets, see Behrman et al (1996).

DEVELOPMENT OF JOINTS

Joints begin to develop during the sixth week (Fig. 16–4A), and by the end of the eighth week they resemble adult joints. The terms *articulation* and *joint* are used synonymously to refer to the structural arrangements that join two or more bones together at their place of meeting. Joints are classified as:

- Fibrous joints
- Cartilaginous joints
- Synovial joints

Joints with little or no movement are classified according to the type of material holding the bones together; for example, the bones involved in fibrous joints are joined by fibrous tissue.

Fibrous Joints

During the development of this type of joint, the interzonal mesenchyme between the developing bones differentiates into dense fibrous tissue (Fig. 16–4D); for example, the sutures of the skull are fibrous joints.

Cartilaginous Joints

During the development of cartilaginous joints, the interzonal mesenchyme between the developing bones differentiates into hyaline cartilage (e.g., the costochondral joints) or fibrocartilage (Fig. 16–4C), such as the pubic symphysis between the bodies of the pubic bones (Moore, 1992).

Synovial Joints

During the development of this common type of joint (e.g., the knee joint), the interzonal mesenchyme between the developing bones differentiates as follows (Fig. 16–4B):

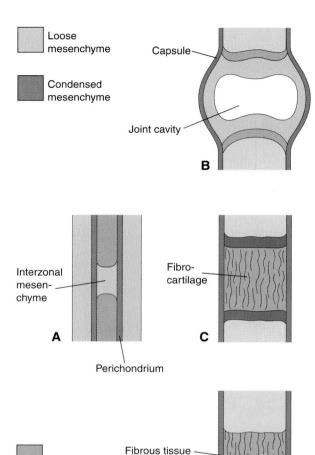

■ **Figure 16–4.** Schematic drawings illustrating the development of joints during the sixth and seventh weeks. *A,* Condensed mesenchyme continues across the gap, or interzone, between the developing bones, enclosing some mesenchyme (the interzonal mesenchyme) between them. This primitive joint may differentiate into *B,* a synovial joint; *C,* a cartilaginous joint; or *D,* a fibrous joint.

- Peripherally it forms the capsular and other ligaments.
- Centrally it disappears, and the resulting space becomes the joint or synovial cavity.
- Where it lines the fibrous capsule and articular surfaces, it forms the synovial membrane, a part of the articular capsule.

Probably as a result of joint movements, the mesenchymal cells subsequently disappear from the surfaces of the articular cartilages.

DEVELOPMENT OF AXIAL SKELETON

The axial skeleton is composed of the following:

- Skull
- Vertebral column
- Ribs
- Sternum

During formation of this part of the skeleton, the cells in the sclerotomes of the somites change their position (Fig. 16–1). During the fourth week they surround the neural tube (primordium of spinal cord) and the notochord, the structure around which the primordia of the vertebrae develop. This positional change of the sclerotomal cells is effected by differential growth of the surrounding structures and not by active migration of sclerotomal cells.

Development of Vertebral Column

During the precartilaginous or mesenchymal stage, mesenchymal cells from the sclerotomes are found in three main areas (Fig. 16–5A):

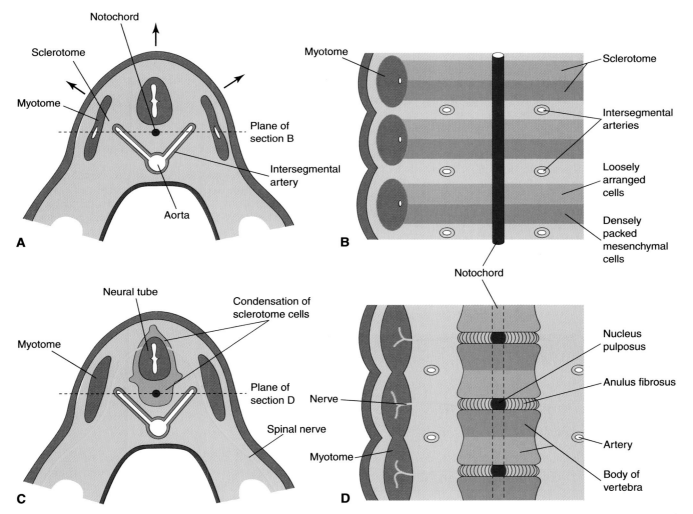

■ **Figure 16–5.** *A,* Transverse section through a 4-week embryo. The arrows indicate the dorsal growth of the neural tube and the simultaneous dorsolateral movement of the somite remnant, leaving behind a trail of sclerotomal cells. *B,* Diagrammatic frontal section of this embryo showing that the condensation of sclerotomal cells around the notochord consists of a cranial area of loosely packed cells and a caudal area of densely packed cells. *C,* Transverse section through a 5-week embryo, showing the condensation of sclerotomal cells around the notochord and neural tube, which forms a mesenchymal vertebra. *D,* Diagrammatic frontal section illustrating that the vertebral body forms from the cranial and caudal halves of two successive sclerotomal masses. The intersegmental arteries now cross the bodies of the vertebrae, and the spinal nerves lie between the vertebrae. The notochord is degenerating except in the region of the intervertebral disc, where it forms the nucleus pulposus.

- Around the notochord
- Surrounding the neural tube
- In the body wall

In a frontal section of a 4-week embryo, the sclerotomes appear as paired condensations of mesenchymal cells around the notochord (Fig. 16-5B). Each sclerotome consists of loosely arranged cells cranially and densely packed cells caudally. Some densely packed cells move cranially opposite the center of the myotome, where they form the **intervertebral disc** (Fig. 16-5C and D). The remaining densely packed cells fuse with the loosely arranged cells of the immediately caudal sclerotome to form the mesenchymal **centrum**, the primordium of the body of a vertebra. Thus each centrum develops from two adjacent sclerotomes and becomes an intersegmental structure. The nerves now lie in close relationship to the intervertebral discs, and the *intersegmental arteries* lie on each side of the vertebral bodies. In the thorax, the dorsal intersegmental arteries become the *intercostal arteries*.

The **notochord** degenerates and disappears where it is surrounded by the developing vertebral bodies. Between the vertebrae the notochord expands to form the gelatinous center of the intervertebral disc, the **nucleus pulposus** (Fig. 16-5D). This nucleus is later surrounded by the circularly arranged fibers that form the **anulus fibrosus**. The nucleus pulposus and anulus fibrosus together constitute the **intervertebral disc**. The mesenchymal cells, surrounding the neural tube, form the vertebral (neural) arch. The mesenchymal cells in the body wall form the costal processes, which form ribs in the thoracic region.

Chordoma

Remnants of the notochord may persist and give rise to a **chordoma**. About a third of these slowly growing malignant tumors occur at the base of the skull and extend to the nasopharynx. They infiltrate bone and are difficult to remove. Few patients survive longer than 5 years (Rubin and Farber, 1988). Chordomas also develop in the lumbosacral region.

CARTILAGINOUS STAGE OF VERTEBRAL DEVELOPMENT

During the sixth week, chondrification centers appear in each mesenchymal vertebra (Fig. 16-6A and B).

The two centers in each centrum fuse at the end of the embryonic period to form a cartilaginous centrum. Concomitantly the centers in the vertebral arches fuse with each other and the centrum. The spinous and transverse processes develop from extensions of chondrification centers in the vertebral arch. Chondrification spreads until a cartilaginous vertebral column is formed.

BONY STAGE OF VERTEBRAL DEVELOPMENT

Ossification of typical vertebrae begins during the embryonic period and usually ends by the 25th year. There are two primary ossification centers, ventral and dorsal, for the centrum (Fig. 16-6C). These **primary ossification centers** soon fuse to form one center. Three primary centers are present by the end of the embryonic period:

- One in the centrum
- One in each half of the vertebral arch

Ossification becomes evident in the vertebral arches during the eighth week. At birth each vertebra consists of three bony parts connected by cartilage (Fig. 16-6D). The bony halves of the vertebral arch usually fuse during the first 3 to 5 years. The arches first unite in the lumbar region, and union progresses cranially. The vertebral arch articulates with the centrum at cartilaginous **neurocentral joints**. These articulations permit the vertebral arches to grow as the spinal cord enlarges. These joints disappear when the vertebral arch fuses with the centrum during the third to sixth years. Five **secondary ossification centers** appear in the vertebrae after puberty:

- One for the tip of the spinous process
- One for the tip of each transverse process
- Two *anular epiphyses*, one on the superior and one on the inferior rim of the vertebral body (Fig. 16-6E and F)

The **vertebral body** is a composite of the anular epiphyses and the mass of bone between them. The vertebral body includes the centrum, parts of the vertebral arch, and the facets for the heads of the ribs. All secondary centers unite with the rest of the vertebra around 25 years of age. Exceptions to the typical ossification of vertebrae occur in the atlas (C1), axis (C2), C7, lumbar vertebrae, sacrum, and coccyx. For details of their ossification, consult Bannister et al (1995) and Moore (1992).

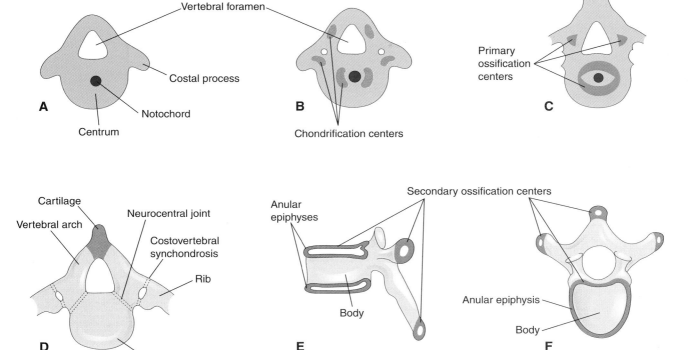

■ **Figure 16–6.** Drawings illustrating the stages of vertebral development. *A,* Mesenchymal vertebra at 5 weeks. *B,* Chondrification centers in a mesenchymal vertebra at 6 weeks. *C,* Primary ossification centers in a cartilaginous vertebra at 7 weeks. *D,* Thoracic vertebra at birth consisting of three bony parts. Note the cartilage between the halves of the vertebral arch and between the arch and the centrum (neurocentral joint). *E* and *F,* Two views of a typical thoracic vertebra at puberty showing the location of the secondary centers of ossification.

Variation in the Number of Vertebrae

About 95% of people have 7 cervical, 12 thoracic, 5 lumbar, and 5 sacral vertebrae. About 3% of people have one or two more vertebrae, and about 2% have one less. To determine the number of vertebrae, it is necessary to examine the entire vertebral column because an apparent extra (or absent) vertebra in one segment of the column may be compensated for by an absent (or extra) vertebra in an adjacent segment—for example, 11 thoracic-type vertebrae with 6 lumbar-type vertebrae.

Development of Ribs

The ribs develop from the mesenchymal costal processes of the thoracic vertebrae (Fig. 16–6*A*). They become cartilaginous during the embryonic period and ossify during the fetal period. The original site of union of the costal processes with the vertebra is replaced by *costovertebral joints.* These are the plane type of synovial joint (Fig. 16–6*D*). Seven pairs of ribs (1 to 7) — **true ribs** — attach through their own cartilages to the sternum. Five pairs of ribs (8 to 12) — **false ribs** — attach to the sternum through the cartilage of another rib or ribs. The last two pairs of ribs (11 and 12) do not attach to the sternum; they are **floating ribs**.

Development of Sternum

A pair of mesenchymal vertical bands, **sternal bars**, develop ventrolaterally in the body wall. *Chondrification* occurs in these bars as they move medially. They fuse craniocaudally in the median plane to form cartilaginous models of the manubrium, sternebrae (segments of the sternal body), and xiphoid process. Fusion at the inferior end of the sternum is sometimes incomplete; as a result, the xiphoid process in these infants is bifid or perforated. Centers of ossification appear craniocaudally in the sternum before birth, except that for the xiphoid process, which appears during childhood.

Development of Skull

The skull develops from mesenchyme around the developing brain. The skull consists of:

- The **neurocranium**, a protective case for the brain

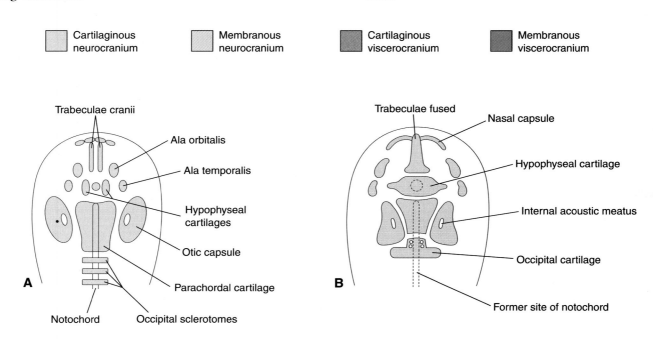

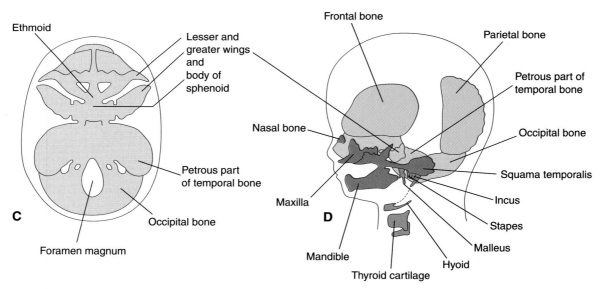

■ **Figure 16–7.** Diagrams illustrating stages in the development of the skull. *A* to *C* are views of the base of the developing skull (viewed superiorly). *D* is a lateral view. *A,* Six weeks, showing the various cartilages that will fuse to form the chondrocranium. *B,* Seven weeks, after fusion of some of the paired cartilages. *C,* Twelve weeks, showing the cartilaginous base of the skull or chondrocranium formed by the fusion of various cartilages. *D,* Twenty weeks, indicating the derivation of the bones of the fetal skull.

• The **viscerocranium**, the skeleton of the face

See Hall and Miyake (1995) for details of molecular events related to chondrogenesis in the craniofacial skeleton.

CARTILAGINOUS NEUROCRANIUM

Initially the cartilaginous neurocranium, or **chondrocranium,** consists of the cartilaginous base of the developing skull, which forms by fusion of several cartilages (Fig. 16-7A to D). Later endochondral ossification of the chondrocranium forms the bones of the base of the skull. The ossification pattern of these bones has a definite sequence, beginning with the occipital bone, basisphenoid bone (body of sphenoid), and ethmoid bone.

The **parachordal cartilage**, or **basal plate**, forms around the cranial end of the notochord (Fig. 16-7A) and fuses with the cartilages derived from the sclerotome regions of the occipital somites. This cartilaginous mass contributes to the base of the occipital bone; later, extensions grow around the cranial end of the spinal cord and form the boundaries of the foramen magnum (Fig. 16-7C).

The **hypophyseal cartilage** forms around the developing pituitary gland (hypophysis cerebri) and fuses to form the body of the sphenoid bone. The *trabeculae cranii* fuse to form the body of the ethmoid bone, and the *ala orbitalis* forms the lesser wing of the sphenoid bone. *Otic capsules* develop around the otic vesicles, the primordia of the internal ears (see Chapter 20), and form the petrous and mastoid parts of the temporal bone. *Nasal capsules* develop around the nasal sacs (see Chapter 11) and contribute to the formation of the ethmoid bone.

THE MEMBRANOUS NEUROCRANIUM

Intramembranous ossification occurs in the mesenchyme at the sides and top of the brain, forming the **calvaria** (cranial vault). During fetal life the flat bones of the calvaria are separated by dense connective tissue membranes that form fibrous joints, the **sutures** (Fig. 16-8). Six large fibrous areas — **fontanelles** — are present where several sutures meet (Moore and Agur, 1995). The softness of the bones and their loose connections at the sutures enable the calvaria to undergo changes of shape during birth, called molding. During **molding of the fetal skull** (adaptation of the fetal head to the pelvic cavity during birth), the frontal bone becomes flat, the occipital bone is drawn out, and one parietal bone slightly overrides the other one. Within a few days after birth, the shape of the calvaria usually returns to normal.

CARTILAGINOUS VISCEROCRANIUM

These parts of the fetal skull are derived from the cartilaginous skeleton of the first two pairs of pharyngeal arches (see Chapter 11).

• The dorsal end of the *first arch cartilage* (Meckel cartilage) forms two middle ear bones, the malleus and incus.
• The dorsal end of the *second arch cartilage* (Reichert cartilage) forms the stapes of the middle ear and the styloid process of the temporal bone. Its ventral end ossifies to form the lesser cornu (L. horn) and superior part of the body of the hyoid bone.
• The third, fourth, and sixth arch cartilages form only in the ventral parts of the arches. The *third arch cartilages* give rise to the greater cornua and inferior part of the body of the hyoid bone.
• The *fourth and sixth arch cartilages* fuse to form the laryngeal cartilages, except for the epiglottis.

MEMBRANOUS VISCEROCRANIUM

Intramembranous ossification occurs in the maxillary prominence of the first pharyngeal arch (see Chapter 11) and subsequently forms the squamous temporal, maxillary, and zygomatic bones. The squamous temporal bones become part of the neurocranium. The mesenchyme in the mandibular prominence of the first arch condenses around its cartilage (Meckel cartilage) and undergoes intramembranous ossification to form the mandible. Some endochondral ossification occurs in the median plane of the chin and in the mandibular condyle.

NEWBORN SKULL

After recovering from molding, the newborn skull is rather round and its bones are thin. Like the fetal skull (Fig. 16-8), it is large in proportion to the rest of the skeleton, and the face is relatively small compared with the calvaria. The small facial region of the skull results from the following:

• The small size of the jaws
• The virtual absence of paranasal (air) sinuses
• The underdevelopment of the facial bones at birth

POSTNATAL GROWTH OF SKULL

The fibrous sutures of the newborn calvaria permit the brain to enlarge during infancy and childhood. The increase in the size of the calvaria is greatest during the first 2 years, the period of most rapid postnatal

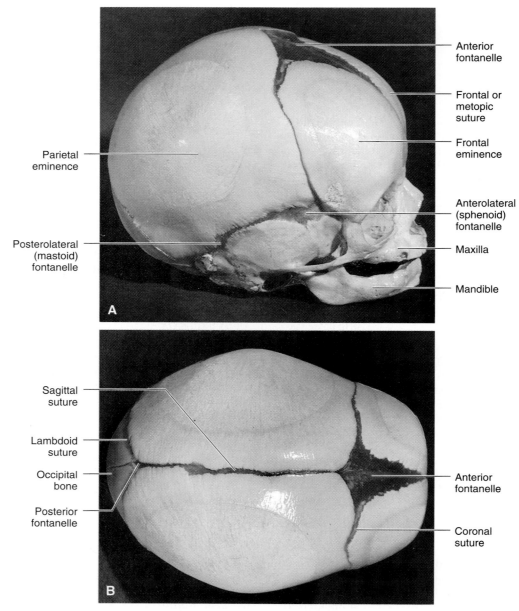

Parietal eminence

Posterolateral (mastoid) fontanelle

Anterior fontanelle

Frontal or metopic suture

Frontal eminence

Anterolateral (sphenoid) fontanelle

Maxilla

Mandible

Sagittal suture

Lambdoid suture

Occipital bone

Posterior fontanelle

Anterior fontanelle

Coronal suture

■ **Figure 16–8.** Photographs of a fetal skull showing the bones, fontanelles, and connecting sutures. *A,* Lateral view. *B,* Superior view. The posterior and anterolateral fontanelles disappear because of growth of surrounding bones, within 2 or 3 months after birth, but they remain as sutures for several years. The posterolateral fontanelles disappear in a similar manner by the end of the first year and the anterior fontanelle by the end of the second year. The halves of the frontal bone normally begin to fuse during the second year, and the frontal or metopic suture is usually obliterated by the eighth year. The other sutures disappear during adult life, but the times when the sutures close are subject to wide variations.

growth of the brain. The calvaria normally increases in capacity until about 16 years of age. After this, it usually increases slightly in size for 3 to 4 years because of thickening of its bones. There is also rapid growth

of the face and jaws, coinciding with eruption of the primary or deciduous teeth. These facial changes are more marked after the secondary or permanent teeth erupt (see Chapter 21). There is concurrent enlargement of the frontal and facial regions, associated with the increase in the size of the paranasal sinuses. Most paranasal sinuses are rudimentary or absent at birth. Growth of these sinuses is important in altering the shape of the face and in adding resonance to the voice.

Klippel-Feil Syndrome (Brevicollis)

The main features of this syndrome are short neck, low hairline, and restricted neck movements. In most cases the number of cervical vertebral bodies is fewer than normal. In some cases there is a lack of segmentation of several elements of the cervical region of the vertebral column. The number of cervical nerve roots may be normal, but they are small, as are the intervertebral foramina. Patients with this syndrome are often otherwise normal, but the association of this anomaly with other congenital anomalies is not uncommon.

Spina Bifida

Failure of fusion of the halves of the vertebral arch results in a major defect — spina bifida. The incidence of this vertebral defect ranges from 0.04 to 0.15%, and it occurs more frequently in girls than in boys (Sarwark, 1996). Spina bifida results from failure of fusion of the halves of the vertebral arch. **Spina bifida occulta** is commonly observed in radiographs of the cervical, lumbar, and sacral regions. Frequently only one vertebra is affected. Spina bifida occulta is a relatively minor, insignificant anomaly of the vertebral column that usually causes no clinical symptoms. It can be diagnosed in utero by sonography (Filly, 1991). Spina bifida occulta of the first sacral vertebra occurs in about 20% of vertebral columns that are examined radiographically (Behrman et al, 1996). The spinal cord and spinal nerves are usually normal, and neurologic symptoms are commonly absent. The skin over the bifid vertebral arch is intact, and there may be no external evidence of the vertebral defect. Sometimes the anomaly is indicated by a dimple or a tuft of hair. In about 3% of normal adults, there is spina bifida occulta of the atlas. At other cervical levels this condition is rare, and, when present, it is sometimes accompanied by other abnormalities of the cervical region of the vertebral column. **Spina bifida cystica**, a severe type of spina bifida involving the spinal cord and meninges, is discussed in Chapter 19. Neurologic symptoms are present in these cases.

Accessory Ribs

Accessory ribs, usually rudimentary, result from the development of the costal processes of cervical or lumbar vertebrae (Fig. 16-6A). These processes form ribs in the thoracic region. The most common type of accessory rib is a **lumbar rib**, but it usually causes no problems (Moore, 1992). **Cervical ribs** occur in 0.5 to 1% of people (Fig. 16-9A). A cervical rib is attached to the seventh cervical vertebra and may be unilateral or bilateral (McNally et al, 1990). Pressure of a cervical rib on the brachial plexus or the subclavian artery often produces symptoms (Moore and Agur, 1995).

Fused Ribs

Fusion of ribs occasionally occurs posteriorly when two or more ribs arise from a single vertebra. Fused ribs are often associated with a hemivertebra (Fig. 16-9B).

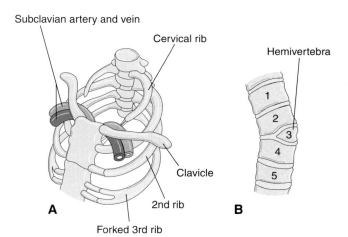

■ **Figure 16-9.** Drawings of vertebral and rib abnormalities. *A,* Cervical and forked ribs. Observe that the left cervical rib has a fibrous band that passes posterior to the subclavian vessels and attaches to the sternum. This condition very likely produced neurovascular changes in the left upper limb. *B,* Anterior view of the vertebral column showing a hemivertebra. The right half of the third thoracic vertebra is absent. Note the associated lateral curvature (scoliosis) of the vertebral column.

Hemivertebra

The developing vertebral bodies have two chondrification centers that soon unite. A hemivertebra results from failure of one of the chondrification centers to appear and subsequent failure of half of the vertebra to form (Fig. 16-9B). These defective vertebrae produce **scoliosis** (lateral curvature) of the vertebral column (Moore, 1992). There are other causes of scoliosis (e.g., myopathic scoliosis resulting from weakness of the spinal muscles).

Rachischisis

The term *rachischisis* (cleft vertebral column) refers to the vertebral abnormalities in a complex group of anomalies (*axial dysraphic disorders*) that primarily affect axial structures (Fig. 16-10C). In these infants the neural folds fail to fuse, either because of faulty induction by the underlying notochord or because of the action of teratogenic agents on the neuroepithelial cells in the neural folds. The neural and vertebral defects may be extensive or be restricted to a small area.

Acrania

In this condition the calvaria is absent, and extensive defects of the vertebral column are often present (Fig. 16-10). Acrania associated with **meroanencephaly** or **anencephaly** (partial absence of the brain) occurs about once in 1000 births and is incompatible with life. Meroanencephaly results from failure of the cranial end of the neural tube to close during the fourth week. This anomaly causes subsequent failure of the calvaria to form (Fig. 16-10A and B).

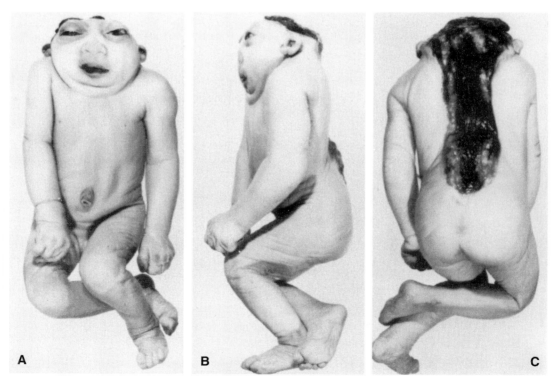

■ **Figure 16-10.** Photographs of anterior (A), lateral (B), and posterior (C) views of a newborn infant with acrania (absence of calvaria), meroanencephaly (partial absence of brain), rachischisis (extensive cleft in vertebral arches of the vertebral column), and myeloschisis (severe anomaly of spinal cord). Infants with these severe craniovertebral anomalies involving the brain and spinal cord usually die within a few days after birth. For more information about meroanencephaly and spina bifida with myeloschisis, see Chapter 19.

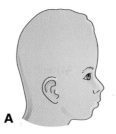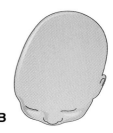

A   **B**

■ **Figure 16–12.** Drawings illustrating skull anomalies. *A,* Oxycephaly (turricephaly), showing the towerlike skull resulting from premature closure of the coronal suture. *B,* Plagiocephaly, illustrating an asymmetric skull resulting from premature closure of the coronal and lambdoid sutures on the left side.

Craniosynostosis

Several skull deformities result from premature closure of the skull sutures. Prenatal closure results in the most severe abnormalities. The cause of craniosynostosis is unknown, but genetic factors appear to be important. These abnormalities are much more common in males than in females, and they are often associated with other skeletal anomalies. The type of deformed skull produced depends upon which sutures close prematurely. If the sagittal suture closes early, the skull becomes long, narrow, and wedge-shaped—**scaphocephaly** (Fig. 16–11). This type of skull deformity constitutes about half the cases of craniosynostosis. Another 30% of cases involve premature closure of the coronal suture, which results in a high, towerlike skull—**oxycephaly** or turricephaly (Fig. 16–12*A*). If the coronal or lambdoid suture closes prematurely on one side only, the skull is twisted and asymmetric—**plagiocephaly** (Fig. 16–12*B*).

Microcephaly

Infants with this condition are born with a normal-sized or slightly small calvaria. The fontanelles close during early infancy, and the sutures close during the first year. This anomaly is not caused by premature closure of sutures. Microcephaly is the result of abnormal development of the central nervous system (CNS) in which the brain and, consequently, the skull fail to grow. Generally, microcephalics are severely mentally retarded. This CNS anomaly is discussed in Chapter 19.

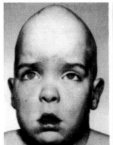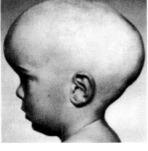

■ **Figure 16–11.** Photographs of a boy with a long, wedge-shaped skull (scaphocephaly) resulting from craniosynostosis—premature closure of the sagittal suture. (From Laurence KM, Weeks R, Abnormalities of the central nervous system. *In* Norman AP [ed]: *Congenital Abnormalities of Infancy,* 2nd ed. Oxford, Blackwell Scientific Publications, 1971.)

DEVELOPMENT OF APPENDICULAR SKELETON

The appendicular skeleton consists of the pectoral and pelvic girdles and the limb bones. Mesenchymal bones form during the fifth week as condensations of mesenchyme appear in the limb buds. During the sixth week the mesenchymal bone models in the limbs undergo chondrification to form hyaline cartilage bone models (Fig. 16–13*A* to *E*). The clavicle initially develops by intramembranous ossification, and it later forms growth cartilages at both ends. The models of the pectoral girdle (shoulder girdle) and upper limb bones appear slightly before those of the pelvic girdle and lower limbs; the bone models appear in a proximodistal sequence. Patterning in the developing limbs is regulated by **homeobox-containing (HOX) genes**. The molecular mechanisms of these HOX genes in limb morphogenesis remain uncertain (Muragaki et al, 1996).

Ossification begins in the long bones by the eighth week of embryonic development and initially occurs in the diaphyses of the bones from **primary centers of ossification** (Fig. 16–3*B* and *C*). By 12 weeks primary ossification centers have appeared in nearly all bones of the limbs (Fig. 16–14). The clavicles begin to ossify before any other bones in the body. The femora are the next bones to show traces of ossification. The first indication of ossification in the cartilaginous model of a long bone is visible near the center of the future body (shaft); this is the primary center of ossification. Primary centers appear at different times in different bones; however, most of them appear between the 7th and 12th weeks of development. Virtually all primary centers of ossification are present at birth. The part of a bone ossified from a primary center is the **diaphysis.**

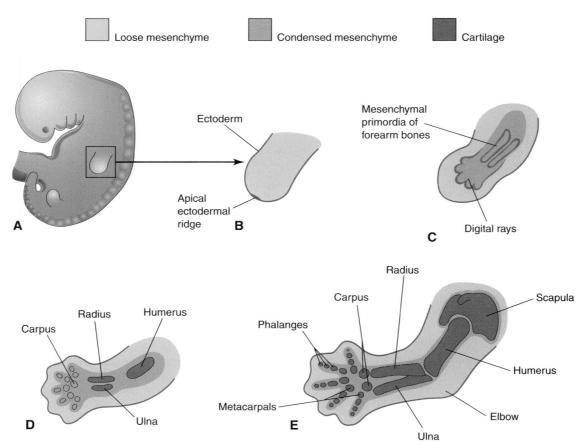

■ **Figure 16–13.** *A,* An embryo at about 28 days, showing the early appearance of the limb buds. *B,* Schematic drawing of a longitudinal section through an upper limb bud. The apical ectodermal ridge has an inductive influence on the mesenchyme in the limb bud; it promotes growth of the mesenchyme and appears to give it the ability to form specific cartilaginous elements. *C,* Similar sketch of an upper limb bud at about 33 days, showing the mesenchymal primordia of the limb bones. The digital rays are mesenchymal condensations that undergo chondrification and ossification to form the bones of the hand. *D,* Upper limb at 6 weeks showing the cartilage models of the bones. *E,* Later in the sixth week showing the completed cartilaginous models of the bones of the upper limb.

The secondary ossification centers of the bones at the knee are the first to appear. The centers for the distal end of the femur and the proximal end of the tibia usually appear during the last month of intrauterine life (34 to 38 weeks after fertilization). Consequently, they are usually present at birth; however, most secondary centers of ossification appear after birth. The part of a bone ossified from a secondary center is the **epiphysis.**

The bone formed from the primary center in the diaphysis does not fuse with that formed from the secondary centers in the epiphyses until the bone grows to its adult length. This delay enables lengthening of the bone to continue until the final size is reached. During bone growth, a plate of cartilage —

the **epiphyseal cartilage plate** — intervenes between the diaphysis and the epiphysis (Fig. 16-3). The epiphyseal plate is eventually replaced by bone development on each of its two sides, diaphyseal and epiphyseal. When this occurs, growth of the bone ceases.

Bone Age

Bone age is a good index of general maturation. Determination of the number, size, and fusion of epiphyseal centers from radiographs is a commonly used

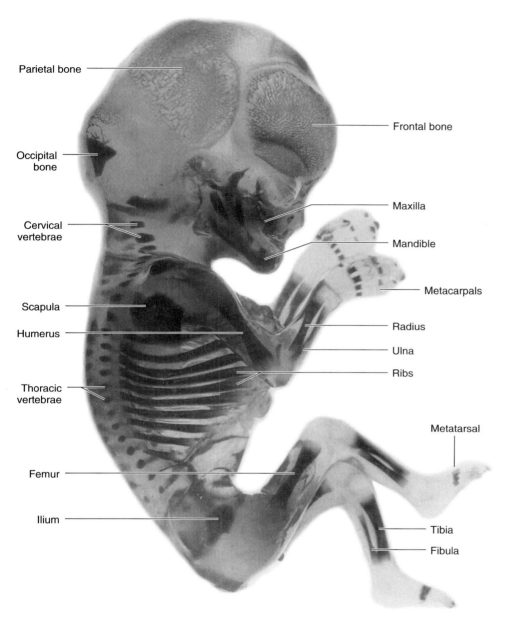

Parietal bone

Frontal bone

Occipital bone

Cervical vertebrae

Maxilla

Mandible

Metacarpals

Scapula

Humerus

Radius

Ulna

Ribs

Thoracic vertebrae

Metatarsal

Femur

Ilium

Tibia

Fibula

■ **Figure 16–14.** Alizarin-stained and cleared 12-week human fetus. Observe the degree of progression of ossification from the primary centers of ossification, which are endochondral in the appendicular and axial parts of the skeleton except for most of the cranial bones (i.e., those that form the calvaria). Observe that the carpus and tarsus are wholly cartilaginous at this stage, as are the epiphyses of all long bones. (Courtesy of Dr. Gary Geddes, Lake Oswego, Oregon.)

method. A radiologist determines the bone age of a person by assessing the ossification centers using two criteria:

- The appearance of calcified material in the diaphysis and/or the epiphysis is specific for each diaphysis and epiphysis and for each bone and sex.
- The disappearance of the dark line representing the epiphyseal cartilage plate indicates that the epiphysis has fused with the diaphysis.

Fusion of the epiphyseal centers, which occurs at specific times for each epiphysis, happens 1 to 2 years earlier in females than in males. Real-time ultrasonography is now increasingly used for the evaluation and measurement of fetal bones, as well as for the determination of gestational age (Filly, 1991).

Generalized Skeletal Malformations

Achondroplasia is the most common cause of **dwarfism**—shortness of stature (see Chapter 9). It occurs about once in 15,000 births. The limbs are bowed and short because of disturbance of endochondral ossification at the epiphyseal cartilage plates, particularly of long bones, during fetal life. The trunk is usually short, and the head is enlarged with a bulging forehead and "scooped-out" nose (flat nasal bone). Achondroplasia is an *autosomal dominant disorder*, and about 80% of cases arise from new mutations; the rate increases with paternal age (Behrman et al, 1996; Thompson et al, 1991).

Hyperpituitarism

Congenital infantile hyperpituitarism, which causes an infant to grow at an abnormally rapid rate, is rare. This may result in **gigantism** (excessive height and body proportions), or *acromegaly* (enlargement of the soft tissues, visceral organs, and bones of the face, hands, and feet). In acromegaly the epiphyseal and diaphyseal centers of the long bones fuse, thereby preventing elongation of these bones. Both gigantism and acromegaly result from an excessive secretion of growth hormone.

Hypothyroidism and Cretinism

A severe deficiency of fetal thyroid hormone production results in cretinism, a condition characterized by growth retardation, mental deficiency, skeletal abnormalities, and auditory and neurologic disorders. Bone age appears as less than chronologic age because epiphyseal development is delayed. Cretinism is very rare except in areas where iodine is lacking in the soil and water. Agenesis of the thyroid gland also results in cretinism.

SUMMARY OF THE SKELETAL SYSTEM

The skeletal system develops from mesenchyme, derived from mesoderm and the neural crest. In most bones, such as the long bones in the limbs, the condensed mesenchyme undergoes chondrification to form cartilage bone models. Ossification centers appear in these models by the end of the embryonic period, and the bones ossify later by *endochondral ossification*. Some bones, the flat bones of the skull for example, develop by *intramembranous ossification*. The vertebral column and ribs develop from mesenchymal cells from the sclerotomes of the somites. Each vertebra is formed by fusion of a condensation of the caudal half of one pair of *sclerotomes* with the cranial half of the subjacent pair of sclerotomes.

The developing skull consists of a neurocranium and a viscerocranium, each of which has membranous and cartilaginous components. The neurocranium forms the *calvaria*, a protective case for the brain. The viscerocranium forms the skeleton of the face. The *appendicular skeleton* develops from endochondral ossification of the cartilaginous bone models, which form from mesenchyme in the developing limbs. Joints are classified as:

- Fibrous joints
- Cartilaginous joints
- Synovial joints

Joints develop from interzonal mesenchyme between the primordia of bones. In a fibrous joint the intervening mesenchyme differentiates into dense fibrous connective tissue. In a cartilaginous joint the mesenchyme between the bones differentiates into cartilage. In a synovial joint, a *synovial cavity* is formed within the intervening mesenchyme by breakdown of the cells. The mesenchyme also gives rise to the synovial membrane and the capsular and other ligaments of the joint.

Although there are numerous types of skeletal anomaly, most of them, except for spina bifida occulta and accessory ribs, are uncommon.

Clinically Oriented Questions

1. What is the most common congenital anomaly of the vertebral column? Where is the defect usually located? Does this congenital anomaly usually cause symptoms (e.g., back problems)?

2. Occasionally rudimentary ribs are associated with the seventh cervical vertebra and the first lumbar vertebra. Are these accessory ribs of clinical importance? What is the embryological basis of accessory ribs?

3. What vertebral defect can produce scoliosis? Define this condition. What is the embryological basis of the vertebral defect?

4. What is meant by the term *craniosynostosis*? What results from this developmental abnormality? Give a common example and describe it.

5. A child presented with characteristics of the Klippel-Feil syndrome. What are the main features of this condition? What vertebral anomalies are usually present?

The answers to these questions are given at the back of the book.

REFERENCES AND SUGGESTED READING

Bannister LH, Berry MM, Collins P, et al: *Gray's Anatomy,* 38th ed. New York, Churchill Livingstone, 1995.

Behrman RE, Kliegman RM, Arvin AM (eds): *Nelson Textbook of Pediatrics,* 15th ed. Philadelphia, WB Saunders, 1996.

Centrella M, Horowitz MC, Wozney JM, McCarthy TL: Transforming growth factor-beta gene family members and bone. *Endocr Rev* 15:27, 1994.

Cohen MM Jr: Syndrome delineation and its implications for the study of pathogenetic mechanisms. *In* Persaud TVN (ed): *Advances in the Study of Birth Defects. Vol 5, Genetic Disorders.* New York, Alan R. Liss, 1982.

Dhem A, Goret-Nicaise M, Dambrain R, et al: Skeletal growth and chondroid tissue. *Arch Ital Anat Embriol* 94:237, 1989.

Dunlop L-LT, Hall BK: Relationships between cellular condensation, preosteoblast formation and epithelial-mesenchymal interactions in initiation of osteogenesis. *Int J Dev Biol* 39:357, 1995.

Dziedzic-Goclawska A, Emerich J, Grzesik W, et al: Differences in the kinetics of the mineralization process in endochondral and intramembranous osteogenesis in human fetal development. *J Bone Miner Res* 3:533, 1988.

Filly RA: Sonographic anatomy of the normal fetus. *In* Harrison MR, Golbus MS, Filly RA (eds): *The Unborn Patient: Prenatal Diagnosis and Treatment,* 2nd ed. Philadelphia, WB Saunders, 1991.

Gartner LP, Hiatt JL: *Color Textbook of Histology.* Philadelphia, WB Saunders, 1997.

Hall BK, Miyake T: Divide, accumulate, differentiate: cell condensation in skeletal development revisited. *Int J Dev Biol* 39:881, 1995.

Mahony BS: Ultrasound evaluation of the fetal musculoskeletal system. *In* Callen PW (ed): *Ultrasonography in Obstetrics and Gynecology,* 3rd ed. Philadelphia, WB Saunders, 1994.

Marin-Padilla M: Cephalic axial skeletal–neural dysraphic disorders: embryology and pathology. *Can J Neurol Sci* 18:153, 1991.

Marks Jr, SC, Popoff SN: Bone cell biology: The regulation of development, structure, and function in the skeleton. *Am J Anat* 183:1, 1988.

McNally E, Sandin B, Wilkins RA: The ossification of the costal element of the seventh cervical vertebra with particular reference to cervical ribs. *J Anat* 170:125, 1990.

Moore KL: *Clinically Oriented Anatomy,* 3rd ed. Baltimore, Williams & Wilkins, 1992.

Moore KL, Agur AMR: *Essential Clinical Anatomy.* Baltimore, Williams & Wilkins, 1995.

Muragaki Y, Mundlos S, Upton J, Olsen BR: Altered growth and branching patterns in synpolydactyly caused by mutations in HOXD 13. *Science* 272:548, 1996.

O'Rahilly R, Müller F, Meyer DB: The human vertebral column at the end of the embryonic period proper. 3. The thoracolumbar region. *J Anat* 168:81, 1990a.

O'Rahilly R, Müller F, Meyer DB: The human vertebral column at the end of the embryonic period proper. 4. The sacrococcygeal region. *J Anat* 168:95, 1990b.

Rubin E, Farber JL (eds): *Pathology.* Philadelphia, JB Lippincott, 1988.

Sarwark JF: Spina bifida. *Pediatr Clin North Am* 43:1151, 1996.

Thompson MW, McInnes RR, Willard HF: *Thompson and Thompson Genetics in Medicine,* 5th ed. Philadelphia, WB Saunders, 1991.

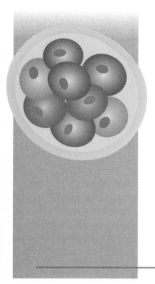

The Muscular System

17

■ The muscular system develops from **mesoderm**, except for the muscles of the iris, which develop from **neuroectoderm** (Uusitalo and Kivela, 1995). Muscle tissue develops **myoblasts**, embryonic muscle cells that are derived from mesenchyme (embryonic connective tissue). MyoD, a member of the family of myogenic regulatory factors, activates transcription of muscle-specific genes and is considered to be an important regulatory gene for the induction of myogenic differentiation (Pin et al, 1997). The induction of myogenesis in mesenchymal cells by MyoD depends on their degree of differentiation (Filvaroff and Derynck, 1996). Much of the mesenchyme in the head is derived from the **neural crest** (see Chapters 5 and 6), particularly the tissues derived from the pharyngeal arches (see Chapter 11); however, the original mesenchyme in the arches gives rise to the musculature of the face and neck (see Table 11–1).

DEVELOPMENT OF SKELETAL MUSCLE

The myoblasts that form the skeletal muscles of the trunk are derived from mesoderm in the myotome regions of the somites (Fig. 17–1A). The limb muscles develop from at least two separate populations of myogenic precursor cells in the limb buds. Recent experimental studies showed that these cells originate from the somites in response to stimuli from nearby tissues (Brand-Saberi et al, 1996). The first indication of **myogenesis** (muscle formation) is the elongation of the nuclei and cell bodies of mesenchymal cells as they differentiate into **myoblasts**. Soon these primordial muscle cells fuse to form elongated, multinucleated, cylindrical structures—**myotubes**. At the molecular level, these events are preceded by gene activation and expression of the MyoD family of muscle-specific basic helix-loop-helix transcription factors in the precursor myogenic cells. For a review of recent work on the genetic control and regulation of muscle differentiation, see Buonanno and Rosenthal (1996) and Pin et al (1997).

Muscle growth during development results from the ongoing fusion of myoblasts and myotubes. **Myofilaments** develop in the cytoplasm of the myotubes during or after fusion of the myoblasts. Soon myofibrils and other organelles characteristic of striated muscle cells develop. Because muscle cells are long and narrow, they are usually called **muscle fibers**. As the myotubes differentiate, they become invested with external laminae, which segregate them from the surrounding connective tissue. Fibroblasts produce the perimysium and epimysium layers of the fibrous sheath; the endomysium is formed by the external lamina, which is derived from the muscle fiber, and reticular fibers. Most skeletal muscle develops before birth, and almost all remaining muscles are formed by the end of the first year. The increase in the size of a muscle after the first year results from an increase in the diameter of the fibers because of the formation of more myofilaments. Muscles increase in length and width in order to grow with the skeleton. Their ultimate size depends on the amount of exercise that is performed. Not all embryonic muscle fibers persist; many of them fail to establish themselves as necessary units of the muscle and soon degenerate.

Myotomes

Each typical myotome part of a somite divides into a dorsal *epaxial division* and a ventral *hypaxial division* (Fig. 17–1B). Each developing **spinal nerve** also divides and sends a branch to each division, the *dorsal primary ramus* supplying the epaxial division and the *ventral primary ramus* the hypaxial division. Some muscles, the intercostal muscles, for example, remain segmentally arranged like the somites, but most myoblasts migrate away from the myotome and form nonsegmented muscles.

DERIVATIVES OF THE EPAXIAL DIVISIONS OF MYOTOMES

Myoblasts from these divisions of the myotomes form the extensor muscles of the neck and vertebral column (Fig. 17–2). The embryonic extensor muscles derived from the sacral and coccygeal myotomes degenerate; their adult derivatives are the dorsal sacrococcygeal ligaments (Moore, 1992).

DERIVATIVES OF THE HYPAXIAL DIVISIONS OF MYOTOMES

Myoblasts from these divisions of the cervical myotomes form the scalene, prevertebral, geniohyoid, and infrahyoid muscles (Fig. 17–2). The thoracic myotomes form the lateral and ventral flexor muscles of the vertebral column, and the lumbar myotomes form the quadratus lumborum muscle. The sacrococcygeal myotomes form the muscles of the pelvic diaphragm (Moore and Agur, 1995) and probably the striated muscles of the anus and sex organs.

Pharyngeal Arch Muscles

The migration of myoblasts from the pharyngeal arches to form the muscles of mastication, facial expression, pharynx, and larynx is described in Chapter 11. These muscles are innervated by pharyngeal arch nerves.

Ocular Muscles

The origin of the extrinsic eye muscles is unclear, but it is thought that they may be derived from mesenchy- mal cells near the prechordal plate (Figs. 17–1 and 17–2). The mesoderm in this area is thought to give rise to three *preotic myotomes*. Myoblasts differentiate from mesenchymal cells derived from these myotomes.

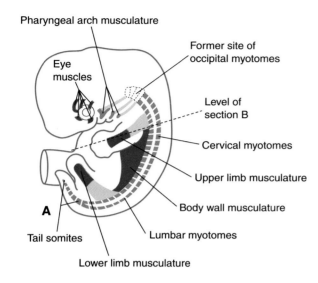

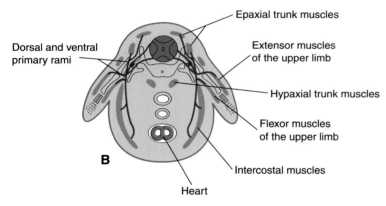

■ **Figure 17–1.** *A,* Sketch of an embryo (about 41 days), showing the myotomes and developing muscular system. *B,* Transverse section of the embryo, illustrating the epaxial and hypaxial derivatives of a myotome. *C,* Similar section of a 7-week embryo, showing the muscle layers formed from the myotomes.

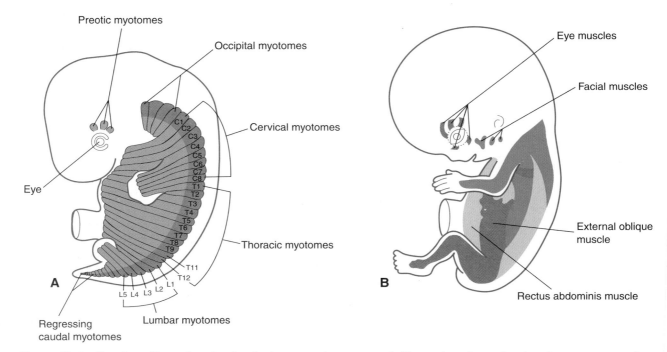

■ **Figure 17–2.** Drawings illustrating the developing muscular system. *A*, Six-week embryo showing the myotome regions of the somites that give rise to most skeletal muscles. *B*, Eight-week embryo showing the developing trunk and limb musculature.

Groups of myoblasts, each supplied by its own cranial nerve (CN III, CN IV, or CN VI), form the extrinsic muscles of the eye.

Tongue Muscles

Initially there are four *occipital (postotic) myotomes*; the first pair disappears. Myoblasts from the remaining myotomes form the tongue muscles, which are innervated by the hypoglossal nerve (CN XII).

Limb Muscles

The musculature of the limbs develops from the myogenic cells (**myoblasts**) surrounding the developing bones (Fig. 17–1). Grafting and gene targeting studies in birds and mammals have demonstrated that at least some of the precursor myogenic cells in the limb buds originate from the somites. These cells are first located in the ventral part of the dermomyotome and are epithelial in nature (see Fig. 16–1*D*). Following mesenchymal-epithelial transformation, the cells then migrate into the primordium of the limb.

DEVELOPMENT OF SMOOTH MUSCLE

Smooth muscle fibers differentiate from splanchnic mesenchyme surrounding the endoderm of the primor-

dial gut and its derivatives (see Fig. 16–1). The smooth muscle in the walls of many blood and lymphatic vessels arises from somatic mesoderm. The muscles of the iris (sphincter and dilator pupillae) and the myoepithelial cells in mammary and sweat glands are thought to be derived from mesenchymal cells that originate from ectoderm. The first sign of differentiation of smooth muscle is the development of elongated nuclei in spindle-shaped myoblasts. During early development, new myoblasts continue to differentiate from mesenchymal cells but do not fuse; they remain mononucleated. During later development, division of existing myoblasts gradually replaces the differentiation of new myoblasts in the production of new smooth muscle tissue. As smooth muscle cells differentiate, filamentous but nonsarcomeric contractile elements develop in their cytoplasm, and the external surface of each cell acquires a surrounding external lamina. As smooth muscle fibers develop into sheets or bundles, they receive autonomic innervation; fibroblasts and muscle cells synthesize and lay down collagenous, elastic, and reticular fibers.

DEVELOPMENT OF CARDIAC MUSCLE

Cardiac muscle develops from splanchnic mesenchyme surrounding the developing heart tube (see Chapter 15). **Cardiac myoblasts** differentiate from the primordial myocardium. Heart muscle is recognizable in the fourth week and likely develops through expression of cardiac-specific genes. Immunohistochemical studies have revealed a spatial distribution of "tissue-specific" antigens (myosin heavy chain isoforms) in the embryonic heart between the fourth and eighth weeks of development (Wessels et al, 1991). **Cardiac muscle fibers** arise by differentiation and growth of single cells, unlike striated skeletal muscle fibers that develop by fusion of cells. Growth of cardiac muscle fibers results from the formation of new myofilaments. The myoblasts adhere to each other as in developing skeletal muscle, but the intervening cell membranes do not disintegrate; these areas of adhesion give rise to **intercalated discs** (Cormack, 1993). Late in the embryonic period, special bundles of muscle cells develop with relatively few myofibrils and relatively larger diameters than typical cardiac muscle fibers. These atypical cardiac muscle cells—**Purkinje fibers**—form the conducting system of the heart (see Chapter 15).

Anomalies of Muscles

Absence of one or more skeletal muscles is more common than is generally recognized. Usually only a single muscle is absent on one side of the body, or only part of the muscle fails to develop. Occasionally the same muscle or muscles may be absent on both sides of the body. Any muscle in the body may occasionally be absent; common examples are the sternocostal head of the pectoralis major (Fig. 17-3), the palmaris longus, trapezius, serratus anterior, and quadratus femoris (Moore, 1992). Absence of the pectoralis major, often

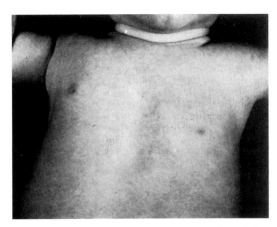

■ **Figure 17–3.** Photograph of the thorax of an infant with congenital absence of the left pectoralis major muscle. Note the absence of the anterior axillary fold on the left and low location of the left nipple. (From Behrman RE, Kliegman RM, Arvin AM (eds): *Nelson Textbook of Pediatrics,* 15th ed. Philadelphia, WB Saunders, 1996.)

its sternal part, is usually associated with syndactyly (fusion of digits). These anomalies are part of the *Poland syndrome*. Absence of the pectoralis major is occasionally associated with absence of the mammary gland and/or hypoplasia of the nipple (Fig. 17-3).

Some muscular anomalies are of a more vital nature, such as **congenital absence of the diaphragm**, which is usually associated with severe *pulmonary atelectasis* (incomplete expansion of the lungs or part of a lung) and pneumonitis (pneumonia). Absence of muscles of the anterior abdominal wall may be associated with severe gastrointestinal and genitourinary anomalies, exstrophy of the bladder, for example (see Chapter 14). Occasionally individuals with congenital absence of a muscle develop **muscular dystrophy** in later life. The most common association is between congenital absence of the pectoralis major muscle and the Landouzy-Dejerine facioscapulohumeral form of muscular dystrophy (Mastaglia, 1974). Both muscle development and muscle repair have distinctive dependence upon expression of muscle regulatory genes (Megeney et al, 1996; Anderson et al, 1996).

Variations in Muscles

All muscles are subject to a certain amount of variation, but some are affected more often than others. Certain muscles are functionally vestigial, such as those of the external ear and scalp. Some muscles present in other primates appear in only some humans (e.g., the sternalis muscle). Variations in the form, position, and attachments of muscles are common and are usually functionally insignificant.

The sternocleidomastoid muscle is sometimes injured at birth, resulting in **congenital torticollis** (Moore, 1992). There is fixed rotation and tilting of the head because of fibrosis and shortening of the sternocleidomastoid muscle on one side (Fig. 17-4). Some cases of torticollis (wryneck) result from tearing of fibers of the sternocleidomastoid muscle during childbirth (Moore and Persaud, 1998). Although birth trauma is commonly considered a cause of congenital torticollis, the fact that the condition has been observed in infants delivered by cesarean section suggests that there are other causes in some cases (Davids et al, 1993; Behrman et al, 1996).

Accessory Muscles

Accessory muscles occasionally develop, and some are clinically significant. For example, an *accessory soleus muscle* is present in about 6% of the population (Agur, 1998). It has been suggested that the primordium of

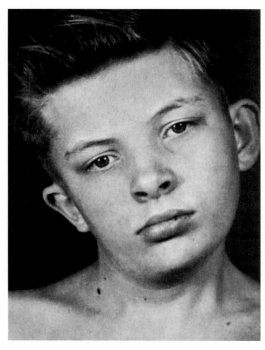

■ **Figure 17–4.** Photograph of the head and neck of a 12-year-old boy with congenital torticollis (wryneck). Shortening of the right sternocleidomastoid muscle has caused tilting of the head to the right and turning of the chin to the left. There is also asymmetric development of the face and skull. (From Behrman RE, Vaughan VC III: *Nelson Textbook of Pediatrics,* 13th ed. Philadelphia, WB Saunders, 1987.)

the soleus muscle undergoes early splitting to form an accessory soleus (Romanus et al, 1986).

SUMMARY OF THE MUSCULAR SYSTEM

Most skeletal muscle is derived from the myotome regions of somites. Some head and neck muscles are derived from pharyngeal arch mesoderm. The limb muscles develop from myogenic precursor cells, which are derived from somites. Cardiac muscle and most smooth muscle are derived from splanchnic mesoderm. Absence or variation of some muscles is common and is usually of little consequence.

Clinically Oriented Questions

1. A newborn infant was born with the prune-belly syndrome caused by failure of the abdominal musculature to develop normally. What do you think would cause this congenital anomaly? What other severe urinary anomaly results from abnormal development of the anterior abdominal wall?

2. A boy asked his mother why one of his nipples was much lower than the other one. She was unable to explain this anomaly to her son. How would you explain this low position of the nipple?

3. An 8-year-old girl asked her doctor why the muscle on one side of her neck was so prominent. What would you tell her? What could happen if this muscle was not treated?

4. After strenuous exercise a young athlete complained of pain on the posteromedial aspect of his ankle. He was told he had an accessory calf muscle. Is this possible? If so, what is the embryologic basis of this anomaly?

The answers to these questions are given at the back of the book.

REFERENCES AND SUGGESTED READING

Agur AMR: Personal communication, 1998.

Anderson JE, McIntosh L, Garrett K, et al: The absence of MyoD increases MDX mouse dystrophy and reduces muscle repair. *Molec Biol Cell Supp* 7:468a, 1996.

Behrman RE, Kliegman RM, Arvin AM (eds): *Nelson Textbook of Pediatrics,* 15th ed. Philadelphia, WB Saunders, 1996.

Brand-Saberi B, Müller TS, Wilting J, et al: Scatter factor/hepatocyte growth factor (SF/HGF) induces emigration of myogenic cells at interlimb level in vivo. *Dev Biol* 179:303, 1996.

Buonanno A, Rosenthal N: Molecular control of muscle diversity and plasticity. *Dev Genet* 19:95, 1996.

Cormack DH: *Essential Histology.* Philadelphia, JB Lippincott, 1993.

Davids JR, Wenger DR, Mubarak SJ: Congenital muscular torticollis: Sequela of intrauterine or perinatal compartment syndrome. *J Pediatr Orthop* 13:141, 1993.

Dubowitz V: *Muscle Disorders in Childhood,* 2nd ed. Philadelphia, WB Saunders, 1995.

Filvaroff EH, Derynck R: Induction of myogenesis in mesenchymal cells by MyoD depends on their degree of differentiation. *Dev Biol* 178:459, 1996.

Mahony BS: Ultrasound evaluation of the fetal musculoskeletal system. *In* Callen PW (ed): *Ultrasonography in Obstetrics and Gynecology,* 2nd ed. Philadelphia, WB Saunders, 1994.

Mastaglia FL: The growth and development of skeletal muscles. *In* Davis JA, Dobbing J (eds): *Scientific Foundations of Paediatrics.* Philadelphia, WB Saunders, 1974.

Megeney A, Kablar B, Garrett K, et al: MyoD is required for myogenic stem cell function in adult skeletal muscle. *Genes Dev* 10:1173, 1996.

Moore KL: *Clinically Oriented Anatomy,* 3rd ed. Baltimore, Williams & Wilkins, 1992.

Moore KL, Agur AMR: *Essential Clinical Anatomy.* Baltimore, Williams & Wilkins, 1995.

Moore KL, Persaud TVN: *The Developing Human: Clinically Oriented Embryology,* 6th ed. Philadelphia, WB Saunders, 1998.

Pin CL, Ludolph DC, Cooper ST, et al: Distal regulatory elements control MRF4 gene expression in early and late myogenic cell populations. *Dev Dyn* 208:299, 1997.

Romanus B, Lindahl S, Stener B: Accessory soleus muscle. A clinical and radiographic presentation of eleven cases. *J Bone Joint Surg* 68A:731, 1986.

Uusitalo M, Kivela T: Development of cytoskeleton in neuroectodermally derived epithelial and muscle cells of human eye. *Invest Ophthalmol Vis Sci* 36:2584, 1995.

Wessels A, Vermeulen JL, Viragh S, et al: Spatial distribution of "tissue-specific" antigens in the developing heart and skeletal muscle. II. An immunohistochemical analysis of myosin heavy chain isoform expression patterns in the embryonic heart. *Anat Rec* 229:355, 1991.

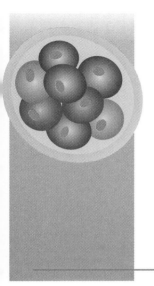

The Limbs

18

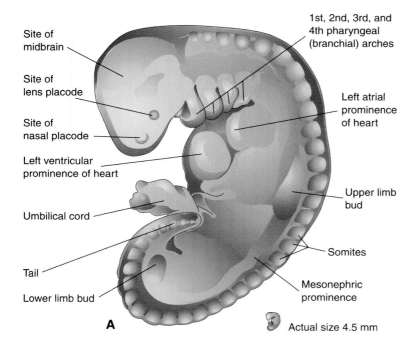

Site of midbrain

Site of lens placode

Site of nasal placode

Left ventricular prominence of heart

Umbilical cord

Tail

Lower limb bud

1st, 2nd, 3rd, and 4th pharyngeal (branchial) arches

Left atrial prominence of heart

Upper limb bud

Somites

Mesonephric prominence

A   Actual size 4.5 mm

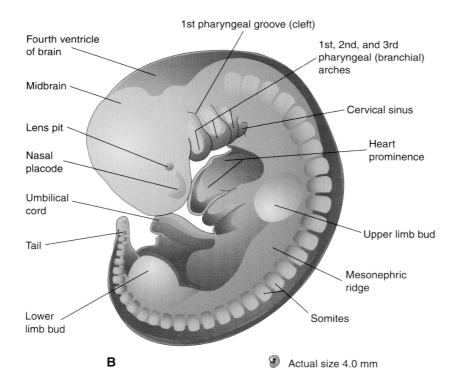

Fourth ventricle of brain

Midbrain

Lens pit

Nasal placode

Umbilical cord

Tail

Lower limb bud

1st pharyngeal groove (cleft)

1st, 2nd, and 3rd pharyngeal (branchial) arches

Cervical sinus

Heart prominence

Upper limb bud

Mesonephric ridge

Somites

B   Actual size 4.0 mm

■ **Figure 18–1.** *A*, Lateral view of a human embryo at Carnegie stage 13, about 28 days. The upper limb buds appear as swellings on the ventrolateral body wall. The lower limbs are not as well developed. *B*, Lateral view of an embryo at Carnegie stage 14, about 32 days. The upper limb buds are paddleshaped, and the lower limb buds are flipperlike. (Modified from Nishimura H, Semba R, Tanimura T, Tanaka O: *Prenatal Development of the Human with Special Reference to Craniofacial Structures: An Atlas.* Washington, DC, National Institute of Health, 1977.)

The general features of limb development are described and illustrated in Chapter 6. Development of limb bones is described in Chapter 16, and formation of limb musculature is outlined in Chapter 17. The purpose of this chapter is to consolidate this material and provide more information about limb development.

EARLY STAGES OF LIMB DEVELOPMENT

The **limb buds** first appear as small elevations of the ventrolateral body wall during the fourth week (Fig. 18-1A). Limb development begins with the activation of a group of mesenchymal cells in the lateral mesoderm (Carlson, 1994). Homeobox-containing (HOX) genes regulate patterning in vertebrate limb development (Muragaki et al, 1996; Cohn et al, 1997). The limb buds form deep to a thick band of ectoderm. The upper limb buds are visible by day 26 or 27, and the lower limb buds appear a day or two later. Each limb bud consists of a mass of mesenchyme covered by ectoderm. The mesenchyme is derived from the somatic layer of lateral mesoderm. The limb buds elongate by the proliferation of the mesenchyme within them. The upper limb buds appear disproportionately low on the embryo's trunk because of the early development of the cranial half of the embryo.

The early stages of limb development are alike for the upper and lower limbs; however, development of the upper limb buds precedes that of the lower limb buds by about 2 days (Fig. 18-1A and B). In addition, there are distinct differences between the development of the hand and foot because of their form and function. The upper limb buds develop opposite the caudal cervical segments, and the lower limb buds form opposite the lumbar and upper sacral segments.

At the apex of each limb bud the ectoderm thickens to form an **apical ectodermal ridge** (AER). Interaction between the AER and mesenchymal cells in the limb is essential to limb development (Hinrichsen et al, 1994). The AER, a multilayered epithelial structure (Fig. 18-2), interacts with mesenchyme in the limb bud, promoting outgrowth of the bud (Carlson, 1994). *The AER exerts an inductive influence on the limb mesenchyme that initiates growth and development of the limbs.* The mesenchyme adjacent to the AER consists of undifferentiated, rapidly proliferating cells, whereas mesenchymal cells proximal to it differentiate

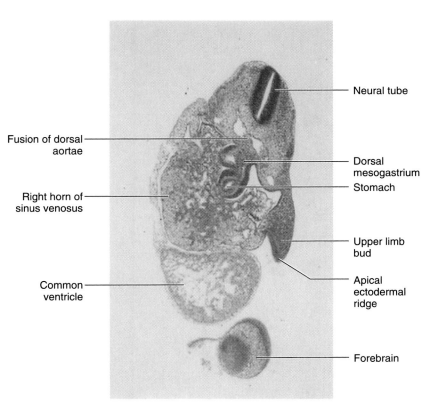

Neural tube

Fusion of dorsal aortae

Dorsal mesogastrium

Stomach

Right horn of sinus venosus

Upper limb bud

Common ventricle

Apical ectodermal ridge

Forebrain

■ **Figure 18-2.** Oblique section of an embryo at Carnegie stage 13, about 28 days. Observe the flipperlike upper limb bud lateral to the embryonic heart. (From Moore KL, Persaud, TVN, Shiota K: *Color Atlas of Clinical Embryology.* Philadelphia, WB Saunders, 1994.)

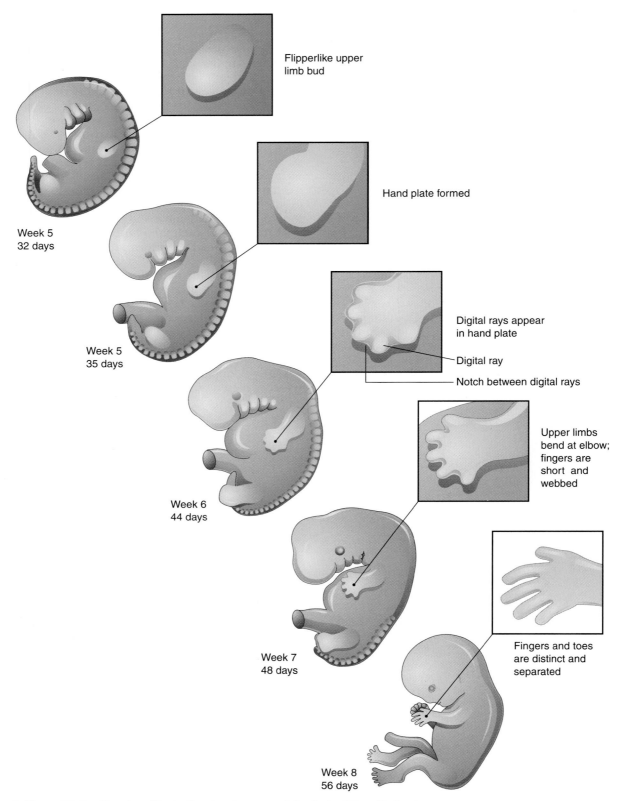

Flipperlike upper limb bud

Hand plate formed

Digital rays appear in hand plate

Digital ray

Notch between digital rays

Upper limbs bend at elbow; fingers are short and webbed

Fingers and toes are distinct and separated

Week 5
32 days

Week 5
35 days

Week 6
44 days

Week 7
48 days

Week 8
56 days

■ **Figure 18–3.** Drawings illustrating development of the limbs (32 to 56 days).

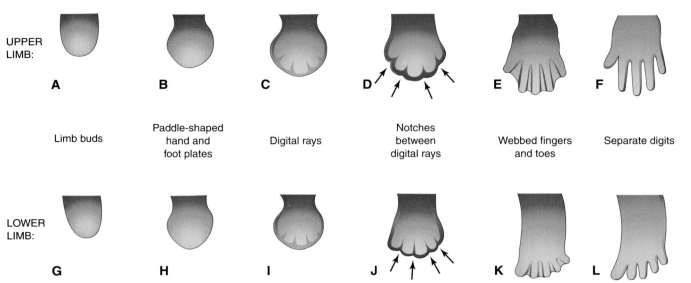

UPPER LIMB:

A — Limb buds

B — Paddle-shaped hand and foot plates

C — Digital rays

D — Notches between digital rays

E — Webbed fingers and toes

F — Separate digits

LOWER LIMB:

G   H   I   J   K   L

■ **Figure 18–4.** Drawings illustrating development of the hands and feet between the fourth and eighth weeks. The early stages of limb development are alike, except that development of the hands precedes that of the feet by a day or so: A, 27 days; B, 32 days; C, 41 days; D, 46 days; E, 50 days; F, 52 days; G, 28 days; H, 36 days; I, 46 days; J, 49 days; K, 52 days; L, 56 days.

into blood vessels and cartilage bone models. Members of the transforming growth factor–gene family, activin-A and bone morphogenetic proteins, play an important role in bone development and remodeling (Centrella et al, 1994; Russell, 1996). The distal ends of the flipperlike limb buds flatten into paddlelike hand and foot plates (Fig. 18–3).

By the end of the sixth week, mesenchymal tissue in the **hand plates** has condensed to form **digital rays** (Figs. 18–3 and 18–4A to C). These mesenchymal condensations outline the pattern of the digits (fingers). During the seventh week, similar condensations of mesenchyme form digital rays in the **foot plates** (Fig. 18–4E to I). At the tip of each digital ray, a part of the AER induces development of the mesenchyme into the mesenchymal primordia of the bones (phalanges) in the digits. The intervals between the digital rays are occupied by loose mesenchyme. Soon the intervening regions of mesenchyme break down, forming *notches between the digital rays* (Figs. 18–3 and 18–4D and J). As this tissue breakdown progresses, separate digits are produced by the end of the eighth week. **Programmed cell death** (apoptosis) is responsible for the tissue breakdown in the interdigital regions, and it is probably mediated by signaling molecules known as **bone morphogenetic proteins**. Blocking these cellular and molecular events could account for **syndactyly**, webbing or fusion of fingers or toes (Zou and Niswander, 1996).

FINAL STAGES OF LIMB DEVELOPMENT

As the limbs elongate during the early part of the fifth week, mesenchymal models of the bones are formed by cellular aggregations (Fig. 18–5A and B). **Chondrification centers** appear later in the fifth week. By the end of the sixth week, the entire limb skeleton is cartilaginous (Fig. 18–5C and D). **Osteogenesis of long bones** begins in the seventh week from primary ossification centers in the middle of the cartilaginous models of the long bones. **Primary ossification centers** are present in all long bones by the 12th week (see Chapter 16). Ossification of the carpal (wrist) bones begins during the first year after birth.

As the long bones form, myoblasts aggregate and form a large muscle mass in each limb bud (see Fig. 17–1). In general, this muscle mass separates into dorsal (extensor) and ventral (flexor) components. The mesenchyme in the limb bud gives rise to bones, ligaments, and blood vessels (Fig. 18–5). From the dermomyotome regions of the somites, myogenic precursor cells also migrate into the limb bud and later differentiate into **myoblasts**—precursors of muscle cells (see Hinrichsen et al, 1994, for more information). The cervical and lumbosacral myotomes contribute to the muscles of the pectoral and pelvic girdles.

Early in the seventh week the limbs extend ventrally. The developing upper and lower limbs rotate in

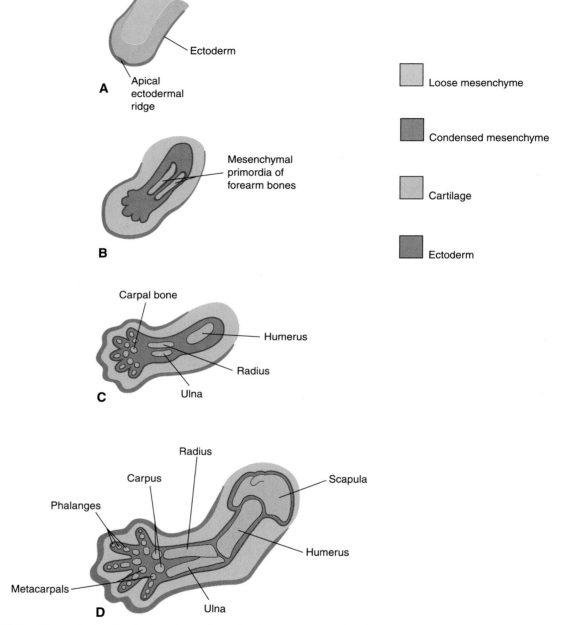

■ **Figure 18-5.** Schematic longitudinal sections of the developing upper limb of a human embryo, showing development of the cartilaginous bones.

opposite directions and to different degrees (Figs. 18-6 and 18-7A to D):

- *The upper limbs rotate laterally through 90 degrees* on their longitudinal axes; thus, the future elbows point dorsally and the extensor muscles lie on the lateral and posterior aspects of the limb.

- *The lower limbs rotate medially* through almost 90 degrees; thus, the future knees face ventrally and the extensor muscles lie on the anterior aspect of the lower limb.

It should now be clear that the radius and the tibia are homologous bones, as are the ulna and fibula, just

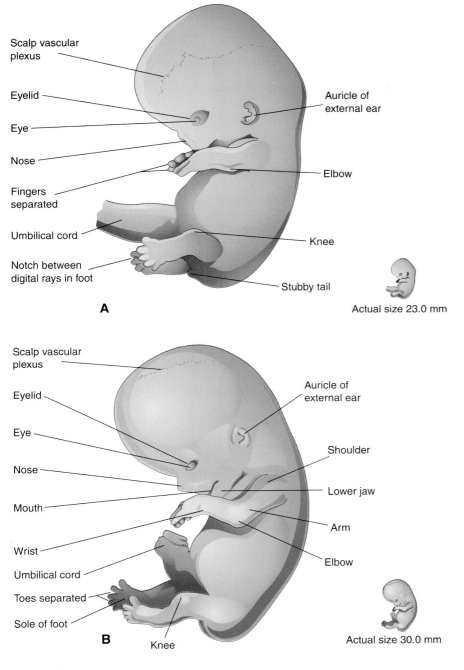

Scalp vascular plexus

Eyelid

Eye

Nose

Fingers separated

Umbilical cord

Notch between digital rays in foot

Auricle of external ear

Elbow

Knee

Stubby tail

A

Actual size 23.0 mm

Scalp vascular plexus

Eyelid

Eye

Nose

Mouth

Wrist

Umbilical cord

Toes separated

Sole of foot

Auricle of external ear

Shoulder

Lower jaw

Arm

Elbow

Knee

B

Actual size 30.0 mm

■ **Figure 18–6.** *A,* Lateral view of an embryo at Carnegie stage 21, about 52 days. The fingers are separated, and the toes are beginning to separate. Note that the feet are fan-shaped. *B,* Lateral view of an embryo at Carnegie stage 23, about 56 days. All regions of the limbs are apparent, and the digits in the hands and feet are separated. (Modified from Nishimura H, Semba R, Tanimura T, Tanaka O: *Prenatal Development of the Human with Special Reference to Craniofacial Structures: An Atlas.* Washington, DC, National Institute of Health, 1977.)

as the thumb and great toe are homologous digits. Originally the flexor aspect of the limbs is ventral and the extensor aspect dorsal, and the preaxial and postaxial borders are cranial and caudal, respectively (Fig. 18–7*A* and *D*). **Synovial joints** appear at the beginning of the fetal period, coinciding with functional differentiation of the limb muscles and their innervation.

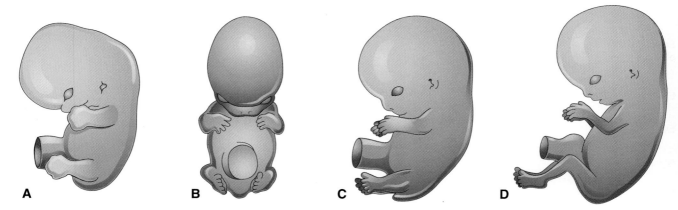

■ **Figure 18–7.** Drawings illustrating positional changes of the developing limbs of human embryos. *A*, About 48 days, showing the limbs extending ventrally and the hand and foot plates facing each other. *B*, About 51 days, showing the upper limbs bent at the elbows and the hands curved over the thorax. *C*, About 54 days, showing the soles of the feet facing medially. *D*, About 56 days. Note that the elbows now point caudally and the knees cranially.

DERMATOMES AND CUTANEOUS INNERVATION OF LIMBS

Because of its relationship to the growth and rotation of the limbs, the cutaneous segmental nerve supply of the limbs is considered in this chapter rather than in

Chapter 19 on the nervous system. See Lamb (1988) for details on the embryology of the peripheral nerves in relation to the innervation of the muscle fibers in the limbs. **Motor axons** arising from the spinal cord enter the limb buds during the fifth week and grow into the dorsal and ventral muscle masses. **Sensory**

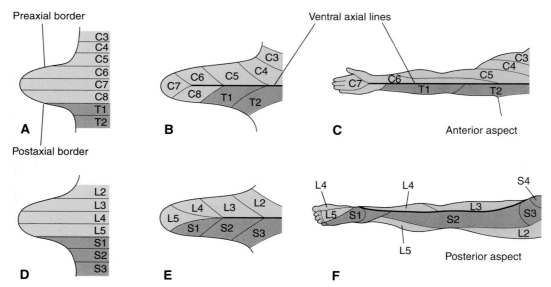

■ **Figure 18–8.** Diagrams illustrating development of the dermatomal patterns of the limbs. The axial lines indicate where no sensory overlap is present. *A* and *D*, Ventral aspect of the limb buds early in the fifth week. At this stage the dermatomal patterns show the primitive segmental arrangement. *B* and *E*, Similar views later in the fifth week, showing the modified arrangement of dermatomes. *C* and *F*, The dermatomal patterns in the adult upper and lower limbs. The primitive dermatomal pattern has disappeared, but an orderly sequence of dermatomes can still be recognized. In *F*, note that most of the original ventral surface of the lower limb lies on the back of the adult limb. This results from the medial rotation of the lower limb that occurs toward the end of the embryonic period. In the upper limb the ventral axial line extends along the anterior surface of the arm and forearm. In the lower limb, the ventral axial line extends along the medial side of the thigh and knee to the posteromedial aspect of the leg to the heel.

axons enter the limb buds after the motor axons and use them for guidance (Carlson, 1994). **Neural crest cells**, the precursors of Schwann cells, surround the motor and sensory nerve fibers in the limbs and form the *neurolemmal* (Schwann cell) and *myelin sheaths* (see Chapter 19).

A **dermatome** is the area of skin supplied by a single spinal nerve and its spinal ganglion. During the fifth week, the peripheral nerves grow from the developing limb plexuses (brachial and lumbosacral) into the mesenchyme of the limb buds (Fig. 18-8*A*, *B*, *D*, and *E*). The spinal nerves are distributed in segmental bands, supplying both dorsal and ventral surfaces of the limb buds. As the limbs elongate, the cutaneous distribution of the spinal nerves migrates along the limbs and no longer reaches the surface in the distal part of the limbs. Although the original dermatomal pattern changes during growth of the limbs, an orderly sequence of distribution can still be recognized in the adult (Fig. 18-8*C* and *F*). In the upper limb observe that the areas supplied by C5 and C6 adjoin the areas supplied by T2, T1, and C8, but the overlap between them is minimal at the *ventral axial line*.

A **cutaneous nerve area** is the area of skin supplied by a peripheral nerve. Cutaneous nerve areas and dermatomes show considerable overlapping. If the dorsal root supplying the area is cut, the dermatomal patterns indicate that there may be a slight deficit in the area indicated. Because there is overlapping of dermatomes, a particular area of skin is not exclusively innervated by a single segmental nerve. The limb dermatomes may be traced progressively down the lateral aspect of the upper limb and back up its medial aspect. A comparable distribution of dermatomes occurs in the lower limbs, which may be traced down the ventral aspect and then up the dorsal aspect of the lower limb. When the limbs descend they carry their nerves with them; this explains the oblique course of the nerves arising from the brachial and lumbosacral plexuses.

BLOOD SUPPLY TO THE LIMBS

The limb buds are supplied by branches of the *intersegmental arteries* (Fig. 18-9*A*), which arise from the aorta and form a fine capillary network throughout the mesenchyme. The primitive vascular pattern consists of a **primary axial artery** and its branches (Fig. 18-9*B*), which drain into a peripheral marginal sinus. Blood in the **marginal sinus** drains into a peripheral vein. The vascular pattern changes as the limbs develop, chiefly by vessels sprouting from existing vessels. The new vessels coalesce with other sprouts to form new vessels. The primary axial artery becomes

the **brachial artery** in the arm and the **common interosseous artery** in the forearm, which has anterior and posterior interosseous branches. The ulnar and radial arteries are terminal branches of the brachial artery. As the digits form, the marginal sinus breaks up and the final venous pattern, represented by the basilic and cephalic veins and their tributaries, develops. In the thigh the primary axial artery is represented by the **deep artery of the thigh** (profunda femoris artery). In the leg the primary axial artery is represented by the anterior and posterior tibial arteries (Moore, 1992).

ANOMALIES OF LIMBS

Minor limb anomalies are relatively common, but they can usually be corrected surgically. Although minor anomalies are usually of no serious medical consequence, they may serve as indicators of more serious anomalies and they may be part of a recognizable pattern of defects (Jones, 1997).

The most critical period of limb development is from 24 to 36 days after fertilization. This statement is based on clinical studies of infants exposed to thalidomide, a potent human teratogen that produced limb defects and other anomalies (Newman, 1986). Exposure to a potent teratogen before day 33 may cause severe anomalies, such as absence of the limbs and hands (Figs. 18-10*A* and 18-11*C*). Exposure to a teratogen from days 34 to 36 produces absence or hypoplasia of the thumbs (Fig. 18-12*B*). Consequently, a teratogen that could cause absence of the limbs or parts of them must act before the end of the critical period of limb development. Many severe limb anomalies occurred from 1957 to 1962 as a result of maternal ingestion of **thalidomide**. This drug, widely used as a sedative and antinauseant, was withdrawn from the market in December 1961. Since that time similar limb anomalies have rarely been observed. Because thalidomide is still available as an investigational agent, it must be emphasized that *thalidomide is absolutely contraindicated in women of childbearing age* (Behrman et al, 1996).

Major limb anomalies appear about twice in 1000 newborns (Connor and Ferguson-Smith, 1988). Most of these defects are caused by genetic factors.

Limb Defects

The terminology used to describe limb deficiencies in this book follows the international nomenclature, in which only two basic descriptive terms are used:

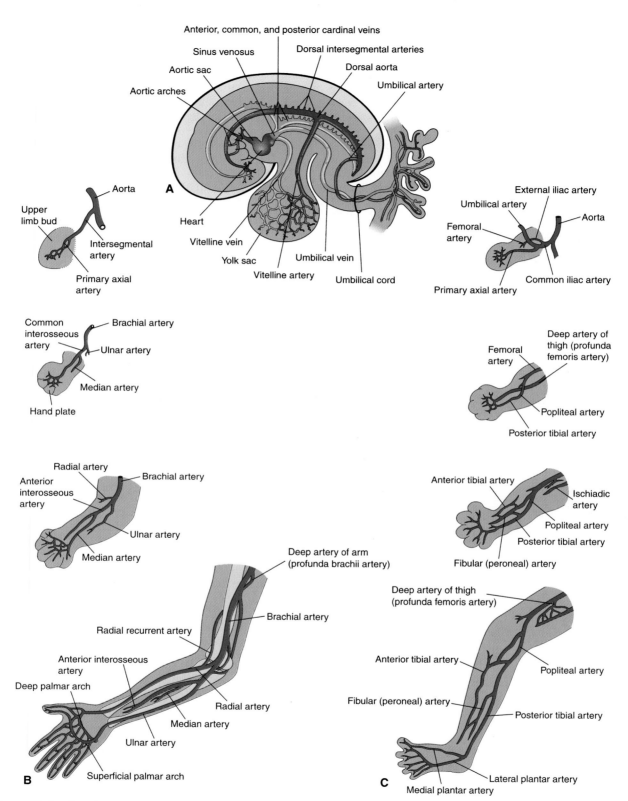

■ **Figure 18–9.** Development of limb arteries. *A*, Sketch of the primitive cardiovascular system in a 4-week embryo, about 26 days. *B*, Development of arteries in the upper limb. *C*, Development of arteries in the lower limb.

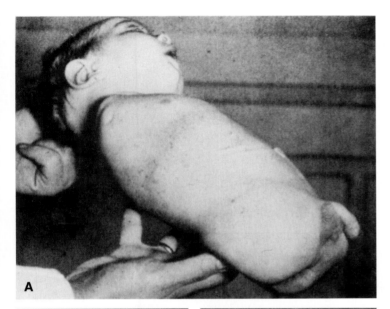

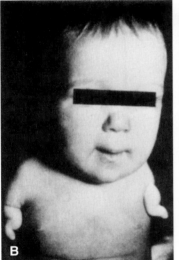

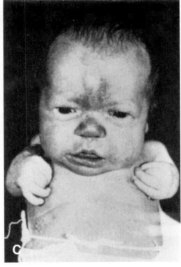

■ **Figure 18–10.** Limb anomalies caused by thalidomide. *A*, Quadruple amelia: absence of the upper and lower limbs. *B*, Meromelia of the upper limbs: the limbs are represented by rudimentary stumps. *C*, Meromelia with the rudimentary upper limbs attached directly to the trunk. (From Lenz W, Knapp K: Foetal malformations due to thalidomide. *Ger Med Mon* 7: 253, 1962).

- *Amelia*, complete absence of a limb or limbs
- *Meromelia* (Gr. *meros*, part, and *melos*, extremity), partial absence of a limb or limbs

Descriptive terms such as *hemimelia, peromelia, ectromelia,* and *phocomelia* are not used in current nomenclature because of their imprecision.

Cleft Hand and Cleft Foot

In these rare lobster-claw deformities, one or more central digits are absent, resulting from failure of development of one or more digital rays (Fig. 18–11*E* and *F*). The hand or foot is divided into two parts that oppose each other like lobster claws. The remaining digits are partially or completely fused (syndactyly).

Congenital Absence of Radius

The radius is partially or completely absent. The hand deviates laterally (radially), and the ulna bows with the concavity on the lateral side of the forearm. This anomaly results from failure of the mesenchymal primordium of the radius to form during the fifth week of development. Absence of the radius is usually caused by genetic factors.

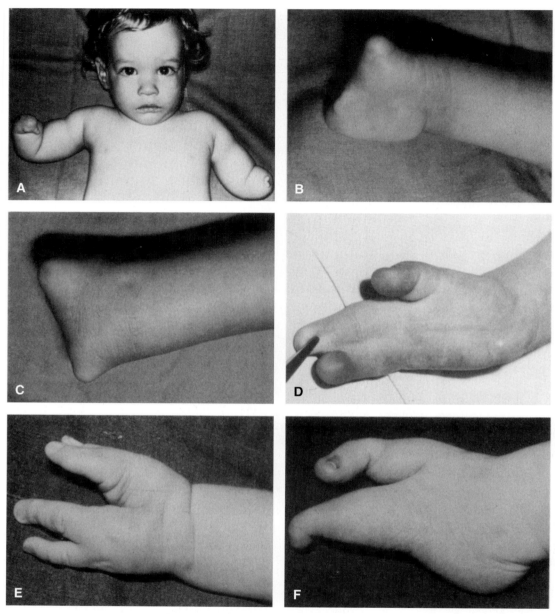

■ **Figure 18–11.** Various types of meromelia (partial absence of limbs). *A*, Absence of the hands and most of the forearms. *B*, Absence of the digits. *C*, Absence of the hand. *D*, Absence of the fourth and fifth digits and syndactyly of the second and third digits. *E*, Absence of the third digit, resulting in a cleft hand. *F*, Absence of the second and third toes and syndactyly of the fourth and fifth toes, resulting in a cleft foot. (*D* from Swenson O: *Pediatric Surgery.* New York, Appleton-Century-Crofts, 1958.)

Brachydactyly

Shortness of the digits (fingers or toes) is uncommon and is the result of reduction in the length of the phalanges (Fig. 18–12*A*). This anomaly is usually inherited as a dominant trait and is often associated with shortness of stature.

Polydactyly

Supernumerary digits are common (Figs. 18–12*C* and *D* and 18–14). Often the extra digit is incompletely formed and lacks proper muscular development; it is thus useless. If the hand is affected, the extra digit is most commonly medial or lateral rather than central.

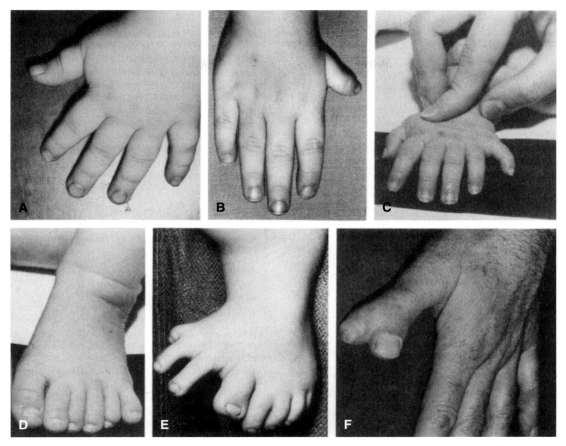

■ **Figure 18–12.** Various types of limb anomaly. *A*, Brachydactyly. *B*, Hypoplasia of the thumb. *C*, Polydactyly showing a supernumerary fifth finger. *D*, Polydactyly showing a supernumerary fifth toe. *E*, Partial duplication of the foot. *F*, Partial duplication of the thumb. (*C* and *D* from Swenson O: *Pediatric Surgery.* New York, Appleton-Century-Crofts, 1958.)

In the foot the extra toe is usually on the lateral side. Polydactyly is inherited as a dominant trait.

Syndactyly

Syndactyly occurs in 1 in 2200 births (Behrman et al, 1996). Cutaneous syndactyly (simple webbing of digits) is the most common limb anomaly (Fig. 18–15*A* and *D*). It is more frequent in the foot than in the hand (Fig. 18–13). **Cutaneous syndactyly** results from failure of the webs to degenerate between two or more digits. In severe cases there is fusion of several digits (Fig. 18–15*B*, *E*, and *F*). In some cases there is fusion of the bones (synostosis). **Osseous syndactyly** occurs when the notches between the digital rays fail to develop during the seventh week; as a result, separation of the digits does not occur. Syndactyly is most frequently observed between the third and fourth fingers (Fig. 18–11*D*) and between the second and third toes (Fig. 18–13). It is inherited as a simple dominant or simple recessive trait (Thompson et al, 1991).

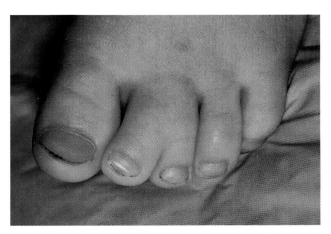

■ **Figure 18–13.** Syndactyly of the second and third toes. (Courtesy of Dr. A. E. Chudley, Section of Genetics and Metabolism, Department of Pediatrics and Child Health, Children's Hospital and University of Manitoba, Winnipeg, Manitoba, Canada.)

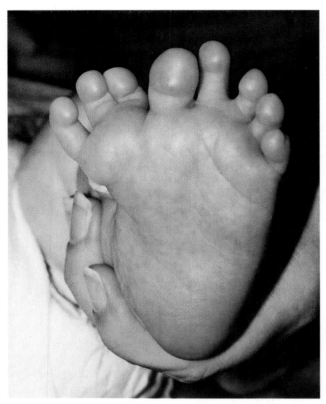

■ **Figure 18–14.** Polydactyly showing partial duplication of the right foot and toes. (Courtesy of Dr. A. E. Chudley, Section of Genetics and Metabolism, Department of Pediatrics and Child Health, Children's Hospital and University of Manitoba, Winnipeg, Manitoba, Canada.)

Congenital Clubfoot

Any deformity of the foot involving the talus (ankle bone) is called clubfoot or talipes (L. *talus*, heel, ankle and *pes*, foot). Clubfoot is a common anomaly, occurring about once in 1000 births. It is characterized by an abnormal position of the foot that prevents normal weight-bearing. As the child develops, he or she tends to walk on the ankle rather than on the sole of the foot. **Talipes equinovarus,** the most common type of clubfoot (Fig. 18–15*C*), occurs about twice as frequently in males. The sole of the foot is turned medially and the foot is inverted. There is much uncertainty about the cause of clubfoot (Robertson and Corbett, 1997). Although it is commonly stated that clubfoot results from abnormal positioning or restricted movement of the fetus's lower limbs in utero, the evidence for this is inconclusive. When the abnormal position of the foot results from the position of the fetus in utero, the foot can easily be positioned

normally (Nichols and Zwelling, 1997). Hereditary factors are involved in some cases, and it appears that environmental factors are involved in most cases. Clubfoot appears to follow a **multifactorial pattern of inheritance**; hence, any intrauterine position that results in abnormal positioning of the feet may cause clubfeet if the fetus is genetically predisposed to this deformity.

Congenital Dislocation of the Hip

This deformity occurs in about 1 of every 1500 newborn infants and is more common in females than in males. The capsule of the hip joint is very relaxed at birth, and the acetabulum of the hip bone and the head of the femur are underdeveloped. The actual dislocation almost always occurs after birth. Two causative factors are commonly given:

- **Abnormal development of the acetabulum** occurs in about 15% of infants with congenital dislocation of the hip, which is common after breech deliveries, suggesting that breech posture during the terminal months of pregnancy may result in abnormal development of the acetabulum and head of the femur.
- **Generalized joint laxity** is often a dominantly inherited condition, which appears to be associated with congenital dislocation of the hip. Congenital dislocation of the hip follows a multifactorial pattern of inheritance (Thompson et al, 1991).

Causes of Limb Anomalies

Anomalies of the limbs originate at different stages of development. Suppression of limb bud development during the early part of the fourth week results in *absence of the limbs*—**amelia** (Fig. 18–10*A*). Arrest or disturbance of differentiation or growth of the limbs during the fifth week results in various types of **meromelia** (Figs. 18–10*B* and *C* and 18–11*A* to *C*). *Meromelia denotes partial absence of a limb.*

Like other congenital anomalies, some limb defects are caused by the following:

- Genetic factors, such as chromosomal abnormalities associated with trisomy 18 (see Chapter 9)
- Mutant genes as in brachydactyly or osteogenesis imperfecta (Marini and Gerber, 1997)
- Environmental factors, such as teratogens like thalidomide
- A combination of genetic and environmental factors (*multifactorial inheritance*), such as congenital dislocation of the hip (Thompson et al, 1991)
- Vascular disruption and ischemia, such as limb reduction defects (Van Allen, 1992)

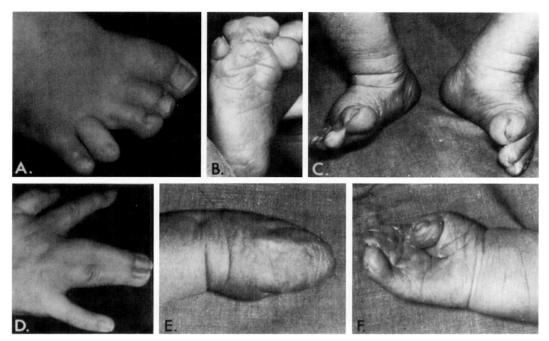

■ **Figure 18–15.** Various types of limb anomaly. *A*, Cutaneous syndactyly showing skin webs between the first and second and second and third toes. *B*, Severe cutaneous syndactyly involving fusion of all the toes except the fifth. *C*, Cutaneous syndactyly associated with clubfoot (talipes equinovarus). *D*, Cutaneous syndactyly involving webbing of the third and fourth fingers. *E* and *F*, Dorsal and palmar views of a child's right hand, showing osseous syndactyly (fusion) of the second to fifth fingers. (*A* and *D* from Swenson O: *Pediatric Surgery.* New York, Appleton-Century-Crofts, 1958.)

A reduced quantity of amniotic fluid (**oligohydramnios**) is commonly associated with limb deformations; however, the significance of in utero mechanical influences on congenital postural deformation is still open to question. For more information on congenital limb defects, see Hoffinger (1996) and Van Heest (1996).

SUMMARY OF LIMB DEVELOPMENT

The limbs begin to appear toward the end of the fourth week as slight elevations of the ventrolateral body wall. The upper limb buds develop about 2 days before the lower limb buds. The tissues of the limb buds are derived from two main sources: mesoderm and ectoderm. The *apical ectodermal ridge* (AER) exerts an inductive influence on the limb mesenchyme, promoting growth and development of the limbs. The limb buds elongate by proliferation of the mesenchyme within them. *Programmed cell death* is an important mechanism in limb development, such as in the formation of the digits. Limb muscles are derived from mesenchyme (myogenic precursor cells) originating in the somites. The muscle-forming cells (myoblasts) form dorsal and ventral muscle masses. Nerves grow into the limb buds after the muscle masses have formed. Most blood vessels of the limb buds arise as buds from the aorta and cardinal veins.

Initially, the developing limbs are directed caudally; later, they project ventrally; and finally, they rotate on their longitudinal axes. The upper and lower limbs rotate in opposite directions and to different degrees. The majority of limb anomalies are caused by genetic factors; however, many limb abnormalities probably result from an interaction of genetic and environmental factors (multifactorial inheritance). Relatively few congenital anomalies of the limbs can be attributed to specific environmental teratogens, except those resulting from thalidomide.

Clinically Oriented Questions

1. An acquaintance of ours had a baby with very short limbs. His trunk is normally proportioned, but his

head is slightly larger than normal. Both parents have normal limbs, and these problems have never occurred in either of their families. Could her ingestion of drugs during pregnancy have caused these abnormalities? If not, what is the probable cause of these skeletal disorders? Could they occur again if they have more children?

2. My sister is interested in marrying a man with very short fingers (*brachydactyly*). He says that two of his relatives have exhibited short fingers, but none of his brothers or sisters has them. My sister has normal digits and so has everyone else in our family. She asked me what the chances are that her children would have brachydactyly if she were to marry him. I know that heredity is involved, but I could not give her a helpful answer. Can you?

3. About a year ago I read in the paper about a woman who had a child with no right hand. She started to take a drug called *Bendectin* to alleviate nausea during the 10th week of her pregnancy (8 weeks after fertilization) and is instituting legal proceedings against the drug company that makes the drug. Does this drug cause limb defects; and, if it does, could it have caused failure of the child's hand to develop?

4. When I was a nurse I saw a baby with *syndactyly* (fused digits) of the left hand and absence of the left sternal head of the pectoralis major muscle. The baby seemed normal except that the nipple on the left side was about 2 inches lower than the other one. What is the cause of these anomalies? Can they be corrected?

5. What is the most common type of clubfoot? How common is it? Describe the feet of infants born with this anomaly.

6. Is syndactyly common? Does it occur more often in the hands than in the feet? What is the embryological basis of syndactyly?

The answers to these questions are given at the back of the book.

REFERENCES AND SUGGESTED READING

Behrman RE, Kliegman RM, Arvin AM (eds): *Nelson Textbook of Pediatrics*, 15th ed. Philadelphia, WB Saunders, 1996.

Carlson BM: *Human Embryology and Developmental Biology*. St. Louis, CV Mosby, 1994.

Centrella M, Horowitz MC, Wozney JM, McCarthy TL: Transforming growth factor-beta gene family members and bone. *Endocrin Rev.* 15:27, 1994.

Cohn MJ, Patel K, Krumlauf R, et al: *HOX* 9 genes and vertebrate limb specification. *Nature* 387:97, 1997.

Connor JM, Ferguson-Smith MA: *Essential Medical Genetics,* 2nd ed. Oxford, Blackwell Scientific Publications, 1988.

Hinrichsen KV, Jacob HJ, Jacob M, et al: Principles of ontogenesis of leg and foot in man. *Ann Anat* 176:121, 1994.

Hoffinger SA: Evaluation and management of pediatric foot deformities. *Pediatr Clin North Am* 43:1091, 1996.

Jones KL: *Smith's Recognizable Patterns of Human Malformation*, 5th ed. Philadelphia, WB Saunders, 1997.

Lamb AH: Aspects of peripheral motor systm development. *Aust Paediatr J* 24 (Suppl 1):37, 1988.

Mahony BS: Ultrasound evaluation of the fetal musculoskeletal system. *In* Callen PW (ed): *Ultrasonography in Obstetrics and Gynecology*, 3rd ed. Philadelphia, WB Saunders, 1994.

Marini JC, Gerber NL: Osteogenesis imperfecta. *JAMA* 277:746, 1997.

Moore KL: *Clinically Oriented Anatomy*, 3rd ed. Baltimore, Williams & Wilkins, 1992.

Muragaki Y, Mundlos S, Upton J, Olsen BR: Altered growth and branching patterns in synpolydactyly caused by mutations in HOXD13. *Science* 272:548, 1996.

Newman CGH: Clinical aspects of thalidomide embryopathy—a continuing preoccupation. *Teratogen Update. Environmentally Induced Birth Risks.* New York, Alan R. Liss, 1986.

Nichols FH, Zwelling E (eds): *Maternal-Newborn Nursing: Theory and Practice*. Philadelphia, WB Saunders, 1997.

Robertson WW Jr, Corbett D: Congenital clubfoot. *Clin Orthop Rel Res* 338:14–18, 1997.

Russell RGG: Cytokines and growth factors involved in bone metabolism and disease. *Bull Royal College of Pathologists* No. 95, ii, 1996.

Thompson MW, McInnes RR, Willard HF: *Thompson and Thompson Genetics in Medicine*, 5th ed. Philadelphia, WB Saunders, 1991.

Van Allen MI: Structural anomalies resulting from vascular disruption. *Pediatr Clin North Am* 39:255, 1992.

Van Heest AE: Congenital disorders of the hand and upper extremity. *Pediatr Clin North Am* 43:1113, 1996.

Zou H, Niswander L: Requirement for BMP signaling in interdigital apoptosis and scale formation. *Science* 272:738, 1996.

The Nervous System

19

■ The nervous system consists of three parts:

- *Central nervous system* (CNS), which includes the brain and spinal cord
- *Peripheral nervous system* (PNS), which includes neurons (nerve cells) outside the CNS and cranial and spinal nerves that connect the brain and spinal cord with peripheral structures
- *Autonomic nervous system* (ANS), which has parts in both the CNS and PNS and consists of neurons that innervate smooth muscle, cardiac muscle, or glandular epithelium or combinations of these tissues (Haines, 1997).

ORIGIN OF THE NERVOUS SYSTEM

The nervous system develops from the **neural plate** (Fig. 19–1*A*), a thickened, slipper-shaped area of embryonic ectoderm. It is the notochord and paraxial mesoderm that induce the overlying ectoderm to differentiate into the neural plate. Signaling molecules appear to involve members of the *transforming growth factor-β* (TGF-β) family, which includes activin and *fibroblast growth factors* (FGFs). Formation of the neural folds, neural tube, and neural crest from the neural plate is illustrated in Figure 19–1*B* to *F*.

- The **neural tube** differentiates into the CNS, consisting of the brain and spinal cord.
- The **neural crest** gives rise to cells that form most of the PNS and ANS, consisting of cranial, spinal, and autonomic ganglia.

Formation of the neural tube—**neurulation**—begins during the early part of the fourth week (22 to 23 days) in the region of the fourth to sixth pairs of somites. At this stage, the cranial two thirds of the neural plate and tube, as far caudal as the fourth pair of somites, represent the future brain, and the caudal one third of the neural plate and tube represents the future spinal cord. Fusion of the neural folds proceeds in cranial and caudal directions until only small areas remain open at both ends (Fig. 19–2*A* and *B*). Here the lumen of the neural tube—**neural canal**—communicates freely with the amniotic cavity. The cranial opening, the *rostral or anterior neuropore*, closes on about the 25th day, and the *caudal or posterior neuropore* 2 days later (Fig. 19–2*C* and *D*). Recently, it has been suggested that multisite initiation of neural tube closure occurs in humans (see Martinez-Frias et al, 1996). Closure of the **neuropores** coincides with the establishment of a blood vascular circulation for the neural tube. The walls of the neural tube thicken to form the brain and the spinal cord (Fig. 19–3). The neural canal of the neural tube is converted into the *ventricular system* of the brain and the *central canal* of the spinal cord.

DEVELOPMENT OF THE SPINAL CORD

The neural tube caudal to the fourth pair of somites develops into the spinal cord (Figs. 19–3 and 19–4). The lateral walls of the neural tube thicken, gradually reducing the size of the neural canal until only a minute **central canal** of the spinal cord is present at 9 to 10 weeks (Fig. 19–4*A* to *C*). Initially the wall of the neural tube is composed of a thick, pseudostratified, columnar neuroepithelium (Fig. 19–4*D*). These neuroepithelial cells constitute the **ventricular zone** (ependymal layer), which gives rise to all neurons and macroglial cells (macroglia) in the spinal cord (Fig. 19–5). Macroglial cells are the larger types of neuroglial cell (e.g., astrocytes and oligodendrocytes). Soon a **marginal zone** composed of the outer parts of the neuroepithelial cells becomes recognizable (Fig. 19–4*E*). This zone gradually becomes the *white matter of the spinal cord* as axons grow into it from nerve cell bodies in the spinal cord, spinal ganglia, and brain. Some dividing neuroepithelial cells in the ventricular zone differentiate into primordial neurons—**neuroblasts.** These embryonic cells form an **intermediate zone** (mantle layer) between the ventricular and marginal zones. Neuroblasts become neurons as they develop cytoplasmic processes (Fig. 19–5).

The primordial supporting cells of the CNS—**glioblasts** (spongioblasts)—differentiate from neuroepithelial cells, mainly after neuroblast formation has ceased. The glioblasts migrate from the ventricular zone into the intermediate and marginal zones. Some glioblasts become **astroblasts** and later *astrocytes,* whereas others become **oligodendroblasts** and eventually *oligodendrocytes* (Fig. 19–5). When the neuroepithelial cells cease producing neuroblasts and glioblasts, they differentiate into *ependymal cells,* which form the **ependyma** (ependymal epithelium) lining the central canal of the spinal cord.

Microglial cells (microglia), which are scattered throughout the gray and white matter, are small cells that are derived from *mesenchymal cells* (Fig. 19–5). Microglial cells invade the CNS rather late in the fetal period after it has been penetrated by blood vessels. Microglia develop from blood cells of the monocyte-macrophage lineage, which enter the CNS with the blood vessels (Hutchins et al, 1997).

Proliferation and differentiation of neuroepithelial cells in the developing spinal cord produce thick walls and thin roof and floor plates (Fig. 19–4*B*). Differen-

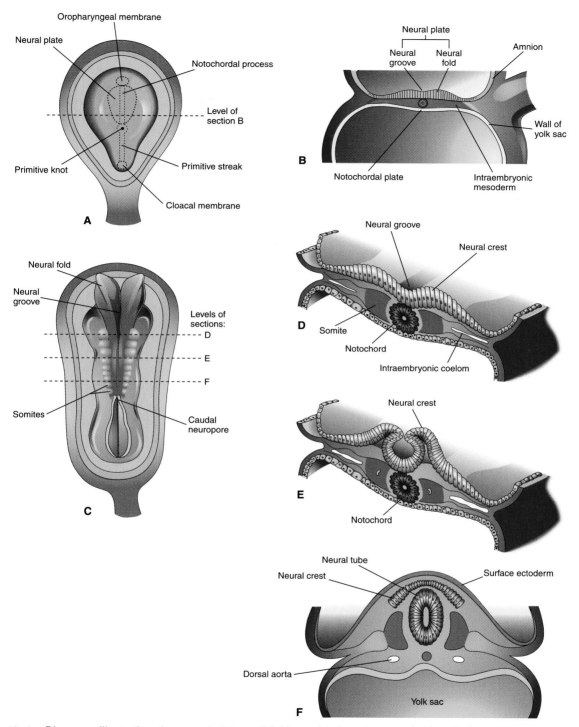

■ **Figure 19–1.** Diagrams illustrating the neural plate and folding of it into the neural tube. *A,* Dorsal view of an embryo of about 18 days, exposed by removing the amnion. *B,* Transverse section of the embryo showing the neural plate and early development of the neural groove. The developing notochord is also shown. *C,* Dorsal view of an embryo of about 22 days. The neural folds have fused opposite the fourth to sixth somites but are widely spread apart at both ends. *D* to *F,* Transverse sections of this embryo at the levels shown in *C,* illustrating formation of the neural tube and its detachment from the surface ectoderm. Note that some neuroectodermal cells are not included in the neural tube but remain between it and the surface ectoderm as the neural crest.

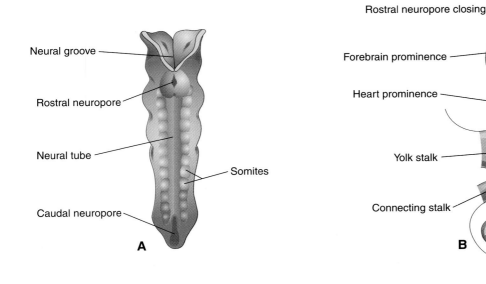

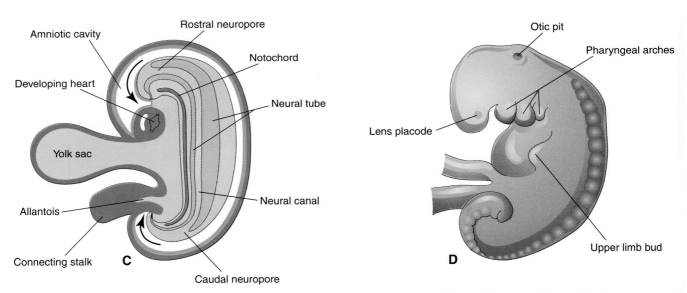

■ **Figure 19–2.** *A,* Dorsal view of an embryo of about 23 days showing advanced fusion of the neural folds, forming the neural tube. *B,* Lateral view of an embryo of about 24 days showing the forebrain prominence and closing of the rostral neuropore. *C,* Diagrammatic sagittal section of this embryo showing the transitory communication of the neural canal with the amniotic cavity *(arrows). D,* Lateral view of an embryo of about 27 days. Note that the neuropores shown in *B* are closed.

tial thickening of the lateral walls of the spinal cord soon produces a shallow longitudinal groove on each side — the **sulcus limitans** (Figs. 19–4*B* and 19–6). This groove separates the dorsal part, the **alar plate** (lamina), from the ventral part, the **basal plate** (lamina). The alar and basal plates produce longitudinal bulges extending through most of the length of the developing spinal cord. This regional separation is of

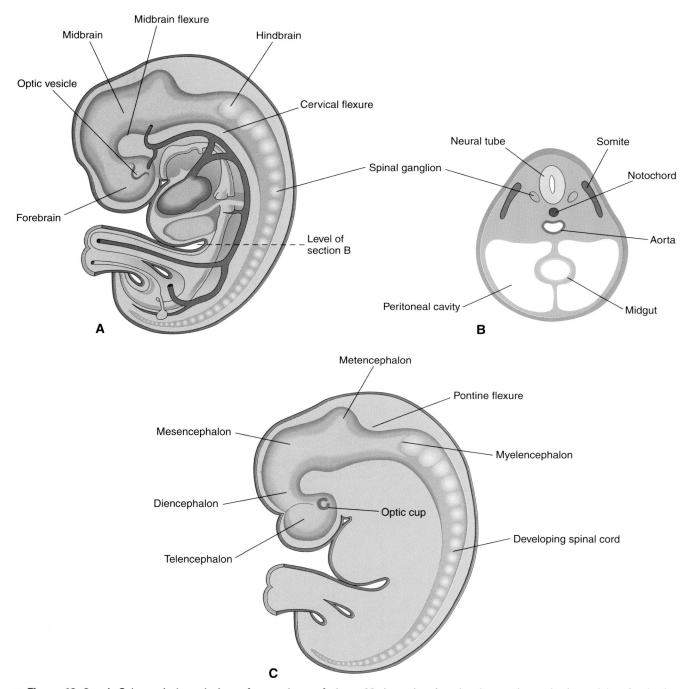

■ **Figure 19–3.** *A,* Schematic lateral view of an embryo of about 28 days showing the three primary brain vesicles: forebrain, midbrain, and hindbrain. Two flexures demarcate the primary divisions of the brain. *B,* Transverse section of this embryo showing the neural tube that will develop into the spinal cord in this region. The spinal (dorsal root) ganglia derived from the neural crest are also shown. *C,* Schematic lateral view of the central nervous system of a 6-week embryo showing the secondary brain vesicles and pontine flexure. The flexure (bend) occurs as the brain grows rapidly.

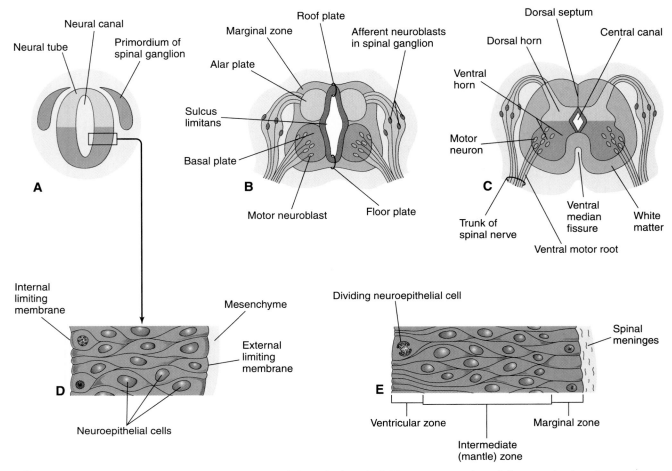

■ **Figure 19–4.** Diagrams illustrating development of the spinal cord. *A*, Transverse section of the neural tube of an embryo of about 23 days. *B* and *C*, Similar sections at 6 and 9 weeks, respectively. *D*, Section of the wall of the neural tube shown in A. *E*, Section of the wall of the developing spinal cord showing its three zones. In *A* to *C*, note that the neural canal of the neural tube is converted into the central canal of the spinal cord.

fundamental importance because the alar and basal plates are later associated with afferent and efferent functions, respectively.

Cell bodies in the alar plates form the dorsal gray columns that extend the length of the spinal cord. In transverse sections of the cord, these columns are the **dorsal (gray) horns** (Fig. 19-7). Neurons in these columns constitute afferent nuclei, and groups of these nuclei form the **dorsal gray columns.** As the alar plates enlarge, the *dorsal septum* or raphe forms (Parkinson and Del Bigio, 1996). Cell bodies in the basal plates form the ventral and lateral gray columns. In transverse sections of the spinal cord, these columns are the **ventral (gray) horns** and **lateral**

(gray) horns, respectively. Axons of ventral horn cells grow out of the spinal cord and form the **ventral roots of the spinal nerves** (Fig. 19-7). As the basal plates enlarge, they bulge ventrally on each side of the median plane. As this occurs, the *ventral median septum* forms, and a deep longitudinal groove — the **ventral median fissure** — develops on the ventral surface of the spinal cord.

Development of Spinal Ganglia

The unipolar neurons in the spinal ganglia (dorsal root ganglia) are derived from **neural crest cells** (Figs. 19-8 and 19-9). The axons of cells in the spinal

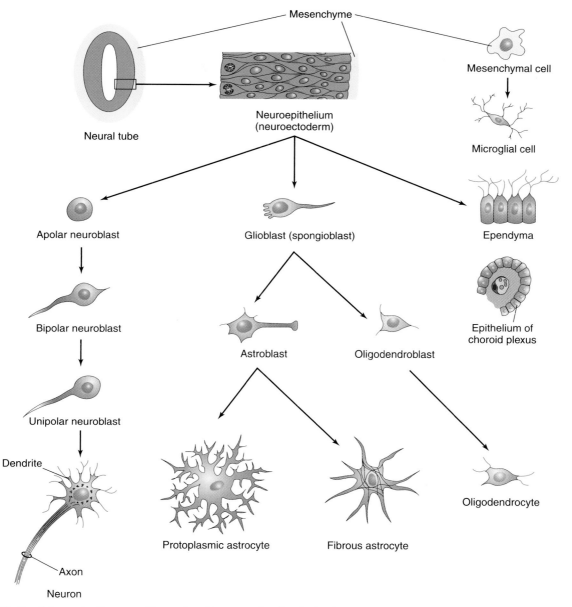

■ **Figure 19-5.** Schematic diagrams illustrating histogenesis of cells in the central nervous system. After further development the multipolar neuroblast *(lower left)* becomes a nerve cell or neuron. Neuroepithelial cells give rise to all neurons and macroglial cells. Microglial cells are derived from mesenchymal cells that invade the developing nervous system with the blood vessels.

ganglia are at first bipolar, but the two processes soon unite in a T-shaped fashion. Both processes of spinal ganglion cells have the structural characteristics of axons, but the peripheral process is a dendrite in that conduction is toward the cell body. The peripheral processes of spinal ganglion cells pass in the spinal nerves to sensory endings in somatic or visceral structures (Fig. 19-8). The central processes enter the spinal cord and constitute the *dorsal roots of the spinal nerves.*

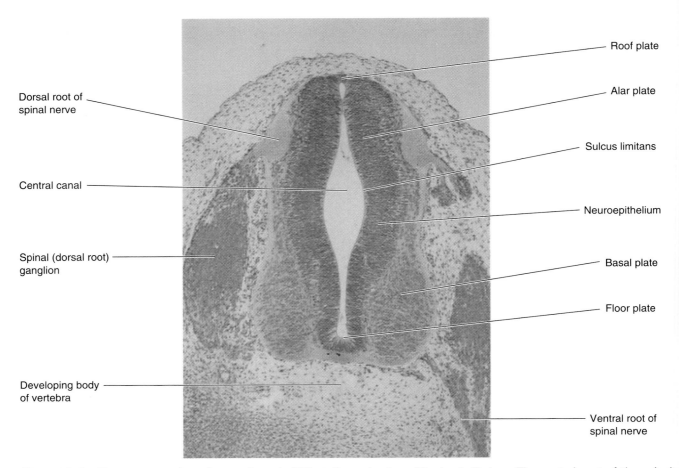

Dorsal root of
spinal nerve

Central canal

Spinal (dorsal root)
ganglion

Developing body
of vertebra

Roof plate

Alar plate

Sulcus limitans

Neuroepithelium

Basal plate

Floor plate

Ventral root of
spinal nerve

■ **Figure 19–6.** Transverse section of an embryo (×100) at Carnegie stage 16, about 40 days. The ventral root of the spinal nerve is composed of nerve fibers arising from neuroblasts in the basal plate (developing ventral horn of spinal cord), whereas the dorsal root is formed by nerve processes arising from neuroblasts in the spinal (dorsal root) ganglion.

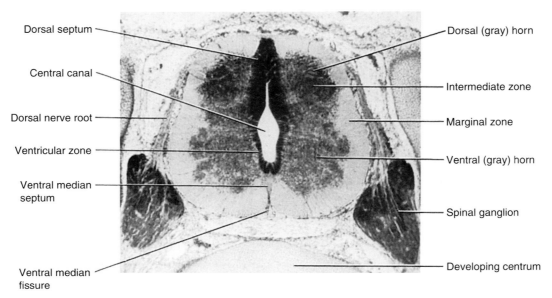

Dorsal septum

Central canal

Dorsal nerve root

Ventricular zone

Ventral median
septum

Ventral median
fissure

Dorsal (gray) horn

Intermediate zone

Marginal zone

Ventral (gray) horn

Spinal ganglion

Developing centrum

■ **Figure 19–7.** Photomicrograph of a transverse section of the developing spinal cord in a 20-mm human embryo of about 50 days (×60). (Courtesy of Professor Jean Hay [retired], Department of Anatomy, University of Manitoba, Winnipeg, Manitoba, Canada.)

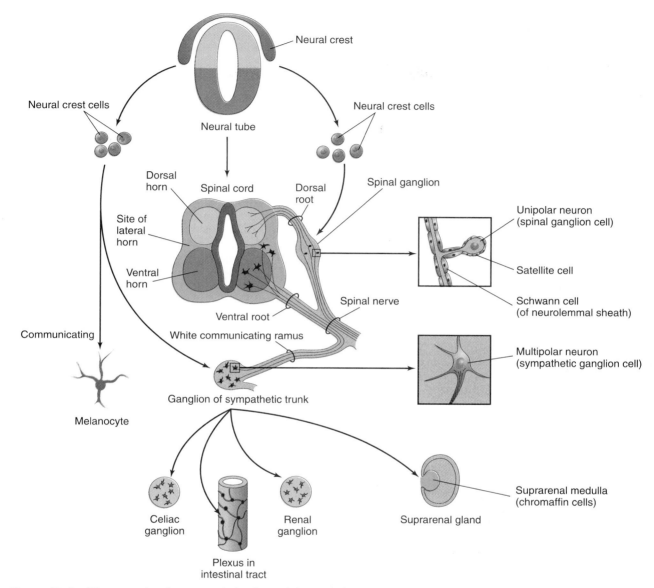

■ Figure 19–8. Diagrams showing some derivatives of the neural crest. Neural crest cells also differentiate into the cells in the afferent ganglia of cranial nerves and many other structures (see Chapter 6). The formation of a spinal nerve is also illustrated.

Development of Spinal Meninges

The mesenchyme surrounding the neural tube condenses to form a membrane called the *primordial meninx* (membrane). The external layer of this membrane, which is of mesodermal origin, thickens to form the **dura mater** (Fig. 19–10). The internal layer remains thin and forms the *pia-arachnoid,* composed of **pia mater** and **arachnoid mater;** together these layers constitute the leptomeninges. *Neural crest cells* mingle with the mesenchyme, forming the **leptomeninges,** and appear to be involved in the function of the pia mater. Fluid-filled spaces appear within the leptomeninges that soon coalesce to form the **subarachnoid space.** The origin of the pia mater and arachnoid from a single layer is indicated in the adult by the numerous delicate strands of connective tissue *(arachnoid trabeculae)* that pass between the pia and arachnoid (Moore, 1992). Embryonic **cerebrospinal fluid** (CSF), which may provide a nutrient medium for

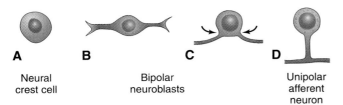

A Neural crest cell

B Bipolar neuroblasts

C

D Unipolar afferent neuron

■ **Figure 19–9.** Diagrams illustrating successive stages in the differentiation of a neural crest cell into a unipolar afferent neuron in a spinal ganglion.

the epithelial neural tissues, begins to form during the fifth week.

Positional Changes of Spinal Cord

The spinal cord in the embryo extends the entire length of the vertebral canal (Fig. 19–10A). The spinal nerves pass through the intervertebral foramina near their levels of origin. Because the vertebral column and dura mater grow more rapidly than the spinal cord, this relationship does not persist. The caudal end of the spinal cord gradually comes to lie at relatively higher levels. At 6 months it lies at the level of the first sacral vertebra (Fig. 19–10B). The spinal cord in the newborn terminates at the level of the second or third lumbar vertebra (Fig. 19–10C). The spinal cord in the adult usually terminates at the inferior border of the first lumbar vertebra (Fig. 19–10D). This is an average level because the caudal end of the spinal cord may be as superior as the 12th thoracic vertebra or as inferior as the third lumbar vertebra (Moore, 1992). As a result, the spinal nerve roots, especially those of the lumbar and sacral segments, run obliquely from the spinal cord to the corresponding level of the vertebral column. The nerve roots inferior to the end of the cord — the **conus medullaris** — form a sheaf of nerve roots, the **cauda equina** (L. horse's tail). Although the dura mater and arachnoid mater usually end at S2 vertebra in adults, the pia mater does not.

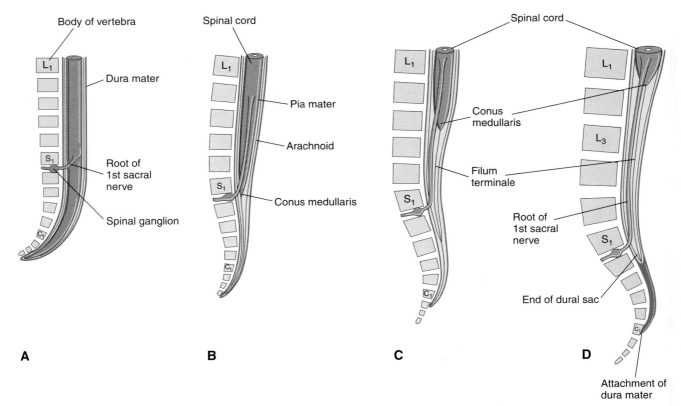

■ **Figure 19–10.** Diagrams showing the position of the caudal end of the spinal cord in relation to the vertebral column and meninges at various stages of development. The increasing inclination of the root of the first sacral nerve is also illustrated. *A*, Eight weeks. *B*, Twenty-four weeks. *C*, Newborn. *D*, Adult.

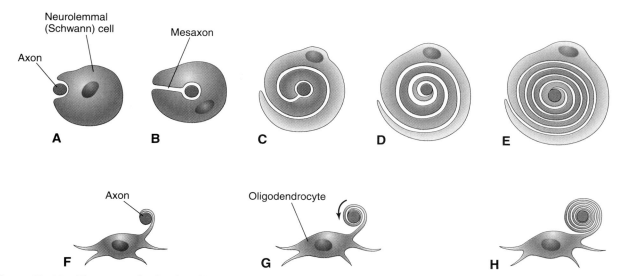

■ **Figure 19–11.** Diagrammatic sketches illustrating myelination of nerve fibers. *A* to *E,* Successive stages in the myelination of an axon of a peripheral nerve fiber by a neurolemmal or Schwann cell. The axon first indents the cell; the Schwann cell then rotates around the axon as the mesaxon (site of invagination) elongates. The cytoplasm between the layers of cell membrane gradually condenses. Cytoplasm remains on the inside of the sheath between the myelin and axon. *F* to *H,* Successive stages in the myelination of a nerve fiber in the central nervous system by an oligodendrocyte. A process of the neuroglial cell wraps itself around an axon, and the intervening layers of cytoplasm move to the body of the cell.

Distal to the caudal end of the spinal cord, the pia mater forms a long fibrous thread, the **filum terminale** (Fig. 19–10*C* and *D*), which also indicates the line of regression of the caudal end of the embryonic spinal cord. This thread extends from the conus medullaris and attaches to the periosteum of the first coccygeal vertebra.

Myelination of Nerve Fibers

Myelin sheaths in the spinal cord begin to form during the late fetal period and continue to form during the first postnatal year. In general, fiber tracts become myelinated at about the time they become functional. The **myelin sheaths** surrounding nerve fibers within the spinal cord are formed by **oligodendrocytes.** The plasma membranes of these cells wrap around the axon, forming a number of layers (Fig. 19–11*F* to *H*). The myelin sheaths around the axons of peripheral nerve fibers are formed by the plasma membranes of **neurolemmal (Schwann) cells,** which are analogous to oligodendrocytes. These neuroglial cells are derived from **neural crest cells** that migrate peripherally and wrap themselves around the axons of somatic motor neurons and preganglionic autonomic motor neurons as they pass out of the CNS (Figs. 19–8 and 19–11*A* to *E*). These cells also wrap themselves around both the central and peripheral processes of somatic and visceral sensory neurons, as well as around the axons of postganglionic autonomic motor neurons. For more details of this process, see Hutchins et al (1997). Beginning at about 20 weeks, the nerve fibers have a whitish appearance, resulting from the deposition of myelin. Motor roots are myelinated before sensory roots.

CONGENITAL ANOMALIES OF THE SPINAL CORD

Most congenital anomalies of the spinal cord result from defective closure of the neural tube during the fourth week of development. These **neural tube defects** (NTDs) affect the tissues overlying the spinal cord: meninges, vertebral arch, muscles, and skin (Fig. 19–12*B* to *D*). Anomalies involving the vertebral arches are referred to as **spina bifida.** This term denotes *nonfusion of the embryonic halves of the vertebral arches,* which is common to all types of spina bifida. Severe anomalies also involve the spinal cord and meninges. Spina bifida ranges from clinically significant types to minor anomalies that are unimportant.

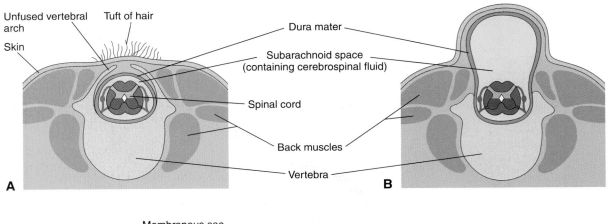

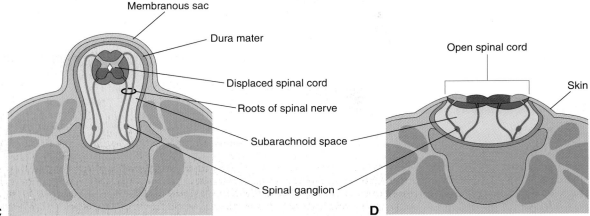

■ **Figure 19–12.** Diagrammatic sketches illustrating various types of spina bifida and the commonly associated anomalies of the vertebral arch, spinal cord, and meninges. *A*, Spina bifida occulta. Observe the unfused vertebral arch. *B*, Spina bifida with meningocele. *C*, Spina bifida with meningomyelocele. *D*, Spina bifida with myeloschisis. The types illustrated in *B* to *D* are referred to collectively as spina bifida cystica because of the cystlike sac that is associated with them.

Spina Bifida Occulta

This *defect in the vertebral arch* (neural arch) is the result of failure of the embryonic halves of the arch to grow normally and fuse in the median plane (Fig. 19–12*A*). Spina bifida occulta occurs in L5 or S1 vertebrae in about 10% of otherwise normal people (Moore, 1992). In its most minor form, the only evidence of its presence may be a small dimple with a tuft of hair arising from it (Fig. 19–13). Spina bifida occulta usually produces no clinical symptoms. A small percentage of affected infants have functionally significant defects of the underlying spinal cord and dorsal roots (Behrman et al, 1996).

Spina Bifida Cystica

Severe types of spina bifida, involving protrusion of the spinal cord and/or meninges through the defect in the vertebral arches, are referred to collectively as *spina bifida cystica* because of the cystlike sac that is associated with these anomalies (Figs. 19–12*B* to *D*, 19–14, and 19–15). Spina bifida cystica occurs about once in every 1000 births. When the sac contains meninges and CSF, the anomaly is called **spina bifida with meningocele** (Fig. 19–12*B*). The spinal cord and spinal roots are in their normal position, but spinal cord abnormalities may be present. If the spinal cord and/or nerve roots are included in the sac, the anomaly is called **spina bifida with**

and/or anal sphincters) is common with lumbosacral meningomyeloceles (Fig. 19-17). Spina bifida cystica and/or meroanencephaly is strongly suspected in utero when the level of alpha-fetoprotein (AFP) in the amniotic fluid is high (see Chapter 8). Alpha-fetoprotein may also be elevated in the maternal blood serum.

Myeloschisis

The most severe type of spina bifida is **spina bifida with myeloschisis** (Figs. 19-12D and 19-18). In these cases the spinal cord in the affected area is open because the neural folds failed to fuse (Gr. *schisis*, a cleaving). As a result, the spinal cord is represented by a flattened mass of nervous tissue. Spina bifida with myeloschisis results from failure of the caudal neuropore to close at the end of the fourth week.

Causes of Neural Tube Defects

Nutritional and environmental factors undoubtedly play a role in the production of NTDs. Studies have shown that vitamins and folic acid supplements taken prior to conception reduce the incidence of NTDs (Murphy et al, 1996). Certain drugs increase the risk of meningomyelocele (e.g., valproic acid). This anticonvulsant causes NTDs in 1 to 2% of pregnancies if given during early pregnancy (fourth week of development) when the neural folds are fusing. For more information about NTDs, see Behrman et al (1996) and Moore and Persaud (1998).

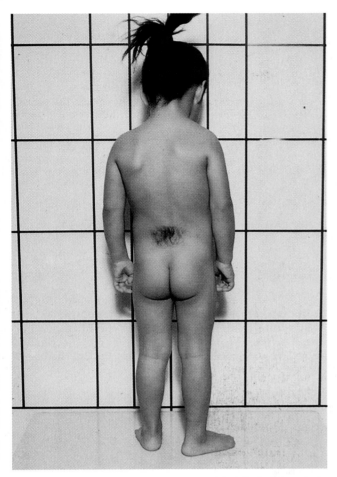

■ **Figure 19-13.** Photograph of a female child with a hairy patch in the lumbosacral region indicating the site of a spina bifida occulta. (Courtesy of A. E. Chudley, MD, Section of Genetics and Metabolism, Department of Pediatrics and Child Health, Children's Hospital and University of Manitoba, Winnipeg, Manitoba, Canada.)

meningomyelcele (Figs. 19-12C and 19-14). Meningoceles are rare compared with meningomyeloceles (Filly, 1994).

Severe cases of spina bifida with meningomyelocele involving several vertebrae are often associated with partial absence of the brain—**meroanencephaly** or **anencephaly** (Fig. 19-16). Spina bifida cystica shows varying degrees of neurological deficit, depending on the position and extent of the lesion. There is usually a corresponding dermatome loss of sensation, along with complete or partial skeletal muscle paralysis. The level of the lesion determines the area of anesthesia (area of skin without sensation) and the muscles affected. **Sphincter paralysis** (bladder

DEVELOPMENT OF THE BRAIN

The neural tube cranial to the fourth pair of somites develops into the brain. Fusion of the neural folds in the cranial region and closure of the rostral neuropore forms **three primary brain vesicles** from which the brain develops (Fig. 19-19). The three primary brain vesicles form the

- *Forebrain* (prosencephalon)
- *Midbrain* (mesencephalon)
- *Hindbrain* (rhombencephalon)

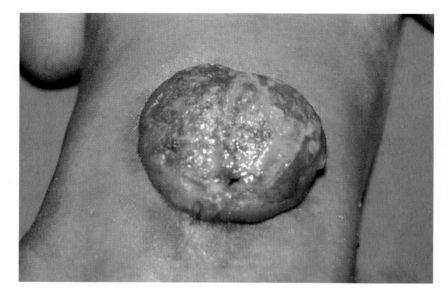

■ **Figure 19-14.** Photograph of the back of a newborn with a large lumbar meningomyelocele (myelomeningocele). The neural tube defect is covered with a thin membrane. (Courtesy of A. E. Chudley, MD, Section of Genetics and Metabolism, Department of Pediatrics and Child Health, Children's Hospital and University of Manitoba, Winnipeg, Manitoba, Canada.)

During the fifth week the forebrain partly divides into two secondary vesicles, the *telencephalon* and *diencephalon;* the midbrain does not divide; the hindbrain partly divides into the *metencephalon* and *myelencephalon.* Consequently, there are **five secondary brain vesicles.**

Brain Flexures

During the fourth week the embryonic brain grows rapidly and bends ventrally with the head fold. This produces the **midbrain flexure** in the midbrain region and the **cervical flexure** at the junction of the hindbrain and spinal cord (Fig. 19–20). Later, unequal growth of the brain between these flexures produces the **pontine flexure** in the opposite direction. This flexure results in thinning of the roof of the hindbrain. Initially the primordial brain has the same basic structure as the developing spinal cord; however, the brain flexures produce considerable variation in the outline of transverse sections at different levels of the brain and in the position of the gray and white matter. The **sulcus limitans** extends cranially to the junction of the midbrain and forebrain, and the alar and basal plates are recognizable only in the midbrain and hindbrain.

Hindbrain

The **cervical flexure** demarcates the hindbrain from the spinal cord (Fig. 19–20A). Later, this junction is arbitrarily defined as the level of the superior rootlet of the first cervical nerve, which is located roughly at

the foramen magnum. The **pontine flexure,** located in the future pontine region, divides the hindbrain into caudal (myelencephalon) and rostral (metencephalon) parts. The myelencephalon becomes the **medulla ob-**

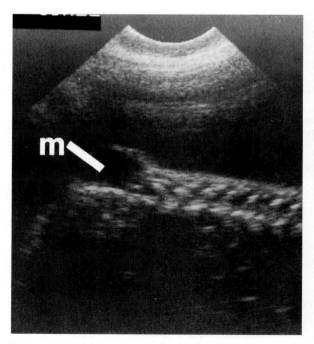

■ **Figure 19-15.** Ultrasound scan of a 14-week fetus showing a cystlike protrusion representing a meningomyelocele (m) in the sacral region of the vertebral column. The well-formed vertebral arches of the vertebrae superior to the neural tube defect are clearly visible. (Courtesy of Lyndon M. Hill, MD, Magee-Women's Hospital, Pittsburgh, Pennsylvania.)

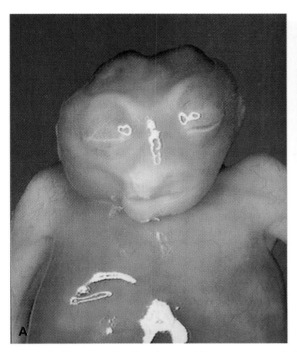

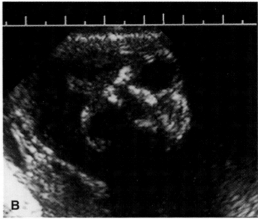

■ **Figure 19–16.** *A,* Photograph of a fetus with meroanencephaly or anencephaly. The neural tube defect was detected by ultrasonography at 18 weeks' gestation *(B).* Note the absence of the calvaria and the large orbits. (Courtesy of Wesley Lee, MD, Division of Fetal Imaging, Department of Obstetrics and Gynecology, William Beaumont Hospital, Royal Oak, Michigan.)

longata and the metencephalon the **pons** and **cerebellum.** The cavity of the hindbrain becomes the fourth ventricle and the central canal in the caudal part of the medulla.

MYELENCEPHALON

The caudal part of the myelencephalon (closed part of the medulla oblongata) resembles the spinal cord both

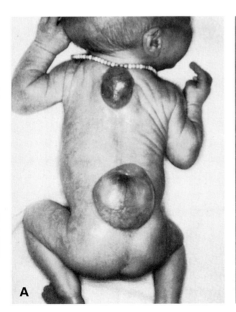

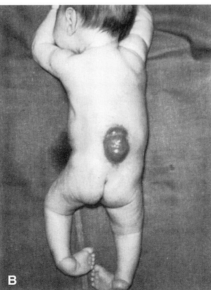

■ **Figure 19–17.** Photographs of infants with spina bifida cystica. *A,* spina bifida with meningomyelocele in the thoracic and lumbar regions. *B,* Spina bifida with myeloschisis in the lumbar region. Note that nerve involvement has affected the lower limbs. (Courtesy of Dwight Parkinson, MD, Department of Surgery and Department of Human Anatomy and Cell Science, University of Manitoba, Winnipeg, Manitoba, Canada.)

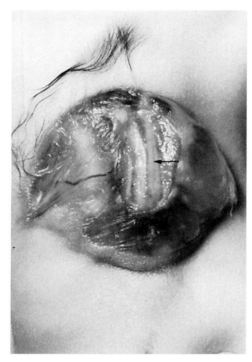

■ **Figure 19–18.** Photograph of an infant's back, exhibiting spina bifida with myeloschisis in the lumbar region. The open spinal cord *(arrow)* is covered by a delicate, semitransparent membrane. This anomaly is the result of a defect in closure of the neural tube during the fourth week (Fig. 19–12*D*). Note the tufts of hair on the surrounding skin. (From Laurence KM, Weeks R: Abnormalities of the central nervous system. *In* Norman AP (ed): *Congenital Abnormalities in Infancy,* 2nd ed. Edinburgh, Blackwell Scientific Publications, 1971.)

developmentally and structurally (Fig. 19–20*B*). The neural canal of the neural tube forms a small central canal. Unlike those of the spinal cord, neuroblasts from the alar plates in the myelencephalon migrate into the marginal zone and form isolated areas of gray matter—the **gracile nuclei** medially and the **cuneate nuclei** laterally. These nuclei are associated with correspondingly named tracts that enter the medulla from the spinal cord. The ventral area of the medulla contains a pair of fiber bundles—**pyramids**—which consist of corticospinal fibers descending from the developing cerebral cortex.

The rostral part of the myelencephalon ("open" part of the medulla) is wide and rather flat, especially opposite the pontine flexure (Fig. 19–20*C* and *D*). The pontine flexure causes the lateral walls of the medulla to move laterally like the pages of an open book. It also causes the roof plate to become stretched and greatly thinned. In addition, the cavity of this part of the myelencephalon (part of the future fourth ventricle) becomes somewhat rhomboidal (diamond-shaped). As the walls of the medulla move laterally, the alar plates come to lie lateral to the basal plates. As the positions of the plates change, the motor nuclei generally develop medial to the sensory nuclei (Fig. 19–20*C*). Neuroblasts in the basal plates of the medulla, like those in the spinal cord, develop into motor neurons. In the medulla the neuroblasts form nuclei (groups of nerve cells) and organize into three cell columns on each side (Fig. 19–20*D*). From medial to lateral, they are as follows:

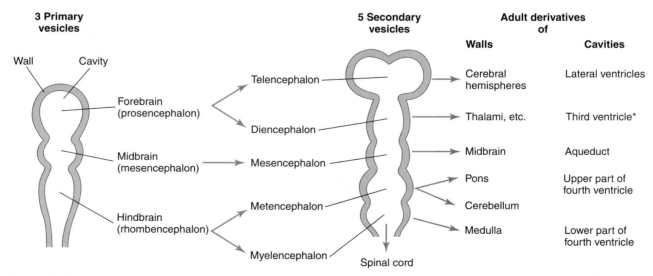

■ **Figure 19–19.** Diagrammatic sketches of the brain vesicles, indicating the adult derivatives of their walls and cavities. *The rostral (anterior) part of the third ventricle forms from the cavity of the telencephalon; most of the third ventricle is derived from the cavity of the diencephalon.

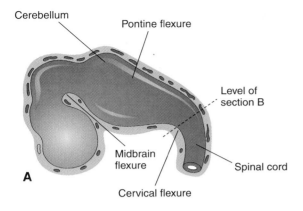

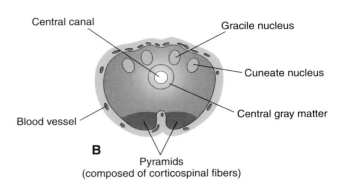

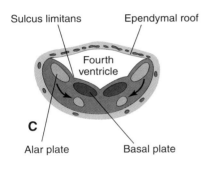

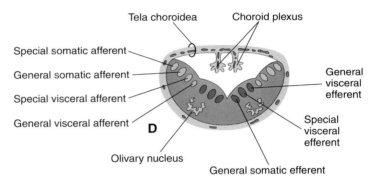

■ **Figure 19–20.** *A*, Sketch of the developing brain at the end of the fifth week showing the three primary divisions of the brain and the brain flexures. *B*, Transverse section of the caudal part of the myelencephalon (developing closed part of the medulla). *C* and *D*, Similar sections of the rostral part of the myelencephalon (developing "open" part of the medulla) showing the position and successive stages of differentiation of the alar and basal plates. The arrows in *C* show the pathway taken by neuroblasts from the alar plates to form the olivary nuclei.

- *General somatic efferent,* represented by neurons of the hypoglossal nerve
- *Special visceral efferent,* represented by neurons innervating muscles derived from the pharyngeal arches (see Chapter 11)
- *General visceral efferent,* represented by some neurons of the vagus and glossopharyngeal nerves

Neuroblasts of the alar plates form neurons that are arranged in four columns on each side. From medial to lateral, they are as follows:

- *General visceral afferent,* receiving impulses from the viscera
- *Special visceral afferent,* receiving taste fibers
- *General somatic afferent,* receiving impulses from the surface of the head
- *Special somatic afferent,* receiving impulses from the ear

Some neuroblasts from the alar plates migrate ventrally and form the neurons in the **olivary nuclei** (Fig. 19–20*C* and *D*).

METENCEPHALON

The walls of the metencephalon form the pons and cerebellum, and its cavity forms the superior part of the fourth ventricle (Fig. 19–21*A*). As in the rostral part of the myelencephalon, the pontine flexure causes divergence of the lateral walls of the pons, which spreads the gray matter in the floor of the fourth ventricle. As in the myelencephalon, neuroblasts in each basal plate develop into motor nuclei and organize into three columns on each side.

The **cerebellum** develops from thickenings of dorsal parts of the alar plates. Initially the cerebellar swellings project into the fourth ventricle (Fig. 19–21*A* and *B*). As the swellings enlarge and fuse in the median

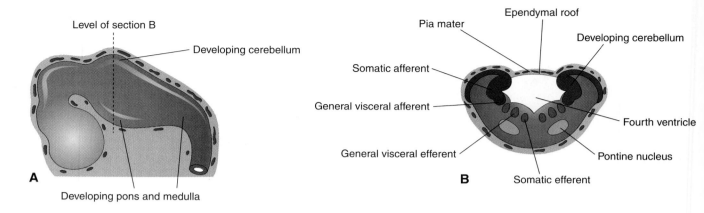

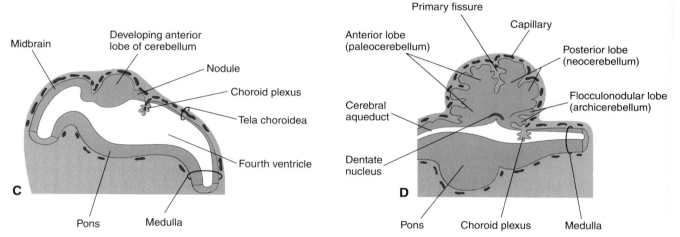

■ **Figure 19–21.** *A,* Sketch of the developing brain at the end of the fifth week. *B,* Transverse section of the metencephalon (developing pons and cerebellum) showing the derivatives of the alar and basal plates. *C* and *D,* Sagittal sections of the hindbrain at 6 and 17 weeks, respectively, showing successive stages in the development of the pons and cerebellum.

plane, they overgrow the rostral half of the fourth ventricle and overlap the pons and medulla (Fig. 19–21*D*). Some neuroblasts in the intermediate zone of the alar plates migrate to the marginal zone and differentiate into the neurons of the **cerebellar cortex.** Other neuroblasts from these plates give rise to central nuclei, the largest of which is the **dentate nucleus.** Cells from the alar plates also give rise to the pontine nuclei, the cochlear and vestibular nuclei, and the sensory nuclei of the trigeminal nerve. The structure of the cerebellum reflects its phylogenetic development (Fig. 19–21*C* and *D*). For discussion of the phylogenetic development of the cerebellum, see Moore and Persaud (1998).

Nerve fibers connecting the cerebral and cerebellar cortices with the spinal cord pass through the mar-

ginal layer of the ventral region of the metencephalon. This region of the brain stem is the **pons** (L. bridge) because of the robust band of nerve fibers that crosses the median plane and forms a bulky ridge on its anterior and lateral aspects.

Choroid Plexuses and Cerebrospinal Fluid (CSF)

The thin ependymal roof of the fourth ventricle is covered externally by *pia mater,* derived from mesenchyme associated with the hindbrain (Fig. 19–21*C* and *D*). This vascular pia mater, together with the ependymal roof, forms the **tela choroidea.** Because of the active proliferation of the pia mater, the tela choroidea invaginates the fourth ventricle, where it differentiates into the **choroid plexus.** Similar choroid plexuses develop in the roof of the third ventricle and in the medial walls of the lateral ventricles. The choroid plexuses secrete **CSF.** The thin roof of the fourth ventricle evaginates in three locations. These outpouchings rupture to form openings. The median and **lateral apertures** (foramen of Magendie and foramina of Luschka, respectively) permit the CSF to enter the **subarachnoid space** from the fourth ventricle. The main site of absorption of CSF into the venous system is through the **arachnoid villi,** which are protrusions of the arachnoid into the dural venous sinuses (Moore, 1992). These villi consist of a thin, cellular layer de-

rived from the epithelium of the arachnoid and the endothelium of the sinus.

Midbrain

The midbrain (mesencephalon) undergoes less change than any other part of the developing brain, except for the most caudal part of the hindbrain. The neural canal narrows and becomes the **cerebral aqueduct** (Fig. 19–21D), a canal that connects the third and fourth ventricles. Neuroblasts migrate from the alar plates of the midbrain into the *tectum* (roof) and aggregate to form four large groups of neurons, the paired *superior and inferior colliculi* (Fig. 19–22B),

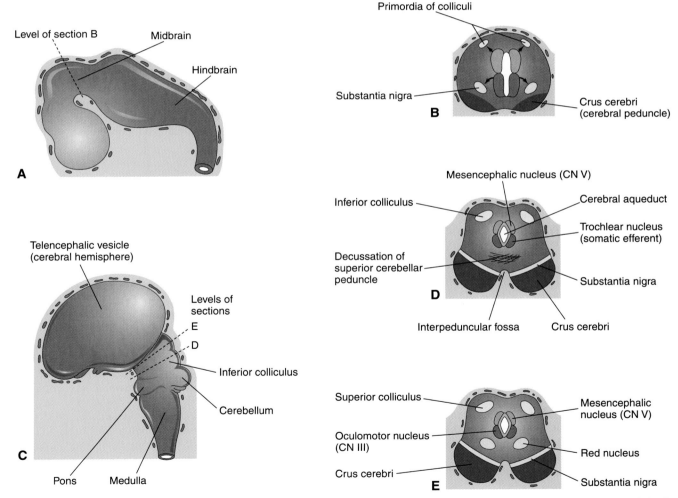

■ **Figure 19–22.** *A,* Sketch of the developing brain at the end of the fifth week. *B,* Transverse section of the developing midbrain showing the early migration of cells from the basal and alar plates. *C,* Sketch of the developing brain at 11 weeks. *D* and *E,* Transverse sections of the developing midbrain at the level of the inferior and superior colliculi, respectively.

which are concerned with visual and auditory reflexes, respectively. Neuroblasts from the basal plates may give rise to groups of neurons in the **tegmentum** (red nuclei, nuclei of the third and fourth cranial nerves, and the reticular nuclei). The **substantia nigra,** a broad layer of gray matter adjacent to the cerebral peduncle (Fig. 19-22D and E), may also differentiate from the basal plate, but some authorities believe that it is derived from cells in the alar plate that migrate ventrally. Fibers growing from the cerebrum form the cerebral peduncles anteriorly (Fig. 19-22B). The **cerebral peduncles** become progressively more prominent as more descending fiber groups (corticopontine, corticobulbar, and corticospinal) pass through the developing midbrain on their way to the brain stem and spinal cord.

Forebrain

As closure of the rostral neuropore occurs, two lateral outgrowths—**optic vesicles**—appear (Fig. 19-3A), one on each side of the forebrain. The optic vesicles are the primordia of the *retinae* and *optic nerves* (see Chapter 20). A second pair of diverticula soon arise more dorsally and rostrally; these are the **cerebral vesicles** or telencephalic vesicles (Fig. 19-22C). They are the primordia of the **cerebral hemispheres,** and their cavities become the *lateral ventricles* (Fig. 19-23A and B). The rostral or anterior part of the forebrain, including the primordia of the cerebral hemispheres, is the **telencephalon,** and the caudal or posterior part of the forebrain is the **diencephalon.** The cavities of the telencephalon and diencephalon contribute to the formation of the **third ventricle,** although the cavity of the diencephalon contributes more.

DIENCEPHALON

Three swellings develop in the lateral walls of the third ventricle, which later become the *epithalamus, thalamus,* and *hypothalamus* (Fig. 19-23C to E). The **thalamus** is separated from the epithalamus by the *epithalamic sulcus* and from the hypothalamus by the *hypothalamic sulcus.* The latter sulcus is not a continuation of the sulcus limitans into the forebrain and does not, like the sulcus limitans, divide sensory and motor areas. The thalamus develops rapidly on each side and bulges into the cavity of the third ventricle, reducing it to a narrow cleft.

The **hypothalamus** arises by proliferation of neuroblasts in the intermediate zone of the diencephalic walls, ventral to the hypothalamic sulci. Later a number of nuclei concerned with endocrine activities and homeostasis develop. A pair of nuclei, the **mamillary bodies,** form pea-sized swellings on the ventral surface of the hypothalamus (Fig. 19-23C). The **epithalamus** develops from the roof and dorsal portion of the lateral wall of the diencephalon. Initially the epithalamic swellings are large, but later they become relatively small. The **pineal body** develops as a median diverticulum of the caudal part of the roof of the diencephalon (Fig. 19-23C and D). Proliferation of cells in its walls soon converts it into a solid cone-shaped gland.

The Pituitary Gland (Fig. 19-24; Table 19-1). The pituitary gland (hypophysis cerebri) is ectodermal in origin. It develops from two sources:

- An upgrowth from the *ectodermal roof of the stomodeum*—the *hypophysial pouch*
- A downgrowth from the neuroectoderm of the diencephalon—the *neurohypophysial bud*

This double embryonic origin explains why the pituitary gland is composed of two completely different types of tissue.

- The **adenohypophysis** (glandular part) or anterior lobe arises from oral ectoderm.
- The **neurohypophysis** (nervous part) or posterior lobe originates from neuroectoderm.

At the middle of the fourth week, a diverticulum—the **hypophysial pouch** or *Rathke pouch*—projects from the roof of the stomodeum and lies adjacent to the floor (ventral wall) of the diencephalon (Fig. 19-24A and B). By the fifth week this pouch has elongated and become constricted at its attachment to the oral epithelium, giving it a nipple-like appearance (Fig. 19-24C). By this stage it has come into contact with the **infundibulum** (derived from neurohypophysial bud), a ventral downgrowth (diverticulum) of the diencephalon (Fig. 19-24C). The parts of the pituitary gland that develop from the ectoderm of the stomodeum—pars anterior, pars intermedia, and pars tuberalis—form the **adenohypophysis** (Table 19-1). The stalk of the hypophysial pouch passes between the chondrification centers of the developing presphenoid and basisphenoid bones of the skull (Fig. 19-24E). During the sixth week the connection of the pouch with the oral cavity degenerates and disappears.

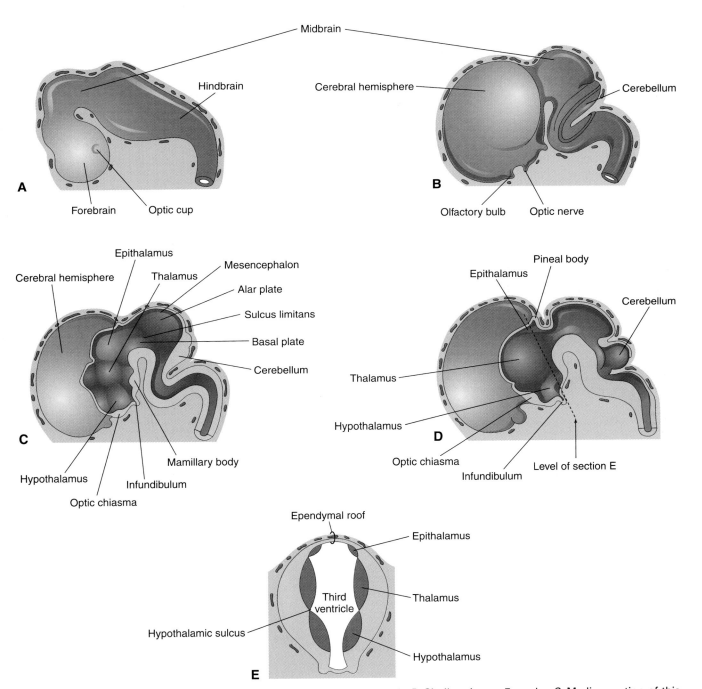

■ **Figure 19–23.** *A,* External view of the brain at the end of the fifth week. *B,* Similar view at 7 weeks. *C,* Median section of this brain showing the medial surface of the forebrain and midbrain. *D,* Similar section at 8 weeks. *E,* Transverse section of the diencephalon showing the epithalamus dorsally, the thalamus laterally, and the hypothalamus ventrally.

Pharyngeal Hypophysis and Craniopharyngioma

A remnant of the stalk of the hypophysial (Rathke) pouch may persist and form a *pharyngeal hypophysis* in the roof of the oropharynx (Fig. 19–24F). Occasion-

ally **craniopharyngiomas** develop in the pharynx or in the basisphenoid (posterior part of sphenoid bone) from remnants of the stalk of the hypophysial pouch, but most often they form in and/or superior to the sella turcica (Moore, 1992).

Cells of the anterior wall of the hypophysial or Rathke pouch proliferate actively and give rise to the

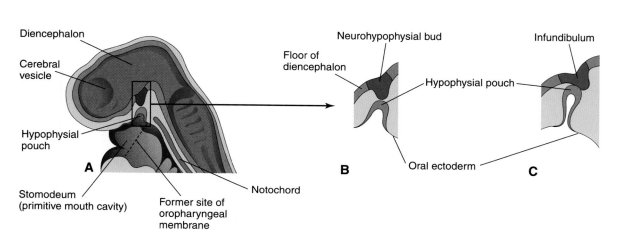

Hypophysial pouch of stomodeum (upgrowth from roof of primitive mouth)

Infundibulum of diencephalon (downgrowth from floor of forebrain)

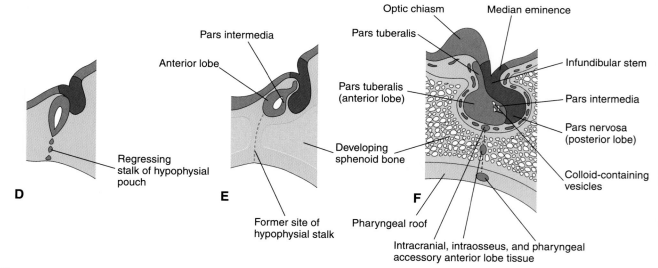

■ **Figure 19–24.** Diagrammatic sketches illustrating development of the pituitary gland. *A*, Sagittal section of the cranial end of an embryo of about 36 days showing the hypophysial (Rathke) pouch, an upgrowth from the stomodeum, and the neurohypophysial bud, a downgrowth from the forebrain. *B* to *D*, Successive stages of the developing pituitary gland. By 8 weeks, the pouch loses its connection with the oral cavity and is in close contact with the infundibulum and the posterior lobe (neurohypophysis) of the pituitary gland. *E* and *F*, Later stages showing proliferation of the anterior wall of the hypophysial pouch to form the anterior lobe (adenohypophysis) of the pituitary gland.

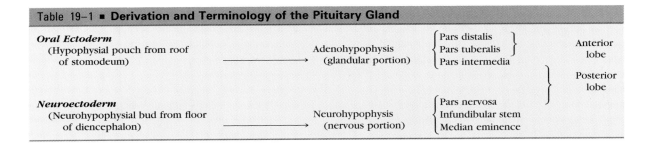

Oral Ectoderm	Adenohypophysis	Pars distalis	Anterior
(Hypophysial pouch from roof of stomodeum)	⟶ (glandular portion)	Pars tuberalis } Pars intermedia	lobe
			Posterior lobe
Neuroectoderm	Neurohypophysis	Pars nervosa	
(Neurohypophysial bud from floor of diencephalon)	⟶ (nervous portion)	Infundibular stem Median eminence	

Table 19-1 ■ Derivation and Terminology of the Pituitary Gland

pars distalis of the pituitary gland. Later a small extension, the **pars tuberalis,** grows around the infundibular stem. The extensive proliferation of the anterior wall of the hypophysial (Rathke) pouch reduces its lumen to a narrow cleft (Fig. 19-24E). This residual cleft is usually not recognizable in the adult gland, but it may be represented by a zone of cysts. Cells in the posterior wall of the hypophysial or Rathke pouch do not proliferate; they give rise to the thin, poorly defined **pars intermedia** (Fig. 19-24F). The part of the pituitary gland that develops from the neuroectoderm of the brain (infundibulum) is the **neurohypophysis** (Table 19-1). The **infundibulum** gives rise to the *median eminence, infundibular stem,* and *pars nervosa.*

TELENCEPHALON

The telencephalon consists of a median part and two lateral diverticula, the **cerebral vesicles** (Figs. 19-23A and 19-24A). These diverticula are the primordia of the **cerebral hemispheres.** The cavity of the median portion of the telencephalon forms the extreme anterior part of the third ventricle. At first, the cerebral vesicles are in wide communication with the cavity of the third ventricle through the **interventricular foramina** (Fig. 19-25). As the cerebral hemispheres expand, they cover successively the diencephalon, midbrain, and hindbrain. The hemispheres eventually meet each other in the midline, flattening their medial surfaces. The mesenchyme trapped in the longitudinal

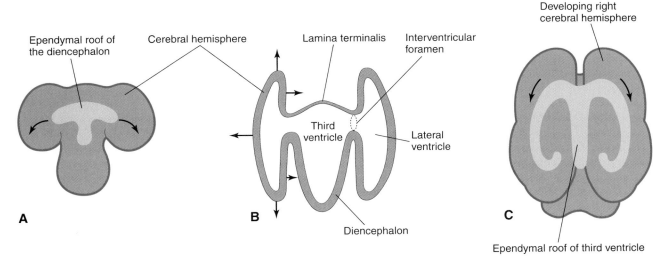

■ **Figure 19-25.** *A,* Sketch of the dorsal surface of the forebrain indicating how the ependymal roof of the diencephalon is carried out to the dorsomedial surface of the cerebral hemispheres. *B,* Diagrammatic section of the forebrain showing how the developing cerebral hemispheres grow from the lateral walls of the forebrain and expand in all directions until they cover the diencephalon. The arrows indicate some directions in which the hemispheres expand. The rostral wall of the forebrain, the *lamina terminalis,* is very thin. *C,* Sketch of the forebrain showing how the ependymal roof is finally carried into the temporal lobes as a result of the C-shaped growth pattern of the cerebral hemispheres.

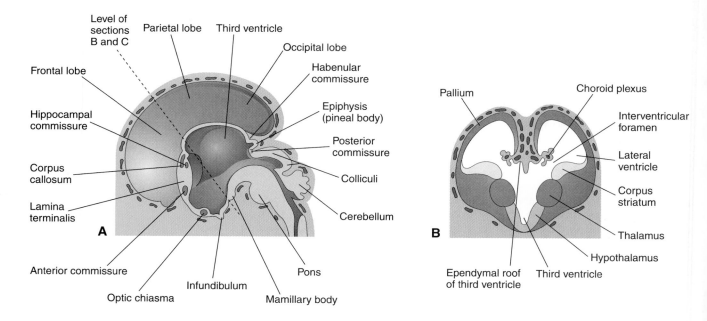

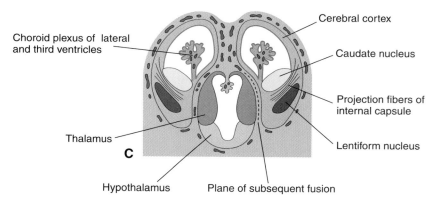

■ **Figure 19–26.** *A*, Drawing of the medial surface of the forebrain of a 10-week embryo showing the diencephalic derivatives, the main commissures, and the expanding cerebral hemispheres. *B*, Transverse section of the forebrain at the level of the interventricular foramina, showing the corpus striatum and choroid plexuses of the lateral ventricles. *C*, Similar section at about 11 weeks showing division of the corpus striatum into the caudate and lentiform nuclei by the internal capsule. The developing relationship of the cerebral hemispheres to the diencephalon is also illustrated.

fissure between them gives rise to the **falx cerebri,** a median fold of dura mater (Moore, 1992).

The **corpus striatum** appears during the sixth week as a prominent swelling in the floor of each cerebral hemisphere (Fig. 19–26*B*). The floor of each hemisphere expands more slowly than their thin cortical walls because it contains the rather large corpus striatum; consequently, the cerebral hemispheres become C-shaped (Fig. 19–27). The growth and curvature of the hemispheres also affect the shape of

the lateral ventricles. They become roughly C-shaped cavities filled with CSF. The caudal end of each cerebral hemisphere turns ventrally and then rostrally, forming the temporal lobe; in so doing, it carries the ventricle (forming the temporal horn) and **choroid fissure** with it (Fig. 19–27). Here, the thin medial wall of the hemisphere is invaginated along the choroid fissure by vascular pia mater to form the *choroid plexus of the temporal horn* (Fig. 19–26*B*).

As the cerebral cortex differentiates, fibers passing

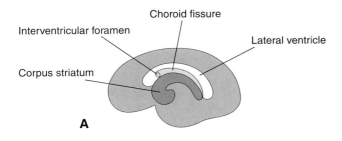

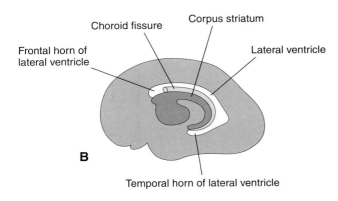

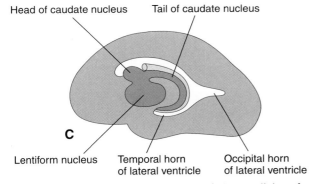

■ **Figure 19–27.** Schematic diagrams of the medial surface of the developing right cerebral hemisphere, showing the development of the lateral ventricle, choroid fissure, and corpus striatum. *A,* At 13 weeks. *B,* At 21 weeks. *C,* At 32 weeks.

U-shaped turn to gain the roof of the temporal or inferior horn.

Cerebral Commissures

As the cerebral cortex develops, groups of fibers — **commissures** — connect corresponding areas of the cerebral hemispheres with one another (Fig. 19–26). The most important of these commissures cross in the **lamina terminalis,** the rostral end of the forebrain. This lamina extends from the roof plate of the diencephalon to the optic chiasma. It is the natural pathway from one hemisphere to the other. The first commissures to form, the anterior commissure and hippocampal commissure, are small fiber bundles that connect phylogenetically older parts of the brain. The **anterior commissure** connects the olfactory bulb and related brain areas of one hemisphere with those of the opposite side. The **hippocampal commissure** connects the hippocampal formations (Haines, 1997).

The largest cerebral commissure is the **corpus callosum** (Fig. 19–26*A*), which connects neocortical areas. The corpus callosum initially lies in the lamina terminalis, but fibers are added to it as the cortex enlarges; as a result, it gradually extends beyond the lamina terminalis. The rest of the **lamina terminalis** lies between the corpus callosum and the fornix. It becomes stretched to form the thin **septum pellucidum,** a thin plate of brain tissue (Koshi et al, 1997). At birth the corpus callosum extends over the roof of the diencephalon. The **optic chiasm,** which develops in the ventral part of the lamina terminalis (Fig. 19–26*A*), consists of fibers from the medial halves of the retinae, which cross to join the optic tract of the opposite side.

The walls of the developing cerebral hemispheres initially show the three typical zones of the neural tube (ventricular, intermediate, and marginal); later a fourth one, the subventricular zone, appears. Cells of the intermediate zone migrate into the marginal zone and give rise to the cortical layers. The gray matter is thus located peripherally, and axons from its cell bodies pass centrally to form the large volume of white matter — the **medullary center.**

Initially the surface of the hemispheres is smooth (Fig. 19–28*A*); however, as growth proceeds, **sulci** (grooves or furrows) and **gyri** (convolutions or elevations) develop (Fig. 19–28*B* to *C*). The sulci and gyri permit a considerable increase in the surface area of the cerebral cortex without requiring an extensive increase in cranial size. As each cerebral hemisphere grows, the cortex covering the external surface of the corpus striatum grows relatively slowly and is soon overgrown (Fig. 19–28*C*). This buried cortex, hidden from view in the depths of the lateral sulcus

to and from it pass through the **corpus striatum** and divide it into the *caudate* and *lentiform nuclei.* This fiber pathway — the **internal capsule** (Fig. 19–26*C*) — becomes C-shaped as the hemisphere assumes this form. The **caudate nucleus** becomes elongated and C-shaped, conforming to the outline of the lateral ventricle (Fig. 19–27*A* to *C*). Its pear-shaped head and elongated body lie in the floor of the frontal horn and body of the lateral ventricle; whereas its tail makes a

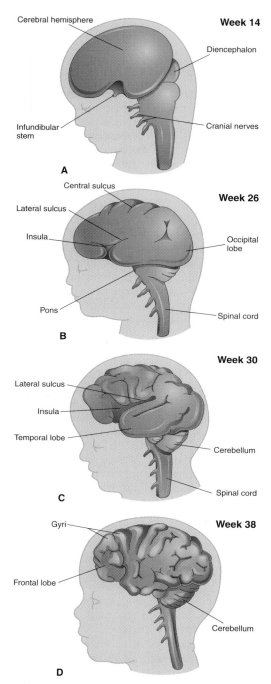

A Week 14

Cerebral hemisphere
Diencephalon
Infundibular stem
Cranial nerves

B Week 26

Central sulcus
Lateral sulcus
Insula
Occipital lobe
Pons
Spinal cord

C Week 30

Lateral sulcus
Insula
Temporal lobe
Cerebellum
Spinal cord

D Week 38

Gyri
Frontal lobe
Cerebellum

■ **Figure 19–28.** *A* to *C*, Sketches of lateral views of the left cerebral hemisphere, diencephalon, and brain stem showing successive stages in the development of the sulci and gyri in the cerebral cortex. Note the gradual narrowing of the lateral sulcus and burying of the insula (L. *island*), an area of cerebral cortex that is concealed from surface view. Note that the surface of the cerebral hemispheres grows rapidly during the fetal period, forming many convolutions (gyri), which are separated by many grooves (sulci).

(fissure) of the cerebral hemisphere, is the **insula** (L. *island*).

CONGENITAL ANOMALIES OF THE BRAIN

Because of the complexity of its embryologic history, abnormal development of the brain is common (about 3 per 1000 births). Most major congenital anomalies of the brain, such as meroanencephaly (anencephaly) and meningoencephalocele, result from defective closure of the rostral neuropore during the fourth week (Fig. 19-29*C*) and involve the overlying tissues (meninges and calvaria). The factors causing the NTDs are genetic, nutritional, and/or environmental in nature (Shaw et al, 1996). Congenital anomalies of the brain may be caused by alterations in the morphogenesis or histogenesis of the nervous tissue, or they can result from developmental failures occurring in associated structures (notochord, somites, mesenchyme, and skull).

Abnormal histogenesis of the cerebral cortex can result in seizures and various types of **mental retardation.** Subnormal intellectual development may also result from exposure of the embryo/fetus during the 8- to 16-week period of development to certain viruses and high levels of radiation (see Chapter 9). Prenatal factors may be involved in the development of **cerebral palsy;** however, this central motor deficit most often results from a normal fetus's brain being damaged at birth. Cerebral palsy is one of the most crippling conditions of childhood (Behrman et al, 1996).

Cranium Bifidum

Defects in the formation of the cranium *(cranium bifidum)* are often associated with congenital anomalies of the brain and/or meninges. Defects of the cranium are usually in the median plane of the calvaria (Fig. 19-29*A*). The defect is often in the squamous part of the occipital bone and may include the posterior part of the foramen magnum. When the defect is small, usually only the meninges herniate and the anomaly is a **cranial meningocele,** or cranium bifidum with meningocele (Fig. 19-29*B*).

Cranium bifidum associated with herniation of the brain and/or its meninges occurs about once in every 2000 births. When the cranial defect is large, the meninges and part of the brain (Gr. *enkephalos*) herniate, forming a **meningoencephalocele** (Fig. 19-29*C*). If the protruding brain contains part of the ventricular system, the anomaly is a **meningohydroencephalocele** (Figs. 19-29*D* and 19-30).

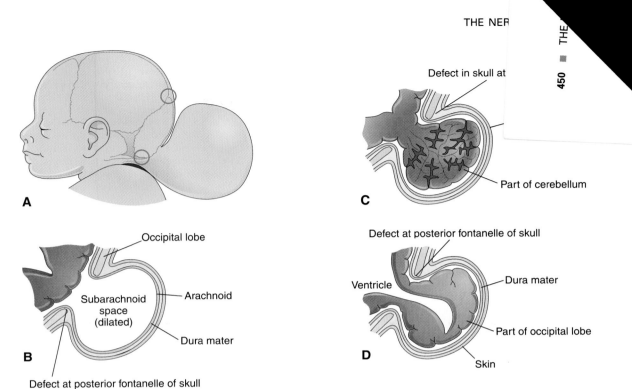

A

C

Defect in skull at

Part of cerebellum

Occipital lobe

Subarachnoid
space
(dilated)

Arachnoid

Dura mater

B

Defect at posterior fontanelle of skull

Defect at posterior fontanelle of skull

Ventricle

Dura mater

Part of occipital lobe

D

Skin

■ **Figure 19–29.** Schematic drawings illustrating cranium bifidum (bony defect in cranium) and various types of herniation of the brain and/or meninges. *A*, Sketch of the head of a newborn infant with a large protrusion from the occipital region of the skull. The upper red circle indicates a cranial defect at the posterior fontanelle. The lower red circle indicates a cranial defect near the foramen magnum. *B*, Meningocele consisting of a protrusion of the cranial meninges that is filled with cerebrospinal fluid. *C*, Meningoencephalocele consisting of a protrusion of part of the cerebellum that is covered by meninges and skin. *D*, Meningohydroencephalocele consisting of a protrusion of part of the occipital lobe that contains part of the posterior horn of a lateral ventricle.

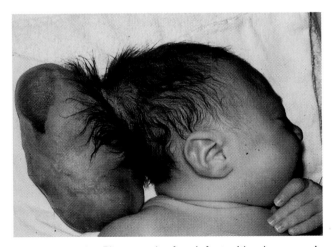

■ **Figure 19–30.** Photograph of an infant with a large meningoencephalocele in the occipital area. (Courtesy of Dr. A. E. Chudley, Section of Genetics and Metabolism, Department of Pediatrics and Child Health, Children's Hospital and University of Manitoba, Winnipeg, Manitoba, Canada.)

Exencephaly and Meroanencephaly

These severe anomalies of the brain result from failure of the rostral neuropore to close during the fourth week of development. As a result, the forebrain primordium is abnormal and development of the calvaria is defective (Fig. 19-31). Most of the infant's brain is extruding from the skull—**exencephaly.** Because of the abnormal structure and vascularization of the embryonic exencephalic brain, the nervous tissue undergoes degeneration. The remains of the brain appears as a spongy, vascular mass consisting mostly of hindbrain structures. Although this NTD is called **anencephaly** (Gr. *an,* without, and *enkephalos,* brain), a rudimentary brain stem and functioning neural tissue are always present in living infants (Filly, 1994). For this reason, meroanencephaly (Gr. *meros,* part) is a better name for this anomaly. **Meroanencephaly** is a

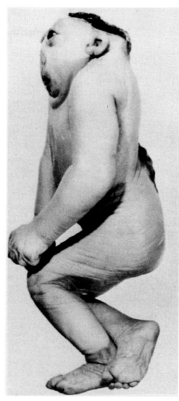

■ **Figure 19-31.** Photograph of an infant with acrania (absence of calvaria), meroanencephaly (absence of most of the brain), rachischisis (failure of fusion of several vertebral arches), and spina bifida with myeloschisis (failure of closure of the neural folds).

common *lethal anomaly,* occurring at least once in every 1000 births. It is two to four times more common in females than in males. *Meroanencephaly usually has a multifactorial inheritance* (Thompson et al, 1991). An excess of amniotic fluid **(polyhydramnios)** is often associated with meroanencephaly, possibly because the fetus lacks the neural control for swallowing amniotic fluid; thus, the fluid does not pass into the intestines for absorption and subsequent transfer to the placenta for disposal.

Microcephaly

In this uncommon condition, the calvaria and brain are small but the face is normal size (Fig. 19-32). These infants are *grossly mentally retarded* because the brain is underdeveloped—**microencephaly.** Microcephaly (Gr. *mikros,* small, and *kephale,* head) is the

result of *microencephaly* (Gr. *mikros,* small, and *enkephalos,* brain) because growth of the calvaria is largely the result of pressure from the growing brain. The cause of microcephaly is often uncertain. Some cases appear to be genetic in origin (autosomal recessive), and others are caused by environmental factors such as a cytomegalovirus infection in utero (see Chapter 9). Exposure to large amounts of ionizing radiation, infectious agents, and certain drugs (maternal alcohol abuse) during the fetal period are contributing factors in some cases. Microcephaly can be detected in utero by ultrasonography. Successive scans carried out over the period of gestation are helpful in assessing the rate of growth of the fetal cranium. A small head may result from *premature synostosis* (osseous union) of all the cranial sutures (see Chapter 16), but the calvaria is thin with exaggerated convolutional markings.

Hydrocephalus

Significant enlargement of the head usually results from an imbalance between the production and ab-

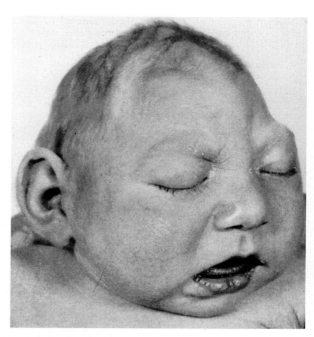

■ **Figure 19-32.** Photograph of an infant with microcephaly showing the typical normal-sized face and small calvaria, which is covered with loose, wrinkled skin. (From Laurence KM, Weeks R: Abnormalities of the central nervous system. *In* Norman AP (ed): *Congenital Abnormalities in Infancy,* 2nd ed. Edinburgh, Blackwell Scientific Publications, 1971.)

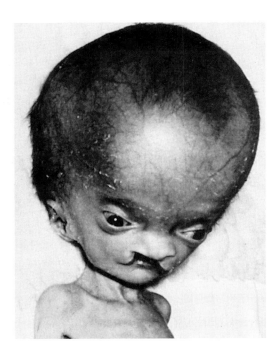

■ **Figure 19-33.** Photograph of an infant with hydrocephalus and bilateral cleft palate.

sorption of CSF; as a result, there is **an excess of CSF** in the ventricular system of the brain (Fig. 19-33). *Hydrocephalus results from impaired circulation and absorption of CSF or, in very rare cases, from increased production of CSF* by a choroid plexus adenoma. Impaired circulation of CSF often results from **congenital aqueductal stenosis** (Fig. 19-34). The cerebral aqueduct is narrow or consists of several minute channels. In a few cases aqueductal stenosis is transmitted by an X-linked recessive trait (Behrman et al, 1996), but most cases appear to result from a *fetal viral infection* (e.g., cytomegalovirus or *Toxoplasma gondii* [see Chapter 9]) or prematurity associated with intraventricular hemorrhage. Blood in the subarachnoid space may cause obliteration of the cisterns or arachnoid villi.

Blockage of CSF circulation results in dilation of the ventricles proximal to the obstruction and in pressure on the cerebral hemispheres (Fig. 19-34). This squeezes the brain between the ventricular fluid and the bones of the calvaria. In infants the internal pressure results in an accelerated rate of expansion of the brain and calvaria because the fibrous sutures of the calvaria are not fused. **Hydrocephalus usually refers to obstructive or noncommunicating hydrocephalus,** in which all or part of the ventricular system is enlarged. All ventricles are enlarged if the

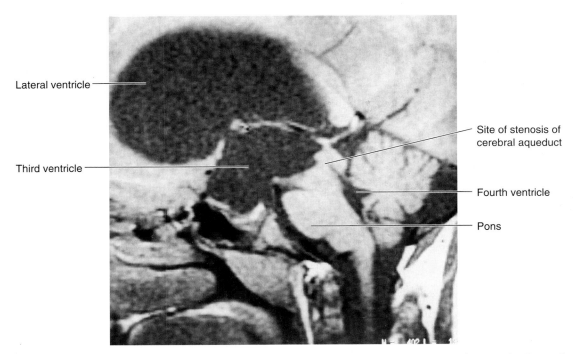

Lateral ventricle

Third ventricle

Site of stenosis of cerebral aqueduct

Fourth ventricle

Pons

■ **Figure 19-34.** Congenital stenosis of the cerebral aqueduct. This sagittal magnetic resonance image of a 9-month-old infant with a large head shows very large lateral and third ventricles. The cerebrospinal fluid appears dark in these images. The cerebral aqueduct appears as a dark line of fluid ventral to the tectum of the midbrain. The cranial end of the aqueduct is stenotic (narrow), which results in the absence of dark cerebrospinal fluid. (Courtesy of Gerald S. Smyser, MD, Altru Health System, Grand Forks, North Dakota.)

apertures of the fourth ventricle or the subarachnoid spaces are blocked, whereas the lateral and third ventricles are dilated when only the cerebral aqueduct is obstructed. Hydrocephalus resulting from obliteration of the subarachnoid cisterns or malfunction of the arachnoid villi is **nonobstructive** or **communicating hydrocephalus.** Although hydrocephalus may be associated with spina bifida cystica (Fig. 19–17), enlargement of the head may not be obvious at birth. Hydrocephalus often produces thinning of the bones of the calvaria, prominence of the forehead, atrophy of the cerebral cortex and white matter, and compression of the basal ganglia and diencephalon.

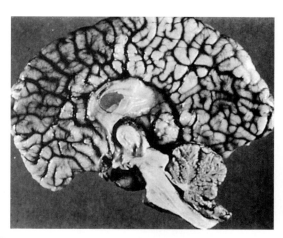

■ **Figure 19–35.** Brain of a child with a thoracolumbar meningomyelocele, showing the Arnold-Chiari malformation. The anomaly consists of elongation of the medulla with inferior displacement of the vermis of the cerebellum through the foramen magnum into the vertebral canal. (From Taeusch HW, Ballard RA, Avery ME (eds): *Schaffer and Avery's Diseases of the Newborn,* 6th ed. Philadelphia, WB Saunders, 1991.)

Holoprosencephaly

Teratogens, such as high doses of alcohol, can destroy embryonic cells in the median plane of the embryonic disc during the third week, producing a wide range of birth defects resulting from defective formation of the forebrain—**holoprosencephaly.** The infants have a small forebrain, and the lateral ventricles often merge to form one large ventricle. Defects in forebrain development often cause facial anomalies resulting from a reduction of tissue in the frontonasal prominence (see Chapter 11). Holoprosencephaly is often indicated when the eyes are abnormally close together *(hypotelorism).*

Arnold-Chiari Malformation

This is the most common congenital anomaly involving the cerebellum (Fig. 19–35). A tonguelike projection of the medulla and *inferior displacement of the vermis of the cerebellum herniates through the foramen magnum into the vertebral canal* (Taeusch et al, 1991). The condition results in a type of communicating hydrocephalus in which there is interference with the absorption of CSF; as a result, the entire ventricular system is distended. The **Arnold-Chiari** or **Chiari malformation** occurs once in every 1000 births and is frequently associated with spina bifida with meningomyelocele, spina bifida with myeloschisis, and hydrocephaly. The cause of the Arnold-Chiari malformation is uncertain; however, the posterior cranial fossa is abnormally small in some infants.

Mental Retardation

Congenital impairment of intelligence may result from various genetically determined conditions (e.g., Down syndrome). Mental retardation may result from the action of a mutant gene or from a chromosomal abnormality (e.g., an extra chromosome 13, 18, or 21). Chromosomal abnormalities and mental deficiency are discussed in Chapter 9. **Maternal alcohol abuse is the most common cause of mental retardation.** The 8- to 16-week period of human development is the period of greatest sensitivity for *fetal brain damage resulting from large doses of radiation* (Persaud, 1990). By the end of the 16th week, most neuronal proliferation and cell migration to the cerebral cortex are completed. Cell depletion of sufficient degree in the cerebral cortex results in severe mental retardation. Therapeutic abortion is often recommended when exposure exceeds 10,000 mrad (Behrman et al, 1996). Disorders of protein, carbohydrate, or fat metabolism may also cause mental retardation. *Maternal and fetal infections* (e.g., syphilis, rubella virus, toxoplasmosis, and cytomegalovirus) and cretinism are commonly associated with mental retardation (Moore and Persaud, 1998). Retarded mental development throughout the *postnatal growth period* can result from birth injuries, toxins (e.g., lead), cerebral infections (e.g., meningitis), cerebral trauma resulting from head injuries, and poisoning. For a complete discussion of mental retardation and its many causes, see Behrman et al (1996).

DEVELOPMENT OF THE PERIPHERAL NERVOUS SYSTEM

The PNS consists of cranial, spinal, and visceral nerves and cranial, spinal, and autonomic ganglia. The PNS develops from various sources, mostly from the *neural crest* (Evans and Hutchins, 1997). All sensory cells (somatic and visceral) of the PNS are derived from **neural crest cells.** The cell bodies of these sensory cells are located outside the CNS. With the exception of the cells in the spiral ganglion of the cochlea and the vestibular ganglion of CN VIII (vestibulocochlear nerve), all peripheral sensory cells are at first bipolar, but the two processes soon unite to form a single process and a unipolar type of neuron (Fig. 19-9D). This process has peripheral and central branches or processes. The peripheral process terminates in a sensory ending, whereas the central process enters the spinal cord or brain (Fig. 19-8). The sensory cells in the ganglion of CN VIII remain bipolar.

The cell body of each afferent neuron is closely invested by a capsule of modified Schwann cells—**satellite cells** (Fig. 19-8)—which are derived from neural crest cells. This capsule is continuous with the neurolemmal sheath of Schwann cells that surrounds the axons of afferent neurons. External to the satellite cells is a layer of connective tissue that is continuous with the endoneurial sheath of the nerve fibers. This connective tissue and the endoneurial sheath are derived from mesenchyme.

Neural crest cells in the developing brain migrate to form sensory ganglia only in relation to the trigeminal (CN V), facial (CN VII), vestibulocochlear (CN VIII), glossopharyngeal (CN IX), and vagus (CN X) nerves. Neural crest cells also differentiate into multipolar neurons of the *autonomic ganglia* (Fig. 19-8), including ganglia of the sympathetic trunks that lie along the sides of the vertebral bodies; collateral, or prevertebral, ganglia in plexuses of the thorax and abdomen (e.g., the cardiac, celiac, and mesenteric plexuses); and parasympathetic, or terminal, ganglia in or near the viscera (e.g., the submucosal or Meissner plexus). Cells of the paraganglia—**chromaffin cells** —are also derived from the neural crest. The term *paraganglia* includes several widely scattered groups of cells that are similar in many ways to medullary cells of the suprarenal (adrenal) glands. The cell groups largely lie retroperitoneally, often in association with sympathetic ganglia. The carotid and aortic bodies also have small islands of chromaffin cells associated with them. These widely scattered groups of chromaffin cells constitute the **chromaffin system.** Neural crest cells also give rise to melanoblasts (the precursors of the *melanocytes*) and cells of the medulla of the suprarenal gland.

Spinal Nerves

Motor nerve fibers arising from the spinal cord begin to appear at the end of the fourth week (Figs. 19-4 and 19-6 to 19-8). The nerve fibers arise from cells in the *basal plates* of the developing spinal cord and emerge as a continuous series of rootlets along its ventrolateral surface. The fibers destined for a particular developing muscle group become arranged in a bundle, forming a **ventral nerve root.** The nerve fibers of the **dorsal nerve** root are formed by axons derived from neural crest cells that migrate to the dorsolateral aspect of the spinal cord, where they differentiate into the cells of the **spinal ganglion** (Figs. 19-7 to 19-9). The central processes of neurons in the spinal ganglion form a single bundle that grows into the spinal cord, opposite the apex of the dorsal horn of gray matter (Fig. 19-4B and C). The distal processes of spinal ganglion cells grow toward the ventral nerve root and eventually join it to form a **spinal nerve.** Immediately after being formed, a mixed spinal nerve divides into dorsal and ventral primary rami (L. branches). The **dorsal primary ramus,** the smaller division, innervates the dorsal axial musculature (see Fig. 17-1), vertebrae, posterior intervertebral joints, and part of the skin of the back. The **ventral primary ramus,** the major division of each spinal nerve, contributes to the innervation of the limbs and ventrolateral parts of the body wall. The major **nerve plexuses** (cervical, brachial, and lumbosacral) are formed by ventral primary rami.

As each limb bud develops, the nerves from the spinal cord segments opposite to it elongate and grow into the limb. The nerve fibers are distributed to its muscles, which differentiate from myogenic cells that originate from the somites (see Chapter 17). The skin of the developing limbs is also supplied in a segmental manner. Early in development, successive ventral primary rami are joined by connecting loops of nerve fibers, especially those supplying the limbs (e.g., the *brachial plexus* [Moore, 1992]). The dorsal division of the trunks of these plexuses supply the extensor muscles and the extensor surface of the limbs, and the ventral divisions of the trunks supply the flexor muscles and the flexor surface. The dermatomes and cutaneous innervation of the limbs are described in Chapter 18.

Cranial Nerves

Twelve pairs of cranial nerves form during the fifth and sixth weeks of development. They are classified into three groups, according to their embryological origins.

SOMATIC EFFERENT CRANIAL NERVES

The trochlear (CN IV), the abducent (CN VI), the hypoglossal (CN XII), and the greater part of the oculomotor (CN III) nerves are homologous with the ventral roots of spinal nerves (Fig. 19–36). The cells of origin of these nerves are located in the *somatic efferent column* (derived from the basal plates) of the brain stem. Their axons are distributed to the muscles derived from the head myotomes (preotic and occipital; see Fig. 17–2).

The **hypoglossal nerve** (CN XII) resembles a spinal nerve more than do the other somatic efferent cranial nerves. Cranial nerve XII develops by the fusion of the ventral root fibers of three or four occipital nerves (Fig. 19–36A). Sensory roots, corresponding to the dorsal roots of spinal nerves, are absent. The somatic motor fibers originate from the *hypoglossal nucleus,* consisting of motor cells resembling those of the ventral horn of the spinal cord. These fibers leave the ventrolateral wall of the medulla in several groups, the *hypoglossal nerve roots,* which converge to form the common trunk of CN XII (Fig. 19–36B). They grow rostrally and eventually innervate the muscles of the tongue, which are thought to be derived from the occipital myotomes (see Fig. 17–2). With development of the neck, the hypoglossal nerve comes to lie at a progressively higher level.

The **abducent nerve** (CN VI) arises from nerve cells in the basal plates of the metencephalon. It passes from its ventral surface to the posterior of the three preotic myotomes from which the lateral rectus muscle of the eye is thought to originate.

The **trochlear nerve** (CN IV) arises from nerve cells in the somatic efferent column in the posterior part of the midbrain. Although a motor nerve, it emerges from the brain stem dorsally and then passes ventrally to supply the superior oblique muscle of the eye.

The **oculomotor nerve** (CN III) supplies most of the muscles of the eye (i.e., the superior, inferior, and medial recti) and inferior oblique muscles, which are thought to be derived from the first preotic myotomes.

NERVES OF THE PHARYNGEAL ARCHES

Cranial nerves V, VII, IX, and X supply the embryonic pharyngeal arches; thus, the structures that develop

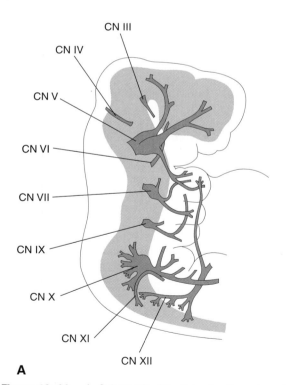

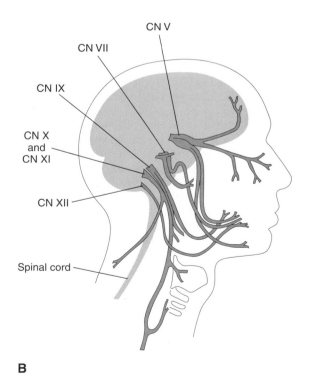

A

B

■ **Figure 19–36.** *A,* Schematic drawing of a 5-week embryo showing the distribution of most of the cranial nerves, especially those supplying the pharyngeal arches. *B,* Schematic drawing of the head and neck of an adult, showing the general distribution of most of the cranial nerves.

from these arches are innervated by these cranial nerves (Fig. 19–36A; see Table 11–1).

The **trigeminal nerve** (CN V) is the nerve of the first pharyngeal arch, but it has an ophthalmic division that is not a pharyngeal arch component. *Cranial nerve V is chiefly sensory and is the principal sensory nerve for the head.* The large **trigeminal ganglion** lies beside the rostral end of the pons, and its cells are derived from the most anterior part of the neural crest. The central processes of cells in this ganglion form the large sensory root of CN V, which enters the lateral portion of the pons. The peripheral processes of cells in this ganglion separate into three large divisions (ophthalmic, maxillary, and mandibular nerves). Their sensory fibers supply the skin of the face as well as the lining of the mouth and nose (see Fig. 11–7). The *motor fibers of CN V* arise from cells in the most anterior part of the *special visceral efferent column* in the metencephalon. The motor nucleus of CN V lies at the midlevel of the pons. The fibers leave the pons at the site of the entering sensory fibers and pass to the muscles of mastication and to other muscles that develop in the mandibular prominence of the first pharyngeal arch (see Table 11–1). The mesencephalic nucleus of CN V differentiates from cells in the midbrain that extend rostrally from the metencephalon.

The **facial nerve** (CN VII) is the nerve of the second pharyngeal arch. It consists mostly of motor fibers that arise principally from a nuclear group in the *special visceral efferent column* in the caudal part of the pons. These fibers are distributed to the *muscles of facial expression* and to other muscles that develop in the mesenchyme of the second pharyngeal arch (see Table 11–1). The small general visceral efferent component of CN VII terminates in the peripheral autonomic ganglia of the head. The sensory fibers of CN VII arise from the cells of the *geniculate ganglion.* The central processes of these cells enter the pons, and the peripheral processes pass to the greater superficial petrosal nerve and, via the chorda tympani nerve, to the taste buds in the anterior two thirds of the tongue.

The **glossopharyngeal nerve** (CN IX) is the nerve of the third pharyngeal arch. Its motor fibers arise from the special and, to a lesser extent, general visceral efferent columns of the anterior part of the myelencephalon. Cranial nerve IX forms from several rootlets that arise from the medulla just caudal to the developing internal ear. All the fibers from the special visceral efferent column are distributed to the stylopharyngeus muscle, which is derived from mesenchyme in the third pharyngeal arch (see Table 11–1). The general efferent fibers are distributed to the otic ganglion from which postganglionic fibers pass to the parotid and posterior lingual glands. The *sensory fibers of CN IX* are distributed as general sensory and special visceral afferent fibers (taste fibers) to the posterior part of the tongue.

The **vagus nerve** (CN X) is formed by fusion of the nerves of the fourth and sixth pharyngeal arches (see Table 11–1). It has large visceral efferent and visceral afferent components that are distributed to the heart, to the foregut and its derivatives, and to a large part of the midgut. The nerve of the fourth pharyngeal arch becomes the **superior laryngeal nerve,** which supplies the cricothyroid muscle and constrictor muscles of the pharynx. The nerve of the sixth pharyngeal arch becomes the **recurrent laryngeal nerve,** which supplies various laryngeal muscles.

The **accessory nerve** (CN XI) has two separate origins (Fig. 19–36). The cranial root is a posterior extension of CN X, and the spinal root arises from the cranial five or six cervical segments of the spinal cord. The fibers of the cranial root emerge from the lateral surface of the medulla, where they join the vagus nerve and supply the muscles of the soft palate and intrinsic muscles of the larynx. The fibers of the spinal root supply the sternocleidomastoid and trapezius muscles (Moore, 1992).

SPECIAL SENSORY NERVES

The **olfactory nerve** (CN I) arises from the olfactory bulb. The olfactory cells are bipolar neurons that differentiate from cells in the epithelial lining of the primitive nasal sac. The axons of the olfactory cells are collected into 18 to 20 bundles around which the *cribriform plate* of the ethmoid bone develops. These unmyelinated nerve fibers end in the olfactory bulb.

The **optic nerve** (CN II) is formed by more than 1 million nerve fibers that grow into the brain from neuroblasts in the primitive retina. Because the optic nerve develops from the evaginated wall of the forebrain, it actually represents a fiber tract of the brain. Development of the optic nerve is described in Chapter 20.

The **vestibulocochlear nerve** (CN VIII) consists of two kinds of sensory fiber in two bundles; these fibers are known as the vestibular and cochlear nerves. The **vestibular nerve** originates in the semicircular ducts, and the **cochlear nerve** proceeds from the cochlear duct, in which the **spiral organ** (of Corti) develops. The bipolar neurons of the vestibular nerve have their cell bodies in the vestibular ganglion. The central processes of these cells terminate in the *vestibular nuclei* in the floor of the fourth ventricle. The bipolar neurons of the *cochlear nerve* have their cell bodies in the spiral ganglion. The central processes of these cells end in the ventral and dorsal *cochlear nuclei* in the medulla.

DEVELOPMENT OF THE AUTONOMIC NERVOUS SYSTEM

Functionally, the autonomic system can be divided into sympathetic (thoracolumbar) and parasympathetic (craniosacral) parts.

Sympathetic Nervous System

During the fifth week, *neural crest cells* in the thoracic region migrate along each side of the spinal cord, where they form paired cellular masses (ganglia) dorsolateral to the aorta (Fig. 19–8). All these segmentally arranged **sympathetic ganglia** are connected in a bilateral chain by longitudinal nerve fibers. These ganglionated cords—**sympathetic trunks**—are located on each side of the vertebral bodies. Some neural crest cells migrate ventral to the aorta and form neurons in the **preaortic ganglia,** such as the celiac and mesenteric ganglia (Fig. 19–8). Other neural crest cells migrate to the area of the heart, lungs, and gastrointestinal tract, where they form terminal ganglia in sympathetic organ plexuses, located near or within these organs.

After the sympathetic trunks have formed, axons of sympathetic neurons located in the **intermediolateral cell column** (lateral horn) of the thoracolumbar segments of the spinal cord pass through the ventral root of a spinal nerve and a **white ramus communicans** (connecting branch) to a paravertebral ganglion (Fig. 19–8). There they may synapse with neurons or ascend or descend in the sympathetic trunk to synapse at other levels. Other preganglionic fibers pass through the paravertebral ganglia without synapsing, forming splanchnic nerves to the viscera. The postganglionic fibers course through a **gray ramus communicans,** passing from a sympathetic ganglion into a spinal nerve; hence, the sympathetic trunks are composed of ascending and descending fibers.

Parasympathetic Nervous System

The preganglionic parasympathetic fibers arise from neurons in nuclei of the brain stem and in the sacral region of the spinal cord. The fibers from the brain stem leave through the oculomotor (CN III), facial (CN VII), glossopharyngeal (CN IX), and vagus (CN X) nerves. The postganglionic neurons are located in peripheral ganglia or in plexuses near or within the structure being innervated (e.g., the pupil of the eye and salivary glands).

Congenital Aganglionic Megacolon

Congenital aganglionic megacolon or **Hirschsprung disease** results from absence of ganglion cells in the wall of the large intestine, extending proximally and continuously from the anus for a variable distance. Hirschsprung disease is the most common cause of lower intestinal obstruction in the neonate, with an overall incidence of 1 in 5000 births (Fig. 19–37). The absence of innervation of the colon results from failure of enteric neuronal precursors to migrate into the wall of the lower bowel (Naftel and Hardy, 1997). The affected segment of colon is paralyzed in a constricted state, which results in distention of the proximal, normally innervated bowel. The aganglionic segment is limited to the rectosigmoid colon in 75% of cases. The clinical symptoms of Hirschsprung disease usually begin within 48 hours of birth with the delayed passage of meconium (fetal feces). Males are affected more often than females (4:1).

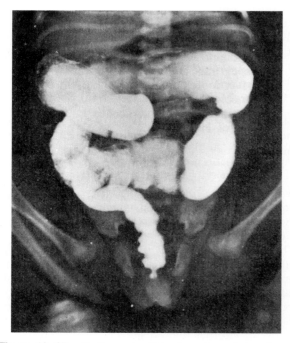

■ **Figure 19–37.** Radiograph of the large bowel showing rectosigmoid narrowing and dilation of the proximal colon, resulting from congenital aganglionic megacolon (Hirschsprung disease). (From Avery ME, Taeusch HW (eds): *Schaffer's Diseases of the Newborn,* 5th ed. Philadephia, WB Saunders, 1984.)

SUMMARY OF THE NERVOUS SYSTEM

The CNS develops from a dorsal thickening of ectoderm — the **neural plate** — which appears around the middle of the third week. The neural plate is induced by the underlying **notochord** and paraxial mesoderm. The neural plate becomes infolded to form a **neural groove** that has **neural folds** on each side. When the neural folds begin to fuse to form the **neural tube,** beginning during the fourth week, some neuroectodermal cells are not included in it but remain between the neural tube and surface ectoderm as the **neural crest.**

The cranial end of the neural tube forms the brain, the primordia of which are the forebrain, midbrain, and hindbrain. The **forebrain** gives rise to the cerebral hemispheres and diencephalon. The embryonic **midbrain** becomes the adult midbrain, and the **hindbrain** gives rise to the pons, cerebellum, and medulla oblongata. The remainder of the neural tube becomes the spinal cord. The **neural canal,** the lumen of the neural tube, becomes the ventricles of the brain and the central canal of the spinal cord. The walls of the neural tube thicken by proliferation of its neuroepithelial cells. These cells give rise to all nerve and macroglial cells in the CNS. The microglia differentiate from mesenchymal cells that enter the CNS with the blood vessels.

The **pituitary gland** develops from two completely different parts:

- An ectodermal upgrowth from the stomodeum — the *hypophysial pouch* — forms the **adenohypophysis**
- A neuroectodermal downgrowth from the diencephalon — the *neurohypophysial bud* — forms the **neurohypophysis** (Table 19-1)

Cells in the cranial, spinal, and autonomic ganglia are derived from **neural crest cells,** which originate in the neural crest. Schwann cells, which myelinate the axons external to the spinal cord, also arise from neural crest cells. Similarly, most of the autonomic nervous system and all chromaffin tissue, including the suprarenal medulla, develop from neural crest cells.

There are three types of congenital anomaly of the nervous system:

- Structural anomalies caused by abnormal organogenesis, such as neural tube defects resulting from defective closure of the neural tube
- Disturbances in the organization of the cells of the nervous system (e.g., the effects of high doses of radiation and severe malnutrition) that result in mental retardation

- Errors of metabolism, which are often inherited, cause mental retardation because of an accumulation of toxic substances (e.g., phenylketonuria) or a deficiency of essential substances (e.g., congenital hypothyroidism)

Congenital anomalies of the CNS are common (about 3 per 1000 births). Defects in the closure of the neural tube account for most severe anomalies (e.g., spina bifida cystica). The anomalies include the overlying tissues. Some anomalies of the CNS are caused by genetic factors (e.g., numerical chromosomal abnormalities such as trisomy 21); others result from environmental factors such as infectious agents, drugs, and metabolic disease. However, *most CNS anomalies are caused by a combination of genetic and environmental factors.* Gross congenital anomalies (e.g., meroanencephaly) are incompatible with life. Other severe anomalies (e.g., spina bifida with meningomyelocele) cause functional disability (e.g., muscle paralysis in the lower limbs). Severe abnormalities of the CNS also result from congenital anomalies of the ventricular system of the brain. **There are two main types of hydrocephalus:**

- *Obstructive* or *noncommunicating hydrocephalus* (blockage of CSF flow in the ventricular system)
- *Nonobstructive* or *communicating hydrocephalus* (blockage of CSF flow in the subarachnoid space)

In most cases, congenital hydrocephalus is associated with spina bifida with meningomyelocele.

Mental retardation may result from chromosomal abnormalities occurring during gametogenesis, from metabolic disorders, from maternal alcohol abuse, or from infections occurring during prenatal life. Various postnatal conditions (e.g., cerebral infection or trauma) may also cause abnormal mental development.

Clinically Oriented Questions

1. Are neural tube defects (NTDs) hereditary? The reason I ask is because my mother had a baby with spina bifida cystica and my sister had one with meroanencephaly. Is my sister likely to have another child with an NTD? Can meroanencephaly and spina bifida be detected early in fetal life?

2. I recently read in the paper about a baby born with no cerebral hemispheres and yet its head appeared normal; however, the baby exhibited excessive sleepiness, continuous crying when awake, and feeding problems. What is this condition called? What is its embryologic basis? Do these children usually survive?

3. I have heard that pregnant women who are heavy drinkers may have babies who exhibit mental and growth retardation. Is this true? I have seen women get drunk during pregnancy and their babies seem to be normal. Is there a safe threshold for alcohol consumption during pregnancy?

4. My aunt told me that my cigarette smoking during pregnancy probably caused the slight mental retardation of my baby. I am not a heavy smoker. Is my aunt's accusation correct?

5. Do all types of spina bifida cause loss of motor function in the lower limbs? Which type of spina bifida cystica is more common and serious? How are infants with spina bifida cystica treated?

The answers to these questions are given at the back of the book.

REFERENCES AND SUGGESTED READING

Behrman RE, Kliegman RM, Arvin AM (eds): *Nelson Textbook of Pediatrics*, 15th ed. Philadelphia, WB Saunders, 1996.

Brumfield CG, Aronin PA, Cloud GA, Davis RO: Fetal myelomeningocele. Is antenatal ultrasound useful in predicting neonatal outcome. *J Reprod Med* 40:26, 1995.

Carlson BM: *Human Embryology and Developmental Biology*. St. Louis, Mosby-Year Book, 1994.

Evans OB, Hutchins JB: Development of the nervous system. *In* Haines DE (ed): *Fundamental Neuroscience*. New York, Churchill Livingstone, 1997.

Filly RA: Ultrasound evaluation of the fetal neural axis. *In* Callen PW (ed): *Ultrasonography in Obstetrics and Gynecology,* 3rd ed. Philadelphia, WB Saunders, 1994.

Graham DI, Lantos PL (eds): *Greenfield's Neuropathology,* 6th ed. New York, Oxford University Press, 1997.

Haines DE (ed): *Fundamental Neuroscience*. New York, Churchill Livingstone, 1997.

Hutchins JB, Naftel, JP, Ard MD: The cell biology of neurons and glia. *In* Haines DE (ed): *Fundamental Neuroscience*. New York, Churchill Livingstone, 1997.

Koshi R, Koshi T, Jeyaseelan L, Vettivel S: Morphology of the corpus callosum in human fetuses. *Clin Anat* 10:22, 1997.

Martinez-Frias ML, Urioste M, Bermejo E, et al: Epidemiological analysis of multi-site closure failure of neural tube in humans. *Am J Med Genet* 66:64, 1996.

Moore KL: *Clinically Oriented Anatomy,* 3rd ed. Baltimore, Williams & Wilkins, 1992.

Moore KL, Persaud TVN: *The Developing Human: Clinically Oriented Embryology,* 6th ed. Philadelphia, WB Saunders, 1998.

Müller F, O'Rahilly R: Development of anencephaly and its variants. *Am J Anat* 190:193, 1991.

Murphy M, Seagroatt V, Hey K, et al: Neural tube defects 1974–1994 —down but not out. *Arch Dis Child* 75:F133, 1996.

Naftel JP, Hardy SGP: Visceral motor pathways. *In* Haines DE (ed): *Fundamental Neuroscience*. New York, Churchill Livingstone, 1997.

Noden DM: Spatial integration among cells forming the cranial peripheral neurons. *J Neurobiol* 24:248, 1993.

Parkinson D, Del Bigio MR: Posterior "septum" of human spinal cord: Normal developmental variations, composition, and terminology. *Anat Rec* 244:572, 1996.

Persaud TVN: Abnormal development of the central nervous system. *Anat Anz* 150:44, 1981.

Persaud TVN: *Environmental Causes of Human Birth Defects*. Springfield, IL, Charles C Thomas, 1990.

Sarwark JL: Spina bifida. *Pediatr Clin North Am* 43:1151, 1996.

Shaw GM, Velie EM, Shaffer D: Risk of neural tube defect—affected pregnancies among obese women. *JAMA* 275:1093, 1996.

Taeusch HW, Ballard RA, Avery ME (eds): *Schaffer and Avery's Diseases of the Newborn,* 6th ed. Philadelphia, WB Saunders, 1991.

Thompson MW, McInnes RR, Willard HF: *Thompson and Thompson Genetics in Medicine,* 5th ed. Philadelphia, WB Saunders, 1991.

Wyllie R: Congenital aganglionic megacolon (Hirschsprung disease). *In* Behrman RE, Kliegman RM, Arvin AM (eds): *Nelson Textbook of Pediatrics,* 15th ed. Philadelphia, WB Saunders, 1996.

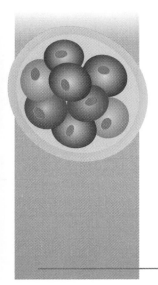

The Eye and Ear

20

DEVELOPMENT OF THE EYE

Early eye development results from a series of inductive signals. For a flow chart of major inductive events and tissue transformations in eye development, see Carlson (1994). The eyes or visual organs are derived from four sources:

- Neuroectoderm of the forebrain
- Surface ectoderm of the head
- Mesoderm between the above layers
- Neural crest cells.

The neuroectoderm of the forebrain differentiates into the retina, the posterior layers of the iris, and the optic nerve. The surface ectoderm of the head forms the lens of the eye and the corneal epithelium. The mesoderm between the neuroectoderm and surface ectoderm gives rise to the fibrous and vascular coats of the eye. Mesenchymal cells are derived from mesoderm but neural crest cells migrate into the mesenchyme from the neural crest and differentiate into the choroid, sclera, and corneal endothelium. Homeobox-containing genes play an important role in the development of the vertebrate eye (Mathers et al, 1997).

Eye development is first evident at the beginning of the fourth week. **Optic grooves** (sulci) appear in the neural folds at the cranial end of the embryo (Fig. 20-1A and B). As the neural folds fuse to form the **forebrain,** the optic grooves evaginate to form hollow diverticula—the **optic vesicles**—which project from the wall of the forebrain into the adjacent mesenchyme (Fig. 20-1C). The cavities of the optic vesicles are continuous with the cavity of the forebrain. Formation of optic vesicles is induced by the mesenchyme adjacent to the developing brain, probably through a chemical mediator. As the bulblike optic vesicles grow, their distal ends expand and their connections with the forebrain constrict to form hollow **optic stalks** (Fig. 20-1D). The optic vesicles soon come in contact with the surface ectoderm, and their lateral surfaces become indented.

Concurrently, the surface ectoderm adjacent to the optic vesicles thickens to form **lens placodes,** the primordia of the lenses (Fig. 20-1C). Formation of lens placodes is induced by the optic vesicles after the surface ectoderm has been conditioned by the underlying mesenchyme (Carlson, 1994). An inductive message passes from the optic vesicles, stimulating the surface ectodermal cells to form the lens primordia. The lens placodes invaginate as they sink deep to the surface ectoderm, forming **lens pits** (Figs. 20-1D and 20-2). The edges of the lens pits approach each other and fuse to form spherical **lens vesicles** (Fig. 20-1F and H), which soon lose their connection with the surface ectoderm. Development of the lenses from the lens vesicles is described after formation of the eyeball is discussed.

As the lens vesicles are developing, the optic vesicles invaginate to form double-walled **optic cups** (Figs. 20-1H and 20-2). The opening of each cup is large at first but its rim infolds around the lens (Fig. 20-3A). By this stage, the lens vesicles have lost their connection with the surface ectoderm and have entered the cavities of the optic cups (see Fig. 20-4). Linear grooves—**optic fissures**—develop on the ventral surface of the optic cups and along the optic stalks (Figs. 20-1E to H and 20-3A to D). The optic fissures contain vascular mesenchyme from which the hyaloid blood vessels develop. The **hyaloid artery,** a branch of the *ophthalmic artery,* supplies the inner layer of the optic cup, the lens vesicle, and the mesenchyme in the optic cup (Figs. 20-1H and 20-3). The **hyaloid vein** returns blood from these structures. As the edges of the optic fissure fuse, the hyaloid vessels are enclosed within the optic nerve (Fig. 20-3C to F). Distal parts of the hyaloid vessels eventually degenerate, but proximal parts persist as the **central artery and vein of the retina** (see Fig. 20-6D).

Development of the Retina

The retina develops from the walls of the **optic cup,** an outgrowth of the forebrain (Figs. 20-1 and 20-2). The outer, thinner layer of the optic cup becomes the **retinal pigment epithelium** and the inner, thicker layer differentiates into the multilayered **neural retina.** During the embryonic and early fetal periods, the two retinal layers are separated by an **intraretinal space,** which is the original cavity of the optic cup. This space gradually disappears as the two layers of the retina fuse (see Fig. 20-6D), but this fusion is never firm; hence, when an adult eyeball is dissected, the neural retina is often separated from the retinal pigment epithelium. Because the optic cup is an outgrowth of the forebrain, the layers of the optic cup are continuous with the wall of the brain. Under the influence of the developing lens, the inner layer of the optic cup proliferates to form a thick **neuroepithelium** (Fig. 20-4). Subsequently the cells of this layer differentiate into the **neural retina,** the light-sensitive region of the eye, containing photoreceptors (*rods and cones*) and the cell bodies of neurons (e.g., bipolar and ganglion cells).

Because the optic vesicle invaginates as it forms the optic cup, the neural retina is "inverted"; that is, light-sensitive parts of the photoreceptor cells are adjacent to the retinal pigment epithelium. As a result, light must pass through most of the retina before reaching the receptors; however, because the retina is thin and transparent, it does not form a barrier to light. The

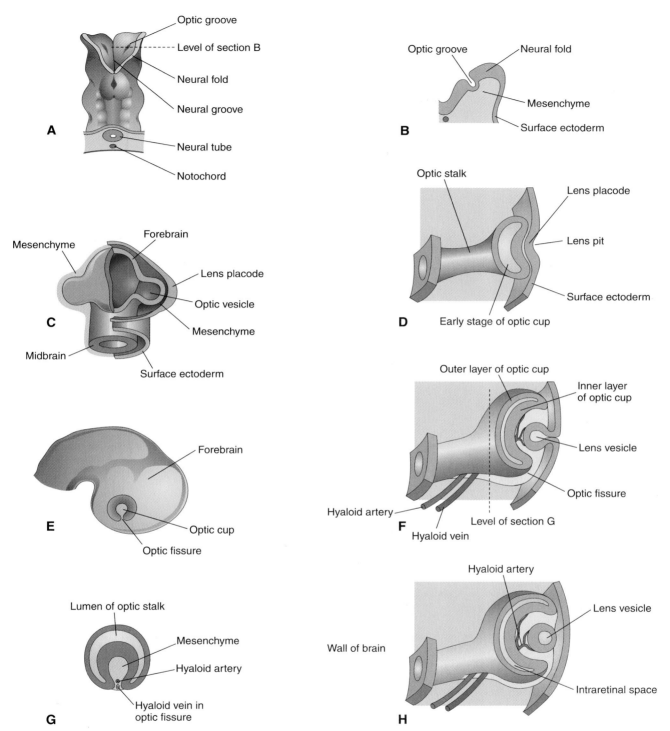

Figure 20–1. Drawings illustrating early stages of eye development. *A,* Dorsal view of the cranial end of an embryo of about 22 days showing the optic sulci or grooves, the first indication of eye development. Note that the neural folds have not fused to form the primary forebrain vesicles at this stage. *B,* Transverse section of a neural fold showing the optic sulcus. *C,* Schematic drawing of the forebrain of an embryo of about 28 days, showing its covering layers of mesenchyme and surface ectoderm. *D, F,* and *H,* Schematic sections of the developing eye illustrating successive stages in the development of the optic cup and lens vesicle. *E,* Lateral view of the brain of an embryo of about 32 days, showing the external appearance of the optic cup. *G,* Transverse section of the optic stalk showing the optic fissure and its contents. Note that the edges of the optic fissure are growing together, thereby completing the optic cup and enclosing the central artery and vein of the retina in the optic stalk and cup.

461

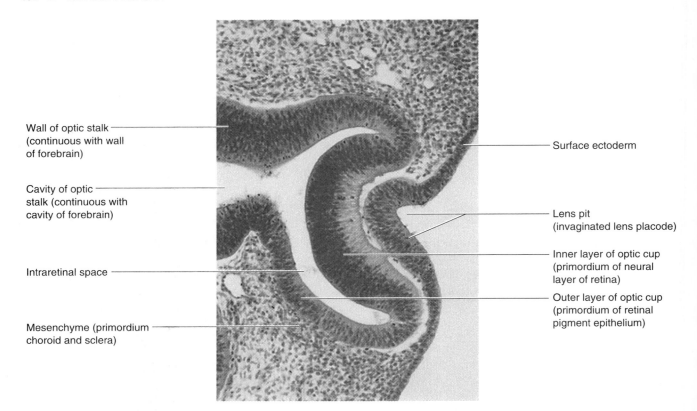

Wall of optic stalk
(continuous with wall
of forebrain)

Cavity of optic
stalk (continuous with
cavity of forebrain)

Intraretinal space

Mesenchyme (primordium
choroid and sclera)

Surface ectoderm

Lens pit
(invaginated lens placode)

Inner layer of optic cup
(primordium of neural
layer of retina)

Outer layer of optic cup
(primordium of retinal
pigment epithelium)

■ **Figure 20–2.** Photomicrograph of a sagittal section of the eye of an embryo (×200) at Carnegie stage 14, about 32 days. Observe the primordium of the lens (invaginated lens placode), the walls of the optic cup (primordium of the retina), and the optic stalk, the primordium of the optic nerve. (From Moore KL, Persaud TVN, Shiota K: *Color Atlas of Clinical Embryology.* Philadelphia, WB Saunders, 1994.)

axons of ganglion cells in the superficial layer of the neural retina grow proximally in the wall of the optic stalk to the brain (see Figs. 19–3 and 19–4). As a result, the cavity of the optic stalk is gradually obliterated as the axons of the many ganglion cells form the **optic nerve** (Fig. 20–3F).

Myelination of optic nerve fibers is incomplete at birth. After the eyes have been exposed to light for about 10 weeks, myelination is complete, but the process normally stops short of the optic disc. The normal newborn infant can see but not too well; it responds to changes in illumination and is able to fixate points of contrast. Visual acuity has been estimated to be in the range of 20/400 (Nelson, 1996). At 2 weeks the infant shows a more sustained interest in large objects.

Congenital Anomalies of the Eye

Because of the complexity of eye development, many anomalies occur, but most of them are uncommon. The type and severity of the anomaly depend upon the embryonic stage during which development is disrupted. Several environmental teratogens cause congenital eye defects (Stromland et al, 1991; see Chapter 9). Most common eye anomalies result from *defects in closure of the optic fissure* (Wright, 1997). For descriptions and illustrations of rare congenital eye anomalies, such as *cyclopia* (single eye), see Moore and Persaud (1998).

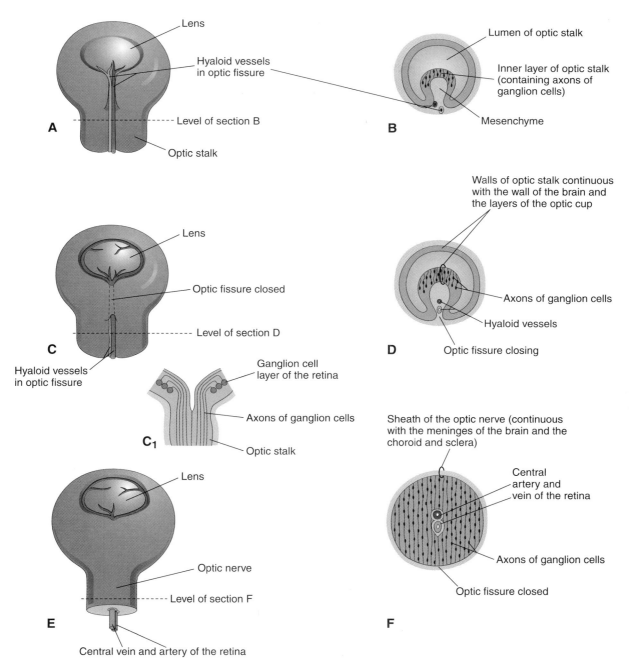

■ **Figure 20-3.** Diagrams illustrating closure of the optic fissure and formation of the optic nerve. *A, C,* and *E,* Views of the inferior surface of the optic cup and stalk, showing progressive stages in the closure of the optic fissure. *C₁,* Schematic sketch of a longitudinal section of a part of the optic cup and stalk, showing axons of ganglion cells of the retina growing through the optic stalk to the brain. *B, D,* and *F,* Transverse sections of the optic stalk, showing successive stages in closure of the optic fissure and formation of the optic nerve. The optic fissure normally closes during the sixth week. Defects in closure of the fissure result in coloboma of the iris and/or retina. Note that the lumen of the optic stalk is gradually obliterated as axons of ganglion cells accumulate in the inner layer of the optic stalk as the optic nerve forms.

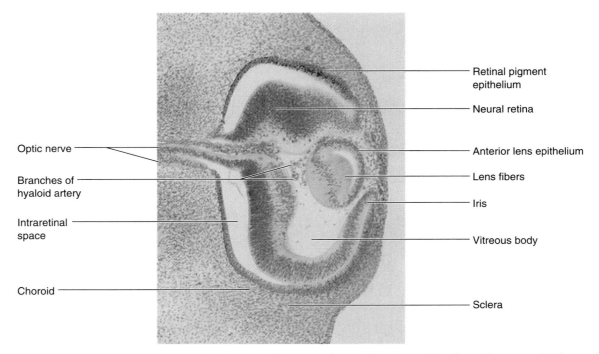

Figure 20–4. Photomicrograph of a sagittal section of the eye of an embryo (×100) at Carnegie stage 18, about 44 days. Observe that the posterior wall of the lens vesicle forms the lens fibers. The anterior wall does not change appreciably as it becomes the anterior lens epithelium. (From Nishimura H [ed]: *Atlas of Human Prenatal Histology.* Tokyo, Igaku-Shoin, 1983.)

Congenital Detachment of the Retina

Congenital detachment of the retina occurs when the inner and outer layers of the optic cup fail to fuse during the fetal period to form the retina and obliterate the intraretinal space (Figs. 20–3 and 20–4). The separation of the neural and pigmented layers of the retina may be partial or complete. Retinal detachment may result from unequal rates of growth of the two retinal layers; as a result, the layers of the optic cup are not in perfect apposition. Sometimes the layers of the optic cup appear to have fused and separated later; such secondary detachments usually occur in association with other anomalies of the eye and head. Knowledge about eye development makes it clear that where there is a detached retina it is not a detachment of the entire retina because the retinal pigment epithelium remains firmly attached to the underlying choroid. The detachment is at the site of adherence of the outer and inner layers of the optic cup. Although separated from the retinal pigment epithelium, the neural retina retains its blood supply (central artery of retina), derived from the embryonic hyaloid artery. Normally the retinal pigment epithelium becomes firmly fixed to the choroid, but its attachment to the neural retina is not firm; hence, a **detached retina** may follow a blow to the eyeball, as may occur during a boxing match. As a result, fluid accumulates between the layers and vision is impaired.

Coloboma of the Retina

This defect is characterized by a localized gap in the retina, usually inferior to the optic disc. The defect is bilateral in most cases. *A typical coloboma results from defective closure of the optic fissure.*

Development of the Ciliary Body

The ciliary body is the wedge-shaped extension of the choroid (Gartner and Hiatt, 1997). Its medial surface projects toward the lens, forming fingerlike **ciliary processes** (Fig. 20–5). The pigmented portion of the ciliary epithelium is derived from the outer layer of

Nonpigmented portion of
the ciliary epithelium
(continuous with the
neural layer of the retina)

Pigmented portion of
the ciliary epithelium
(continuous with the pigment
epithelium of the retina)

Ciliary
processes

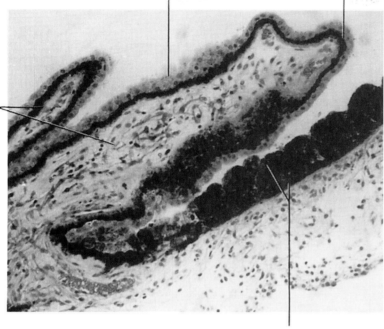

■ **Figure 20–5.** Photomicrograph of the root of the adult iris (*right*) and ciliary processes, showing ciliary and iridial parts of the retina (×215). (From Leeson TS, Leeson CR [eds]: *Histology,* 3rd ed. Philadelphia, WB Saunders, 1976.)

Double-layered epithelium of the iris
(continuous with the neural and
pigmented layers of the retina)

the optic cup and is continuous with the retinal pigment epithelium (Figs. 20–5 and 20–6*D*). The nonpigmented portion of the ciliary epithelium represents the anterior prolongation of the neural retina, in which no neural elements differentiate. The smooth **ciliary muscle** responsible for focusing the lens and the connective tissue in the ciliary body develop from mesenchyme located at the edge of the optic cup in the region between the anterior scleral condensation and the ciliary pigment epithelium.

Development of the Iris

The iris develops from the rim of the optic cup, which grows inward and partially covers the lens (Figs. 20–5 and 20–6*D*). The two layers of the optic cup have remained thin in this area. The epithelium of the iris represents both layers of the optic cup; it is continuous with the double-layered epithelium of the ciliary body and with the retinal pigment epithelium and neural retina. The connective tissue framework (stroma) of the iris is derived from neural crest cells

that migrate into the iris (Carlson, 1994). The **dilator pupillae** and **sphincter pupillae muscles** of the iris are *derived from neuroectoderm of the optic cup.* They appear to arise from the anterior epithelial cells of the iris. These smooth muscles result from a transformation of epithelial cells into smooth muscle cells.

Color of the Iris

The iris is typically light blue or gray in most newborn infants. It acquires its definitive color as pigmentation occurs during the first 6 to 10 months. It is the concentration and distribution of pigment-containing cells —**chromatophores**—in the loose vascular connective tissue of the iris that determines eye color. If the melanin pigment is confined to the pigmented epithelium on the posterior surface of the iris, the eye appears blue. If melanin is also distributed throughout the stroma of the iris, the eye appears brown.

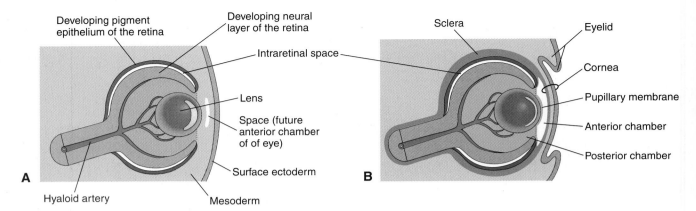

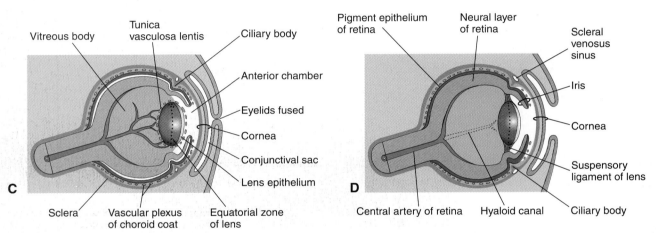

■ **Figure 20–6.** Diagrammatic drawings of sagittal sections of the eye, showing successive developmental stages of the lens, retina, iris, and cornea. *A,* Five weeks. *B,* Six weeks. *C,* Twenty weeks. *D,* Newborn. Note that the layers of the optic cup fuse to form the retinal pigment epithelium and neural retina and that they extend anteriorly as the double epithelium of the ciliary body and its iris. The retina and optic nerve are formed from the optic cup and optic stalk (outgrowths to the brain). At birth the eye is about three-quarters adult size. Most growth occurs during the first year. After puberty, growth of the eye is negligible.

Coloboma of the Iris

In these infants there is a defect in the inferior sector of the iris or a notch in the pupillary margin, giving the pupil a keyhole appearance (Fig. 20-7). The coloboma may be limited to the iris, or it may extend deeper and involve the ciliary body and retina. *A typical coloboma results from failure of closure of the optic fissure during the sixth week.* The defect may be genetically determined or may be caused by environmental factors. A simple coloboma of the iris is frequently hereditary and is transmitted as an autosomal dominant characteristic (Behrman et al, 1996).

Development of the Lens

The lens develops from the **lens vesicle,** a derivative of the surface ectoderm (Fig. 20-1). The anterior wall of this vesicle, composed of cuboidal epithelium, does not change appreciably as it becomes the **subcapsular lens epithelium** (Fig. 20-6C). The nuclei of the tall columnar cells forming the posterior wall of the lens vesicle undergo dissolution. These cells lengthen considerably to form highly transparent epithelial cells, the **primary lens fibers.** As these fibers grow, they gradually obliterate the cavity of the lens vesicle (Figs. 20-6A to C, 20-8 and 20-9). The rim of the lens is known as the **equatorial zone** or region because it is located midway between the anterior and posterior poles of the lens. The cells in the equatorial zone are

the **hyaloid artery** (Figs. 20-4 and 20-6); however, it becomes avascular in the fetal period when this part of the artery degenerates. After this occurs, the lens depends on diffusion from the aqueous humor in the anterior chamber of the eye, which bathes its anterior surface, and from the vitreous humor in other parts. The developing lens is invested by a vascular mesenchymal layer, the **tunica vasculosa lentis.** The anterior part of this capsule is the *pupillary membrane* (Fig. 20-6B and C). The part of the hyaloid artery that supplies the tunica vasculosa lentis disappears during the late fetal period. As a result, the tunica vasculosa lentis and pupillary membrane degenerate (Fig. 20-6D); however, the **lens capsule** produced by the anterior lens epithelium and the lens fibers persists. The lens capsule represents a greatly thickened basement membrane and has a lamellar structure because of its development. The former site of the hyaloid artery is indicated by the **hyaloid canal** in the vitreous body (Fig. 20-6D), which is usually inconspicuous in the living eye.

The **vitreous body** forms within the cavity of the optic cup (Fig. 20-6C). It is composed of **vitreous humor,** an avascular mass of transparent, gelled, intercellular substance. The **primary vitreous humor** is derived from mesenchymal cells of neural crest origin. The primary vitreous humor does not increase, but it is surrounded by a gelatinous **secondary vitreous humor,** the origin of which is uncertain (Wright, 1997).

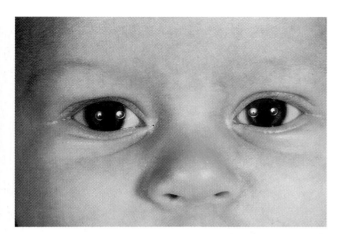

■ **Figure 20-7.** Bilateral coloboma of the iris. Observe the defect in the inferior part of the iris (at the 6-o'clock position). (Courtesy of A. E. Chudley, MD, Section of Genetics and Metabolism, Department of Pediatrics and Child Health, Children's Hospital, University of Manitoba, Winnipeg, Manitoba, Canada.)

cuboidal; as they elongate, they lose their nuclei and become **secondary lens fibers.** These fibers are added to the external sides of the primary lens fibers. Although secondary lens fibers continue to form during adulthood and the lens increases in diameter, the primary lens fibers must last a lifetime.

The developing lens is supplied by the distal part of

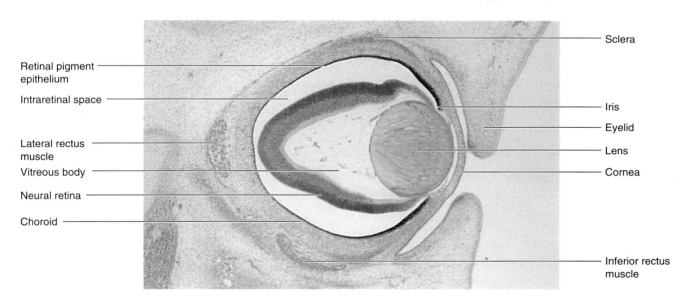

■ **Figure 20-8.** Photomicrograph of a sagittal section of the eye of an embryo (×50) at Carnegie stage 23, about 56 days. Observe the developing neural retina and the retinal pigment epithelium. The intraretinal space normally disappears as these two layers of the retina fuse. (From Moore KL, Persaud TVN, Shiota K: *Color Atlas of Clinical Embryology.* Philadelphia, WB Saunders, 1994.)

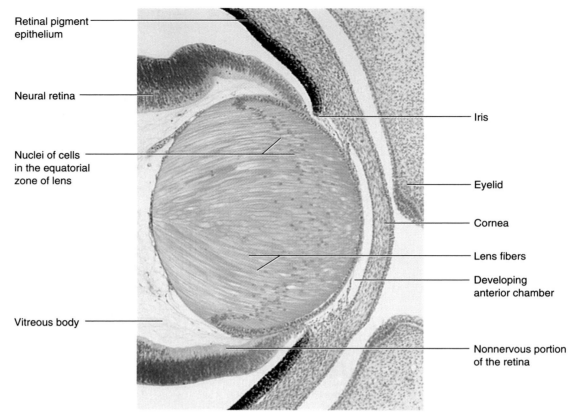

■ **Figure 20–9.** Photomicrograph of a sagittal section of a portion of the developing eye of an embryo (×280) at Carnegie stage 23, about 56 days. Observe that the lens fibers have elongated and obliterated the cavity of the lens vesicle. Note that the inner layer of the optic cup has thickened greatly to form the neural retina and that the outer layer is heavily pigmented (retinal pigment eqithelium). (From Moore KL, Persaud TVN, Shiota K: *Color Atlas of Clinical Embryology.* Philadelphia, WB Saunders, 1994.)

Persistence of the Hyaloid Artery

The distal part of the hyaloid artery normally degenerates as its proximal part becomes the central artery of the retina. If a small part of the artery persists distally, it may appear as a freely moving, nonfunctional vessel or as a wormlike structure projecting from the optic disc. Sometimes the hyaloid artery remnant may appear as a fine strand traversing the vitreous body. In other cases a remnant of the hyaloid artery may form a cyst. In unusual cases, the entire distal part of the artery persists and extends from the optic disc through the vitreous body to the lens. In most of these infants, the eye is microphthalmic (very small), but in some cases the eye is otherwise normal.

Development of Aqueous Chambers

The **anterior chamber of the eye** develops from a cleftlike space that forms in the mesenchyme located between the developing lens and cornea (Figs. 20–4 and 20–9). The mesenchyme superficial to this space forms the substantia propria of the cornea and the mesothelium of the anterior chamber. After the lens is established, it induces the surface ectoderm to develop into the epithelium of the cornea and the conjunctiva. The **posterior chamber of the eye** develops from a space that forms in the mesenchyme posterior to the developing iris and anterior to the developing lens. When the pupillary membrane disappears and the pupil forms (Fig. 20–6C and D), the anterior and posterior chambers of the eye are able to communicate with each other through a circumferential **scleral venous sinus**

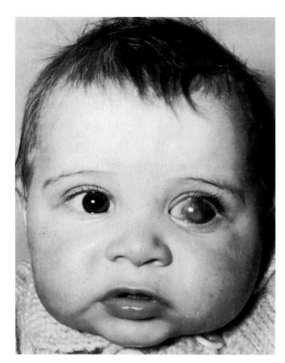

■ **Figure 20-10.** Child with congenital glaucoma of the left eye. (Courtesy of C. A. Brown, MD, Consultant Ophthalmologist, Bristol Eye Hospital, England.)

(sinus venosus sclerae, canal of Schlemm). This sinus (canal) is the *outflow site of aqueous humor* from the anterior chamber of the eye to the venous system.

Congenital Glaucoma

Abnormal elevation of intraocular pressure in newborn infants usually results from abnormal development of the drainage mechanism of the aqueous humor during the fetal period (Fig. 20-10). *Intraocular tension* rises because of an imbalance between the production of aqueous humor and its outflow. This imbalance may result from abnormal development of the *scleral venous sinus* in the iridocorneal angle or angle of the anterior chamber (Fig. 20-6D). Congenital glaucoma is usually caused by recessive mutant genes, but the condition may result from a rubella infection during early pregnancy (see Chapter 9).

Congenital Cataracts

In this condition the lens is opaque and frequently appears grayish white. Blindness results. Many lens opacities are inherited, dominant transmission being more common than recessive or sex-linked transmission (Behrman et al, 1996). Some congenital cataracts are caused by teratogenic agents, particularly the *rubella virus* (Fig. 20-11), that affect early development of the lenses. The lenses are vulnerable to **rubella virus** between the fourth and seventh weeks when primary lens fibers are forming. Cataract and other ocular abnormalities caused by the rubella virus could be completely prevented if immunity to rubella were conferred on all women of reproductive age. Physical agents, such as **radiation,** can also damage the lens and produce cataracts. For a discussion of other causes of congenital cataracts, see Moore and Persaud (1998).

Development of the Cornea

The cornea is formed from three sources:

• The external **corneal epithelium** is derived from **surface ectoderm**
• The embryonic connective tissue or mesenchyme is derived from **mesoderm,** which is continuous with the developing sclera.
• **Neural crest cells** migrate from the lip of the optic cup through the embryonic connective tissue and differentiate into the **corneal endothelium.**

Formation of the cornea is induced by the lens vesicle. The inductive influence results in transformation of the surface ectoderm into the transparent avascular cornea, the part of the fibrous tunic of the eye that bulges out of the orbit.

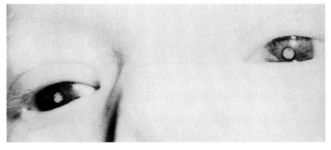

■ **Figure 20-11.** Typical bilateral congenital cataracts resulting from the teratogenic effects of the rubella virus. (Courtesy of Richard Bargy, MD, Department of Ophthalmology, Cornell-New York Hospital, New York, New York.)

Development of the Choroid and Sclera

The mesenchyme surrounding the optic cup (largely of neural crest origin) reacts to the inductive influence of the retinal pigment epithelium by differentiating into an inner vascular layer, the **choroid,** and an outer fibrous layer, the **sclera** (Fig. 20-6). The sclera develops from a condensation of the mesenchyme external to the choroid and is continuous with the stroma of the cornea. Toward the rim of the optic cup, the choroid becomes modified to form the cores of the **ciliary processes,** consisting chiefly of capillaries supported by delicate connective tissue. The first choroidal blood vessels appear during the 15th week; by the 22nd week, arteries and veins can be distinguished.

Edema of the Optic Disc

The optic nerve is surrounded by three sheaths, which evaginate with the optic vesicle and stalk; consequently, they are continuous with the meninges of the brain.

- The outer dural sheath from the dura mater is thick and fibrous and blends with the sclera of the eye.
- The intermediate sheath from the arachnoid mater is thin.
- The inner sheath from the pia mater is vascular and closely invests the optic nerve and central vessels of the retina as far as the optic disc.
- Cerebrospinal fluid is present in the subarachnoid space between the intermediate and inner sheaths of the optic nerve.

The relationship of the sheaths of the optic nerve to the meninges of the brain and the subarachnoid space is important clinically (Moore and Agur, 1995). An increase in CSF pressure (often resulting from increased intracranial pressure) slows venous return from the retina, causing papilledema (fluid accumulation) of the optic disc. This occurs because the retinal vessels are covered by pia mater and lie in the extension of the subarachnoid space that surrounds the optic nerve.

Development of the Eyelids

The eyelids develop during the sixth week from neural crest mesenchyme and from two folds of skin that grow over the cornea (Fig. 20-6B). The eyelids adhere to one another by the beginning of the 10th week, and remain adherent until the 26th to 28th weeks (Fig. 20-6C). While the eyelids are adherent, there is a closed **conjunctival sac** anterior to the cornea; when the eyes begin to open, the **bulbar conjunctiva** is reflected over the anterior part of the sclera and the surface epithelium of the cornea. The **palpebral conjunctiva** lines the inner surface of the eyelids. For a detailed account of the development of the eyelids, see Wright (1997). The eyelashes and glands are derived from the surface ectoderm in a manner similar to that described for other parts of the integument (see Chapter 21). The connective tissue and tarsal plates develop from mesenchyme in the developing eyelids. The *orbicularis oculi muscle* is derived from the mesenchyme in the second pharyngeal arch (see Chapter 11) and is supplied by its nerve (CN VII).

Congenital Ptosis of the Eyelid

Drooping of the upper eyelids at birth is relatively common (Fig. 20-12). Ptosis (blepharoptosis) may result from failure of normal development of the **levator**

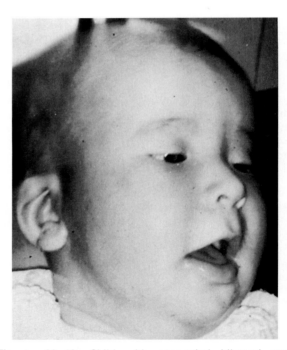

■ Figure 20-12. Child with congenital bilateral ptosis. Drooping of the upper eyelid usually results from abnormal development or failure of development of the levator palpebrae superioris, the muscle that elevates the eyelid. In bilateral cases, as here, the infant contracts the frontalis muscle of the forehead in an attempt to raise the eyelids. (From Avery ME, Taeusch HW Jr: *Schaffer's Diseases of the Newborn,* 5th ed. Philadelphia, WB Saunders, 1984.)

THE EYE AND EAR ■ 471

palpebrae superioris muscle (Moore, 1992). Congenital ptosis (Gr. a falling) may also result from prenatal injury or abnormal development of the superior division of the **oculomotor nerve** (CN III), which supplies this muscle. If ptosis is associated with inability to move the eyeball superiorly, there is also failure of the superior rectus muscle of the eye to develop normally. *Congenital ptosis is hereditary;* an isolated defect is usually transmitted as an autosomal dominant trait (Nelson, 1996). Congenital ptosis is associated with several syndromes; for details, see Behrman et al (1996).

Coloboma of the Eyelid

Large defects of the eyelid (**palpebral coloboma**) are uncommon (Fig. 20–13). Most colobomas are usually characterized by a small notch in the upper eyelid, but the defect may involve almost the entire lid. Coloboma of the lower eyelid is rare. Palpebral colobomas appear to result from local developmental disturbances in the formation and growth of the eyelid.

Development of Lacrimal Glands

At the superolateral angles of the orbits, the lacrimal glands develop from a number of solid buds that are evaginations of the surface ectoderm. The buds branch and become canalized to form the ducts and alveoli of the glands. The lacrimal glands are small at birth and do not function fully until about 6 weeks; hence, the newborn infant does not produce tears when it cries.

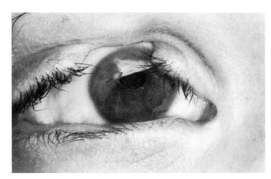

■ **Figure 20–13.** Photograph of the eye of a child with a coloboma of the iris and upper eyelid. (From Brown CA: Abnormalities of the eyes and associated structures. *In* Norman AP (ed): *Congenital Abnormalities in Infancy,* 2nd ed. Edinburgh, Blackwell Scientific Publications, 1971.)

Tears are often not present with crying until 1 to 3 months (Nelson, 1996).

DEVELOPMENT OF THE EAR

The ear is composed of three anatomic parts:

* The *external ear,* consisting of the auricle (pinna), the external acoustic (auditory) meatus, and the external layer of the tympanic membrane (eardrum)
* The *middle ear,* consisting of a chain of three auditory ossicles (small ear bones), which connect the internal layer of the tympanic membrane to the oval window of the internal ear
* The *internal ear,* consisting of the vestibulocochlear organ, which is concerned with both hearing and balance.

The external and middle parts are concerned with the transference of sound waves from the exterior to the internal ear, which converts the sound waves into nerve impulses and registers changes in equilibrium.

Development of Internal Ear

The internal (inner) ear is the first of the three anatomic parts to begin development. Early in the fourth week a thickening of surface ectoderm, the **otic placode,** appears on each side of the myelencephalon, the caudal part of the hindbrain (Fig. 20–14A and B). Inductive influences from the notochord and paraxial mesoderm stimulate the surface ectoderm to form the otic placodes. Each otic placode soon invaginates and sinks deep to the surface ectoderm into the underlying mesenchyme. In so doing it forms an **otic pit** (Fig. 20–14C and D). The edges of the otic pit soon come together and fuse to form an **otic vesicle** (otocyst), the primordium of the *membranous labyrinth* (Fig. 20–14E to G). The otic vesicle soon loses its connection with the surface ectoderm, and a diverticulum grows from the otic vesicle and elongates to form the **endolymphatic duct** and **sac** (Fig. 20–15A to E). Two regions of the otic vesicle are now recognizable:

* A dorsal **utricular part,** from which the endolymphatic duct, utricle, and semicircular ducts arise
* A ventral **saccular part,** which gives rise to the saccule and cochlear duct in which the spiral organ (of Corti) is located

Three flat, disklike diverticula grow out from the utricular part of the developing **membranous laby-**

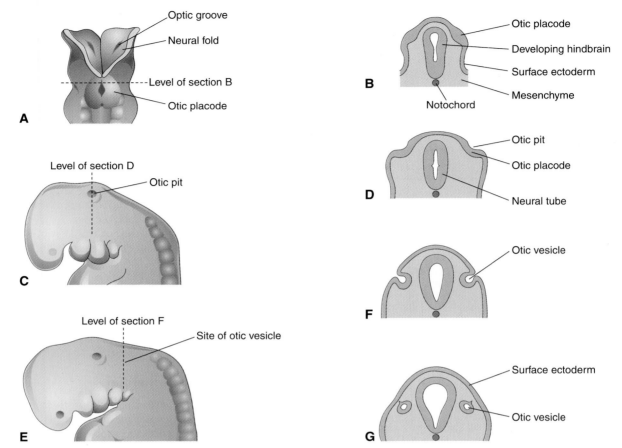

■ **Figure 20–14.** Drawings illustrating early development of the internal ear. *A,* Dorsal view of a 4-week embryo (about 22 days), showing the otic placodes. *B, D, F,* and *G,* Schematic coronal sections illustrating successive stages in the development of otic vesicles. *C* and *E,* Lateral views of the cranial region of embryos, about 24 and 28 days, respectively.

rinth. Soon the central parts of these diverticula fuse and disappear (Fig. 20-15*B* to *E*). The peripheral unfused parts of the diverticula become the **semicircular ducts,** which are attached to the utricle and are later enclosed in the **semicircular canals** of the bony labyrinth. Localized dilatations, the **ampullae,** develop at one end of each semicircular duct. Sensory nerve endings — cristae ampullares — differentiate in these ampullae and in the utricle and saccule (maculae utriculi and sacculi).

From the ventral saccular part of the otic vesicle, a tubular diverticulum — the **cochlear duct** — grows and coils to form the *membranous cochlea* (Fig. 20-15*C* to *E*). A connection of the cochlea with the saccule, the **ductus reuniens,** soon forms. The **spiral organ** (of Corti) differentiates from cells in the wall of the cochlear duct (Fig. 20-15*F* to *I*). Ganglion cells

of the eighth cranial nerve migrate along the coils of the membranous cochlea and form the **spiral ganglion** (cochlear ganglion). Nerve processes extend from this ganglion to the **spiral organ,** where they terminate on the hair cells. The cells in the spiral ganglion retain their embryonic bipolar condition; that is, they do not become unipolar like spinal ganglion cells.

Inductive influences from the otic vesicle stimulate the mesenchyme around the otic vesicle to condense and differentiate into a cartilaginous **otic capsule** (Fig. 20-15*F*). It was suggested from the results of histochemical and in vitro studies that the transforming growth factor-β (TGF-β) may play a role in modulating epithelial-mesenchymal interaction in the internal ear and in directing the formation of the otic capsule (Frenz et al, 1991). As the **membranous labyrinth**

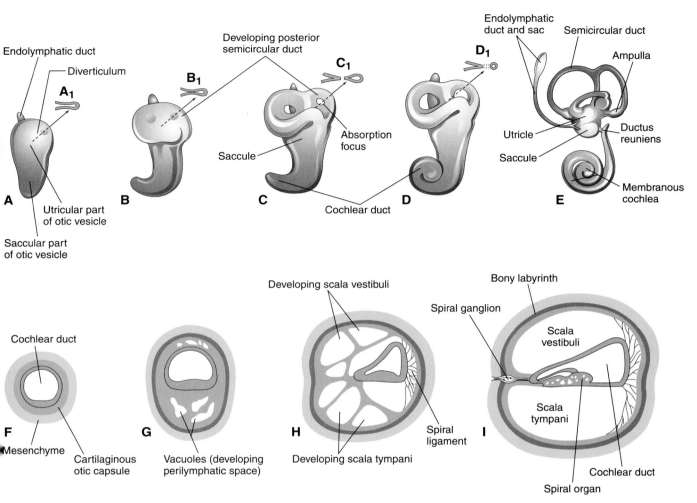

Figure 20–15. Drawings of the otic vesicle showing development of the membranous and bony labyrinths of the internal ear. *A* to *E*, Lateral views showing successive stages in the development of the otic vesicle into the membranous labyrinth from the fifth to eighth weeks. *A₁* to *D₁*, Diagrammatic sketches illustrating development of a semicircular duct. *F* to *I*, Sections through the cochlear duct showing successive stages in the development of the spiral organ (of Corti) and the perilymphatic space from the 8th to the 20th weeks.

enlarges, vacuoles appear in the cartilaginous otic capsule, which soon coalesce to form the **perilymphatic space.** The membranous labyrinth is now suspended in **perilymph** (fluid in perilymphatic space). The perilymphatic space related to the cochlear duct develops two divisions, the **scala tympani** and **scala vestibuli** (Fig. 20–15*H* and *I*). The cartilaginous otic capsule later ossifies to form the **bony labyrinth** of the internal ear. The internal ear reaches its adult size and shape by the middle of the fetal period (20 to 22 weeks).

Development of the Middle Ear

Development of the tubotympanic recess (Fig. 20–16*B*) from the first pharyngeal pouch is described in Chapter 11. The proximal part of the tubotympanic recess forms the **pharyngotympanic tube** (auditory tube). The distal part of the tubotympanic recess expands and becomes the **tympanic cavity** (Fig. 20–16*C*), which gradually envelops the **auditory ossicles** (malleus, incus, and stapes), their tendons and ligaments, and the chorda tympani nerve. All these struc-

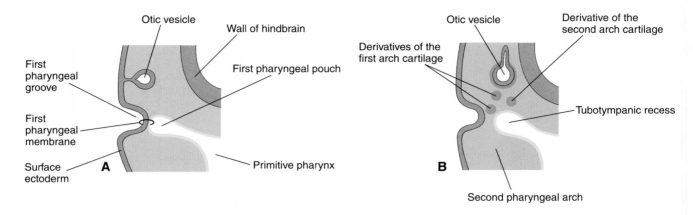

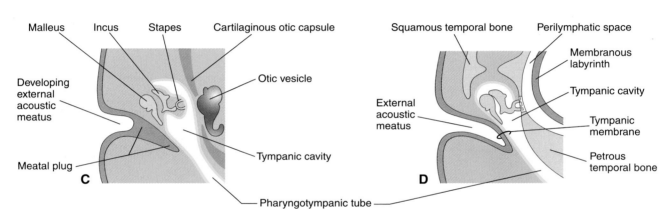

■ **Figure 20–16.** Schematic drawings illustrating development of the external and middle ear. Observe the relationship of these parts of the ear to the otic vesicle, the primordium of the internal ear. *A*, Four weeks, illustrating the relation of the otic vesicle to the pharyngeal apparatus. *B*, Five weeks, showing the tubotympanic recess and pharyngeal arch cartilages. *C*, Later stage, showing the tubotympanic recess (future tympanic cavity and mastoid antrum) beginning to envelop the ossicles. *D*, Final stage of ear development, showing the relationship of the middle ear to the perilymphatic space and the external acoustic meatus. Note that the tympanic membrane develops from three germ layers: surface ectoderm, mesoderm, and endoderm of the tubotympanic recess.

tures receive a more or less complete epithelial investment. From a study of early human embryos and fetuses, it has been suggested that an epithelial-type organizer located at the tip of the tubotympanic recess probably plays a role in the early development of the middle ear and tympanic membrane (Michaels, 1988).

During the late fetal period, expansion of the tympanic cavity gives rise to the **mastoid antrum,** located in the petromastoid part of the temporal bone (Moore, 1992). The mastoid antrum is almost adult size at birth; however, *no mastoid cells are present in newborn infants.* By 2 years of age the mastoid cells are well-developed and produce conical projections of the temporal bones, the **mastoid processes.** The middle ear continues to grow through puberty (Behrman

et al, 1996). Development of the **auditory ossicles** (middle ear bones) is described in Chapter 11. The *tensor tympani,* the muscle attached to the malleus, is derived from mesenchyme in the first pharyngeal arch and is innervated by CN V, the nerve of this arch. The *stapedius muscle* is derived from the second pharyngeal arch and is supplied by CN VII, the nerve of that arch.

Development of the External Ear

The **external acoustic meatus** develops from the dorsal end of the first pharyngeal groove (cleft). The ectodermal cells at the bottom of this funnel-shaped tube proliferate to form a solid epithelial plate, the

meatal plug (Fig. 20-16C). Late in the fetal period the central cells of this plug degenerate, forming a cavity that becomes the internal part of the external acoustic meatus (Fig. 20-16D). This meatus is relatively short at birth; because of this, care must be taken not to injure the tympanic membrane. The external acoustic meatus attains its adult length around the ninth year.

The primordium of the **tympanic membrane** is the first pharyngeal membrane, which separates the first pharyngeal groove from the first pharyngeal pouch (Fig. 20-16A). As development proceeds, mesenchyme grows between the two parts of the pharyngeal membrane and differentiates into the collagenic fibers in the tympanic membrane. The external covering (very thin skin) of the tympanic membrane is derived from the surface ectoderm, whereas its internal lining is derived from the endoderm of the tubotympanic recess. To summarize, the tympanic membrane develops from three sources:

- *Ectoderm* of the first pharyngeal groove
- *Endoderm* of the tubotympanic recess, a derivative of the first pharyngeal pouch
- *Mesoderm* of the first and second pharyngeal arches

The **auricle** (pinna) develops from six mesenchymal proliferations in the first and second pharyngeal arches. The prominences—**auricular hillocks**—surround the first pharyngeal groove (Fig. 20-17A). As the auricle grows, the contribution by the first arch is reduced (Fig. 20-17B to D). The lobule (earlobe) is the last part to develop. The auricles begin to develop at the base of the neck (Fig. 20-17A and B). As the mandible develops, the auricles move to their normal position at the side of the head. (Fig. 20-17D). The external ears continue to grow through puberty. The parts of the auricle derived from the first pharyngeal arch are supplied by its nerve, the mandibular branch of the trigeminal nerve; the parts derived from the second arch are supplied by cutaneous branches of the **cervical plexus,** especially the lesser occipital and greater auricular nerves. The facial nerve of the second pharyngeal arch has few cutaneous branches; some of its fibers contribute to the sensory innervation of the skin in the mastoid region and probably in small areas on both aspects of the auricle (Moore, 1992).

Congenital Deafness

Because formation of the internal ear is independent of development of the middle and external ears, congenital impairment of hearing may be the result of

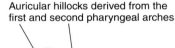
Auricular hillocks derived from the first and second pharyngeal arches

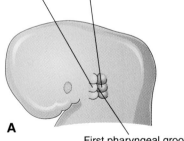

A

First pharyngeal groove

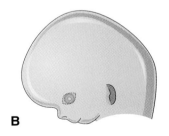

B

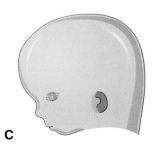

C

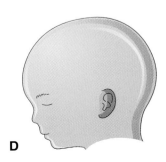

D

■ **Figure 20-17.** Drawings illustrating development of the auricle. *A,* Six weeks. Note that three auricular hillocks are located on the first pharyngeal arch and three on the second arch. *B,* Eight weeks. *C,* Ten weeks. *D,* Thirty-two weeks. As the mandible and teeth develop, the auricles move from the neck to the side of the head.

maldevelopment of the sound-conducting apparatus of the middle and external ears (De la Cruz and Doyle, 1994) or of the neurosensory structures in the internal ear. Most types of congenital deafness are caused by genetic factors. In **deaf-mutism** the ear abnormality is usually perceptive in type. Congenital deafness may be associated with several other head and neck anomalies as a part of the *first arch syndrome* (see Chapter 11). Abnormalities of the malleus and incus are often associated with this syndrome. A *rubella infection* during the critical period of development of the internal ear, particularly the seventh and eighth weeks, can cause maldevelopment of the spiral organ and deafness. Congenital deafness may also be associated with maternal goiter, which may result in fetal hypothyroidism. **Congenital fixation of the stapes** results in conductive deafness in an otherwise normal ear. Failure of differentiation of the *anular ligament*, which attaches the base of the stapes to the fenestra vestibuli (Moore, 1992), results in fixation of the stapes to the bony labyrinth.

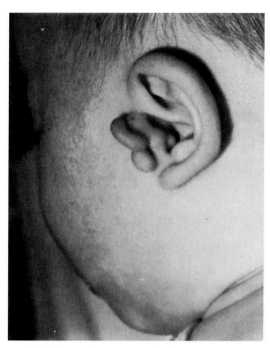

■ **Figure 20–18.** Photograph of a child with two auricular appendages (skin tags), which resulted from the formation of accessory auricular hillocks. (From Swenson O: *Pediatric Surgery.* New York, Appleton-Century-Crofts, 1958.)

Auricular Abnormalities

Severe anomalies of the external ear are rare, but minor deformities are common (Behrman et al, 1996). A wide normal variation exists in the shape of the auricle. Almost any minor auricular defect may occasionally be found as a usual feature in a particular family (Jones, 1997). Minor anomalies of the auricles may serve as indicators of a specific pattern of congenital anomalies. For example, the auricles are often abnormal in shape and low-set in infants with chromosomal syndromes such as trisomy 18 and in infants affected by maternal ingestion of certain drugs (e.g., trimethadione).

Auricular Appendages

Auricular appendages (skin tags) are common and result from the development of accessory auricular hillocks (Fig. 20–18). The appendages usually appear anterior to the auricle, more often unilaterally than bilaterally. The appendages, often with narrow pedicles, consist of skin but they may contain some cartilage.

Microtia

Microtia (small auricle) results from suppressed development of the auricular hillocks (Fig. 20–19). This anomaly often serves as an indicator of associated anomalies, such as an atresia of the external acoustic meatus and middle ear anomalies.

Preauricular Sinuses

Pitlike cutaneous depressions or shallow sinuses are commonly located in a triangular area anterior to the auricle (Fig. 20–20). The sinuses are usually narrow tubes or shallow pits that have pinpoint external openings. Some sinuses contain a vestigial cartilaginous mass. Preauricular sinuses may be associated with internal anomalies, such as deafness and kidney malformations. The embryological basis of auricular sinuses is uncertain, but some are related to abnormal development of the auricular hillocks and defective closure of the dorsal part of the first pharyngeal groove. This cleft normally disappears as the external auditory meatus forms. Other auricular sinuses appear to represent ectodermal folds that are sequestered during formation of the auricle (Moll, 1991). Preauricular sinuses are familial and frequently bilateral. They are asymptomatic and have only minor cosmetic importance; however, they often develop serious infections. *Auricular fistulas* (narrow canals) connecting the exterior with the tympanic cavity or the tonsillar sinus are extremely rare.

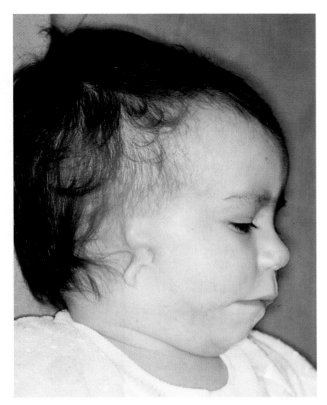

■ **Figure 20–19.** Child with a small rudimentry auricle (microtia). She also had several other congenital anomalies. (Courtesy of A. E. Chudley, MD, Section of Genetics and Metabolism, Department of Pediatrics and Child Health, Children's Hospital, University of Manitoba, Winnipeg, Manitoba, Canada.)

Atresia of the External Acoustic Meatus

Blockage of this auditory canal results from failure of the meatal plug to canalize (Fig. 20–16C). Usually the deep part of the meatus is open, but the superficial part is blocked by bone or fibrous tissue. Most cases are associated with the *first arch syndrome* (see Chapter 11). Often abnormal development of both the first and second pharyngeal arches is involved. Usually the auricle is also severely affected and anomalies of the iddle and/or internal ear are sometimes present. Atresia of the external acoustic meatus can occur bilaterally or unilaterally and usually results from autosomal dominant inheritance.

Absence of the External Acoustic Meatus

Absence of the external acoustic meatus is rare; often the auricle is normal (Fig. 20–21). This anomaly results from failure of inward expansion of the first pharyngeal groove and failure of the meatal plug to disappear (Fig. 20–16C).

SUMMARY OF DEVELOPMENT OF THE EYE

The first indication of the eye is the **optic groove,** which forms at the beginning of the fourth week. The groove deepens to form a hollow **optic vesicle** that projects from the forebrain. The optic vesicle contacts the surface ectoderm and induces development of the **lens placode,** the primordium of the lens. As the lens

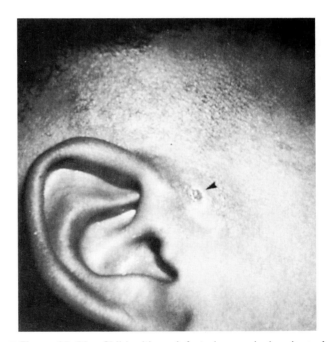

■ **Figure 20–20.** Child with an infected preauricular sinus. A small patch of chronic granulation tissue is seen at the external orifice of the sinus *(arrowhead)*. (From Raffensperger JG (ed): *Swenson's Pediatric Surgery,* 5th ed. New York, Appleton & Lange, 1990.)

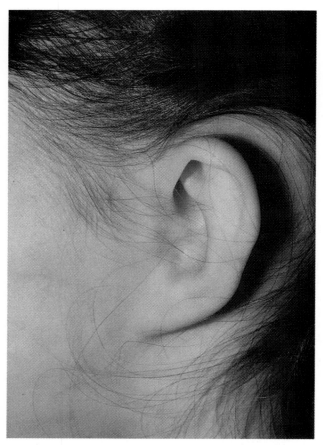

■ **Figure 20–21.** Child with no external acoustic meatus; however, the auricle is normal. A CT scan revealed normal middle and internal ear structures. (Courtesy of A. E. Chudley, MD, Section of Genetics and Metabolism, Department of Pediatrics and Child Health, Children's Hospital, University of Manitoba, Winnipeg, Manitoba, Canada.)

placode invaginates to form a **lens pit** and **lens vesicle,** the optic vesicle invaginates to form an **optic cup.** The retina forms from the two layers of the optic cup.

• The retina, the optic nerve fibers, the muscles of the iris, and the epithelium of the iris and ciliary body are derived from the *neuroectoderm* of the forebrain. The sphincter and dilator muscles of the iris develop from the ectoderm at the rim of the optic cup.
• The *surface ectoderm* gives rise to the lens and the epithelium of the lacrimal glands, eyelids, conjunctiva, and cornea.

• The *mesoderm* gives rise to the eye muscles, except those of the iris, and to all connective and vascular tissues of the cornea, iris, ciliary body, choroid, and sclera.

There are many **ocular anomalies,** but most of them are rare. The eye is very sensitive to the teratogenic effects of infectious agents (e.g., cytomegalovirus and rubella virus). The most serious defects result from disturbances of development during the fourth to sixth weeks, but defects of sight may result from infection of tissues and organs by certain microorganisms during the fetal period (e.g., rubella virus and *Treponema pallidum,* the microorganism that causes syphilis). Most ocular anomalies are caused by defective closure of the optic fissure during the sixth week (e.g., coloboma of the iris). *Congenital cataract* and *glaucoma* may result from intrauterine infections (e.g., rubella virus), but most congenital cataracts are inherited.

SUMMARY OF DEVELOPMENT OF THE EAR

The **otic vesicle** develops from the surface ectoderm during the fourth week. The vesicle develops into the **membranous labyrinth** of the internal ear. The otic vesicle divides into two parts:

• A dorsal utricular part, which gives rise to the utricle, semicircular ducts, and endolymphatic duct
• A ventral saccular part, which gives rise to the saccule and cochlear duct

The cochlear duct gives rise to the **spiral organ** (of Corti). The **bony labyrinth** develops from the mesenchyme adjacent to the membranous labyrinth. The epithelium lining the tympanic cavity, mastoid antrum, and **pharyngotympanic tube** (auditory tube) is derived from the endoderm of the tubotympanic recess, which develops from the first pharyngeal pouch. The **auditory ossicles** (malleus, incus, and stapes) develop from the dorsal ends of the cartilages in the first two pharyngeal arches.

The epithelium of the **external acoustic meatus** develops from the ectoderm of the first pharyngeal groove (cleft). The tympanic membrane is derived from three sources:

• Endoderm of the first pharyngeal pouch
• Ectoderm of the first pharyngeal groove
• Mesenchyme between the above layers

The auricle develops from six **auricular hillocks,** which form from mesenchymal prominences around the margins of the first pharyngeal groove. These hillocks fuse to form the auricle.

Congenital deafness may result from abnormal development of the membranous labyrinth and/or bony labyrinth, as well as from abnormalities of the auditory ossicles. *Recessive inheritance is the most common cause of congenital deafness,* but a rubella virus infection near the end of the embryonic period is a major environmental factor known to cause abnormal development of the spiral organ and defective hearing. There are many minor, clinically unimportant anomalies of the auricle; however, they alert the clinician to the possible presence of associated major anomalies (e.g., defects of the middle ear). Low-set, severely malformed ears are often associated with chromosomal abnormalities, particularly trisomy 18 and trisomy 13.

contaminated fish. Can you explain how these anomalies could be caused by methyl mercury?

The answers to these questions are given at the back of the book.

Clinically Oriented Questions

1. If a woman has rubella (German measles) during the first trimester of her pregnancy, what are the chances that the eyes and ears of the embryo/fetus will be affected? What is the most common manifestation of late fetal rubella infection in babies? If a pregnant woman is exposed to rubella, can it be determined if she is immune to the infection?

2. My grandmother told me that a good way of preventing the congenital anomalies caused by German measles is by the purposeful exposure of young girls to rubella (German measles). Is this the best way for me to prevent having a blind and deaf baby resulting from rubella infection during pregnancy? If not, what can be done to provide immunization against rubella infection?

3. A nurse told me that deafness and tooth defects occurring during childhood can result from what she called "fetal syphilis." Is this true? If so, how could this happen? Can these congenital defects be prevented?

4. I recently read that blindness and deafness can result from herpes virus infections. Is this true? If so, which herpes viruses are involved? What are the infant's chances of normal development?

5. I read in the paper that methyl mercury exposure in utero can cause mental retardation, deafness, and blindness. The mother had apparently been eating

REFERENCES AND SUGGESTED READING

Behrman RE, Kliegman RM, Arvin AM (eds): *Nelson Textbook of Pediatrics,* 15th ed. Philadelphia, WB Saunders, 1996.

Carlson, BM: *Human Embryology and Developmental Biology.* St. Louis, Mosby-Year Book, 1994.

De la Cruz A, Doyle KJ: Ossiculoplasty in congenital hearing loss. *Otolaryngol Clin North Am* 27:799, 1994.

Frenz DA, Van de Water TR, Galinovic-Schwartz V: Transforming growth factor beta: does it direct otic capsule formation. *Ann Otol Rhinol Laryngol* 100:301, 1991.

Gartner LP, Hiatt JL: *Color Textbook of Histology.* Philadelphia, WB Saunders, 1997.

Gorlin RJ, Toriello HV, Cohen MM Jr: *Hereditary Hearing Loss and its Syndromes.* New York, Oxford University Press, 1995.

Jones KL: *Smith's Recognizable Patterns of Human Malformation,* 5th ed. Philadelphia, WB Saunders, 1997.

Mathers PH, Grinberg A, Mahon KA, Jamrich M: The *Rx* homeobox gene is essential for vertebrate eye development. *Nature* 387:603, 1997.

Michaels L: Evolution of the epidermoid formation and its role in the development of the middle ear and tympanic membrane during the first trimester. *J Otolaryngol* 17:22, 1988.

Moll M: Congenital earpits or auricular sinuses. *Acta Path Microbiol Scand* 99:96, 1991.

Moore KL: *Clinically Oriented Anatomy,* 3rd ed. Baltimore, Williams & Wilkins, 1992.

Moore KL, Agur AMR: *Essential Clinical Anatomy.* Baltimore, Williams & Wilkins, 1995.

Moore KL, Persaud TVN: *The Developing Human. Clinically Oriented Embryology,* 6th ed. Philadelphia, WB Saunders, 1998.

Nelson L: Disorders of the eye. *In* Behrman RE, Kliegman RM, Arvin AM (eds): *Nelson Textbook of Pediatrics,* 15th ed. Philadelphia, WB Saunders, 1996.

Noden DM, Van de Water TR: Genetic analyses of mammalian ear development. *Trends Neurosci* 15:235, 1992.

Penfold PL, Provis JM, Madigan MC, et al: Angiogenesis in normal human retinal development: the involvement of astrocytes and macrophages. *Graefes Arch Clin Exp Ophthalmol* 228:255, 1990.

Stromland K, Miller M, Cook C: Ocular teratology. *Surv Ophthalmol* 35:429, 1991.

Takayama S, Yamamoto M, Hashimoto K, Itoh H: Immunohistochemical study in the developing optic nerves in human embryos and fetuses. *Brain Develop* 13:307, 1991.

Tripathi BJ, Tripathi RC, Livingston AM, Borisuth NSC: The role of growth factors in the embryogenesis and differentiation of the eye. *Am J Anat* 192:442, 1991.

Twefik TL, Der Kaloustian VM (eds): *Congenital Anomalies of the Ear, Nose, and Throat.* Oxford, Oxford University Press, 1996.

Wilson RS, Char F: Drug-induced ocular malformations. *In* Persaud TVN (ed): *Advances in the Study of Birth Defects.* Vol. 7: *Central Nervous System and Craniofacial Malformations.* New York, Alan R Liss, 1982.

Wright KW: Embryology and eye development. *In* Wright KW (ed): *Textbook of Ophthalmology.* Baltimore, Williams & Wilkins, 1997.

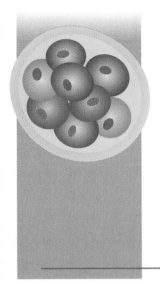

The Integumentary System

21

▪ The integumentary system consists of the skin and its derivatives: sweat glands, nails, hair, sebaceous glands, and arrector pili muscles. The system also includes the mammary glands and teeth. At the external orifices, the digestive tract for example, the mucous membrane and integument (L. covering) are continuous.

DEVELOPMENT OF SKIN

The skin — one of the largest structures of the body — is a complex organ system that forms a protective covering for the body. The skin consists of two layers that are derived from two different germ layers (Fig. 21 – 1): ectoderm and mesoderm.

- The **epidermis** is a superficial epithelial tissue, which is derived from surface ectoderm.
- The **dermis** is a deeper layer composed of dense, irregularly arranged connective tissue, which is derived from mesoderm. The meshwork of embryonic connective tissue or **mesenchyme** derived from mesoderm forms the connective tissues of the dermis.

Ectodermal (epidermal)/mesenchymal (dermal) interactions involve mutual inductive mechanisms (Collins, 1995). Skin structures vary from one part of the body to another. For example, the skin of the eyelids is thin and soft and has fine hairs, whereas the skin of the eyebrows is thicker and has coarse hairs. The embryonic skin at 4 to 5 weeks consists of a single layer of surface ectoderm overlying the mesenchyme (Fig. 21 – 1).

Epidermis

During the first and second trimesters, epidermal growth occurs in stages, which result in an increase in epidermal thickness. The primordium of the epidermis is the layer of surface ectodermal cells (Fig. 21 – 1A). These cells proliferate and form a layer of squamous epithelium, the **periderm,** and a basal germinative layer (Fig. 21 – 1B). The cells of the periderm continually undergo keratinization and desquamation and are replaced by cells arising from the **basal layer.** The exfoliated peridermal cells form part of a white greasy substance — the **vernix caseosa** — that covers the fetal skin. Later, the vernix (L. varnish) contains sebum, the secretion from sebaceous glands in the skin. The vernix protects the developing skin from constant exposure to amniotic fluid with its urine content during the fetal period. In addition, the vernix caseosa facilitates birth of the fetus because of its slippery nature.

The basal germinative layer of the epidermis becomes the **stratum germinativum,** which produces

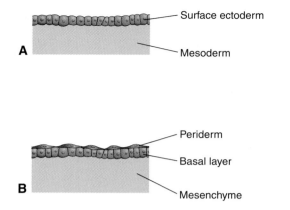

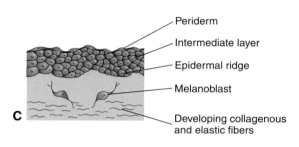

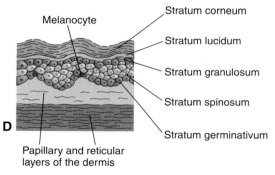

▪ **Figure 21–1.** Drawings illustrating successive stages in skin development. *A,* Four weeks. *B,* Seven weeks. *C,* Eleven weeks. The cells of the periderm continually undergo keratinization and desquamation. The exfoliated peridermal cells form part of the vernix caseosa. *D,* Newborn. Note the position of the melanocytes in the basal layer of the epidermis and the way their branching processes extend between the epidermal cells to supply them with melanin.

new cells that are displaced into the layers superficial to it. By 11 weeks, cells from the stratum germinativum have formed an **intermediate layer** (Fig. 21 – 1C). Replacement of peridermal cells continues until about the 21st week; thereafter, the periderm disappears and the **stratum corneum** forms (Fig. 21 – 1D).

Proliferation of cells in the stratum germinativum also forms **epidermal ridges,** which extend into the developing dermis. These ridges begin to appear in embryos of 10 weeks and are permanently established by the 17th week. The epidermal ridges produce grooves on the surface of the palms of the hands and the soles of the feet, including the digits. The type of pattern that develops is determined genetically and constitutes the basis for examining fingerprints in criminal investigations and medical genetics.

Dermatoglyphics is the study of the patterns of the epidermal ridges of the skin. Abnormal chromosome complements affect the development of ridge patterns; for example, infants with Down syndrome have distinctive patterns on their hands and feet that are of diagnostic value (see Chapter 9).

Late in the embryonic period, **neural crest cells** migrate into the mesenchyme in the developing dermis and differentiate into **melanoblasts.** Later these cells migrate to the dermoepidermal junction and differentiate into **melanocytes** (Fig. 21–1D). The differentiation of melanoblasts into melanocytes involves the formation of pigment granules. Recent studies have shown that melanocytes appear in the developing skin at 40 to 50 days, immediately after the migration of neural crest cells (Holbrook et al, 1989). In white races, the cell bodies of melanocytes are usually confined to basal layers of the epidermis; however, their dendritic processes extend between the epidermal cells. Only a few melanin-containing cells are normally present in the dermis. The melanocytes begin producing **melanin** (Gr. *melas,* black) before birth and distribute it to the epidermal cells. Pigment formation can be observed prenatally in the epidermis of dark-skinned races. Increased amounts of melanin are produced in response to ultraviolet light. The relative content of melanin in the melanocytes accounts for the different colors of skin.

The transformation of the surface ectoderm into a multilayered epidermis results from continuing inductive interactions with the dermis (Carlson, 1994). Skin is classified as thick or thin based on the thickness of the epidermis (Gartner and Hiatt, 1997).

- **Thick skin** covers the palms and soles; it lacks hair follicles, arrector pili muscles, and sebaceous glands but has sweat glands.
- **Thin skin** covers most of the rest of the body; it contains hair follicles, arrector pili muscles, sebaceous glands, and sweat glands (Fig. 21–2).

Dermis

The dermis develops from mesenchyme, which is derived from the mesoderm underlying the surface ectoderm. Most of the mesenchyme that differentiates into the connective tissue of the dermis originates from the somatic layer of lateral mesoderm, but some of it is derived from the dermatomes of the somites (see Chapter 16). By 11 weeks, the mesenchymal cells have begun to produce collagenous and elastic connective tissue fibers (Fig. 21–1D). As the **epidermal ridges** form, the dermis projects into the epidermis, forming **dermal ridges.** Capillary loops develop in some of these ridges and provide nourishment for the epidermis. Sensory nerve endings form in others. The developing afferent nerve fibers apparently play an important role in the spatial and temporal sequence of dermal (papillary) ridge formation (Moore and Munger, 1989). The development of the *dermatomal pattern of innervation of the skin* is described in Chapter 18.

The blood vessels in the dermis begin as simple, endothelium-lined structures that differentiate from mesenchyme. As the skin grows, new capillaries grow out from the simple vessels. Such simple capillary-like vessels have been observed in the dermis at the end of the fifth week. Some capillaries acquire muscular coats through differentiation of myoblasts developing in the surrounding mesenchyme and become arterioles and arteries. Other capillaries, through which a return flow of blood is established, acquire muscular coats and become venules and veins. As new blood vessels form, some transitory ones normally disappear. By the end of the first trimester, the major vascular organization of the fetal dermis is established (Johnson and Holbrook, 1989).

Glands of the Skin

Two kinds of glands, sebaceous and sweat glands, are derived from the epidermis and grow into the dermis. The mammary glands develop in a similar manner.

SEBACEOUS GLANDS

Most sebaceous glands develop as buds from the sides of developing epithelial root sheaths of hair follicles (Fig. 21–2). The glandular buds grow into the surrounding embryonic connective tissue and branch to form the primordia of several alveoli and their associated ducts. The central cells of the alveoli break down, forming an oily secretion—**sebum**—that is released into the hair follicle and passes to the surface of the skin, where it mixes with desquamated peridermal cells to form **vernix caseosa.** Sebaceous glands, independent of hair follicles (e.g., in the glans penis and labia minora) develop in a similar manner from buds from the epidermis.

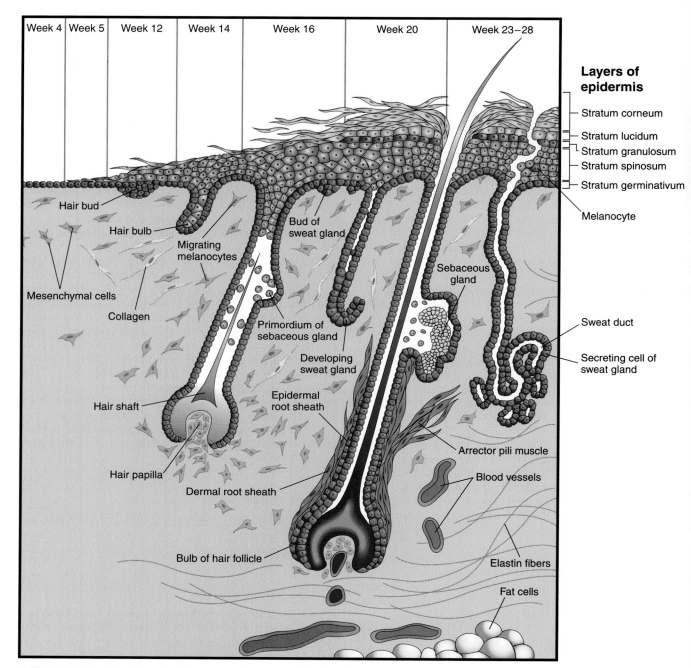

■ **Figure 21–2.** Drawing showing successive stages in the development of a hair and its associated sebaceous gland and arrector pili muscle. Note that the sebaceous gland develops as an outgrowth from the side of the hair follicle.

SWEAT GLANDS

Eccrine sweat glands are located in the skin throughout most of the body. They develop as epidermal downgrowths into the underlying mesenchyme (Fig. 21–2). As the bud elongates, its end coils to form the primordium of the secretory part of the gland (Fig. 21–3A to C). The epithelial attachment of the developing gland to the epidermis forms the primordium of the duct. The central cells of the primor-

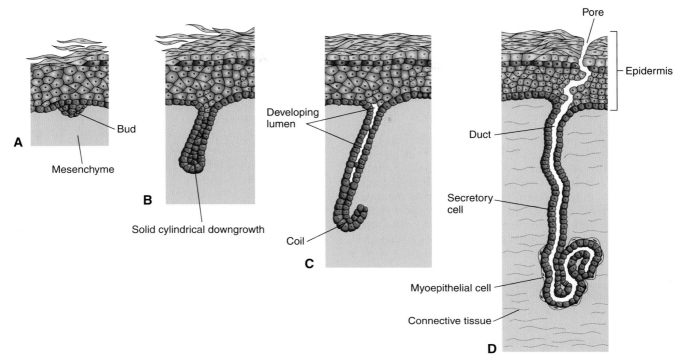

■ **Figure 21–3.** Diagrams illustrating successive stages in the development of a sweat gland. *A* and *B,* The gland develops at about 20 weeks as a solid growth of epidermal cells into the mesenchyme. *C,* Its terminal part coils and forms the body of the gland. The central cells degenerate to form the lumen of the gland. *D,* The peripheral cells differentiate into secretory cells and contractile myoepithelial cells.

dial ducts degenerate, forming a lumen. The peripheral cells of the secretory part of the gland differentiate into myoepithelial and **secretory cells** (Fig. 21-3*D*). The **myoepithelial cells** are thought to be specialized smooth muscle cells that assist in expelling sweat from the glands. Eccrine sweat glands begin to function shortly after birth.

The distribution of the large **apocrine sweat glands** in humans is mostly confined to the axilla, pubic, and perineal regions, and areolae of the nipples. They develop from downgrowths of the stratum germinativum of the epidermis that give rise to hair follicles. As a result, the ducts of these glands open, not onto the skin surface as do ordinary sweat glands, but into the upper part of hair follicles superficial to the openings of the sebaceous glands.

DEVELOPMENT OF HAIR

Hairs begin to develop early in the fetal period (9th to 12th weeks), but they do not become easily recognizable until about the 20th week (see Chapter 7). Hairs are first recognizable on the eyebrows, upper lip, and chin. A hair follicle begins as a proliferation of the stratum germinativum of the epidermis and extends into the underlying dermis (Fig. 21-2). The **hair bud** soon becomes club-shaped, forming a **hair bulb.** The epithelial cells of the hair bulb constitute the **germinal matrix,** which later produces the hair. The hair bulb (primordium of hair root) is soon invaginated by a small mesenchymal **hair papilla** (Fig. 21-2). The peripheral cells of the developing hair follicle form the **epithelial root sheath,** and the surrounding mesenchymal cells differentiate into the **dermal root sheath.** As cells in the germinal matrix proliferate, they are pushed toward the surface, where they become keratinized to form the **hair shaft.** The hair grows through the epidermis on the eyebrows and upper lip by the end of the 12th week.

The first hairs that appear—**lanugo hairs** (L. *lana,* wool)—are fine, soft, and lightly pigmented. Lanugo hairs begin to appear toward the end of the 12th week and are plentiful by 17 to 20 weeks. These hairs help to hold the vernix caseosa on the skin. Lanugo hairs are replaced during the perinatal period by coarser hairs. This hair persists over most of the body, except in the axillary and pubic regions, where it is replaced at puberty by even coarser terminal hairs. In males, similar coarse hairs also appear on the face and often on the chest. **Melanoblasts** migrate into the hair bulbs and differentiate into **melanocytes.** The melanin produced by these cells is transferred to the hair-forming cells in the germinal matrix several weeks before birth. The relative content of melanin accounts for different hair colors. **Arrector pili muscles,** small bundles of smooth muscle fibers, differentiate from the mesenchyme surrounding the hair follicle and attach to the dermal root sheath of the hair follicles and the papillary layer of the dermis (Fig. 21–2). Contractions of the arrector pili muscles depress the skin over their attachment and elevate the skin around the hair shafts, forming tiny "goose bumps" on the surface of the skin. The arrector pili muscles are poorly developed in the hairs of the axilla and in certain parts of the face. The hairs forming the eyebrows and the cilia forming the eyelashes have no arrector pili muscles.

Disorders of Keratinization

Ichthyosis (Gr. *ichthys,* fish) is a general term that is applied to a group of disorders resulting from excessive keratinization. The skin is characterized by dryness and fishskin-like scaling, which may involve the entire body surface. A **harlequin fetus** results from a rare keratinizing disorder that is inherited as an autosomal recessive trait (Behrman et al, 1996). The skin is markedly thickened, ridged, and cracked. Affected infants have a grotesque appearance, and most of them die during the first week of life. A **collodion baby** is covered at birth by a thick, taut membrane that resembles collodion or parchment. This membrane cracks with the first respiratory efforts and begins to fall off in large sheets. Complete shedding may take several weeks, occasionally leaving normal-appearing skin. **Lamellar ichthyosis** (Fig. 21–4) is an autosomal recessive disorder. A newborn infant with this condition may first appear to be a collodion baby, but the scaling persists. Growth of hair may be curtailed, and development of sweat glands is often impeded. Affected infants often suffer severely in hot weather because of their inability to sweat.

Angiomas of the Skin

These vascular anomalies are developmental defects in which some transitory and/or surplus primitive blood or lymphatic vessels persist. These anomalies are called **angiomas,** even though they may not be true tumors. Those composed of blood vessels may be

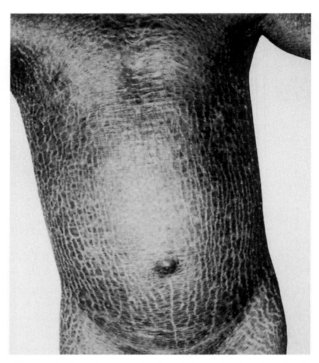

■ **Figure 21–4.** Photograph of an infant with lamellar ichthyosis, a congenital disorder of keratinization of the skin that is characterized by pronounced scaling involving the entire body. (From Behrman RE, Kliegman RM, Arvin AM [eds]: *Nelson Textbook of Pediatrics,* 15th ed. Philadelphia, WB Saunders, 1996.)

mainly arterial, venous, or cavernous, but they are often of a mixed type. Angiomas composed of lymphatics are called cystic lymphangiomas or **cystic hygromas** (see Chapter 15). True angiomas are benign tumors of endothelial cells, usually composed of solid or hollow cords; the hollow cords contain blood. Various terms are used to describe angiomatous anomalies ("birthmarks"). **Nevus flammeus** denotes a flat, pink or red, flamelike blotch that often appears on the posterior surface of the neck. A portwine stain or **hemangioma** is a larger and darker angioma than nevus flammeus and is nearly always anterior or lateral on the face and/or neck. It is sharply demarcated when it is near the median plane, whereas the common angioma (pinkish red blotch) may cross the median plane.

Albinism

In *generalized albinism,* an autosomal recessive trait, the skin, hair, and retina lack pigment; however, the iris usually shows some pigmentation. Albinism occurs

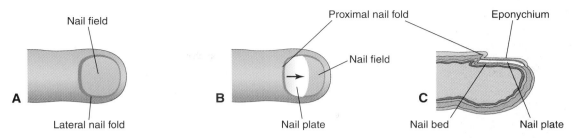

■ **Figure 21–5.** Diagrams illustrating successive stages in the development of a fingernail. *A,* The first indication of a nail is a thickening of the epidermis, the nail field, at the tip of the digit. *B,* As the nail plate develops, it slowly grows toward the tip of the digit. *C,* The fingernail reaches the end of the digit before birth.

when the melanocytes fail to produce melanin because of the lack of the enzyme tyrosinase. In *localized albinism* — **piebaldism** — an autosomal dominant trait, there is a lack of melanin in patches of skin and/or hair.

DEVELOPMENT OF NAILS

Toenails and fingernails begin to develop at the tips of the digits at about 10 weeks (Fig. 21–5). Development of fingernails precedes that of toenails by about 4 weeks (see Chapter 7). The primordia of nails appear as thickened areas or fields of epidermis at the tip of each digit. Later these **nail fields** migrate onto the dorsal surface (Fig. 21–5A), carrying their innervation from the ventral surface. The nail fields are surrounded laterally and proximally by folds of epidermis, the **nail folds.** Cells from the proximal nail fold grow over the nail field and become keratinized to form the **nail plate** (Fig. 21–5B). At first the developing nail is covered by superficial layers of epidermis, the **eponychium** (Fig. 21–5C). This later degenerates, exposing the nail, except at its base, where it persists as the **cuticle.** The skin under the free margin of the nail is the **hyponychium.** The fingernails reach the fingertips by about 32 weeks; the toenails reach the toetips by about 36 weeks. Nails that have not reached the tips of the digits at birth indicate prematurity.

Deformed Nails

This disorder occurs occasionally and may be a manifestation of a generalized skin disease or systemic disease. A number of congenital diseases demonstrate nail defects (for details, see Behrman et al, 1996).

DEVELOPMENT OF MAMMARY GLANDS

Mammary glands are a modified and highly specialized type of sweat gland. **Mammary buds** begin to develop during the sixth week as solid downgrowths of the epidermis into the underlying mesenchyme (Fig. 21-6C). These changes occur in response to an inductive influence from the mesenchyme (Carlson, 1994). The mammary buds develop from the thickened **mammary ridges** (lines), which are thickened strips of ectoderm extending from the axillary to the inguinal regions (Fig. 21–6A). The mammary ridges appear during the fourth week but normally persist in humans only in the pectoral area, where the breasts develop (Fig. 21–6B). Each primary bud soon gives rise to several secondary mammary buds that develop into **lactiferous ducts** and their branches (Fig. 21–6D and E). Canalization of these buds is induced by placental sex hormones entering the fetal circulation. This process continues until late gestation, and by term 15 to 20 lactiferous ducts are formed. The fibrous connective tissue and fat of the mammary gland develop from the surrounding mesenchyme.

During the late fetal period the epidermis at the site of origin of the mammary gland becomes depressed, forming a shallow **mammary pit** (Fig. 21–6E). The nipples are poorly formed and depressed in newborn infants. Soon after birth the nipples usually rise from the mammary pits because of proliferation of the surrounding connective tissue of the **areola,** the circular area of skin around the nipple (Fig. 21–6F). The smooth muscle fibers of the nipple and areola differentiate from surrounding mesenchymal cells. The rudimentary mammary glands of newborn males and females are identical and are often enlarged. Some secretion, often called "**witch's milk**", may be produced. These transitory changes are caused by maternal hormones passing through the placental membrane into the fetal circulation.

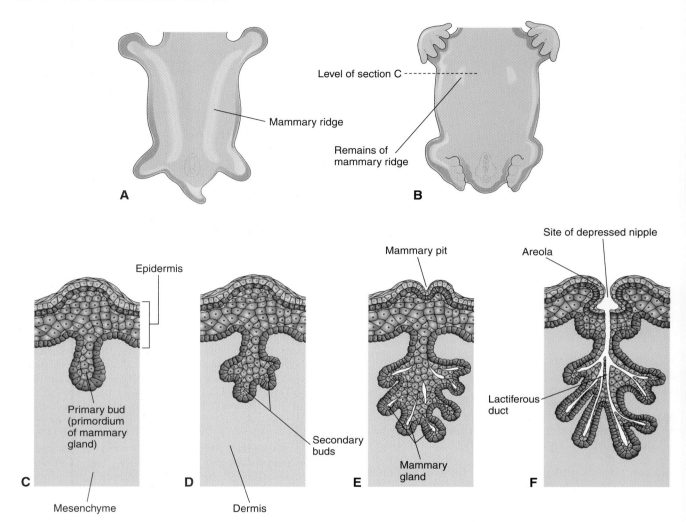

■ **Figure 21–6.** Drawings illustrating the development of mammary glands. *A*, Ventral view of an embryo of about 28 days showing the mammary ridges. *B*, Similar view at 6 weeks showing the remains of these ridges. *C*, Transverse section of a mammary ridge at the site of a developing mammary gland. *D*, *E*, and *F*, Similar sections showing successive stages of breast development between the 12th week and birth.

Only the main lactiferous ducts are formed at birth and the mammary glands remain underdeveloped until puberty. The mammary glands develop similarly and are of the same structure in both sexes. In females the glands enlarge rapidly during puberty (Fig. 21 – 7), mainly because of fat and other connective tissue development. Growth of the duct system also occurs because of the raised levels of circulating estrogens. Progestogens, prolactin, corticoids, and growth hormone also play a role (Gartner and Hiatt, 1997). If pregnancy occurs, the mammary glands complete their development owing to the raised estrogen levels and the sustained increase in the levels of progesterone.

The intralobular ducts undergo rapid development, forming buds that become alveoli. The breasts become hemispherical in shape (Fig. 21 – 7*D* and *E*), largely because of the deposition of fat. Full development occurs at about 20 years (Fig. 21 – 7*E*).

Gynecomastia

The rudimentary mammary glands in males normally undergo no postnatal development. Gynecomastia (Gr.

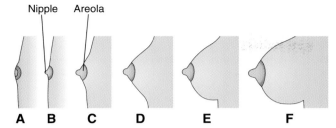

Nipple   Areola

A   B   C   D   E   F

■ **Figure 21–7.** Sketches showing progressive stages in the postnatal development of the breast. *A,* Newborn. *B,* Child. *C,* Early puberty. *D,* Late puberty. *E,* Young adult. *F,* Pregnant female. Note that the nipple is inverted at birth (*A*). Normally it elevates during childhood to form the usual nipple. Failure of this process to occur gives rise to an inverted nipple. At puberty (12 to 15 years), the breasts enlarge because of development of the mammary glands and the increased deposition of fat.

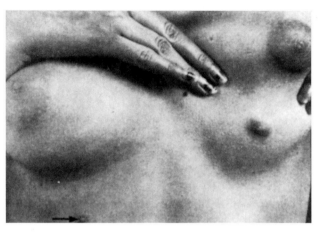

■ **Figure 21–8.** Photograph of a woman with a supernumerary nipple on the right (*arrow*) and a small supernumerary breast inferior to the normal left one. (From Haagensen CD: *Diseases of the Breast,* 3rd ed. Philadelphia, WB Saunders, 1986.)

gyne, woman, and *mastos,* breast) refers to excessive development of the male mammary tissue. It occurs in most newborn males because of stimulation of the glandular tissue by maternal sex hormones. This effect disappears in a few weeks (Behrman et al, 1996). During midpuberty, about two thirds of boys develop varying degrees of hyperplasia of the breasts. The subareolar hyperplasia may persist for a few months to 2 years. A decreased ratio of testosterone to estradiol is found in boys with gynecomastia (Behrman et al, 1996). About 80% of males with Klinefelter syndrome have gynecomastia (see Chapter 9).

Aplasia of the Breast

The breasts of a postpubertal female often differ somewhat in size. Marked differences are regarded as anomalies because both glands are exposed to the same hormones at puberty. In these cases there is often associated rudimentary development of muscles, usually the pectoralis major (see Chapter 17).

Supernumerary Breasts and Nipples

An extra breast (**polymastia**) or nipple (**polythelia**) occurs in about 1% of the female population (Fig. 21–8) and is an inheritable condition. An extra breast or nipple usually develops just inferior to the normal breast. **Supernumerary nipples** are also relatively

common in males; often they are mistaken for moles. An extra breast or nipple usually develops just inferior to the normal breast. Less commonly, supernumerary breasts or nipples appear in the axillary or abdominal regions. In these positions the nipples or breasts develop from extra mammary buds that develop along the mammary ridges. They usually become obvious in women when pregnancy occurs. About one third of affected persons have two extra nipples or breasts. Supernumerary mammary tissue very rarely occurs in a location other than along the course of the mammary ridges. It probably develops from tissue that was displaced from these ridges.

DEVELOPMENT OF TEETH

Two sets of teeth normally develop: the primary dentition or **deciduous teeth** and the secondary dentition or **permanent teeth.** Teeth develop from:

- Oral ectoderm
- Mesoderm
- Neural crest cells

The enamel is derived from ectoderm of the oral cavity; all other tissues differentiate from the surrounding mesenchyme derived from mesoderm and neural crest cells. Experimental evidence suggests that **neural crest cells** are imprinted with morphogenetic information before or shortly after they migrate from the **neural crest** (Carlson, 1994). As the mandible and maxilla grow to accommodate the developing teeth, the shape of the face changes. **Odontogenesis** (tooth

Table 21–1 ■ The Order and Usual Time of Eruption of Teeth and the Time of Shedding of Deciduous Teeth		
Tooth	**Usual Eruption Time**	**Shedding Time**
Deciduous		
Medial incisor	6–8 mos	6–7 yr
Lateral incisor	8–10 mos	7–8 yr
Canine	16–20 mos	10–12 yr
First molar	12–16 mos	9–11 yr
Second molar	20–24 mos	10–12 yr
Permanent*		
Medial incisor	7–8 yr	
Lateral incisor	8–9 yr	
Canine	10–12 yr	
First premolar	10–11 yr	
Second premolar	11–12 yr	
First molar	6–7 yr	
Second molar	12 yr	
Third molar	13–25 yr	

(Modified from Moore KL: *Clinically Oriented Anatomy*, 3rd ed. Baltimore, Williams & Wilkins, 1992.)

* The permanent teeth are not shed. If they are not properly cared for or disease of the gingiva develops, they may have to be extracted.

development) is initiated by the inductive influence of neural crest mesenchyme on the overlying ectoderm. Tooth development is a continuous process; however, it is usually divided into stages for descriptive purposes on the basis of the appearance of the developing tooth. Not all teeth begin to develop at the same time. The first tooth buds appear in the anterior mandibular region; later tooth development occurs in the anterior maxillary region and then progresses posteriorly in both jaws. Tooth development continues for years after birth (Table 21–1). The first indication of tooth development occurs in the sixth week as a thickening of the oral epithelium, a derivative of the surface ectoderm. These U-shaped bands—**dental**

laminae—follow the curves of the primitive jaws (Figs. 21–9*A* and 21–10*A*).

Bud Stage of Tooth Development

Each dental lamina develops 10 centers of proliferation from which swellings—**tooth buds**—grow into the underlying mesenchyme (Figs. 21–9*B* and 21–10*B*). These tooth buds develop into the first or **deciduous teeth,** which were given this name because they are shed during childhood (Table 21–1). There are 10 tooth buds in each jaw, one for each deciduous tooth. The tooth buds for **permanent teeth** that have deciduous predecessors begin to appear at about 10 weeks from deep continuations of the dental lamina (Fig. 21–10*D*). They develop lingual (toward the tongue) to the deciduous **tooth buds.** The permanent molars that have no deciduous predecessors develop as buds from posterior extensions of the dental laminae. The tooth buds for the permanent teeth appear at different times, mostly during the fetal period. The buds for the second and third permanent molars develop after birth.

Cap Stage of Tooth Development

As each tooth bud is invaginated by mesenchyme—the primordium of the dental papilla—it becomes cap-shaped (Fig. 21–10*C*). The ectodermal part of the developing tooth, the **enamel organ** (dental organ), eventually produces enamel. The internal part of each cap-shaped tooth, the **dental papilla,** is the primordium of the dental pulp. Together, the dental papilla and enamel organ form the **tooth germ** (Gartner and Hiatt, 1997). The outer cell layer of the enamel organ is the **outer enamel epithelium,** and the inner cell layer lining the "cap" is the **inner enamel epithelium** (Fig. 21–10*D*). The central core of loosely ar-

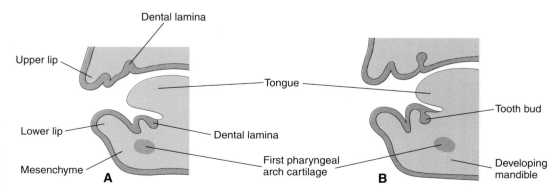

■ **Figure 21–9.** Diagrammatic sketches of sagittal sections through the developing jaws, illustrating early development of the teeth. *A*, Early in the sixth week, showing the dental laminae. *B*, Later in the sixth week, showing tooth buds arising from the dental laminae.

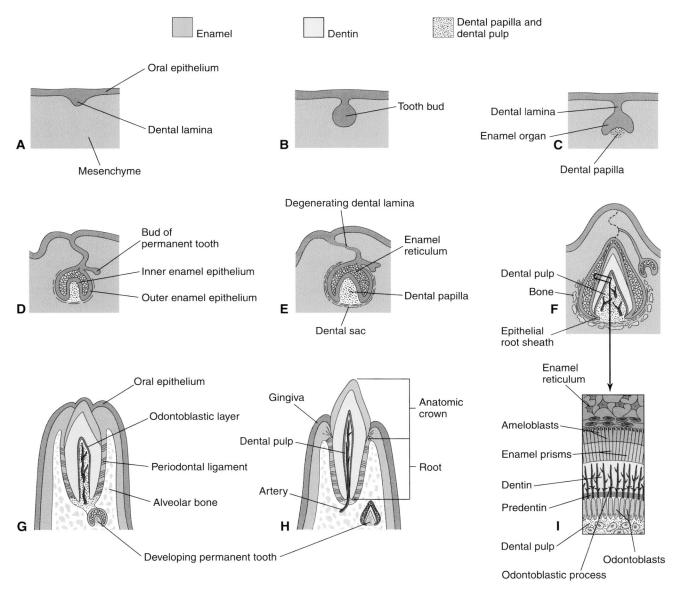

■ **Figure 21–10.** Schematic drawings of sagittal sections illustrating successive stages in the development and eruption of an incisor tooth. *A*, Six weeks, showing the dental lamina. *B*, Seven weeks, showing the tooth bud developing from the dental lamina. *C*, Eight weeks, showing the cap stage of tooth development. *D*, Ten weeks, showing the early bell stage of a deciduous tooth and the bud stage of a permanent tooth. *E*, Fourteen weeks, showing the advanced bell stage of tooth development. Note that the connection (dental lamina) of the tooth to the oral epithelium is degenerating. *F*, Twenty-eight weeks, showing the enamel and dentin layers. *G*, Six months postnatal, showing early tooth eruption. *H*, Eighteen months postnatal, showing a fully erupted deciduous incisor tooth. The permanent incisor tooth now has a well-developed crown. *I*, Section through a developing tooth showing ameloblasts (enamel producers) and odontoblasts (dentin producers).

ranged cells between the layers of enamel epithelium is the **enamel (stellate) reticulum.** As the enamel organ and dental papilla of the tooth develop, the mesenchyme surrounding the developing tooth condenses to form the **dental sac,** a vascularized capsular

structure (Fig. 21–10*E*). The dental sac is the primordium of the cementum and periodontal ligament. The **cementum** is the bonelike rigid connective tissue covering the root of the tooth. The **periodontal ligament** is the fibrous connective tissue that surrounds the root of the tooth, separating it from and attaching it to the alveolar bone (Fig. 21 – 10*G*).

Bell Stage of Tooth Development

As the enamel organ differentiates, the developing tooth assumes the shape of a bell (see Fig. 21 – 13*D* and *E*). The mesenchymal cells in the dental papilla adjacent to the inner enamel epithelium differentiate into **odontoblasts,** which produce **predentin** and deposit it adjacent to the epithelium. Later, the predentin calcifies and becomes **dentin.** As the dentin thickens, the odontoblasts regress toward the center of the

■ **Figure 21–11.** Photomicrograph of the crown and neck of a tooth (×17). (From Gartner LP, Hiatt JL: *Color Textbook of Histology.* Philadelphia, WB Saunders, 1997.)

dental papilla; however, their fingerlike cytoplasmic processes — **odontoblastic processes** or Tomes processes — remain embedded in the dentin (Fig. 21 – 10*F* and *I*). The yellowish dentin is the second hardest tissue in the body (Gartner and Hiatt, 1997). It overlies and protects the brittle enamel, the hardest tissue in the body, from being fractured (Fig. 21 – 11).

Cells of the inner enamel epithelium differentiate into **ameloblasts,** which produce enamel in the form of prisms (rods) over the dentin. As the **enamel** increases, the ameloblasts regress toward the outer enamel epithelium. Enamel and dentin formation begins at the tip (cusp) of the tooth and progresses toward the future root. The **root of the tooth** begins to develop after dentin and enamel formation is well advanced. The inner and outer enamel epithelia come together in the neck region of the tooth where they form a fold, the **epithelial root sheath** (Fig. 21 – 10*F*). This sheath grows into the mesenchyme and initiates root formation. The odontoblasts adjacent to the epithelial root sheath form dentin that is continuous with that of the crown. As the dentin increases, it reduces the pulp cavity to a narrow **root canal** through which the vessels and nerves pass. The inner cells of the dental sac differentiate into **cementoblasts,** which produce cementum that is restricted to the root. **Cementum** is deposited over the dentin of the root and meets the enamel at the neck of the tooth **(cementoenamel junction).**

As the teeth develop and the jaws ossify, the outer cells of the dental sac also become active in bone formation. Each tooth soon becomes surrounded by bone, except over its crown. The tooth is held in its **alveolus** (bony socket) by the strong **periodontal ligament,** a derivative of the dental sac (Fig. 21 – 10*G* and *H*). Some fibers of this ligament are embedded in the cementum; other fibers are embedded in the bony wall of the alveolus. The periodontal ligament is located between the cementum of the root and the bony alveolus.

Tooth Eruption

As the teeth develop, they begin a continuous slow movement toward the oral cavity (Fig. 21 – 10). The mandibular teeth usually erupt before the maxillary teeth, and girls' teeth usually erupt sooner than boys' teeth. The child's dentition contains **20 deciduous teeth.** The complete adult dentition consists of 32 teeth. As the root of the tooth grows, its crown gradually erupts through the oral epithelium. The part of the oral mucosa around the erupted crown becomes the **gingiva** (gum). Usually eruption of the deciduous

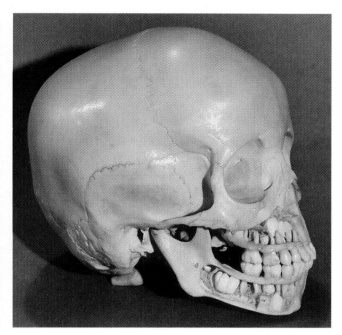

■ **Figure 21–12.** Photograph of a 4-year-old child's skull. Bone has been removed to show the relation of the developing permanent teeth to the erupted deciduous teeth.

teeth occurs between the 6th and 24th months after birth (Table 21–1). The mandibular medial or **central incisors** usually erupt 6 to 8 months after birth, but this process may not begin until 12 or 13 months in some children. Despite this, all 20 deciduous teeth are usually present by the end of the second year in healthy children. Delayed eruption of all teeth may indicate a systemic or nutritional disturbance such as hypopituitarism or hypothyroidism (Behrman et al, 1996).

The **permanent teeth** develop in a manner similar to that described for deciduous teeth. As a permanent tooth grows, the root of the corresponding deciduous tooth is gradually resorbed by **osteoclasts.** Consequently, when the deciduous tooth is shed, it consists only of the crown and the uppermost part of the root. The permanent teeth usually begin to erupt during the sixth year and continue to appear until early adulthood (Fig. 21–12; Table 21–1). The shape of the face is affected by the development of the paranasal sinuses and the growth of the maxilla and mandible to accommodate the teeth (see Chapter 11). It is the lengthening of the **alveolar processes** (bony sockets supporting the teeth) that results in the increase in depth of the face during childhood.

Natal Teeth

Natal teeth are erupted at birth (L. *natus,* birth). There are usually two in the position of the mandibular incisors. Natal teeth are observed in about 1 in 2000 newborn infants (Behrman et al, 1996). Natal teeth may produce maternal discomfort during breast-feeding. In addition, the infant's tongue may be lacerated or the teeth may detach and be aspirated; for these reasons natal teeth are sometimes extracted.

Enamel Hypoplasia

Defective enamel formation causes pits and/or fissures in the enamel (Fig. 21–13). These defects result from temporary disturbances of enamel formation. Various factors may injure ameloblasts, the enamel builders, such as nutritional deficiency, tetracycline therapy, and infectious diseases such as measles. **Rickets** during the critical period of permanent tooth development is the most common known cause of enamel hypoplasia. Rickets, a disease in children who are deficient in vitamin D, is characterized by disturbance of ossification of the epiphyseal cartilages and disorientation of cells at the metaphysis (see Chapter 16).

Variations of Tooth Shape

Abnormally shaped teeth are relatively common (Fig. 21-13A to G). Occasionally there are spherical masses of enamel—**enamel pearls**—attached to the tooth. They are formed by aberrant groups of ameloblasts. In other children, the maxillary lateral incisor teeth may have a slender, tapering shape (peg-shaped incisors). **Congenital syphilis** affects the differentiation of the permanent teeth, resulting in screwdriver-shaped incisors, with central notches in their incisive edges.

Numerical Abnormalities

One or more supernumerary teeth may develop or the normal number of teeth may fail to form (Fig. 21-13H and I). **Supernumerary teeth** usually develop in the area of the maxillary incisors and disrupt the position

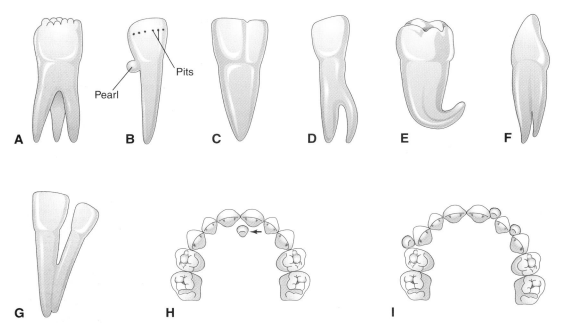

■ **Figure 21–13.** Drawings illustrating common anomalies of teeth. *A,* Irregular raspberry-like crown. *B,* Enamel pearl and pits. *C,* Incisor tooth with a double crown. *D,* Abnormal division of root. *E,* Distorted root. *F,* Branched root. *G,* Fused roots. *H,* Hyperdontia with a supernumerary incisor tooth in the anterior region of the palate (*arrow*). *I,* Hyperdontia with 13 deciduous teeth in the maxilla (upper jaw) instead of the normal 10.

and eruption of normal teeth. The extra teeth commonly erupt posterior to the normal ones. In **partial anodontia,** one or more teeth are absent. Congenital absence of one or more teeth is often a familial trait. In **total anodontia,** no teeth develop; this very rare condition is usually associated with *congenital ectodermal dysplasia* (Behrman et al, 1996).

Abnormally Sized Teeth

Disturbances during the differentiation of teeth may result in gross alterations of dental morphology, such as *macrodontia* (large teeth) and *microdontia* (small teeth).

Fused Teeth

Occasionally a tooth bud divides or two buds partially fuse to form fused teeth (Fig. 21–13*C* and *G*). This condition is commonly observed in the mandibular incisors of the primary dentition. "Twinning" of teeth results from division of the tooth bud. In some cases

the permanent tooth does not form; this suggests that the deciduous and permanent tooth primordia fused to form the primary tooth.

Dentigerous Cyst

In rare cases a cyst develops in a mandible, maxilla, or maxillary sinus that contains an unerupted tooth. The dentigerous (tooth-bearing) cyst develops because of cystic degeneration of the enamel reticulum of the enamel organ of an unerupted tooth. Most cysts are deeply situated in the jaw and are associated with misplaced or malformed secondary teeth that have failed to erupt.

Amelogenesis Imperfecta

The enamel is soft and friable because of hypocalcification, and the teeth are yellow to brown in color. The teeth are covered with only a thin layer of abnormally formed enamel through which the yellow underlying dentin is visible (Johnsen, 1996). This gives a darkened appearance to the teeth. This autosomal dominant trait affects about 1 in every 20,000 children.

Dentinogenesis Imperfecta

This condition is relatively common in white children (Fig. 21–14). The teeth are brown to gray-blue with an opalescent sheen because the odontoblasts fail to differentiate normally and poorly calcified dentin results (Johnsen, 1996). Both deciduous and permanent teeth are usually involved. The enamel tends to wear down rapidly, exposing the dentin. This anomaly is inherited as an autosomal dominant trait (Thompson et al, 1991).

Discolored Teeth

Foreign substances incorporated into the developing enamel discolor the teeth. The hemolysis (liberation of hemoglobin) associated with erythroblastosis fetalis or hemolytic disease of the newborn (see Chapter 8) may produce blue to black discoloration of the teeth. *All tetracyclines are extensively incorporated into the enamel of teeth.* The critical period of risk is from about 14 weeks of fetal life to the 10th postnatal month for primary teeth, and from about 14 weeks of fetal life to the 16th postnatal year for permanent

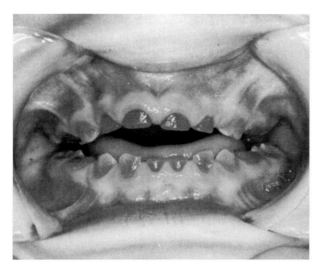

■ **Figure 21–14.** Photograph of the teeth of a child with dentinogenesis imperfecta. (From Thompson MW: *Genetics in Medicine,* 4th ed. Philadelphia, WB Saunders, 1986.)

teeth (Johnsen, 1996). Tetracyclines produce brownish yellow discoloration (mottling) and enamel hypoplasia because they interfere with the metabolic processes of the ameloblasts. The enamel is completely formed on all but the third molars by about 8 years of age. For this reason, *tetracyclines should not be administered to pregnant women or children under 8 years of age* (Shepard, 1992).

SUMMARY OF THE INTEGUMENTARY SYSTEM

The skin and its appendages develop from ectoderm, mesoderm, and neural crest cells. The epidermis is derived from surface ectoderm. Melanocytes are derived from **neural crest cells** that migrate into the epidermis. Cast-off cells from the epidermis mix with secretions of sebaceous glands to form the **vernix caseosa,** a whitish, greasy coating for the skin. This fatty substance protects the epidermis, probably making it more waterproof, and facilitates birth because of its slipperiness.

Hairs develop from downgrowths of the epidermis into the dermis. By about 20 weeks the fetus is completely covered with fine, downy hairs — **lanugo hairs.** These hairs are shed by birth or shortly thereafter and are replaced by coarser hairs. Most **sebaceous glands** develop as outgrowths from the sides of hair follicles; however, some glands develop as downgrowths of the epidermis into the dermis. **Sweat glands** also develop from epidermal downgrowths into the dermis. **Mammary glands** develop in a similar manner.

Congenital anomalies of the skin are mainly **disorders of keratinization** (ichthyosis) and pigmentation (albinism). Abnormal blood vessel development results in various types of **angioma.** Nails may be absent or malformed. Hair may be absent or excessive. Absence of mammary glands is rare, but supernumerary breasts (polymastia) or nipples (polythelia) are relatively common.

Teeth develop from ectoderm, mesoderm, and neural crest cells. The enamel is produced by **ameloblasts,** which are derived from the oral ectoderm; all other dental tissues develop from mesenchyme, derived from mesoderm and neural crest cells. The common **congenital anomalies of teeth** are defective formation of enamel and dentin, abnormalities in shape, and variations in number and position. **Tetracyclines** are extensively incorporated into the enamel of developing teeth and produce brownish yellow discoloration and hypoplasia of the enamel. Consequently, they should not be prescribed for pregnant women or children under 8 years of age.

Clinically Oriented Questions

1. I recently heard someone talking about her baby that she said was born without skin. Is this possible? If possible, could such a baby survive?

2. I once saw a dark-skinned person with patches of white skin on his face, chest, and limbs. He even had a white forelock. What is this condition called and what is its developmental basis? Is there any treatment for these skin defects?

3. I was told that some male babies have enlarged breasts at birth. Is this an indication of abnormal sex development? I have also heard that some males develop breasts during puberty. Are they intersexes?

4. A nurse told me about a girl who developed a breast in her axilla during puberty. She also said that this girl had extra nipples on her upper abdomen. What is the embryological basis for these anomalies?

5. I recently read in the newspaper that a baby was born with two teeth. Would these be normal teeth? Is this a common occurrence? Are they usually extracted?

The answers to these questions are given at the back of the book.

REFERENCES AND SUGGESTED READING

Behrman RE, Kliegman RM, Arvin AM (eds): *Nelson Textbook of Pediatrics,* 15th ed. Philadelphia, WB Saunders, 1996.

Beller F: Development and anatomy of the breast. *In* Mitchell GW Jr, Bassett LW (eds): *The Female Breast and Its Disorders.* Baltimore, Williams & Wilkins, 1990.

Booth DH, Persaud TVN: Congenital absence of the breast. *Anat Anz* 155:23, 1984.

Carlson BM: *Human Embryology and Developmental Biology.* St. Louis, CV Mosby, 1994.

Casasco A, Calligaro A, Casasco M, et al: Early stages of ameloblast differentiation as revealed by immunogold detection of enamel matrix proteins. *Proc R Microsc Soc* 30:113, 1995.

Collins P: Embryology and development. *In* Bannister LH, Berry MM, Collins P, et al (eds): *Gray's Anatomy: The Anatomical Basis of Medicine and Surgery,* 38th ed. New York, Churchill Livingstone, 1995.

Darmstadt GL, Lane AT: The skin. *In* Berhman RE, Kliegman RM, Arvin AM (eds): *Nelson Textbook of Pediatrics,* 15th ed. Philadelphia, WB Saunders, 1996.

Gartner LP, Hiatt JL: *Color Textbook of Histology.* Philadelphia, WB Saunders, 1997.

Holbrook KA, Underwood RA, Vogel AM, et al: The appearance, density and distribution of melanocytes in human embryonic and fetal skin revealed by the anti-melanoma monoclonal antibody. *Anat Embryol* 180:443, 1989.

Johnsen DC: The oral cavity. *In* Behrman RE, Kliegman RM, Arvin AM (eds): *Nelson Textbook of Pediatrics,* 15th ed. Philadelphia, WB Saunders, 1996.

Johnson CL, Holbrook KA: Development of human embryonic and fetal dermal vasculature. *J Invest Dermatol* 93(Suppl):105, 1989.

Moore KL: *Clinically Oriented Anatomy,* 3rd ed. Baltimore, Williams & Wilkins, 1992.

Moore KL, Persaud TVN: *The Developing Human: Clinically Oriented Embryology,* 6th ed. Philadelphia, WB Saunders, 1998.

Moore SJ, Munger BL: The early ontogeny of the afferent nerves and papillary ridges in human digital glabrous skin. *Dev Brain Res* 48: 119, 1989.

Shephard TH: *Catalog of Teratogenic Drugs,* 6th ed. Baltimore, The Johns Hopkins University Press, 1992.

Ten Cate AR: Development of the tooth. *In* Ten Cate AR (ed): *Oral Histology. Development, Structure, and Function,* 4th ed. St. Louis, CV Mosby, 1994.

Thompson MW, McInnes RR, Willard HF: *Thompson and Thompson Genetics in Medicine,* 5th ed. Philadelphia, WB Saunders, 1991.

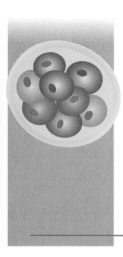

Answers to Clinically Oriented Questions

Chapter 1

1. You should not attempt to reproduce the timetables of development. They are presented as an overview of human development before birth. Neither should you try to memorize the criteria for the stages (e.g., that stage 3 begins on day four when there are 12 or more blastomeres). These stages are used by embryologists when they are describing embryos in detail. You should, however, be able to describe human development to laypersons, and some of the sketches in the timetables are helpful when explaining human development to them.

2. The term *conceptus* is used to refer to the embryo and its membranes (amnion, chorion, yolk sac, and allantois). The embryo is a part of the conceptus. The term *conceptus* refers to the products of conception, that is, everything that develops from the zygote.

3. Everyone, especially those in the health sciences, should know about conception, contraception, and how people develop, both normally and abnormally. Health professionals are expected to give intelligent answers to the questions people ask, such as, When does the baby's heart start to beat? When does it look like a human being? When does it move its limbs?

4. Animal and human embryos look very much alike for the first few weeks; for example, they both have pharyngeal arches and tails. After the seventh week, human embryos do not resemble animal embryos, mainly because the head looks human and the tail disappears (see drawings on p. 501).

5. Physicians date pregnancies from the last normal menstrual period (LNMP) because it is a date that is usually remembered by women. It is not possible to detect the precise time of ovulation and fertilization; however, tests and ultrasound imaging can be done to detect when ovulation is likely to occur and when pregnancy has occurred. These tests are not routinely performed because of the costs involved. When dating pregnancies using LNMP, physicians are aware that the age of the developing human is about 2 weeks less than the "menstrual or gestational age," and they base their decisions on this; for example, concerning the embryo's vulnerability to drugs.

6. *The zygote has the potential to develop into a human being*, just as an acorn has the potential to develop into an oak tree. The zygote is a single cell, whereas a human being consists of many cells. Human development begins at fertilization.

Chapter 2

1. The hymen usually ruptures during the perinatal period, forming the vaginal orifice. This opening usually enlarges during childhood as the result of physical activity. Contrary to popular myth, the rupture of this mucous membrane surrounding the vaginal orifice or the absence of bleeding resulting from tearing during initial intercourse is not necessarily an indication of the loss of virginity.

2. The term *erection* is rarely used when referring to the sexual excitement of a female; however, the clitoris—homologous to the penis—enlarges ("erects") when it is stimulated and the female is sexually aroused. It is a highly sensitive female sex organ.

3. Pregnant women do not menstruate, even though there may be some bleeding at the usual time of menstruation. This blood leaks from the intervillous space because of partial separation of the placenta. Because there is no shedding of the endometrium, this is not menstrual fluid. In unusual cases, periodic bleeding may occur every month during pregnancy; again, this is loss of blood from the placenta.

4. It depends on when she forgot to take the pill. If it was at midcycle, ovulation might occur and pregnancy could result. The taking of two pills the next day would not likely prevent ovulation.

5. *Coitus interruptus* refers to withdrawal of the penis from the vagina before ejaculation occurs. It depends on the self-discipline of the couple to part before climax of the male (i.e., ejaculation). Not only is this difficult to do, but it is neither reliable nor psychologically acceptable. Often a few sperms are expelled from the penis with the secretions of one of the auxiliary sex glands (e.g., the seminal vesicles) before ejaculation occurs. One of these sperms could fertilize the oocyte.

6. *Spermatogenesis* refers to the complete process of sperm formation. *Spermiogenesis* is the transformation of a spermatid into a sperm. Therefore, spermiogenesis is the final stage of spermatogenesis (see the text for illustrations and details).

7. An IUD may inhibit the capacitation of sperms and their transport through the uterus to the fertilization site in the uterine tube; in this case, it would be a *contraceptive device*. More likely, the IUD produces endometrial changes that present a hostile environment for the blastocyst; as a result, the blastocyst does not implant. In this case, the IUD would be a *contraimplantation device* that results in the death and absorption of the embryo when it is a week or so old.

8. The youngest mother on record gave birth at 5 years and 8 months. This was a *highly unusual occurrence* that resulted from precocious sexual development, ovulation, and sexual intercourse. Wide variations exist in the onset of puberty (menarche) in females; however, the most common age range in North America is 11 to 13 years.

Chapter 3

1. The ovarian and endometrial (menstrual) cycles cease between 47 and 55 years of age, the average being 48. Menopause results from the gradual cessation of gonadotropin production by the pituitary gland; however, it does not mean that ovaries have exhausted their supply of oocytes. The risk of the Down syndrome and other trisomies is increased in the children of women who are 35 years of age or older. *Spermatogenesis also decreases after the age of 45*, and the number of nonviable and abnormal sperms increases with age. Nevertheless, sperm production continues until old age, and some very old men have fathered children. The risk of producing abnormal gametes is much less common than in women; however, older men are more likely to have accumulated mutations that the child might inherit. Chromosomal mutations may produce congenital anomalies (see Chapter 9).

2. Considerable research on new contraceptive methods is being conducted, including the development

of contraceptive pills for men. This research includes experimental work on nonhormonal prevention of spermatogenesis and stimulation of immune responses to sperms. Arresting the development of millions of sperms on a continuous basis is much more difficult than arresting the development of a single oocyte monthly.

3. It is not known that polar bodies are ever fertilized; however, it has been suggested that dispermic chimeras result from fusion of a fertilized oocyte with a fertilized polar body. Chimeras are rare individuals who are composed of a mixture of cells from two zygotes. More likely, dispermic chimeras result from the fusion of DZ twin zygotes early in development. DZ twins are derived from two zygotes. If a polar body were fertilized and remained separate from the normal zygote, it might form a small embryo; however, it is doubtful that it would survive.

4. The common cause of spontaneous abortions during the first week of development is usually chromosomal abnormalities, such as those resulting from nondisjunction. Failure of production of an adequate amount of hCG by the corpus luteum in the ovary could also result in an early spontaneous abortion. For more discussion, see Chapter 3.

5. Yes, it is; however, this phenomenon is extremely rare. The term *superfecundation* indicates fertilization by separate acts of coitus of two or more oocytes that are ovulated at approximately the same time. In lower mammals that are characterized by multiple births and promiscuity (e.g., cats and dogs), superfecundity is common. In such cases, littermates are quite different and have characteristics of the different fathers. The possibility of this process occurring in humans cannot be discounted because evidence exists from DZ (nonidentical) twins belonging to different blood groups, which cannot be accounted for in any other way.

6. There are not too many differences. *Conception* means to become pregnant. *Fertilization* occurs when a sperm fuses with an oocyte; when this occurs, conception takes place. *Impregnation* means to make pregnant (a male impregnates a female).

7. Essentially, yes. *Mitosis* is the usual process of cell reproduction that results in the formation of daughter cells. *Cleavage* is the series of mitotic cell divisions occurring in the zygote after it forms. This process results in the formation of daughter cells—*blastomeres*. The expressions "cleavage division" and "mitotic division" mean the same when referring to the dividing zygote.

8. The nutritional requirements of the dividing zygote are not great. The blastomeres are nourished partly by the sparse yolk granules in these cells; however, the nutrients come mainly from the secretions of the uterine tubes and later from the uterine glands.

9. Yes. One of the blastomeres could be removed, and the Y chromosome could be identified by staining the cell with quinacrine mustard (see Chapter 7). Blastomeres of a female embryo lack a fluorescent body (Y chromosome). This staining technique could be available to couples with a family history of sex-linked genetic diseases (e.g., hemophilia or muscular dystrophy) and to women who have already given birth to a child with such a disease and are reluctant to have more children. In these cases, only female embryos developing in vitro would be transferred to the uterus.

Chapter 4

1. "Implantation bleeding" refers to the loss of small amounts of blood from the implantation site of a blastocyst that occurs at the expected time of menstruation. Persons unfamiliar with this possible occurrence may interpret the bleeding as light menstrual flow; in such cases, they would give the wrong date for their LNMP. This blood is not menstrual fluid; it is blood from the intervillous space of the developing placenta.

2. Drugs or other agents do not cause congenital anomalies if taken during the first 2 weeks of development. A teratogenic drug either damages all the embryonic cells, killing the embryo, or it injures only a few cells and the embryo recovers to develop normally. Despite this fact, it is unwise to give known teratogenic drugs to a female during her reproductive years. If she has a malignant tumor and needs chemotherapy, contraceptive techniques should be used because many chemotherapeutic drugs are teratogenic (see Chapter 9).

3. The term "interception" is sometimes used when referring to *postcoital contraception*. Interceptive pills (e.g., composed of ethinyl estradiol and norgestrel) may be given after a sexual assault to prevent a sperm from fertilizing an oocyte (if present). The risk of pregnancy from unprotected midcycle intercourse is up to 30%.

4. The insertion of an *IUD* usually prevents implantation of a blastocyst in the uterus; however, it does not prevent a sperm from entering the uterine tubes and fertilizing an oocyte if one is present. Because the endometrium is hostile to implantation, a blasto-

cyst could develop and implant in the uterine tube (i.e., an ectopic tubal pregnancy).

5. *Abdominal pregnancies are very uncommon.* Although such a pregnancy can result from primary implantation of a blastocyst in the abdomen, most of them are believed to result from the ectopic implantation of a blastocyst that spontaneously aborted from the uterine tube. The risk of severe maternal bleeding and fetal mortality is high in cases of abdominal pregnancy; however, if the diagnosis is made late in pregnancy and the patient (mother) is free of symptoms, the pregnancy may be allowed to continue until the viability of the fetus is ensured (e.g., 32 weeks). It would then be delivered by cesarean section.

6. Yes, but it is very rare. An intrauterine and ectopic tubal pregnancy is more common.

Chapter 5

1. Yes, if they become pregnant soon after they stop taking the pills. It takes from 1 to 3 months for normal menstrual cycles to occur. If pregnancy occurs before this time, a spontaneous abortion may occur a week or so after the first missed menstrual period. Most embryos have been found to have severe chromosomal abnormalities. For this reason, most physicians recommend that other contraceptive techniques be used for 2 to 3 months after cessation of birth control pills in order to allow normal menstrual cycles to occur.

2. Yes. Traditionally, the fourth to eighth weeks were considered to be the embryonic period; however, the third week is now included because important stages of embryonic development occur during the third week (e.g., early development of the nervous and cardiovascular systems).

3. *Menstrual extraction* or aspiration refers to suction or vacuum curettage of the uterus, usually within 5 to 8 weeks after a missed menstrual period. Menstrual extraction or aspiration is often a euphemistic term for an early abortion. The conceptus is evacuated using an electrically powered vacuum source.

4. Yes, certain drugs can produce congenital anomalies (see Chapter 9). Antineoplastic agents (antitumor drugs) can produce severe skeletal and neural tube defects in the embryo, such as meroanencephaly (partial absence of the brain), if administered during the third week.

5. Yes, risks to the mother and her embryo are increased. Increased maternal age is a predisposing factor to certain medical conditions (e.g., kidney disorders and hypertension). Preeclampsia—a hypertensive disorder of pregnancy characterized by increased blood pressure and edema, for example, occurs more frequently in older pregnant women than in younger ones. Advanced maternal age also produces a significantly increased risk to the embryo/fetus. Most common are birth defects associated with chromosomal abnormalities, such as Down syndrome and trisomy 13 (see Chapter 9); however, women over 40 often have normal children.

Chapter 6

1. During the first few weeks, human embryos resemble the embryos of several other species because of common characteristics (e.g., large head, pharyngeal arches, and tail); thereafter, embryos acquire characteristics that are distinctly human (e.g., loss of the tail and the human appearance of the face and limbs (see drawings of embryos of four species). The distinctive feature of early human embryos is the large prominence formed by the heart.

2. Early in the eighth week embryos look different from 9-week fetuses because of their webbed toes and stubby tails; however, by the end of the eighth week, embryos and early fetuses appear similar. The name change is made to indicate that a new phase of development (rapid growth and differentiation) has begun and that the most critical period of development is completed.

3. This common question is difficult to answer because views are affected by religion and one's peers. The scientific answer is that the embryo has human potential, and no other, from the time of fertilization because of its human chromosome constitution. Three things are definite:

   • Human development begins at fertilization.

   • The zygote and early embryo are living human organisms.

   • The embryo acquires distinctive human characteristics during the eighth week, such as loss of the tail and the appearance of the face.

4. No. During the embryonic period more similarities than differences exist in the external genitalia (see Chapter 14). It would be impossible to tell by ultrasound examination whether the primordial sexual organ (genital tubercle at 5 weeks and phallus at 7 weeks) will become a penis or a clitoris. Sexual differences are not clear until the early fetal period

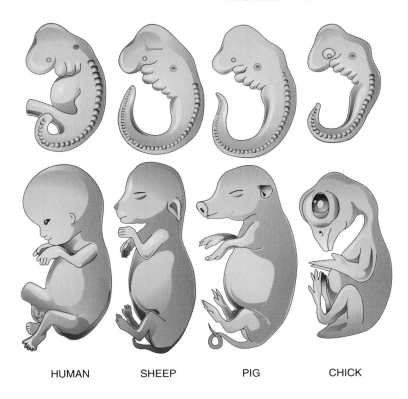

HUMAN SHEEP PIG CHICK

(10th to 12th week). Sex chromatin patterns and chromosome analysis of embryonic cells obtained during amniocentesis can reveal the chromosomal sex of the embryo (see Chapter 7).

5. A *primigravida* is a woman who is pregnant for the first time (L. *primus*, first, and *gravida*, pregnant woman). *Primipara* is a woman who has given birth for the first time to an infant or infants, alive or dead, weighing 500 gm or more or having a gestation of 20 weeks or more. A mother who has previously had a spontaneous abortion at 6 weeks is referred to as a multigravida because she has been pregnant more than once. *Primip* is an abbreviation for the term *primipara*, a woman who has given birth to her first child; hence, "primips" are women who have babies for the first time.

Chapter 7

1. Ultrasound examinations have shown that mature embryos (8 weeks) and young fetuses (9 weeks) show spontaneous movements, such as twitching of the trunk and limbs. Although the fetus begins to move its back and limbs during the 12th week, the mother cannot feel her baby move until the 16th to 20th week. Women who have born several children

(multigravida) usually detect this movement — *quickening* — sooner than women who are pregnant for the first time because they know what fetal movements feel like. Quickening is the first time a woman recognizes fetal movement, which is often perceived as a faint flutter (quivering motion).

2. About 70% of pregnant women experience *nausea* and vomiting ("morning sickness") during the first trimester. Although the urge to vomit usually occurs in the morning, it may occur any time. Nausea and vomiting are often the first symptoms that a woman experiences in early pregnancy. Although some nausea is felt by most women at some time during pregnancy, a majority of women do not experience vomiting. The increase in hormones (hCG and progesterone) is thought to be the main cause of nausea. Usually eating dry crackers and restricting water intake during meals dispels the nauseated feeling. Some women require medication (prescribed by a physician) to relieve the symptoms.

3. No. Although the fetus is competing with the mother for the nutrients and calcium in her blood, the fetus cannot remove calcium from the mother's teeth if she is following a balanced diet as recommended by national guidelines, maintains good oral hygiene, and has regular dental checkups. The fetus

needs calcium for mineralization of its skeleton and tooth formation; therefore, the mother's intake of calcium should be sufficient for her and the fetus. If the maternal calcium intake is inadequate, fetal requirements are met by demineralization of the maternal skeleton.

4. At present it cannot be stated with certainty that periconceptional vitamin supplementation is effective in reducing the incidence of NTDs (e.g., spina bifida); however, preliminary studies are encouraging. It has been shown that the risk of a mother having a child with NTD is significantly lower when vitamin supplementation is used. However, no consensus exists that vitamins are helpful in preventing these defects in most at-risk pregnancies.

5. There is no risk of damaging the fetus during amniocentesis when ultrasonography is used to locate the position of the fetus; hence, the needle will not injure it. The risk of inducing an abortion is slight (about 0.5%). Maternal or fetal infection is an unlikely complication when the procedure is performed by a trained person using modern techniques such as ultrasonography.

Chapter 8

1. A stillbirth is the birth of a dead fetus (stillborn infant) that weighs at least 500 gm and is at least 20 weeks old. A stillborn (fetus) shows no evidence of life. Stillborn infants occur about three times more frequently among mothers over the age of 40 than among women in their 20s. It is true that more male fetuses are stillborn than females. The reason for this is unknown.

2. Sometimes the umbilical cord is abnormally long and wraps around part of the fetus, such as the neck or a limb. This "cord accident" obstructs blood flow in the umbilical vein to the fetus and in the umbilical arteries from the fetus to the placenta. If the fetus does not receive sufficient oxygen and nutrients, it dies. A true knot in the umbilical cord, formed when the fetus passes through a loop in the cord, also obstructs blood flow through the cord. *Prolapse of the umbilical cord* may also be referred to as a "cord accident." This occurs when the cord prolapses into the cervix at the level of a presenting part (often the head). This creates pressure on the cord and prevents the fetus from receiving adequate oxygen. Prolapse may cause fetal death or brain damage. Entanglement of the cord around the fetus can also cause congenital defects (e.g., absence of a forearm).

3. Most "over-the-counter" pregnancy tests are based on the presence of hCG. These tests are capable of detecting the relatively large amounts of hCG that are in the woman's urine. Such tests are positive a short time (a week or so) after the first missed period. HCG is produced by the syncytiotrophoblast of the chorion. These tests usually give an accurate diagnosis of pregnancy; however, a physician should be consulted as soon as possible because some tumors (*choriocarcinomas*) also produce this hormone.

4. The "bag of waters" is a layperson's term for the amniotic sac containing amniotic fluid (largely composed of water). Sometimes the chorionic and amniotic sacs rupture before labor begins, allowing the fluid to escape. *Premature rupture of the membranes (PROM) is the most common event leading to premature labor (birth).* PROM may complicate the birth process; however, it is not a "dry birth." Sometimes sterile saline is infused into the uterus by way of a catheter to alleviate fetal distress—*amnioinfusion*. PROM may also allow a vaginal infection to spread to the fetus. Prolapse of the cord commonly occurs following PROM.

5. The term *fetal distress* is synonymous with *fetal hypoxia*—decreased oxygenation to the fetus resulting from a general decrease of maternal oxygen content of the blood, decreased oxygen-carrying capacity, or diminished blood flow. Fetal distress exists when the fetal heart rate falls below 100 beats per minute. *Pressure on the umbilical cord* causes fetal distress in about 1 in 200 deliveries resulting from impairment of blood supply to the fetus. In these cases, the fetal body compresses the umbilical cord as it passes through the cervix and vagina. *Fetal stress* results from hypoxia and cardiac anomalies (see the text for more details).

6. Yes, this statement is true for DZ twins but not for MZ twins. DZ twinning is an autosomal recessive trait that is carried by the daughters of mothers of twins; hence, *DZ twinning is hereditary*. MZ twinning, on the other hand, is a random occurrence that is not genetically controlled.

Chapter 9

1. No evidence indicates that the occasional use of aspirin in *recommended therapeutic dosages* is harmful during pregnancy; however, large doses at subtoxic levels (e.g., for rheumatoid arthritis) have not been proven to be harmless to the embryo and fetus. Hence, women who take one or two aspirins for a headache need not worry about producing

anomalies in their embryo/fetus. All pregnant women should discuss the use of over-the-counter medications with their physicians.

2. A woman who is addicted to a habit-forming drug (e.g., heroin) and takes it during pregnancy is almost certain to give birth to a child who shows signs of drug addiction. The fetus's chances of survival until birth, however, are not good; mortality and premature birth rates are high among fetuses of drug-addicted mothers.

3. All drugs prescribed in North America are tested for teratogenicity before they are marketed. The thalidomide tragedy, however, clearly demonstrated the need for improved methods for detecting potential human teratogens. Thalidomide was not teratogenic in pregnant mice and rats; however, it is a potent teratogen in humans during the fourth to sixth weeks of pregnancy. Because it is unethical to test the effects of drugs on embryos who are to be aborted, no way exists of preventing some human teratogens from being marketed. Human teratologic evaluation depends on retrospective epidemiologic studies and the reports of astute physicians. This is the way thalidomide teratogenicity was detected. Most new drugs contain a disclaimer in the accompanying package insert, such as, "This drug has not been proven safe for pregnant women." Some drugs may be used if, in the opinion of the physician, the potential benefits outweigh the possible hazards. All known teratogenic drugs that may be taken by a pregnant woman are available only through prescription by a physician.

4. Cigarette smoking during pregnancy is harmful to the embryo and fetus. Its most adverse effect is *intrauterine growth retardation*. Women who stop smoking during the first half of pregnancy have infants with birth weights closer to those of nonsmokers. Decreased placental blood flow, thought to be a nicotine-mediated effect, is believed to cause decreased intrauterine blood flow. No conclusive evidence exists that maternal smoking causes congenital anomalies. The growth of the fetus of a woman who smokes but does not inhale is still endangered because nicotine, carbon monoxide, and other harmful substances are absorbed into the maternal bloodstream through the mucous membranes of the mouth and throat, as well as through the lungs. These substances are then transferred to the embryo/fetus through the placenta. Hence, refraining from inhaling smoke is safer; however, smoking in any manner during pregnancy is not advisable.

5. Ample evidence indicates that most drugs do not cause congenital anomalies in human embryos; however, a pregnant woman should take only drugs that are essential and recommended by her physician. A pregnant woman with a severe lower respiratory infection, for example, would be unwise to refuse drugs recommended by her doctor to cure her illness; her health and that of her embryo or fetus could be endangered by the infection. Most drugs, including sulfonamides, meclizine, penicillin, antihistamines, and Bendectin are considered safe drugs. Similarly, local anesthetic agents, dead vaccines, and salicylates (e.g., aspirin) in low doses are not known to cause congenital anomalies. See the text for more information.

Chapter 10

1. Yes, it is. When a baby is born with a congenital diaphragmatic hernia (CDH), its stomach and liver may be in its thorax (chest); however, this is uncommon. Usually, the abnormally placed viscera are intestines. The viscera enter the thorax through a posterolateral defect in the diaphragm, usually on the left side.

2. Yes, it can. A baby born with CDH may survive; however, the mortality rate is high (about 76%). Treatment must be given immediately. A feeding tube is inserted into the stomach, and the air and gastric contents are aspirated with continuous suction. The displaced viscera are replaced into the abdominal cavity, and the defect in the diaphragm is surgically repaired. Infants with large diaphragmatic hernias, operated on within 24 hours after birth, have survival rates of 40 to 70%. CDH can be repaired before birth; however, this intervention carries considerable risk to the fetus and mother.

3. It depends upon the degree of herniation of the abdominal viscera. With a moderate hernia, the lungs may be mature but small. With a severe degree of herniation, lung development is reduced. Most babies with CDH die, but not because of the defect in the diaphragm or viscera in the chest; they die because the lung on the affected side is hypoplastic (underdeveloped).

4. Yes, it is possible to have a small CDH and not be aware of it. Some small diaphragmatic hernias may remain asymptomatic into adulthood and are discovered only during a routine radiographic or ultrasound examination of the chest. His lung on the affected side probably developed normally because there would be little or no pressure on his lungs during prenatal development.

Chapter 11

1. "Harelip" is the old, incorrect term for cleft lip. It was given this name because the hare (a mammal resembling a large rabbit) has a divided upper lip. It is not an accurate comparison, however, because the cleft in the hare's lip is in the median (central) part of the upper lip, whereas most human clefts are lateral to the median plane.

2. No. Both statements are inaccurate. All embryos have grooves in their upper lips where the maxillary prominences meet the merged medial nasal prominences; however, normal embryos do not have cleft lips. When lip development is abnormal, the tissue in the floor of the lip groove breaks down, forming a cleft lip.

3. The risk in your case is the same as for the general population—about 1 per 1000 (see text).

4. Although environmental factors may be involved, it is reasonable to assume that your son's cleft lip and cleft palate were hereditary and recessive in their expression. This would mean that your husband also carried a concealed gene for cleft lip and that his family was equally responsible for your son's anomalies.

5. Minor anomalies of the auricle of the external ear are common, and usually they are of no serious medical or cosmetic consequence. About 14% of newborn infants have minor morphologic abnormalities, and less than 1% of them have other defects. The child's abnormal ears could be considered branchial anomalies because the external ears develop from six small auricular hillocks (swellings) of the first two pairs of pharyngeal arches; however, such minor abnormalities of ear shape would not normally be classified in this way.

Chapter 12

1. The fetus cannot breathe before birth because the airways and primordial alveoli are distended with liquid. The fetal lungs do not function as organs of gas exchange; however, breathing movements are practiced by the fetus. Rapid, irregular respiratory movements occur during the terminal stages of pregnancy. The lungs must develop in such a way that they can assume their breathing role as soon as the baby is born. Intra-alveolar fluid is rapidly replaced by air after birth.

2. The stimuli that initiate breathing at birth are multiple (see text). "Slapping the buttocks" used to be a common physical stimulus; however, this action is usually unnecessary. Under normal circumstances, the infant's breathing begins promptly, which suggests that it is a reflex response to the sensory stimuli of exposure to air and touching. The changes in blood gases after interruption of the placental circulation are also important in stimulating breathing, such as the fall in oxygen tension and pH and the rise in PCO_2. Therefore, "slapping the buttocks" is not usually necessary.

3. *Hyaline membrane disease (HMD)*, a common cause of the respiratory distress syndrome (RDS), occurs after the onset of breathing in infants with immature lungs and a *deficiency of pulmonary surfactant*. The incidence of RDS is about 1% of all live births and is the leading cause of death in newborn infants (see text). It occurs mainly in infants who are born prematurely. HMD is caused by environmental factors (mainly surfactant deficiency).

4. A 22-week fetus is viable and, if born prematurely and given special care in a neonatal intensive care unit, may survive. Chances of survival, however, are poor for infants who weigh less than 600 gm because the lungs are immature and incapable of adequate alveolar-capillary gas exchange. Furthermore, the fetus's brain is not usually differentiated sufficiently to permit regular respiration.

Chapter 13

1. Undoubtedly, the baby had *congenital hypertrophic pyloric stenosis,* a diffuse hypertrophy (enlargement) and hyperplasia of smooth muscle in the pyloric part of the stomach. This condition produces a hard mass ("tumor"); however, it is not a true tumor. It is a benign enlargement and is definitely not a malignant tumor. The muscular enlargement causes the exit canal (pyloric canal) to be narrow. In response to the outflow obstruction and vigorous peristalsis, the vomiting is projectile, as in the case of your sister's baby. Surgical relief of the pyloric obstruction is the usual treatment. The cause of pyloric stenosis is not known; however, it is thought to have a *multifactorial inheritance*; that is, genetic and environmental factors are probably involved.

2. It is true that infants with Down syndrome have an increased incidence of *duodenal atresia.* They are also more likely to have an *imperforate anus* and other congenital defects (e.g., *atrial septal defects*). These anomalies are likely caused by the abnormal chromosome constitution of the infants (i.e., three instead of two chromosomes 21). The atresia can be corrected surgically by bypassing the pyloric obstruction—a *duodenoduodenostomy* (see text).

3. In very uncommon cases when the intestines return to the abdomen, they rotate in a clockwise direction rather than in the usual counterclockwise manner. As a result, the cecum and appendix are located on the left side — *situs inversus abdominis*. Left-sided cecum and appendix could also result from a *mobile cecum*. If the cecum does not become fixed to the posterior abdominal wall, the cecum and appendix are freely movable and could migrate to the left side.

4. Undoubtedly, the nurse's friend had an *ileal (Meckel) diverticulum*, a finger-like outpouching of the ileum. This common anomaly is sometimes referred to as a "second appendix," which is a misnomer. An ileal diverticulum produces symptoms that are similar to those produced by appendicitis. It is also possible that the person had a *duplication of the cecum*, which would result in two appendices.

5. Hirschsprung disease or *congenital megacolon* (Gr. *megas*, big) is the most common cause of obstruction of the colon in newborn infants. The cause of the condition is *failure of migration of neural crest cells into the wall of the intestine*. As these cells form neurons, there is a deficiency of the nerve cells that innervate the muscular wall of the bowel. When the wall collapses, obstruction occurs and constipation results (see text for illustrations).

6. No, she was not. If the baby had an *umbilicoileal fistula*, the abnormal canal connecting the ileum and umbilicus could permit the passage of feces from the ileum to the umbilicus. This occurrence would be an important diagnostic clue to the presence of such a fistula. Urine could also drip from the umbilicus if the urachus were patent (*urachal fistula*).

Chapter 14

1. Most people with a horseshoe kidney have no urinary problems. These abnormal kidneys are usually discovered at autopsy, during diagnostic imaging, or in the dissecting room. Nothing needs to be done with the abnormal kidney unless infection of the urinary tract occurs that cannot be controlled. In some cases the urologist may divide the kidney into two parts and fix them in positions that do not result in urinary stagnation.

2. His developing kidneys probably fused during the sixth to eighth weeks as they "migrated" from the pelvis. The fused kidneys then ascended toward the normal position on one side or the other. Usually no problems are associated with fused kidneys;

however, surgeons have to be conscious of the possibility of this condition and recognize it for what it is. Removal of fused pelvic kidneys would be a catastrophic error because they represent the only kidneys the person has.

3. Some true hermaphrodites marry; however, most of them do not. These people have both ovarian and testicular tissue (see text). Although spermatogenesis is uncommon, ovulation is not. Pregnancy and childbirth have been observed in a few patients; however, this is very unusual.

4. By 48 hours after birth a definite gender assignment can be made in most cases. The parents are told that their infant's genital development is incomplete and that tests are needed to determine whether the baby is a boy or girl. They are usually advised against announcing their infant's birth to their friends until the appropriate sex has been assigned. The buccal smear test for the identification of sex chromatin is done as soon as possible. Chromatin-positive cells — those with sex chromatin in their nuclei — almost always indicate a female. Chromatin-negative cells usually indicate a male; however, study of the baby's chromosomes may be required before sex can be assigned. Hormone studies may also be required.

5. Virilization (masculinization) of the female fetus resulting from *congenital adrenal hyperplasia* (CAH) is the most common cause of ambiguous external genitalia resulting in intersexuality. In other cases the androgens enter the fetal circulation following maternal ingestion of androgenic hormones. In unusual cases, the hormones are produced by a tumor on one of the mother's suprarenal glands (see text). Partial or complete fusion of the urogenital folds or labioscrotal swellings is the result of exposure to androgens prior to the 12th week of development. Clitoral enlargement occurs after this; however, androgens do not cause sexual ambiguity because the other external genitalia are fully formed by this time.

Chapter 15

1. Heart murmurs are sounds transmitted to the thoracic wall from turbulence of blood in the heart or great arteries. Loud murmurs often represent narrowing or *stenosis of one of the semilunar valves* (aortic or pulmonary valve). A ventricular septal defect or a patent foramen ovale may also produce a loud murmur.

2. Congenital heart defects are common. They occur

in 6 to 8 of every 1000 newborns and represent about 10% of all congenital anomalies. Ventricular septal defects (VSDs) are the most common type of heart anomaly. They occur more frequently in males than females. The reason for this is unknown.

3. The cause of most congenital anomalies of the cardiovascular system is unknown. In about 8% of children with heart disease, a genetic basis is clear. Most of these are associated with obvious chromosomal abnormalities (e.g., trisomy 21) and deletion of parts of chromosomes. *Down syndrome* is associated with congenital heart disease in 50% of cases. The maternal ingestion of drugs, such an antimetabolites and Coumadin (an anticoagulant), has been shown to be associated with a high incidence of cardiac defects. Evidence suggests that heavy consumption of alcohol during pregnancy may cause heart defects; however, it is impossible to say whether the excessive use of alcohol by your friend caused her baby's heart condition.

4. Several viral infections are associated with congenital cardiac defects (see Chapter 9); however, only the *rubella virus* is known to cause cardiovascular disease (e.g., patent ductus arteriosus). *Measles* is a general term that is used for two different viral diseases. *Rubeola* (common measles) does not cause cardiovascular defects; however, *rubella* (German measles) does. *Rubella virus vaccine* is available and is effective in preventing the development of rubella infection in a woman who has not had the disease and is planning to have a baby. It will subsequently prevent the rubella syndrome from developing in her baby as well. Because of the potential hazard of the vaccine to the embryo, the vaccine is given only if there is assurance that there is no likelihood of pregnancy for the next 2 months.

5. This anomaly is called *transposition of the great arteries* (TGA) because the positions of the great vessels (aorta and pulmonary trunk) are reversed (see the text for details and illustrations). Survival after birth depends on mixing between the pulmonary and systemic circulations (e.g., through an ASD or patent foramen ovale). TGA occurs in slightly more than 1 per 5000 live births and is more common in male infants (almost 2:1). Most infants with this severe cardiac anomaly die during the first months of life; however, corrective surgery can be done in those who survive for several months. Initially, an ASD may be created to increase mixing between the systemic and pulmonary circulations. Later, an arterial switch operation (reversing the aorta and pulmonary trunk) can be performed; however, more commonly, a baffle is inserted in the atrium to divert systemic venous blood through the mitral valve, left ventricle, and pulmonary artery to the lungs, and pulmonary venous blood through the tricuspid valve, right ventricle, and aorta. This physiologically corrects the circulation.

6. Very likely the one twin has *dextrocardia*. Usually this is of no clinical significance. In some cases the heart is simply displaced to the right; in others, the right and left chambers are completely transposed. In the condition represented by your friend, the heart presents a mirror image of the normal cardiac structure. This occurs during the fourth week of development when the heart tube rotates to the left rather than to the right.

Chapter 16

1. The most common congenital anomaly of the vertebral column is *spina bifida occulta*. This defect of the vertebral arch of the first sacral and/or last lumbar vertebra is present in about 10% of people. The defect also occurs in cervical and thoracic vertebrae. The spinal cord and nerves are usually normal, and neurologic symptoms are usually absent. Spina bifida occulta does not cause back problems in most people; occasionally, however, it may be associated with neurologic or musculoskeletal disturbances.

2. A rib associated with the seventh cervical vertebra is of clinical importance because it may compress the subclavian artery and/or brachial plexus, producing symptoms of artery and nerve compression. In most cases, cervical ribs produce no symptoms. These ribs develop from the costal processes of the seventh cervical vertebra. Lumbar ribs are common and have a similar embryologic basis; that is, they result from development of the costal processes of the first lumbar vertebra.

3. A hemivertebra can produce a lateral curvature of the vertebral column (*scoliosis*). A hemivertebra is composed of one half of a body, a pedicle, and a lamina. This anomaly results when mesenchymal cells from the sclerotomes on one side fail to form the primordium of half of a vertebra. As a result, more growth centers are found on one side of the vertebral column; this imbalance causes the vertebral column to bend laterally.

4. *Craniosynostosis* indicates premature closure of one or more of the cranial sutures. This developmental abnormality results in malformations of the skull. *Scaphocephaly*—a long narrow skull—results from premature closure of the sagittal suture. This type of craniosynostosis accounts for about 50% of the

cases of premature closure of cranial sutures (see text).

5. The features of Klippel-Feil syndrome are short neck, low hairline, and restricted neck movements. In most cases, the number of cervical vertebral bodies is fewer than normal.

Chapter 17

1. The *prune belly syndrome* results from partial or complete absence of abdominal musculature. Usually the abdominal wall is so thin that the organs are easily palpated. This syndrome is usually associated with malformations of the urinary tract, especially the urinary bladder—*exstrophy* (see Chapter 14).

2. Absence of the sternocostal part of the left pectoralis major muscle is usually the cause of an abnormally low nipple and areola. Despite its numerous and important actions, absence of all or part of the pectoralis major muscle usually causes no disability. The actions of other muscles associated with the shoulder joint compensate for the partial absence of this muscle.

3. The sternocleidomastoid muscle (SCM) was prominent. The SCM attaches the mastoid process to the clavicle and sternum; hence, continued growth of the side of the neck results in tilting and rotation of the head. This relatively common condition—*congenital torticollis* (wryneck)—may occur because of injury to the muscle during birth. Tearing of some muscle fibers may have occurred, resulting in bleeding into the muscle. Over several weeks, necrosis of some fibers occurred, and the blood was replaced by fibrous tissue. This resulted in shortening of the muscle and pulling of the child's head to one side. If the condition is not corrected, the shortened muscle could distort the shape of the face on the affected side.

4. The young athlete probably had an accessory soleus muscle. It is present in about 6% of people. This anomaly probably results from splitting of the primordium of the muscle into two parts.

Chapter 18

1. The ingestion of drugs did not cause the child's short limbs. The infant has a skeletal disorder—*achondroplasia*. This type of short-limbed dwarfism has an incidence of 1 in 10,000 and shows an autosomal dominant inheritance (see text). About 80%

of these infants are born of normal parents, and presumably the condition results from fresh mutations (changes of genetic material) in the parents' germ cells. Most achondroplastic people have normal intelligence and lead normal lives within their physical capabilities. If the parents of an achondroplastic child have more children, the risk of having another child with this condition is slightly higher than the population risk; however, the risk for the achondroplastic person's own children is 50%.

2. *Brachydactyly* is an autosomal dominant trait; that is, it is determined by a dominant gene. If your sister (likely bb) marries the brachydactylous man (likely Bb), the risk is 50% for a brachydactylous child and 50% for a normal child. It would be best for her to discuss her obvious concern with a medical geneticist.

3. Bendectin, an antinauseant, does not produce limb defects in human embryos. Several epidemiologic studies have failed to show an increased risk of birth defects after exposure to Bendectin or its separate ingredients during early pregnancy. In the case you describe, the mother took the drug more than 3 weeks after the end of the critical period of limb development (24 to 36 days after fertilization). Consequently, even a known limb teratogen such as *thalidomide* could not have caused failure of the child's hand to develop if ingested after 36 days of development. Most limb reduction defects have a genetic basis.

4. *Syndactyly* (fusion of digits) is the most common type of limb anomaly. It varies from cutaneous webbing between the digits to synostosis (union of phalanges, the bones of the digits). Syndactyly is more common in the foot than in the hand. This anomaly occurs when separate digital rays fail to form in the fifth week or the webbing between the developing digits fails to break down during the eighth week.

5. The most common type of clubfoot is *talipes equinovarus*, occurring in about 1 of every 1000 newborn infants (see Chapter 18 for illustration). In this deformation, the soles of the feet are turned medially and the feet are sharply plantarflexed. The feet are fixed in the tiptoe position, resembling the foot of a horse (L. *equinus*, horse).

6. Syndactyly is very common and is more common in the foot than in the hand. This anomaly occurs when separate digital rays fail to form or the webbing between the digits fails to break down.

Chapter 19

1. Neural tube defects (NTDs) are hereditary. Mero-anencephaly (anencephaly) and spina bifida cystica have a multifactorial inheritance; that is, both genetic and environmental factors are involved. Nutritional factors may be implicated. After the birth of one child with an NTD, the risk of a subsequent child having an NTD is divided about equally between the two defects. The recurrence risk in the United Kingdom, where NTDs are common (7.6 per 1000 in South Wales and 8.6 per 1000 in Northern Ireland), is about 1 in 25. It is probably about 1 in 50 in North America. NTDs can be detected prenatally by a combination of ultrasound scanning and measurement of alpha-fetoprotein levels in amniotic fluid (see text).

2. The condition described is *hydranencephaly*, an extremely rare anomaly. Most of both cerebral hemispheres are reduced to membranous sacs that contain CSF. Absence of cerebral hemispheres can result from different developmental disturbances. The condition most likely results from vascular occlusion of both internal carotid arteries resulting from a severe intrauterine infection. In some cases, hydranencephaly appears to be a severe type of intrauterine hydrocephalus (hence, the prefix *hydro-* in the designation). These infants usually do not survive longer than 3 months.

3. Mental retardation and growth retardation are the most serious aspects of the *fetal alcohol syndrome*. Average IQ scores are 60 to 70. It has been estimated that the incidence of mental retardation resulting from heavy drinking during pregnancy may be as high as 1 per every 400 live births. Heavy drinkers are those who consume five or more drinks on one occasion, with a consistent daily average of 45 ml of absolute alcohol. At present, no safe threshold for alcohol consumption during pregnancy is known. Most physicians recommend complete abstinence from alcohol during pregnancy.

4. No conclusive evidence indicates that maternal smoking affects the mental development of a fetus; however, cigarette smoking compromises oxygen supply to the fetus because blood flow to the placenta is decreased during smoking (see Chapters 8 and 9). Because it is well established that heavy maternal smoking seriously affects physical growth of the fetus and is a major cause of IUGR, it is not wise for mothers to smoke during pregnancy. The reduced oxygen supply to the brain could affect intellectual development, even though the effect may be undetectable. Abstinence gives the fetus the best chance for normal development.

5. Most laypeople use the designation "spina bifida" in a general way. They are unaware that the common type, *spina bifida occulta,* is usually clinically insignificant. It is an isolated finding in up to 20% of radiographically examined vertebral columns. Most people are unaware that they have this vertebral defect, and most physicians would not tell them about it because it produces no symptoms unless it is associated with an NTD or an abnormality of the spinal nerve roots. The various types of *spina bifida cystica* are of clinical significance (see text for details and illustrations). Meningomyelocele is a more severe defect than meningocele because neural tissue is included in the lesion. Because of this, the function of abdominal and limb muscles may be affected. Meningoceles are usually covered with skin, and motor function in the limbs is usually normal unless associated developmental defects of the spinal cord or brain are present. Management of infants with spina bifida cystica is complex and involves several medical and surgical specialties. Spinal meningocele is obviously easier to correct surgically than spinal meningomyelocele, and the prognosis is also better.

Chapter 20

1. The chance of significant damage to the embryo/fetus after a rubella infection depends primarily on the timing of the viral infection (see Chapter 9). In cases of primary maternal infection during the first trimester of pregnancy, the overall risk of embryonic/fetal infection is about 20%. It is estimated that about 50% of the pregnancies end in spontaneous abortion, stillbirth, or congenital anomalies (deafness, cataract, glaucoma, and mental retardation). When infection occurs at the end of the first trimester, the probability of congenital anomalies is only slightly higher than for an uncomplicated pregnancy. Certain infections occurring late in the first trimester, however, may result in severe eye infections (e.g., chorioretinitis), which may affect visual development. *Deafness is the most common manifestation of late fetal rubella infection* (i.e., during the second and third trimesters). If a pregnant woman is exposed to rubella, an antibody test can be performed. If she is determined to be immune, she can be reassured that her embryo/fetus will not be affected by the virus. Preventive measures are essential for the protection of the embryo. It is especially important that girls obtain immunity to ru-

bella before they reach childbearing age; for example, by active immunization.

2. The purposeful exposure of young girls to rubella (German measles) is not recommended by physicians. Although complications resulting from such infections are uncommon, neuritis and arthritis occasionally occur (inflammation of nerves and joints, respectively). *Encephalitis* (inflammation of the brain) occurs in about 1 in 6000 cases; furthermore, the rubella infection is often subclinical (difficult to detect) and yet represents a risk to pregnant women. The chance of injury to embryos is possible because the danger period is greatest when the eyes and ears are developing. This occurs early enough in pregnancy that some women would be unaware that they are pregnant. A much better way of providing immunization against rubella is the administration of live-virus vaccine. This is given to children over 15 months of age and to nonpregnant postpubertal females who can be reasonably relied upon not to become pregnant within 3 months of immunization.

3. *Congenital syphilis* ("fetal syphilis") results from the transplacental transmission of the microorganism *Treponema pallidum*. The transfer from untreated pregnant women may occur throughout pregnancy; however, it usually takes place during the last trimester (see Chapter 8). Deafness and tooth deformities commonly develop in these children. These anomalies can be prevented by treating the mother early in pregnancy. The microorganism that causes syphilis is very sensitive to penicillin, an antibiotic that does not harm the fetus.

4. Several viruses in the herpes virus family can cause fetal blindness and deafness during infancy. The *cytomegalovirus* can cross the placenta, be transmitted to the infant during birth, and be passed to the baby in breast milk. *Herpes simplex viruses* (usually type 2 or genital herpes) are usually transmitted just before or during birth. The chances for normal development of infected infants are not good. Some of them develop microcephaly, seizures, deafness, and blindness.

5. *Methylmercury is teratogenic in human embryos*, especially to the developing brain (see Chapter 9). Because the eyes and internal ears develop as outgrowths from the brain, it is understandable how their development is also affected. Besides the methylmercury that passes from the mother to the embryo/fetus through the placenta, the newborn infant may receive more methylmercury from breast milk. Sources of methylmercury have included fish from contaminated water, flour made from methylmercury-treated seed grain, and meat eaten from animals raised on contaminated food.

Chapter 21

1. Congenital absence of skin is very uncommon. Patches of skin (several centimeters in diameter) may be absent, most often from the scalp, but patches of skin may also be missing from the trunk and limbs. Affected infants usually survive because healing of the lesions is uneventful and takes 1 to 2 months. A hairless scar persists. The cause of congenital absence of hair—*aplasia cutis congenita*—is usually unknown. Most cases are sporadic; however, several well-documented pedigrees demonstrate autosomal dominant transmission of this skin defect.

2. The white patches of skin on a dark-skinned person result from *partial albinism* (piebaldism). This defect, which also affects light-skinned persons, is a heritable disorder transmitted by an autosomal dominant gene. Ultrastructural studies show an absence of melanocytes in the depigmented areas of skin. Presumably the cause is a genetic defect in the differentiation of melanoblasts. These skin and hair defects are not amenable to treatment; however, they can be covered with cosmetics and hair dyes.

3. The breasts, including the mammary glands within them, of males and females are similar at birth. Breast enlargement in a newborn infant is common and results from stimulation by maternal hormones that enter the infant's blood through the placenta. Therefore, enlarged breasts are a normal occurrence in male infants and do not indicate abnormal sex development. Similar physiologic *pubertal gynecomastia* occurs in some males during their early teens as a result of decreased levels of testosterone. The breast enlargement is usually transitory. *Familial gynecomastia* is an X-linked or autosomal dominant sex-linked trait. Gynecomastia also occurs in about 50% of males with the *Klinefelter syndrome* (described in Chapter 9 and illustrated in Figure 9–7). These boys and men are not intersexes because their external and internal genitalia are normal except that their testes are small because of the degeneration of seminiferous tubules.

4. An extra breast (polymastia) or nipple (polythelia) is common. The axillary breast may enlarge during puberty, or it may not be noticed until pregnancy occurs. The embryologic basis of extra breasts and

nipples is the presence of mammary ridges that extend from the axillary to the inguinal regions. Usually, only one pair of breasts develops; however, breasts can develop anywhere along the mammary ridges. The extra breast or nipple is usually just superior or inferior to the normal breast. An axillary breast or nipple is very uncommon.

5. Teeth present at birth are natal teeth (L. *natalis*, to be born). A more appropriate term would be *congenital teeth* (L. *congenitus*, born with). *Natal teeth* are erupted at birth and are observed in about 1 in 2000 newborn infants. Usually two mandibular medial (central) incisors are present. The presence of natal teeth usually suggests that early eruption of other teeth will occur. Because natal teeth may detach and be aspirated into the lungs, the natal teeth are sometimes extracted. Often they fall out on their own.

Note: Page numbers in *italics* refer to illustrations; page numbers followed by t refer to tables.